								He $1s^2$
			B† $2s^2 2p^1$	C† $2s^2 2p^2$	N† $2s^2 2p^3$	O $2s^2 2p^4$	F $2s^2 2p^5$	Ne $2s^2 2p^6$
			Al† $3s^2 3p^1$	Si† $3s^2 3p^2$	P† $3s^2 3p^3$	S† $3s^2 3p^4$	Cl† $3s^2 3p^5$	A $3s^2 3p^6$
Ni ‡** $d^8 4s^2$	Cu ‡** $3d^{10} 4s^1$	Zn ‡ $3d^{10} 4s^2$	Ga† $4s^2 4p^1$	Ge †§ $4s^2 4p^2$	As †§ $4s^2 4p^3$	Se † $4s^2 4p^4$	Br † $4s^2 4p^5$	Kr $4s^2 4p^6$
Pd ‡** $4d^{10}$	Ag ‡** $4d^{10} 5s^1$	Cd ‡** $4d^{10} 5s^2$	In † $5s^2 5p^1$	Sn †§ $5s^2 5p^2$	Sb †§ $5s^2 5p^3$	Te † $5s^2 5p^4$	I † $5s^2 5p^5$	Xe $5s^2 5p^6$
Pt ‡** $...6s^1$	Au ‡** $5d^{10} 6s^1$	Hg †** $5d^{10} 6s^2$	Tl ** $6s^2 6p^1$	Pb †§ $6s^2 6p^2$	Bi †§ $6s^2 6p^3$	Po $6s^2 6p^4$	At $6s^2 6p^5$	Rn $6s^2 6p^6$

One may classify the elements, in a very qualitative way, according to the types of atoms with which they seem to coordinate most firmly. The groups, of course, merge into each other:

*Most of these form complexes in which oxygen is the donor atom. Fluoro complexes are also well known. The tendency to coordinate with other non-metals increases toward the lower right of this area.

†Known chiefly in complexes in which oxygen is the donor atom.

‡Known chiefly in complexes in which nitrogen is the donor atom.

**Form stable complexes in which the donor atom is a halogen, sulfur, phosphorus, or carbon. The tendency to form complexes containing other non-metals, and the lighter halogens, increases toward the upper left of this area.

§Form stable complexes in which sulfur is the donor atom.

THE CHEMISTRY

of the

COORDINATION COMPOUNDS

Edited by

JOHN C. BAILAR, JR.

University of Illinois

Urbana, Illinois

DARYLE H. BUSCH

Editorial Assistant

American Chemical Society

Monograph Series

REINHOLD PUBLISHING CORPORATION

NEW YORK

CHAPMAN & HALL, LTD., LONDON

1956

REINHOLD PUBLISHING CORPORATION

Publishers of Chemical Engineering Catalog, Chemical Materials Catalog, "Automatic Control," "Materials & Methods"; Advertising Management of the American Chemical Society

Printed in the U.S.A. by
THE WAVERLY PRESS, INC., BALTIMORE, MD.

B. & T.

Athens, Tennessee

Contributors

Fred Basolo	Raymond N. Keller
B. P. Block	Stanley Kirschner
Robert C. Brasted	Ernest H. Lyons, Jr.
Clayton F. Callis	J. A. Mattern
Leallyn B. Clapp	Niels C. Nielsen
William E. Cooley	Thomas D. O'Brien
Bodie E. Douglas	Robert W. Parry
Gunther L. Eichhorn	James V. Quagliano
Stanley J. Gill	R. L. Rebertus
Roy D. Johnson	Carl L. Rollinson
Hans B. Jonassen	Donald H. Wilkins

General Introduction

American Chemical Society's Series of Chemical Monographs

By arrangement with the Interallied Conference of Pure and Applied Chemistry, which met in London and Brussels in July, 1919, the American Chemical Society was to undertake the production and publication of Scientific and Technologic Monographs on chemical subjects. At the same time it was agreed that the National Research Council, in cooperation with the American Chemical Society and the American Physical Society, should undertake the production and publication of Critical Tables of Chemical and Physical Constants. The American Chemical Society and the National Research Council mutually agreed to care for these two fields of chemical progress. The American Chemical Society named as Trustees, to make the necessary arrangements of the publication of the Monographs, Charles L. Parsons, secretary of the Society, Washington, D. C.; the late John E. Teeple, then treasurer of the Society, New York; and the late Professor Gellert Alleman of Swarthmore College. The trustees arranged for the publication of the ACS Series of (a) Scientific and (b) Technological Monographs by the Chemical Catalog Company, Inc. (Reinhold Publishing Corporation, successor) of New York.

The Council of the American Chemical Society, acting through its Committee on National Policy, appointed editors (the present list of whom appears at the close of this sketch) to select authors of competent authority in their respective fields and to consider critically the manuscripts submitted.

The first Monograph of the Series appeared in 1921. After twenty-three years of experience certain modifications of general policy were indicated. In the beginning there still remained from the preceding five decades a distinct though arbitrary differentiation between so-called "pure science" publications and technologic or applied science literature. By 1944 this differentiation was fast becoming nebulous. Research in private enterprise had grown apace and not a little of it was pursued on the frontiers of knowledge. Furthermore, most workers in the sciences were coming to see the artificiality of the separation. The methods of both groups of workers are the same. They employ the same instrumentalities, and frankly recognize that their objectives are common, namely, the search for new knowledge for the service of man. The officers of the Society therefore combined the two editorial Boards in a single Board of twelve representative members.

Also in the beginning of the Series, it seemed expedient to construe rather broadly the definition of a Monograph. Needs of workers had to be recognized. Consequently among the first hundred Monographs appeared works in the form of treatises covering in some instances rather broad areas. Because such necessary works do not now want for publishers, it is considered advisable to hew more strictly to the line of the Monograph character, which means more complete and critical treatment of relatively restricted areas, and, where a broader field needs coverage, to subdivide it into logical subareas. The prodigious expansion of new knowledge makes such a change desirable.

These Monographs are intended to serve two principal purposes: first, to make available to chemists a thorough treatment of a selected area in form usable by persons working in more or less unrelated fields to the end that they may correlate their own work with a larger area of physical science discipline; second, to stimulate further research in the specific field treated. To implement this purpose the authors of Monographs are expected to give extended references to the literature. Where the literature is of such volume that a complete bibliography is impracticable, the authors are expected to append a list of references critically selected on the basis of their relative importance and significance.

Preface

Werner's coordination theory has been a guiding principle in inorganic chemistry and in the theory of valence since its publication sixty years ago. Indeed, it might be said to underlie our modern concepts of molecular structure. The current theories of acidity, basicity, amphoterism, and hydrolysis grew directly from it, and the assumption of the complete ionization of solid salts is implicit in it. In recent years, the coordination theory has found increasing application in many types of chemical work. For example, its usefulness in the selection of organic precipitants for metallic ions and in explaining biological phenomena are well known. It is also the basis for our understanding of the role of metal ions in leather tanning, in the dyeing of cloth, and in regulating plant growth. Coordinating agents are used in winning metals from their ores, in electroplating, in catalyzing reactions and in obviating the effects of undesirable catalyses, in precipitating metallic ions and in preventing their precipitation, and in many other ways. Still other uses await study and exploration.

So much interest has developed in the theory of coordination and in coordination compounds in recent years that a need has arisen for a book describing them. I began the preparation of such a book several years ago, but the literature on the coordination compounds is so vast, and is growing so rapidly, that it soon became apparent that the task is too great for one person. I have therefore asked some of my students and former students to help me with it. I am grateful to them for their help, and proud to present their work.

No attempt has been made to cover the chemistry of coordination compounds completely—to do so would require many volumes. Rather, we have attempted to select ideas which are fundamental and stimulating and applications which are both illustrative and useful. Even so, it has been necessary to omit extensive discussion of such important topics as the use of complex ions as catalysts, metal ion deactivators, methods of preparing complex ions, and the details of many physical methods which are used in the study of coordination compounds.

In the interest of saving space, we have often used a single reference number for several related articles. When one of these articles is referred to later, it is designated by the original number, followed by a letter of the alphabet which shows its position in the list.

Our thanks are due to Prof. N. J. Leonard, Prof. C. S. Vestling, Prof.

vii

H. A. Laitinen and Dr. Eleanora C. Gyarfas who have read portions of the manuscript, and have made valuable suggestions concerning them.

In addition to serving as a coauthor, Dr. Daryle H. Busch has assisted a great deal with the editorial work, and I wish to express special gratitude to him. Without his excellent help, it is doubtful if the work could have been completed.

A person who has never written a book may wonder why authors so frequently acknowledge the patience and understanding of their wives. These are, indeed, not idle words. Many of the hours which went into the working on this book were taken from evenings which would otherwise have been spent with my family or from time which might have been spent in doing the many odd jobs that fall to the lot of every householder. My wife has not only borne this with patience and understanding, but has lent valuable advice and encouragement. To her goes my most grateful acknowledgment.

JOHN C. BAILAR, JR.

Urbana, Illinois
June, 1956

Contents

ix

1. A General Survey of the Coordination Compounds

John C. Bailar Jr., and Daryle H. Busch*

University of Illinois, Urbana, Illinois

Since coordination compounds differ greatly in nature and stability, chemists are not completely agreed on a simple definition of the term. Early workers in the field had few of the modern physical-chemical tools at their disposal, and if a material satisfied the law of definite proportions, they were inclined to consider it a compound. For example, crystals of the composition $(NH_4)_3ZnCl_5$ are readily obtained from an aqueous solution containing zinc chloride and ammonium chloride. These can be recrystallized without change of composition, and the substance was long considered to be a complex compound in which zinc shows a coordination number of five. X-ray analysis has shown, however, that only four of the chlorine atoms are close to the zinc while the fifth is much more distant. Similarly, the clathrates were once believed to be coordination compounds.

According to the theory of Sidgwick and Lowry, a coordinate bond (and hence, a coordination compound) can be formed between any atom or ion which can accept a share in a pair of electrons (the acceptor) and any atom or ion which can furnish a pair of electrons (the donor). The donor is nonmetallic—it may be part of a neutral molecule, like CO, H_2O, or NH_3, or part of an ion, like Cl^-, $CO_3^=$ or $NH_2CH_2COO^-$. Ordinarily, an acceptor requires several donors, which may be alike or different. The resulting complex may be a positive ion, a negative ion, or a neutral molecule.

Even if we accept the idea that a coordinate bond consists of a shared pair (or pairs) of electrons, a question remains as to the nature and the necessary degree of such sharing. In many cases, the donor and acceptor are bound in such a way that the reaction of formation is not reversible to any detectable degree. In aqueous solution, the hexamminecobalt(III) ion $[Co(NH_3)_6]^{+++}$, shows no detectable dissociation[1] and the analogous tris(ethylenediamine)cobalt(III) ion, $[Co\ en_3]^{+++}$, retains its optical activity in solution for many weeks at ordinary temperatures. Both of these

---

* Now at Ohio State University, Columbus, Ohio.

1. Flagg, *J. Am. Chem. Soc.*, **63**, 957 (1941).

ions are stable in concentrated hydrochloric acid, and react only slowly with hydrogen sulfide and with sodium hydroxide.

The copper(II) tetrammine ion, $[Cu(NH_3)_4]^{++}$, can be easily detected in solution by its deep blue color, and its salts can be crystallized from solution. It is of a different order of stability from the cobalt(III) hexammine ion, however, as it is readily destroyed by acids or by heating. In solution, it exists in equilibrium with $[Cu(H_2O)_4]^{++}$ and ammonia. The fact that the formation of the complex is accompanied by a color change, by a change in oxidation-reduction potential of the copper(II), and by other changes in properties clearly indicates that there is a true chemical bond between the copper ion and the ammonia molecules.

Sodium chloride absorbs ammonia when under pressure, but liberates it when the pressure is released[2]. No doubt there are attractive or adsorptive forces which tend to hold the two substances together, but they are weak and poorly characterized.

In general, the small, highly charged cations form the most stable co-ordinate bonds, and it is often mistakenly supposed that the ability to form complexes is limited to the transition metals. This is far from being so, as is seen from the fact that the beryllium derivative of acetylacetone can be distilled without decomposition at 270°C.

Even the alkali metal ions form complexes, as shown by the work of Sidgwick and Brewer[3]. They found that sodium benzoyl acetone has the properties of a salt; it is insoluble in nonpolar solvents, and upon heating it chars instead of melting. If recrystallized from 95 per cent ethanol, it takes up two molecules of water from the solvent, yielding a dihydrate that melts at 115°C and is appreciably soluble in toluene. It is evident that the dihydrate is a chelated compound.

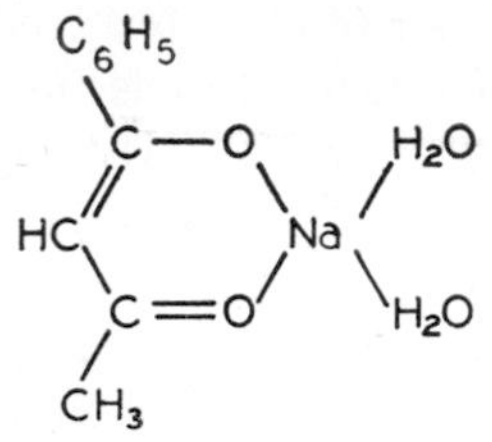

Salicylaldehyde (and similar compounds) also forms sodium chelates[3, 4, 5, 6].
The nature of the electron sharing is discussed in Chapters 3 and 4.

2. Clark, *Am. J. Sci.*, **7**, 1 (1924).
3. Sidgwick and Brewer, *J. Chem. Soc.*, **127**, 2379 (1925); Brewer, *J. Chem. Soc.*, **1931**, 361.
4. Hantzsch, *Ber.*, **39**, 3089 (1906).
5. Weygand and Forkel, *J. prakt. Chem.*, **116**, 293 (1927).
6. Brady and Bodger, *J. Chem. Soc.*, **1932**, 952.

Suffice it to say here that stability depends upon many factors and cannot be directly correlated with bond type. Among the many other factors that are important in determining stability are charge on the acceptor atom, nature of the donor atom and of the molecule of which it is a part, chelation, cationic, anionic, or neutral nature of the complex, and the nature of the ion with which it is associated (if the complex is an ion).

The relationship between the donor and acceptor atoms is especially interesting. Nearly all of the complexes of the light metals (Periodic groups IA, IIA, IIIB, IVB) contain oxygen as the donor atom. It may be furnished in the form of water, hydroxide ion, an oxyanion, an alcohol, ether, ketone, or in a variety of other ways. These light metals seldom coordinate with molecules containing nitrogen, sulfur, carbon, or the halogens. Vanadium, at the head of group VB, is a powerful oxygen coordinator, but also shows some ability to form ammines and complex cyanides. Proceeding across the periodic table toward the right from vanadium, we encounter elements which easily coordinate with nitrogen. Thus, chromium forms a large number of ammines, most of which are slowly destroyed in water solution. The ammines of manganese are still less stable, and neither iron(II) or iron(III) ion reacts with ammonia in water solution to give ammines. These ions coordinate instead with hydroxyl ions generated in the water by the addition of ammonia. With cobalt, nickel, copper, and zinc, however, stable ammines are formed. The ions of these metals retain the ability to coordinate with oxygen in even greater degree than do the ions of the lighter metals, but the tendency to form links with nitrogen is still more pronounced. Starting with vanadium, too, we see an increasing tendency to coordinate with carbon—all the elements from vanadium to zinc form stable cyanides, those from chromium to nickel form carbonyls, and copper, at least, forms compounds with olefinic substances. The ability of the metals in this series to combine with sulfur also increases toward copper. Vanadium, chromium and manganese occur in nature in oxide ores, iron both in oxide and sulfide ores, and cobalt, nickel, copper and zinc largely as sulfide ores.

In the fifth and sixth series of the periodic table, there is an increased tendency to form stable complexes with halides. This is present in the fourth series to some degree, but is increasingly important in the later series, as is illustrated by the solubility of silver chloride in hydrochloric acid and the reaction of platinum and gold with chlorine water and aqua regia to form $[PtCl_6]^=$ and $[AuCl_4]^-$.

The elements of Periodic groups VIII, IB, and IIB are of special interest. All of them form complex cyanides, but only palladium, silver, platinum, rhodium, and mercury are known to form compounds with the ethylenic double bond. All of them form ammines (the ammines of mercury readily lose protons, but the metal-nitrogen bond remains), but the platinum metals and gold form few complexes containing a metal-oxygen bond. This does not mean that such a bond is not stable, but only that the metal-halide and metal-sulfur bonds are more stable.

The metals of periodic groups IIIA, IVA, and VA form many complexes in which the donor atom is oxygen, sulfur, or a halogen. Compounds in which the donor is carbon or nitrogen are much less common.

THE DONOR PROPERTIES OF THE HALOGENS

The halide ions often coordinate strongly, and halo- complexes are well known; fluorosilicates, bromoplatinates, and iodomercurates are familiar. These ions are often thought of as substituted oxy- anions, but this has arisen through pedagogic convenience rather than strict parallelism, for while a halide ion occupies one coordination position, just as an oxide "ion" does, its electrovalence is 1 instead of 2. Thus the statement that Na_2SiF_6 is analogous to Na_2SiO_3 is somewhat misleading, for in solid sodium silicate, the silicate ions are linked together through oxygen atoms in such a way that each silicon is surrounded by four oxygens, while in the fluorosilicate, each silicon is surrounded by six fluorines. A much closer analogy exists between the halide ions and the hydroxyl ion, as is shown by the series $H_2[PtCl_6]$; $H_2[PtCl_5(OH)]$; $H_2[PtCl_4(OH)_2]$; $H_2[PtCl_3(OH)_3]$; $H_2[PtCl_2(OH)_4]$; $H_2[PtCl(OH)_5]$; $H_2[Pt(OH)_6]$, all of the members of which are known except the fourth. These acids, or their alkali salts, can be obtained from the chloro-platinate by stepwise substitution of hydroxo- groups for chloro-groups[7, 8, 9, 10].

For convenience, the complexes formed by halide ions may be considered to be of two general types; those containing only halide ions as ligands (with the possible exception of solvent molecules) and those containing halide ions as a less abundant donor species, as is the case among the halopentammines of cobalt(III) and chromium(III). Although the stabilities of complexes is generally dependent both on the nature of the central metal ion and on the nature of the donor group, these complexes may be grossly divided into two major stability groups; i.e., those very stable complexes of the heavy metals, such as the platinum group metals and mercury, which give only a faint test for halide ion in water solution, and those relatively labile halide complexes of the type formed by the elements of the first transition group and, in general, the more electropositive metals. These

7. Miolati and Bellucci, Z. anorg. Chem., **26**, 209 (1901).
8. Miolati, Z. anorg. Chem., **22**, 445 (1900).
9. Miolati, Z. anorg. Chem., **33**, 251 (1903).
10. Bellucci, Z. anorg. Chem., **44**, 168 (1905).

two major stability groups correspond to the penetration and normal complexes discussed in Chapter 4.

Many of the reported halide complexes of metallic elements are characterized solely by the composition of solids obtained from solutions of mixed halides. The weakness of this type of evidence as a criterion for complex formation is exemplified by the fact that the compound written as $K_2CuCl_4 \cdot 2H_2O$ has been shown by x-ray means to exist as copper(II) chloride 2-hydrate admixed with potassium chloride in the crystal lattice[11].

Occurrence and Nature of the "Strictly" Halide Complexes

In order to facilitate an understanding of the extent of the occurrence of halo- complexes, and to illustrate the trends occurring among the families and periods of the periodic system of elements, a brief discussion of the halide complexes follows.

Family IIA. In group IIA, only tetrafluoroberyllate ion, $[BeF_4]^=$, is well characterized. Its salts bear marked resemblance to sulfates[12]. This is not unexpected since tetrafluoroberyllate ion is isoelectronic and isosteric with sulfate and also approximately the same size[13]. Mitra[14] reports that monohydroxytrifluoroberyllate resembles sulfate even more closely, citing such evidence as the isomorphism of the salts. The corresponding chloro- complex is much less stable, evidence for its existence being confined to freezing point behavior of beryllium chloride-alkali chloride mixtures[15]. Double fluorides of magnesium with alkali metal ions have been reported; however, their complexity is unlikely since the crystal structure of $KMgF_3$ is close-packed and does not show discrete anionic complexes[16].

Family IIB. Complexes with all four halide ions are reported for zinc and cadmium. In the solid state, the complexes seem to vary from $[ZnX_3]^-$ and $[CdX_3]^-$ to $[ZnX_5]^=$ and $[CdX_6]^{4-}$. However, it seems probable that $[ZnX_4]^=$ represents the maximum ratio of halide to zinc in true combination (see page 1). Studies of complex halides of cadmium[17], zinc[18], and

11. Hendricks and Dickinson, *J. Am. Chem. Soc.*, **49**, 2149 (1927).
12. Kruss and Moroht, *Ann.*, **260**, 161 (1890); Ray, *et al.*, *Z. anorg. Chem.*, **201**, 289 (1931); **205**, 257 (1932); **206**, 209 (1936); **227**, 32, 103 (1936); **241**, 165 (1939).
13. Ray and Sarkar, *J. Ind. Chem. Soc.*, **6**, 987 (1929); Ghosh, Mitra, and Ray: *J. Ind. Chem. Soc.*, **30**, 221 (1953).
14. Mitra, *Science and Culture*, **18**, 393 (1953).
15. Schmidt, *Ann. chim.*, [X] **11**, 351 (1929); O'Daniel and Tscheischwile, *Z. Krist.*, **104**, 124 (1942).
16. Wells, "Structural Inorganic Chemistry," p. 89, London, Oxford University Press, 1948.
17. Leden, *Z. phys. Chem.*, **188**, 160 (1941); Ermolevka and Makkaveeva, *Zhur. Obschchei Khim.*, **22**, 1741 (1952); Markman and Tur'yan; *Zhur. Obschchei Khim.*, **22**, 1926 (1952); Strocchi, *Gazz. chim. ital.*, **80**, 234 (1950).
18. Strocchi, *Gazz. chim. ital.*, **79**, 41, 270 (1949).

mercury(II)[19] in solution support the possibility that the most characteristic species are $[MX_3]^-$ and $[MX_4]^=$. The order of stability of the cadmium and mercury complexes is $I > Br > Cl$ (There is some doubt that fluoride ion form complexes with these two metals in solution).

Family IIIA. The halide complexes of group IIIA illustrate the inversion in relative stability of the $[MX_n]^{(n-3)-}$ anions upon descending the series. The fluoro- complexes of aluminum are by far the best characterized and most stable of all the haloaluminates. The anion $[Al F_6]^=$ is remarkable in a number of ways. It represents the only 6-coordinate haloaluminate, the only class of haloaluminates which may be prepared in water[20], the only haloaluminates occurring in nature, and it is apparently the monomeric parent unit of a family of condensed fluoroaluminates all of which contain hexafluoroaluminate units in their solid structures[21]. However, some doubt remains concerning the nature of the complex species existing in solutions of aluminum ions and fluoride ions[22]. Chloride and bromide form complexes, $M[AlX_4]$, with the corresponding simple aluminum(III) halides in organic solvents[20] or from melts of the mixed halides[23]. The tetrahedral AlX_4 unit also exists in the liquid and vapor states of the aluminum(III) halides, which are dimeric[24].

The halide complexes of gallium(III) are relatively rare, the best known species being the fluorides[25], $[GaF_6]^=$ and $[GaF_5(H_2O)]^=$. There is little indication that the remaining halides have any great tendency to form complexes with gallium(III) ions. In contrast to this behavior, and to the behavior of aluminum, indium(III) and thallium(III) form well characterized complexes with chloride and bromide (and iodide in the case of

19. Sherrill, *Z. phys. Chem.*, **43**, 705 (1903); **47**, 103 (1904); Garrett, *J. Am. Chem. Soc.*, **61**, 2744 (1939); Nayar, Srivastava, and Nyar, *J. Ind. Chem. Soc.*, **29**, 241, 248, 250 (1952); Kazi and Desai, *Current Sci.*, (*India*), **22**, 15 (1953); Ellendt and Cruse, *Z. physik. Chem.*, **201**, 130 (1952).

20. Malquori, *Atti R.*, [6] **5**, 510 (1927); [6] **7**, 745 (1928).

21. Thilo, *Naturwiss.*, **26**, 529 (1938); Brosset, *Z. anorg. Chem.*, **235**, 139 (1937).

22. Savchenko and Tananaev, *J. Gen. Chem.*, *U.S.S.R.*, **21**, 2505 (1951); cf. *Chem. Abs.*, **47**, 5836e (1953); Tananaev and Nekhamkina, *Trudy Komissii Anal. Khim.*, *Akad. Nauk. S.S.S.R.*, **3**, 89 (1951); cf. *Chem. Abstracts*, **47**, 5835e (1953).

23. Kendall, Crittenden, and Miller, *J. Am. Chem. Soc.*, **45**, 969 (1923); Plotnikov and Gorenbein, *J. Gen. Chem. Russ.*, **5**, 1108 (1935).

24. Harris, Wood, and Ritter, *J. Am. Chem. Soc.*, **73**, 3151 (1951); Gerding and Smit, *Z. physik. Chem.*, **50B**, 171 (1941); Deville and Troast, *Compt. rend.*, **45**, 821 (1857); Palmer and Elliott, *J. Am. Chem. Soc.*, **60**, 1852 (1938); Smits, Meijering, and Kamermans, *Proc. Acad. Sci.*, (*Amsterdam*), **34**, 1327 (1931); Smits and Meijering, *Z. physik. Chem.*, **41B**, 98 (1938).

25. Hannebahn and Klemm, *Z. anorg. Chem.*, **229**, 341 (1936); Pugh, *J. Chem. Soc.*, **1937**, 1046, 1959.

thallium)[26, 27, 28]. They apparently form no fluoro- complexes. The most typical species is $[MX_6]^=$, although the enneachlorodithallate(III) ion, $[Tl_2Cl_9]^=$ has been studied extensively[29].

From such observations it is commonly suggested that the more electropositive cations; i.e., Al^{+++} and Ga^{+++}, tend to form electrostatically bound complexes and, in consequence, show their greatest affinities for the most electronegative halogens. On the other hand, the relatively less electropositive ions, In^{+++} and Tl^{+++}, show a much greater tendency to form covalent bonds, and for that reason are most susceptible to complexation with the larger, more easily polarized halide ions.

Family IVA. Similar behavior is observed among the elements of group IVA (excluding carbon). Only the octahedral[30] hexafluorosilicate exists in the case of silicon, while germanium(IV) forms the analogous $[GeF_6]^=$ ion[31] and the relatively unstable hexachlorogermanate[32]. The complexes $[SnX_6]^=$ are reported for all four of the halides[33]. That fewer halogen complexes are formed by lead(IV) is a direct result of the strongly oxidizing nature of the ion.

Family VA. Tripositive arsenic and antimony are almost unique in their ability to exist either as the central atom in a complex species or as the donor atom in complexing with another metal ion (a property which is probably shared only by selenium and tellurium). The latter role will be discussed at

26. Hoard and Goldstein, *J. Chem. Phys.*, **3**, 645 (1935).
27. Klug and Alexander, *J. Am. Chem. Soc.*, **70**, 3064 (1948).
28. Benoit, *Bull. soc. chim., France*, **1949**, 518.
29. Hoard and Goldstein, *J. Chem. Phys.*, **3**, 199 (1935); Powell and Wells, *J. Chem. Soc.*, **1935**, 1008.
30. Ketelaar, *Z. Krist.*, **92**, 155 (1935); Hoard and Vincent, *J. Am. Chem. Soc.*, **62**, 3126 (1940).
31. Müller, *J. Am. Chem. Soc.*, **43**, 1087 (1921); Wykoff and Müller, *Am. J. Sci.*, [5] **13**, 346 (1927).
32. Laubengayer, Billings, and Newkirk, *J. Am. Chem. Soc.*, **62**, 546 (1946).
33. Skrabal and Gruber, *Monats.*, **38**, 19 (1917); Briggs, *Z. anorg. Chem.*, **82**, 441 (1913); Casey and Wyckoff, *Z. Krist.*, **89**, 469 (1934); Dickinson, *J. Am. Chem. Soc.*, **44**, 276 (1922); Ketelaar, Rietdyk, and Stoverer, *Rec. trav. chim.*, **56**, 907 (1937); Gosteanu, *Ber.*, **60**, 1312 (1927); Seubert, *Ber.*, **20**, 793 (1887); Brauner, *J. Chem. Soc.*, **65**, 393 (1894).

some length later (page 78). Species of the types $[MX_4]^-$ and $[MX_5]^=$ have been reported (for M = As, X = Cl or Br [34]; for M = Sb or Bi, X = F or Cl [35]). Bismuth(III) and antimony(III) also form hexahalo-anions. Recent x-ray investigations of complex antimony(III) fluorides [36] have been interpreted as showing that the pair of "s" electrons of the antimony are stereochemically active. Thus, K_2SbF_5, which contains discrete SbF_5 units, is not strictly 5-coordinate but is octahedral

Similarly, the ion $[Sb_2F_7]^-$, in its cesium salt, is probably made up of two trigonal bipyramids sharing a fluoride ion at a common apex and with one corner of each equatorial plane occupied by an electron pair.

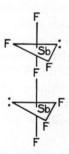

The only halide complex of arsenic(V) is $[AsF_6]^-$ [37]. The anions $[SbX_6]^-$ have been reported for X = F, Cl, or Br. The bromide complexes differ from the chloro- and fluoro- species in being highly colored and readily hydrolyzed. They may be polybromides of antimony(III) [37d]. Bismuth(V) does not form the fluoro- complex corresponding to that of antimony, but gives $[BiOF_6]^=$ instead [38].

First Transition Series. By far the most interesting halide complexes occurring among the metals of the first transition series are the fluoride

34. Petzold, *Z. anorg. Chem.*, **214**, 355, 365 (1933); Dehr, *J. Am. Chem. Soc.*, **48**, 275 (1926).
35. Gutbier and Müller, *Z. anorg. Chem.*, **128**, 137 (1923); Ephriam and Masimann, *Ber.* **54**, 396 (1921).
36. Bystrom and Wilhelmi, *Arkiv Kemi*, **3**, 373, 461 (1952); Byström, *Nature*, **167**, 780 (1951).
37. Schrewelius, *Z. anorg. Chem.*, **223**, 1935 (1935); Weinland and Feige, *Ber.*, **36**, 244, 252 (1903); Petzold, *Z. anorg. Chem.*, **215**, 92 (1933).
38. Ruff, *Z. anorg. Chem.*, **57**, 220 (1908).

complexes. Some of these are uniquely stable toward hydrolysis while others may support unusually high oxidation states for the metal ions. The relative resistance of some of the fluoro- complexes to dissociation or hydrolysis in aqueous medium, as compared to the remaining halo- complexes, is an indication of the relative affinities of the transition ions for these donors. It is obvious that the affinity for fluoride ion in these cases must exceed that for the oxygen donor species of the solvent water, and it is likely that the affinity for oxygen donors is greater than that for chloride or bromide, although our picture is greatly distorted in this latter case by the omnipresence of water as the solvent. The extreme difficulty with which fluoride ion is oxidized apparently makes the existence of strongly oxidizing metal fluoride complexes possible; however, it is not true that the highest known electrovalences of a given metal invariably occur in fluoride complexes. Figure 1.1 illustrates this point by comparing oxy- complexes of the elements of the first transition series with the corresponding fluoro- complexes. The general character of the fluoride complexes of these metals may be judged from the fact that most of the complexes containing higher valence states, such as heptafluorocobaltate(IV), are decomposed by water[39]. Some of the complexes of the more common oxidation states are much more stable.

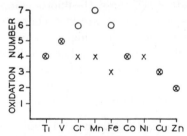

Fig. 1.1. Maximum valencies of the elements of the first transition series.
o = Maximum valencies found in oxy- complexes.
X = Maximum valencies found in fluro- complexes.

The fluoro- complexes[40] of iron(III) are noteworthy because of their importance in analytical chemistry. Iron(III) also forms relatively stable complexes with chloride ion as indicated by their extractability from aqueous hydrochloric acid with ether[41].

Cobalt(II) forms a number of complex fluorides and chlorides[42]. Physico-

39. Klemm and Huss, Z. anorg. allgem. Chem., 258, 221 (1949).
40. Remy and Busch, Ber., 66, 961 (1933).
41. Dodson, Forney, and Swift, J. Am. Chem. Soc., 58, 2573 (1936); Lindquist, Arkiv Kemi Min. Geol., 24A, No. 1 (1947).
42. Gmelin, "Handbuch der Anorganisen Chemie," Vol. 58A, pp. 398–461, Berlin, Verlag Chimie G.m.b., 1932.

chemical studies[43] on solutions of cobalt(II) halides in the presence of excess halide ion indicate the existence of $[CoX_4]^=$, the stability of the complexes decreasing in the order $Cl^- > Br^- > I^-$. Even the chloro complex is not very stable, its formation being detectable spectrophotometrically only in hydrochloric acid which is at least $2N$. A fluoro- complex of tetrapositive cobalt, K_3CoF_7, has been prepared[39] by fluorination of mixtures of potassium chloride and cobalt(II) chloride. It is fairly stable toward reduction, but at $450°$ is slowly converted by hydrogen to potassium hexafluorocobaltate(III).

The halide complexes of dipositive nickel are poorly characterized, the fluoride compounds being best known. When treated with elemental fluorine at elevated temperatures, mixtures of potassium chloride and nickel chloride yield potassium hexafluoronickelate(IV)[39], which is readily hydrolyzed and may be reduced to K_2NiF_4.

The composition of K_2MnF_6 coupled with the presence of manganese(IV) in a soluble compound justifies the assumption that the substance is a true complex[39, 44, 45]. Manganese(III) forms fluoro- and chloro- complexes having five halogen atoms and, presumably, one water molecule attached to each manganese[46].

Complex titanium halides of the form $[TiX_6]^=$, where X = F, Cl, or Br, have been characterized[47, 48]. Of these, the fluoro- complex is the most stable.

The halo- complexes of vanadium are best characterized for the tripositive oxidation state of the metal ion, higher valent vanadium tending to form oxy- and hydroxyhalo- complexes. The hexafluorovanadates(III) and pentafluoroaquovanadates have been identified[49], as have complex chlorides of the type $M_2[VCl_5(H_2O)]^{50}$. Tripositive chromium also forms halo- complexes of the type $M_2[CrX_5H_2O]^{44}$ and hexafluorochromates(III)[51].

43. Barvinok, *Zhur. fiz. Khim.*, *U.S.S.R.*, **22**, 1100 (1948); *Zhur. Obshchei Khim.*, **19**, 612, 1028 (1949); Varadi, *Acta Univ. Szeged., chim. et phys.*, **2**, 175 (1949); **3**, 62 (1950).
44. Weinland and Laurenstein, *Z. anorg. allgem. Chem.*, **20**, 40 (1899); Jenssen and Bardte, *Angew. Chem.*, **65**, 304 (1953).
45. Bode and Wendt, *Z. anorg. Chem.*, **269**, 165 (1952); Cox and Sharpe, *J. Chem. Soc.* **1953**, 1783.
46. Weinland and Dinkelacker, *Z. anorg. Chem.*, **60**, 173 (1908).
47. Ruff and Ipsen, *Ber.*, **36**, 1777 (1903); Rumpf, *Compt. rend.*, **202**, 950 (1936); Rosenheim and Schütte, *Z. anorg. Chem.*, **26**, 239 (1901).
48. Cox and Sharpe, *J. Chem. Soc.*, **1953**, 1783; Wernet, *Z. anorg. allgem. Chem.*, **272**, 279 (1953).
49. Neumann, *Ann.*, **244**, 336 (1888); Werner and Gubser, *Ber.*, **34**, 1579 (1901); Christensen, *J. prakt. Chem.*, [2] **35**, 161 (1887); Schulter, *Compt. rend.*, **152**, 1107, 1261 (1911).
50. Stähler, *Ber.*, **37**, 4411 (1904).
51. Fabris, *Gazz. chim. ital.*, **20**, 582 (1890); Helmolt, *Z. anorg. Chem.*, **3**, 125 (1898).

Scandium forms several complex halides, among which are the fluoro-complexes $[ScF_4]^-$, $[ScF_5]^=$, and $[ScF_6]^\equiv$. There is some evidence that the remaining elements of periodic family IIIB also form fluoro- complexes, although these are not so well characterized as those of the other transition elements[52]. The complexity of $KLaF_4$ is unlikely since the crystal structure indicates the presence of no finite $[LaF_4]^-$ groups[53].

Although copper(I) complexes are known[54] with chloride, bromide, and iodide ions, no fluoride complexes appear to exist. A great variety of complex halides has been reported for copper(II). The complexity of some of the double salts formed by copper(II) chloride and copper(II) bromide with alkali halides is in doubt since x-ray data show that $K_2CuCl_4 \cdot 2H_2O$ and $(NH_4)_2CuBr_4 \cdot 2H_2O$ exist as lattice compounds of the simple salts. However, physical evidence indicates that $[CuCl_3]^-$ and $[CuCl_4]^=$ do exist[55]. The latter is reported to be a distorted tetrahedron[56]. Copper(III) has been reported in K_3CuF_6[39].

The relatively greater tendency of the metallic ions of the first transition series to form complex ions with fluoride and chloride rather than with bromide and iodide and the general tendency of the complexes to dissociate or hydrolyze in solution appears to justify the supposition that the binding force involved is essentially electrostatic. This suggestion is supported by the considerable stability of hexafluoroferrate(III) and hexafluorotitanate(IV) which involve electronic states normally associated with unusually stable gaseous ions (Chapter 3).

Second and Third Transition Series and Family IB. In contrast to the elements of subgroups IIIA, IVA, VA, and VIA, the elements of the three transition series show a marked increase in the importance of their higher oxidation states as the atomic weight of the metal increases. This is related to the types of compounds formed by each element, since high oxidation states ions usually exist in covalent compounds. The halide complexes of the platinum metals include some of the most widely known complex ions. This is doubtless a consequence of the fact that their simple compounds are for the most part "simple" in name only (for example, platinum(II) chloride is not salt-like but exists as bridged, covalent, giant molecules).

Complexes of the type $[PtX_6]^=$ have been characterized for all four of the

52. Dergunov, *Doklady Akad. Nauk*, *S.S.S.R.*, **85**, 1025 (1952); cf. *Chem. Abs.* **47**, 1524b (1953).
53. Ref. 16, p. 290.
54. Szabo and Szabo, *Z. physik. Chem.*, **166**, 288 (1933); Fontana, Gorin, Kidder, and Meredith, *Ind. Eng. Chem.*, **44**, 363 (1952); Harris, *J. Proc. Roy. Soc.*, *N.S. Wales*, **85**, 138 (1952).
55. Rossi and Strocchi, *Gazz. chim. ital.*, **78**, 725 (1948). (see Ref. 72c)
56. Helmholz and Kruh, *J. Am. Chem. Soc.*, **74**, 1176 (1952).

common halides, the chloride and bromide being the easiest to prepare[57]. The iodo complex tends to liberate iodine with the reduction of the platinum to the dipositive state[58], while salts of hexafluoroplatinate(IV) readily hydrolyze. The complex fluorides have been prepared by heating the addition product of the chloroplatinate and bromine trifluoride[59]. They are diamagnetic, indicating d^2sp^3 hybridization and covalent bonding (despite the high electronegativity of the fluorine). The Pt—F bond distance is greater than that expected for a covalent link, which indicates that the bond has a considerable degree of ionic character[60]. Mixed halo- complexes, such as $[PtCl_4Br_2]^=$, have been prepared[61], as well as the series of hydroxychloro-anions $[PtCl_n(OH)_{6-n}]^=$ (page 4). The planar tetrahalide complexes of platinum(II) have been prepared with chloride, bromide, and iodide. Salts of these anions are generally obtained by reduction of the corresponding hexahaloplatinate(IV) salts with sulfur dioxide[62], potassium oxalate[62b, 62c, 63], potassium hydrogen sulfite[64], hydrogen sulfide[65], potassium hypophosphite[66], or hydrazine salts[67]. Grinberg[68] has suggested that reduction by hydrazine salts proceeds in two steps:

$$K_2PtCl_6 + N_2H_4 \cdot 2HCl \rightarrow Pt^0 + N_2 + 2KCl + 6HCl$$

$$2KCl + K_2PtCl_6 + Pt^0 \rightarrow 2K_2PtCl_4$$

In support of this argument, Grinberg has shown that hexachloroplatinate ion is reduced to tetrachloroplatinate(II) by platinum black which has been freshly prepared by the reduction of hexachloroplatinate(IV) with hydrazine sulfate. Exchange experiments have shown that halide ions of platinum(II) complexes are labile, the bromide of $[PtBr_4]^=$ being subject to complete exchange; however, the central platinum atom does not undergo

57. Weber, *J. Am. Chem. Soc.*, **30**, 29 (1908); Rudnick and Cooke, *J. Am. Chem. Soc.*, **39**, 633 (1917); Bielmann and Arduson, *Ber.*, **36**, 1365 (1903); Gutbier and Bauriedel, *Ber.*, **41**, 4243 (1908).
58. Datta, *J. Chem. Soc.*, **103**, 426 (1913).
59. Sharpe, *J. Chem. Soc.*, **1950**, 3444; **1953**, 197; Schlesinger and Tapley, *J. Am. Chem. Soc.*, **46**, 276 (1924).
60. Mellor, Report of the Brisbane meeting of the Australian and New Zealand Assoc. for the Advancement of Science, Vol. XXVIII, 131, May 1951.
61. Klement, *Z. anorg. Chem.*, **164**, 195 (1927).
62. Claus, *Ann.*, **107**, 137 (1858); Klason, *Ber.*, **37**, 1360 (1904); Vezes, *Bull. soc. chim.*, [3] **19**, 879 (1898).
63. Mikhelis, *Zhur. priklad. Khim.*, **26**, 221 (1953); cf. *Chem. Abs.*, **47**, 11060i (1953).
64. Lea, *Am. J. Sci.*, [3] **48**, 398, 400 (1894).
65. Böttger, *J. prakt. Chem.*, [1] **91**, 251 (1863).
66. Lea, *Am. J. Sci.*, [3] **48**, 397 (1894).
67. Gil'degershel and Shagesultanova, *Zhur. priklad. Khim.*, **26**, 222 (1953); Cooley and Busch, unpublished experiments (1954).
68. Grinberg, *Zhur. priklad. Khim.*, **26**, 224 (1953).

exchange[69]. The rates of exchange vary in the order $CN^- > I^- > Br^- > Cl^-$. It is, at first thought, paradoxical that the complexes having the greater thermodynamic stabilities exchange most rapidly ($\Delta F_{form.}$: $[PtCl_4]^=$, -21.8; $[PtBr_4]^=$, -24.5). This ease of "self-displacement" may be a peculiarity of planar complexes since ferrocyanide ion does not exchange with cyanide ion in water[70]. The diammine $Pt(NH_3)_2Br_3$ which was once thought to contain tripositive, 5-coordinate platinum has been shown rather to exist as a molecular compound of $[Pt^{II}(NH_3)_2Br_2]$ and $[Pt^{IV}(NH_3)_2Br_4]$[71].

In contrast to platinum, the tetrapositive oxidation state of palladium is rather unstable. The hexachloro- and hexabromopalladate(IV) anions may be prepared[72] in much the same way as are the platinum complexes; however, their solutions are unstable toward evolution of the halogen and they both react with aqueous ammonia to liberate nitrogen. The hexafluoropalladate(IV) has recently been prepared by Sharpe[73]. Its salts are yellow; they darken rapidly in air and are immediately hydrolyzed in cold water. Salts of the planar tetrahalopalladate(II), $[PdX_4]^=$, are known[74] for $X = Cl$, Br, and I.

The great affinity of palladium(II) for halide ions may be seen from the dissociation constant[75] of $[PdCl_4]^=$ ($K_d = 6 \times 10^{-14}$). The supposed palladium(III) complex, $M_2Pd^{III}Cl_5$[76] probably contains both palladium(II) and palladium(IV).

The tendency for higher oxidation states to become more stable with increasing atomic weight of the metal is illustrated by cobalt, rhodium, and iridium. The only strictly halogen complexes in which cobalt has an oxidation number greater than two are the fluoro- complexes. Dipositive rhodium, on the other hand, forms no complexes. Rhodium is tripositive in all of its halogen complexes except the recently reported rhodium(IV) fluoro-

69. Grinberg and Filinov, *Compt. rend. acad. sci., U.R.S.S.*, **23**, 912 (1939); cf. *Chem. Abs.* **34**, 1246² (1940); **31**, 453 (1941); cf. *Chem. Abs.*, **37**, 571⁹ (1943); Grinberg, *Bull. acad. sci., U.R.S.S., Ser. phys.*, 349 (1940); cf. *Chem. Abs.* **35**, 3895³ (1941).
70. Grinberg and Nikol'skaya, *Zhur. priklad. Khim.*, **24**, 893 (1951); cf. *Chem. Abs.* **47**, 4709a (1953).
71. Cohen and Davidson, *J. Am. Chem. Soc.*, **73**, 1955 (1951); Brossett, *Arkiv Kemi Min. Geol.*, **25A**, No. 19 (1948).
72. Puche, *Compt. rend.*, **200**, 1206 (1935); **208**, 656 (1939); Rosenheim and Maas, *Z. anorg. Chem.*, **18**, 331 (1898); Gutbier and Krell, *Ber.*, **38**, 2385 (1905).
73. Sharpe, *J. Chem. Soc.*, **1953**, 197.
74. Gutbier, *Ber.*, **38**, 2107 (1905); Gutbier and Krell, *Ber.*, **38**, 3969 (1905); Gutbier, Krell and Janssen, *Z. anorg. Chem.*, **47**, 23, 1292 (1906); Gutbier and Woernle, **47**, 2716 (1906); Gutbier and Fellner, *Z. anorg. Chem.*, **95**, 129 (1916); Dickinson, *J. Am. Chem. Soc.*, **44**, 2404 (1922); Cox and Preston, *J. Chem. Soc.*, **1933**, 1089; Theilacker, *Z. anorg. Chem.*, **234**, 161 (1937).
75. Templeton, Watt, and Garner, *J. Am. Chem. Soc.*, **65**, 1608 (1943).
76. Wöhler and Martin, *Z. anorg. Chem.*, **57**, 398 (1908).

complexes[77]. Three formulations are reported for the halorhodiates(III), M_2RhX_5, M_3RhX_6, and $M_3Rh_2X_9$. All three types are known for bromide and chloride[78], but the only fluoro- complex is the ion $[RhF_6]^\equiv$. The structures of most of these compounds are still open to question.

Both tripositive and tetrapositive iridium form complexes with chloride and bromide. The iridium(III) complexes are of the types $[IrX_6]^\equiv$ and $[IrX_5(H_2O)]^{=\ [79]}$, whereas iridium(IV) is found in the anion $[IrX_6]^=$, (X = Br, Cl, or F). The hexabromo compound is unstable toward evolution of bromine[80].

Ruthenium(III) and ruthenium(IV) form a variety of complex halides and aquohalo- or hydroxohalo- complexes. Ruthenium trichloride apparently exists in several hydrated forms, analogous to the hydrate isomers of chromium(III) (see Chapter 7)[81]. Some of the probable "hydrate isomers" are $Ru(H_2O)Cl_3$, which contains no ionizable chloride, and the reported cis and trans forms of $[RuCl_2(H_2O)_2]Cl$. Dwyer and Backhouse[81] suggest that the ruthenium is 6-coordinate in all of these complexes. As compared to the similar platinum compounds, halide complexes of ruthenium show a marked tendency to hydrolyze and to retain water in their coordination spheres. As with the platinum analogues, $[RuBr_6]^=$ is less easily hydrolyzed than $[RuCl_6]^{=\ [81]}$. Ruthenium(III) forms two types of anionic chloro- complexes $[RuCl_6]^\equiv$ and $[RuCl_5(H_2O)]^=$, while ruthenium(IV) forms the complexes formulated as $[RuCl_6]^=$ and $[RuCl_5(OH)]^{-\ [82,\ 83,\ 84]}$. It has been shown that $[RuCl_5(OH)]^=$ is actually dimeric in the crystalline state, having the structure $[Cl_5Ru—O—RuCl_5]^{4-}$ (see p. 167). Fluorination of hexachlororuthenate(IV) yields a white crystalline compound of the composition K_2RuF_8, which hydrolyzes readily and darkens on standing[85]. It is possible that ruthenium(VI) is present, and that it is octacoordinate.

77. Weise and Klemm, Z. anorg. allgem. Chem., **272,** 211 (1953); Sharpe, J. Chem. Soc., **1950,** 3444.
78. Delepine, Bull. soc. chim., Belg., **36,** 108 (1927); Gutbier and Bertsch, Z. anorg. Chem., **129,** 67 (1923); Meyer and Hoehne, Z. anorg. Chem., **231,** 372 (1937); Meyer, Kawkzyk, and Hoehne, **232,** 410; Poulenc, Compt. rend., **190,** 639 (1930); Ann. chim., [Xi] **4,** 567 (1935).
79. Delepine, Bull. soc. chim., [4] **3,** 901 (1908); Delepine-Tard, Ann. chim. phys., [10] **4,** 282 (1935).
80. Delepine, Ann. chim. phys., [9] **7,** 277 (1917); Schlesinger and Topley, J. Am. Chem. Soc., **46,** 276 (1924); Dobroborskaya, Zhur. priklad. Khim., **26,** 223 (1953); cf. Chem. Abs., **47,** 1106lg (1953).
81. Dwyer and Backhouse, J. Proc. Roy. Soc., N.S. Wales, **83,** 138 (1949).
82. Gutbier and Niemann, Z. anorg. Chem., **141,** 312 (1924); Howe, J. Am. Chem. Soc., **49,** 2389 (1927); Charonnat, Ann. chim., [10] **16,** 72 (1931); Compt. rend., **181,** 867 (1925).
83. Howe, J. Am. Chem. Soc., **26,** 942 (1904).
84. Charonnat, Compt. rend., **180,** 1271 (1925).
85. Aynsley, Peacock, and Robinson, Chem. Ind., **1952,** 1002.

The hexahalo- salts M_3OsX_6 and M_2OsX_6 are reported where X = Cl or Br in the first case[86] and for X = F, Cl, Br, or I, in the latter[87]. Recrystallization of the hexachloro- and hexabromoosmiate(IV) salts from dilute halogen acid leads to hydrolysis. Mixed halogen complexes, such as $[OsCl_5Br]^=$ and $[OsCl_3Br_3]^=$, and hydroxohalo- complexes, such as $[OsX_5(OH)]^=$, are also reported[88]. Osmium also forms halo- complexes in its higher oxidation states. Osmium(VI) exists in the tetrahaloosmyl complexes $[OsO_2X_4]^{=89}$, and the oxydihaloosmyl complexes $[OsO_3X_2]^{=90}$. X-ray data show that the salts $M_2[OsO_2X_4]$ are similar in crystal structure to potassium hexachloroplatinate(IV)[91]. Fluoride ion combines with osmium (VIII) fluoride to produce a white solid that may be a 9- or 10-coordinate complex[92]; the material has not been analyzed. Dissolution of osmium(VIII) oxide in fluoride solution leads to the formation of unstable compounds which presumably contain complex anions, such as $[OsO_4F_2]^{=93}$.

The halo- complexes of rhenium are intermediate in character between those of the platinum metals and those of the remaining transition elements. Thus, rhenium(IV) forms complexes of the type $[ReX_6]^=$ with fluoride (like the IVB, VB, and VIB metals) and also with the other halogens, even iodide (a behavior more to be expected of the platinum metals)[94]. An interesting similarity is found between some rhenium(IV) and rhenium(V) chloro- complexes and those of ruthenium(III) and ruthenium(IV). In addition to hexachlororhenate(IV), the pentachlororhenium complexes $[Re^{IV}Cl_5(OH)]^=$, $[Re^VCl_5O]^=$, and $[Re^{IV}_2Cl_{10}O]^{4-}$ also exist[94f].

Molybdenum and tungsten form complex halides or oxyhalides in their di-, tri-, penta-, and hexavalent states. Tripositive molybdenum forms fluoro- and chloro- complexes of the types $[MoX_5(H_2O)]^=$ and $[MoX_6]^{=95}$.

86. Claus and Jacoby, *J. prakt. Chem.*, **90**, 78 (1863); Crowell, Brenton, and Evenson, *J. Am. Chem. Soc.*, **60**, 1105 (1938).
87. Ruff and Tscherch, *Ber.*, **46**, 932 (1913); Dwyer and Gibson, *Nature*, **165**, 1012 (1950); Wintrebert, *Ann. chim. phys.*, [7] **28**, 133 (1903).
88. Krauss and Wilkin, *Z. anorg. Chem.*, **137**, 360 (1924).
89. Wintrebert, *Ann. chim. phys.*, [7] **28**, 54, 86 (1903).
90. Wintrebert, *Ann. chim. phys.*, [7] **28**, 114 (1901).
91. Hoard and Grenko, *Z. Krist.*, **87**, 100 (1934).
92. Ruff and Tscherch, *Ber.*, **46**, 929 (1913).
93. Tschugaev, *Compt. rend.*, **167**, 162 (1918); Krauss and Wilkin, *Z. anorg. Chem.*, **145**, 151 (1925).
94. Ruff and Kwasnik, *Z. anorg. Chem.*, **219**, 76 (1934); Schmid, *Z. anorg. Chem.*, **212**, 187 (1933); Hölemann, *Z. anorg. Chem.*, **211**, 195 (1933); Noddack and Noddack, *Z. anorg. Chem.*, **215**, 129 (1933); Briscoe, Roderson, and Rudge, *J. Chem. Soc.*, **1931**, 3218; Jezowska-Trzebiatowska, *Trav. soc. sci. et lettres Wroclaw*, Ser. B, **39**, 5 (1953).
95. Rosenheim and Braun, *Z. anorg. Chem.*, **46**, 320 (1905); Foerster and Fricke, *Z. angew. Chem.*, **36**, 458 (1923).

However, only the dimeric anion $[W_2Cl_9]^=$ is known for tungsten(III)[96] (for structure, see page 7). It seems likely that a tungsten-tungsten bond is present in this anion since the substance is diamagnetic[97]. The most stable oxyhalo- complexes of molybdenum and tungsten in their penta- and hexa-positive states are fluoro- complexes, such as $[Mo^{VI}O_2F_4]^=$, $[W^{VI}O_2F_4]^=$, and $[Mo^VOF_5]^=$, all of which are isomorphous with $[Nb^VOF_5]^=$. The affinity of fluoride ion for hexavalent molybdenum and tungsten may be illustrated by the fact that most of the precipitation and color reactions of molybdate and tungstate ions are masked by the presence of fluoride ion[98].

An interesting feature of the halogen complexes of niobium and tantalum is the occurrence of high coordination numbers (see Chapter 10). This is undoubtedly associated with the fact that the only significant strictly halogen complexes of these metals are those of the fluoride ion. Both of these elements form heptafluoro- anions of the type $[M^VF_7]^=$. Their structures are discussed on page 393. In addition, tantalum(V) forms an 8-coordinate fluoro- complex $[TaF_8]^=$ which exists in the form of a tetragonal antiprism[99]. Six-coordinate hexafluoroniobate(V) is also known, as is its tantalum analog[100]. The heptafluorotantalate(V) is somewhat more stable than the niobium(V) compound which hydrolyzes to $[NbOF_5]^=$, and this difference has served in helping to separate the two metals. Oxyhalo- complexes are formed by both metals, the oxyfluorides being the most stable.

The same trends are observable among the halogen complexes of zirconium and hafnium, the outstanding characteristics being variable coordination number and decreasing stability of the complexes with increasing atomic weight of the halide. The latter point is illustrated by the fact that zirconium dioxide is dissolved by hydrofluoric acid and that only the fluoro-complexes are stable in aqueous media[101]. The chloro- and bromo- complexes are prepared in alcohol[102]. The complexes are of the types $[MX_5]^-$, $[MX_5(H_2O)]^=$, $[MX_6]^=$, $[MX_7]^=$ (see Chapter 10). The structure of the supposed 5-coordinate species is still open to question[103]. The fluoro- complexes are used in the separation of hafnium and zirconium[104].

96. Olsson, *Ber.*, **46**, 566 (1913); Olsson, Collenberg, and Sandved, *Z. anorg. chem.*, **130**, 16 (1923).
97. Brossett, *Nature*, **135**, 824 (1935); Pauling, *Chem. Eng. News*, **1947**, 2970.
98. Feigl, *Ann. Chem. Acta*, **2**, 397 (1948).
99. Hoard, *J. Am. Chem. Soc.*, **61**, 1252 (1939); **64**, 633 (1942); de Marigroc, *Compt. rend.*, **63**, 85 (1866); Hoard, Paper presented at 6th annual symposium, Div. Phys. and Inorg. Chem., Columbus, Ohio, Dec., 1941.
100. Hahn and Putter, *Z. anorg. Chem.*, **120**, 71 (1922).
101. Connick and McVey, *J. Am. Chem. Soc.*, **71**, 3182 (1949).
102. Schwarz and Giese, *Z. anorg. Chem.*, **176**, 209 (1928); Rosenheim and Frank, *Ber.*, **38**, 812 (1905).
103. Haendler and Robinson, *J. Am. Chem. Soc.*, **75**, 3846 (1953); Haendler, Wheeler, and Robinson, *J. Am. Chem. Soc.*, **74**, 2352 (1952).
104. Larsen, Fernelius, and Quill, *Ind. Eng. Chem., Anal. Ed.*, **15**, 512 (1943); Schultz

The solubilities of the silver halides increase sharply as the concentration of excess halide ion is increased[105]. The study of this solubility dependence indicates the formation of a series of complexes ranging from $[Ag_3X]^{++}$ to $[AgX_4]^{\equiv}$, and possibly $[Ag_2X_6]^{4-}$ [106]. The order of stability of both silver and gold halide complexes is $I > Br > Cl$ (as is also commonly observed among the platinum metals). The silver complexes best known in the solid state are of the types $[AgX_2]^-$ and $[AgX_3]^{=}$ [107]. Unipositive gold normally forms 2-coordinate, linear complexes of the type $[AuCl_2]^-$ [108], while gold(III) forms 4-coordinate, planar complexes of the type $[AuX_4]^-$ [109]. Gold forms many bridged halogen compounds (page 19). The substance having the empirical formula $CsAuCl_3$ should be formulated as $Cs_2Au^IAu^{III}Cl_6$, containing equivalent amounts of gold(I) and gold(III) (see Chapter 9).

Complexes Containing Halide Groups as a Less Abundant Donor Species

Many metals, especially those of the platinum group, form halo- complexes containing three, four, or five halide groups; however, with the exception of the hexafluorocobaltate(III), cobalt(III) complexes are not known with more than three halide groups. Indeed, the mixed complexes which have been most significant in the development of the coordination theory are those which contain one, two, or three coordinated halides and five, four or three neutral groups. Chloropentamminecobalt(III) chloride, $[Co(NH_3)_5Cl]Cl_2$, is one of the longest known cobalt(III) ammines and is the chief product obtained by atmospheric oxidation of solutions containing cobalt(II) chloride, ammonium chloride, and ammonium hydroxide. The coordinated chloride is only slowly removed by the action of silver nitrate, even when heated. The salt serves, however, as a starting material for the preparation of many other cobalt(III) ammines, not only by replacement of the chloride, but also by replacement of one of the ammonia molecules. Heating with ammonium carbonate, for example, gives carbonatotetramminecobalt(III) chloride, $[Co(NH_3)_4CO_3]Cl$. It has also been utilized in

and Larsen, *J. Am. Chem. Soc.*, **72**, 3610 (1950); Huffman and Lilly, *J. Am. Chem. Soc.*, **73**, 2902 (1951).

105. Eber and Schühly, *J. prakt. Chem.*, **158**, 176 (1941); *Z. anorg. allgem. Chem.*, **248**, 32 (1941).

106. Bern and Leden, *Svensk. Kem. Tidskr.*, **65**, 88 (1953); *Z. Naturforsch.*, **89**, 719 (1953); Chateau and Pounadiev, *Science et indus. phot.*, **23**, 225 (1952); Yatsimirskii, *Doklady Akad. Nauk.*, *S.S.S.R.*, **77**, 819 (1951); cf. *Chem. Abs.*, **45**, 7462 (1951).

107. Forbes and Cole, *J. Am. Chem. Soc.*, **43**, 2492 (1921); Harris and Schafer, *J. Proc. Roy. Soc.*, *N.S. Wales*, **85**, 148 (1952); Harris, *J. Proc. Roy. Soc.*, *N.S. Wales* **85**, 142 (1952).

108. Lengfield, *Am. Chem. J.*, **26**, 324 (1901).

109. Cox and Webster, *J. Chem. Soc.*, **1936**, 1635.

studies directed at elucidation of the mechanism of substitution reactions of 6-coordinate complexes[110].

The two forms of dichlorobis(ethylenediamine)cobalt(III) chloride, [Co en$_2$ Cl$_2$]Cl, are used in the preparation of other ethylenediamine cobalt salts. Both the *cis* and *trans* forms of this complex are readily prepared, and are stable in water solution for some time, though the change in color of the solution indicates aquation; the *cis*-dibromobis(ethylenediamine)cobalt(III) ion rearranges with extreme ease to the *trans* form, and both isomers aquate rapidly; the corresponding iodo compounds are not known.

Chloropentamminechromium(III) chloride, [Cr(NH$_3$)$_5$Cl]Cl$_2$, is obtained, together with the hexammine, by the action of liquid ammonia on anhydrous chromium(III) chloride. Once formed, the pentammine is converted to the hexammine with extreme slowness, which may be due, however, to the very slight solubility of the pentammine in liquid ammonia.

cis-Dichlorobis(ethylenediamine)chromium(III) chloride is most easily obtained by the thermal decomposition of tris(ethylenediamine)chromium(III) chloride. The reverse reaction takes place very slowly when the dichloro- salt is suspended in ethylenediamine. Complexes of very similar type are also encountered in the chemistries of the platinum metals.

In general, the complexes containing halo- groups as less abundant donor species may be grouped according to the same classification as that given for the strictly halide complexes; i.e., those which show little tendency to dissociate in solution (penetration complexes), and those which change upon dissolution in a polar solvent as a result of displacement by solvent molecules (normal complexes). Only the first class of compounds is of great significance here since the more labile species cannot experience a change in the state of aggregation without extensive change in their natures. Thus, [Fe(NH$_3$)$_2$Cl$_2$] cannot be dissolved in water and subsequently recovered, while many strictly halide complexes may dissociate in solution but still be recoverable in the original form upon removal of the solvent.

Complexes Involving Halogen Bridges

The halide ions sometimes donate pairs of electrons to two metallic ions simultaneously, forming a "bridge." Aluminum chloride (page 6) and rhenium(III) chloride[111] have been shown to have the structures

110. Brønsted, *Z. physik. Chem.*, **102**, 169 (1922); Garrick, *Trans. Faraday Soc.*, **33**, 486 (1937); Lamb and Fairball, *J. Am. Chem. Soc.*, **45**, 378 (1923); Lamb and Marden, *J. Am. Chem. Soc.*, **33**, 1873 (1911); Adell, *Z. anorg. allgem. Chem.*, **249**, 251 (1942).

and other volatile metal halides are probably similar. The dimeric tertiary phosphine and arsine compounds also contain double halide bridges (page 81) and a number of olefin complexes and thio ether complexes have been formulated in the same way (see page 83). Alkyl derivatives of gold bromide are dimeric and probably have the structure[112]

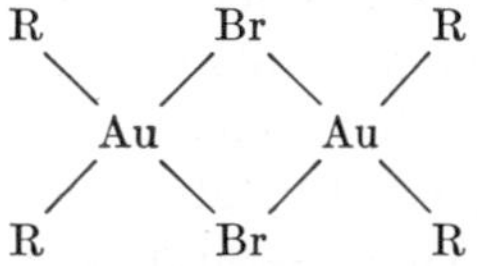

$$
\begin{array}{ccccc}
\text{R} & & \text{Br} & & \text{R} \\
& \diagdown \;\diagup & & \diagdown \;\diagup & \\
& \text{Au} & & \text{Au} & \\
& \diagup \;\diagdown & & \diagup \;\diagdown & \\
\text{R} & & \text{Br} & & \text{R}
\end{array}
$$

The presence of double bridges in platinum(II) chloride results in the formation of an infinite chain of $PtCl_4$ groups.

In addition to double halogen bridges, triple or single bridges may be formed. The triple bridge is illustrated by ions of the type $[M^{III}_2X_9]^{\equiv}$ (see page 7), while single halogen bridges occur in such species as $[AlF_5]^=$ (page 389). The compounds

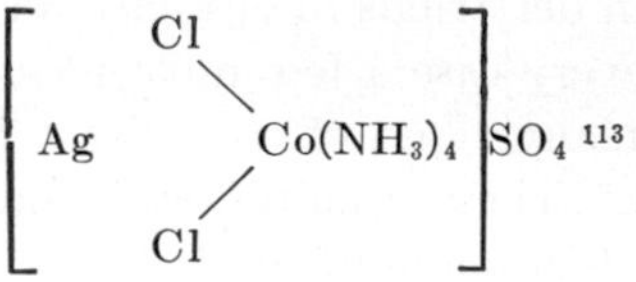

$$
\left[\text{Ag} \underset{\text{Cl}}{\overset{\text{Cl}}{\diagup}} \text{Co(NH}_3)_4 \right] \text{SO}_4 \;^{113} \quad \text{and}
$$

$$
\left[\text{Ag} \underset{\text{Cl}}{\overset{\text{Cl}}{\diagup}} \text{Co(NH}_3)_3(\text{H}_2\text{O}) \right] \text{SO}_4 \;^{114}
$$

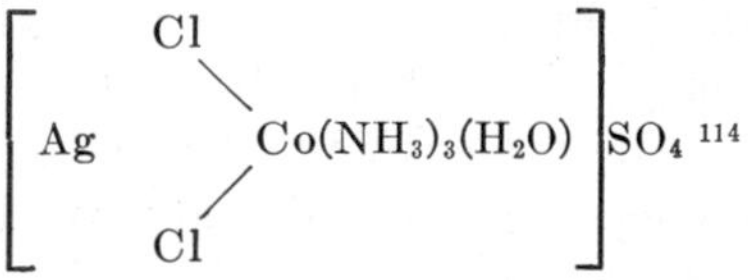

may also exemplify single bridges. When silver ion is added to a solution of the dichlorotetramminecobalt(III) ion, silver chloride does not precipitate at once, but the silver ions lose their ionic property through coordination with the chloride of the cobalt(III) complex. The ion so formed is not stable, however, and slowly precipitates silver chloride.

The phenomenon of "interaction absorption" is often observed in bridged halogen complexes. When the halides (cyanides, or oxides) of a metal in two different oxidation states are associated in a single molecule or ion (or possibly in such relatively less intimate admixture as crystal compounds or solutions—the point is not clear), a high degree of color is developed. Thus, $CuCl_2 \cdot CuCl$; $SbCl_3 \cdot SbCl_5$; $SnCl_2 \cdot SnCl_4$; $Cs_2Au^IAu^{II}Cl_9$; and $[Pd(NH_3)_2Br_2] \cdot [Pd(NH_3)_2Br_4]$ are all highly colored[60]. In none of these cases

111. Wriggee and Biltz, *Z. anorg. allgem. Chem.*, **228**, 372 (1936).
112. Gibson and Simonsen, *J. Chem. Soc.*, **1930**, 2531; Buroway, *et al.*, *J. Chem. Soc.*, **1937**, 1690.
113. Werner, *Z. anorg. Chem.*, **14**, 31 (1897).
114. Werner, *Z. anorg. Chem.*, **15**, 155 (1897).

has conclusive evidence for an intermediate oxidation state of the metal been obtained; indeed, strong evidence indicates the nonexistence of such states. In the first example the ridiculous assumption of the ion $Cu^{1.5+}$ would be necessary, while in the case of the diammino palladium compound, x-ray data and magnetic behavior definitely preclude the existence of the intermediate state. Nonetheless, a resonance between the two oxidation states produces high color and probably renders the two metal atoms indistinguishable. The probablity that a halogen (or similar) bridge is necessary for this phenomenon is supported by the fact that rapid electron exchange occurs between the coordinately saturated complexes, $[Os^{II}dipy_3]^{++}$ and $[Os^{III}dipy_3]^{+++}$, without the development of high color[115].

The Donor Properties of Oxygen

Hydrate Formation

All metallic ions apparently form hydrates in aqueous solution, frequently surrounding themselves with large numbers of molecules of water. Part of this water is held by van der Waals forces only, but it is difficult to escape the conclusion that in every case a few molecules at least are coordinated to the metallic ion. In many cases, of course, the hydrates can be crystallized from the solution.* These usually retain only enough molecules of water to satisfy the coordination number of the metallic ion, but sometimes, as with the alums, stable hydrates contain more than this amount. To account for these we may assume that (a) the excess water is not chemically combined, but is held in place by the demands of the lattice structure, (b) the coordination number of the metal is abnormal, (c) second and even third coordination spheres are formed, (d) the molecules of water are polymeric or (e) part of the water is combined with anion. It is often assumed that water of hydration which is not lost at 100°C must be chemically combined, but this does not necessarily follow, for lattice compounds sometimes show considerable stability. On the other hand, chemically combined water may escape from salts at low temperatures—even at room temperature—if the anion is one which readily coordinates with the cation, thus displacing the water from the coordination sphere.

Werner recognized that water molecules are sometimes held by feeble, nonchemical forces in writing formulas such as $[Co(NH_3)_5Cl]Cl_2 \cdot H_2O$. The water may be removed from this compound without changing its properties except for disruption of the crystal lattice, while dehydration of the isomeric $[Co(NH_3)_5H_2O]Cl_3$ is accompanied by change in color and solubility, and by loss of ionic function of one chloride ion.

115. Dwyer, Mellor, and Gyarfas, *Nature*, **166**, 176 (1950).

* Many anions also have the power of combining with water—this union takes place through hydrogen bonding.

In his early papers, Werner[116] also gave expression to the thought that several coordination spheres can form around a positive ion. He argued that when water molecules form a coordination sphere around a positive ion, a negative charge is induced on the inner surface of the sphere, so that the outer surface bears a positive charge, just as the metal ion itself does. This enables it to attract another sphere of water molecules, which will likewise bear an induced charge. The process may be repeated several times.

Closely related to this hypothesis was the thought that water exists in hydrates in the polymeric form. In view of the fact that water as such is associated, this is not an unreasonable assumption, though Werner had little experimental evidence on which to support it. The fact that many salts contain exactly twice as many water molecules as can be explained by the coordination theory made it an easy assumption. Such an explanation seems naive, but the fact that "multiple coordination spheres" do exist in solution cannot be denied. Their existence has been demonstrated by the diffusion studies of Brintzinger (Chapter 18) and by the polarographic work of Laitinen and his co-workers[117].

As is to be expected, the ease with which metallic ions form hydrates increases with increasing charge and with decreasing radius. The ions of the alkali metals except lithium and sodium are seldom hydrated in the solid state, and the hydrates of these two are unstable; divalent ions of the lighter metals are usually hydrated (unless they exist in highly insoluble compounds) and trivalent ions, nearly always so. In any periodic group the stability of the hydrates is greatest for the smallest ions, while the *number* of water molecules normally held is greatest for the large ions. Even in complexes in which water molecules undoubtedly occupy positions in a true coordination sphere, the nature of the oxygen-metal bond varies a great deal. Hunt and Taube[118] showed that the water in the hydrated forms of Al^{+++}, Ga^{+++} and Th^{4+} exchange with the solvent water in about three minutes, so the metal-oxygen bond must have a considerable degree of ionic character. The hydrated chromium(III) ion, on the other hand, exchanges very slowly, the halftime being about forty hours. They made the observation, also, that all of the cations studied show a greater affinity for H_2O^{18} than for H_2O^{16}. The hydrated cobalt(III) ion exchanges rapidly. This is probably not due to a lack of covalent bonding, but to a rapid electron exchange between the hydrated cobalt(III) and cobalt(II) ions, and a rapid exchange between the latter and the solvent water[119].

116. Werner, *Z. anorg. Chem.*, **3**, 267 (1893).
117. Laitinen, Bailar, Holtzclaw, and Quagliano, *J. Am. Chem. Soc.*, **70**, 2999 (1948); Laitinen, Frank and Kivalo, *J. Am. Chem. Soc.*, **75**, 2865 (1953).
118. Hunt and Taube, *J. Chem. Phys.*, **18**, 757 (1950); **19**, 602 (1951).
119. Friedman, Taube, and Hunt, *J. Chem. Phys.*, **18**, 759 (1950).

Hydroxyl Coordination

The hydroxide ion has a strong coordinating tendency, partly because it has three pairs of unshared electrons, but chiefly because of its negative charge. The hydrates of highly charged metallic ions readily lose protons with the formation of hydroxo complexes:

$$[Al(H_2O)_6]^{+++} \rightarrow H^+ + [Al(H_2O)_5OH]^{++} \rightarrow H^+ + [Al(H_2O)_4(OH)_2]^+, \text{ etc.}$$

The aquo ammine complexes undergo the same type of reaction: $[Co(NH_3)_5H_2O]^{+++} \rightleftharpoons [Co(NH_3)_5OH]^{++} + H^+$. The phenomenon underlies our present theories of acidity, hydrolysis and amphoterism, and is discussed in Chapter 12.

The hydroxide group can act as a bridging group between two metallic ions, under which conditions it is almost entirely devoid of basic properties. This bridge forming ability may extend to great lengths and an interesting theory of colloidal oxides has been based upon it (Chapter 13).

Werner's postulate that basic salts are polynuclear complexes held together by hydroxyl groups[120] has been shown, by x-ray studies, to be untenable in most cases. The basic chlorates and perchlorates of lead have not been studied by x-ray analysis, but the conductivities and other properties of their solutions indicate that they have the structures

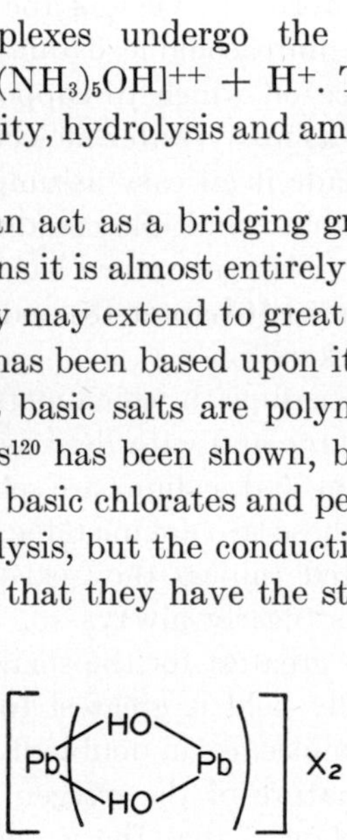

and

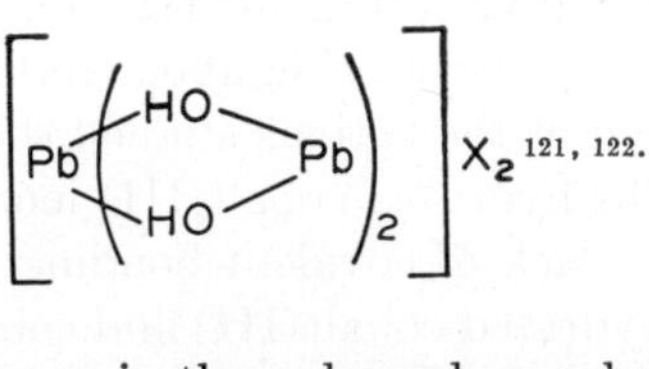

"Ol" bridges are common in the polynuclear cobalt complexes. The chief constituent of Vortmann's sulfate, which is obtained by oxidation of an

120. Werner, *Ber.*, **40**, 4441 (1907).
121. Weinland and Stroh, *Ber.*, **55**, 2219, 2706 (1922).
122. Weinland and Paul, *Z. anorg. Chem.*, **129**, 243 (1923).

ammoniacal solution of a cobalt salt, is

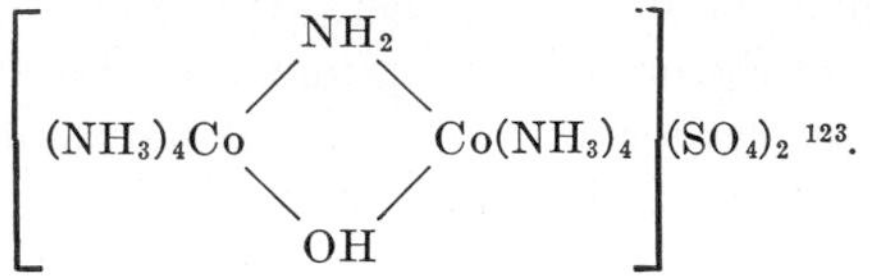

$$\left[(NH_3)_4Co \underset{OH}{\overset{NH_2}{\diagup\diagdown}} Co(NH_3)_4 \right] (SO_4)_2 \ ^{123}.$$

Such ions as

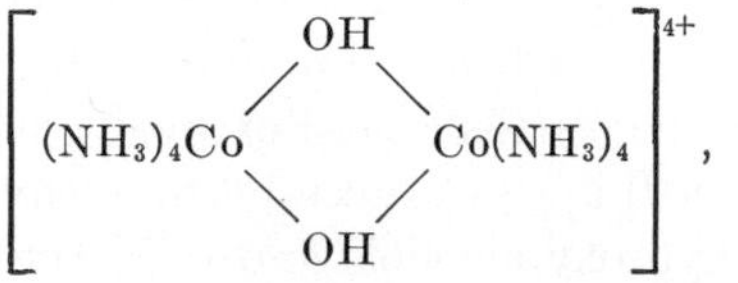

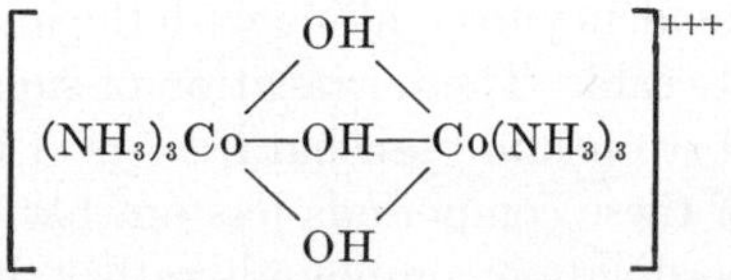

$$\left[(NH_3)_4Co \underset{OH}{\overset{OH}{\diagup\diagdown}} Co(NH_3)_4 \right]^{4+} ,$$

$$\left[(NH_3)_3Co\text{—}OH\text{—}Co(NH_3)_3 \underset{OH}{\overset{OH}{\diagup\diagdown}} \right]^{+++}$$

and

$$\left[Co \left(\underset{HO}{\overset{HO}{\diagdown\diagup}} Co(NH_3)_4 \right)_3 \right]^{6+}$$

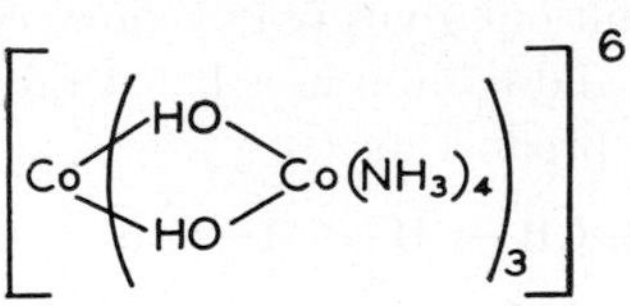

have been known for many years. The hexol salt is of special interest, as it was the first strictly inorganic compound to be resolved into optical antipodes[124]. Adamson, Ogata, Grossman, and Newbury[125] have come to the conclusion that Durrant's salt has the bimolecular structure

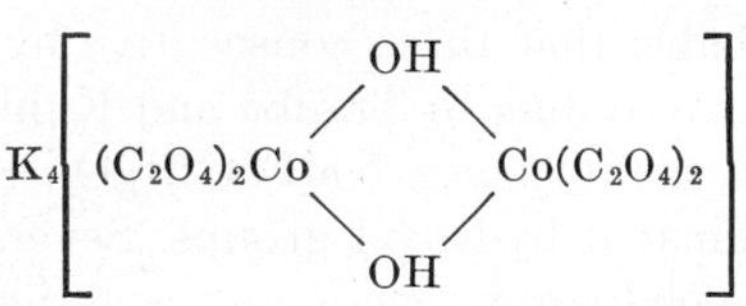

$$K_4 \left[(C_2O_4)_2Co \underset{OH}{\overset{OH}{\diagup\diagdown}} Co(C_2O_4)_2 \right].$$

Alcohols and Ethers

The organic derivatives of water, the alcohols and ethers, show much less tendency to form coordination compounds than does water; nevertheless, a

123. Werner, *Ber.*, **40**, 4609 (1907).
124. Werner, *Ber.*, **47**, 3087 (1914).
125. Adamson, Ogata, Grossman, and Newbury, O.N.R. Contract 23809, Technical
    Report, March 1954.

large number of such compounds is known. The compounds of the alcohols are more stable than those of the ethers, the stability in each series decreasing as the size of the organic group increases. Because of the chelation effect, the polyhydric alcohols form somewhat more stable compounds than do the monohydric alcohols. Glycol is able to displace water from hydrates of heavy metals, each alcoholic hydroxyl group taking the place of one molecule of water in the coordination sphere[126]. Glycerol ordinarily behaves as a bidentate donor, also, adjacent hydroxyl groups coordinating. The third hydroxyl group is prevented from combination by steric factors. The divalent ions of the alkaline earths[127], and of cobalt, nickel, copper, and zinc, all form compounds in this way, those of the heavy metals being rather unstable. Other polyhydroxy alcohols and even the sugars form coordination compounds, the tendency to combine with the ions of the alkaline earths being particularly noticeable. The purification of sugar through the precipitation of calcium and strontium "saccharates" is of interest in this connection. The structure of these compounds has not been studied in detail, but they are evidently coordination compounds rather than salts.

In the presence of polyhydric alcohols such as mannitol and sorbitol, sodium hydroxide does not precipitate iron(III) ion[128]. Addition of barium chloride to such basic solutions gives pale yellow, crystalline products containing the alcohol, iron, and barium in a 1:1:1 ratio. Traube and Kuhbier write the formula of this product as

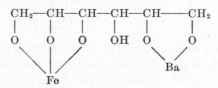

but they cite no evidence to support such a formulation. Scale models indicate that it is improbable that three consecutive hydroxyl groups are coordinated to the iron. According to Traube and Kuhbier, treatment of this product with sodium sulfate gives $Na[FeC_6H_{10}O_6] \cdot 3H_2O$, in which there must be two uncoordinated hydroxyl groups. Several similar compounds containing sugars or polyhydroxy acids and a variety of metal ions have been prepared and analyzed, but their structures have not been determined[129]. Some of these oxidize in the air to formic acid, carbon dioxide, and similar compounds[130].

126. Grün and Bockisch, *Ber.*, **41**, 3465 (1908); Grün and Boedecker, *Ber.*, **43**, 1051 (1910).
127. Grün and Husmann, *Ber.*, **43**, 1291 (1910).
128. Traube and Kuhbier, *Ber.*, **65**, 187 (1932).
129. Traube and Kuhbier, *Ber.*, **66**, 1545 (1933); **69**, 2655 (1936).
130. Traube and Kuhbier, *Ber.*, **65**, 190 (1932); **69**, 2664 (1936).

The ethanolamines can coordinate through either oxygen or nitrogen. Tettamanzi and Carli[131] found that triethanolamine forms addition compounds of the type $MX_2 \cdot 2 N(C_2H_4OH)_3$ (where M is Co, Ni, Cu, Cd, Pb, Ca, Mg, or Sr), some of the compounds being hydrated. No study of the structures of these compounds has been made, but in view of the structural similarity of triethanolamine and nitrilotriacetic acid, one may assume the presence of chelate rings, their number depending upon the coordination number of the metal ion:

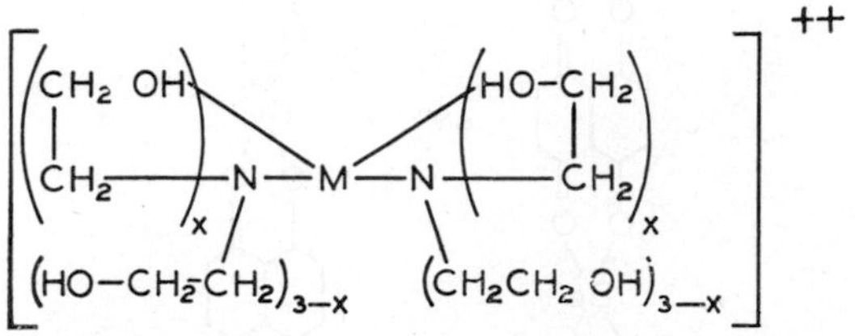

$$\left[\begin{pmatrix} \text{CH}_2\ \text{OH} \\ | \\ \text{CH}_2 \end{pmatrix}_x \text{N} - \text{M} - \text{N} \begin{pmatrix} \text{HO} - \text{CH}_2 \\ | \\ \text{CH}_2 \end{pmatrix}_x \right]^{++}$$
$$\left(\text{HO} - \text{CH}_2\text{CH}_2 \right)_{3-x} \quad \left(\text{CH}_2\text{CH}_2\ \text{OH} \right)_{3-x}$$

Ethers form addition compounds with a wide variety of compounds. Confirmation of this is found in the high solubility of the heteropolyacids, of uranyl nitrate, and of magnesium iodide, in ethers. The best known of the ether coordination compounds are those formed with the Grignard reagent. Spacu[132] has prepared some interesting compounds in which ether and pyridine share the coordination sphere: $[Mg\ py_4(ether)_2]Br_2$ and $[Mg\ py_5\ ether]I_2$.

The formation of a deep color in the well known iron(III) chloride test for phenols indicates that phenols form compounds with the heavy metals. In the thermometric, conductometric, and spectrophotometric titration of phenol with iron(III) chloride, Banerjee and Haldar[133] find breaks at molar ratios of 1:3 and 1:6. Upon electrolysis, the iron(III) ion goes to the anode. These findings suggest the reactions

$$Fe^{+++} \rightarrow [Fe(OC_6H_5)_3]^0 \rightarrow [Fe(OC_6H_5)_6]^=$$

Catechol, because of the effect of chelation, forms stable complexes with the heavy metals:

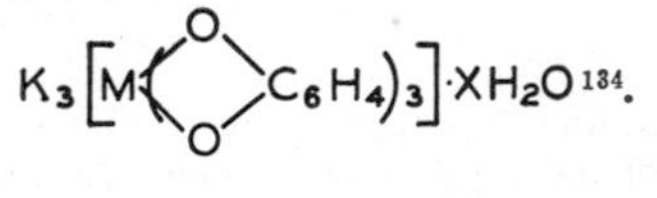

$$K_3 \left[M \left(\underset{O}{\overset{O}{\diagdown}} C_6H_4 \right)_3 \right] \cdot XH_2O \ ^{134}.$$

131. Tettamanzi and Carli, *Gazz. chim. ital.*, **63**, 566 (1933); **64**, 315 (1934); *Atti accad. sci. Torino, Classe sci. fis., mat. nat.*, **68**, 500 (1933); Garelli, *Atti accad. sci. Torino, Classe sci. fis., mat. nat.*, **68**, 398 (1933).
132. Spacu, *Bul. Soc. Stiinte Cluj*, **1**, 72 (1921).
133. Banerjee and Haldar, *Nature*, **165**, 1012 (1950).
134. Weinland and Binder, *Ber.*, **45**, 148, 1113 (1912); **46**, 874 (1913); Weinland and Walther, *Z. anorg. Chem.*, **126**, 141 (1923).

If the phenolic group can take part in the formation of a chelate ring with some other strongly coordinating group, very stable complexes may be formed. Thus, naphthazarin reacts quantitatively with beryllium ion to give the complexes

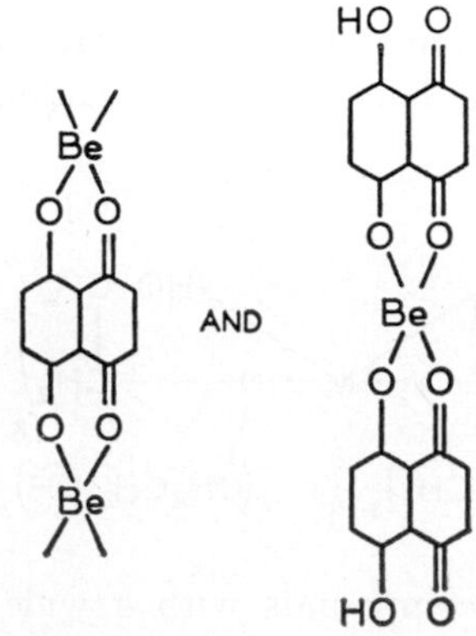

in which the coordinated oxygen atoms are doubtless equivalent[135].

Peroxide Coordination

Many salts have been shown to crystallize with hydrogen peroxide "of crystallization" [136]. In some cases, at least, this may be chemically combined with the salt, as is shown by cryoscopic measurements[137].

The peroxo group may serve as a bridge between two cobalt ions. When an ammoniacal cobalt(II) solution is allowed to stand in the air, the first product formed is a brown decammine-μ-peroxo-dicobalt(III) salt, $[(NH_3)_5Co-O_2-Co(NH_3)_5]X_4$[138], which upon further oxidation is converted to the deep green $[(NH_3)_5Co-O_2-Co(NH_3)_5]X_5$ in which one of the cobalt atoms seems to have achieved a valence of 4+. The dicobalt(III) salts are reduced to cobalt(II) by four equivalents of arsenic(III) oxide (one equivalent for each cobalt and two for the peroxo group) while the cobalt(III)-cobalt(IV) salts require five equivalents of reducing agent. The brown dicobalt(III) salt is diamagnetic, whereas the cobalt(III)-cobalt(IV) salt is paramagnetic[139].

135. Underwood, Toribara, and Neuman, *J. Am. Chem. Soc.*, **72**, 5597 (1950).
136. Tanatar, *Ber.*, **32**, 1544 (1899); *Z. anorg. Chem.*, **28**, 255 (1901); Rudenko, *J. Russ. Phys. Chem. Soc.*, **44**, 1209 (1912); Kazanetzkii, *J. Russ. Phys. Chem. Soc.*, **46**, 1110 (1914).
137. Jones and Murray, *Am. Chem. J.*, **30**, 205 (1903); Maass and Hatcher, *J. Am. Chem. Soc.*, **44**, 2472 (1922).
138. Vortmann, *Monatshefte*, **6**, 404 (1885); Werner and Mylius, *Z. anorg. Chem.*, **16**, 245 (1898); Werner, *Ann.*, **375**, 1 (1910).
139. Gleu and Rehm, *Z. anorg. allgem. Chem.*, **237**, 79 (1938).

"Vortman's sulfate" is a mixture of materials, containing the sulfates of

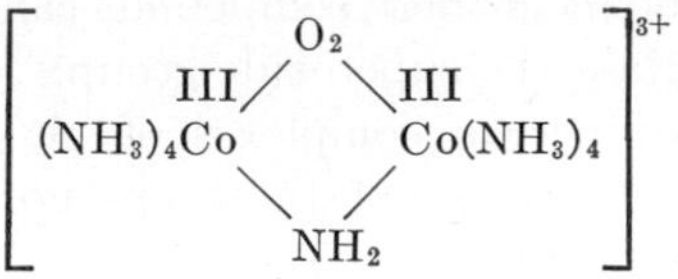

$$
\left[\begin{array}{c} O_2 \\ III \diagup \quad \diagdown III \\ (NH_3)_4Co \qquad Co(NH_3)_4 \\ \diagdown \diagup \\ NH_2 \end{array} \right]^{3+} \text{(A)} \quad \text{and} \quad \left[\begin{array}{c} O_2 \\ III \diagup \quad \diagdown IV \\ (NH_3)_4Co \qquad Co(NH_3)_4 \\ \diagdown \diagup \\ NH_2 \end{array} \right]^{4+} \text{(B)}
$$

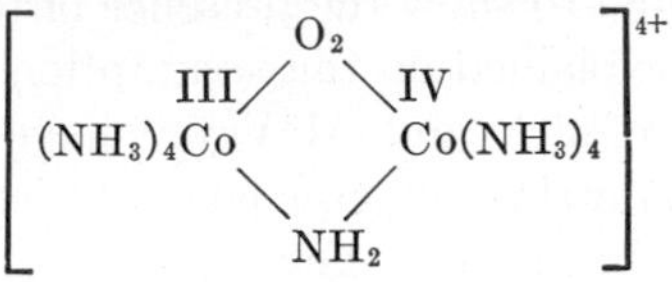

Compound B, on warming with sulfuric acid, liberates one and a half atoms of oxygen, and on further heating, two-thirds of an atom of nitrogen, leaving the cobalt in the dipositive state. These reactions, again, confirm the tetravalency of one cobalt atom. The surprising stability of these compounds is illustrated by the reaction

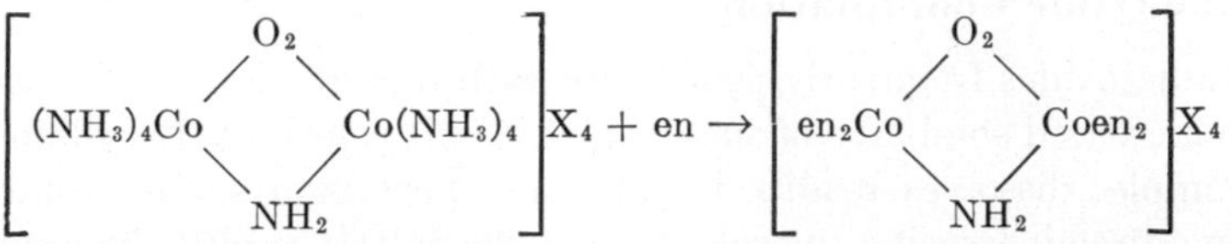

$$
\left[\begin{array}{c} O_2 \\ \diagup \diagdown \\ (NH_3)_4Co \qquad Co(NH_3)_4 \\ \diagdown \diagup \\ NH_2 \end{array} \right] X_4 + en \rightarrow \left[\begin{array}{c} O_2 \\ \diagup \diagdown \\ en_2Co \qquad Coen_2 \\ \diagdown \diagup \\ NH_2 \end{array} \right] X_4
$$

Compound B and its ethylenediamine analog are both paramagnetic[140]. The ethylenediamine compound can be reduced to the dicobalt(III) state by nitrite, hydrazine, ferrocyanide, arsenite or thiosulfate, but not by hydroxylamine, hydrogen peroxide or mercury(I) ion. The product of the reduction can then be reoxidized to the Co(III)-Co(IV) state by treatment with permanganate, hypochlorite, bromine, bromate, or nitric acid, but not by dichromate, peroxide, or mercury(II), iron(III) or silver ions. These reactions establish the reduction potential at about one volt.

The peroxo- group in compound B can be replaced by other groups with reduction of the cobalt to the 3+ condition. Thus

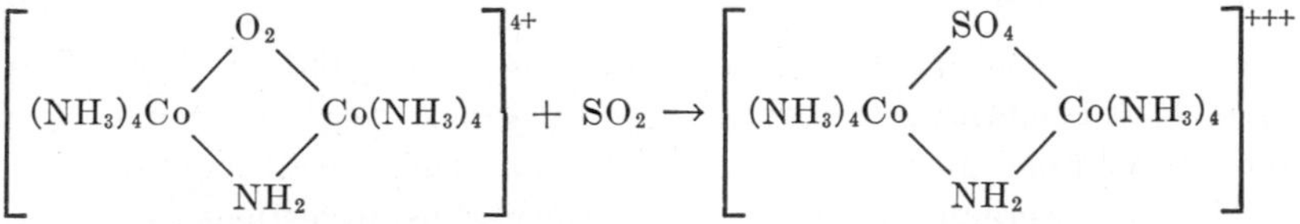

$$
\left[\begin{array}{c} O_2 \\ \diagup \diagdown \\ (NH_3)_4Co \qquad Co(NH_3)_4 \\ \diagdown \diagup \\ NH_2 \end{array} \right]^{4+} + SO_2 \rightarrow \left[\begin{array}{c} SO_4 \\ \diagup \diagdown \\ (NH_3)_4Co \qquad Co(NH_3)_4 \\ \diagdown \diagup \\ NH_2 \end{array} \right]^{+++}
$$

Among the other doubly bridged cobalt(III), cobalt(IV) compounds described by Werner the triply bridged compound

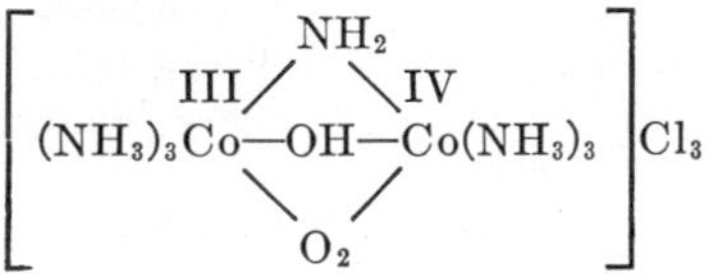

$$
\left[\begin{array}{c} NH_2 \\ III \diagup \quad \diagdown IV \\ (NH_3)_3Co-OH-Co(NH_3)_3 \\ \diagdown \diagup \\ O_2 \end{array} \right] Cl_3
$$

is worthy of note[141].

140. Malatesta, *Gazz. chim. ital.*, **72**, 287 (1942).
141. Werner, *Ann.*, **375**, 104 (1910).

Brimm[142] has pointed out that most of the results which have been interpreted to show the presence of tetrapositive cobalt in these compounds can be explained on the assumption that they contain the superoxide group.

Connick and McVey[143] have identified two peroxo complexes of plutonium(IV) in aqueous solution. While the structures of these are not finally proved, they seem to contain the rings

$$\left[\begin{array}{c} OH \\ Pu \diagup \diagdown Pu \\ \diagdown \diagup \\ O_2 \end{array}\right]^{5+} \quad \text{and} \quad \left[\begin{array}{c} O_2 \\ Pu \diagup \diagdown Pu \\ \diagdown \diagup \\ O_2 \end{array}\right]^{4+}$$

Metallic Oxide Coordination

Metallic oxides frequently coordinate with metallic ions, as is evidenced by the increased solubility of such oxides in salt solutions. Beryllium oxide, for example, dissolves readily in saturated beryllium sulfate solution, at the same time increasing the solubility of the sulfate itself[144]. The solubility relations indicate that each beryllium ion combines with four beryllium oxide molecules. The compound $[Be(BeO)_4]SO_4$ is more soluble than its analog $[Be(H_2O)_4]SO_4$. The structure given for the complex is supported by the lowering of the freezing point, which indicates that addition of beryllium oxide to a solution of beryllium sulfate does not increase the number of ions in solution. Beryllium selenate gives the same result as the sulfate. A related situation is found in the anion commonly described as $[RuCl_5OH]^=$, but which is shown by crystal analysis to be the oxo complex $[Cl_5Ru—O—RuCl_5]^{4-}$ [145].

Oxyanion Coordination

The anions of all oxyacids have donor properties, but in very different degree. It is sometimes said that the nitrate and perchlorate ions do not enter into complex formation, but this is not true. Nitratopentamminecobalt(III) salts were prepared by some of the earliest investigators, and were described in detail by Jörgensen[146]. Later investigations have led to the preparation of $[Co(NH_3)_3(NO_3)_3]$,[147] $[Co(NH_3)_4(NO_3)_2]NO_3 \cdot H_2O$,[148] and

142. Brimm, private communication. Quoted in Kleinberg "Unfamiliar Oxidation States," p. 100, University of Kansas Press, 1950.
143. Connick and McVey, National Nuclear Energy Series, Vol. 14B (The Transuranium Elements), p. 445, 1949.
144. Sidgwick and Lewis, *J. Chem. Soc.*, **1926**, 1287.
145. Mellor, Report of the Brisbane meeting of the Australian and New Zealand Association for the Advancement of Science, **28**, 137 (1951).
146. Jörgensen, *J. prakt. Chem.*, [2] **23**, 227 (1881).
147. Jörgensen, *Z. anorg. Chem.*, **5**, 185 (1894).
148. Birk, *Z. anorg. allgem. Chem.*, **164**, 241 (1927).

[Co en$_2$(NO$_3$)$_2$]NO$_3 \cdot$H$_2$O[149]. The last two are shown to be dinitrate salts rather than aquo nitrato salts by the fact that the loss of water does not change the properties greatly.

Transference measurements on solutions of plutonium(IV) in $1M$ HNO$_3$ indicate the existence of the complex [Pu(NO$_3$)]$^+$, which coordinates with more nitrate ions as the concentration of HNO$_3$ is increased. In $5M$ acid, the bright green ion [Pu(NO$_3$)$_6$]$^=$ is present, and (NH$_4$)$_2$[Pu(NO$_3$)$_6$] can be crystallized from the solution. Thorium shows a similar behavior, giving a salt which is isomorphous with the plutonium(IV) and cerium(IV) compounds[150].

G. F. Smith and his students have demonstrated the existence of both nitrate and perchlorate cerium(IV) ions[151] but the exact structure of the ions is not yet clear. The oxidation-reduction potential of the cerium(III)-cerium(IV) couple varies greatly with the nature of the acid present. In $1N$ acid, the electrode potentials (referred to the normal hydrogen electrode) are HClO$_4$, 1.70 volts; HNO$_3$, 1.61 volts; H$_2$SO$_4$, 1.44 volts; HCl, 1.28 volts. This variation indicates that either the Ce(III) or the Ce(IV) or both, combine with the anion of the acid. Duval[152] has reported pentamminecobalt complexes in which chlorate, bromate, iodate and perchlorate groups occupy the sixth coordination position.

The sulfate ion can occupy either one coordination position, or two. In either event, of course, it contributes a charge of minus two to the ion of which it becomes a part. The first type of compound is illustrated by sulfatopentamminecobalt(III) bromide, [Co(NH$_3$)$_5$SO$_4$]Br[153], which is prepared by heating the chloropentammine chloride with concentrated sulfuric acid. The sulfate group in the coordination sphere is not readily replaced, but is precipitated by boiling with barium salts. The ion slowly aquates on standing in solution:

$$[Co(NH_3)_5SO_4]^+ + H_2O \rightarrow [Co(NH_3)_5(H_2O)]^{+++} + SO_4^-$$

Sulfato-aquo complexes of several types evidently exist in aqueous solutions of chromium(III) sulfate[154].

Cases in which the sulfate group occupies two positions in the same coordination sphere are not as well known. The double sulfates of iron, chrom-

149. Schramm, *Z. anorg. allgem. Chem.*, **180,** 170 (1929).
150. Hindman, National Nuclear Energy Series, Vol. 14B (The Transuranium Elements), p. 388, 1949.
151. Smith, Sullivan, and Frank, *Ind. Eng. Chem., Anal. Ed.*, **8,** 449 (1936); Smith and Getz, *Ind. Eng. Chem., Anal. Ed.*, **10,** 191 (1938); Kott, thesis, University of Illinois, 1940.
152. Duval, *Ann. Chim.*, **18,** 241 (1932).
153. Jörgensen, *J. prakt. Chem.*, [2] **31,** 270 (1885).
154. Erdmann, *Angew. Chem.*, **64,** 500 (1952).

ium and the rare earths may contain the anions $[M(SO_4)_3]^=$, but they are too unstable to exist in solution. The case of potassium iridium sulfate, $3K_2SO_4 \cdot Ir_2(SO_4)_3 \cdot 2H_2O$ or $K_3[Ir(SO_4)_3] \cdot H_2O$, is perhaps a little more certain, for this salt does not give the characteristic tests for sulfate ion[155]. Weinland and Sierp[156] have prepared alkaloid salts of the acids $H_3[Fe(SO_4)(C_2O_4)_2]$ and $H_3[Fe(SO_4)_2(C_2O_4)]$, in which the sulfate group is evidently doubly coordinated. Duff[157] claims to have prepared [Co en$_2$SO$_4$]Br·H$_2$O, but Job[158] and Ephraim and Flugel[159] believe the salt to be [Co en$_2$(H$_2$O)SO$_4$]Br, in which the sulfato group occupies only one coordination position. In any event, the sulfate group is not held very tenaciously, for in solution the complex ion is rapidly converted to [Co en$_2$(H$_2$O)$_2$]$^{+++}$.

Several cases are known in which the sulfato group acts as a bridge between two metal atoms, but in every case it must evidently be accompanied by some other bridging group. When octammine-μ-amino-ol-dicobalt(III) chloride,

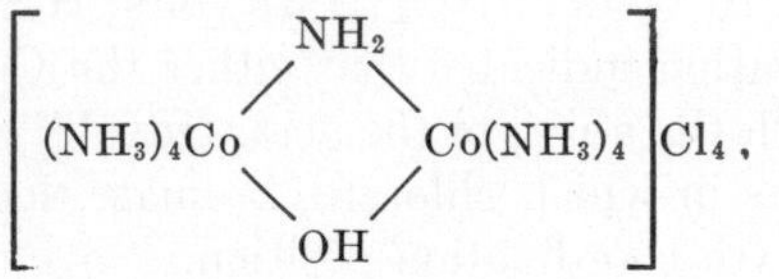

$$\left[\ (NH_3)_4Co\ \begin{array}{c} NH_2 \\ \diagup\ \ \diagdown \\ \ \\ \diagdown\ \ \diagup \\ OH \end{array}\ Co(NH_3)_4\ \right]Cl_4 \ ,$$

is heated with sulfuric acid, the "ol" bridge is replaced by a sulfato bridge:

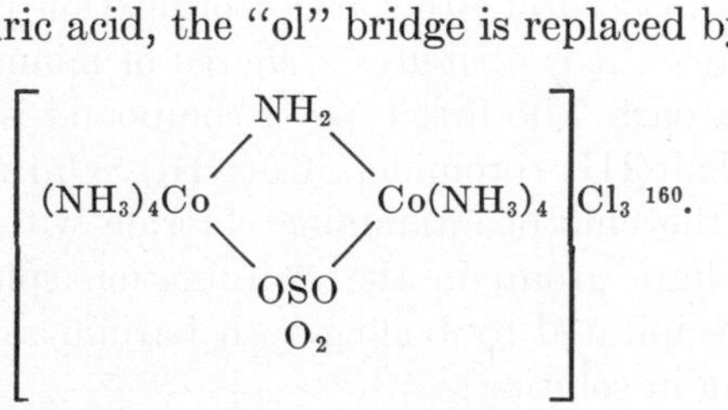

$$\left[\ (NH_3)_4Co\ \begin{array}{c} NH_2 \\ \diagup\ \ \diagdown \\ \ \\ \diagdown\ \ \diagup \\ OSO \\ O_2 \end{array}\ Co(NH_3)_4\ \right]Cl_3 \ ^{[160]}.$$

The sulfato bridge is eliminated by heating with concentrated hydrochloric acid; chloroaquo-octammine-μ-amino-dicobalt(III) chloride

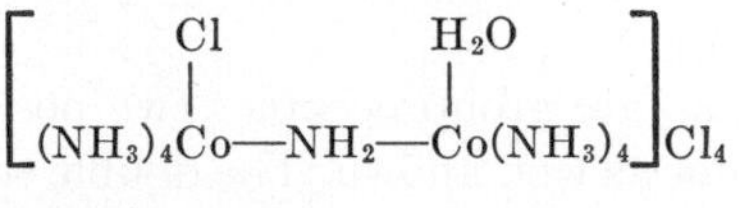

$$\left[\ \begin{array}{ccc} Cl & & H_2O \\ | & & | \\ (NH_3)_4Co & -NH_2- & Co(NH_3)_4 \end{array}\ \right]Cl_4$$

results. The μ-amino-sulfato compounds are also obtained[161] by the action of sulfur dioxide upon salts of the μ-amino-peroxo series (see page 27).

155. Delepine, *Compt. rend.*, **142**, 1525 (1906).
156. Weinland and Sierp, *Z. anorg. Chem.*, **117**, 59 (1921).
157. Duff, *J. Chem. Soc.*, **121**, 450 (1922).
158. Job, *Bull. soc. chim.*, [4] **33**, 15 (1923).
159. Ephraim and Flügel, *Helv. chim. Acta*, **7**, 727 (1924).
160. Werner, Beddow, Baselli, and Steinitzer, *Z. anorg. Chem.*, **16**, 109 (1898).
161. Werner, *Ann.*, **375**, 15 (1910).

Gibson and his co-workers[162] have studied a case of a very different type of sulfate bridging. The substance $(C_2H_5)_4Au_2SO_4$ was found to be a dimer in acetone, and probably has the structure

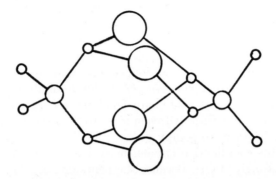

Foss and Gibson[163] have reported a similar compound in which the phenyl phosphate group, $C_6H_5OPO_3^=$, replaces the sulfate.

The sulfate ion has the rather unusual ability to form hydrates; metallic sulfates usually crystallize from solution with one molecule of water more than other salts containing the same metallic ion. Thus the vitriols of the divalent ions of magnesium, zinc, cadmium, vanadium, chromium, manganese, cobalt, and nickel are heptahydrates and that of copper is a pentahydrate. In these complexes, two oxygens of the sulfate ion are hydrogen bonded to the water.

The tellurate and iodate ions are remarkable in that when they coordinate with copper, they stabilize the trivalent state, forming such complexes as $[Cu(TeO_6)_2]^{9-}$ and $[Cu(IO_6)_2]^{7-}$ [164, 165].

The bleaching of solutions of iron(III) chloride by addition of phosphate ion indicates the existence of phosphate complexes[166]. Ricci[167] advanced evidence for the existence of $H_3[FeCl_3PO_4]$ and $H_3[FeCl_3AsO_4]$, but later work indicates that the complexes probably contain no chlorine. Jensen[168] found the solubility of $FePO_4$ and $AlPO_4$ to rise with increasing phosphate ion concentration, but to be independent of the chloride ion concentration.

162. Gibson and Weller, *J. Chem. Soc.*, **1941**, 102; Evens and Gibson, *J. Chem. Soc.*, **1941**, 109.
163. Foss and Gibson, *J. Chem. Soc.*, **1949**, 3075.
164. Malatesta, *Gazz. chim. ital.*, **71**, 467, 580 (1941).
165. Lister, *Can. J. Chem.*, **31**, 638 (1953).
166. Weinland and Ensgraber, *Z. anorg. Chem.*, **84**, 340 (1914).
167. Ricci and Meduri, *Gazz. chim. ital.*, **64**, 235 (1934); Ricci and Lamonica, *Gazz. chim. ital.*, **64**, 294 (1934); Ricci and Saraceno, thesis, University of Messina, 1929.
168. Jensen, *Z. anorg. allgem. Chem.*, **221**, 1 (1934).

Di-, tri- and polyphosphates all show a remarkable ability to form stable complexes, even with the alkaline earth ions, so some of them have found wide use industrially (Chapter 23). Pyrophosphate complexes of many metals have been studied in solution by a variety of physical methods. For example, Haldar[169] has studied the pyrophosphate complexes of Cu^{++}, Ni^{++}, and Co^{++} by thermometric and conductometric titrations, and by magnetic, cryoscopic, and transport measurements. He finds evidence for the existence of two series of complexes, $[M(P_2O_7)]^=$ and $[M(P_2O_7)_2]^{6-}$. Watters and Aaron[170] report, in addition, copper complexes with $Cu:P_2O_7{}^{4-}$ ratios of 2:1 and 4:1, which, however, exist only in dilute solutions.

The carbonate ion forms coordinate bonds easily, as witnessed by its strong tendency to unite with hydrogen ions. In the metal ammines such as $[Co(NH_3)_4CO_3]^+$ it seems to occupy two coordination positions. In view of the fact that this coordination entails the formation of a four-membered ring, it is surprisingly stable. Because the pentammine $[Co(NH_3)_5CO_3]Cl \cdot H_2O$ gives an alkaline reaction, and because he thought that the molecule of water could not be removed without destruction of the complex, Werner was of the opinion that the formula of the salt should be written $[Co(NH_3)_5HCO_3]Cl(OH)$[171]. Lamb and Mysels[172], however, found that all of the water can be removed without destruction of the complex, so it is evidently not essential to the constitution of the complex. On the other hand, the carbonato complex does undergo aquation in water solution, first yielding $[Co(NH_3)_5HCO_3]^{++}$ and then $[Co(NH_3)_5(H_2O)]^{+++}$[173]. The analagous ion, $[Co(NH_3)_4CO_3]^+$, aquates to $[Co(NH_3)_4(HCO_3)H_2O]^{++}$, and then to $[Co(NH_3)_4(H_2O)_2]^{+++}$[174]. Stranks and Harris[175] studied the exchange in solution of C-labelled carbonate with the carbonate in $[Co(NH_3)_4CO_3]^+$ and Yankwich and McNamara[176] did the same with $[Co\ en_2CO_3]^+$. The exchange takes place through the intermediate formation of a bicarbonate complex.

By using labeled oxygen, Taube and his students demonstrated that in the cases of $[Co(NH_3)_5CO_3]^+$ and $[Co(NH_3)_4CO_3]^+$ exchange does not involve rupture of the cobalt-oxygen link, but rather, of the carbon-oxygen bond[177].

169. Haldar, *Science and Culture*, **14**, 340–1 (1949); *Nature*, **166**, 744 (1950).
170. Watters and Aaron, *J. Am. Chem. Soc.*, **75**, 611 (1953).
171. Werner, *Ber.* **40**, 4101 (1907)
172. Lamb and Mysels, *J. Am. Chem. Soc.*, **67**, 468 (1945).
173. Lamb and Stevens, *J. Am. Chem. Soc.*, **61**, 3229 (1939).
174. Harris and Stranks, *Trans. Faraday Soc.*, **48**, 137 (1952).
175. Stranks and Harris, *J. Chem. Phys.*, **19**, 257 (1951).
176. Yankwich and McNamara, *J. Chem. Phys.*, **20**, 1325 (1952).
177. Hunt, Rutenberg, and Taube, *J. Am. Chem. Soc.*, **74**, 268 (1952); Posey and Taube, *J. Am. Chem. Soc.*, **75**, 4099 (1953).

McCutcheon and Schuele[178] have recently isolated the interesting ion $[Co(CO_3)_3]^=$ as the hexamminecobalt(III) salt; its existence clearly indicates that the carbonate ion can fill two coordination positions.

Organic Anion Coordination

Many organic anions form stable coordination compounds. Formate and acetate ions form strong bonds, but monocarboxylic acids with longer chains show a rapidly decreasing ability to coordinate. Formate and acetate often bind two metal atoms together, each oxygen of the carboxyl group linking to a different metal atom,

$$\begin{array}{c} R \\ | \\ M\text{—}OC\text{=}O\text{—}M. \end{array}$$

When the carboxyl group is attached to only one metal atom, however, it fills but one position in the coordination sphere. Complexes of the types $[Co(NH_3)_5OOC\,CH_3]^{++}$ [179] and $[Co(NH_3)_5OOCH]^{++}$ [180] are well known and easily prepared. The solubilities[181] and stabilities[182] of several similar complexes containing a variety of aliphatic anions have been studied.

Gott and Bailar[183] were able to effect a partial resolution of α-chloropropionic and α-bromopropionic acids through the formation of stable cobalt complexes containing levo-propylenediamine, $[Co\ l\text{-}pn_2(OOC\cdot CHX\cdot CH_3)_2]^+$.

The solubility of lead sulfate in solutions of sodium acetate has inspired much research, and many formulas have been postulated for the complexes which are formed[184]. Weinland and his students[121] report the isolation of the polynuclear complex ions

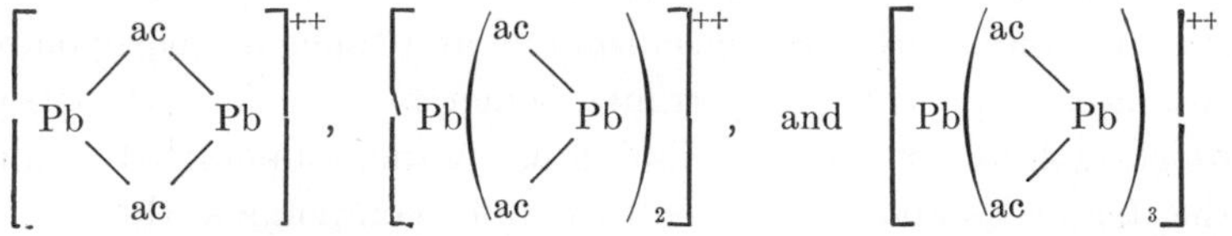

$$\left[\begin{array}{c} ac \\ Pb\diamond Pb \\ ac \end{array}\right]^{++} ,\quad \left[Pb\left(\begin{array}{c}ac\\ \\ac\end{array}Pb\right)\right]^{++}_2 ,\quad \text{and}\quad \left[Pb\left(\begin{array}{c}ac\\ \\ac\end{array}Pb\right)\right]^{++}_3$$

Toropeva and Batyrshine[185], however, report only the formation of $[Pbac]^+$, $[Pbac_3]^-$, and $[Pbac_4]^=$, the last being the most important in analytical work.

178. McCutcheon and Schuele, *J. Am. Chem. Soc.*, **75**, 1845 (1953).
179. Basolo, *Inorganic Syntheses*, **4**, 171 (1953).
180. Yatsimirskii, *J. Gen. Chem. (U.S.S.R.)*, **20**, 1408 (1950).
181. Linhard and Rau, *Z. anorg. allgem. Chem.*, **271**, 121 (1952).
182. Bunton and Llewellyn, *J. Chem. Soc.*, **1953**, 1692.
183. Gott and Bailar, *J. Am. Chem. Soc.*, **74**, 4820 (1952).
184. Weinland, "Einfuhrung in die Chemie der Komplexverbindungen," Second Edition, pp. 391–400, Enke, Stuttgart, 1924.
185. Toropova and Batyrshina, *Zhur. Anal. Khim.*, **4**, 337 (1949).

The "basic acetate" method of separating the ions of the trivalent metals in qualitative analysis involves the formation of acetate complexes. Weinland and his students studied many of these[184] and isolated some very complex materials which they thought were true chemical entities.

Among the examples in which the carboxyl group forms a bridge between two metal atoms are the "basic" beryllium salts, $Be_4O(OOC \cdot R)_6$, in which R represents CH_3 , C_2H_5 , etc. These compounds are readily formed and are stable, volatile, and soluble in nonpolar solvents. Structural studies[186] indicate the presence of a central oxygen surrounded tetrahedrally by four beryllium ions. Each edge of the tetrahedron is composed of the grouping
$$R$$
Be—O—C—O—Be. Similar compounds of zinc[187] and zirconium, $(ZrO)_4O(OOCR)_6$,[188] are known.

The oxalate ion forms a great many stable coordinate compounds, usually acting as bidentate group. The best known are those of the types $[M^{II}Ox_3]^{4-}$, $[M^{III}Ox_3]^{\equiv}$, and $[M^{III}Ox_2]^-$. The tris-(oxalato) complexes have been studied extensively, especially in regard to their stereochemistry. (Chapter 8). The oxalate group can share the coordination sphere with ammonia, ethylenediamine, water, or other groups. Oxalatobis(ethylenediammine) cobalt(III) chloride, [Co en$_2$Ox]Cl, is readily obtained by the action of an alkali oxalate upon the dichloro salt[189]; the corresponding chromium salt is prepared by the action of ethylenediamine upon the tris-(oxalato) salt[190]. Hamm and Davis[191] have studied the formation of these ions by the reaction of $[Cr(H_2O)_6]^{+++}$ and oxalate ion, and Hamm[192] has followed the rate of isomerization of $[Cr(H_2O)_2Ox_2]^-$ in water solution. He postulates that upon collision with the ion, a water molecule knocks one end of an oxalate group away from the chromium and takes its place; on return of the oxalate, either the cis- or trans- isomer may be formed, depending upon which molecule of water is eliminated. A small amount of alkali converts the diaquo compounds to hydroxoaquo- compounds, the cis isomer

186. Bragg and Morgan, *Proc. Roy. Soc. London,* **A104,** 437 (1923); Morgan and Astbury, *Proc. Roy. Soc. London,* **A112,** 441 (1926); Pauling and Sherman, *Proc. Natl. Acad. Sci.,* **20,** 340 (1934).
187. Auger and Robin, *Compt. rend.,* **178,** 1546 (1924); Wyart, *Bull. Soc. Fr. Min.,* **49,** 148 (1926).
188. Tanatar and Kurowski, *Chem. Centralblatt,* **1908** (1) 1523.
189. Werner and Vilmos, *Z. anorg. Chem.,* **21,** 153 (1899); Price and Brazier, *J. Chem. Soc.,* **107,** 1376, 1726 (1915).
190. Werner and Schwarz, *Ann.,* **405,** 222 (1914).
191. Hamm and Davis, *J. Am. Chem. Soc.,* **75,** 3085 (1953).
192. Hamm, *J. Am. Chem. Soc.,* **75,** 609 (1953).

of which is converted upon heating into the tetrakis(oxalato)-μ-diol-salt,

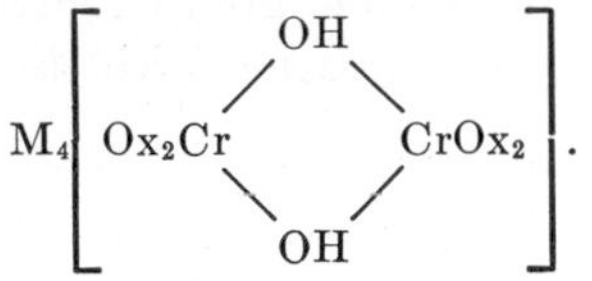

$$M_4\left[\begin{array}{c} OH \\ / \quad \backslash \\ Ox_2Cr \qquad CrOx_2 \\ \backslash \quad / \\ OH \end{array}\right].$$

Larger amounts of alkali change the diaquo salts to dihydroxo salts, still without breaking the chromium-oxalate linkage.

Weinland and Paul[122] have isolated several compounds of the ion $[Pb_2Ox]^{++}$, in which all four of the oxygen atoms are probably bonded to the metal:

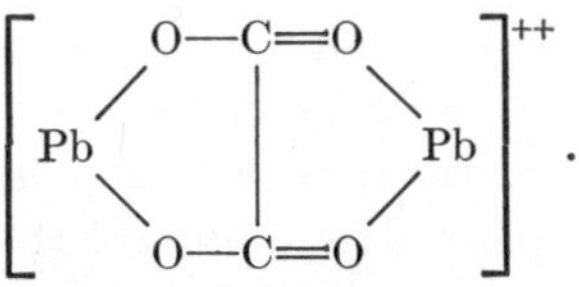

$$\left[\begin{array}{c} O—C=O \\ / \quad | \quad \backslash \\ Pb \qquad \qquad Pb \\ \backslash \quad | \quad / \\ O—C=O \end{array}\right]^{++}.$$

Solubility studies[193] have indicated the existence of analagous ions of zinc and cadmium.

The stability of the oxalato complexes is largely due, no doubt, to the formation of five-membered rings. Compounds are known, however, in which rings are not formed. Grünberg's method of determining the configuration of cis-trans isomers of the type $[Pt(NH_3)_2X_2]^{194}$ is based upon the inability of the trans-isomer to yield a chelate oxalato derivative. (See Chapter 9).

The oxalate ion, like the sulfate ion, forms hydrates. Werner has pointed out[195] that a large number of compounds containing complex oxalate anions crystallize with water, even if the cation is one which is usually anhydrous.

The malonate ion coordinates with metallic ions to give a six-membered ring, which is not as stable as the five-membered ring formed from the oxalate ion. Schramm has studied the formation of malonatotetrammine-cobalt(III) compounds in some detail[196]. Anions of other dibasic organic acids form cations of the type $[Co\ en_2A]^+$, but seem unable to form anionic complexes like those formed by oxalates and malonates. Complexes of some difunctional acids are discussed in Chapter 6.

α-Hydroxy acids often coordinate readily, the hydroxyl and carboxyl group both coordinating, and the chelation effect enhancing the stability

193. Vosburgh and Beckman, *J. Am. Chem. Soc.*, **62**, 1028 (1940).
194. Grünberg, *Helv. chim. Acta*, **14**, 455 (1931).
195. Werner, "New Ideas on Inorganic Chemistry," Translated by Hedley, p. 113, London, Longmans, Green & Co., 1911.
196. Schramm, *Z. anorg. allgem. Chem.*, **180**, 161 (1929).

of the compounds formed. The hydrogen of the hydroxyl group may be lost simultaneously, so that the organic group contributes a charge of minus two to the complex. Thus, coordination with the copper(II) ion gives

$$
\left[\mathrm{Cu} \left\langle \begin{array}{l} \mathrm{O - C = O} \\ \quad | \\ \mathrm{O - CHR} \end{array} \right\rangle_2 \right]^{=}
$$

The copper complexes containing glycollic and lactic acids are not very stable[197] but those containing the stronger salicylic and mandelic acids are easily isolated[198]. Boron forms stable compounds even with the simpler α-hydroxy acids[199], and Boesken and his co-workers were able to resolve the bis-(α-hydroxybutyro)borate ion[200] as well as the bis(salicylato)borate ion[201].

The work of Jantsch[202] on the rare earth glycolates and lactates indicates that some chelation takes place. His values for the equivalent conductances of various lanthanum salts are as follows:

	ν	λ
acetate	1024	89.5
phenylacetate	1200	91.2
glycolate	1200	70.3
lactate	1024	54.1

Salicylate ion differs from its meta- and para- isomers in being able to form chelate rings, which greatly stabilizes its coordination[203]. Many recent studies have been made on solutions of metal ions and α-hydroxy acids, such as salicylic, lactic, citric, glycollic, and tartaric; these studies lead to a knowledge of the compositions and stabilities of the complexes formed, but do not give information on their structures. The work of Bertin-Batsch and of Bobtelsky and his collaborators[204] is typical.

The compounds of the α-amino acids are of great stability, and have received extensive study. Ley[205] and Bruni and Fornara[206] suggested that

197. Wark, *J. Chem. Soc.*, **123**, 1815 (1923).
198. Wark, *J. Chem. Soc.*, **1927**, 1753.
199. Rosenheim and Vermehren, *Ber.*, **57**, 1337 (1924).
200. Boeseken, Muller, and Japhongjouw, *Rec. trav. chim.*, **45**, 919 (1926).
201. Boeseken and Meulenhoff, *Proc. Acad. Sci. Amsterdam*, **27**, 174 (1924).
202. Jantsch, *Z. anorg. allgem. Chem.*, **153**, 9 (1926); Jantsch and Grünkraut, *Z. anorg. allgem. Chem.*, **79**, 305 (1913).
203. Bertin-Batsch, *Ann. chim.*, **7**, 481 (1952).
204. Bobtelsky and Heitner, *Bull. soc. chim. France*, **1951**, 494; Bobtelsky and Graus, *J. Am. Chem. Soc.*, **75**, 4172 (1953); Bobtelsky and Bar-Gadda, *Bull. soc. chim. France*, **1953**, 276, 687.
205. Ley, *Z. Elektrochem.*, **10**, 954 (1904).
206. Bruni and Fornara, *Atti accad. Lincei*, [5] **13**, II, 26 (1904); Bruni, *Z. Elektrochem.*, **11**, 93 (1905).

copper glycine is an inner complex. The deep blue color of the compound indicates copper-nitrogen linkages, and the possibility of the formula $Cu(NH \cdot CH_2COOH)_2$ is eliminated by the fact that N,N-diethylglycine gives an analagous compound. The compound is a nonelectrolyte, and it is evident that the copper is coordinately saturated, for it absorbs ammonia only very slowly. Finally, the properties of copper glycine are very similar to those of diamminecopper(II) acetate $[Cu(OOCCH_3)_2(NH_3)_2]$, which seems to justify the formula

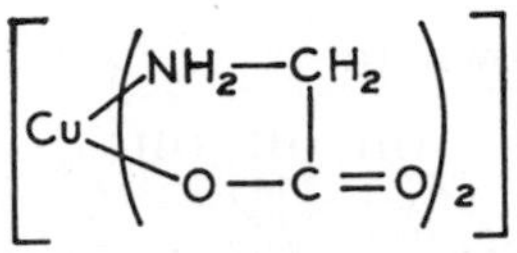

$$\left[Cu \left\langle \begin{matrix} NH_2-CH_2 \\ | \\ O-C=O \end{matrix} \right\rangle_2 \right]$$

The copper(II) compounds of α-amino acids are so stable that they do not respond to most of the usual tests for copper(II) ion. Hydrogen sulfide deposits copper sulfide, and boiling alkalies precipitate copper oxide, but both reactions take place slowly. The opening of the ring by ammonia to give $[Cu(NH_3)_2(OOCCH_2NH_2)_2]$[207] is an interesting reaction. The remarkable stability of the copper chelate of the α-amino acid group is illustrated by the work of Kurtz[208] who studied several acids of the type

$$NH_2-(CH_2)_x-\underset{\underset{NH_2}{|}}{CH}-COOH,$$

where $X = 2, 3,$ or 4 (α,γ-diaminobutyric acid, ornithine, and lysine). In each case the usual properties of the carboxyl group and the adjacent amino group are completely masked, but the other amino group retains its characteristic behavior, and Kurtz was able to carry out reactions on it, without affecting the coordinated amino group.

The cobalt complexes of the α-amino acids, $[Coamac_3]$, exist in two stereoisomeric forms (see page 283), both of which are remarkably stable, being unattacked by 50 per cent sulfuric acid. Elliott[209] has utilized this stability in the preparation of highly insoluble and stable "super complexes" by the reaction of cobalt(III) hydroxide with

$$HOOC-\underset{\underset{NH_2}{|}}{CH}-(CH_2)_n-\underset{\underset{NH_2}{|}}{CH}-COOH \quad .$$

Chromium(III) forms inner complexes which are similar but of less stability; they are slowly decomposed by hot acids, by sodium hydroxide, and

207. Ley, *Ber.*, **42**, 354 (1909).
208. Kurtz, *J. Biol. Chem.*, **122**, 477 (1937-8); **180**, 1253 (1949).
209. Elliott, thesis, University of Illinois, 1943.

to a degree, by boiling water. Keller[210] has studied the reactions of a large number of α-amino acids with chromium(III) hydroxide and chromammines in boiling water. In all cases compounds of the formula [Cr(amac)₃] seem to form, but are quickly hydrolyzed to

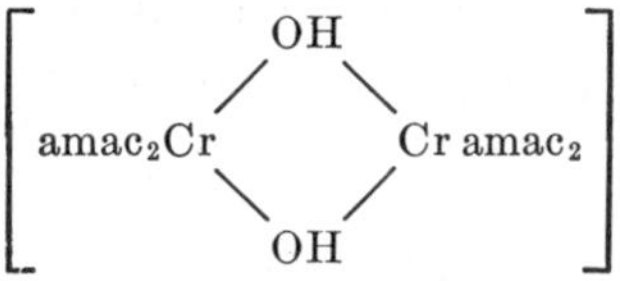

$$
\left[\text{amac}_2\text{Cr} \underset{\text{OH}}{\overset{\text{OH}}{\diamond}} \text{Cr amac}_2 \right]
$$

which in turn hydrolyze slowly to

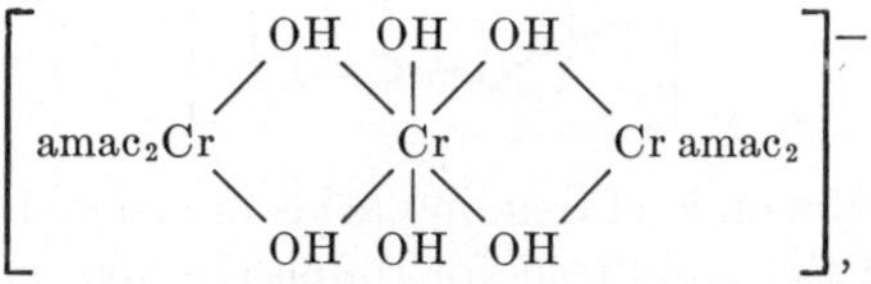

$$
\left[\text{amac}_2\text{Cr} \begin{array}{c} \text{OH OH OH} \\ \diagup\diagdown | \diagup\diagdown \\ \text{Cr} \\ \diagdown\diagup | \diagdown\diagup \\ \text{OH OH OH} \end{array} \text{Cr amac}_2 \right]^-,
$$

and more complex products. Cobalt amino acid compounds undergo the same reactions, but much more slowly.

Platinum does not readily coordinate with oxygen, but the coordinating tendency of the α-amino acids is so great that such compounds as

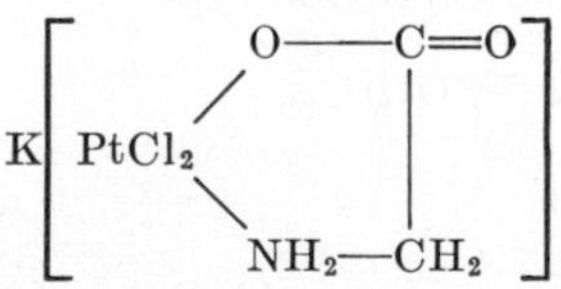

$$
K\left[\text{PtCl}_2 \begin{array}{c} \text{O}——\text{C}=\text{O} \\ \diagup \qquad | \\ \diagdown \qquad | \\ \text{NH}_2——\text{CH}_2 \end{array} \right] \quad \text{and} \quad \left[\text{Pt}\left(\begin{array}{c} \text{O}—\text{C}=\text{O} \\ | \qquad | \\ \text{NH}_2—\text{CH}_2 \end{array} \right)_2 \right]
$$

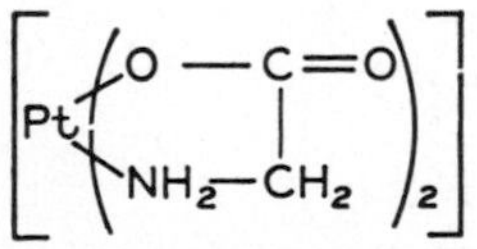

can be formed[211, 212, 213]. Even α-amino acids containing tertiary nitrogen atoms will coordinate with platinum strongly, as is shown by the optical resolution of the ion

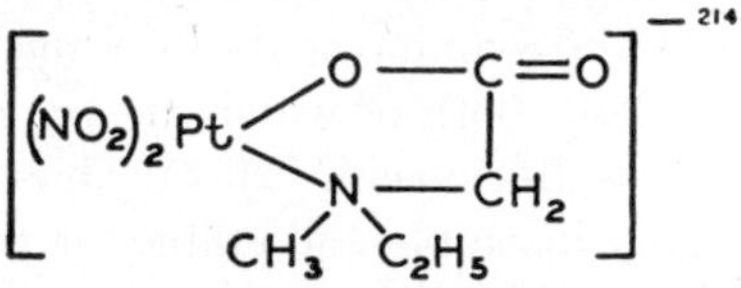

$$
\left[(\text{NO}_2)_2\text{Pt} \begin{array}{c} \text{O}—\text{C}=\text{O} \\ \diagup \qquad | \\ \diagdown \qquad | \\ \text{N}——\text{CH}_2 \\ \diagup \diagdown \\ \text{CH}_3\ \text{C}_2\text{H}_5 \end{array} \right]^{-214}
$$

Heterocyclic acids having a carboxyl group in the α-position to the ring nitrogen (picolinic, quinolinic, quinaldinic, etc.) form inner complexes. The compounds with iron(II), which are deeply colored, have been studied by

210. Keller, thesis, University of Illinois, 1940.
211. Ley and Ficken, Ber., 45, 377 (1912).
212. Grinberg and Ptitzuin, Ann. inst. platine, No. 9, 55 (1932).
213. Grinberg and Ptitzuin, Ann. inst. platine, No. 11, 77 (1933).
214. Kuebler and Bailar, J. Am. Chem. Soc., 74, 3535 (1952).

Ley and his co-workers[215]. The corresponding copper(II) compounds are light in color, and are probably not coordination compounds.

The β-amino acids also form inner complexes with the transition metals, but these are less stable than those of the α-acids. Hearn[216] has shown that α-amino acids can be distinguished from the β-acids by the fact that the former react with cobalt(III) hydroxide to give colored complexes, while the latter do not.

The γ-, δ-, and ε-amino acids do not form chelate rings with metals, so form normal salts[217].

Among the amino acids, the derivatives of acetic acid are particularly noteworthy for their chelating ability. The tridentate iminodiacetic acid gives many complexes, which in general are more stable than those of glycine. For example, the first and second stability constants of the zinc complex of glycine are 4.8 and 4.1, while for the zinc complex of iminodiacetic acid they are 7.8 and 5.7[218]. Nitrilotriacetic acid forms still more stable complexes, the two dissociation constants for the zinc complex being 10.5 and 3.0[219]. The great difference between the two values in the case of the triacetic acid doubtless reflects the fact that the zinc ion cannot accept all of the possible donor groups in two of the donor anions. The complex which is formed in this case[220] is

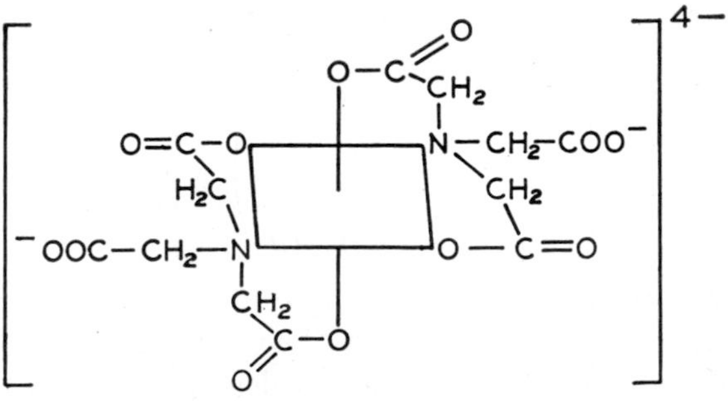

The most remarkable of the acetic acid derivatives, however, is ethylenediaminetetraacetic acid (often abbreviated EDTA or H_4Y). This substance is potentially hexadentate, but complexes in which only four or five groups are coordinating are well known. The complexes of EDTA are remarkably stable, so have been investigated extensively from the industrial point of

215. Ley, Schwarte, and Münnich, *Ber.*, **57**, 349 (1924).
216. Hearn, thesis, University of Illinois, 1951.
217. Tschugaeff and Serbin, *Compt. rend.*, **151**, 1361 (1910); Pfeiffer and Lübbe, *J. prakt. Chem.*, [2] **136**, 321 (1933).
218. Flood and Loras, *Tids. Kjemi, Bergsvesen Met.*, **6**, 83 (1945).
219. Schwarzenbach, *Chimia*, **3**, 1 (1949).
220. Schwarzenbach and Biedermann, *Helv. Chim. Acta*, **31**, 331 (1948).

view. More than four hundred and fifty articles were published during 1952 describing uses of this reagent or stability constants of its metal derivatives. It has been used in water softening (Chapter 23), electroplating, controlling the metal content of dye baths, in removing lead and other heavy metals from the human system, in the treatment of chlorosis in plants, and in many other ways.

The stability of the EDTA complexes is illustrated by the fact that neither the copper(II) or the nickel compound is destroyed by sodium or ammonium hydroxide. The nickel compound is not attacked by dimethyl-glyoxime or hydrogen sulfide, but is destroyed by potassium cyanide. The copper compound gives the usual reactions of Cu^{++} when treated with potassium cyanide, hydrogen sulfide, or potassium ferrocyanide[221].

The ability of ethylenediaminetetraacetic acid to form stable complexes depends upon the fact that when it coordinates it forms multiple fused five-membered chelate rings. Pfeiffer and Simons[222] compared the calcium derivatives of methylaminediacetic acid

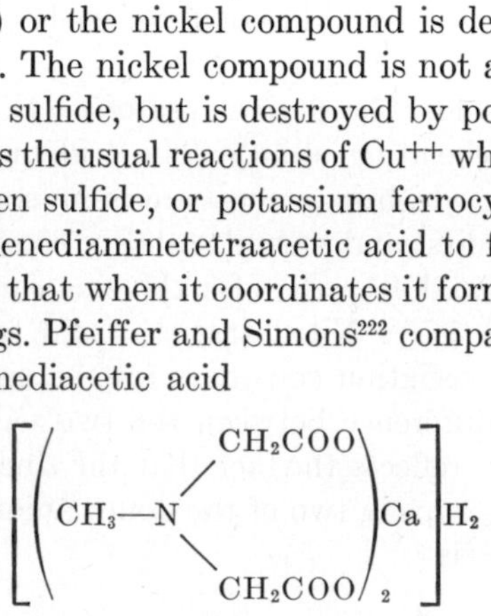

$$\left[\left(CH_3-N\begin{array}{l}{}^{CH_2COO}\\{}_{CH_2COO}\end{array}\right)_2 Ca\right]H_2$$

and ethylenediaminetetraacetic acid,

$$\left[\left(-CH_2-N\begin{array}{l}{}^{CH_2COO}\\{}_{CH_2COO}\end{array}\right)_2 Ca\right]H_2$$

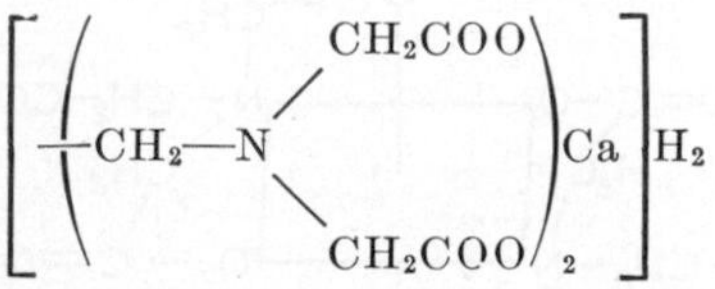

which differ only in that the two nitrogen atoms in the latter are linked together through the ethylene bridge. The methylamine complex reacts slowly with oxalate ion to precipitate calcium oxalate, but the ethylenediamine complex does not. Pfeiffer and Simons came to the conclusion that these complexes are hexadentate, for the structurally similar $HOOCCH(CH_3)NHCH_2CH_2NCH(CH_3)COOH$ does not form a stable calcium complex.

Several studies have been made of the effect of ring size on the stability of complexes of this type. Schwarzenbach and Ackermann[223] investigated the series $(HOOCCH_2)_2N(CH_2)_nN(CH_2COOH)_2$, where n varies from two to five. In general, the stability of the alkaline earth compounds decreases as "n" increases. When "n" is 4 or 5, the two ends of the molecule seem

221. Brintzinger and Hesse, *Z. anorg. allgem. Chem.*, **249**, 113 (1942).
222. Pfeiffer and Simons, *Ber.*, **76B**, 847 (1943).
223. Schwarzenbach and Ackermann, *Helv. Chim. Acta*, **31**, 1029 (1948).

able to act independently, for complexes of the type M_2Y can be formed. Chaberek and Martell[224] found the stabilities of the complexes of ethylenediaminediacetic-dipropionic acid to be considerably less than those of the tetraacetic acid.

Some cases are known in which EDTA does not act as a hexadentate coordinator, even though six positions are open to it. Thus, Schwarzenbach[225] prepared the compounds $[CoHYBr]^-$ and $[CoHY(NO_2)]^-$. Removal of the bromide or nitro group allows the unattached carboxyl group to coordinate with the cobalt to form $[CoY]^-$. Busch[226] has shown that the palladium(II) chelate has the structure

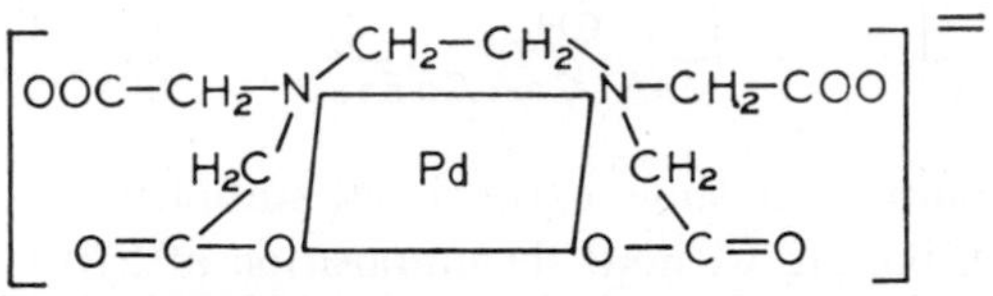

$$\left[\begin{array}{c} OOC-CH_2-N \overset{CH_2-CH_2}{\diagdown} N-CH_2-COO \\ H_2C \quad Pd \quad CH_2 \\ O=C-O \quad O-C=O \end{array} \right]^=$$

The stereochemistry of the EDTA complexes is discussed in Chapter 8.

Carbonyl Coordination

The carbonyl group of aldehydes has rather weak donor properties, but addition compounds of aldehydes with several of the light metals, such as magnesium[227], and with the weakly basic elements, such as tin and antimony,[228] are known. The carbonyl group of esters also forms rather weak coordinate links with these metals[229]. Simple aliphatic ketones show similar behavior.

The 1,3-dicarbonyl compounds, through their ability to enolize, form stable chelate rings with a large number of metals. In many cases the compounds so obtained are nonionic, insoluble in water, soluble in nonpolar solvents, and volatile. Acetylacetone has received the most attention in this regard, but dibenzoyl methane, benzoylacetone, acetoacetic ester, salicylaldehyde, benzoyl pyruvic acid, and o-hydroxyacetone are important. Thenoyltrifluoroacetone (TTA),

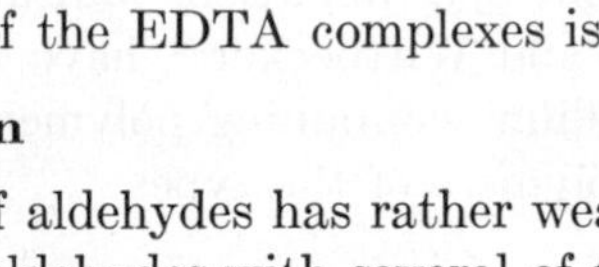

$$\underset{S}{\overset{O \quad\quad O}{\underset{\|}{\overset{\|}{C}}-CH_2-\underset{\|}{\overset{\|}{C}}-CF_3}}$$

224. Chaberek and Martell, *J. Am. Chem. Soc.*, **74**, 6228 (1952).
225. Schwarzenbach, *Helv. Chim. Acta*, **32**, 839 (1949).
226. Busch and Bailer, *J. Am. Chem. Soc.*, in press, 1956.
227. Menschutkin, *Izvest. St. Petersburg Polytech. Inst.*, **6**, 39 (1906).
228. Menschutkin, *J. Russ. Phys. Chem. Soc.*, **44**, 1929 (1912); Rosenheim and Stellman, *Ber.*, **34**, 3377 (1901); Pfeiffer, *Ann.*, **376**, 296 (1910).
229. Menschutkin, *Izvest. St. Petersburg Polytech. Inst.*, **4**, 101 (1905); **6**, 101 (1906); Lewy, *J. prakt. Chem.*, **37**, 480 (1846).

has received much attention because of the great stability of its compounds. The classic paper of Morgan and Moss on the acetylacetone compounds[230] reviews the literature up to 1914 and describes the preparation of many compounds. Metallic ions having a coordination number twice the ionic charge give nonelectrolytic complexes:

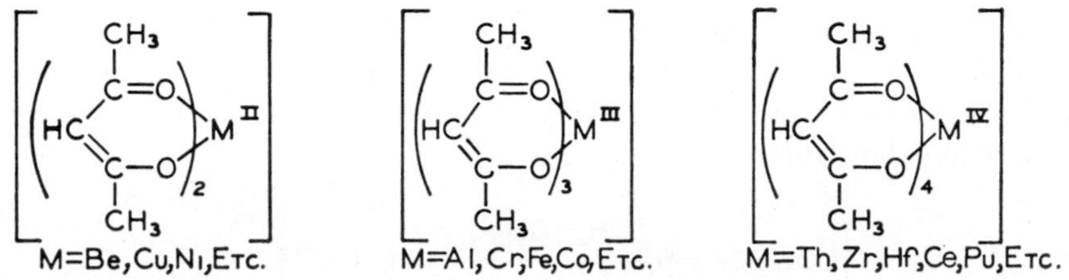

$$M=Be,Cu,Ni,Etc. \qquad M=Al,Cr,Fe,Co,Etc. \qquad M=Th,Zr,Hf,Ce,Pu,Etc.$$

Many of these compounds show exceptional stability, the beryllium complex, for example, boiling without decomposition at 270°C at atmospheric pressure. Molecular weight determinations indicate that these compounds are monomeric. Wilkins and Wittbecker[231] have utilized this stability in the preparation of beryllium containing polymers. They report that tetraketones form linear polymers of the types

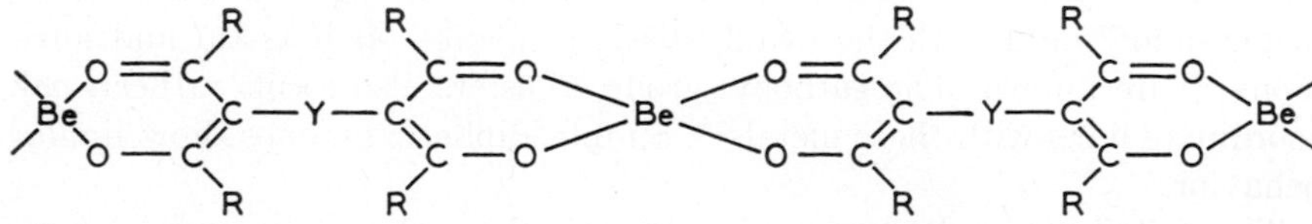

AND

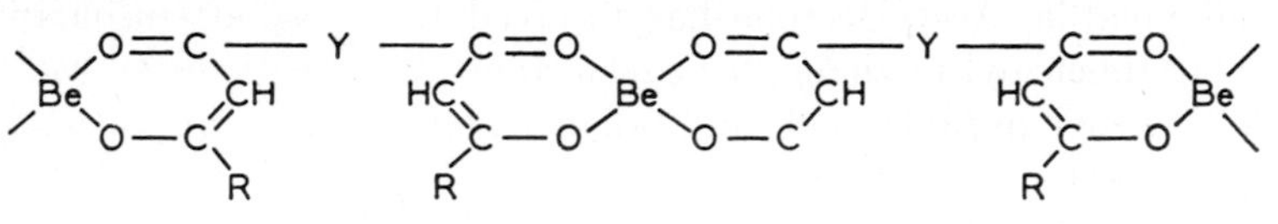

where Y is any one of a variety of organic groups.

There is, however, some popular misconception as to the stability of the diketone chelates. The statements that the rare earths can be separated through the volatility of their acetylacetonates[232], and that the molecular weights of the rare earth acetylacetonates can be determined by their vapor

230. Morgan and Moss, *J. Chem. Soc.*, **105**, 189 (1914).
231. Wilkins and Wittbecker, U. S. Patent 2,659,711 (Nov. 17, 1953).
232. Ephraim, "Inorganic Chemistry," English Edition by Thorne, London, Gurney and Jackson, 1926.

densities[233] are incorrect—scandium acetylacetonate is readily volatile[230, 234], but those of the true rare earths decompose on heating[235, 236]. Brimm[236] found that the rare earth compounds of dibenzoylmethane and benzoylacetone are readily decomposed by traces of moisture with the formation of $[M(diketone)_2(OH)(H_2O)]$. These compounds are soluble in organic solvents, but are not volatile.

When the coordination number of the central ion is less than twice the electrovalence, cationic compounds are formed, as illustrated by the compounds containing boron, silicon and titanium[237]

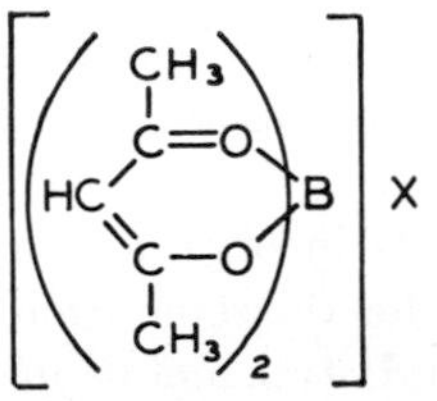

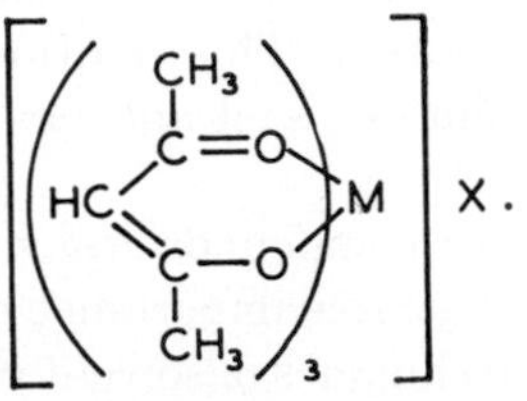

M= Si ,Ti

These compounds are of special interest because of their stereochemical possibilities and because they show typical metalloid elements in the role of cations. Similar compounds of other 1,3-diketones have been described[238].

If, on the other hand, the coordination number of the central atom is more than twice the electrovalence, the coordination sphere will tend to fill itself with other neutral groups[237]. Iron(II) forms the compounds

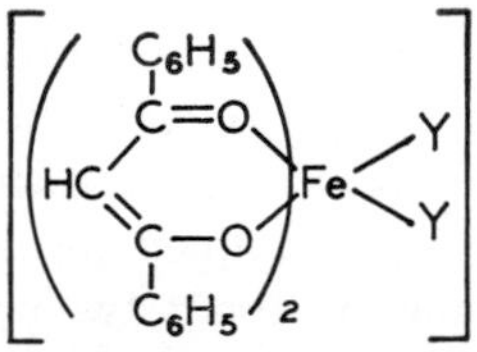

$Y = NH_3, py, \frac{1}{2}en, \phi NHNH_2,$
PIPERIDINE, NICOTINE

all of which are soluble in organic solvents, insoluble in water, and deeply colored[239]. On heating in vacuo the ammonia compound is converted to dibenzoylmethane iron.

233. Hein, "Chemische Koordinationtheorie," p. 153, Zurich, Hirzel Verlag, 1950.
234. Meyer and Winter, Z. anorg. Chem., 67, 414 (1910).
235. Urbain, Ann. chim., [7] 19, 212 (1900).
236. Brimm, thesis, University of Illinois, 1940.
237. Dilthey, Ber., 36, 923 (1903); 37, 588 (1904); Ann., 344, 300 (1905).
238. Dilthey, Ber., 36, 1595, 3207 (1903); J. prakt. Chem., [2] 111, 147 (1925).
239. Emmert and Gsottschneider, Ber., 66, 1871 (1933).

2,4-Pentanediono-dimethyl thallium

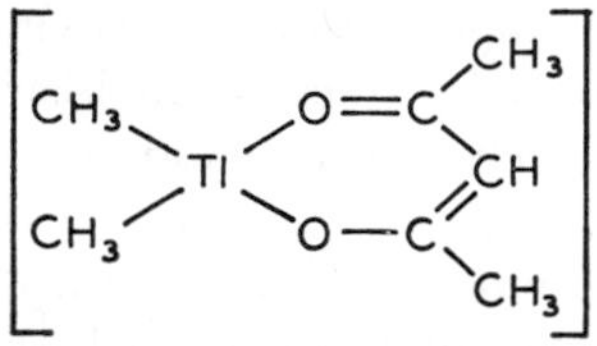

has unusual properties[240]. It is soluble in benzene, has a low melting point, and sublimes readily. On the other hand, it is also soluble in water, giving an alkaline solution. This solution shows the usual properties of the dimethyl thallium ion, so it appears that the coordinate bonds are broken by water.

The diketone compounds which are soluble in organic compounds have achieved considerable importance as agents for the separation of metal ions through the techniques of solvent extraction. If two metals in aqueous solution, are in equilibrium with a diketone, if the equilibrium constants are different and if the complexes are soluble in a solvent immiscible with water, the metals can be separated by liquid-liquid extraction[241]. Since the extent of dissociation of the complex of any metal can be changed by changing the pH of the solution, the method is widely applicable. If a specified metal is to be separated from several others, the pH is adjusted so that that metal (and those with smaller dissociation constants) will be extracted into the organic layer. This is then extracted with water, the pH of which is adjusted to allow only the extraction of the metal in question, since its complex has the largest dissociation constant of those now present. Bolomey and Wish[242] used this technique to separate radioberyllium from the other metals obtained with it by cyclotron bombardment. Huffman and Beaufait[243] employed the method to separate zirconium and hafnium, using thenoyltrifluoroacetone as the complex former. The distribution coefficient of the zirconium complex is about twenty times that of the hafnium complex, so excellent separation was achieved.

This extraction technique can also be used to determine the formulas of complexes and the degree of hydrolysis of metal ions in aqueous solution, as was shown by Connick and McVey in their study of the zirconium ion[244]. By determining the extraction coefficient of the zirconium complex of then-

240. Menzies, Sidgwick, Fox, and Cutliffe, *J. Chem. Soc.*, **1928**, 1288.
241. Calvin, Manhattan Project Report CN-2486, December 1944; *Experientia*, **6**, 135 (1950).
242. Bolomey and Wish, *J. Am. Chem. Soc.*, **72**, 4483 (1950).
243. Huffman and Beaufait, *J. Am. Chem. Soc.*, **71**, 3179 (1949).
244. Connick and McVey, *J. Am. Chem. Soc.*, **71**, 3182 (1949).

oyltrifluoroacetone between benzene and water as a function of the TTA activity in benzene, they were able to establish the composition of the chelate as [Zr(TTA)$_4$]. By measuring the distribution of the zirconium between the benzene and water phases as a function of pH, they then demonstrated that in the pH range -0.4 to 2.0, the zirconium ion exists largely as a mixture of Zr^{4+} and Zr(OH)$^{+++}$.

Steinbach and Freiser[245] have suggested that the complexing agent (acetylacetone, in their example) can serve also as the solvent for the complex. Using this technique, they have effected the analytical separation of zinc and copper ions.

Oxygen Carrying Chelates

Hemoglobin and hemocyanin were long considered to be unique in their ability to absorb and release oxygen, but several types of synthetic compounds are now known which possess this property. Their behavior is illustrated by a simple experiment: If cobalt nitrate solution is treated with ammonium chloride and ammonium hydroxide in the absence of air, a pink precipitate forms. When air is bubbled through the suspension, a brown color develops, but when nitrogen is substituted for the air, the pink color returns. This cycle can be repeated many times. Interestingly enough, the experiment fails if ethylenediamine is substituted for ammonia.

Pfeiffer, Breith, Lubbe, and Tsumaki[246] reported that bis-(salicylal)ethylenediiminecobalt(II)

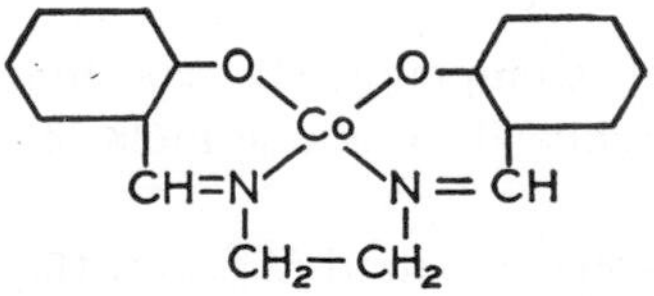

(A)

darkens in air. Tsumaki[247] found that this is due to absorption of oxygen and that the process is reversible. It has since been found that other cobalt chelates also show this property. Calvin and his students and Diehl and his students have studied compound (A) and many derivatives of it. Diehl[248] reports that the parent compound contains one-half mole of water per cobalt atom, and believes that two molecules of the chelate are held together

245. Steinbach and Freiser, *Anal. Chem.*, **25**, 881 (1953).
246. Pfeiffer, Breith, Lubbe, and Tsumaki, *Ann.*, **503**, 84 (1933).
247. Tsumaki, *Bull. Chem. Soc. Japan*, **13**, 252 (1938).
248. Diehl and co-workers (Hach, Harrison, Liggett, Chao, Brouns, Curtis, Henselmeir, Schwandt, Mathews), *Iowa State Coll. J. Sci.*, **21**, 271, 278, 287, 311, 316, 326, 335 (1947); **22**, 91, 110, 126, 129, 141, 150, 165 (1948); **23**, 273 (1949).

by an aquo bridge. This is a unique situation, for no other cases of aquo bridges are known. Calvin and his group[249] have studied compound (A) and some of its derivatives from the structural point of view. Both Calvin and Diehl report that most of these compounds exist in several different isomeric forms, only one of which (for each compound) is active toward oxygen. Compound (A) is paramagnetic, apparently having one unpaired electron per cobalt atom. Diehl reports that it does not absorb carbon monoxide or nitrous oxide, but that it absorbs nitric oxide and nitrogen dioxide. He is of the opinion that it will absorb other paramagnetic gases, but not diamagnetic ones.

When put under pressure of oxygen, these materials, either in the solid state or in solution in quinoline or similar solvents, absorb one mole of oxygen for each two moles of chelate, and release it again when the pressure is decreased. In each repetition of the cycle, however, there is a small amount of irreversible oxidation, so the ability to absorb oxygen gradually decreases.

Calvin's group also prepared compound (B)

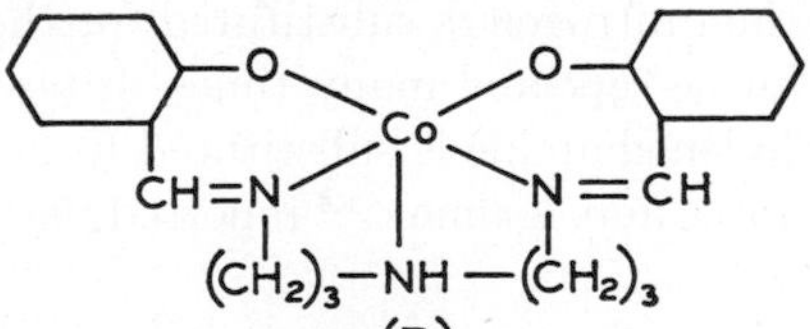

(B)

and several analogs of it. Compound (B) has three unpaired electrons per cobalt atom, and reversibly absorbs one mole of oxygen per atom of cobalt[250].

Calvin's x-ray studies on compound (A) show that it crystallizes in layers, with holes running through the layers. These holes are big enough to contain oxygen molecules, and the passages between them, while smaller, are sufficiently large to allow such molecules to go through without great difficulty.

Cobalt(II) histidine chelates in water solution will absorb oxygen reversibly[251]. Histidine compounds of iron are oxidized irreversibly, while those of nickel and copper are not oxidized at all. The unoxygenated cobalt histidine complex is paramagnetic to the extent of three unpaired electrons per cobalt atom, while the oxygenated compound is diamagnetic. Hearon is of the opinion that cobalt is four covalent in this compound, and that the

249. Calvin and co-workers (Bailes, Wilmarth, Barkelew, Aranoff, Hughes), J. Am. Chem. Soc., **68**, 2254, 2257, 2263, 2267, 2273 (1946).
250. Harle and Calvin, J. Am. Chem. Soc., **68**, 2612 (1946).

amino acid is coordinated to the metal only through nitrogen atoms

Two molecules of this chelate absorb one molecule of oxygen. It does not combine with carbon monoxide. According to Hearon[251d, e], the oxygenated molecule has either the structure

(g is a molecule of water or some other neutral group)

OR

Michaelis[252] has also measured the magnetic susceptibility of the cobalt histidine compounds.

The properties of hemoglobin and its oxygen carrying capacity are discussed in Chapter 21. Like the other oxygen carrying chelates, it is paramagnetic when deoxygenated, but diamagnetic in the oxygenated form[253]. As is well known, it combines with carbon monoxide more firmly than with oxygen, and with cyanide ion or pyridine still more firmly.

THE DONOR PROPERTIES OF SULFUR

The donor properties of sulfur are quite different from those of oxygen. In general, they are somewhat more restricted as regards the nature of the acceptor atom, but in some types of compounds, they are exceptionally

251. Burk, Hearon, Caroline, and Schade, *J. Biol. Chem.*, **165**, 723 (1946); Burke, Hearon, Levy, and Schade, *Federation Proc.*, **6**, 242 (1947); Hearon, *Federation Proc.*, **6**, 259. 260 (1947); *J. Nat. Cancer Inst.*, **9**, 1 (1948); Hearon, Burk, and Schade, *J. Natl. Cancer Inst.*, **9**, 337 (1949).
252. Michaelis, *Arch. Biochem.*, **14**, 17 (1942).
253. Pauling and Coryell, *Proc. Natl. Acad. Sci.*, **22**, 159, 210 (1936).

strong. The thioethers, for example, form much more stable compounds than the corresponding oxyethers. The coordination of sulfide (or hydrosulfide) ion with the sulfides of arsenic, antimony, tin, copper, and mercury is well known and is of great importance in qualitative analysis. Similarly, the preferential coordination of sulfide ion plays an important part in the metallurgies of copper and nickel. The Orford process exploits the amphoteric behavior of copper and iron toward sulfide in the separation of these metals from nickel. The separation is not quantitative, but repetition of the process gives further separation.

Thiohydrate Formation

Liquid hydrogen sulfide shows little resemblance to water in its solvent properties[254], although some inorganic salts dissolve in it. A few thiohydrates have been isolated[255, 256, 257] and thiohydrolysis probably takes place through the formation of unstable thiohydrates. Morgan and Ledbury[258] concluded that organic sulfides coordinate readily with those metals which occur as sulfides in nature, or which form very stable sulfides. They also found that the reactions of metal ions with dimethyldithiolethylene show analogies to their reactions with hydrogen sulfide. Thus, copper(II) and gold(III) chlorides, which are readily reduced by hydrogen sulfide, form the compounds

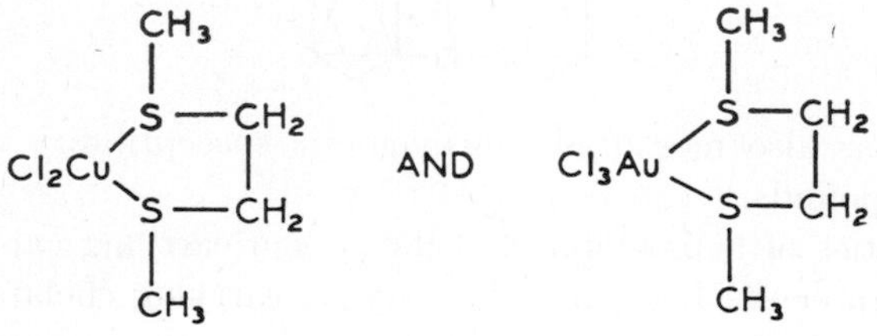

which readily revert to copper(I) and gold(I) compounds. Tschugaeff[259] found that of the dithioethers, $RS(CH_2)_nSR$ ($n = 0, 1, 2, 3, 5$), only the compounds having $n = 2$ formed stable, well-characterized chelates.

Dithiane, $C_4H_8S_2$, forms complexes with the ions of the coinage metals, platinum, mercury, and cadmium[260]. The ratio of dithiane to metal varies

254. Antony and Magri, *Gazz. chim. ital.*, **35**, 206 (1905).
255. Plotnikov, *J. Russ. Phys. Chem. Soc.*, **45**, 1162 (1913).
256. Biltz and Keunecke, *Z. anorg. allgem. Chem.*, **147**, 171 (1925).
257. Ralston and Wilkinson, *J. Am. Chem. Soc.*, **50**, 258 (1928).
258. Morgan and Ledbury, *J. Chem. Soc.*, **121**, 2882 (1922).
259. Tschugaeff, *Ber.*, **41**, 2222 (1908); Tschugaeff and Kobljanski, *Z. anorg. Chem.*, **83**, 8 (1913); Tschugaeff, *Compt. rend.*, **154**, 33 (1912); Tschugaeff and Subbotin, *Ber.*, **43**, 1200 (1910).
260. Bouknight and Smith, *J. Am. Chem. Soc.*, **61**, 28 (1939).

from two to one, as in $2AgNO_3 \cdot C_4H_8S_2$, to one to two, as in $AgNO_3 \cdot 2C_4H_8S_2$. The cation in the former may have the bridge structure

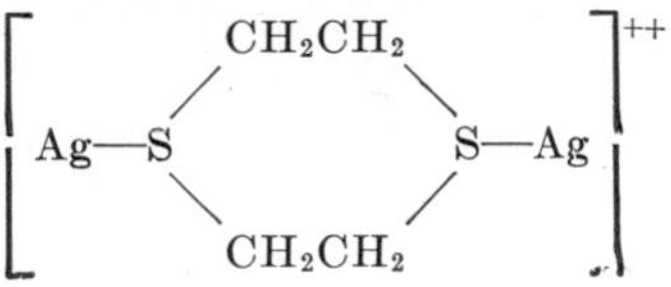

Thioethers and Thiols

Pfeiffer[261] has pointed out that the thioethers show a strong tendency to unite with salts of such metals as nickel, copper, and zinc, and, especially with those of platinum and palladium. Diethyl sulfide reacts with platinum(II) chloride to give three compounds of the empirical formula $Pt(SEt_2)_2Cl_2$, the yellow α- and β-isomers being the trans and cis compounds, respectively[262], and the γ-isomer being the dimer $[Pt(SEt_2)_4]$ $[PtCl_4]$[263]. The α- and β-forms are easily converted into each other by crystallization from suitable solvents. The differences between these α- and β- forms are so much greater than is usually shown by cis-trans isomers that Angell, Drew, and Wardlaw concluded that the isomerism is structural rather than spatial[264a]. They proposed the formulas

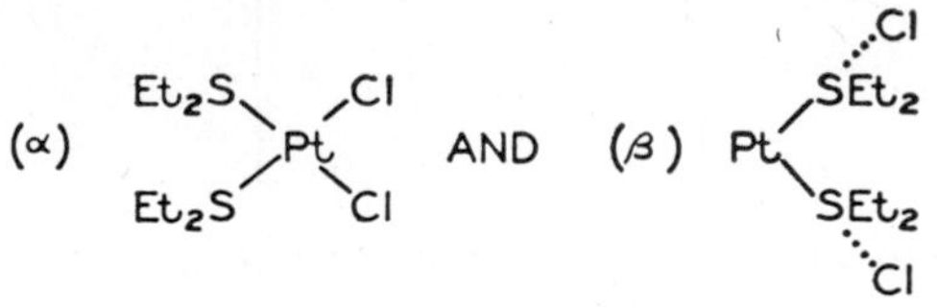

but Drew and Wyatt[264b] later concluded that the α-salt has the trans structure:

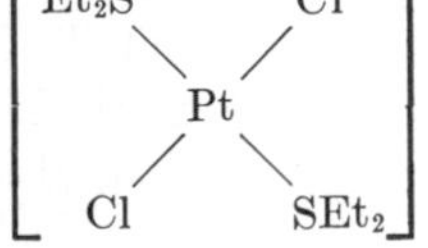

The great differences in the two isomers may be explained on the basis of the strong trans influence of the coordinated sulfur.

261. Pfeiffer, "Organische Molekulverbindungen," p. 159, Second Edition, Stuttgart, Enke, 1927.
262. Jensen, *Z. anorg. allgem. Chem.*, **225**, 97, 115 (1935).
263. Tschugaeff and Benewolensky, *Z. anorg. Chem.*, **82**, 420 (1913); Drew, Preston, Wardlaw, and Wyatt, *J. Chem. Soc.*, **1933**, 1294; Cox, Saenger and Wardlaw, *J. Chem. Soc.*, **1934**, 182.
264a. Angell, Drew, and Wardlaw, *J. Chem. Soc.*, **1930**, 349.
264b. Drew and Wyatt, *J. Chem. Soc.*, **1934**, 56.

The ion $[Pt(SEt_2)_4]^{++}$ is unstable, and its salts with simpler anions have not been isolated in the solid state. The iodide apparently cannot exist even in solution[265]. With ions such as $[PtCl_4]^=$, $[PtCl_6]^=$, and $[Pt(NO_2)_4]^=$, however, it forms stable, insoluble salts. Upon heating or solution, chloroplatinites of this type frequently rearrange to a mixture of the α- and β-monomeric forms:

$$[Pt(SMe_2)_4][PtCl_4] \rightarrow 2[Pt(SMe_2)_2Cl_2]^{263b,c}$$

The chloroplatinate decomposes on heating to give a mixture of $[Pt(SEt_2)_2Cl_2]$ and $[Pt(Et_2S)_2Cl_4]^{263}$.

Several tetrahalides of the type $[Pt(R_2S)_2X_4]$ are known[264, 265, 266]. Several of them have been shown to exist in α- and β-forms, which are readily interconvertible.

Disulfides behave similarly, but occupy two positions in the coordination sphere. The compound

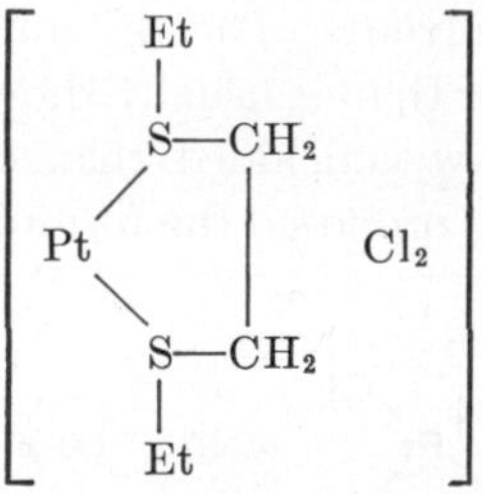

which may serve as an example, cannot exist in a *trans* form, but β- and γ- forms analagous to those described above have been prepared. The β-form reacts with ethylenediamine to give the rather unstable mixed compound $[Pt\ es\ en]Cl_2{}^{265}$. Bennett, Mosses, and Statham[267] were of the opinion that dithioether complexes of the type $[Pt\ es\ X_2]$ should exist in racemic and meso forms because of the asymmetry of the donor atoms, but they were unable to isolate the two geometrical isomers. Mann, however,[268] resolved a compound containing coordinated sulfur as its center of asymmetry (see page 325).

The dibenzylsulfide complex $[Au\{S(C_7H_7)_2\}Cl_2]$ is noteworthy because its simplest formula suggests the possibility that it may contain gold(II)[269].

265. Tschugaeff and Fraenkel, *Compt. rend.*, **154**, 33 (1912).
266. Blomstrand and Weibull, *J. prakt. Chem.*, [2] **38**, 352 (1888); Blomstrand and Enebuske, *J. prakt. Chem.*, [2] **38**, 365 (1888); Blomstrand and Rudelius, *J. prakt. Chem.*, [2] **38**, 508 (1888); Blomstrand and Löndahl, *J. prakt. Chem.*, [2] **38**, 515 (1888).
267. Bennett, Mosses, and Statham, *J. Chem. Soc.*, **1930**, 1668.
268. Mann, *J. Chem. Soc.*, **1930**, 1745.
269. Herman, *Ber.*, **38**, 2813 (1905); Ray and Sen, *J. Ind. Chem. Soc.*, **7**, 67 (1930).

Such is not the case, however, as the substance is diamagnetic[270]. From the molecular weight, electrical conductivity, magnetic susceptibility, and crystallographic data it is concluded that the substance is a lattice compound containing equivalent amounts of gold(I) and gold(III), $[Au(SR_2)Cl] \cdot [Au(SR_2)Cl_3]$[270].

Iridium(III)[271] and rhodium(III)[272] form the species $[M(SR_2)_3Cl_3]$. The iridium complex has been separated into its isomeric forms. The anionic complex $[Ir(SR_2)_2Cl_4]^-$ has also been prepared[273]. Surprisingly, treatment of these complexes with amines results in the replacement of the thioether groups first[273].

Livingstone and Plowman[274] have prepared some halogen bridged complexes of *o*-methylmercaptobenzoic acid which contain different metal ions.

$(M = Hg^{II} \text{ or } Cu^{II})$.

Most of the remarkable hexadentate chelating agents of Dwyer and Lions (Chapter 8) contain two coordinating sulfur atoms. A fine demonstration of the much greater affinity of cobalt(III) for ether-type sulfur than for ether-type oxygen is found in the fact that so long as one sulfur atom is present, the complexes are resolvable into optical isomers, while substitution of oxygen atoms for both sulfurs leads to cobalt(III) complexes which are too unstable to resolve[275].

Gonick, Fernelius, and Douglas[276] determined the formation constants of a series of sulfur and nitrogen containing chelating agents with the ions of copper, nickel, cobalt, zinc, and silver. A comparison of the data with similar data for a series of analagous polyamines indicated that nitrogen is probably a stronger donor for the metals studied, except silver. However, 2-aminoethanethiol, which coordinates as a negative ion, forms the most stable complexes of the entire group.

270. Brain, Gibson, Jarvis, Phillips, Powell, and Tyabji, *J. Chem. Soc.*, **1952**, 3686.
271. Ray and Adhikari, *J. Ind. Chem. Soc.*, **9**, 251 (1932); Ray, Adhikari, and Ghosh, *J. Ind. Chem. Soc.*, **10**, 279 (1933).
272. Dwyer and Nyholm, *J. Proc. Roy. Soc. N.S. Wales*, **78**, 67 (1944).
273. Ray and Ghosh, *J. Ind. Chem. Soc.*, **13**, 138 (1936); Ray, Adhikari, and Ghosh, *J. Ind. Chem. Soc.*, **10**, 275 (1933); Ray and Adhikari, *J. Ind. Chem. Soc.*, **11**, 517 (1934); Lebedinskii and Gurin, *Compt. rend. acad. sci. U.R.S.S.*, **40**, 322 (1943).
274. Livingstone and Plowman, *J. Proc. Roy. Soc.*, *N.S. Wales*, **85**, 116 (1952).
275. Dwyer, Gill, Gyarfas, and Lions, *J. Am. Chem. Soc.*, **75**, 1526 (1953).
276. Gonick, Fernelius, and Douglas, Technical Report to O.N.R., Oct. 15, 1953.

In addition to the marked stability of complexes containing the negative mercaptide ion toward dissociation in solution, stabilization of the ligand or of a high oxidation state of the metal may occur. Thus, the complex

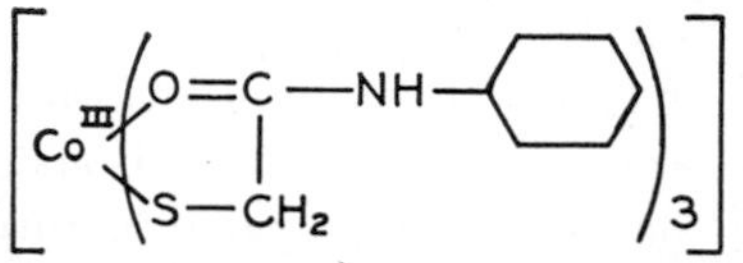

$$\left[Co^{III} \left(\begin{array}{l} O = C - NH - \bigcirc \\ | \\ S - CH_2 \end{array} \right)_3 \right]$$

stabilizes the ligand toward oxidation (when uncomplexed it is rapidly oxidized by air to the disulfide) and at the same time stabilizes the strongly oxidizing cobalt(III) species[277]. The great specificity of the metal ion in this behavior is illustrated by comparison with the reaction of thioglycolic acid and iron ions. In air-free alkaline solution, the complex

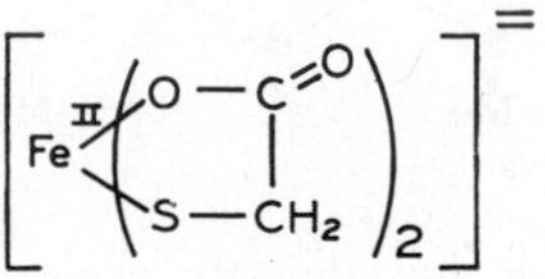

$$\left[Fe^{II} \left(\begin{array}{l} O - C \stackrel{O}{=} \\ | \\ S - CH_2 \end{array} \right)_2 \right]^{=}$$

is formed. Air oxidizes the iron(II) ion to iron(III) which in turn catalyzes the oxidation of the ligand to the corresponding disulfide[278].

Gold complexes of α-thiol fatty acids may prove useful in the treatment of such maladies as tuberculosis and leprosy[279]. The complex formed from diethylgold monobromide and 2-aminoethanethiol is also of interest. From its molecular weight it is assigned the structure

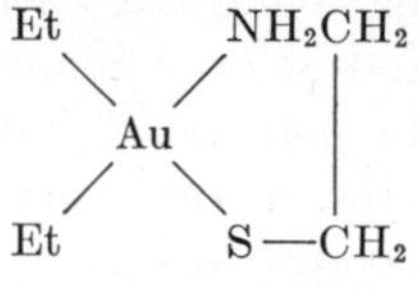

$$\begin{array}{ccc} Et & NH_2CH_2 \\ \diagdown \diagup & | \\ Au & | \\ \diagup \diagdown & | \\ Et & S - CH_2 \end{array}$$

However, the compound is remarkable in that the coordinated sulfur atom is quite reactive. The compound reacts explosively with methyl iodide and more moderately with ethyl bromide. The picrate salt of the product of treatment with ethyl bromide was shown to be identical with the complex prepared from S-ethyl-2-aminoethanethiol[280].

277. Feigl, *Nature*, **161**, 435 (1948); *Anal. Chem.*, **21**, 1298 (1949).
278. Leussing and Kolthoff, *J. Am. Chem. Soc.*, **75**, 3904 (1953).
279. Kundu, *J. Ind. Chem. Soc.*, **29**, 592 (1952).
280. Ewens and Gibson, *J. Chem. Soc.*, **1949**, 431.

The ability of seleno- and telluromercaptides and ethers to form complexes similar to those of the sulfur analogs is illustrated by the mercury(II) halide complexes used in the characterization of these donor molecules[281]. Gould and McCullough[282] have expressed the opinion that diarylselenoxides coordinate to mercury(II) through the selenium atom.

Thiocarbonyl Coordination

Many thiocarbonyl compounds show strong donor properties. Among the simplest of these is thiourea, which coordinates through the sulfur rather than through nitrogen, thus occupying only one coordination position. Thiourea coordinates with salts of almost all of the heavy metals. With compounds of tripositive iridium[283] and rhodium[284] it forms whole series of compounds, such as [Ir tu$_3$Cl$_3$], [Ir tu$_4$Cl$_2$]Cl, [Ir tu$_5$Cl]Cl$_2$, and [Ir tu$_6$]Cl$_3$. Thiourea reacts with the *cis* and *trans* isomers of platinum(II) compounds of the type [Pt a$_2$X$_2$] yielding different products and in so doing serves as the basis of Kurnakov's test which is widely used to distinguish between the isomers[285]. (Chapter 9) Another interesting application of thiourea to the chemical determination of structure is found in the work of Gent and Gibson[286] with the dimeric [Et$_2$Au SCN]$_2$. The failure of the complex to react with such nitrogen bases as ammonia, dipyridyl, and ethylenediamine, and its reaction with thiourea to produce [Et$_2$Au(SCN)tu] is interpreted to mean that the thiocyanate is coordinated through the sulfur, and that the original compound has the structure

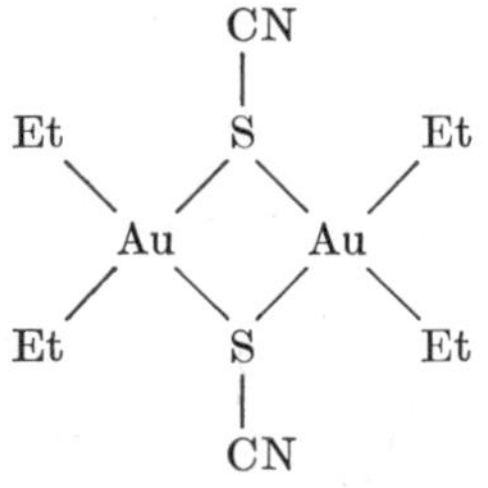

$$
\begin{array}{ccccc}
 & & \text{CN} & & \\
 & & | & & \\
\text{Et} & & \text{S} & & \text{Et} \\
 & \diagdown \;/ & & \diagdown \;/ & \\
 & \text{Au} & & \text{Au} & \\
 & /\; \diagdown & & /\; \diagdown & \\
\text{Et} & & \text{S} & & \text{Et} \\
 & & | & & \\
 & & \text{CN} & &
\end{array}
$$

Jensen has studied the compounds formed between thiosemicarbazide

281. Morgan and Burstall, *J. Chem. Soc.*, **1929**, 1096; **1930**, 1497; **1931**, 173; Carr and Pearson, *J. Chem. Soc.*, **1938**, 282; Krafft and Lyons, *Ber.*, **27**, 1761 (1894).
282. Gould and McCullough, *J. Am. Chem. Soc.*, **73**, 3195 (1951).
283. Lebedinskii, Shapiro, and Kasatkina, *Ann. inst. platine, U.S.S.R.*, No. **12**, 93 (1935).
284. Lebedinskii and Volkov, *Ann. inst. platine, U.S.S.R.*, No. **12**, 79 (1935).
285. Kurnakov, *J. Russ. Phys. Chem. Soc.*, **25**, 565 (1893); cf. *Chem. Centr.*, **65**, I, 460 (1894).
286. Gent and Gibson, *J. Chem. Soc.*, **1949**, 1835.

and platinum(II)[287], palladium(II)[287], and nickel[288] ions. The thiosemicarbazide molecule occupies two coordination positions, evidently coordinating thus

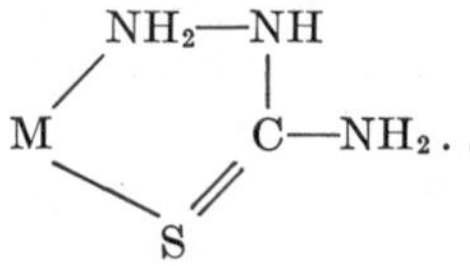

$$
\begin{array}{c}
NH_2-NH \\
M \quad\quad\quad C-NH_2 . \\
S
\end{array}
$$

Upon the addition of thiosemicarbazide, potassium chloropalladate(II) first gives [Pd thio$_2$][PdCl$_4$] and then [Pd thio$_2$]Cl$_2$. If this latter compound is heated in weakly acid solution, it changes to the insoluble inner complex

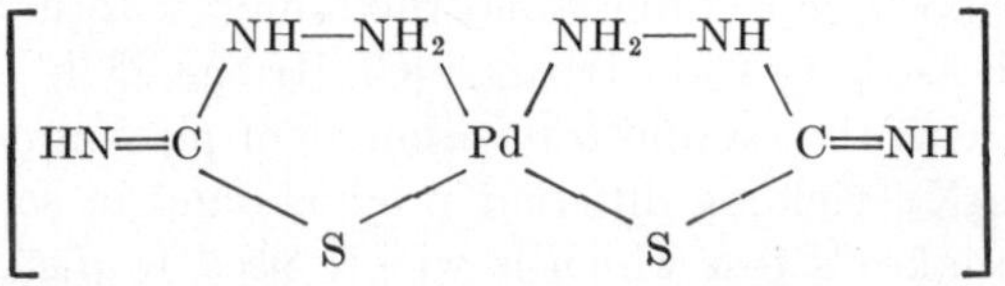

$$
\left[\begin{array}{cc}
NH-NH_2 \quad NH_2-NH \\
HN=C \quad\quad Pd \quad\quad C=NH \\
S \quad\quad\quad S
\end{array} \right] .
$$

There is evidence that this exists in two, presumably cis-trans-, forms. The platinum and nickel compounds behave similarly.

Diketonedithiosemicarbazone (thiazone) and its homologs

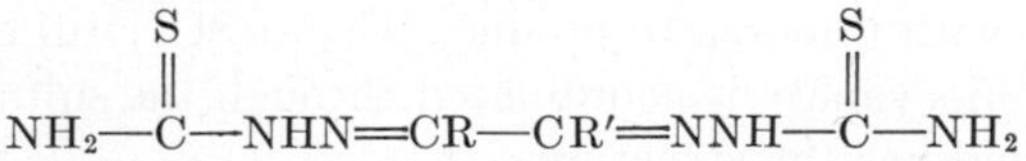

$$
\begin{array}{cc}
S & S \\
\| & \| \\
NH_2-C-NHN=CR-CR'=NNH-C-NH_2
\end{array}
$$

act as tetradentate ligands forming inner complexes with copper(II) and nickel(II) ions

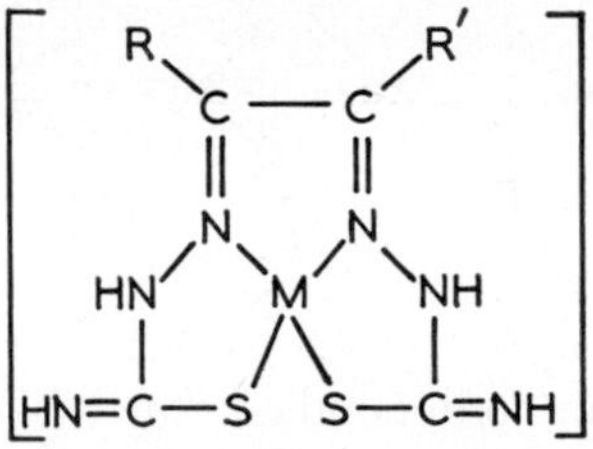

$$
\left[\begin{array}{c}
R \quad\quad R' \\
C - C \\
\| \quad\quad \| \\
N \quad N \\
HN \quad M \quad NH \\
\| \quad\quad \| \\
HN=C-S \quad S-C=NH
\end{array} \right]
$$

These complexes are quite stable, dissolving in strong acid as the soluble salts, [M(thiazone)]X$_2$[289].

Ammonium dithiocarbazide reacts with platinum(II) in a manner comparable both to thiourea and to thiosemicarbazide. With trans-[Pt(NH$_3$)$_2$Cl$_2$]

287. Jensen, Z. anorg. allgem. Chem., **221**, 6 (1934).
288. Jensen, Z. anorg. allgem. Chem., **221**, 11 (1934).
289. Bähr and Hess, Z. anorg. allgem. Chem., **268**, 351 (1952).

the reaction is

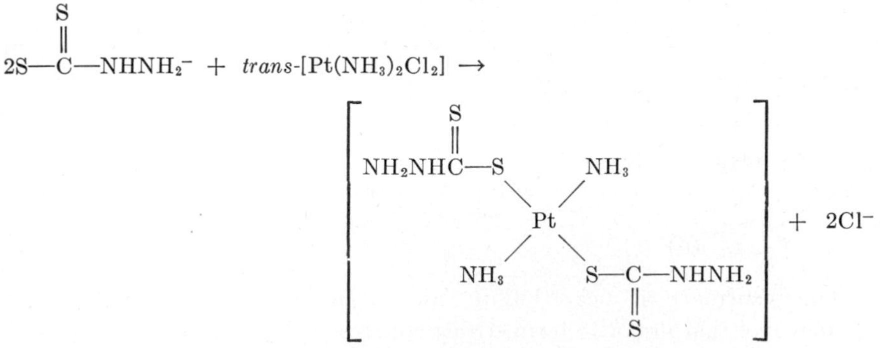

$$2S-\overset{\overset{\textstyle S}{\|}}{C}-NHNH_2^- + \textit{trans-}[Pt(NH_3)_2Cl_2] \rightarrow$$

$$\left[\begin{array}{cc} NH_2NH\overset{\overset{\textstyle S}{\|}}{C}-S & NH_3 \\ \diagdown & \diagup \\ & Pt \\ \diagup & \diagdown \\ NH_3 & S-C-NHNH_2 \\ & \| \\ & S \end{array}\right] + 2Cl^-$$

while the cis-isomer undergoes the reaction

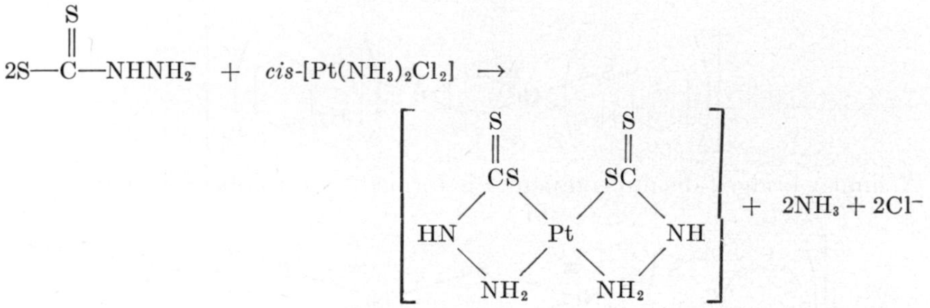

$$2S-\overset{\overset{\textstyle S}{\|}}{C}-NHNH_2^- + \textit{cis-}[Pt(NH_3)_2Cl_2] \rightarrow$$

$$\left[\begin{array}{cc} \overset{\textstyle S}{\|} & \overset{\textstyle S}{\|} \\ CS & SC \\ \diagup\diagdown & \diagup\diagdown \\ HN \quad Pt \quad NH \\ \diagdown\diagup & \diagdown\diagup \\ NH_2 & NH_2 \end{array}\right] + 2NH_3 + 2Cl^-$$

From these reactions and the fact that tetrammineplatinum(II) ion is not attacked by the dithiocarbazide ion, it is concluded that the sulfur groups may displace chloride rapidly but that the ammonia is displaced only as a consequence of the trans influence of the coordinated sulfur[290].

Inner complexes are formed by cobalt(II), cobalt(III), nickel(II), and palladium(II) with thiodicyandiamidine (guanyl thiourea),

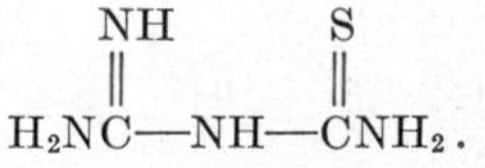

$$H_2N\overset{\overset{\textstyle NH}{\|}}{C}-NH-\overset{\overset{\textstyle S}{\|}}{C}NH_2.$$

Copper differs by forming a complex of the type [Cu(thicy) SO₄]. The cobalt, copper, and palladium complexes decompose in warm alkali, depositing insoluble metal sulfides, thus providing evidence for the participation of

290. Chernyaev and Mashentsev, *Izvest. Sektora Platiny i Drugikh Blagorod. Metal. Inst. Obshchei i Neorg. Khim., Akad. Nauk S.S.S.R.*, **23**, 72 (1949); cf. *Chem. Abs.* **45**, 2812d (1951); Mashentsev and Chernyaev, *Doklady Akad. Nauk S.S.S.R.*, **79**, 803 (1951); cf. *Chem. Abs.* **46**, 2949g (1952).

the sulfur atom in coordination (A). The nickel complex fails to give this test and is thought to have structure B[291].

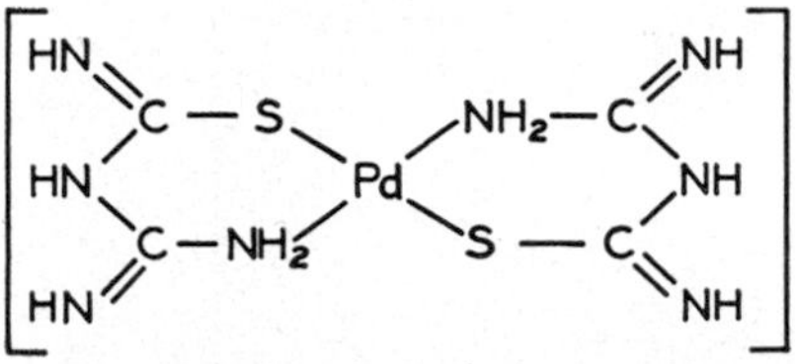

(A) 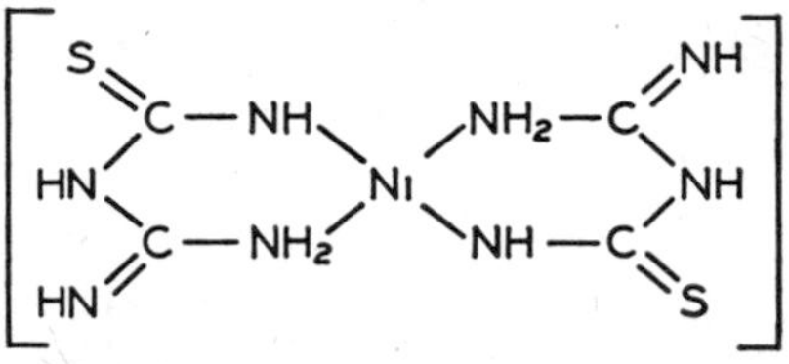   (B)

The occurrence of nickel(IV) in sulfur complexes testifies to the great tendency of that donor to form strong covalent bonds. Hieber and Brück[292] found that air oxidation of a strongly alkaline suspension of the nickel(II) complex of o-aminothiophenol produces the deep blue complex

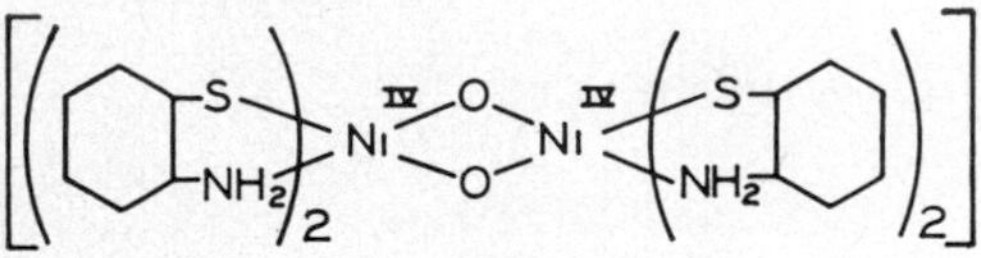

A similar bridged disulfo compound is formed by dithiobenzoic acid

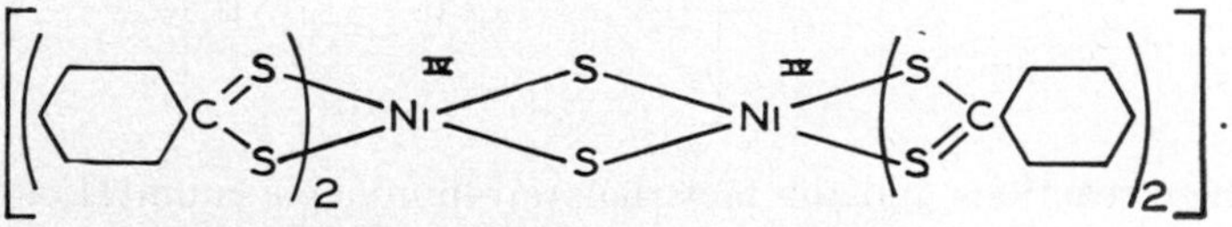

Dithiooxamide (rubeanic acid) forms insoluble complexes with nickel, and copper ions[293]. These substances have the properties of inner salts, and because of the steric requirements of the ligand, they exist as bridged polymers

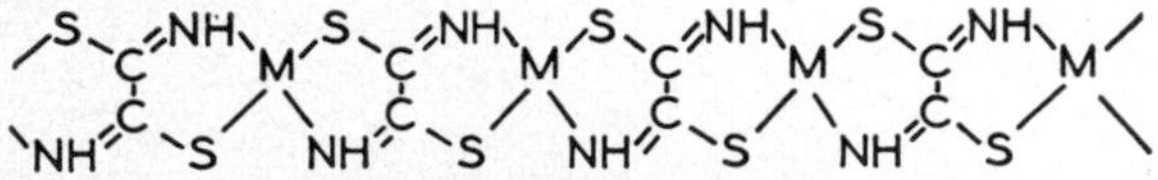

Amon and Kane[294] have used the linear nature and the light absorption of this polymer in the manufacture of a device for the polarization of light. A sheet of plastic is soaked in a solution of dithiooxamide, which causes the precipitation of the complex within the plastic. When the plastic sheet is

291. Ray and Chaudhury, J. Ind. Chem. Soc., 27, 673 (1950); Poddar and Ray, J. Ind. Chem. Soc., 29, 279 (1952).
292. Hieber and Brück, Naturwiss., 36, 312 (1949).
293. Jensen, Z. anorg. Chem., 252, 227 (1944); Ray, Z. anal. Chem., 79, 95 (1929).
294. Amon and Kane, U.S. Patent 2 505 085, April 25, 1950.

stretched in one direction, the polymer chains are oriented parallel to each other. The bridging ability of this donor molecule is also illustrated in the dimeric derivative of diethylgold monobromide[295].

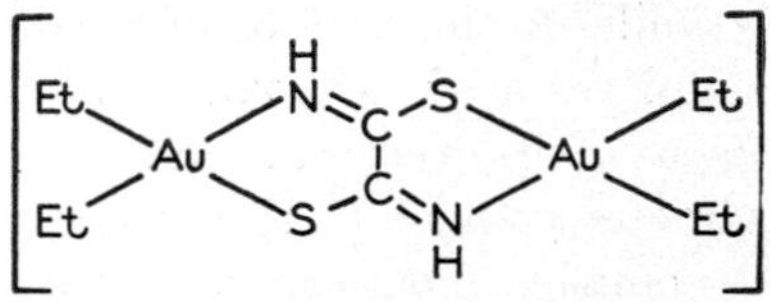

Other Sulfur Donors

The thiocyanate ion has unshared pairs of electrons on both the sulfur and the nitrogen. Werner at one time[296] supposed the two isomers of $[Co\ en_2(NCS)_2]^+$ to be structurally different, one having a cobalt-nitrogen link and the other a cobalt-sulfur link. This hypothesis was based upon the fact that the thiocyanate group of one of the isomers is destroyed by chlorine, leaving the nitrogen (in the form of ammonia) in union with the metal, while the thiocyanate group of the other isomer is completely eliminated by this treatment. Werner later found[297], however, that the two compounds are stereoisomers, and that the thiocyanate group is attached to the metal through the nitrogen in both cases. The sulfur of the thiocyanate group probably does have strong donor properties, however, and in the case of gold it is the sulfur atom which preferentially coordinates Werner reported that silver nitrate does not precipitate silver thiocyanate from a solution of $[Co(NH_3)_5(NCS)]^{++}$ or similar complexes but the silver loses its ionic character. He supposed that the silver coordinates with the sulfur[298]. Waggener, Mattern, and Cartledge[299] however, have found the stability of these dinuclear complexes to be much less than reported by Werner.

The sulfite group evidently occupies only one coordination position in most cases, and from the fact that salts of the ion $[Co(NH_3)_4(SO_3)_2]^-$ are yellow or brown, it may be inferred that these compounds contain a sulfur-cobalt link.

The action of sulfite ion on platinum(II) complexes is also most easily explained on the basis of a metal-sulfur bond. Sulfite acts differently[300] on

295. Ewens and Gibson, *J. Chem. Soc.*, **1949**, 431.
296. Werner and Braunlich, *Z. anorg. Chem.*, **22**, 91, 123 (1900).
297. Werner, *Ann.*, **386**, 1 (1912).
298. Werner, *Ann.*, **386**, 50 (1912).
299. Waggener, Mattern, and Cartledge, abstracts, 122*nd* meeting, American Chemical Society, Sept. 1952.
300. Gurin, *Doklady Akad. Nauk S.S.S.R.*, **50**, 201 (1945).

the cis- and trans- isomers of dichlorodiammineplatinum(II)

$$cis\text{-}[Pt(NH_3)_2Cl_2] + 4Na_2SO_3 \rightarrow Na_6[Pt(SO_3)_4] + 2NaCl + 2NH_3$$

$$trans\text{-}[Pt(NH_3)_2Cl_2] + 2Na_2SO_3 \rightarrow trans\text{-}Na_2[Pt(NH_3)_2(SO_3)_2] + 2NaCl$$

This behavior is quite similar to the reaction of these isomers with thiourea.

Aside from the complexes with aromatic nitrogen molecules, ruthenium(II) is best known in its very unusual sulfite complexes. Treatment of chloropentammineruthenium(III) ion with sodium bisulfite produces the two complex compounds, $[Ru^{II}(NH_3)_4(SO_3H)_2]$ and $Na_4[Ru^{II}(NH_3)_2(SO_3)_2(SO_3H)_2]\cdot 6H_2O$. The dipositive oxidation state of the ruthenium was verified by analysis and magnetic measurements[301]. Upon dissolution in acid, $[Ru^{II}(NH_3)_4(SO_3H)_2]$ is converted to $[Ru^{II}(NH_3)_4(SO_2)X]X$. The action of ammonium hydroxide on the dibisulfitotetrammine produces the nonelectrolyte, $[Ru^{II}(NH_3)_5(SO_3)]$[302]. This compound is also sensitive to acid, transforming to $[Ru^{II}(NH_3)_5(SO_2)]^{++}$.

Rhodium(III) and iridium(III) form complexes of the type $M^I_3[M^{III}(NH_3)_3(SO_3)_3]$[303]. Iridium also forms a compound in which the sulfite group is reported to be bidentate, $[Ir(SO_3)_3Cl_2]^{5-}$, but the alternate possibility of halogen bridging has not been disproved.

Riley[304] has prepared salts of the dark red selenitopentamminecobalt(III) ion, $[Co(NH_3)_5(SeO_3)]^+$, but his experiments did not show whether the selenite group is attached through the selenium or through the oxygen. Several selenite complexes of nickel, copper, and cobalt have been obtained by Ray and Ghosh[305], who found them to be less stable than the corresponding sulfite compounds.

The thiosulfate group, with unshared electrons on both oxygen and sulfur, could conceivably coordinate through either or both. When it occupies but one coordination position, union with the metal evidently takes place through the oxygen, for the ion $[Co(NH_3)_5S_2O_3]^+$ is red[306]. This ion is very stable, for it is formed when $[Co(NH_3)_5Cl]S_2O_3$ or $[Co(NH_3)_5Br]S_2O_3$ is allowed to stand at 35 to 40°C[307]. The stability of the thiosulfate-cobalt bond is further attested by the reaction of $[Co(NH_3)_5S_2O_3]^+$ with potassium cyanide, which yields $K_4[Co(S_2O_3)(CN)_5]$.[308] Duff[157] reported the prepara-

301. Gleu, Breuel, and Rehm, Z. anorg. allgem. Chem., **235,** 201 (1938).
302. Gleu and Breuel, Z. anorg. allgem. Chem., **235,** 211 (1938).
303. Lebedinskii and Shenderetskaya, Izvest. Sektora. Platiny i Drugikh Blagorod. Metal., Inst. Obshchei i Neorg. Khim. Akad. Nauk S.S.S.R., **21,** 164 (1948); cf. Chem. Abs., **44,** 10565a (1950); Gurin, Doklady Akad. Nauk S.S.S.R., **56,** 217 (1935); cf. Chem. Abs. **43,** 1676a (1949).
304. Riley, J. Chem. Soc., **1928,** 2985.
305. Ray and Ghosh, J. Indian Chem. Soc., **13,** 494 (1936).
306. Ray, J. Indian Chem. Soc., **4,** 64 (1927).
307. Sarkar and Das-Gupta, J. Ind. Chem. Soc., **7,** 835 (1930).
308. Ray, J. Ind. Chem. Soc., **4,** 325 (1927).

tion of [Co en$_2$ S$_2$O$_3$]Br·3H$_2$O, which he thought contained a doubly co-ordinated thiosulfate group. The evidence for this is slight, however, and the correct formula may well be [Co en$_2$ (H$_2$O)S$_2$O$_3$]Br·2H$_2$O. Weinland[309] has suggested, but without experimental evidence, that the double potassium bismuth thiosulfate is

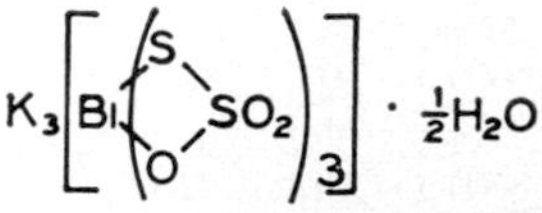

$$K_3\left[Bi\left(\begin{array}{c} S \\ \diagdown \\ \diagup \\ O \end{array}SO_2\right)_3\right] \cdot \tfrac{1}{2}H_2O$$

in which coordination takes place through both oxygen and sulfur. The fixation process in photography depends upon the formation of thiosulfato-silver anions, of which several have been reported[310]. If coordination takes place through the oxygen, sulfates should give analagous compounds.

The Donor Properties of Nitrogen

The solvent properties of ammonia closely resemble those of water, and solvation is as important in ammonia solutions as it is in aqueous solutions. The donor properties of nitrogen are as strong, or stronger, than those of oxygen, and some of the metal-ammonia compounds show remarkable stability. Many of them (including those of cobalt, chromium and the platinum metals) do not lose ammonia when heated above 200°C or when treated with sodium hydroxide or hydrochloric acid. The ammines of copper, silver, zinc, and several other metals are equally well known, but are much less stable, and are decomposed by dilute acids or bases. Ammines of the alkali and alkaline earth metals are completely decomposed by water, and some of them are stable only at low temperatures.

Ammines

The hydrates, especially those of the highly charged metallic ions, readily liberate hydrogen ions, with the formation of aquohydroxo complexes. An analagous reaction takes place with ammines, but it is less pronounced than with hydrates. From a study of the ammines of rhodium, Grünberg and Faermann[311] concluded that the acid dissociation of coordinated water is 10^5 times as great as that of coordinated ammonia. The loss of protons by ammines is particularly noticeable with the complexes of the very heavy metals, as is illustrated by the formation of HgNH$_2$Cl when mercuric chloride is treated with ammonia. Other illustrations involve the ammines of

309. Weinland, "Einführung in die Chemie der Komplexverbindungen," Second Ed., p. 148, Stuttgart, Enke, 1924.
310. Bassett and Lemon, *J. Chem. Soc.*, **1933**, 1423; Ashihara and Matsuda, *Kogaku Shuho, Kyushu Univ.* (*Technological Reports, Kyushu Univ.*), **25**, 11 (1952); cf. *Chem. Abs.*, **47**, 12075g (1953).

TABLE 1.1. COLORS OF SOME ANHYDROUS SALTS, AND THEIR HYDRATES
AND AMMONATES

$CoCl_2$	$[Co(H_2O)_6]Cl_2$	$[Co(NH_3)_6]Cl_2$
Blue	Red	Rose
$CuCl_2$	$[Cu(H_2O)_4]Cl_2$	$[Cu(NH_3)_4]Cl_2$
Brown	Blue	Deep Blue
$NiCl_2$	$[Ni(H_2O)_6]Cl_2$	$[Ni(NH_3)_6]Cl_2$
Light brown	Green	Blue
$CrCl_3$	$[Cr(H_2O)_6]Cl_3$	$[Cr(NH_3)_6]Cl_3$
Violet	Gray-violet	Yellow
	$[Cr(H_2O)_5Cl]Cl_2 \cdot H_2O$	$[Cr(NH_3)_5Cl]Cl_2$
	Green	Rose red
	$[Cr(H_2O)_4Cl_2]Cl \cdot 2H_2O$	$[Cr(NH_3)_4Cl_2]Cl$
	Green	cis- violet
		trans- green

platinum[311, 312], gold[313], and osmium[314]. Ammines of the lighter elements
also lose protons to some extent, as is indicated by the fact that the hydrogen atoms in such complexes as $[Co(NH_3)_6]^{+++}$ are readily exchanged for
deuterium when placed in heavy water[315].

Water and ammonia, coordinated to ions of the same metal, do not always stabilize the same valence state (Chapter 11). For example, hydrated
cobalt(III) compounds are very strong oxidizing agents, while ammoniated
cobalt(II) compounds are strong reducing agents. The hydrates and ammines often show similar colors, but this is by no means a general rule.
Table 1.1 summarizes a few examples. Peters[316] made the first systematic
and extended study of the stability of ammines. He subjected ninety seven
salts to the action of dry ammonia gas at atmospheric pressure and by
measuring the volume of ammonia absorbed in each case, calculated the
formulas of the ammines obtained. Following Peters, Ephraim[317], W.
Biltz[318], Clark[319, 320], and others studied the reactions of salts with anhydrous

311. Grünberg, Z. anorg. Chem., **138**, 333 (1924); Grünberg and Faermann, ibid., **193**, 193 (1930).
312. Tschugaeff, Z. anorg. Chem., **137**, 1 (1924).
313. Block and Bailar, J. Am. Chem. Soc., **73**, 4722 (1951).
314. Dwyer and Hogarth, J. Am. Chem. Soc., **75**, 1008 (1953).
315. Anderson, Briscol, and Spoor, J. Chem. Soc., **1943**, 361.
316. Peters, Zeit anorg. Chem., **77**, 137 (1912).
317. Ephraim, Z. phys. Chem., **81**, 513, 539 (1913); **83**, 196 (1913); Ber., **45**, 1322 (1912); **46**, 3103, 3742 (1913); **47**, 1828 (1914); **48**, 41, 624, 629, 1638, 1770 (1915); **49**, 2007 (1916); **50**, 529, 1069, 1088 (1917); **51**, 130, 644, 706 (1918); **52**, 236, 241, 940, 957 (1919); **53**, 548 (1920); **54**, 973 (1921).
318. Biltz and co-workers, Z. phys. Chem., **82**, 688 (1913); Z. anorg. allgem. Chem., **83**, 163, 177 (1913); **89**, 97, 134, 141 (1914); **109**, 89, 132 (1919); **114**, 161, 174, 241 (1920); **119**, 97, 115 (1921); **123**, 31 (1922); **124**, 235, 322 (1922); **125**, 269 (1922); **127**, 1 (1923); **129**, 1, 161 (1923); **130**, 93 (1923); Z. Elektrochem., **26**, 374 (1920); Angew. Chem., **33**, 313 (1920).

ammonia. They prepared and studied hundreds of ammines in order to find out what factors are important in determining stability. While a great deal was learned about the stabilities of ammines, little light was thrown on the structures of such compounds as $AlCl_3 \cdot 9NH_3$, $AlCl_3 \cdot 5NH_3$ and $AlCl_3 \cdot 1NH_3$[320] and compounds containing very large amounts of ammonia, such as $TlCl_4 \cdot 20NH_3$[321]. Doubtless many of these are "lattice compounds" only.

The ammines which are of chief interest are those of the transition metals and the metals of periodic groups IB and IIB. Even among these, there are great differences in stability. For example, iron ammines cannot be obtained in the presence of water; copper ammines and cobalt(II) ammines exist in water solution, and can be crystallized from such solutions, but they are immediately destroyed by acids. Cobalt(III) and platinum ammines can be recrystallized from solutions of strong acids, and the hydroxides $[Co(NH_3)_6](OH)_3$ and $[Pt(NH_3)_6](OH)_4$ are sufficiently stable to allow their easy preparation[322]. This, of course, may be a measure of rate of decomposition rather than of intrinsic stability, but it is of tremendous practical importance.

The nature of the anion is of great importance in determining the stability of some metal ammines. Weitz[323] observed that the ammines of gold are stable if the anion is an oxy-anion such as nitrate, perchlorate, phosphate or oxalate, and the ammonia groups cannot be removed by the action of the oxyacids. They are destroyed, however, by halides, presumably because the halide ion replaces part of the ammonia in the coordination sphere. Tomlinson, Ottoson, and Audrieth[324] have called attention to the explosive character of cobalt(III) and chromium(III) ammines in which oxidizing groups are present in the coordination sphere or as anions.

It is of interest that the ammines which are easily decomposed by acids (e.g., those of Cu, Ag, and Zn) are easily formed by the addition of ammonia to a solution of the metal ion. The ammines which are not rapidly destroyed by acids are not readily formed. Thus, the addition of an excess of ammonia to a solution of a chromium(III) salt ordinarily precipitates the hydroxide; the hexammine is formed in good yield only by the action of liquid ammonia on anhydrous chromium(III) chloride in the presence of a catalyst[325]. The hexammine cobalt(III) ion is not obtained by aerial oxida-

319. Clark, Quick, and Harkins, *J. Am. Chem. Soc.*, **42**, 2438 (1920); Clark and Buckner, *J. Am. Chem. Soc.*, **44**, 230 (1922).
320. Clark, *Am. J. Sci.*, **7**, 1 (1924).
321. Young, *J. Am. Chem. Soc.*, **57**, 997 (1935).
322. Hecht, *Z. anorg. allgem. Chem.*, **270**, 215 (1952).
323. Weitz, *Ann.*, **410**, 117 (1915).
324. Tomlinson, Ottoson, and Audrieth, *J. Am. Chem. Soc.*, **71**, 375 (1949).
325. Oppegard and Bailar, *Inorganic Syntheses*, III, 153 (1950).

tion of an ammoniacal cobalt(II) solution except in the presence of a catalyst[326]. Dwyer and Hogarth[327] could prepare the ion $[Os(NH_3)_6]^{+++}$ only by the treatment of $[Os(NH_3)_5Br]^{++}$ with ammonia under pressure.

Ammonia can, of course, share the coordination sphere with other donor groups. In his first paper[116], Werner pointed out that ammonia molecules can be displaced, one by one, from the coordination sphere, either by other neutral groups such as water, or by negative groups. If the metal-ammonia bond is stable, the groups which share the coordination sphere with ammonia may be replaced by other groups to form a great variety of compounds. The following reactions are typical[327]:

$$[Os(NH_3)_5Br]^{++} \xrightarrow{\text{Ag}_2\text{O}} [Os(NH_3)_5OH]^{++} \underset{\text{H}_2\text{O}}{\overset{\text{HCl}}{\rightleftharpoons}} [Os(NH_3)_5Cl]^{++}$$

The amide group, like the hydroxide group, has two pairs of unshared electrons and coordinates readily with certain metals. Mercury amido chloride illustrates this. The NH_2^- group can also act as a bridge between two acceptor atoms (p. 23). The imino group frequently acts as a bridge also, as in

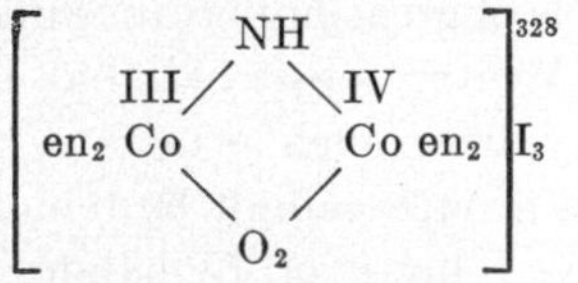

$$\left[\begin{array}{c} \mathrm{NH} \\ \mathrm{III}\diagup\quad\diagdown\mathrm{IV} \\ \mathrm{en_2\,Co}\qquad\mathrm{Co\ en_2} \\ \diagdown\quad\diagup \\ \mathrm{O_2} \end{array} \right]\mathrm{I_3}\ [328]$$

and

$$\mathrm{K_2}\left[\begin{array}{c} \mathrm{NH} \\ \diagup\quad\diagdown \\ \mathrm{(NH_3)_3PtI}\qquad\mathrm{PtI(NH_3)_3} \\ \diagdown\quad\diagup \\ \mathrm{NH} \end{array} \right]\ [329].$$

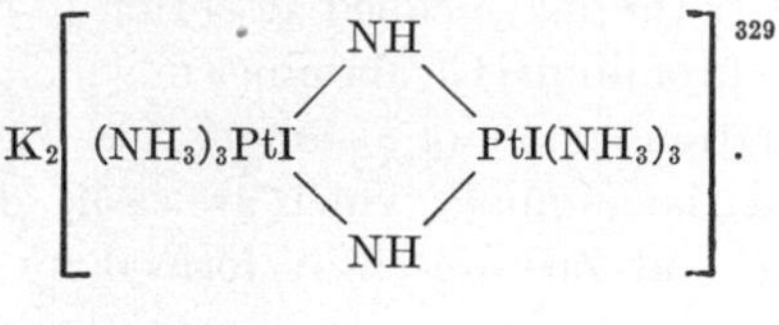

Aliphatic Amines

The aliphatic monoamines coordinate less readily than does ammonia, and the compounds so formed are less stable than the ammines. However, this point is often overemphasized, for some rather stable coordination compounds of the aliphatic amines do exist. The secondary amines coordinate less readily than do the primary, and the tertiary amines are almost devoid of ability to coordinate with metal ions. This is probably due

326. Bailar and Work, *J. Am. Chem. Soc.*, **67**, 176 (1945).
327. Dwyer and Hogarth, *J. Proc. Roy. Soc. N.S. Wales*, **84**, 117 (1951).
328. Werner, *Ann.*, **375**, 74 (1910).
329. Cleve, *Öfvers. K. Vet. Akad. Forh.*, **27**, 777 (1870); **28**, 175 (1871).

to steric factors, for the tertiary amines coordinate firmly with the hydrogen ion; that is, they are strong bases. Straumanis and Circulis[330] have described compounds of the mercury and copper halides with ethylamine, propylamine, butylamine, dimethylamine, and diethylamine. Jörgensen[331] prepared platinum(II) complexes containing methyl, ethyl, and propylamines, and Drew and Tress[332] have extended his study to include the preparation of the stereoisomeric forms of $[Pt(CH_3NH_2)_2Cl_2]$. These are stable enough that they can be oxidized to $[Pt(CH_3NH_2)_2Cl_4]$. Gil'dengershel[333] prepared $[Pt(CH_3NH_2)_4Cl_2]Cl_2$ by the action of methylamine on potassium chloroplatinate, and purified it by recrystallization from hydrochloric acid. Chernyaev[334] has prepared three of the four possible isomers of $[[Pt\ en(CH_3NH_2)(NO_2)Cl_2]Cl$, and has resolved one of them, as well as $[Pt\ en(CH_3NH_2)(NO_2)_2Cl]Cl$. Finally, Meisenheimer and Kiderlen[335] have introduced various primary amines into the coordination sphere of cobalt by the reaction

$$[Co\ en_2Cl_2]Cl + amine \rightarrow [Co\ en_2\ amine\ Cl]Cl_2$$

Even aromatic amines form fairly stable compounds in this way. Primary amines which are weaker bases than aniline, and secondary amines, do not enter the complex, but bring about more complicated reactions[336, 337].

If chelation can take place to form five-membered rings, the stability of the compounds is greatly enhanced (Chapter 5). Ethylenediamine is the simplest and the most important of such bases, and its compounds have played an important part in the development of the coordination theory. 1,2-Diaminopropane (propylenediamine) also forms stable compounds, which are similar to those containing ethylenediamine, but are usually more soluble. Isobutylenediamine[338], 2,3-diaminobutane[339], stilbenediamine[338, 340], and several other 1,2-diamines have been shown to form stable chelate rings. Pearson, Boston, and Basolo[341] have prepared com-

330. Straumanis and Circulis, Z. anorg. allgem. Chem., 230, 65 (1936).
331. Jörgensen, J. prakt. Chem., 33, 530 (1886).
332. Drew and Tress, J. Chem. Soc., 1935, 1212.
333. Gil'dengershel, Zhur. Priklad. Khim. (J. Applied Chem.), 23, 487 (1950).
334. Chernyaev, Ann. inst. platine No. 8, 37 (1931).
335. Meisenheimer and Kiderlen, Ann., 438, 238 (1924).
336. Ablov, Bull. soc. chim., [5] 3, 2270 (1936); 4, 1783 (1937).
337. Bailar and Clapp, J. Am. Chem. Soc., 67, 171 (1945).
338. Mills and Quibell, J. Chem. Soc., 1935, 839; Lidstone and Mills, J. Chem. Soc., 1939, 1754.
339. Bailar and Balthis, J. Am. Chem. Soc., 58, 1474 (1936).
340. Williams, thesis, University of Illinois, 1951.
341. Pearson, Boston and Basolo, J. Am. Chem. Soc., 75, 3089 (1953).

pounds of the type

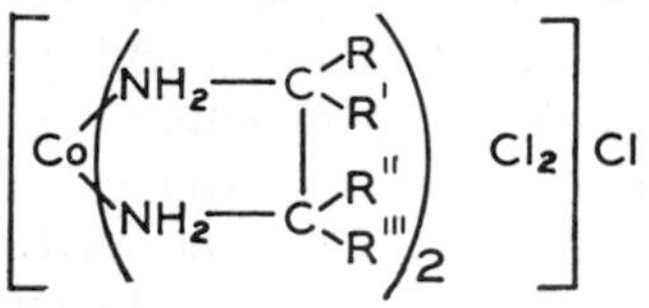

$$\left[Co \left(\begin{matrix} NH_2 - C \begin{matrix} R \\ R' \end{matrix} \\ NH_2 - C \begin{matrix} R'' \\ R''' \end{matrix} \end{matrix} \right)_2 \quad Cl_2 \right] Cl$$

in which the R's represent hydrogen or methyl. As the number of methyl groups is increased, crowding becomes pronounced, and, in water solution, the coordinated chlorides are more easily replaced by water molecules.

Trimethylenediamine forms six-membered rings, which compare favorably in stability with those of ethylenediamine[297, 342]. Mann[343] has prepared coordination compounds of several metals with bases of the type $(NH_2CH_2)_2CHX$, where $X = CH_3$, Br, SCN, and OH. Tetramethylenediamine and the higher homologs in the series apparently cannot form rings at all in aqueous solution. Diamines having four, five, ten and eighteen carbon atoms have been investigated[344]. Pfeiffer[345] has shown, however, that tetramethylenediamine and hexamethylenediamine will form chelates from alcohol solution.

The polyamines $NH_2CH_2CH_2(NHCH_2CH_2)_nNH_2$ ($n = 1, 2, 3,$ or 4) are strong coordinators, (even though part of the nitrogen atoms are secondary), because they form multiple ring systems. Diethylenetriamine acts as a tridentate base toward copper(II) and nickel(II) ions, giving complexes of the types [Cu dien Cl]$^+$ and [Cu dien$_2$]$^{++}$. In the second case, because of the stereochemical properties of the base, copper assumes a coordination number of six[346, 347]. Jonassen and his students prepared platinum and palladium-triethylenetetramine complexes [Pt trien]$^{++}$ and [Pd trien]$^{++}$[348], and [Ni$_2$ trien$_3$]$^{4+}$. The [Ni$_2$ trien$_3$]$^{4+}$ is paramagnetic, so must consist of two tetrahedra[349]. Basolo[350] prepared a series of cobalt complexes of the types

342. Bailar and Work, J. Am. Chem. Soc., **68**, 232 (1946).
343. Mann, J. Chem. Soc., **1927**, 2904; **1928**, 1261.
344. Pfeiffer and Haimann, Ber., **36**, 1063 (1903); Pfeiffer and Lübbe, J. prakt. Chem., [2] **136**, 321 (1933); Tschugaeff, Ber., **39**, 3190 (1906); Tschugaeff, J. prakt. Chem., [2] **75**, 159 (1907); Werner, Ber., **40**, 61 (1907); McReynolds, thesis, University of Illinois, 1938.
345. Pfeiffer, Naturwiss., **35**, 190 (1948).
346. Mann, J. Chem. Soc., **1934**, 466.
347. Breckenridge, Canadian J. Research, **26B**, 11 (1948).
348. Jonassen and Cull, J. Am. Chem. Soc., **71**, 4097 (1949).
349. Jonassen and Douglas, J. Am. Chem. Soc., **71**, 4094 (1949).
350. Basolo, J. Am. Chem. Soc., **70**, 2634 (1948).

[Co trien X_2] and [Co trien Y], where X is Cl, NO_2 and NH_3 and Y is CO_3 or en. He also obtained [Co_2 $trien_3$]$^{6+}$, an ion of unusually high ionic charge. Jonassen and Fry[351] have isolated the cobalt(II) complex of tetraethylene-pentamine.

β,β',β''-Triaminotriethylamine behaves as a quadridentate amine in spite of the reluctance of tertiary nitrogen to coordinate. Mann and Pope[352] prepared the platinum(II) and platinum(IV) complexes [Pt tren]Cl_2 and [Pt tren Cl_2]Cl_2. The palladium(II) and nickel ions form the ion [M tren]$^{++}$ and nickel forms also the ion [Ni_2 $tren_3$]$^{4+}$, in which the coordination number of nickel is evidently six[353]. Mann[354] prepared several salts of the ion [Co tren(SCN)$_2$]$^+$. By treatment of [Co en$_2$Cl$_2$]$^+$ with the same base, Jaeger and Koets[355] obtained salts of an ion which they thought to be [(Co en$_2$)$_3$tren$_2$]$^{9+}$, but attempts to repeat this work[356] have been unsuccessful, and it seems that Jaeger and Koets probably had [Co tren en]$^{+++}$.

Cases are known in which the polyamines coordinate without using all of their nitrogen atoms[357]. α,β,γ-Triaminopropane can act either as a bidentate or tridentate group[358] depending upon the metal ion involved and the conditions of the experiment. If only two amino groups coordinate, they are on adjacent carbon atoms.

Ethylenediamine, and presumably other, similar bases, sometimes coordinate through only one nitrogen. Chernyaev and Fedorova[359] prepared a compound whose formula they write [Pt(en·HCl)·NH$_3$·Cl$_2$]. Mild alkalies close the ring with the formation of [Pt enNH$_3$Cl]Cl, and chlorine oxidizes the compound to [Pt(enHCl)(NH$_3$)Cl$_4$]. This platinum(IV) compound hydrolyzes to [(NH$_3$)(H$_2$O)Cl$_3$PtenPtCl$_3$(H$_2$O)(NH$_3$)]Cl$_2$, in which the ethylenediamine acts as a bridge between the two platinum atoms. Job[360] has adduced evidence for the existence of [Ag en$_2$]$^+$ and [Tl en]$^+$ ions, which are analagous to [Ag(NH$_3$)$_2$]$^+$ and [Tl(NH$_3$)]$^+$, and hence contain monocoordinated ethylenediamine. Di-n-propylgold(III) bromide reacts with

351. Jonassen and Fry, *J. Am. Chem. Soc.*, **75**, 1524 (1953).
352. Mann and Pope, *Proc. Roy. Soc. London*, **109A**, 444 (1925).
353. Mann and Pope, *J. Chem. Soc.*, **1926**, 482.
354. Mann, *J. Chem. Soc.*, **1929**, 409.
355. Jaeger and Koets, *Z. anorg. allgem. Chem.*, **170**, 347 (1928).
356. Middleton (1952) and Rebertus (1954), unpublished work, University of Illinois.
357. Mann, *J. Chem. Soc.*, **1934**, 466; Job and Brigando, *Compt. rend.*, **210**, 438 (1940).
358. Mann and Pope, *J. Chem. Soc.*, **1926**, 2675; *Nature*, **119**, 351 (1927); Mann, *J. Chem. Soc.*, **1926**, 2681; **1927**, 1224; **1928**, 890; **1929**, 651.
359. Chernyaev and Fedorova, *Ann. secteur platine, Inst. chim. gen.* (*U.S.S.R.*), No. **14**, 9 (1937).
360. Job, *Compt. rend.*, **176**, 442 (1923); **184**, 1066 (1927).

ethylenediamine to form a compound which is formulated

$$
\begin{array}{ccccc}
\mathrm{Pr} & & \mathrm{Br} & \mathrm{Br} & \mathrm{Pr}^{\,361,} \\
\diagdown & \diagup & & \diagdown & \diagup \\
& \mathrm{Au} & & & \mathrm{Au} \\
\diagup & \diagdown & & \diagup & \diagdown \\
\mathrm{Pr} & & \mathrm{NH_2{-}CH_2{-}CH_2{-}NH_2} & & \mathrm{Pr}
\end{array}
$$

On heating, one of the gold atoms loses its two propyl groups, retaining its hold on the bromine and the nitrogen:

$$
\begin{array}{ccccc}
\mathrm{Pr} & & \mathrm{Br} & \mathrm{Br} & \\
\diagdown & \diagup & & \diagdown & \\
& \mathrm{Au} & & & \mathrm{Au} \,. \\
\diagup & \diagdown & & \diagup & \\
\mathrm{Pr} & & \mathrm{NH_2CH_2CH_2NH_2} & &
\end{array}
$$

The treatment of Zeise's salt, $K[Pt(C_2H_4)Cl_3]$, with ethylenediamine results in the formation of a dinuclear complex in which the ethylenediamine acts as a bridging group[362]

$$
\left[
\begin{array}{ccccc}
\mathrm{C_2H_4} & & \mathrm{Cl} & \mathrm{Cl} & \mathrm{C_2H_4} \\
\diagdown & \diagup & & \diagdown & \diagup \\
& \mathrm{Pt} & & & \mathrm{Pt} \\
\diagup & \diagdown & & \diagup & \diagdown \\
\mathrm{Cl} & & \mathrm{NH_2CH_2CH_2NH_2} & & \mathrm{Cl}
\end{array}
\right].
$$

Gilman and Woods[363] have prepared a compound which they believe to have the structure $(CH_3)_3AuNH_2CH_2CH_2NH_2Au(CH_3)_3$. In this case ring formation is impossible because only one coordination position is open on each gold atom.

Pfeiffer and Glaser[364] have studied the donor properties of N-substituted ethylenediamines. With copper(II) perchlorate, N-methyl and N,N'-diethylethylenediamine give blue-violet compounds analgous to [Cu en$_2$] (ClO$_4$)$_2$. The corresponding N-diethyl compound is ruby red at room temperature, but assumes the blue-violet color above 44°. The same investigators report that the reaction of N-methyl-N'-diethyl ethylenediamine and N-triethyl ethylenediamine with copper perchlorate do not give compounds which are analagous to those of the less highly substituted bases, but correspond to the formula [Cu OH diamine]ClO$_4$. They are probably dimeric, the copper atoms being linked together through two ol bridges. These compounds, like the others, are thermochromic, changing from blue-violet to ruby-red when they are cooled in liquid air.

361. Burawoy and Gibson, *J. Chem. Soc.*, **1935**, 219; Burawoy, Gibson, and Holt, *J. Chem. Soc.*, **1935**, 1024.
362. Hel'man, *Compt. rend. acad. sci. U.R.S.S.*, **38**, 243 (1943).
363. Gilman and Woods, *J. Am. Chem. Soc.*, **70**, 550 (1948).
364. Pfeiffer and Glaser, *J. prakt. Chem.*, [2], **151**, 134 (1938); **153**, 300 (1939).

The remarkably stable tris-(N-hydroxethylethylenediamine)cobalt(III) complex[365] shows none of the characteristic reactions of aliphatic hydroxyl groups, even though the usual formulation would indicate that the hydroxyl groups are not coordinated to the metal.

Aromatic Amines

Aromatic diamines form quite unstable coordination compounds. Hieber and his co-workers have shown that ortho-phenylenediamine usually occupies only one coordination position[366] but that the para isomer occupies two[367]. They give the latter the rather improbable formula

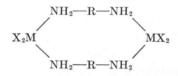

Diamino-biphenyls seem to have somewhat stronger donor properties. 2,2'-Diamino-biphenyl forms cobalt(III) complexes corresponding to those of ethylenediamine[368] and several stable compounds of benzidine and tolidine have been reported[369]. The empirical formulas indicate that these bases occupy two coordination positions, but there is no evidence that both amino groups attach themselves to the same metal atom.

Heterocyclic Amines

The heterocyclic amines, although they contain tertiary nitrogen, coordinate readily, and a large number of pyridine complexes has been described. In general, these resemble the corresponding ammonia compounds. Davis and his students[370] have found the stability of certain nickel and zinc pyridine compounds to decrease as the temperature is lowered. For example, $Nipy_4(SCN)_2$ is stable at room temperatures, but decomposes at $-3°$. It may be that the coordinating tendency of the thiocyanate group, relative to that of pyridine, increases with falling temperature till, at $-3°$, it displaces the pyridine.

In this, as in other cases, chelation greatly enhances coordination, and metals which ordinarily do not coordinate with nitrogen form stable com-

365. Keller and Edwards, *J. Am. Chem. Soc.*, **74**, 215 (1952).
366. Hieber, Schlieszmann, and Ries, *Z. anorg. allgem. Chem.*, **180**, 89 (1929); Hieber and Ries, *Z. anorg. allgem. Chem.*, **180**, 225 (1929).
367. Hieber and Ries, *Z. anorg. allgem. Chem.*, **180**, 105 (1929).
368. Middleton: thesis, University of Illinois, 1938.
369. Tettamanzi, *Atti accad. Torino, Classe sci. fis., mat. nat.*, **69**, 225 (1935); Spacu and Dima, *Bull. Soc. Stiinte Cluj*, **8**, 549 (1937).
370. Davis and Batchelder, *J. Am. Chem. Soc.*, **52**, 4069 (1930); Davis and Ou, *J. Am. Chem. Soc.*, **56**, 1061, 1064 (1934).

pounds with α-pyridyl hydrazine[371], α-pyridyl pyrrole[372], 2,2'-dipyridyl and 1,10-phenanthroline. Many coordination compounds of 2,2'-dipyridyl have been prepared. As far as is known, dipyridyl always acts as a bidentate coordinating agent. The stability of some of its coordination compounds is truly remarkable. For example, [Ni dipy$_3$]$^{++}$ is destroyed only very slowly by sodium hydroxide or ammonium sulfide[373]. Prussian blue is completely destroyed in the cold by the addition of 2,2'-dipyridyl[374].

Research on the dipyridyl complexes has centered largely on their stereochemistry, the stabilization of unusual valence states by coordination with dipyridyl, and the usefulness of the complexes in analytical chemistry (Chapter 20).

While many substituted derivatives of 2,2'-dipyridyl form complexes, substituents in the 6,6' positions may prevent coordination. Thus, 2-pyridyl-2'-quinoline, and 2,2'-diquinoline fail to react with octahedral metal ions[375], as does 6,6'-dimethyl-2,2'-dipyridyl[376].

The stabilization of valence states by coordination with dipyridyl is illustrated by the cases of silver and chromium. If present as the dipyridyl complex, Ag(I) can be oxidized to the Ag(II) complex and isolated as [Ag dipy$_2$]$^{++}$ [377, 378]. Hein and Herzog[379] report that the reduction of [Cr dipy$_3$]$^{+++}$ in the presence of perchlorate ion gives [Cr dipy$_3$]ClO$_4$, a deep blue compound, unstable in air, insoluble in water, but soluble in methanol, ethanol and pyridine.

2,2',2''-Terpyridyl and 2,2',2'',2'''-tetrapyridyl coordinate through all of their nitrogen atoms. The iron(II) ion fills its coordination sphere by combination with two molecules of terpyridyl[380]; the platinum(II) ion, having a coordination number of only four, forms compounds of the type [Pt tripyCl]Cl[381]. Tetrapyridyl gives compounds such as [Ag tetrapy]NO$_3$,

371. Emmert and Schneider, Ber., 66, 1875 (1933).
372. Emmert and Brandl, Ber., 60, 2211 (1927).
373. Jaeger and Van Dijk, Proc. Acad. Sci. Amsterdam, 37, 10 (1934); 37, 618 (1934); 39, 164 (1936); Z. anorg. allgem. Chem., 227, 273 (1936).
374. Barbieri, Atti X° congr. intern. chim., 2, 583 (1938).
375. Smirnoff, Helv. chim. Acta, 4, 802 (1921).
376. Willink and Wibaut, Rec. Trav. Chim., 54, 275 (1935).
377. Barbieri and Malaguti, Atti acad. nazl. Lincei, Rend. classe sci. fis., mat. e nat., 8, 619 (1950).
378. Malaguti, Atti acad. nazl Lincei, Rend. classe sci. fis., mat. e. nat., 9, 349 (1950).
379. Hein and Herzog, Z. anorg. allgem. Chem., 267, 337 (1952).
380. Morgan and Burstall, J. Chem. Soc., 1932, 20.
381. Morgan and Burstall, J. Chem. Soc., 1934, 1498.

[Co(II) tetrapy]Cl$_2$, and [Pt(II) tetrapy][PtCl$_6$][381, 382].
1,10-Phenanthroline

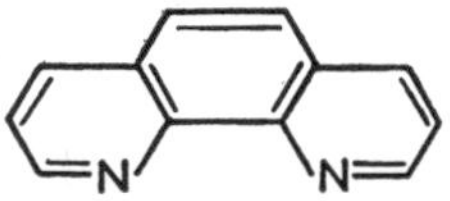

resembles 2,2'-dipyridyl in its coordinating ability, but gives somewhat more stable complexes. Even beryllium and magnesium, which seldom coordinate with nitrogen compounds, form complex ions containing three molecules of 1,10-phenanthroline[383].

The complexes of 1,10-phenanthroline are chiefly of interest because of their stereochemistry (Chapter 8), their usefulness in analytical chemistry (Chapter 20), and the ability of 1,10-phenanthroline to stabilize unusual valence states of some of the metals (Chapter 11).

Hydrazine Coordination

Hydrazine forms many coordination compounds, though their number is somewhat limited because of the reducing action of hydrazine. Compounds of the noble metals, and of metals in their higher oxidation states, are thus quite unstable. Efforts to prepare compounds of cobalt(III), for example, have been unsuccessful. Most hydrazine complexes which have been isolated as solids do not contain enough hydrazine molecules to fill the coordination sphere, so it has been suggested that hydrazine serves as a bidentate ligand. This, however, necessitates the formation of a three-membered ring. Goremykin[384] treated potassium chloroplatinate(II) with $N_2H_4 \cdot HCl$ and obtained a product which he believes to be [PtCl$_2$(N$_2$H$_5$)$_2$]Cl$_2 \cdot 2H_2O$. On heating, this goes to [PtCl$_2$(N$_2$H$_4$)(N$_2$H$_5$)]Cl, which reacts with pyridine to form [PtCl$_2$(N$_2$H$_4$)$_2$]. If this interpretation is correct, hydrazine is acting as a monodentate donor.

Schwarzenbach and Zobist[385], using the Bjerrum technique, have shown that in solution, zinc ion can coordinate with four molecules of hydrazine and nickel ion with six. Rebertus, Laitinen and Bailar[386] have shown, polarographically, that zinc ion forms a tetrahydrazine complex.

382. Morgan and Burstall, *J. Chem. Soc.*, **1938**, 1672, 1675.
383. Pfeiffer and Werdelman, *Z. anorg. Chem.*, **261**, 197 (1950).
384. Goremykin, *Compt. rend. acad. sci. U.R.S.S.*, **33**, 227 (1941).
385. Schwarzenbach and Zobist, *Helv. chim. Acta*, **35**, 1291 (1952).
386. Rebertus, Laitinen, and Bailar, *J. Am. Chem. Soc.*, **75**, 3051 (1953); Rebertus, thesis, University of Illinois, 1954.

Biguanide Coordination

Biguanide,

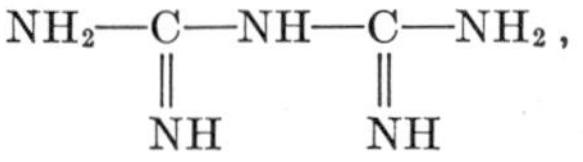

$$NH_2—C—NH—C—NH_2,$$
$$\overset{\|}{NH}\qquad\overset{\|}{NH}$$

is a remarkable coordinating material which has been studied extensively by Ray and his students. Only two of the five nitrogen atoms coordinate; these are on different carbon atoms. When coordination takes place, a hydrogen atom is lost from each molecule of biguanide. The uncoordinated nitrogen atoms still have basic properties, so salts may be formed. Many substituted biguanides have powerful coordinating ability. Among these are phenylbiguanide,

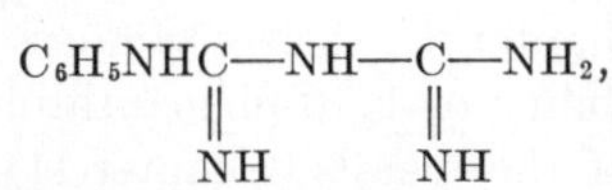

$$C_6H_5NHC—NH—C—NH_2,$$
$$\overset{\|}{NH}\qquad\overset{\|}{NH}$$

N,N′ diphenylbiguanide, N,N′-diethylbiguanide, N-phenyl-N′methyl biguanide, ethylenedibiguanide

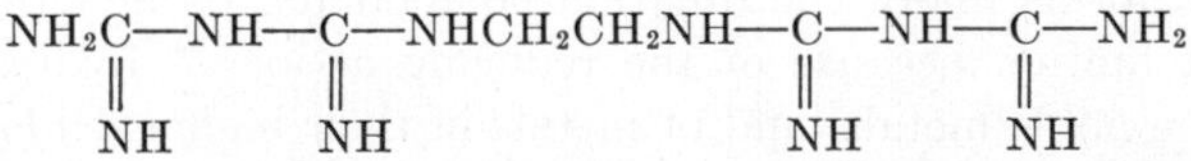

$$NH_2C—NH—C—NHCH_2CH_2NH—C—NH—C—NH_2$$
$$\overset{\|}{NH}\qquad\overset{\|}{NH}\qquad\qquad\overset{\|}{NH}\qquad\overset{\|}{NH}$$

and meta-phenylenedibiguanide

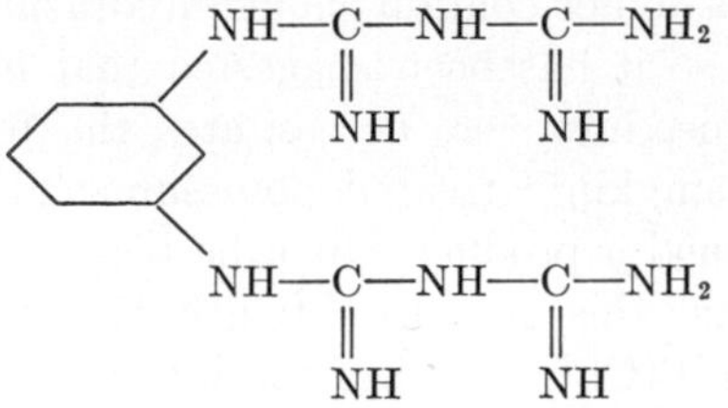

$$NH—C—NH—C—NH_2$$
$$\overset{\|}{NH}\qquad\overset{\|}{NH}$$

$$NH—C—NH—C—NH_2$$
$$\overset{\|}{NH}\qquad\overset{\|}{NH}$$

Bivalent metal ions such as Cu^{++} and Ni^{++} form stable complexes with the biguanides. The copper complex is stable enough that the metal in it is not reduced by iodide, sulfite, thiosulfate, or other anions that commonly reduce copper(II) to copper(I)[387]. When the biguanide is unsymmetrically substituted, as in phenylbiguanide, the copper(II) and nickel complexes exist in two cis and trans forms[388]. Ghosh and Chatterjee, however, isolated only one form of each of the metal bis(methylphenylbiguanides)[389].

387. Ray and Bagchi, *J. Indian Chem. Soc.*, **16,** 617 (1939).
388. Ray and Chakravarty, *J. Indian Chem. Soc.*, **18,** 609 (1941).
389. Ghosh and Chatterjee, *J. Indian Chem. Soc.*, **30,** 369 (1953).

The tervalent metal ions give remarkably stable complexes of the type

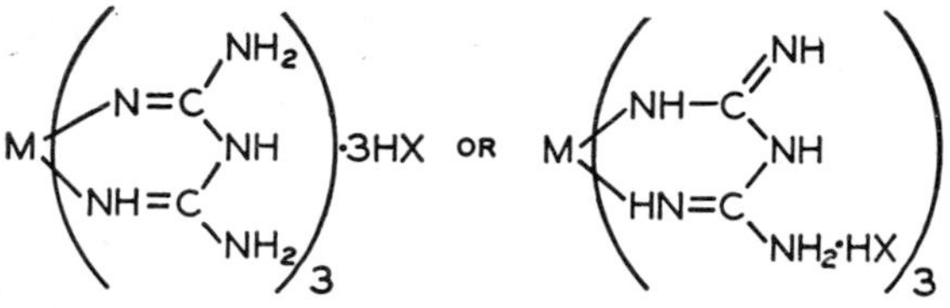

Ray and his students have published a long series of articles on these interesting substances[390]. The chromium complexes undergo slow hydrolysis:

$$[Cr(BigH)_3]X_3 + 2H_2O \rightarrow [Cr(BigH)_2(OH)H_2O]X_2 .$$

The hydroxoaquobis(biguanides) can hydrolyze further to monobiguanides, but these are unstable. The cobalt(III) complexes are more stable than those of chromium, and, in fact, have been shown to be more stable than the cobalt(III) ammines[391]. The tris(phenylbiguanide)cobalt(III) ion has been resolved into its optical antipodes[392]. Bis(biguanide) cobalt(III) complexes of the types $[Co(BigH)_2X_2]$ and $[Co(BigH)_2XY]$ exist in *cis* and *trans* forms[393]. The dibiguanides are quadridentate[394], apparently attaching themselves to the metal through the $\alpha, \alpha', \gamma, \gamma'$ positions. Ray and Das Sarma[395] have prepared the cobalt(III) meta-phenylenedibiguanide complexes $[Co\ phenylene(BigH)_2X_2]^{+++}$, where $X = NH_3$ or H_2O. These apparently have the trans configuration, for oxalate ion does not seem to be able to replace the two coordinated X groups.

Among the most remarkable derivatives of biguanide is the silver(III) compound of ethylenedibiguanide:

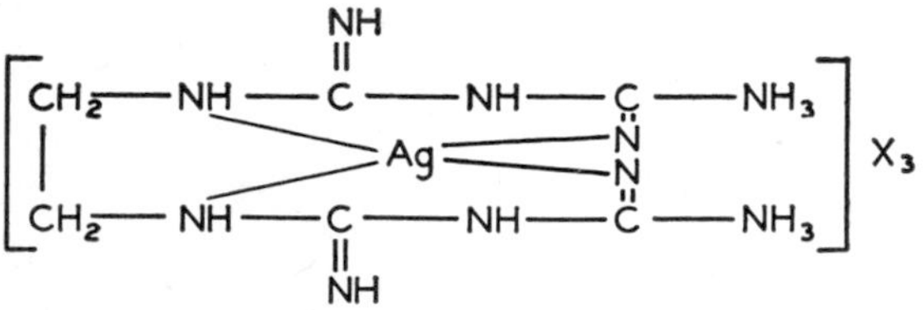

The high valence state of silver is quite stable, but is reduced to silver(I)

390. Ray and co-workers (Saha, Ghosh, Dutt, Battacharya, Suddhanta, Chakravarty, Majumdar, Das Sarma): *J. Indian Chem. Soc.*, **14**, 670 (1937); **15**, 347, 350, 353, 633 (1938); **16**, 621, 629 (1939); **18**, 289, 298 (1941); **19**, 1 (1942); **21**, 47 (1944); **23**, 73 (1946); **25**, 589 (1948); **26**, 137 (1949), and other articles not in the "series".
391. De, Ghosh, and Ray, *J. Indian Chem. Soc.*, **27**, 493 (1950).
392. Shiddhanta, Dutt, and Ray, *J. Indian Chem. Soc.*, **27**, 641 (1950).
393. Ray and Majumdar, *J. Indian Chem. Soc.*, **23**, 73 (1946).
394. Ray and Shiddhanta, *J. Indian Chem. Soc.*, **20**, 200 (1943).
395. Ray and Das Sarma, *J. Indian Chem. Soc.*, **26**, 137 (1949).

by iodide ion[396]. The conductivity and magnetic susceptibility are consistent with the assumption that the compound contains trivalent silver with dsp^2 bonds[397]. Measurement of stability constants shows this to be a very stable substance[398].

Quinoline and Its Derivatives

The nitrogen of quinoline has very weak donor properties, but properly substituted quinolines form stable coordination compounds. 8-Hydroxy-quinoline is a strong complexing agent, and has found wide use in analytical chemistry (Chapter 20). The important compounds are inner complexes

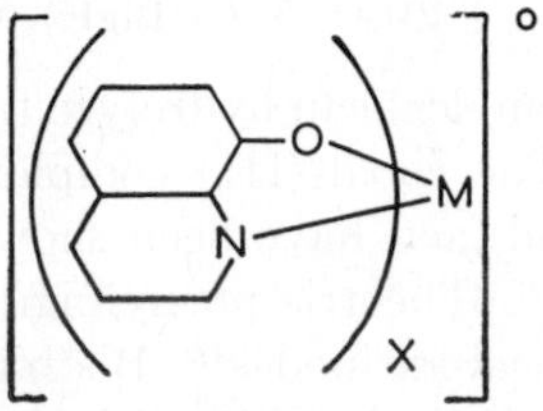

which are insoluble in water, but soluble in organic solvents; this property is utilized in the separation of metal ions, just as it is with the inner complexes of the 1,3 diketones (page 44)[399]. Substituted 8-hydroxyquinolines can often be used to advantage[400].

Inner complexes can often be given water solubility by the introduction of a highly polar group into the complexing agent. If this substituent is distant in the molecule from the donor atoms, it does not disturb the stability or nature of the coordinate bonds. Thus, Liu and Bailar[401] prepared the soluble zinc compound

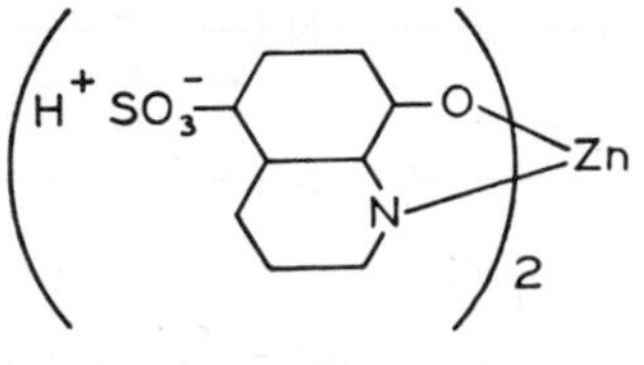

and resolved it into its optical antipodes.

396. Ray, *Nature*, **151**, 643 (1943).
397. Ray and Chakravarty, *J. Indian Chem. Soc.*, **21**, 57 (1944).
398. Sen, Ghosh, and Ray, *J. Indian Chem. Soc.*, **27**, 619 (1950).
399. Moeller: *Ind. Eng. Chem., Anal. Ed.*, **15**, 270, 346 (1943).
400. Moeller and Jackson, *Anal. Chem.*, **22**, 1393 (1950); Moeller and Ramaniah, *J. Am. Chem. Soc.*, **76**, 2022 (1954).
401. Liu and Bailar, *J. Am. Chem. Soc.*, **73**, 5432 (1951).
402. Ley and Ficken, *Ber.*, **50**, 1133 (1917).

Picolinic acid, like other alpha amino acids, forms stable coordination compounds, many of which are inner complexes. The cobalt(III) compound[402] is illustrative of this group.

Phthalocyanines and Porphins

When *o*-dicyanobenzene, *o*-cyanobenzamide, or related substances are heated with metals or their salts, a vigorous exothermic reaction takes place and metal derivatives of phthalocyanine

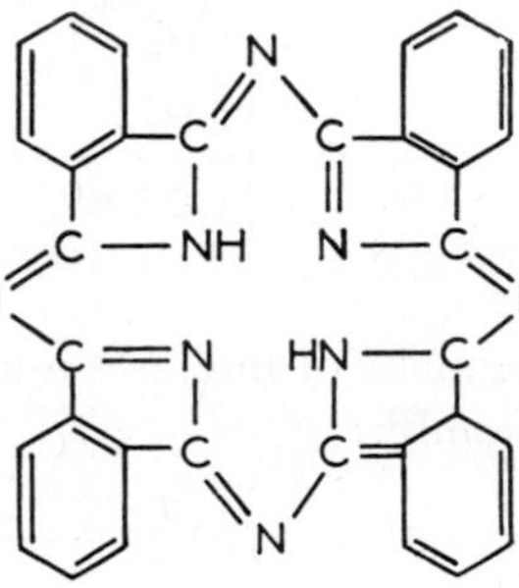

are formed. The metal occupies a position in the center of the molecule. If it be a divalent metal, it displaces the two hydrogen atoms, and coordinates with all four of the nitrogen atoms. Trivalent ions seem to form compounds of the type [Phthalocyanine M]X. The metal derivatives, like the parent substance, are deep blue. Many of them are extremely stable, being unaffected by any but the most vigorous chemical agents; some of them can be sublimed in vacuo above 500°C. This combination of properties makes them valuable as pigments (Chapter 22).

Phthalocyanine is closely related to porphin:

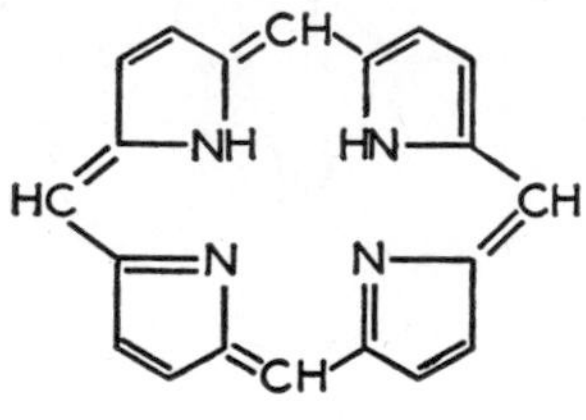

which also gives highly colored metallic derivatives[403]. Porphin is the parent

403. Fischer and Gleim, *Ann.*, **521,** 157 (1935).

substance of chlorophyll and hemin:

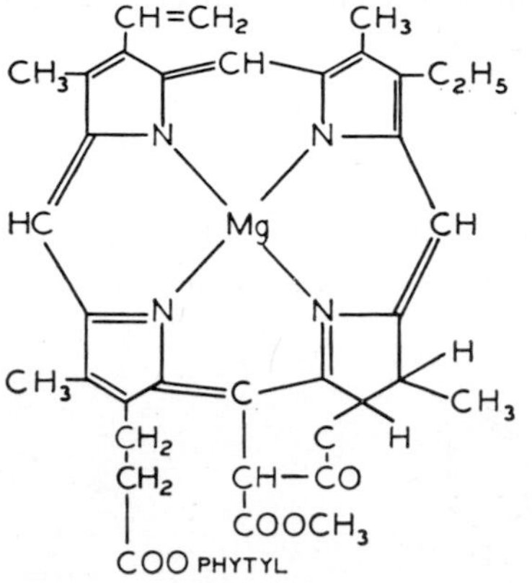

CHLOROPHYLL A 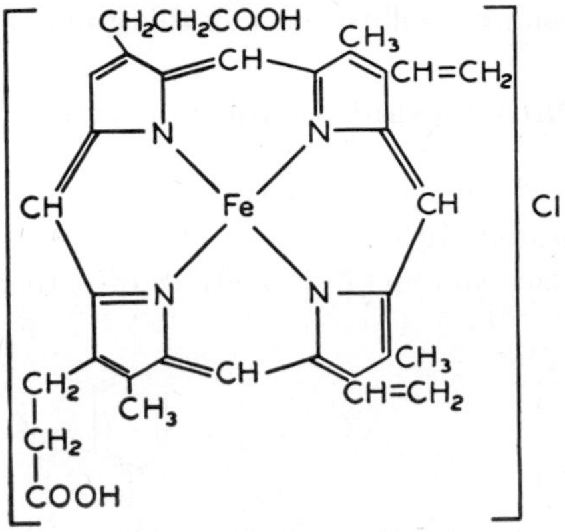   HEMIN

Haemocyanin, the blood pigment of molluscs and crustaceans, is a copper compound of the porphin family.

The Azo Group

The donor properties of the azo group are weak[404], but azo compounds which contain a strong donor (e.g., carboxyl or hydroxy) in a position ortho to the azo group form very stable chelate rings. The complexes so formed are usually highly colored and find use as dyes and pigments (Chapter 22).

The diazo amino compounds have been the subject of an interesting study by Dwyer[405]. The imino hydrogen atom is replaced, at least in some cases, and the nitrogen chain forms a chelate ring with the metal, thus occupying two coordination positions. Examples are

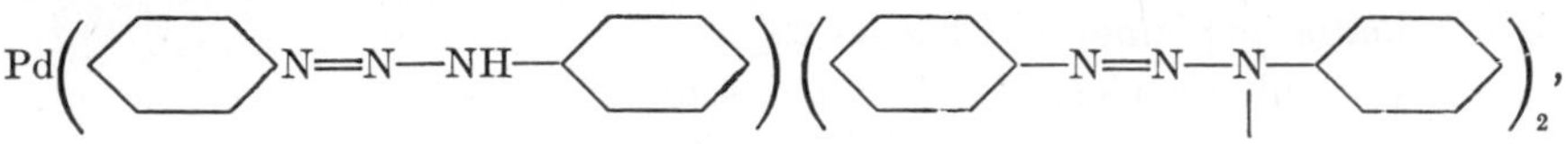

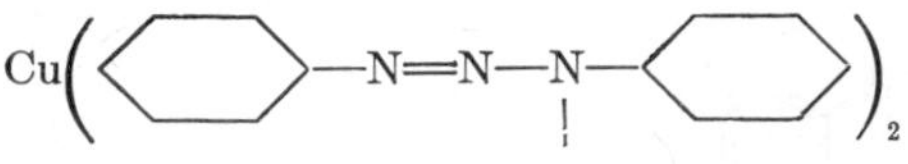

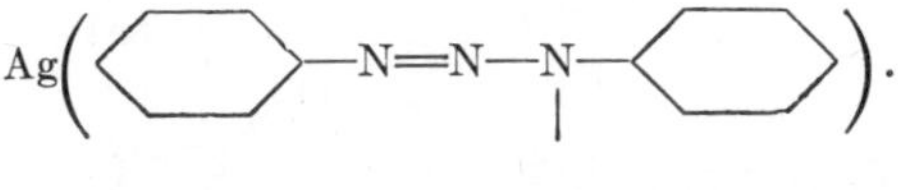

Nitriles

The nitrogen atoms in organic nitriles have fairly strong donor properties, especially toward the heavier metals. The halides of platinum add

404. Kharasch and Ashford, *J. Am. Chem. Soc.*, **58**, 1736 (1936).
405. Dwyer, *J. Am. Chem. Soc.*, **63**, 78 (1941).

nitriles directly[406] to form $PtX_2(RCN)_2$ and $PtX_4(RCN)_2$ (R may be either aliphatic or aromatic). Halogens readily convert the platinum(II) compounds to the platinum(IV), which are not readily reduced again, even by formaldehyde, sulfur dioxide or aluminum and hydrochloric acid.

Lebedinskii and Golovnya[407,408] have carried out the following reactions:

$$[Pt(C_2H_5CN)_2Cl_2] + C_2H_5NH_2 \rightarrow [Pt(C_2H_5NH_2)_4(C_2H_5CN)_2][PtCl_4]$$

$$\downarrow HCl$$

$$[Pt(C_2H_5NH_2)_2Cl_2]$$

$$[Pt(NH_3)_2Cl_2] + CH_3CN \rightarrow [Pt(NH_3)_2(CH_3CN)Cl]Cl$$
$$+ NH_4OH \rightarrow [Pt(NH_3)_4(CH_3CN)]Cl_2$$

$$K[Pt(NH_3)Cl_3] + CH_3CN \rightarrow [Pt(NH_3)(CH_3CN)Cl_2]$$
$$+ NH_4OH \rightarrow [Pt(NH_3)_4(CH_3CN)]Cl_2$$

The platinum in the compound $[Pt(NH_3)_4(CH_3CN)]Cl_2$ does not seem to show the usual coordination number for platinum, and doubtless needs further study. Upon heating with hydrochloric acid, this compound is converted to $[Pt(NH_3)_3Cl]Cl$.

In the presence of acetonitrile, copper(I) coordination compounds are readily formed. They oxidize slowly in the air[409].

Pseudohalides

The cyanide ion has unshared pairs of electrons on both the carbon and the nitrogen atoms, and theoretically, it might coordinate to metals through either of these pairs. Actually, it seems to combine preferentially through the carbon atom, and the simple, mononuclear cyanides are characterized by a metal-carbon link (page 87). The formation of the carbon-metal bond, however, does not preclude the formation of a coordinate bond between the nitrogen and another metal atom. The "super-complex" heavy metal cyanides, such as Prussian blue, are probably built up in this way, as are the organo gold cyanides.

The thiocyanate group also has pairs of electrons on two atoms, and conceivably can coordinate through either nitrogen or sulfur (p. 57). The

406. Ashford, thesis, University of Chicago, 1936. Ashford gives references to several earlier articles on platinum-nitrile addition compounds, the more important being Hofman and Bugge, *Ber.*, **40**, 1772 (1907); Ramberg, *Ber.*, **40**, 2578 (1907); Tschugaeff and Lebedinskii, *Compt. rend.*, **161**, 563 (1915).
407. Lebedinskii and Golovnya, *Izvest. Sektora Platiny i Drugikh Blagorod. Metal., Inst. Obschei i Neorg. Khim., Akad. Nauk. S.S.S.R.*, No. **22**, 168 (1948); cf. *Chem. Abs.*, **44**, 10566a, (1950).
408. Lebedinskii and Golovnya, *Ann. secteur platine, Inst. Chim. gen. (U.S.S.R.)*, No. **16**, 57 (1939).
409. Morgan, *J. Chem. Soc.*, **123**, 2901 (1923).

easy formation of the highly colored iron(III) and cobalt(II) complexes makes them suitable for the qualitative detection of these ions in solution. Several investigations have been made to determine the nature of the ferric thiocyanate complex which exists in such solutions. Møller[410] showed, by conductivity measurements, that there are not more than three thiocyanate groups attached to the iron. Bent and French[411] and Edmonds and Birnbaum[412], from a study of the absorption of light by solutions containing iron(III) and thiocyanate, came to the conclusion that the formula of the complex is $Fe(NCS)^{++}$, neglecting hydration. Schlesinger and Van Valkenburgh[413] showed that in ether solution, the $[Fe(NCS)_6]^{\equiv}$ ion is present. The entire subject has been well reviewed by Lewin and Wagner[414].

The coordinating ability of the azide ion was first studied by Strecker and Oxenius[415], who prepared a series of cobalt(III) compounds. They obtained the ions cis-$[Co(NH_3)_4(N_3)_2]^+$ cis- and trans-$[Co\ en_2(N_3)_2]^+$, and $[Co\ py_4ClN_3]^+$. Linhard and Flygare[416] prepared several salts of the ion $[Co(NH_3)_5N_3]^{++}$ which they report to be similar in color to $[Co(NH_3)_5Cl]^{++}$. The action of sodium azide on a solution of $[Co(NH_3)_4(H_2O)_2]^{+++}$ gave a mixture of the cis and trans forms of $[Co(NH_3)_4(N_3)_2]^{+\ 417}$. That the azide group has strong donor properties is shown by the fact that triazidotriamminecobalt can be prepared by treatment of $[Co(NH_3)_4(H_2O)_2]^{+++}$, $[Co(NH_3)_4(N_3)_2]^+$, or $[Co(NH_3)_5N_3]^{++}$ with azide ion[418]. Straumanis and Circulis[419] prepared stable, slightly soluble compounds which they believed to be nonelectrolytes of the type $[Cu\ R_2(N_3)_2]$ in which R is ammonia or any one of a number of aliphatic or aromatic amines. They also obtained the anions $[Cu(N_3)_6]^{4-}$, $[Cu(N_3)_4]^{\equiv}$, and $[Cu(N_3)_3]^-$. All of the azido complexes are unstable and explosive.

Oximes

The coordinating tendency of the oximes is well known. A lone oxime group does not coordinate firmly, but when it forms part of a chelate ring, the oxime nitrogen has very strong donor properties and oximes are frequently used in inorganic analysis (Chapter 20). Metallic ions having a coordination number of six combine with only two dioxime groups, the

410. Møller, Kem. Maanedsblad, 18, 138 (1937).
411. Bent and French, J. Am. Chem. Soc., 63, 568 (1941).
412. Edmonds and Birnbaum, J. Am. Chem. Soc., 63, 1471 (1941).
413. Schlesinger and Van Valkenburgh, J. Am. Chem. Soc., 53, 1212 (1931).
414. Lewin and Wagner, J. Chem. Ed., 30, 445 (1953).
415. Strecker and Oxenius, Z. anorg. allgem. Chem., 218, 151 (1934).
416. Linhard and Flygare, Z. anorg. Chem., 262, 328 (1950).
417. Linhard, Weigel, and Flygare, Z. anorg. allgem. Chem., 263, 233 (1950).
418. Linhard and Weigel, Z. anorg. allgem. Chem., 263, 245 (1950).
419. Straumanis and Circulis, Z. anorg. allgem. Chem., 251, 341 (1943); 252, 9, 121 (1943).

remaining coordination positions being filled by other donors, as the following cobalt compounds illustrate:

$$[Co(HD)_2(NH_3)_2]X, [Co(HD)_2NH_3X] \text{ and } [Co(HD)_2X_2]^{-} \text{ } {}^{420}.$$

Aniline and substituted anilines can replace the ammonia in the cobalt compounds[421]. Compounds of the type $M'[M'''(HD)_2X_2]$ containing rhodium[422] and iridium[423] have also been described. Only one $=NOH$ group from each *anti*-dioxime molecule liberates a hydrogen ion, as is shown by the fact that the mono-ethers,

$$
\begin{array}{cc}
R\!-\!C\!-\!C\!-\!R & {}^{424,425,426} \\
\parallel \ \ \parallel & \\
HO\!-\!N \ \ N\!-\!OCH_3 &
\end{array}
$$

and the imino and methylimino compounds

$$
\begin{array}{ccc}
C_2H_5\!-\!C\!-\!C\!-\!CH_3 & & C_2H_5\!-\!C\!-\!C\!-\!CH_3 \ {}^{426} \\
\parallel \ \ \parallel & \text{and} & \parallel \ \ \parallel \\
H\!-\!N \ \ N\!-\!OH & & CH_3\!-\!N \ \ N\!-\!OH
\end{array}
$$

give entirely analagous compounds. On the other hand, both hydrogens of an *amphi*-dioxime are replaceable. Nickel, for example, forms rather poorly defined compounds of the type

$$
\begin{array}{c}
R\!-\!C\!\text{---------}\!C\!-\!R \\
\parallel \qquad\qquad \parallel \\
N \qquad\qquad N \\
\diagdown\quad \diagup \\
O \qquad Ni\!-\!O
\end{array}
$$

in which the metal is evidently attached to one nitrogen atom and one oxygen atom[427, 428, 429]. Acids rearrange these to the more stable red modification. The *anti* and *amphi* forms of benzil dioxime react with palladium(II) ion just as they do with the nickel ion. *Syn* dioximes do not yield nickel derivatives[429] but *syn* benzildioxime readily forms a crystalline palladous

420. Tschugaeff, *Ber.*, **39**, 2692 (1906); **41**, 2226 (1908).
421. Ablov, *Bull. soc. chim.*, **7**, 151 (1940).
422. Lebedinskii and Fedorov, *Ann. secteur platine, Inst. chim. gen. (U.S.S.R.)*, No. **15**, 19 (1938).
423. Lebedinskii and Fedorov, *Ann. secteur platine, Inst. chim. gen. (U.S.S.R.)*, No. **15**, 27 (1938).
424. Thilo and Friedrich, *Ber.*, **62**, 2990 (1929).
425. Brady and Muers, *J. Chem. Soc.*, **1930**, 1599.
426. Pfeiffer, *Ber.*, **63**, 1811 (1930).
427. Atack, *J. Chem. Soc.*, **103**, 1317 (1913).
428. Hieber and Leutert, *Ber.*, **62**, 1839 (1929).
429. Meisenheimer and Theilacker, *Ann.*, **469**, 128 (1929).

compound which is said to have the structure

$$\phi - C \underline{\hspace{3cm}} C - \phi \, ^{430}$$

(structure showing two N—O groups bridging to Pd below two C=N double bonds)

Bryson and Dwyer[431] report that β-furfuraldoxime reacts with copper, silver, nickel, and cobalt. The α isomer does not, but on standing in solution with the metal salt, it changes to the β isomer.

THE DONOR PROPERTIES OF PHOSPHORUS AND ARSENIC

Phosphine Coordination

The action of phosphine on metallic salts has been studied by several investigators. Most metallic ions are reduced to metal or to phosphides[432, 433, 434], but some form phosphine addition compounds. Riban[435] found that a solution of copper(I) chloride in hydrochloric acid absorbs phosphine readily, forming the rather unstable compounds $CuCl \cdot PH_3$ and $CuCl \cdot 2PH_3$. Upon gentle warming, these compounds liberate phosphine, while stronger heating generates copper phosphide. These results have been confirmed and extended by Scholder and Pattock[436].

Holtje and his co-workers[437] have made a systematic study of the donor properties of phosphine. They found that in its ability to form coordination compounds, phosphine resembles hydrogen sulfide more closely than it does ammonia. The phosphinates are more stable than the sulfhydrates in every case investigated. Among the more stable compounds reported by these investigators is $AlI_3 \cdot PH_3$, which may be sublimed in vacuo.

Tertiary Phosphine and Arsine Coordination

The tertiary organic phosphines and arsines have strong donor properties, in which regard they are in sharp contrast to the tertiary amines, but are similar to the thioethers. Even the stibines can form addition compounds[438].

430. Dwyer and Mellor, *J. Proc. Roy. Soc. N.S. Wales*, **68**, 107 (1935).
431. Bryson and Dwyer, *J. Proc. Roy. Soc.*, *N.S. Wales*, **74**, 107 (1940).
432. Winkler, *Ann. chim. phys.*, **111**, 443.
433. Keilisch, *Ann.*, **231**, 327 (1885); "Ueber die Einwirkung des Phosphorwasser-stoffs auf Metallsalzlösungen," Berlin, 1885.
434. Scholder, Apel, and Haken, *Z. anorg. allgem. Chem.*, **232**, 1 (1937).
435. Riban, *Compt. rend.*, **88**, 581 (1879); *Bull. soc. chim.*, [2] **31**, 385 (1879).
436. Scholder and Pattock, *Z. anorg. allgem. Chem.*, **220**, 250 (1934).
437. Höltje, *Z. anorg. allgem. Chem.*, **190**, 241 (1930); **209**, 241 (1932); Höltje and Meyer, *Z. anorg. allgem. Chem.*, **197**, 93 (1931); Höltje and Schlegel, *Z. anorg. allgem. Chem.*, **243**, 246 (1940).
438. Jensen, *Z. anorg. allgem. Chem.*, **229**, 225 (1936).

The strong *trans* influence of tertiary phosphines is emphasized by the failure of Kurnakov's rule (Chapter 9) in the reaction of thiourea with [Pt(PEt₃)₂Br₂][439]. The use of several of the phosphine compounds as antiknocks has been patented[440].

Organic phosphines[441] and arsines[442] are often identified through their highly crystalline mercuric halide complexes. These are true coordination compounds, and are soluble in organic solvents.

The most common phosphines and arsines of copper are $CuX \cdot AsR_3$ and $CuX \cdot 2AsR_3$, where X is a halide ion. Those containing a single coordinated arsine group are tetrameric while those containing two arsine groups are presumably monomeric. Nyholm[443] has reported that four molecules of diphenylmethylarsine may be associated with a single copper(I) ion, as in the compounds $[Cu(AsMePh_2)_4][CuX_2]$ and $[Cu(AsMePh_2)_4]X$. This tertiary arsine also forms the nonelectrolytic complex $[Cu(AsMePh_2)_3X]$. Similar behavior[444] was also noted among the *o*-phenylenebis(dimethylarsine) complexes of copper(I). Gold complexes of the form $AuX \cdot MR_3$, where X is Cl^-, Br^-, or NCS^-, and M is arsenic or phosphorus, are monomeric, and some of them can be distilled under reduced pressure. There is evidence[445] that the corresponding cyanides and iodides are polymeric. The extreme stability of these substances is shown by the fact that tributylphosphinegold(I) chloride may be volatilized at atmospheric pressure and triethylphosphinegold(I) chloride[446] dissolves in concentrated hydrochloric acid and in potassium hydroxide without decomposition, and is only slowly reduced to metallic gold by sulfur dioxide. The vapors of $AuCl \cdot PBu_3$ deposit a fine film of gold when passed through a heated tube[447]. Both gold(I) and gold(III) complexes[448] with *o*-phenylenebis(dimethylarsine) have been reported[449].

439. Grinberg and Razumova, *Zhur. Obschei Khim.*, **18**, 282 (1948).
440. Bataafsche Petroleum Maatschappij, French Patent 805 666 (1936); Peski and Melsen, U.S. Patent 2 150 349 (1938).
441. Davies and Jones, *J. Chem. Soc.*, **1929**, 33; Davies, Pearce, and Jones, *J. Chem. Soc.*, **1929**, 1262; Jackson, Davies, and Jones, *J. Chem. Soc.*, **1930**, 2298; Jackson and Jones, *J. Chem. Soc.*, **1931**, 575; Jackson, Davies, and Jones, *J. Chem. Soc.*, **1931**, 2109.
442. Jones, Dyke, Davies, Griffiths, and Webb, *J. Chem. Soc.*, **1932**, 2284; Challenger, Higginbottom, and Ellis, *J. Chem. Soc.*, **1933**, 95; Challenger and Ellis, *J. Chem. Soc.*, **1935**, 398; Challenger and Rawlings, *J. Chem. Soc.*, **1936**, 264; Blicke and Cataline, *J. Am. Chem. Soc.*, **60**, 419 (1938).
443. Nyholm, *J. Chem. Soc.*, **1952**, 1257.
444. Kabesh and Nyholm, *J. Chem. Soc.*, **1951**, 38.
445. Dwyer and Stewart, *J. Proc. Roy. Soc., N.S. Wales*, **83**, 177 (1949).
446. Levi-Malvano, *Atti accad. Lincei*, [5] **17**, i, 847 (1908).
447. Mann and Wells, *Nature*, **140**, 502 (1937); Mann, Wells, and Purdie, *J. Chem. Soc.*, **1937**, 1828.
448. Mann and Purdie, *J. Chem. Soc.*, **1940**, 1235.
449. Nyholm, *Nature*, **168**, 705 (1951).

Recently, compounds of o-phenylenebis(dimethylarsine) (PDA) have been prepared with four or six arsenic atoms coordinated to one metal atom. Iron forms complexes of the formulas $[Fe^{III}(PDA)_2Cl_2]ClO_4$ and $[Fe^{II}(PDA)_2X_2](X = Br^-, I^-,$ or $SCN^-)$[450]. The magnetic moments of the complexes indicate that the iron atom is covalently bound.

Rhodium(III) halides react with o-phenylenebis(dimethylarsine) forming analagous compounds[451]. However, upon reaction with a monodentate tertiary arsine, rhodium(III) halides form two isomeric compounds containing three moles of arsine per mole of rhodium. These are, presumably, $[Rh(AsR_3)_6][RhX_6]$ and $[Rh(AsR_3)_3X_3]$[452]. Rhodium(II) forms a variety of other complexes[453] with tertiary arsines, such as $[Rh(AsR_3)_6]_3[RhX_5(AsR_3)]_2$ and $[Rh(AsR_3)_6][RhX_4(AsR_3)_2]$.

Iridium(II) and iridium(III) also form complexes with tertiary arsines[454]. Dwyer, Humpholtz, and Nyholm[455] have investigated the complexes of diphenylmethylarsine with ruthenium(II) and ruthenium(III). Ruthenium(II) forms the complex $[Ru(AsR_3)_4X_2]$ while ruthenium(III) forms $[Ru(AsR_3)_3X_3]$.

The preparation of nickel complexes of trialkyl compounds of the group V elements has been especially fruitful, as higher valence states of nickel are probably best characterized among these derivatives. Jensen and Nygaard[456] prepared a rather unstable pentacoordinate triethylphosphine complex of tripositive nickel $[NiBr_3(PEt_3)_2]$. The corresponding cobalt(III) complex, $CoCl_3 \cdot 2PEt_3$, has been studied[457]; it is probably of the same configuration as the nickel complex (see Chapter 10, page 392). Nyholm[458] has reported $[Ni(PDA)_2X_2]X$, containing nickel(III), and $[Ni(PDA)_2X_2]$ $(ClO_4)_2$, which contains nickel(IV).

This work[459] on the o-phenylenebis(dimethylarsine) complexes of the metals of the first transition series has been quite significant from the theoretical standpoint. It has been found that this ditertiary arsine reacts with transition metal ions with the formation of strongly covalent bonds only when the metal ion contains d-electrons which are not involved in the

450. Nyholm, *J. Chem. Soc.*, **1950**, 851.
451. Nyholm, *J. Chem. Soc.*, **1950**, 857.
452. Dwyer and Nyholm, *J. Proc. Roy. Soc., N.S. Wales*, **75**, 140 (1942).
453. Dwyer and Nyholm, *J. Proc. Roy. Soc., N.S. Wales*, **76**, 133 (1942).
454. Dwyer and Nyholm, *J. Proc. Roy. Soc., N.S. Wales*, **77**, 116 (1943); **79**, 121 (1946).
455. Dwyer, Humpholtz, and Nyholm, *J. Proc. Roy. Soc., N.S. Wales*, **80**, 217 (1947).
456. Jensen and Nygaard, *Acta. Chem. Scand.*, **3**, 474 (1949).
457. Jensen, *Nature*, **167**, 434 (1951).
458. Nyholm, *J. Chem. Soc.*, **1950**, 2061; **1951**, 2602.
459. Burstall and Nyholm, *J. Chem. Soc.*, **1952**, 3570; Nyholm and Sharpe, *J. Chem. Soc.*, **1952**, 3579.

hybridized group (see Chapter 4). It has been concluded that the stability of arsine and phosphine complexes depends on the formation of double-bonds between the metal and the *donor* atom. This conclusion is not inconsistent with the observation that the more stable complexes containing phosphorus-metal or arsenic-metal bonds occur among the group VIII and IB metals.

Complexes of the tritertiaryarsine, methylbis(3-dimethylarsinopropyl)-arsine(TAS), have been prepared by Barclay and Nyholm[460]. The iron(III) complexes, $[Fe^{III}(TAS)X_3]$, are nonelectrolytes and exhibit magnetic moments corresponding to one unpaired electron. Cobalt(II) iodide forms a similar complex, $[Co^{II}(TAS)I]I$, which contains a single unpaired electron; air oxidation produces diamagnetic $[Co^{III}(TAS)I_3]$. Copper(I) and nickel(II) form the diamagnetic, nonelectrolytic complexes $[Cu(TAS)I]$ and $[Ni(TAS)I_2]$. The possibility of pentacoordinate nickel(II) here is especially interesting in view of the previously mentioned observations of Jensen and Nygaard.

By far the best known compounds in this group, however, are those of platinum and palladium. Cahours and Gal, in 1870, isolated isomeric forms of $PtCl_2 \cdot 2P(CH_3)_3$, $PtCl_2 \cdot 2P(C_2H_5)_3$, and $PtCl_2 \cdot 2As(C_2H_5)_3$. Their work was confirmed by Klason[461] and by Jensen, who extended it to the stibines[438]. Chatt and Wilkins[462] studied the isomerization of palladium compounds of this general type by following the variation in dielectric constant of their solutions. No detectable amount of the *cis* isomer of the arsine or phosphine complexes appears to exist in solution, while as much as 40 per cent of the stibine complex may be *cis*.

Complexes of platinum(IV) with tertiary arsines[463] and phosphines[464] have been prepared in isomeric forms by oxidation of the appropriate isomers of $PtX_2 \cdot 2MR_3$.

Upon treatment with ammonium tetrachloropalladate(II), the bis(phosphine)palladium(II) compounds, $[Pd(PR_3)_2Cl_2]$, are converted to the dinuclear complexes, $[Pd_2(PR_3)_2Cl_4]$. Mann and his co-workers[465] have studied these bridged compounds in some detail. They were at first of the opinion that several forms could exist

460. Barclay and Nyholm, *Chem. and Ind.*, **1953**, 378.
461. Cahours and Gal, *Compt. rend.* **70**, 1380; **71**, 208 (1870). Klason and Wanselin, *J. prakt. Chem.*, [2] **67**, 41 (1903).
462. Chatt and Wilkins, *J. Chem. Soc.*, **1953**, 70.
463. Nyholm, *J. Chem. Soc.*, **1950**, 843.
464. Chatt, *J. Chem. Soc.*, **1950**, 2301.
465. Mann and Purdie, *Chem. and Ind.*, **54**, 814 (1935); *J. Chem. Soc.*, **1935**, 1549; **1936**, 873; Chatt and Mann, *J. Chem. Soc.* **1938**, 1949; Chatt, Mann, and Wells, *J. Chem. Soc.* **1938**, 2086.

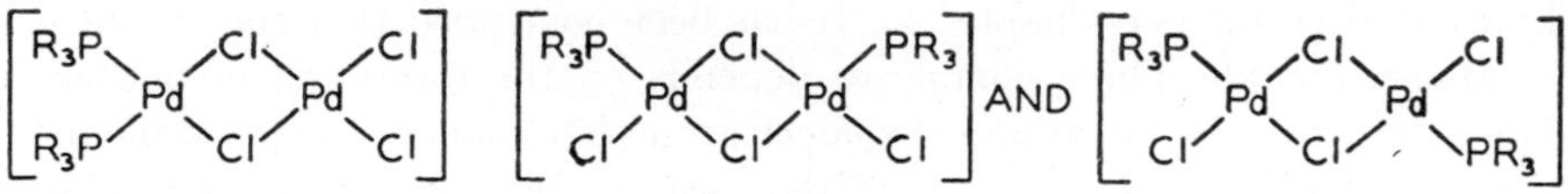

Evidence for the first formula was found in the fact that dipyridyl and nitrites react with these substances, and with the corresponding arsine derivatives, to give mixtures of compounds:

$$(R_3P)_2PdCl_2PdCl_2 + dipy \rightarrow (R_3P)_2PdCl_2 + [(dipy)PdCl_2]$$

$$(R_3As)_2PdCl_2PdCl_2 + 6KNO_2 \rightarrow (R_3As)_2Pd(NO_2)_2 + K_2[Pd(NO_2)_4] + 4KCl$$

On the other hand, aniline, toluene, and pyridine give good yields of mono-phosphine (or arsine) derivatives:

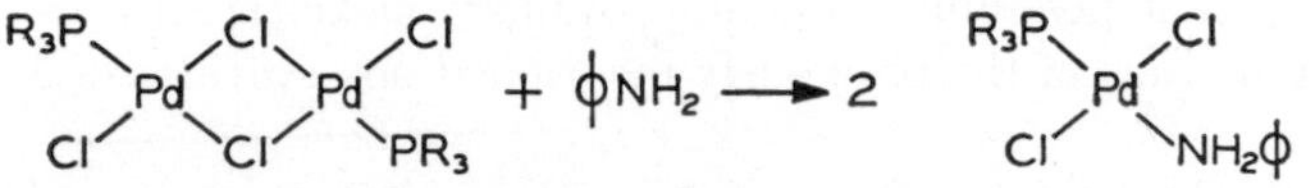

Ethylenediamine splits the butyl phosphine compound unsymmetrically in benzene, but symmetrically in alcohol.

Later evidence, however, showed the earlier hypothesis to be incorrect[466, 467]; the dimeric molecule apparently always has the symmetrical structure. It was shown that compounds of the type $PtCl_2 \cdot (PR_3)_2$ are not primary products of the splitting, but are formed by secondary reactions. The unsymmetrical formulas for the bridged complexes would indicate that compounds of the types

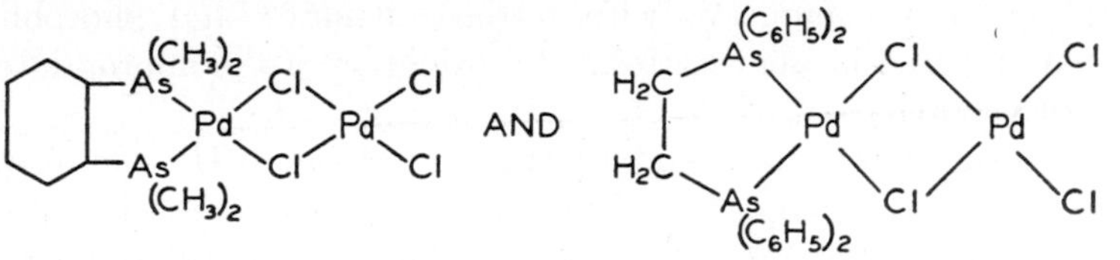

should exist. Chatt and Mann[466] were unable to prepare any such compounds, but obtained

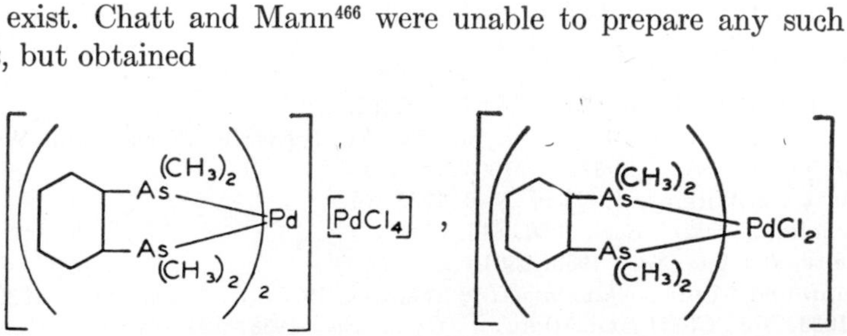

466. Chatt and Mann, *J. Chem. Soc.*, **1939**, 1622.
467. Mann and Wells, *J. Chem. Soc.*, **1938**, 702; Wells, *Proc. Roy. Soc. London*, **A167**, 169 (1938).

and several other interesting substances. Chatt has extended this work to include the tripropylstibine complex[468] of platinum(II). This species behaves essentially as the arsine and phosphine complexes.

Interesting examples of phosphine complexes with bridging groups other than the halide ions are found in the ethyl mercaptan and oxalate bridges[469]:

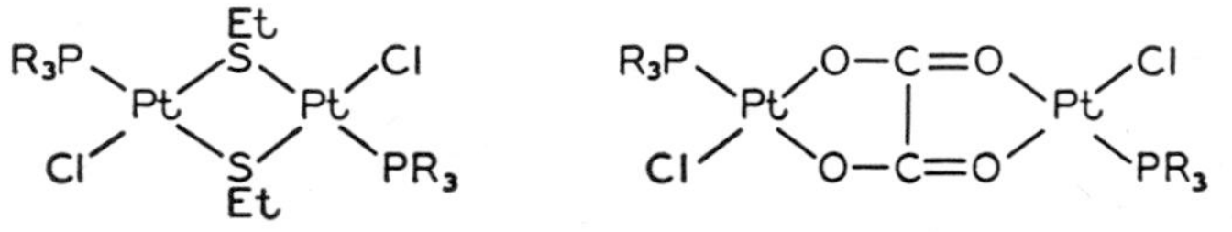

The ethyl mercaptan complex exists in two (*cis-trans?*) forms. A related compound with thiocyanate bridges is reported to exist in the isomeric forms

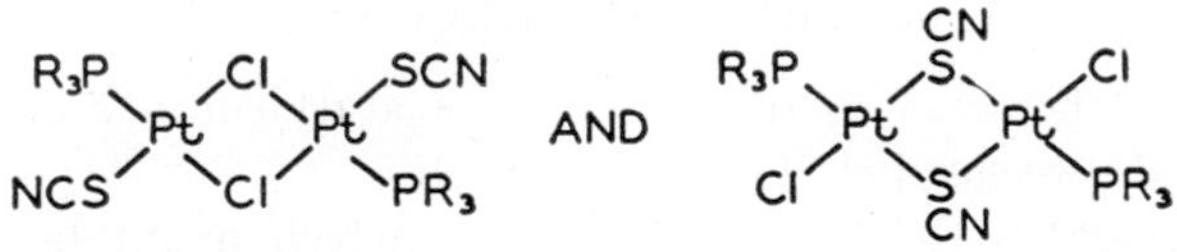

The reported isomerism of the bridged compound trichlorotris(diphenyl-methylarsine)copper(I)copper(II) is interesting[470]. Copper(I) is tetrahedral[471] while copper(II) is planar so that the isomerides were thought to be

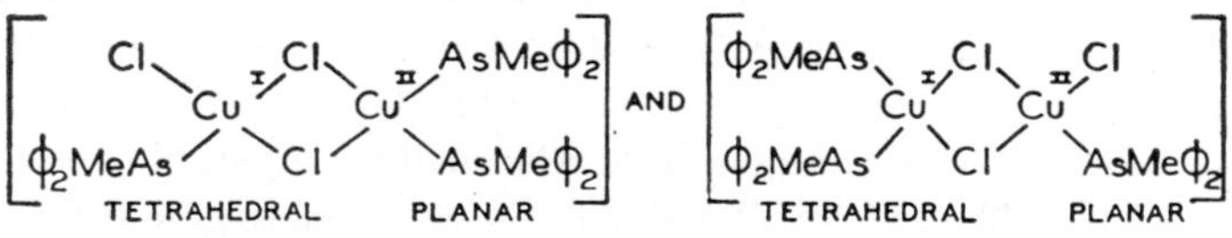

However, it has since been contended that these substances are actually complexes of diphenylmethylarsine oxide and that the reported isomerism was associated with an impurity in one of the forms[472].

The existence of bridged arsine and phosphine complexes containing two different metals is reported by Mann and his co-workers[473]. A series of compounds involving palladium(II) or cadmium bridged to mercury is exemplified by

468. Chatt, *J. Chem. Soc.*, **1951**, 652.
469. Chatt and Hart, *J. Chem. Soc.*, **1953**, 269; *Nature*, **169**, 673 (1952); Chatt, Mann, and Wells, *J. Chem. Soc.*, **1938**, 2086.
470. Mellor, Burrows, and Morris, *Nature*, **141**, 414 (1938).
471. Mellor and Craig, *J. Proc. Roy. Soc., N.S. Wales*, **75**, 27 (1941).
472. Nyholm, *J. Chem. Soc.*, **1951**, 1767.
473. Mann and Purdie, *J. Chem. Soc.*, **1940**, 1230; Allison and Mann, *J. Chem. Soc.*, **1949**, 2915.

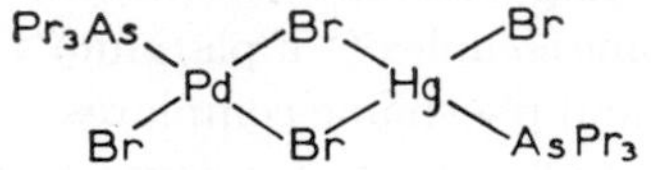

$$\begin{array}{ccc} Pr_3As & Br & Br \\ \diagdown & \diagup \diagdown & \diagup \\ & Pd & Hg \\ \diagup & \diagdown \diagup & \diagdown \\ Br & Br & AsPr_3 \end{array}$$

The compounds $SnX_4 \cdot 2PR_3 (X = Cl^-$ or $Br^-)$ also form mixed-metal, bridged complexes with mercury(II) or palladium(II).

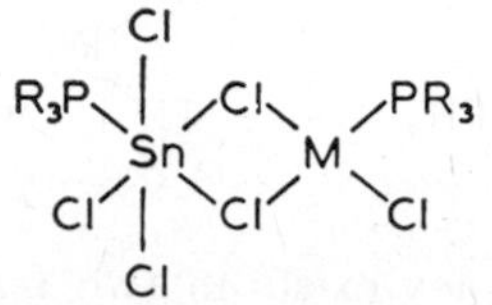

$$\begin{array}{c} Cl \\ R_3P \diagdown \quad | \quad \diagup Cl \diagdown \quad \diagup PR_3 \\ Sn \qquad M \\ Cl \diagup \quad | \quad \diagdown Cl \diagup \quad \diagdown Cl \\ Cl \end{array}$$

Tertiary phosphines react with the carbonyls of iron, cobalt and nickel to produce mixed phosphine-carbonyl complexes:

$$Ni(CO)_4 + PR_3 \text{ (or } 2PR_3) \rightarrow [Ni(PR_3)(CO)_3] \text{ (or } [Ni(PR_3)_2(CO)_2])$$

Their catalytic behavior in the reactions of acetylene has been discussed by Reppe and Sweckendich[474].

Cacodyl oxide, $(CH_3)_2As$—O—$As(CH_3)_2$, which might be expected to coordinate through both arsenic atoms, does so with difficulty, and it usually occupies only one coordination position[475].

Phosphorus(III) Halide Coordination

The "double compounds" formed by phosphorus(III) chloride and bromide with metal halides certainly contain true coordinate links, the phosphorus acting as the donor atom. Platinum(II) chloride and phosphorus(III) chloride, for example, give the highly crystalline compounds $PtCl_2 \cdot PCl_3$ and $PtCl_2 \cdot 2PCl_3$[476]. These react with water to give $PtCl_2 \cdot P(OH)_3$ and $PtCl_2 \cdot 2P(OH)_3$, and with alcohols to form the corresponding esters. Molecular weight determinations have shown the ethyl ester of the monophosphine complex to be dimeric, and hence (presumably)

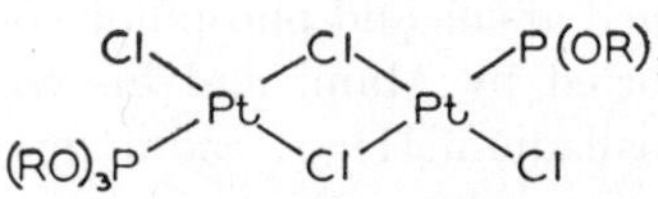

$$\begin{array}{ccc} Cl & Cl & P(OR)_3 \\ \diagdown & \diagup \diagdown & \diagup \\ & Pt & Pt \\ \diagup & \diagdown \diagup & \diagdown \\ (RO)_3P & Cl & Cl \end{array}$$

474. Reppe and Sweckendich, *Ann.*, **560**, 104 (1948).
475. Jensen and Frederiksen, *Z. anorg. allgem. Chem.*, **230**, 34 (1936); Baudrimont, *Compt. rend.*, **55**, 363 (1862); *Ann. chim. phys.*, [4] **2**, 5 (1864); "Recherches sur les chlorures et les bromures de phosphore," Paris, 1864.
476. Schutzenberger, *Compt. rend.*, **70**, 1287, 1414 (1870); *Bull. soc. chim.*, [2] **14**, 97, 178 (1870); Schutzenberger and Fontaine, *Bull. soc. chim.*, [2] **17**, 386, 482 (1872).

The ester $PtCl_2 \cdot 2P(OCH_3)_3$, however, is monomeric[477]:

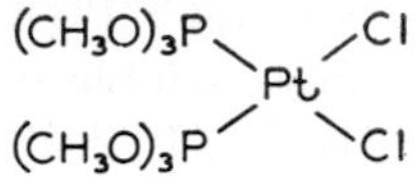

$$(CH_3O)_3P \diagdown \diagup Cl$$
$$Pt$$
$$(CH_3O)_3P \diagup \diagdown Cl$$

The acids and esters react with silver salts, with replacement of the chloride groups, the acids at the same time forming silver salts[476]:

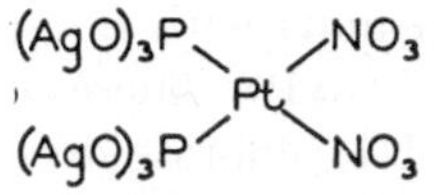

$$(AgO)_3P \diagdown \diagup NO_3$$
$$Pt$$
$$(AgO)_3P \diagup \diagdown NO_3$$

The dimeric esters are readily split by substances which have fairly strong donor properties[476, 478, 479]. Aniline, for example, gives *cis* and *trans* $[PtCl_2 \ P(OC_2H_5)_3(C_6H_5NH_2)]$[480]. $[PtCl_2 2P(OC_2H_5)_3]$ adds two molecules of ammonia, both chlorides becoming ionic. Platinum(II) chloride also forms white, crystalline $[PtCl_2 \cdot (PF_3)_2]$ and red $[PtCl_2 \cdot (PF_3)]_2$ when treated with phosphorus(III) fluoride[481]. Both substances are sensitive to moisture; however, the white compound is thermally stable and may be refluxed in a dry atmosphere without substantial decomposition. It is interesting that phosphorus(III) fluoride, which has no appreciable basic character, should form such stable complex compounds. This behavior is attributed by Chatt[482] to the formation of a double-bond between the phosphorus and the platinum.

As might be expected, palladium(II) chloride forms analagous compounds[483]. The corresponding iridium compounds, which have been studied by Geisenheimer[484] and by Strecker and Schurigin[485], are reported to be much more stable than those of platinum and palladium. $IrCl_3 \cdot 3PCl_3$ does not react with cold alcohol, with cold concentrated sulfuric acid, or with organic bases.

477. Rosenheim and Loewenstamm, *Z. anorg. Chem.*, **37**, 394 (1903).
478. Schutzenberger and Fontaine, *Bull. soc. chim.*, [2] **18**, 101, 148 (1872).
479. Rosenheim and Levy, *Z. anorg. Chem.*, **43**, 34 (1905).
480. Troitskaya, *Zhur. Priklad. Khim.*, **26**, 781 (1953).
481. Chatt and Williams, *J. Chem. Soc.*, **1951**, 3061.
482. Chatt: *Nature*, **165**, 637 (1950).
483. Fink, *Compt. rend.*, **115**, 176 (1892); **123**, 603 (1896); The author's name is spelled Finck in the second reference, but it evidently refers to the same man.
484. Geisenheimer, *Ann. chim. phys.*, [6] **23**, 231 (1891); "Sur les chlorures et bromures double d'iridium et de phosphore," Paris, 1891.
485. Strecker and Schurigin, *Ber.*, **42**, 1767 (1909); Schurigin, "Die Einwirkung von Phosphor-halogeniden auf die Metalle der Platingruppe," Grieswald, 1909.

Gold(I) halides form a similar series of compounds, e.g., $AuCl \cdot PCl_3$[486, 487]. It is not possible to obtain $AuCl \cdot P(OH)_3$, for the phosphorous acid reduces the gold to the metallic state, but $AuCl \cdot P(OC_2H_5)_3$ is quite stable, and is not reduced by sulfur dioxide. It is soluble in ammonium hydroxide with the formation of $AuCl \cdot P(OC_2H_5)_3 \cdot 2NH_3$, from which acids reprecipitate it in the original form. The methyl ester, $AuCl \cdot P(OCH_3)_3$, has been prepared by the action of methanol on $AuCl \cdot PCl_3$ and by the union of trimethyl phosphite and gold(I) chloride. The phenyl ester was prepared by the second method[488].

A series of nickel(0) compounds with phosphorus(III) halides has been prepared from nickel tetracarbonyl[489]. These compounds are of the composition $Ni(PX_3)_4$. Phosphorus(III) fluoride does not completely replace the carbonyl groups from nickel tetracarbonyl; however, the compound $[Ni(PF_3)_4]$ can be prepared by the following reactions

$$[Ni(PCl_3)_4] \text{ or } [Ni(PBr_3)_4] + 4PF_3 \rightarrow [Ni(PF_3)_4] + 4PCl_3 \text{ or } 4PBr_3$$

$$[Ni(PCl_3)_4] + 4SbF_3 \rightarrow [Ni(PF_3)_4] + 4SbCl_3$$

Antimony(III) chloride reacts with nickel and iron carbonyls giving the products $[Ni(CO)_3SbCl_3]$ and $[Fe(CO)_3(SbCl_3)_2]$, respectively[490].

Copper(I) chloride reacts with phosphorus(III) chloride[491], but the compound so formed is reactive and unstable. With methyl alcohol it gives a mixture of copper(I) chloride and $CuCl \cdot P(OCH_3)_3$. Iron(III) chloride gives the volatile compound $FeCl_3 \cdot PCl_3$[492].

THE DONOR PROPERTIES OF CARBON

There are three great classes of coordination compounds in which carbon apparently shares electrons with metals—the ethylenic compounds, the metal carbonyls, and the complex cyanides. The first two of these are the subjects of special chapters in this book, so this section will be devoted to the cyanides and the closely related complexes of metal ions with isonitriles.

Cyanide Coordination

The cyanide ion has unshared electrons both on the carbon atom and on the nitrogen atom, and one might expect to find isomeric series of complexes

486. Lindet, *Compt. rend.*, **98**, 1382 (1884); **101**, 164 (1885); **103**, 1014 (1886); *Bull. soc. chim.*, [2] **42**, 70 (1884); *Ann. chim. phys.*, [6] **11**, 177 (1887). Most of Lindet's conclusions were later confirmed by Levi-Malvano (Ref. 446).
487. Arbuzov and Lovoastrova, *Doklady akad. Nauk. S.S.S.R.*, **84**, 503 (1952).
488. Arbuzov and Shavska, *Doklady akad. Nauk. S.S.S.R.*, **84**, 507 (1952).
489. Irvine and Wilkinson, *Science*, **113**, 742 (1951); Wilkinson, *J. Am. Chem. Soc.*, **73**, 559 (1951).
490. Wilkinson, *J. Am. Chem. Soc.*, **73**, 5502 (1951).
491. Davis and Ehrlich, *J. Am. Chem. Soc.*, **58**, 2151 (1936).
492. Urbain, British Patent 312 685 (May 31, 1928).

corresponding to the nitriles and isonitriles of organic chemistry. Such, however, have not been observed, so it is concluded that the attachment of the cyanide ion to any given metal ion always takes place through the same atom. It is conceivable that some metals share electrons with the carbon and others with the nitrogen, but there is no experimental support for such a hypothesis. The preponderence of the evidence indicates that in complexes of the type $[M(CN)_x]^{y-}$, union is always through the carbon.

Carbon and nitrogen are so close together in atomic number that only the most accurate x-ray measurements can distinguish between them. Such distinction is particularly difficult in the complex metal cyanides, where the heavy metal atom masks the lighter nonmetals. A few such accurate measurements have been made, and all of them support the hypothesis that the metal is attached to carbon[493]. Holzl and his co-workers have come to the same conclusion from chemical studies. They alkylated a number of metal cyanide complexes, and obtained compounds which upon decomposition yielded alkyl isonitriles[494]. In some cases, alkyl amines were also obtained, but in no case were ammonium salts formed in significant amounts. Infrared spectral work by L. H. Jones[495] indicates the existence of the carbon-metal bond. He found that the pattern of infrared active vibrational frequencies for the compounds $KAu(C^{12}N^{14})_2$, $KAu(C^{12}N^{14})(C^{13}N^{14})$, $KAu(C^{13}N^{14})_2$, and $KAu(C^{12}N^{14})(C^{12}N^{15})$ indicates that the bonding is through the carbon. Jones also found that in $[Au(CN)_2]^-$ the $C{\equiv}N$ force constant is greater than in $CH_3C{\equiv}N$. In $CH_3N{\equiv}C$ the $C{\equiv}N$ force constant is considerably less than in $CH_3C{\equiv}N$. This also indicates, but does not prove, that the CN is bound to the gold through the carbon.

The cyanide ion is a powerful coordinating agent, and it frequently displaces all other groups from the coordination sphere, forming ions of the type $[M(CN)_x]^{y-}$. Exceptions to this are found among the carbonyl and nitrosyl cyanides (Chapter 16), and in such complexes as $[Co\ en_2(CN)_2]^+$ [496a], $[Co(CN)_5OH]^{\equiv}$ [496b], $[Co(CN)_4(OH)_2]^{\equiv}$, and $[Fe(CN)_5H_2O]^=$ [497].

Examples of unusual and variable coordination numbers are fairly common among the cyano complexes. Thus, Adamson[498] believes that the formula for potassium cobalt(II) cyanide, which has long been written

493. Hoard, *Z. Krist.*, **84**, 231 (1933); Hoard and Nordsieck, *J. Am. Chem. Soc.*, **61**, 2853 (1939); Powell and Bartindale, *J. Chem. Soc.*, **1945**, 799.

494. Hölzl, *Monats.*, **48**, 71 (1927); **51**, 1, 397 (1929); Hölzl and Xenakis, *Monats.*, **48**, 689 (1927); Hölzl and Viditz, *Monats.*, **49**, 241 (1928); Hölzl and Krichmayr, *Monats.*, **51**, 397 (1929); Hölzl, Meier-Mohar, and Viditz, *Monats.*, **52**, 73; **53–54**, 237 (1929).

495. L. H. Jones, private communication.

496a. Ray and Sarma, *J. Indian Chem. Soc.* **28**, 59 (1951).

496b. Smith, Kleinberg, and Griswold, *J. Am. Chem. Soc.*, **75**, 449 (1953).

497. Hieber, Nast, and Bartenstein, *Z. anorg. allgem. Chem.*, **272**, 32 (1953).

498. Adamson, *J. Am. Chem. Soc.*, **73**, 5710 (1951).

$K_4Co(CN)_6$, is actually $K_3Co(CN)_5$. Even in aqueous solution, the co-ordination number of five is maintained. The familiar copper cyanide plating bath contains both $[Cu(CN)_2]^-$ and $[Cu(CN)_3]^=$, the latter predominating. The infrared spectral studies of L. H. Jones and Penneman[499] have shown that in aqueous solutions containing silver ion, increasing concentration of cyanide ion brings about the successive formation of $[Ag(CN)_2]^-$, $[Ag(CN)_3]^=$, and $[Ag(CN)_4]^{\equiv}$. The tricyano complex exists over a wide range of concentrations, the equilibrium constants between the successive complexes being $K_{3,2} = 0.20 \pm 0.05$ and $K_{4,3} = 13.4 \pm 4$. Under the same conditions, gold(I) forms only $[Au(CN)_2]^-$. The gold and silver complexes are both adsorbed on anion exchange resins, but the gold complex is held much more firmly than is that of silver.

Adamson, Welker, and Volpe[500] have studied the exchange of radiocyanide with some heavy metal cyanides. The rate of exchange for complexes in which the metal shows a coordination number of two or four was found to be immeasurably rapid. With hexacyano manganate(III) it is rapid but measurable, and with the other hexacyano complexes it is negligible. Thus, the rate seems to be a function of coordination number rather than thermodynamic stability. A more detailed study of the exchange between $[Mn(CN)_6]^{\equiv}$ and CN^- showed that the rate of this reaction is proportional to the concentration of cyanomanganate(III), but independent of the concentration of cyanide ion. The authors postulate the existence of an unstable intermediate, $[Mn(CN)_6H_2O]^{\equiv}$, in which manganese shows a coordination number of seven. This is possible for manganese(III), but not for chromium(III), iron(III), or cobalt(III).

The cyanide group acts as a bridging group in polynuclear complexes, both the carbon and the nitrogen atoms sharing electrons with the metals. An interesting example of this is found in dipropyl gold cyanide, which has been shown to be tetrameric and to which the structure

499. Jones and Penneman, *J. Chem. Phys.*, **22**, 965 (1954).
500. Adamson, Welker, and Volpe, *J. Am. Chem. Soc.*, **72**, 4030 (1950); Adamson, Welker, and Wright, *J. Am. Chem. Soc.*, **73**, 4786 (1951).
501. Phillips and Powell, *Proc. Roy. Soc. London*, **A173**, 147 (1939).

has been assigned. The polymeric structure is dictated by the necessity of coordinating four donor groups to each gold atom.

Upon heating, a compound of the type $[R_2Au(CN)]_4$ decomposes to form a substance of the empirical formula R Au CN, which Gibson[502] believes is a linear polymer

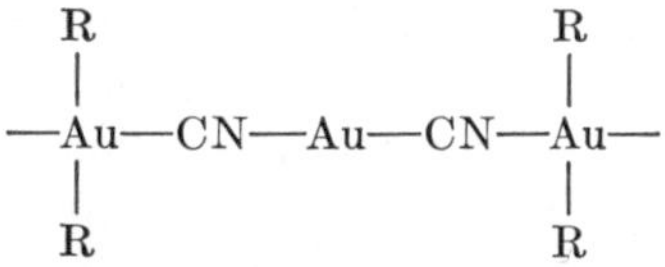

$$
\begin{array}{ccc}
R & & R \\
| & & | \\
-Au-CN-Au-CN-Au- \\
| & & | \\
R & & R
\end{array}
$$

In spite of the stability of the gold-carbon bond, the tetramer $[R_2Au(CN)]_4$ is destroyed by ethylenediamine, giving $[R_2Au\ en][R_2Au(CN)_2]$[503].

In the "simple" cyanides of the heavy metals, linking between the metal atoms takes place, the complexity of the resulting structure depending upon the relative numbers of cyanide ions and metal atoms, and the coordination number of the latter. Silver[504] and gold[505] cyanides have been shown to contain infinite chains of metal atoms held together by cyanide bridges. Mercury(II) cyanide is also said to have a linear structure[506], while the closely related zinc[507] and cadmium[508] compounds are three-dimensional super complexes. Tetracovalent metals which form planar bonds form layer structures. Thus, palladium cyanide is

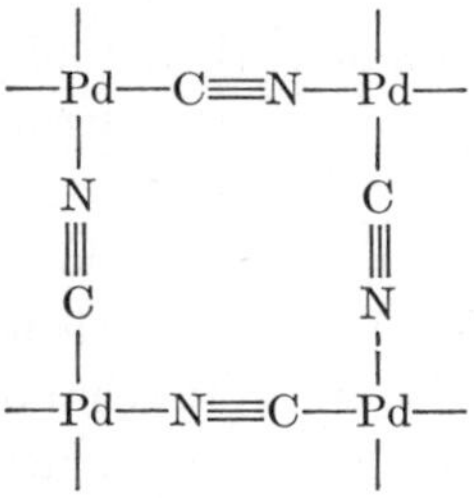

$$
\begin{array}{ccc}
| & & | \\
-Pd-C\equiv N-Pd- \\
| & & | \\
N & & C \\
||| & & ||| \\
C & & N \\
| & & | \\
-Pd-N\equiv C-Pd- \\
| & & |
\end{array}
$$

Long[509] has studied the rate of exchange between $[Ni(CN)_4]^=$ and CN^- and between $[Ni(CN)_4]^=$ and Ni^{++}. The first of these is fast but the second is slow compared with the rate of precipitation of these ions when they are

502. Gibson, *Proc. Roy. Soc. London*, **A173**, 160 (1939).
503. Brain and Gibson, *J. Chem. Soc.*, **1939**, 762.
504. Braekken, *Kgl. Norske Vidensk. Selskabs. Forh.*, II **1929**, 123; West, *Z. Krist.*, **90**, 555 (1935).
505. Zhandov and Shugam, *Acta Physicochim. U.R.S.S.*, **20**, 253 (1945).
506. Hassel, *Z. Krist.*, **64**, 218 (1926); Zhandov and Shugam, *C. R. Acad. Sci. U.R.S.S.*, **45**, 295 (1944).
507. Zhandov, *C. R. Acad. Sci. U.R.S.S.*, **31**, 350 (1941).
508. Shugam and Zhandov, *Acta Physicochim. U.R.S.S.*, **20**, 247 (1945).
509. Long, *J. Am. Chem. Soc.*, **73**, 537 (1951).

mixed with each other. Long concludes that the nickel is bound in two different ways, and that nickel cyanide may be formulated as nickel tetra-cyanonickelate(II), $Ni[Ni(CN)_4]$. Hume and Kolthoff[510] have come to the same conclusion from polarographic studies.

Heavy metal salts of the hexacyano complexes have been studied extensively, especially the ferro- and ferricyanides. It has long been known that the heavy metal ferrocyanides are not simple salts of $H_4[Fe(CN)_6]$. For example, Reihlen and Zimmermann[511] showed that ammonia will extract only part of the cadmium from cadmium ferrocyanide. The complexity of these materials is indicated also by their great insolubility and their colloidal nature. Turnbull's blue, made from an iron(II) salt and a hexacyanoferrate(III), and Prussian blue, made from an iron(III) salt and a hexacyanoferrate(II), were long thought to be different materials, but both chemical and physical studies have shown them to be identical. This comes about because the ions involved react with each other readily:

$$Fe^{+++} + [Fe(CN)_6]^{4-} \rightleftarrows Fe^{++} + [Fe(CN)_6]^{\equiv} \text{ [512]}.$$

When union between the simple cation and the complex anion takes place, the nitrogen of each cyanide group shares electrons with an iron atom, which in turn shares electrons with nitrogen atoms from other complex anions. Thus, a super complex is built up.

The x-ray studies of Keggin and Miles[513] have revealed the structure of the ferro- and ferricyanide pigments. In Berlin green, $Fe[Fe(CN)_6]$, which is made by the reaction of Fe^{+++} and $[Fe(CN)_6]^{\equiv}$, the iron atoms form a cubic, face-centered lattice. (Fig. 1.2). This arrangement is retained in "soluble" Prussian blue (Fig. 1.3), in which half of the iron atoms are in the $3+$ state and half in the $2+$ state. It is impossible to distinguish between these, and it is probable that they are identical, the charge distribution being levelled out by resonance. One potassium ion (or another univalent ion) must be present for each iron(II) ion to maintain electroneutrality. These univalent cations are located in the centers of alternate small cubes. If all of the iron atoms are in the dipositive state, there is an alkali ion at the center of each small cube; the arrangement of the iron atoms is not changed (Fig. 1.4).

510. Hume and Kolthoff, *J. Am. Chem. Soc.*, **72**, 4423 (1950).
511. Reihlen and Zimmermann, *Ann.*, **475**, 101 (1929).
512. Bhattacharya, *J. Indian Chem. Soc.*, **11**, 325 (1934); Davidson, *J. Chem. Ed.*, **14**, 238, 277 (1937).
513. Keggin and Miles, *Nature*, **137**, 577 (1936).

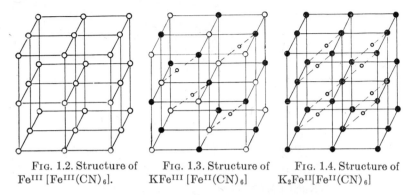

FIG. 1.2. Structure of $Fe^{III}[Fe^{III}(CN)_6]$. FIG. 1.3. Structure of $KFe^{III}[Fe^{II}(CN)_6]$ FIG. 1.4. Structure of $K_2Fe^{II}[Fe^{II}(CN)_6]$

A structure similar to this is probably common to all of the heavy metal ferrocyanides, variations being introduced as the nature of the second metal ion is changed. For example, assuming that the coordination number of silver is two, $Ag_4Fe(CN)_6$ should be formulated as $Ag[Ag_3Fe(CN)_6]$. Since the covalences of silver are linear, each of the coordinated silver atoms must share electrons with the nitrogen atoms of two different $Fe(CN)_6$ units, thus forming a giant polymer.

Examples are known in which coordination with carbon tends to stabilize high oxidation states of the metal ions (i.e., the hexacyanocobaltate(III) ion), but in most cases, metals coordinated to carbon show very low oxidation states. In the metal carbonyls, for example, the metals are in the zero oxidation state and in the salt-like carbonyls and the coordination compounds containing ethylenic substances, the metals are always in their lower oxidation states. The same tendency appears in the complex cyanides, as is exemplified by the compounds $K_2Ni^{(I)}(CN)_3$ and $K_4Ni^{(O)}(CN)_4$. The compound of monovalent nickel was first prepared by Bellucci and Corelli[514] by reducing $K_2[Ni(CN)_4]$ with potassium amalgam. Hydrazine can also be used as the reducing agent[515], but the best method of preparation involves reduction with metallic potassium, using liquid ammonia as the solvent[516]. Bellucci and Corelli supposed that it is similar in structure to $K_2[Cu^I(CN)_3]$, but the fact that it is diamagnetic shows that it must be a polymer. Mellor and Craig[517] proposed that it may be a dimer containing a metal-metal bond, but the x-ray work of Nast and Pfab[515] indicates the presence of a double bridge and they write the structure

514. Bellucci and Corelli, *Z. anorg. Chem.*, **86**, 88 (1914).
515. Nast and Pfab, *Naturwissenschaften*, **39**, 300 (1952).
516. Eastes and Burgess, *J. Am. Chem. Soc.*, **64**, 1187 (1942).
517. Mellor and Craig, *J. Proc. Roy. Soc. N. S. Wales*, **76**, 281 (1943).

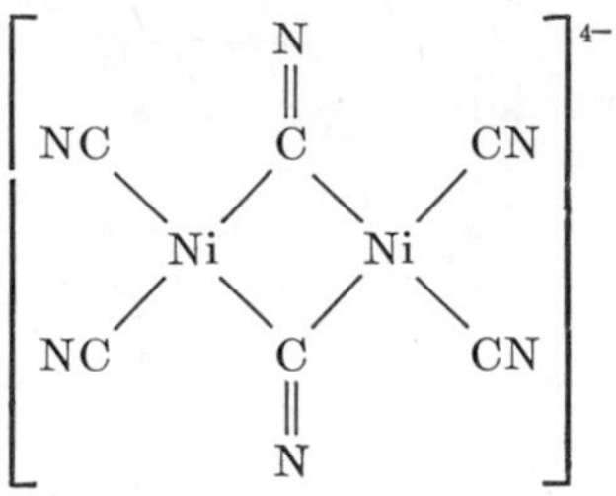

$$\left[\begin{array}{c} N \\ \| \\ NC \diagdown \;\; C \;\; \diagup CN \\ Ni \quad Ni \\ NC \diagup \;\; C \;\; \diagdown CN \\ \| \\ N \end{array}\right]^{4-}$$

The complex ion readily adds nitric oxide and carbon monoxide:

$$K_2[Ni(CN)_3] + NO \rightarrow K_2[Ni(CN)_3NO]^{518}$$

$$K_2[Ni(CN)_3] + CO \rightarrow K_2[Ni(CN)_3CO]^{519}$$

The products are actually more complex than these equations indicate; the carbonyl compound, at least, is evidently a polymer, for it is diamagnetic.

The action of excess potassium on $K_2[Ni(CN)_4]$ in liquid ammonia gives $K_4[Ni(CN)_4]$[516] as a copper-colored solid of very strong reducing powers. Compounds of the formula $K_4[M(CN)_4]$ containing palladium[520] and cobalt[521] have been prepared in analogous fashion.

Kleinberg and Davidson[522] have reduced the hexacyanomanganate(III) ion in liquid ammonia, obtaining a product of the formula $K_5Mn(CN)_6 \cdot K_6Mn(CN)_6 \cdot 2NH_3$. They also have evidence for the existence of a cyano complex of chromium(I)[523].

Isonitrile Coordination

Metal complexes of the isonitriles have been known for a long time, but have received little attention until recent years. Hartley[524] prepared two isomers of "methyl ferrocyanide," and showed that upon treatment with a mixture of alkyl iodide and mercury(II) iodide both isomers were converted to $[Fe(CH_3NC)_4(RNC)_2]I_2 \cdot 2HgI_2$. Both isomers gave the same product when methyl iodide was used, but ethyl iodide gave two isomers[525]. These have been subjected to x-ray analysis[526], and have been shown to be cis- and trans- isomers.

There is a close relationship between the isonitrile-metal complexes and the metal carbonyls. In both, the metal-carbon bond possesses a consider-

518. Hieber, Nast, and Proeschel, Z. anorg. Chem., **256,** 145 (1948).
519. Nast and Krakkay, Z. anorg. Chem., **272,** 233 (1953).
520. Burbage and Fernelius, J. Am. Chem. Soc., **65,** 1484 (1943).
521. Hieber and Bartenstein, Naturwissenschaften, **39,** 300 (1952).
522. Kleinberg and Davidson, J. Am. Chem. Soc., **75,** 2495 (1953).
523. Davidson and Kleinberg, J. Phys. Chem., **57,** 571 (1953).
524. Hartley, J. Chem. Soc., **103,** 1196 (1913).
525. Hartley, J. Chem. Soc., **1933,** 101.
526. Powell and Stanger, J. Chem. Soc., **1939,** 1105.

able degree of double bond character[493c]. The isonitrile complexes can be made by displacement of carbon monoxide from metallic carbonyls. Thus, phenyl isonitrile reacts with nickel carbonyl to give [Ni(ϕNC)$_4$] as long, canary-yellow needles[527, 528]. They are stable, soluble in many organic solvents, but insoluble in water. Iron and chromium carbonyls also react, though more slowly. The resulting compounds have not been fully characterized.

Methyl isonitrile reacts incompletely with nickel carbonyl, giving [Ni(CO)(CH$_3$NC)$_3$]. However, the same reactants in the presence of iodine and pyridine give [Ni(CH$_3$NC)$_4$]. A cobalt complex of the empirical formula [Co$_2$(CO)$_3$(ϕNC)$_5$] is obtained by the action of phenylisonitrile on Hg[Co(CO)$_4$]$_2$ in the presence of iodine and pyridine. Klages, Mönkemeyer, and Heinle[529] have prepared a series of copper(I) complexes, CuCl·xϕNC, (x = 1 − 4), the silver compounds AgNO$_3$(p-CH$_3$C$_6$H$_4$NC)$_x$ (x = 2 and 4), and the mercury(II) and zinc compounds MCl$_2$(p-CH$_3$C$_6$H$_4$NC)$_2$.

The Nomenclature of Coordination Compounds

Werner's system of nomenclature is the basis for the system which has been adopted by the International Union of Pure and Applied Chemistry, and which is now almost universally used[530]. These rules may be summarized as follows[531, 532]:

(1) If the substance is an electrolyte, the cation is named first, then the anion.

(2) The names of all negative coordinating groups end in -o, but those of neutral groups have no characteristic ending. In deference to long established practice, the coordinated water molecule is called *aquo*.

(3) The numbers of coordinating groups of each kind are indicated by the Greek prefixes mono-, di-, tri-, tetra-, etc., unless these groups are complex. In that case, the prefixes bis-, tris-, tetrakis-, etc., are used.

(4) Negative coordinated groups are listed first, then neutral coordinated groups, then the metal. (The reverse order is followed in writing formulas of complexes.)

(5) The oxidation state of the metallic element is indicated by a parenthetical Roman numeral. With cations and neutral molecules, this numeral

527. Hieber, *Z. Naturforsch.*, **5b**, 129 (1950); Hieber and Böckly, *Z. anorg. Chem.*, **262**, 344 (1950).
528. Klages and Mönkemeyer, *Ber.*, **83**, 501 (1950).
529. Klages, Mönkemeyer, and Heinle, *Ber.*, **85**, 109, 126 (1952).
530. Jorissen, Bassett, Damiens, Fichter, and Remy, *J. Am. Chem. Soc.*, **63**, 889 (1941).
531. Fernelius, *Chem. Eng. News*, **26**, 161 (1948); Advances in Chemistry Series, [8], 9 (1953). American Chemical Society.
532. Fernelius, Larsen, Marchi, and Rollinson, *Chem. Eng. News*, **26**, 520 (1948).

follows the name of the metal directly. With anions, the Roman numeral is placed after the name of the complex, which always bears the suffix -*ate*.

Werner's system differed from this chiefly in the mode of designation of oxidation state of the metal. Werner indicated the oxidation state of the metal in cations by the suffixes -a, -o, -i, and -e, indicating $1+$, $2+$, $3+$, and $4+$, respectively. In anions, the same suffixes were used, followed by the ending -ate. In neutral molecules, no suffixes were used.

Fernelius and his co-workers[531, 532] have suggested some useful additions to the system adopted by the International Union. The more important of these have been summarized by Moeller as follows[533]:

(1) The names of coordinated positive groups end in -*ium*.

(2) Positive groups are listed last, after negative and neutral groups.

(3) Groups of the same general nature (i.e., all negative, all neutral, all positive) are listed in alphabetical order without regard to any prefixes designating the numbers of such groups present.

(4) Zero oxidation state for the central element is designated by the Arabic character 0 placed in parentheses.

(5) Coordinated hydrogen salts are named as acids by dropping the word hydrogen and replacing the suffix -*ate* by -*ic*.

(6) Oxidation state of the central element is designated in the usual manner even though the complex is a neutral molecule.

(7) Use of prefixes such as *bis*-, *tris*-, and *tetrakis*-, followed by the name of the coordinated group set off by parentheses is preferred to that of the old designations *di*-, *tri*-, and *tetra*- to indicate numbers of coordinated groups if the names of those groups are complex.

In both the Werner and the I.U.C. systems, the names of bridging coordinated groups (i.e., those which are coordinated to two metal atoms simultaneously) are given after the names of all the other coordinating groups, and are preceded by the Greek letter μ. Bridging groups have their usual names, except the OH group, which is designated as *ol*.

Geometrical isomers of planar ions may be distinguished either by the terms *cis*- and *trans*- or by the numbers 1,2- and 1,3-. For octahedral complexes, these become *cis*- and *trans*- or 1,2- and 1,6-. Where there are more than two kinds of coordinating groups, or more than two of any one kind, the number system is much to be preferred.

The sign of rotation of optical isomers is indicated by *d*-, *l*- (or meso-). If the complex contains optically active coordinating groups, the small letter may be used to designate that fact, and the capital letters D- and L- to indicate the sign of rotation of the complex as a whole.

These rules are exemplified in Table 1.2.

It is customary, in writing formulas of metal coordination compounds, to

533. Moeller, "Inorganic Chemistry," New York, John Wiley & Sons, Inc., 1952.

TABLE 1.2. NOMENCLATURE OF COORDINATION COMPOUNDS

Formula	Name	Note
[Pt(NH₃)₄]Cl₂	tetrammineplatinum(II) chloride	
[Pt(NH₃)₆]Cl₄	hexammineplatinum(IV) chloride	
[Co(NH₃)₅Cl]Cl₂	monochloropentamminecobalt(III) chloride	The prefix "mono" is often omitted.
[Co(NH₃)₄Cl₂]Cl	dichlorotetramminecobalt(III) chloride	May be either cis- or trans- (1,2- or 1,6-)
[Co en₂ (NH₃)₂]Cl₃	diamminebis(ethylenediamine)cobalt(III) chloride	May be either cis- or trans-
[Co en₂ NO₂ Cl]⁺	chloronitrobis(ethylenediamine)cobalt(III) ion	May be either cis- or trans-. Either negative group may be named first
[Cr en₂ H₂O Cl]⁺⁺	chloroaquobis(ethylenediamine)chromium(III) ion	May be either cis- or trans-
NH₄[Cr(NH₃)₄(SO₃)₂]	ammonium disulfitotetramminechromate(III)	May be either cis- or trans-
[Co(NH₃)₃(NO₂)₃]	trinitrotriamminecobalt(III)	May be either 1,2,3 or 1,2,6
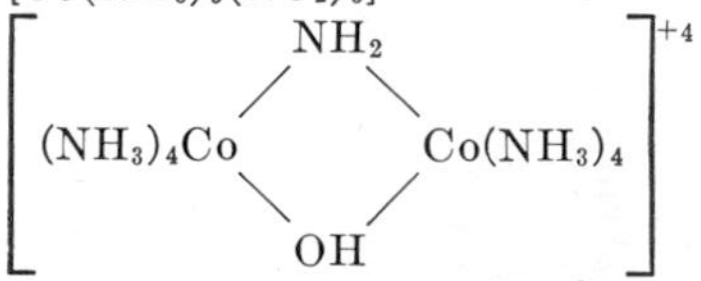 $$\left[(NH_3)_4Co \begin{array}{c} NH_2 \\ \\ OH \end{array} Co(NH_3)_4 \right]^{+4}$$	octammine-μ-amido-ol-dicobalt(III) ion	
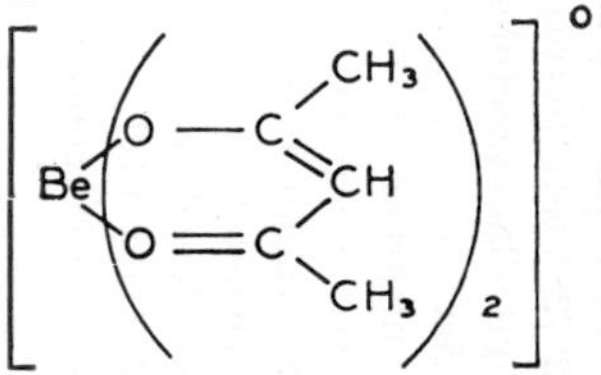 $$\left[Be \begin{array}{c} O=C-CH_3 \\ \quad \quad CH \\ O=C-CH_3 \end{array} \right]^{0}_{2}$$	bis(2,4-pentanediono)beryllium(II)	

TABLE 1.3. SYMBOLS FOR NAMES OF SOME LIGANDS

Name of ligand	Symbol
acetate ion	ac[1]
acetylacetonate ion	acac
alanine anion	alan
amino acid anion	amac
ammonia	a[2]
benzidine	bzd
benzoylacetate ion	benzac
benzylamine	bzl
biguanide	BigH
2,3-butanediamine	bn[3]
isobutanediamine	ibn
citrate anion (monobasic)	ci
cyanide ion	cy[2]
1,2, *trans*-cyclohexanediamine	chxn
1,2, *trans*-cyclopentanediamine	cptn
diallylamine	dlm
2,4-diaminopentane	ptn
dibenzoylmethane	dibenz
diethylenetriamine	dien
dimethylglyoxime monobasic anion	DMG or HD
2,2'-dipyridyl	dipy
ethylamine	etn
ethylenebiguanide	enBigH
ethylenediamine	en
ethylenediamine-acetylacetone	enac
ethylenediaminetetraacetic acid	H_4Y or EDTA
ethylenethiourea or ethylenethiocarbamide	etu
glycine anion	gly
halide	X
hydroxylamine	hx
methyl bis (3-dimethylarsinopropyl) arsine	TAS
oxalate dibasic anion	ox
1,10-phenanthroline	*o*-phen[4]
phenylalanine anion	ϕ ala
phenylbiguanide	ϕ BigH
ortho-phenylenediamine	ph
o-phenylenebis (dimethyl arsine)	PDA
phthalocyanine (dinegative group)	pc
propylenediamine (1,2-diaminopropane)	pn
pyridine	py
stilbenediamine (1,2-diphenylethylenediamine)	stien
2,2',2",2'''-tetrapyridyl	tetrpy
thenoyltrifluoroacetone	TTA
thiourea	tu
thiosemicarbazide	thio
1,2,3-triaminopropane	tn
2,2',2"-triaminotriethylamine	tren or trin
triethylenetetramine	trien
trimethylenediamine	trim
2,2',2"-tripyridyl	tripy

[1] Not to be confused with "Ac" used in organic chemistry to denote the acetyl group.

[2] Obsolete.

[3] May be preceded by *d*, *l*, or *m* (dextro, levo, or meso).

[4] Other symbols commonly used are "phenan" and "ph".

TABLE 1.4. SOME COMPLEX COMPOUNDS NAMED AFTER THEIR DISCOVERERS

Name	Structure	Note
Cleve's Salt	cis-$[Pt(NH_3)_2Cl_4]$	1
Cleve's Triammine	$[Pt(NH_3)_3Cl]Cl$	
Cossa's First Salt	$K[Pt(NH_3)Cl_3]$	
Cossa's Second Salt	$K[Pt(NH_3)Cl_5]$	
Drechsel's Chloride	$[Pt(NH_3)_6]Cl_4$	

Durrant's Salt

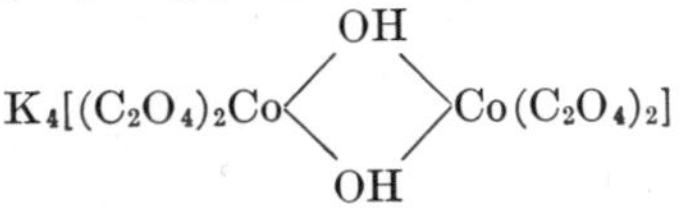

$$K_4[(C_2O_4)_2Co\underset{OH}{\overset{OH}{\diagup\diagdown}}Co(C_2O_4)_2]$$

Erdmann's Salt	$trans$-$K[Co(NH_3)_2(NO_2)_4]$	
Fischer's Salt	$K_3[Co(NO_2)_6]$	
Gerard's Salt	trans-$[Pt(NH_3)_2Cl_4]$	2
Gibbs' Salt	$[Co(NH_3)_3(NO_2)_3]$	
Gro's Salt	$trans$-$[Pt(NH_3)_4Cl_2]Cl_2$	
Litton's Salt	$Na_6[Pt(SO_3)_4]$	3
Magnus' Green Salt	$[Pt(NH_3)_4][PtCl_4]$	4
Magnus' Pink Salt	Two substances of this name are known. The common one is $[Pt(NH_3)_3Cl]_2[PtCl_4]$	
Melano chloride	A mixture, chiefly 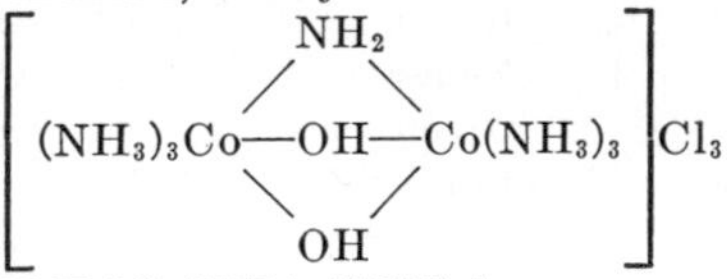	

$$\left[(NH_3)_3Co\underset{OH}{\overset{NH_2}{\diagup\diagdown}}Co(NH_3)_3\right]Cl_3$$

Morland's Salt	$CN_3H_6[Cr(NH_3)_2(SCN)_4]$	5
Peyrone's Salt	cis-$[Pt(NH_3)_2Cl_2]$	6
Recoura's Sulfate	$[Cr(H_2O)_5Cl]SO_4$	
Reinecke's Salt	$NH_4[Cr(NH_3)_2(SCN)_4]$	7
Rieset's First Chloride	$[Pt(NH_3)_4]Cl_2$	
Rieset's Second Chloride	$trans$-$[Pt(NH_3)_2Cl_2]$	8
Roussin's Red Salts	M Fe(NO)$_2$S (M = Na, K, NH$_4$)	
Roussin's Black Salts	M Fe$_4$(NO)$_7$S$_3$ (M = Na, K, Rb, Cs, NH$_4$, or Tl	
Vaquelin's Salt	$[Pd(NH_3)_4][PdCl_4]$	9
Vortmann's Sulfate	A mixture, chiefly	

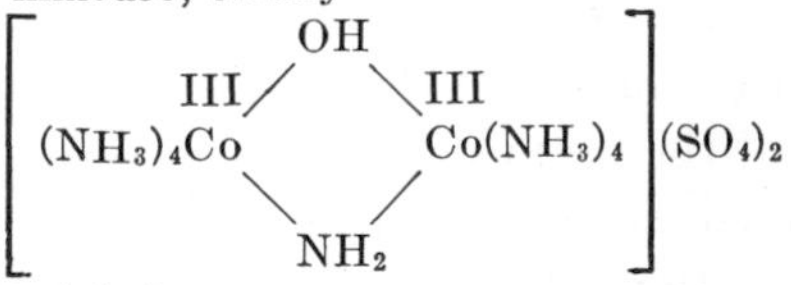

$$\left[(NH_3)_4Co\overset{III}{}\underset{NH_2}{\overset{OH}{\diagup\diagdown}}\overset{III}{}Co(NH_3)_4\right](SO_4)_2$$

containing some

$$\left[(NH_3)_4Co\overset{III}{}\underset{NH_2}{\overset{O_2}{\diagup\diagdown}}\overset{IV}{}Co(NH_3)_4\right](SO_4)_2$$

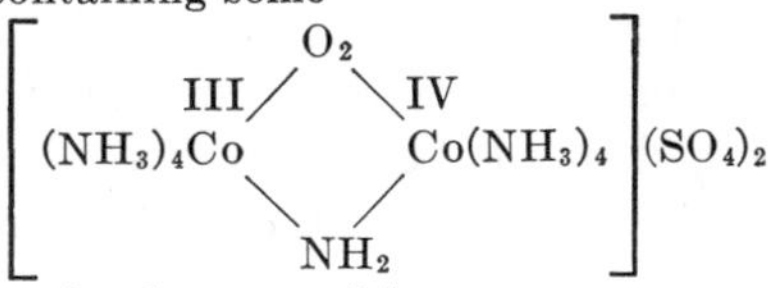

and other materials

Wolffram's Red Salt	Pt(C$_2$H$_5$NH$_2$)$_4$Cl$_3$·2H$_2$O—contains Pt(II) and Pt(IV)	10
Zeise's Salt	$K[PtCl_3·C_2H_4]$	

TABLE 1.4—*Continued*

[1] cf. Gerard's Salt.

[2] cf. Cleve's Salt.

[3] Salts of this type, in which the platinum is replaced by other divalent metals, the ammonia is replaced by other nitrogen bases, or the chloride is replaced by other halides, are often referred to as Magnus salts.

[4] Cox, Pinkard, Wardlaw, and Preston, *J. Chem. Soc.* **1932**, 2527.

[5] The guanidinium analog of Reinicke's salt.

[6] cf. Rieset's Second Chloride.

[7] Discovered by Morland in 1861; investigated by Reinicke in 1863.

[8] cf. Peyrone's salt.

[9] cf. Magnus' Green Salt.

[10] Jensen, *Z. anorg. allgem. Chem.*, **229**, 252 (1936).

TABLE 1.5. SOME NAMES OF COMPLEXES BASED ON COLOR

Name	Color	Structure	Note
Croceo	Yellow	$trans\text{-}[Co(NH_3)_4(NO_2)_2]^+$	
Flavo	Brown	$cis\text{-}[Co(NH_3)_4(NO_2)_2]^+$	
Luteo	Yellow	$[Co(NH_3)_6]^{+++}$	
Praseo	Green	$trans\text{-}[Co(NH_3)_4Cl_2]^+$	1
Purpureo	Purplish-red	$[Co(NH_3)_5Cl]^{++}$	1
Roseo	Rose-red	$[Co(NH_3)_5H_2O]^{+++}$	
Violeo	Violet	$cis\text{-}[Co(NH_3)_4Cl_2]^+$	1

[1] Often used to denote other halopentammines, sometimes with a designation as to the halogen present; thus, $[Co(NH_3)_5Br]^{++}$ is referred to as the bromopurpureo ion.

use symbols for the names of many organic ligands. Table 1.3 lists the symbols used in this book, as well as some others which may be encountered in other reading. Unfortunately, there is not complete uniformity in the use of these abbreviations, which may lead to some confusion. Because of this, some notes and recommendations are included in Table 1.3.

The early workers in the field of complex inorganic compounds did not understand the nature of these substances, so were not able to give them names based upon structure. It was customary, therefore, to name each compound after its discoverer. A few of these early names persist in the current literature, and are listed in Table 1.4.

In 1840, Fremy[534] suggested that the ammines of cobalt be given names descriptive of their colors. He derived such names from the Latin. The system was easily extended to the cobalt compounds containing ethylenediamine and other amines, and to the chromium(III) salts, the colors of which are similar to those of their cobalt(III) analogs. These names are now frequently used to describe classes of compounds. For example, the term

534. Fremy, *Ann. chim. phys.* [3], **35**, 257 (1852); *J. prakt. Chem.*, **57**, 95 (1852).

"luteo," originally used to describe the ion $[Co(NH_3)_6]^{3+}$, has been extended to include also $[Co\ en_3]^{3+}$, $[Co\ dipy_3]^{3+}$, $[Co\ trien_2]^{3+}$, and other cobalt(III) complexes in which six amine nitrogen atoms are coordinated to the cobalt. The terms are sometimes used to describe ammines of metals other than cobalt and chromium, even though the colors are quite at variance with the names suggested by Fremy. For example, Gleu and Rehm[535] use the term "luteo" in reference to the hexammine ruthenium(III) ion, which is colorless. When any metal other than cobalt is meant, it is usual to include the name of the metal. Thus, luteo chromium(III) chloride is $[Cr(NH_3)_6]Cl_3$. The more important of Fremy's "color names" are assembled in Table 1.5.

535. Gleu and Rehm, *Z. anorg. allgem. Chem.*, **227**, 237 (1936).

2. The Early Development of the Coordination Theory

John C. Bailar, Jr.

University of Illinois, Urbana, Illinois

The history of chemistry in the nineteenth century is largely an account of the growth of our knowledge of molecular structure. When the doctrine of constant valence proved so successful in explaining the structures of organic compounds, it was natural that every effort should be made to apply it also to the structures of inorganic substances. Thus it happened that the growth of inorganic chemistry was retarded for over twenty years by the same factor which contributed most to the phenomenal development of our knowledge of the compounds of carbon. Inorganic chemistry is the older of the two fields, and the study of inorganic "complex compounds" antedated the rise of organic chemistry by over fifty years. The structures of hydrates, double salts, and metal ammonia compounds were widely discussed even before the beginning of the nineteenth century. Of these, the ammonia compounds attracted the most attention, for they lent themselves to study by classical methods. The early history of the theory of complex compounds is therefore the history of the ammonates.* The discovery of these substances is usually attributed to Tassaert[1], who observed in 1798 that cobalt salts combine with ammonia.

EARLY THEORIES OF THE STRUCTURE OF AMMINES

Berzelius' Conjugate Theory

The first logical attempt to explain the metal ammonia compounds was made by Berzelius[2], who observed that a metal in "conjugation" with ammonia did not lose its capacity for combination with other substances. He

---

* The term "ammonate" was displaced by the simpler term "ammine" at the suggestion of Werner.

1. Tassaert, *Ann. chim. phys.*, [1] **28,** 92 (1798).
2. Berzelius, "Essai sur la theorie des proportions chimique et sur l'influence chimique de l'electricite," Paris, 1819.

attempted to extend this theory, but without great success, to the double salts and complex cyanides.

Graham's Ammonium Theory

According to Graham's "ammonium" theory[3], metal ammonates are considered to be substituted ammonium compounds. This view, in one form or another, was generally accepted until the time of Werner. Graham made this suggestion in an attempt to explain the structure of diammonium copper(II) salts, in which he supposed one hydrogen atom from each of two ammonium groups had been displaced by copper. Obviously, such a formula can apply only when the number of ammonia groups in the molecule is the same as the electrovalence of the metal—a condition which usually does not hold. Gerhardt[4], Wurtz[5], Rieset[6], A. W. Hofmann[7] and Boedecker[8] suggested modifications of the theory to take care of other cases. According to Rieset and Hofmann, the hydrogen atoms of an ammonium group are replaceable, not only by metals, but also by other ammonium groups. Hofmann represented the compound of cobalt(III) chloride with six molecules of ammonia, for example, as

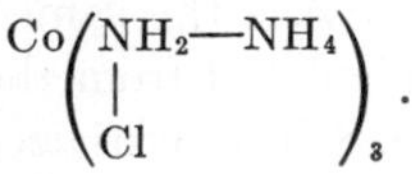

$$Co\left(\begin{array}{c}NH_2{-}NH_4 \\ | \\ Cl\end{array}\right)_3.$$

Some years later the experiments of Jörgensen showed this argument to be fallacious. It does not allow for the existence of similar compounds of tertiary amines[9], and it does not explain why the removal of one molecule of ammonia completely alters the function of one of the chlorine atoms. Boedecker avoided the branching of the chain by assuming that the metal substitutes in an ammonium group which is itself a substituent group: $Co(NH_3{-}NH_3{-}Cl)_3$. The diammonate and tetrammonate of platinum(II) chloride were represented as $Pt(NH_3{-}Cl)_2$ and $Pt(NH_3{-}NH_3{-}Cl)_2$. The question "What prevents further lengthening of the ammonia chain?" was never answered, and was an insurmountable objection to this type of theory.

3. Graham, "Elements of Chemistry," London, 1837. This book is rare, and is best known in Otto's German translation *"Lehrbuch der Chemie,"* Braunschweig, 1840. Graham's suggestion of the ammonium theory appears in Vol. 2, page 741 of the German edition.
4. Gerhardt, *Jahresber. Fortschr. pharm., tech. chem. physik (Liebig)*, **3**, 335 (1850).
5. Wurtz, *Ann. chim. phys.*, [3] **30**, 488 (1850).
6. Rieset, *Ann. chim. phys.*, [3] **11**, 417 (1844).
7. Hofmann, *Ann.*, **78**, 253 (1851).
8. Boedecker, *Ann.*, **123**, 56 (1862).
9. Jörgensen, *J. prakt. Chem.*, [2] **33**, 489 (1886).

Claus' Theory

The theory of Claus[10] met with vigorous opposition, but is all the more interesting on that account, for the parts of it which were most vigorously attacked appeared in only slightly modified form in Werner's theory. Claus believed that, when combined with metallic oxides, ammonia not only does not affect the saturation capacity of the metal, but becomes "passive" as regards its own basicity. His views may be summarized as follows:[11]

(1) The union of several equivalents of ammonia with one equivalent of a metal chloride leads to the formation of a neutral substance, in which the basic property of ammonia is lost, so that the ammonia can no longer be determined by the usual means nor eliminated by double decomposition. Thus, the ammonia is in a different condition than in ordinary ammonium salts. This hypothesis met with a storm of protest, just as Werner's similar suggestion did forty years later. The attack was led by Weltzein[12], who held the term "passive molecule" to be indefinite and confusing, and who believed that every part of a molecule influences every other part, so that no part can be said to be "passive".

(2) If these chlorides are converted to oxides, strong bases are formed. The saturation capacity of these is the same as that of the metal oxides themselves, and cannot be calculated from the number of ammonia molecules combined with the oxide. Schiff[13] criticized this conclusion by pointing out that the oxides of the "ammonia bases" of the metals are much stronger bases than the metal oxides themselves. This criticism seems to rest on a confusion between the "strength" of a base and its "saturation capacity" (i.e., equivalence). It is true that the hydroxides of the metal ammines are strong bases, but the ammonia present in them does not readily combine with the hydrogen ion.

(3) The number of ammonia molecules combined with a molecule of metallic salt is determined by the same factors as the number of molecules of water in the hydrate and the two will be the same. This point of Claus' theory was easy to attack, for many hydrates were known for which analogous ammonia compounds did not seem to exist. The conclusion which Claus drew, however, was restated as an integral part of Werner's theory and has been amply verified.

Blomstrand's Chain Theory

Odling[14] suggested that metallic atoms can substitute for the hydrogen atoms in ammonia just as organic radicals do. The diammonate of plati-

10. Claus, "Beiträge zur Chemie der Platinmetalle," Dorpat, 1854; *Zentralblatt*, **25**, 789 (1854); *Ann.*, **98**, 317 (1856).
11. Reitzenstein, *Z. anorg. Chem.*, **18**, 152 (1898).
12. Weltzein, *Ann.*, **97**, 19 (1856).
13. Schiff, *Ann.*, **123**, 1 (1862).
14. Odling, *Chem. News*, **21**, 289 (1870).

num(II) chloride was construed as being analogous to ethylenediamine hydrochloride: $Pt(NH_2)_2 \cdot 2HCl$ and $C_2H_4(NH_2)_2 \cdot 2HCl$. The chaining of ammonia molecules was compared to the chaining of methylene groups in the hydrocarbons.

Blomstrand[15] made this the basis of his famous theory. Ammonium chloride was represented as $H-NH_3-Cl$, $NH_4NO_3 \cdot NH_3$ as $H-NH_3-NH_3-NO_3$, and $NH_4I \cdot 6NH_3$ as $H(NH_3)_7I$. The terminal hydrogen atom can be replaced by other positive atoms, such as metals. The metal, in fact, stabilizes the chain, and its nature determines the length and stability of the chain. Chains of three ammonia molecules are often found in union with nickel, cobalt, iridium and rhodium, but platinum and copper seem unable to stabilize chains of more than two nitrogen atoms. On the basis of these postulates, Blomstrand wrote the formulas for the tetrammonate of platinum(II) chloride and the hexammonate of cobalt(II) chloride as

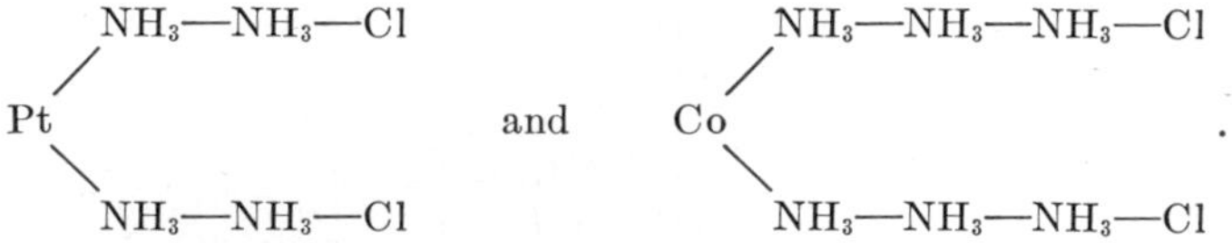

$$\underset{\displaystyle Pt}{\diagup \; NH_3-NH_3-Cl \atop \diagdown \; NH_3-NH_3-Cl} \qquad \text{and} \qquad \underset{\displaystyle Co}{\diagup \; NH_3-NH_3-NH_3-Cl \atop \diagdown \; NH_3-NH_3-NH_3-Cl} \quad .$$

According to Blomstrand, the stability of the ammonia chain is not dependent on its length. Although platinum is unable to stabilize chains of any great length, platinum(II) chloride ammonate is not attacked by hydrogen sulfide or by sodium hydroxide. Chlorine oxidizes the platinum without attacking the ammonia, converting the compound to:

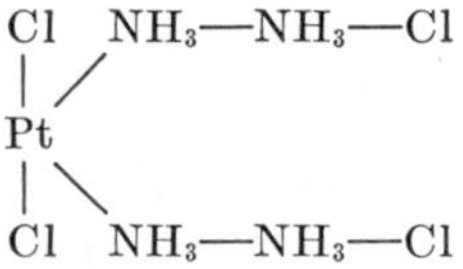

$$\begin{array}{c} Cl \quad NH_3-NH_3-Cl \\ | \diagup \\ Pt \\ | \diagdown \\ Cl \quad NH_3-NH_3-Cl \end{array}$$

in which chlorine is attached to the molecule in two different ways. The validity of this postulate is borne out by experiment, for only half the chlorine is replaced by the action of sodium carbonate, and the second half is only slowly precipitated by silver nitrate. Blomstrand referred to the two types of chloride as the "farther" and "nearer". This expression may have inspired Werner's postulate of "first" and "second" spheres[11].

Jörgensen's Theories

Blomstrand's formulas for the cobalt ammonia compounds became the center of a long controversy between Jörgensen and Werner, and are therefore of considerable interest. Blomstrand believed—and the belief was

15. Blomstrand, "Chemie der Jetztzeit," Heidelberg, 1869; *Ber.*, **4**, 40 (1871).

universal until 1890[16]—that cobalt(III) chloride and its ammonia compounds were dimolecular. In that year, Jörgensen adduced evidence for the simpler molecular weights, and halved Blomstrand's formulas. This did not affect the postulates of Blomstrand's theory, but without this change, Werner's theory might not have been conceived. Blomstrand first supposed the luteo cobalt salts (e.g., $Co_2Cl_6 \cdot 12NH_3$) to have the completely symmetrical structure:

$$Co_2 \begin{cases} NH_3\text{—}NH_3\text{—}Cl \\ NH_3\text{—}NH_3\text{—}Cl \\ NH_3\text{—}NH_3\text{—}Cl \\ NH_3\text{—}NH_3\text{—}Cl \\ NH_3\text{—}NH_3\text{—}Cl \\ NH_3\text{—}NH_3\text{—}Cl \end{cases}$$

and the purpureo salts ($Co_2Cl_6 \cdot 10NH_3$) the structure:

$$Co_2 \begin{cases} NH_3\text{—}Cl \\ NH_3\text{—}NH_3\text{—}Cl \\ NH_3\text{—}NH_3\text{—}Cl \\ NH_3\text{—}NH_3\text{—}Cl \\ NH_3\text{—}NH_3\text{—}Cl \\ NH_3\text{—}Cl \end{cases}$$

But this was soon seen to be incorrect, for the purpureo salt contains chlorine in two very different modes of combination[11, 17].* In a cold solution, silver nitrate precipitates two-thirds of the chlorine at once, and the other third only after long standing. The slight functional difference shown in the formula above can hardly explain such a difference in behavior. Jörgensen[18] prepared a whole series of salts in which the more readily precipitated chlorine is replaced by other groups. He concluded that the chlorine in these salts is combined directly with the metal, while the other negative groups are united with the ammonia. Similar relationships were shown to hold for the chromium[19] and rhodium[20] pentammonate salts. Jörgenson also demonstrated that the "masked" chloride can be replaced by bromine[21], sulfate[22], and other negative groups. These groups, like the chloride in the original purpureo salt, have lost their ionic properties.

* For explanation of nomenclature, see Chapter 1.

16. Jörgensen, *J. prakt. Chem.*, [2] **41**, 429 (1890); Petersen, *Z. phys. Chem.*, **10**, 580 (1892).
17. Gibbs and Genth, "Researches on the Ammonia Cobalt Bases," Washington, 1856.
18. Jörgensen, *J. prakt. Chem.*, [2] **18**, 209 (1878).
19. Jörgensen, *J. prakt. Chem.*, [2] **20**, 105 (1879); **25**, 83 (1882).
20. Jörgensen, *J. prakt. Chem.*, [2] **25**, 346 (1882); **27**, 433 (1883); **40**, 309 (1886).
21. Jörgensen, *J. prakt. Chem.*, [2] **19**, 49 (1879).
22. Jörgensen, *J. prakt. Chem.*, [2] **31**, 262 (1885).

When Jörgensen found[23] that two-thirds of the chlorine in the tetrammonates of the trivalent metals is "masked", he concluded that this should be represented as in direct union with the metal. He formulated these salts as:

$$Co_2 \begin{cases} Cl \\ Cl \\ NH_3-NH_3-NH_3-NH_3-Cl \\ NH_3-NH_3-NH_3-NH_3-Cl \\ Cl \\ Cl \end{cases}$$

and the purpureo and the luteo salts as:

$$Co_2 \begin{cases} Cl \\ NH_3Cl \\ NH_3-NH_3-NH_3-NH_3-Cl \\ NH_3-NH_3-NH_3-NH_3-Cl \\ NH_3Cl \\ Cl \end{cases} \quad \text{and} \quad Co_2 \begin{cases} NH_3Cl \\ NH_3Cl \\ NH_3-NH_3-NH_3-NH_3-Cl \\ NH_3-NH_3-NH_3-NH_3-Cl \\ NH_3-Cl \\ NH_3-Cl \end{cases}$$

Jörgensen showed that the "roseo" salts, which had been thought to be isomeric with the purpureo salts, contain two molecules of water[24]. This water is lost at elevated temperatures, leaving a residue of the purpureo salt. The roseo salts resemble the luteo salts in that all of the negative groups are ionic as well as in solubility, crystalline form, and appearance. Jörgensen concluded that they are luteo salts in which one-sixth of the ammonia molecules are replaced by water.

The roseo tetrammonate salts were also shown to be analogous to the luteo salts, but they contain water in place of one-third of the ammonia molecules. No compounds were known in which more than a third of the ammonia was replaced by water, so it was assumed that the "unchained" ammonia molecules were the ones replaced. The roseo tetrammonia salts were therefore represented as:

$$Co_2 \begin{cases} H_2O-Cl \\ H_2O-Cl \\ NH_3-NH_3-NH_3-NH_3-Cl \\ NH_3-NH_3-NH_3-NH_3-Cl \\ H_2O-Cl \\ H_2O-Cl \end{cases}$$

or, using the simplified formula, as:

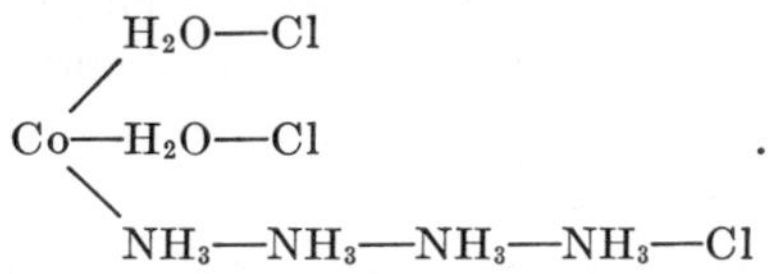

$$Co \begin{array}{l} \nearrow H_2O-Cl \\ -H_2O-Cl \\ \searrow NH_3-NH_3-NH_3-NH_3-Cl \end{array} \quad .$$

23. Jörgensen, *J. prakt. Chem.*, [2] **27**, 433 (1883).
24. Jörgensen, *J. prakt. Chem.*, [2] **29**, 409 (1884); **31**, 49 (1885).

These postulates suggest many questions, some of which Jörgensen attempted to answer by modifications or elaborations of the theory:

Why can cobalt hold only six ammonia molecules? If one of the valences holds a chain of four, why cannot the others also? Can chains of more than four ammonia groups exist? How shall we explain the existence of isomeric compounds?

Jörgensen felt that the chains contain a maximum of four $-NH_3$-groups[25], because of the many examples of tetrammonated compounds, and because the penta- and hexaammonated salts seemed to contain one and two ammonia molecules, respectively, which are different from the other four. He answered the other questions by developing Blomstrand's hypothesis that the three valences of cobalt are different. An example or two[26] will illustrate the argument: The luteo chloride,

$$\begin{array}{l} \gamma NH_3Cl \\ M \; \alpha(NH_3)_4Cl \quad \text{(M represents a trivalent metal)} \\ \beta NH_3Cl \end{array}$$

readily loses one molecule of ammonia to form

$$\begin{array}{l} \gamma Cl \\ M\alpha(NH_3)_4Cl, \\ \beta NH_3Cl \end{array}$$

which in water is converted to the aquo (roseo) salt, which must therefore be

$$\begin{array}{l} \gamma H_2O-Cl \\ M\alpha(NH_3)_4Cl. \\ \beta NH_3Cl \end{array}$$

The diaquo roseo salt,

$$\begin{array}{l} \gamma H_2O-Cl \\ M\alpha(NH_3)_4Cl \\ \beta H_2O-Cl \end{array}$$

readily loses one molecule of water to form a compound which must contain the groups $-Cl$ and $-H_2O-Cl$. But the $-H_2O-Cl$ group in this compound is not like the $-H_2O-Cl$ group in the roseo pentammine. The former loses a molecule of water when heated to 100°C or lower, while no water is lost from the latter until the temperature is well above 100°C. According to Jörgensen, this difference indicates that the β and γ valences are not the same. He cited the fact that the tetrammonates take up one molecule of

25. Jörgensen, Z. anorg. Chem., 5, 147 (1894).
26. Jörgensen, Z. anorg. Chem., 7, 289 (1894).

ammonia or water easily, and a second with difficulty, as further evidence for this view. The isomerism of the "flavo" and "croceo" chlorides was explained by the formulas:

$$\begin{array}{cc} \gamma NO_2 & \gamma NO_2 \\ Co\ \alpha(NH_3)_4Cl & Co\ \alpha NO_2 \\ \beta NO_2 & \beta(NH_3)_4Cl \end{array} \qquad \text{and}$$

Early Theories of the Structure of Hydrates

While these theories of the metal ammonia compounds were being discussed, attempts were also being made to elucidate the structures of the hydrates. The best known of the hydrate theories was that of Wurtz[27], who postulated that the water molecules link themselves to the metal and to each other in rings:

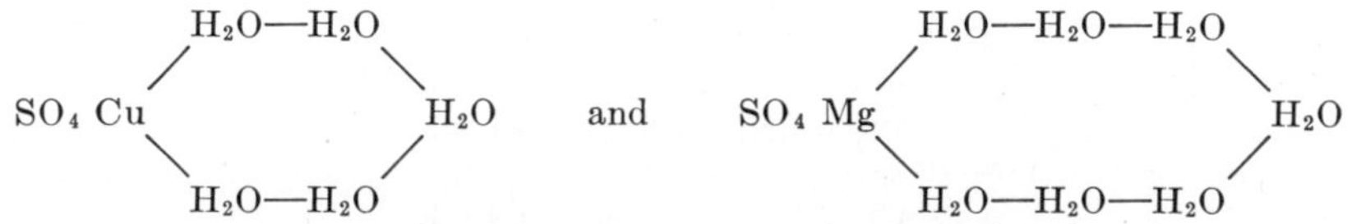

$$SO_4\ Cu \underset{H_2O-H_2O}{\overset{H_2O-H_2O}{\diagup \diagdown}} H_2O \qquad \text{and} \qquad SO_4\ Mg \underset{H_2O-H_2O-H_2O}{\overset{H_2O-H_2O-H_2O}{\diagup \diagdown}} H_2O$$

The assumptions underlying the theory were unsupported by experimental evidence, and it met with little favor.

Early Theories of the Structure of Double Salts

The double salts, especially the double halides, were of great interest, and numerous theories of their constitution were advanced. Bonsdorff[28] and Boullay[29] compared the chlorides to oxides, some of which are acidic and others basic, and they supposed double salts were formed by a sort of neutralization reaction. Others[30, 31] took exception to this theory, but it found wide acceptance. Naquet[32] expressed the view that two chlorine atoms are equivalent to one oxygen, and Blomstrand[15] went so far as to suppose these two chlorine atoms to be linked together through a double bond. On this basis $3KCl \cdot FeCl_3$ and $2KCl \cdot PtCl_4$ become

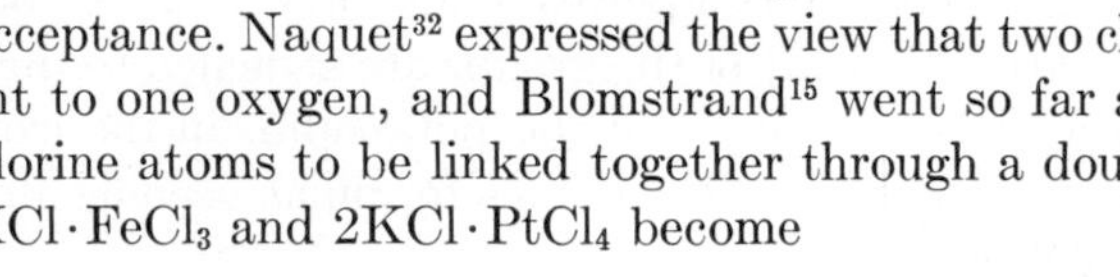

$$Fe \underset{Cl=Cl-K}{\overset{Cl=Cl-K}{\diagup \diagdown}} Cl=Cl-K \qquad \text{and} \qquad Pt \underset{Cl}{\overset{Cl}{\diagdown \diagup}} \overset{Cl=Cl-K}{\underset{Cl=Cl-K}{\diagup \diagdown}}$$

27. Wurtz, "La Theorie Atomique," Paris, 1879.
28. Bonsdorff, *Ann. chim. phys.*, **34**, 142 (1827).
29. Boullay, *Ann. chim. phys.*, **34**, 337 (1827).
30. Liebig, *Ann. chim. phys.*, **35**, 68 (1827).
31. Berzelius, *Jahresber. Fortsch. chem. mineral. (Berzelius)*, **8**, 138 (1829).
32. Naquet, "Principes de Chemie fondee sur les Theories Modernes," Paris, 1867.

There was little experimental evidence to support Blomstrand's suggestion, and it was not widely accepted[33]. Such formulas do not indicate why the potassium should be ionic and the iron and platinum nonionic, nor do they allow for the formation of double chlorides such as $CdCl_2 \cdot 4KCl$, in which the number of molecules of alkali metal chloride exceeds the number of chlorine atoms in the heavy metal chloride. Remsen[34] "solved" the latter difficulty by assuming the formation of halogen rings:

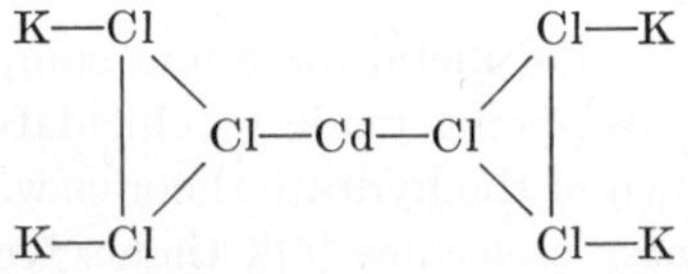

$$
\begin{array}{ccc}
K-Cl & & Cl-K \\
& \diagdown & \diagup \\
\Big| & Cl-Cd-Cl & \Big| \\
& \diagup & \diagdown \\
K-Cl & & Cl-K \\
\end{array}
$$

In 1885 Horstmann[35] wrote the reaction:

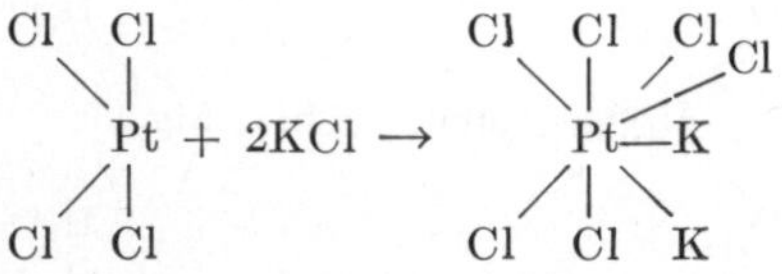

$$
\begin{array}{c}
\underset{Cl}{Cl}\ \underset{}{Cl} \\
\diagdown\ \big| \\
Pt + 2KCl \rightarrow \\
\diagup\ \big| \\
Cl\ \ Cl
\end{array}
\qquad
\begin{array}{c}
Cl\ \ Cl\ \ Cl \\
\diagdown\ \big|\ \diagup{}^{Cl} \\
Pt{-}K \\
\diagup\ \big|\ \diagdown \\
Cl\ \ Cl\ \ K
\end{array}
$$

in analogy to

$$
\begin{array}{c}
H \\
\diagdown \\
H-N + HCl \rightarrow \\
\diagup \\
H
\end{array}
\qquad
\begin{array}{c}
H\ \ \ H \\
\diagdown\ \diagup \\
H-N \\
\diagup\ \diagdown \\
H\ \ \ Cl
\end{array} \quad ,
$$

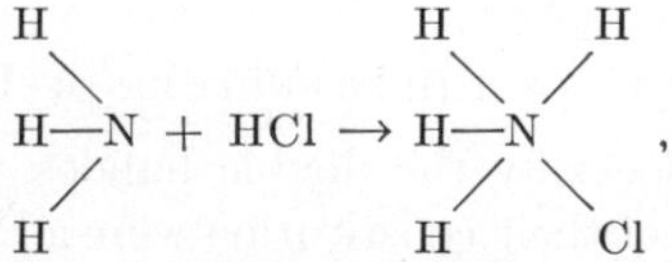

which was the generally accepted mechanism for the reaction of ammonia with hydrochloric acid. By assuming large enough valences for the metals, we can apply this theory to complexes of all sorts. It is, of course, misleading in its implication that all of the groups are attached to the central atom in the same way (the chlorine and the potassium, in the example given). With this feature modified, Horstmann's formulas become almost identical with those of Werner.

WERNER'S COORDINATION THEORY

This, then, is the background on which Werner built. In his paper "Contribution to the Theory of Affinity and Valence" [36] published in 1891, he suggested that an atom does not have a certain number of valence bonds, but that the valence force is exerted over the whole surface of the atom, and

33. Remsen, *Am. Chem. J.*, **11**, 291 (1889).
34. Remsen, *Am. Chem. J.*, **14**, 81 (1892).
35. Horstmann, "Lehrbuch der Physikalischen und Theoretischen Chemie," Braunschweig, 1885.
36. Werner, "Beitrage zue Theorie der Affinität und Valenz," 1891.

can be divided into several units of varying strength, depending on the demands of the atoms which unite with it. Some of its valence force may be left unexpended. This thought is different from the postulate of "primary" and "secondary" valences, but is certainly a forerunner of it. The wide-spread belief that the coordination theory had no roots in earlier theories or in the experience of its author is a mistaken one. It is true, however, that the theory was different from anything which had previously been proposed and that it came in a spectacular way. Pfeiffer[37] has written: "According to his own statement, the inspiration came to him like a flash. One morning at two o'clock he awoke with a start; the long-sought solution of this problem had lodged in his brain. He arose from his bed and by five o'clock in the afternoon the essential points of the coordination theory were achieved." Werner was then twenty-six years old.*

Fundamenental Postulates

The fundamental postulate in Werner's coordination theory is stated in the following way[38] "Even when, to judge by the valence number, the combining power of certain atoms is exhausted, they still possess in most cases the power of participating further in the construction of complex molecules with the formation of very definite atomic linkages. The possibility of this action is to be traced back to the fact that, besides the affinity bonds designated as principal valencies, still other bonds on the atoms, called auxiliary valences, may be called into action." The rest of the theory is an elucidation of the nature, the number, and the spatial distribution of these "auxiliary" valences.† The auxiliary valences were originally conceived as being very different from principal valences, since they do not allow ionization while the principal valences do. Yet according to Werner, there is a connection between them, for if an atom forms strong primary bonds with certain other atoms, it usually forms strong secondary bonds with them too. Thus the alkaline earth oxides are extremely stable, and they combine with water (by secondary valence) with great avidity. Similarly, the very stable sulfides of copper, mercury and arsenic readily form thio complexes. It is pos-

* For biographical sketches of Werner, see G. T. Morgan: *J. Chem. Soc.*, **117**, 1639 (1920); J. Lifschitz, *Z. Elektrochem.*, **26**, 514 (1920); and P. Karrer, *Helv. chim. Acta*, **3**, 196 (1920). These give brief accounts of his theory. The article by Karrer contains a portrait and a list of Werner's publications. P. Pfeiffer, *J. Chem. Ed.*, **5**, 1090 (1928) gives a description of Werner's personal life and a portrait of him.

† The terms "primary" and "secondary" were often used instead of "principal" and "auxiliary."

37. Pfeiffer, *J. Chem. Ed.*, **5**, 1096 (1928); Ostwald's "Klassiker der Exakten Wissenschaften," No. 212, p. 5, Leipzig, Akademische Verlagsgesellschaft, 1924.

38. Werner, "Neuere Anschauungen," 4th Ed. p. 44, Vieweg, Braunschweig, 1920. Quoted from Bass' translation of Schwarz, "The Chemistry of Inorganic Complex Compounds," p. 9, New York, John Wiley & Sons, Inc., 1923.

sible, too, for a primary valence to be converted into a secondary one. In solutions of hexammine chromic chloride, $[Cr(NH_3)_6]Cl_3$,* all of the chlorine is at once precipitated by solutions of silver nitrate. If the dry hexammine be heated somewhat above 100°C, a molecule of ammonia escapes, and simultaneously one-third of the chlorine loses its ionic properties. Werner argued that this means it has become attached by a secondary valence, though of course this does not release a primary valence, and the new compound contains only two chloride ions[39]. Jörgensen and Werner both believed the nonionic chlorine to be attached directly to the metal, in place of the ammonia which had been lost. On standing in water solution, the pentammine undergoes a slow change by which the third chlorine again becomes ionic. Upon evaporation at room temperature, the resulting solution yields crystals of a rose-red pentammine, containing a molecule of water. Jörgensen[40] had shown that this "roseo" compound is closely analogous to the hexammine, and he recognized it as a hexammine in which one ammonia molecule is replaced by water. In this, he and Werner agreed. They disagreed, however, on the fate of the chlorine atom which the water molecule had displaced. Jörgensen believed it to be attached to this water molecule through the quadrivalence of oxygen while Werner felt that it was not attached to any particular atom in the complex, but was attracted by the complex ion as a whole. Werner's postulate clearly foreshadows the theory of ionization of salts in the crystalline state, and has been amply confirmed by x-ray measurements and by other means. At the time of its proposal, however, it was a most revolutionary doctrine, and for many years it met with widespread criticism[41].

The relationship between primary and secondary valence became closer and closer in Werner's mind, and he was finally led to the conclusion that there is no essential difference between the two. This came about through his study of the tetrakis(ethylenediamine)-μ-amino-nitro-dicobalt(III) ion,

---

* The term "ammin" proposed by Werner to designate the metal ammonia compounds, is translated into English as "ammine". Its use in this place is somewhat anachronic, as it was not used in Werner's earlier papers, but we shall use it throughout. The term "ammonate" is still used by some authors to designate simple addition compounds of ammonia with metallic salts. Such compounds can be called "ammines" equally well, however. In the earlier papers, Werner indicated the constituents of the complex ion by enclosing them in parentheses, but he later adopted the use of square brackets.

39. Jörgensen, *J. prakt. Chem.*, [2] **20**, 105 (1879).
40. Jörgensen, *J. prakt. Chem.*, [2] **29**, 409 (1884).
41. See for example, Friend, *J. Chem. Soc.*, **109**, 715 (1916); **119**, 1040 (1921).

$$\left[\text{en}_2 \text{ Co} \underset{NO_2}{\overset{NH_2}{\diamondsuit}} \text{Co en}_2 \right]^{4+ \; 42}.$$

This ion contains two asymmetric cobalt atoms (See Chapter 8) which apparently are not identical. One of them is attached to the amino group by a primary valence and to the nitro group by a secondary valence, while for the other one, these relationships are reversed. Resolution, then, should give a dextro, a levo, and two meso forms. Careful experimentation, however, yielded only one meso form. This compound is completely inactive, indicating the identity of the two asymmetric atoms. Werner may not have been surprised at this discovery, for his first paper[43] draws an analogy between the metal ammine ions and the ammonium ion, in which the hydrogen which is held by "secondary" valence is indistinguishable from the rest.

It has long been known that many of the metal ions form hexammonates and hexahydrates, and that tetraammonates are common. The tetra- and hexacyanides have also long been known as stable, well-defined compounds. From such facts, Werner deduced that each element has only a certain number of secondary valences. Groups attached to the central element by these valences are said to be "coordinated" to it. The "coordination number" of an atom or ion is the number of groups which can be coordinated to it.* While four and six are the most common coordination numbers, coordination numbers of two, three, five, seven and eight are known.

In terms of Werner's theory, the secondary valences of an atom *must* be satisfied. In the case of hexamminechromium(III) chloride, if a molecule of ammonia is driven out, one of the chloride ions will take its place to maintain the coordination number six. A wide variety of neutral groups or negative ions can enter the coordination sphere. When these latter become coordinated, they cease to be ions, of course, and this is indicated by the suffix -o on their names or abbreviated names; thus, "cyano," "chloro," "nitro," and "hydroxo".

If a trivalent metal hexammine chloride loses one molecule of ammonia, one of the three chlorides loses its ionic properties, as has been pointed out. If a second molecule of ammonia is lost, a second chloride becomes nonionic[44]. What will happen if a third ammonia molecule is lost? According to

* When applied to the structure of crystals the term "coordination number" is given a somewhat different meaning; it refers to the number of atoms (or ions) which surround the atom (or ion) in question, and are at equal distances from it, no matter what the nature of the bond between them.

42. Werner, *Ber.*, **46**, 3674 (1913); **47**, 1964, 1978 (1914).
43. Werner, *Z. anorg. Chem.*, **3**, 267 (1893).
44. Jörgensen, *Z. anorg. Chem.*, **5**, 147 (1894).

Jörgensen's own statement[44], he had never considered this point, but it became very important, for his theory and Werner's predicted different behaviors. According to the coordination theory, the third chloride should become nonionic, and a nonelectrolytic molecule should result. Jörgensen had to assume that his postulated ammonia chain would simply be shortened by one nitrogen atom, which would still leave the chloride in the ionic state. Very few triammines of trivalent metals were known at that time, and when Werner pointed out[43] that their properties supported his own theory, Jörgensen objected[44] that the compounds were not sufficiently understood to justify the conclusion.

One of these compounds, $Ir(NH_3)_3Cl_3$, had been described by Palmaer[45], who found that it did not liberate hydrochloric acid when heated with concentrated sulfuric acid. He suggested that it had twice the simplest formula, and was a double salt, $Ir(NH_3)_6Cl_3 \cdot IrCl_3$. Jörgensen showed that a corresponding rhodium double salt could be prepared from the components, and that it did not liberate hydrogen chloride when warmed with sulfuric acid. He pointed out also that Magnus' salt $Pt(NH_3)_4Cl_2 \cdot PtCl_2*$ is resistant to concentrated sulfuric acid, and concluded that this reagent cannot be relied upon to indicate the presence of ionic chlorine.

The other example cited by Werner was Erdmann's $Co(NH_3)_3(NO_2)_3$[46], which was admittedly not a well characterized compound[47]. Several substances of the same composition had been discovered, and Erdmann's description of his compound was incomplete. Investigation of the compound convinced Jörgensen that it has the structure

$$
\begin{array}{l}
\quad\ NO_2 \\
\quad / \\
Co—NH_3—NO_2 \qquad . \\
\quad \backslash \\
\quad\ NH_3—NH_3—NO_2
\end{array}
$$

He converted it to the chloride, which however, contains one molecule of firmly held water; to this compound he assigned the structure

$$
\begin{array}{l}
\quad\ H_2O—Cl \\
\quad / \\
Co—NH_3—Cl \\
\quad \backslash \\
\quad\ NH_3—NH_3—Cl
\end{array}
$$

* We would now give these "double salts" the formulas $[Ir(NH_3)_6]$ $[IrCl_6]$ and $[Pt(NH_3)_4]$ $[PtCl_4]$, which indicate that they do not contain chloride ions.
45. Palmaer, Oefvers, af k. Vet. Acad. Förh, No. 6, 373 (1889); Ber., **22,** 15 (1889).
46. Erdmann, J. prakt. Chem., **97,** 412 (1866).
47. Gibbs, Proc. Amer. Acad., **10,** 16 (1875).

because all of the chlorine is precipitated at once by silver nitrate. This compound is readily converted to Erdmann's "trinitrite," which must then have the structure shown.

The two theories differ also in their predictions as to the result of the loss of another molecule of ammonia, with the production of a diammine. No such compounds were known and this was in accord with Werner's theory. To him, an ammonia molecule cannot be "lost"; it must be replaced by another group. Thus far in the process, the halide ions which accompany the complex have been able to carry out this replacement, but now a new group must be supplied. If this be a negative ion, it will give the complex a negative charge. Reinecke's salt, $NH_4[Cr(NH_3)_2(SCN)_4]$[48] and Erdmann's salt, $NH_4[Co(NH_3)_2(NO_2)_4]$[49] * are examples of this type of compound. There were no examples of the monoammonates, $M_2'[M'''NH_3X_5]$, predicted by Werner, but numerous examples of the final step in the replacement were known; e.g., the heavy metal cyanides, the cobaltinitrites, and the double chlorides.

The tetravalent elements furnish a similar series. Platinum(IV) chloride yields ammines containing six, five, four, three, two, and one molecules of ammonia. All the chloride is readily removed from the first of these. Blomstrand[15] had observed that two of the four chlorine atoms in the tetrammonate are much less reactive than the other two. There are two isomeric forms of the diammonate, which therefore elicited great interest. In accordance with the demands of Werner's theory, both of these are nonionic. The end member of the series is potassium hexachloroplatinate(IV), which does not react with silver nitrate to give silver chloride, but gives silver chloroplatinate, $Ag_2[PtCl_6]$.

Conductivity Studies

To give further support to these views, Werner and Miolati measured the conductivities of a large number of metal ammines[50]. Again, the results seemed to substantiate the coordination theory, but Emil Petersen[51] raised objections to this conclusion. The number of ions found was in some cases greater than predicted by the theory. A case in point is $Co(NH_3)_3(NO_2)_2Cl$, which the theory demands must be a nonelectrolyte, but which showed the conductivity of a uni-univalent electrolyte. Werner explained this by assuming the reaction $[Co(NH_3)_3(NO_2)_2Cl] + H_2O \rightarrow [CO(NH_3)_3(NO_2)_2H_2O]Cl$,

* Erdmann's salt is not to be confused with Erdmann's trinitrotriamminecobalt (III), mentioned above.
48. Reinecke, *Ann.*, **126,** 113 (1863).
49. Erdmann, *J. prakt. Chem.*, **97,** 406 (1866).
50. Werner and Miolati, *Z. physik. Chem.*, **12,** 35 (1893); **14,** 506 (1894); **21,** 225 (1896).
51. Petersen, *Z. physik. Chem.*, **22,** 410 (1897).

TABLE 2.1. EFFECT OF AGING ON THE MOLAR CONDUCTIVITY OF AN AQUEOUS SOLUTION
OF $[Co(NH_3)_4Br_2]Br$
(Molar Concentration, 0.2%)

	$\mu =$
Freshly prepared solution	190.6
5 minutes after the first measurement	288.0
10 minutes after the first measurement	325.5
15 minutes after the first measurement	340.7
20 minutes after the first measurement	347.8
40 minutes after the first measurement	363.5

and supported this by the fact that at 0°C, where the hydration reaction cannot proceed readily, the conductivity is indeed very low. Petersen countered by pointing out that all salts show much lower conductivities at 0° than at 25°C.

Werner and Miolati reported several instances of this kind, and in some of them, had good evidence that reaction with the water does take place. The dark green $Co(NH_3)_4Br_3$ dissolves to give a deep green solution, which rapidly becomes red. At the same time, the conductivity rises, as shown in Table 2.1. It seems to approach that of the diaquotetrammine salt (see Table 2.2), which is bright red. Werner and Miolati wrote the equation:

$$[Co(NH_3)_4Br_2]Br + 2H_2O \rightarrow [Co(NH_3)_4(H_2O)_2]Br_3$$

The "dichro" salt, $Co(NH_3)_3(H_2O)Cl_3$ gave similar results, the solution turning from green through blue to violet;

$$[Co(NH_3)_3(H_2O)Cl_2]Cl + 2H_2O \rightarrow [Co(NH_3)_3(H_2O)_3]Cl_3 .$$

This reaction proceeds so rapidly at room temperature that Werner and Miolati made their conductivity studies at 1°C. The molecular conductivity was compared with those of potassium chloride, barium chloride, and hexamminecobalt(III) chloride at the same temperature, and found to correspond to that of the first; in other words, the salt is composed of two ions.

With those compounds which do not contain readily displaced groups in the coordination sphere, Werner and Miolati obtained results entirely in accord with their expectations. Many of their results are elegantly shown in graphical form in the second paper of their series, and two are reproduced in Figs. 2.1 and 2.2. The conductivities of aquoammine salts are significant in that they support Werner's contention that water molecules and ammonia molecules occupy equivalent positions in the coordination sphere. Some of these are shown in Table 2.2. Petersen[51] repeated some of this work,

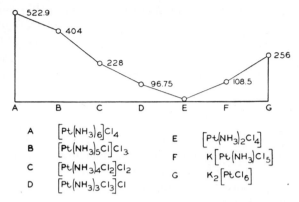

A	$\left[Pt(NH_3)_6\right]Cl_4$
B	$\left[Pt(NH_3)_5Cl\right]Cl_3$
C	$\left[Pt(NH_3)_4Cl_2\right]Cl_2$
D	$\left[Pt(NH_3)_3Cl_3\right]Cl$

E	$\left[Pt(NH_3)_2Cl_4\right]$
F	$K\left[Pt(NH_3)Cl_5\right]$
G	$K_2\left[PtCl_6\right]$

FIG. 2.1. The molar conductivities of 0.1 molar per cent aqueous solutions of some platinum (IV) ammines.*

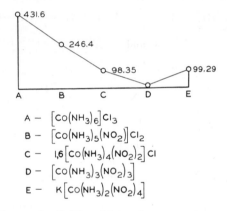

A — $\left[Co(NH_3)_6\right]Cl_3$

B — $\left[Co(NH_3)_5(NO_2)\right]Cl_2$

C — $1,6\left[Co(NH_3)_4(NO_2)_2\right]Cl$

D — $\left[Co(NH_3)_3(NO_2)_3\right]$

E — $K\left[Co(NH_3)_2(NO_2)_4\right]$

FIG. 2.2. The molar conductivities of 0.1 molar per cent aqueous solutions of some cobalt (III) ammines.

TABLE 2.2. MOLAR CONDUCTIVITIES OF SOME COBALT(III) AMMINES AT VARIOUS DILUTIONS

(25°C)

V (liters)	[Co(NH₃)₆]Br₃	[Co(NH₃)₅(H₂O)]Br₃	[Co(NH₃)₄(H₂O)₂]Br₃	[Co(NH₃)₅NO₂](NO₂)₂	[Co(NH₃)₄CO₃]Br
125	343.8	333.6	325.5	—	98.58
250	378.0	365.4	354.8	206.1	101.3
500	401.6	390.3	379.8	225.1	103.5
1000	426.9	412.9	399.5	234.4	106.0
2000	442.2	436.4	417.4	242.8	111.8

* The value for [Pt(NH₃)₅Cl]Cl₃ was not given in the original paper, but has since been determined by Tschugaeff and Wladimiroff: *Compt. rend.*, **160**, 840 (1915).

and his results agree with those of Werner and Miolati. Particularly interesting is his value for the molecular conductivity of $Co(NH_3)_3(NO_2)_3$ (8.4 at a dilution of 800 liters at 25°C) which fully confirms that of Werner and Miolati, and clearly shows the compound to be nonionic. Petersen also attempted to determine the number of ions formed from many of the metal ammonia compounds by measuring the freezing points of their solutions. The results did not agree in all cases with those obtained from the conductivity studies. They did not support Jörgensen's beliefs any better than they did Werner's, but they were used[52] to discredit the conductivity method, upon which Werner's crucial experiments rested.

The coordination theory handles metals of coordination number four just as it does those of coordination number six, and one example will suffice: Platinum(II) chloride forms ammines with two, three, and four molecules of ammonia. The first of these is especially interesting, because two isomeric forms exist. The Blomstrand-Jörgensen theory supposed these to be

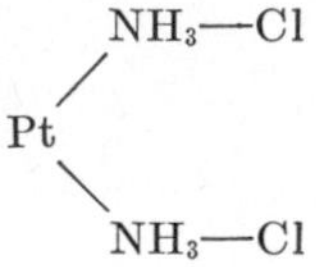

$$
\begin{array}{ccc}
& NH_3{-}Cl & NH_3{-}NH_3{-}Cl \\
& \diagup & \diagup \\
Pt & \quad\quad \text{and} \quad\quad Pt & \\
& \diagdown & \diagdown \\
& NH_3{-}Cl & Cl \\
& (I) & (II)
\end{array}
$$

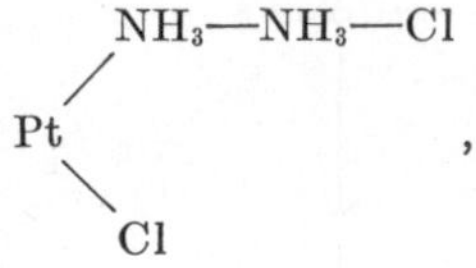

whereas, according to the coordination theory they are stereoisomeric forms ro $[Pt(NH_3)_2Cl_2]$. The older theory would postulate that form (I) can liberate two chloride ions whereas form (II) can liberate only one, but the coordination theory allows no ionization in either case. As far as form (II) is concerned, the data of Table 2.3 clearly support the latter contention.

TABLE 2.3. EFFECT OF AGING ON THE MOLAR CONDUCTIVITY OF AN AQUEOUS SOLUTION OF "PLATOSEMIDIAMMINCHLORID"
(Molar Concentration, 0.1%)

	$\mu =$
Freshly prepared solution	1.17
2 minutes after first measurement	1.81
4 minutes after first measurement	2.41
10 minutes after first measurement	2.61
15 minutes after first measurement	4.33
30 minutes after first measurement	11.03
180 minutes after first measurement	21.87

Form (I), (the "platosamminchlorid"), goes into solution very slowly, and then only with warming, so it was possible to measure the conductivity only after some reaction with the water had taken place. The molar con-

52. Jörgensen, *Z. anorg. Chem.*, **14**, 404 (1897); **19**, 132 (1899).

ductivity, at 25°C and for a 0.1 molar per cent solution, was found to be 22.42. Platinum(II) chloride does not form a monammine, but the compound $K[PtCl_3 \cdot NH_3]$ takes its place in the series. Potassium tetrachloroplatinate(II) represents the complete replacement of ammonia by the chloride ion.

His views on the ion forming properties of the metal ammines thus overthrown, Jörgensen turned his attack on the coordination theory to Werner's postulate that all of the coordinated groups occupy equivalent positions in the complex[53]. He cited several reactions of the hexammines to indicate that four of the ammonia molecules are attached to the metal ion more firmly than the other two. Thus, the aquopentamminecobalt(III) salts, on heating with ammonium carbonate, give carbonatotetrammine salts, and the nitropentammines give dinitrotetrammines when treated with sodium nitrite. In neither case is more ammonia readily removed.

Jörgensen felt also that the reactions of $Co(NH_3)_3(NO_2)_3$ and "croceo" dinitrotetrammine salts indicate that all of the nitro groups are not held to the cobalt in the same way. In each case, the action of hydrochloric acid eliminates one nitro group more readily than the others. Werner had assumed the existence of nitro ($-NO_2$) and nitrito ($-ONO$) groups (in agreement with Jörgensen) to explain the existence of isomeric salts of the composition $Co(NH_3)_5NO_2X_2$. Why, then, argued Jörgensen, does he assume that the "flavo" and "croceo" salts must be stereoisomers rather than structural isomers? If the "croceo" compounds are *trans*-dinitro salts as Werner suggested, the two nitro groups will show identical chemical reactions. In reality, they do not. One of them resembles the nitrous group of the "isoxantho" (nitritopentammine) compounds, and is readily liberated by dilute acids; the other is not attacked.

Jörgensen also found fault with Werner's theory because it predicted the existence of many compounds which were then unknown. Most important among these were the "violeo" (*cis*) dichlorotetramminecobalt(III) salts, which might be expected to be formed upon replacement of the nitro groups of "flavo" (*cis*) dinitrotetrammine compounds by chloride. Such replacement can be effected by the action of dilute hydrochloric acid, but "praseo" salts, rather than "violeo", are formed. Jörgensen called upon Werner, not only to explain the nonexistence of the "violeo" salts, but also the rearrangements which the coordination theory implied in this and similar reactions. Jörgensen also pointed out that many compounds exist which Werner's theory does not satisfactorily explain. Commonest of these are the hydrates, many of which contain more than six molecules of water. Werner's assumption of double water molecules, H_4O_2, was without ex-

53. Jörgensen, *Z. anorg. Chem.*, **19**, 109 (1899).

perimental support, and could explain only a small fraction of the examples known.

Finally, Jörgensen[53] criticized the suggestion that the entrance of a negative group into the complex ion should lower the valence of the complex. In support of his criticism, he quoted Werner to the effect that "the coordinated groups do not change the valence of the metal atom." He argued that if this negative group still saturates one of the primary valences of the metal, it cannot be coordinated.

While some of these criticisms were obviously not well founded, others were thoroughly sound, and challenged Werner's ingenuity and experimental skill to the utmost. Many of the missing compounds were discovered, among them the crucial "violeo" cobalt salts[54]; a theory of rearrangements was devised[55]; the relationship between the primary and secondary valences was clarified[42]; and the octahedral structure of the hexacoordinated complexes was firmly established by the resolution of many compounds into their optical antipodes. The coordination theory, as originally devised, was supported in almost every particular.

54. Werner, *Ber.*, **40,** 4817 (1907).
55. Werner, *Ann.*, **386,** 1 (1912).

3. Modern Developments—The Electrostatic Theory of Coordination Compounds

Robert W. Parry

University of Michigan, Ann Arbor, Michigan

and

Raymond N. Keller

University of Colorado, Boulder, Colorado

Although Werner's ideas regarding the stereochemistry of complex compounds were well substantiated by experiment, widespread dissatisfaction with his postulates of primary and secondary valences served as a strong deterrent to the general acceptance of his entire theory even as late as 1916[1]. Since data available to Werner did not always permit a sound differentiation between the assumed valence types, the coordination theory led to the prediction of a variety of unusual valence states for many common metals. It was justly held that such a theory led to confusion, and Werner's postulates concerning primary and secondary valence bonds were called vague and unfounded[1, 2].

It was not until the development of the electronic theory of valence by Lewis, Kossel, Langmuir, Sidgwick, Fajans, Pauling and others that a self-consistent explanation of valence types evolved. The models which were developed for the electronic theory were so successful in resolving the confusion surrounding the ideas of primary and secondary valence that almost general acceptance of Werner's views soon followed the work of Lewis and his contemporaries.

Modern x-ray diffraction data have now provided unequivocal experimental support for Werner's ideas on stereochemistry. In addition, quantum

1. Friend, *J. Chem. Soc.*, **93**, 260, 1006 (1908); **109**, 715 (1916); **119**, 1040 (1921).
2. Briggs, *J. Chem. Soc.*, **93**, 1564 (1908); *Proc. Chem Soc.*, **24**, 94 (1908); Jorgensen, *Z. phys. chem.*, **144**, 187 (1929); Pfeiffer, *Z. anorg. allgem. Chem.* **112**, 81 (1920); Povarnin, *J. Russ. Phys. Chem. Soc.* **47**, 217, 501, 989 (1915); cf. *Chem. Abs.* **10**, 138 (1916).

mechanics now provides the framework for a more detailed solution of valence problems. Unfortunately, the quantum mechanical approach is extremely complex unless many simplifying assumptions are made; as a result, the simple molecular models suggested by Lewis, Kossel, and others are still of fundamental importance in correlating fact and theory.

THE ELECTROSTATIC MODEL

The Charge-size Ratio

According to the viewpoint first clearly developed by Kossel[3], complexes are held together by the electrostatic* attraction between oppositely charged ions or between ions and dipolar molecules. For example, the fluoroborate ion, $(BF_4)^-$, can be pictured as a triply charged central boron ion to which four fluoride ions are symmetrically bound by electrostatic forces. The hydrated calcium ion, $[Ca(H_2O)_6]^{++}$, may be pictured as a central calcium cation to which six water dipoles are electrostatically bound with octahedral symmetry. Complex ammines, halides, hydrates, and many other compounds may be represented in a similar manner. From considerations of elementary electrostatics, Kossel suggested that those metal ions with high ionic charge† and small ionic radius would form coordination compounds of greatest stability. De[5] pointed out, apparently independently, that the metals whose ions have the highest coordinating ability are those of small atomic volume (and thus of small ionic radius), such as Cr, Fe, Co, Ni, Cu, Ru, Rh, Pd, Os, Ir, Pt, and Au. Since ionic charge and ionic size have opposite effects in determining the electrostatic field of an ion, Cartledge[6] suggested a single arbitrary parameter called the ionic potential, which is defined as the charge of the ion divided by its crystal radius in Ångstrom units. In general, coordinating ability increases with an increase in the ionic potential of the central ion, although a number of qualitative exceptions, such as the high relative stability of the complexes of Hg^{++} and

---

* Electrostatic interaction was implied by earlier workers[2d, 4] but never developed.

† In general, the stability of ammines frequently does increase with increasing charge on the central ion, but this is not always so as is shown by the fact that $FeCl_2 \cdot 6NH_3$ is more stable than $FeCl_3 \cdot 6NH_3$.

3. Kossel, *Z. Elektrochem.*, **26**, 314 (1920); *Z. Phys.*, **1**, 395 (1920); *Naturwissenschaften*, **7**, 339, 360 (1919); **11**, 598 (1923); *Ann. Phys.*, **49**, 229 (1916).

4. Nelson and Falk, *J. Am. Chem. Soc.*, **37**, 274 (1915).

5. De, *J. Chem. Soc.*, **115**, 127 (1919).

6. Cartledge, *J. Am. Chem. Soc.*, **50**, 2855, 2863 (1928); **52**, 3076 (1930); *J. Phys. Colloid Chem.* **55**, 248 (1951).

7. Bjerrum, "Metal Ammine Formation in Aqueous Solution," pp. 75, 87. P. Hasse and Son, Copenhagen, 1941; Irving and Williams, *J. Chem. Soc.*, **1953**, 3202; Bjerrum, *Chem. Revs.*, **46**, 381 (1950).

Cu^+, are known. As early as 1928 Fajans[8] pointed out that the concepts of ion deformation and interpenetration must be used along with any ionic model in order to obtain reasonable agreement between fact and theory. The problem is considered under polarization (see page 125). More recently Irving and Williams[7b] have demonstrated in a most convincing manner that the ionic potential alone is not adequate as a parameter for the estimation of complex stability constants.

Acid-base Phenomena in Coordination Compounds

An extension of the charge-size ratio principle to the hydrolysis of the ions of the first two periods of the periodic table permitted Kossel to treat aqueous acid-base phenomena as a natural consequence of the coordination theory. (See references 3c, 3d, 6, 9 and Chapter 12 for a more thorough treatment of this topic.) This viewpoint readily justifies the acid character of the complex ion, $[Pt(NH_3)_6]^{4+}$ and is effective in explaining acid-base behavior in nonaqueous solvents.*

POLARIZATION AS A FACTOR IN THE IONIC MODEL

Nature of Polarization

Many of the early energy calculations based on the electrostatic model had two rather serious limitations. No provision was made for energy changes involved in lattice expansion or in solution processes; only interaction energy between ion and ligand was considered. Secondly, the existence of rigid, spherically symmetrical ions or molecules was assumed (i.e., the ionic potential was considered as a suitable differentiating parameter). Actually, the electronic clouds of each atom or ion are deformed by the fields which are set up by neighboring ions or dipolar molecules.†

This deformation of ions is related to their polarization. The amount of distortion is determined by the strength of the distorting field and by the

---

* The ideas expressed by Kossel were anticipated to some extent in 1899 by Abegg and Bodlander[10] who discussed the factors influencing coordination. They noted that certain weak bases, such as $Co_2O_3 \cdot H_2O$ become strong bases when coordinated to form complexes such as $[Co(NH_3)_6](OH)_3$,[11] and that weak acids such as HCN form strong acids when coordinated to metal ions, as is illustrated by $H_3[Fe(CN)_6]$.[12]

† The inaccuracy of the approximation of rigid ions was mentioned by Kossel,[3d, 13] but not considered as a major factor in compound stability.

8. Fajans, *Z. Krist.*, **A66**, 321 (1928).

9. Foster, *J. Chem. Ed.*, **17**, 509 (1940).

10. Abegg and Bodlander, *Z. anorg. Chem.*, **20**, 453 (1899).

11. Lamb and Yngve, *J. Am. Chem. Soc.*, **43**, 2352 (1921).

12. Brigando, *Compt. rend.*, **208**, 197 (1939); Ray and Dutt, *Z. anorg. allgem. Chem.*, **234**, 65 (1937).

13. Kossel, *Naturwissenschaften*, **12**, 703 (1924).

magnitude of the force binding the electron cloud to the atomic nucleus. If the electrons are tightly bound (low polarizability), little distortion occurs. If they are loosely bound (large polarizability), the ion may be seriously deformed from its spherical symmetry.

Polarization as a factor in binding forces was first suggested by Haber[14] in 1919 and independently by Debye[15] in 1920. The development of the concept and its applications to chemical theory were due largely to Fajans. Some attempt was also made to apply the idea to structural problems. Hund[16] and Heisenberg[17] used the ideas of polarization to account for the fact that the water molecule is angular instead of linear, as the concept of rigid spherical ions would suggest[18]. The effects of polarization have been reviewed by Fajans[19], Clark[20], and Debye[18]. Quantitative data on the polarizability (deformability) of various ions as measured by their molar refraction were reported by Fajans and Joos[22] and others[21, 23, 24, 25]. These data in the hands of Fajans permitted the modification of the original ionic model to correct for deformation effects. The modified ionic model has been used to correlate both the chemical and physical properties of complexes.

Chemical Properties and the Polarization Model

Stability of Ammines and Hydrates. It is a well known fact that cations such as those of the alkalies and the alkaline earths do not form stable ammonia complexes in water solution. In aqueous solution the hydrate is far more stable than the ammine. For these cations, the metal ion-ammonia bond in solution is weaker than the metal ion-water bond. On the other hand, cations such as copper(II), silver(I), cadmium(II), and zinc(II), which are found in Periodic Groups IB and IIB, form ammine complexes which are much more stable in aqueous solution than are the hydrated ions. For these metals, the metal-ammonia bond is significantly stronger than the metal-water bond. It is also interesting that the coordinating ability of

14. Haber, *Verhandl. deut. physik. Ges.*, **21**, 750 (1919).
15. Debye, *Z. Phys.*, **21**, 178 (1920); **22**, 30 (1921).
16. Hund, *Z. Phys.*, **31**, 81 (1925); **32**, 1 (1925).
17. Heisenberg, *Z. Phys.*, **26**, 196 (1924).
18. Debye, "Polar Molecules," p. 63, New York, The Chemical Catalog Co., Inc. (Reinhold Publishing Corp.), 1929.
19. Fajans, "Radioelements and Isotopes—Chemical Forces," pp. 63 and 76, New York, McGraw-Hill Book Company, 1931.
20. Clark, "The Fine Structure of Matter," Vol. II, Part II, p. 405, "Molecular Polarization," New York, John Wiley & Sons, Inc., 1938.
21. Wasastjerna, *Z. Phys. Chem.*, **101**, 193 (1922).
22. Fajans and Joos, *Z. Phys.*, **23**, 1 (1924).
23. Born and Heisenberg, *Z. Phys.*, **23**, 388 (1924).
24. Mayer and Mayer, *Phys. Rev.*, **43**, 610 (1933).
25. Bauer and Fajans, *J. Am. Chem. Soc.*, **64**, 3023 (1942).

many metal cations with amines varies in the order NH_3 equal to or greater than a primary amine $>$ secondary $>$ tertiary amine,* while the coordinating ability of the phosphines appears to *increase* in the order phosphine to trisubstituted phosphine[26].

The elements oxygen and sulfur in Group VI show relations similar to those observed for the Group V elements. Coordinating ability decreases in the series water, alcohol, ether in a manner analogous to the decrease on going from ammonia to the tertiary amines. On the other hand, coordinating ability increases in the series hydrogen sulfide, mercaptans, thioethers, just as in the case of the phosphines and substituted phosphines. In short, alkyl substitution on the first short period elements, oxygen and nitrogen, decreases their coordinating ability, while alkyl substitution on the second short period elements, sulfur and phosphorus, increases their coordinating ability. While one is probably not justified in claiming that such generalizations are completely explained by the electrostatic-polarization treatment, it is significant that the treatment permits a good correlation between the stability of some of the complexes and certain fundamental properties of the coordinated groups and metal ions.

The fact that some ions coordinate with ammonia more strongly than with water while others coordinate with water in preference to ammonia has been treated by a number of different investigators,[27, 28] using the electrostatic model. Verwey[28d] first recognized that the attraction between an ion and a molecule will depend upon the strength of the electrostatic field around the central cation and upon the total dipole moment of the coordinated molecule. In turn, the total dipole moment of the coordinated group depends upon its permanent dipole moment, P, and upon the induced moment, p'.†
(Total Moment $= P + p'$). The moment induced in a given molecule (p') is determined by the strength of the inducing electrostatic field, E, and the electronic polarizability, α, of the molecule (Total Moment $= P + p' =$

---

* Sidgwick[26a] pointed out that in general the ability to coordinate decreases in the order NH_3, NH_2R, NHR_2, NR_3, but the rule is not inviolate. In the case of $SnCl_4$, all amines coordinate almost equally well. For the iron(III) ion, data are uncertain, but the trend seems to be reversed. Useful data are limited in number.

† The energy for such a system is approximated by the expression $\pi = E\left(P + \dfrac{\alpha E}{2}\right)$ where the factor $\frac{1}{2}$ in the second term compensates for energy expended in inducing the dipole.

26. Sidgwick, *J. Chem. Soc.*, **1941**, 433; Hertel, *Z. anorg. Chem.*, **178**, 200 (1929); Carlson, McReynolds, and Verhoek, *J. Am. Chem. Soc.*, **67**, 1336 (1945); Spike and Parry, *J. Am. Chem. Soc.*, **75**, 2726 (1953).
27. Van Arkel and de Boer, *Rec. trav. chim.*, **47**, 593 (1928).
28. Garrick, *Phil. Mag.*, [7] **9**, 131 (1930); [7], **10**, 76 (1930); (b) [7] **11**, 741 (1931); (c) Magnus, *Z. Phys.*, **23**, 241 (1922); (d) Verwey, *Chem. Weekblad.*, **25**, 250 (1928).

$P + \alpha E$). While water has a higher permanent dipole than ammonia, ammonia has a much higher polarizability which gives a higher induced dipole under the same conditions. Thus the total dipole of the ammonia, $(P + \alpha E)$, in a strong field may easily exceed the total dipole moment of the water molecule in the same field. This line of reasoning then suggests that for inert gas type ions of low charge and large size (small external field, E) water will coordinate more strongly because the induced dipole contribution is small, while for smaller central ions with greater external fields (i.e., greater polarizing power), ammonia will coordinate more easily.

A semiquantitative electrostatic treatment of hydrate and ammine formation by Van Arkel and De Boer[27] suggested that for univalent, noble gas type ions, which are larger than the lithium ion, the hydrate should be more stable than the ammine; for the lithium ion, they should be about equally stable; and for smaller ions of higher field strength than lithium, the ammine should be the more stable. These predictions are in agreement with fact. Bjerrum[7a] was unable to detect any potassium ammine formation in aqueous solution, but the lithium ion forms detectable amounts of ammine complexes in solutions containing ammonia at concentrations above one normal[7a].* In addition, the heat of reaction between lithium bromide and two moles of gaseous ammonia is 12.7 kcal, while that for lithium bromide with two moles of gaseous water is 15.3 kcal. The difference of 2.6 kcal is small and in favor of greater hydrate stability. On the other hand, the small doubly charged beryllium ion forms a much more stable ammine, as is suggested by comparing the heats of reaction for the processes:

$$BeCl_{2(s)} + 4NH_{3(g)} \rightarrow Be(NH_3)_4Cl_{2(s)} + 34.1 \text{ kcal}$$

$$BeCl_{2(s)} + 4H_2O_{(g)} \rightarrow Be(H_2O)_4Cl_{2(s)} + 20.8 \text{ kcal}$$

The behavior of the very small hydrogen ion is in accord with this principle, since it forms an ammine which is much more stable, NH_4^+, than the corresponding hydrate, H_3O^+.

The importance of ion type (i.e., inert gas, palladium, or transition types) in determining field strength around the metal ion must not be overlooked in the electrostatic treatment. Although copper(I) and sodium ions have approximately the same charge-size ratio, the palladium-type copper(I) ion has a much stronger field than the inert gas-type sodium ion. (The ionization potential of sodium is 5.14 ev, that of copper is 7.72.) Failure to recognize this fact has led to unwarranted criticism of the electrostatic approach. The existence of stable ammines of silver(I), copper(I), zinc(II), cad-

---

* It should be noted that this relationship may be obscured if the field is strong enough to force a proton from the water to form a hydroxide ion, [i.e., $B(OH)_3$ forms instead of a complex $B(OH_2)_3^{+++}$].

mium(II), copper(II), and other related ions in water solution seems reasonable, if ion type is considered, since the dipole moment induced in the polarizable ammonia molecule by the strong field of the metal ions more than compensates for the difference between the permanent dipoles of water and ammonia.

Representation of the greater field strength around palladium- and transition-type ions in terms of any physical model is difficult; however, a rather crude illustration may be obtained if the 18 electron shell of the palladium and transition types of ions is regarded as being softer and hence more easily deformed and penetrated than the inert gas type shell. The ease of such deformation is related to the polarizability of the central ion. The silver ion is much more easily polarized than the potassium ion of supposedly equal size[19, 30, 31]. The role of polarization and interpenetration in complex formation may be illustrated by the following drawings which were first suggested by Fajans (Fig. 3.1). In Fig. 3.1A no deformation of either

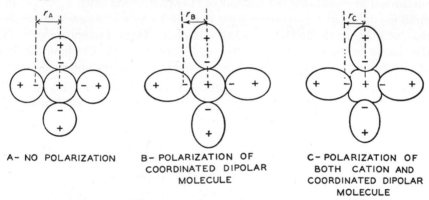

A- NO POLARIZATION   B- POLARIZATION OF COORDINATED DIPOLAR MOLECULE   C- POLARIZATION OF BOTH CATION AND COORDINATED DIPOLAR MOLECULE

FIG. 3.1. The role of deformation in coordination

the cation or dipolar molecule has occurred and the charges are separated by the distance r_A ; in Fig. 3.1B the coordinated groups have been deformed and the negative pole of the groups is pulled in toward the positive cation. In this case, the distance between the positive and negative charges, r_B , is shorter than the distance r_A (Fig. 3.1A) and the resulting potential energy of the system is reduced, giving a greater stability. In Fig. 3.1C both the central ion and the coordinated groups have been deformed, producing a

30. Pauling, "Nature of the Chemical Bond," p. 376, Ithaca, New York, Cornell University Press, 1942.
31. Fajans, *Ceramic Age*, **54**, 288 (1949).

still smaller distance of separation, r_C ; case C represents the most stable bond.*

As the positive charge on the central cation increases, its polarizability decreases. As a result, cation polarizability and deformability are of greatest importance in ions of low charge. Cation deformability and ion size are of major importance in differentiating the A and B subgroups of the periodic table. The A group ions, with 8 outer electrons, are not deformed easily, while the B type ions, with 18 outer electrons, are more easily deformed and penetrated. Since deformation differences are most pronounced with cations of low valence, subgroups IA and IB of the periodic table exhibit the most startling contrasts in behavior. The differences diminish as the charges on the ions increase. As a result, tetravalent ions of *both* Groups IV A and IV B are of low deformability and are very similar in their complexing properties.

The above discussion suggests at least five major factors which must be considered in estimating the amount of energy released when a *free gaseous metal ion* unites with a *gaseous dipolar molecule* to form a *free gaseous complex ion* (i.e., $Ag^+_{(g)} + 2NH_{3(g)} \rightarrow [Ag(NH_3)_2]^+_{(g)}$. These factors include: (1) the charge and size of the central ion (ionic potential); (2) the deformability of the central ion, which is in turn determined by the electronic structure of

---

* Van Arkel and de Boer[27] used the following equation to represent the phenomenon in C. Situation A is represented by omission of terms 2, 3, 4, and 5, while B is represented by omission of terms 3 and 5.

$$\pi = \frac{-eP}{r^2} - \frac{ep'}{r^2} - \frac{2(P + p')P_A}{r^3} + \frac{(p')^2}{2\alpha} + \frac{P_A^2}{2\alpha_A}$$

where π = the potential energy of the gaseous complex ion.

e = the charge on the electron.

P = permanent dipole moment of the coordinated molecule.

p' = the additional dipole moment induced in the coordinated molecule.

r = the distance between the center of the central ion and the center of the dipole of the coordinated molecule.

α = polarizability of the coordinated molecule.

P_A = the dipole or quadripole moment induced in the central metal ion.

α_A = the polarizability or ease of deformation of the central metal ion.

The first term in the expression represents the energy change due to interaction of the permanent dipole and the central ion; the second term, the energy change due to interaction of the induced dipole and the central cation; the third term, interaction between the induced dipole of the cation and the total dipole of the coordinated group; while the fourth and fifth terms represent the energy required to polarize the coordinated molecule and the central cation, respectively.

TABLE 3.1. SOME PHYSICAL PROPERTIES OF AMMONIA, PHOSPHINE, AND ARSINE

Molecule	Dipole Moment (e.s.u.)	H-X Distance	H-X-H Angle	Ht. of Pyramid (Å)	Polarizability $\times 10^{24}$ (α)
NH_3	1.46×10^{-18} [a,b]	1.016Å[a]	$108°$ [a]	3.60[a]	$.22$[b]
PH_3	0.55×10^{-18} [b]	1.46Å[c]	$99°$ [c]	0.67[c]	$.48$[b]
AsH_3	0.16×10^{-18} [b]	1.523Å[d]	$91° 34'$ [d]	0.93[e]	$.58$[b]

[a] Martin, *J. Phys. Colloid Chem.*, **51**, 1400 (1947).

[b] Maryott and Buckley, "Table of Dielectric Constants and Electric Dipole Moments," Natl. Bur. Stats. Circular 537 (1953).

[c] Pauling, *J. Chem. Soc.*, **1948**, 1461; "Valence Commemoratiff Victor Henri, Liege, 1947.

[d] Nielsen, *J. Chem. Phys.*, **20**, 1955 (1952).

[e] Meisenheimer, *Z. Phys. Chem.*, **97**, 304 (1921).

the ion (i.e., inert gas, palladium, or transition type); (3) the magnitude of the permanent dipole in the coordinated molecule; (4) the polarizability of the group to be coordinated (this is important in determining the size of the induced dipole); and (5) the size of the group being coordinated (this influences the distance between the central ion and the center of negative charge in the coordinated group). If a charged ion is being coordinated instead of a dipolar molecule, the charge on the ion will also be important.

Coordination Compounds of Phosphine and Hydrogen Sulfide. Experimentally, it is found that phosphine coordinates much less strongly than ammonia with all of the metal ions which have been studied. This[20] is not unexpected since phosphine has a much smaller permanent dipole moment and a larger central atom than ammonia. Comparative data for ammonia, phosphine, and arsine are cited in Table 3.1. Although the polarizability of the phosphine molecule is twice as large as that of ammonia, the magnitude of the induced dipole is not large enough to overcome the adverse effects of low permanent moment and large molecular size. Holtje and Schlegel[32] prepared the following phosphine complexes:

$CuCl \cdot 2PH_3$ $CuCl \cdot PH_3$ $AgI \cdot 0.5PH_3$

$CuBr \cdot 2PH_3$ $CuBr \cdot PH_3$ $AgI \cdot PH_3$

$CuI \cdot 2PH_3$ $CuI \cdot PH_3$ $AuI \cdot PH_3$

These were unstable as compared to the ammines. One would expect the most stable coordination compounds of phosphine with cations of high polarizing power such as Ag^+, or Hg^{++}. In such a case the induced dipole contribution would be relatively large.

Arsine, of smaller permanent moment (0.15×10^{-18} e.s.u.) than phosphine, coordinates with even greater difficulty, despite the fact that arsine is more polarizable.

32. Holtje and Schlegel, *Z. anorg. Allgem. Chem.*, **243**, 246 (1940).

Hydrogen sulfide bears the same relationship to water that phosphine bears to ammonia. Though hydrogen sulfide is more polarizable than water (refractivity: H_2O = 3.7 cc; H_2S = 9.5 cc[19]), the larger size and smaller permanent moment of the H_2S molecule (H_2O = 1.89 × 10^{-18} e.s.u.; H_2S = about 1.1 × 10^{-18} e.s.u.[20]) reduce its coordinating ability to a point below that of water for ions of low field strength. For ions of high field strength (Hg^{++}, Ag^+, etc.) the hydrogen sulfide coordinates and the protons are forced off to give insoluble metal sulfides.

Coordinating Ability of Alkyl Substituted Hydrides of Group V and Group VI Elements. The coordinating abilities of the alkyl and aromatic derivatives of ammonia, phosphine, water, and hydrogen sulfide also show a fairly good correlation with the permanent dipole moments of the molecules. The decrease in coordinating ability from water to alcohol to ether and from ammonia to primary amine to secondary amine to tertiary amine runs parallel to a decrease in the permanent dipole moment of the molecules. This is shown in Table 3.2. Polarizabilities, where available, are also included. The increase in the coordinating ability in the series H_2S, RHS, R_2S runs parallel to an increase in the dipole moment of the compounds. A similar relationship is noted for the phosphines. Very stable tertiary phosphine complexes have been described by many investigators[37] (see Chapter 1, p. 78).

In a similar manner, the fact that the cyclic tertiary amine, pyridine, coordinates more strongly than most other *tertiary amines* can be correlated with its higher dipole moment, which is even higher than that of ammonia (Table 3.2).

It will also be observed that the polarizability of the bonding electrons[33] (i.e., the electrons on the nitrogen or phosphorus atom) is decreased in all cases by alkyl substitution, but the per cent decrease in going from H_2O to R_2O is much greater (about 24 per cent) than the decrease in going from H_2S to R_2S (about 5 per cent). The per cent decrease in going from NH_3 to R_3N (about 12 per cent) is likewise greater than the per cent decrease in going from PH_3 to R_3P (about 5 per cent). From this it appears that the polarizability factor also favors the differences in relative stabilities outlined above.

33. Reference 34, p. 152.
34. Smyth, "Dielectric Constant and Molecular Structure," p. 192, New York, Chemical Catalog Co., Inc., (Reinhold Publishing Corp.), 1931.
35. Kodama and Parry, unpublished results.
36. Sidgwick, "The Electronic Theory of Valency," p. 152, London, Oxford University Press, 1927.
37. Mann and Purdie, *Chem. and Ind.*, **1935**, 814; Mann, Wells, and Purdie, *J. Chem. Soc.*, **1937**, 1828.

TABLE 3.2. MOLAR REFRACTIVITIES AND DIPOLE MOMENTS OF ALKYL SUBSTITUTED HYDRIDES

Molecule	Refractivity of (33) X in R-X-R	Permanent Dipole Moment × 10^{18} e.s.u.		Coordinating Ability
H_2O	3.7 cc	1.89 (20)	1	
CH_3OH	About 3.2 cc	1.68		
C_2H_5OH		1.69	2	Decrease ↓
n-C_3H_7OH		1.66		
$(CH_3)_2O$	About 2.8 cc	1.29		
$(C_2H_5)_2O$		1.15	3	
$(n$-$C_3H_7)_2O$		1.16		
H_2S	9.6 cc	1.1 (20)	3	
CH_3SH	About 9.4 cc	—		
C_2H_5SH		1.39	2	Decrease ↑
n-C_3H_7SH		1.33		
$(CH_3)_2S$	About 9.1 cc	1.40		
$(C_2H_5)_2S$		1.58	1	
$(n$-$C_3H_7)_2S$		1.55		
NH_3	5.6	1.49 (34)	1	
CH_3NH_2	About 5.1 cc	1.23		
$C_2H_5NH_2$		1.3	2	
$(CH_3)_2NH$	About 4.8	0.96		Decrease ↓
$(C_2H_5)_2NH$		1.20	3	
$(CH_3)_3N$	About 4.7 cc	0.6		
$(C_2H_5)_3N$		0.90	4	
$(C_6H_5)_3N$		0.26		
Pyridine	—	2.1	1	Unusual ability for *tert.* amine.
PH_3	About 11.9 cc	0.55	1	
CH_3PH_2				
$C_2H_5PH_2$	—	1.17 (35)	3	
n-$C_3H_7PH_2$				Decrease ↑
$(CH_3)_2PH$				
$(C_2H_5)_2PH$	—	1.4 (35)	2	
$(CH_3)_3P$				
$(C_6H_5)_3P$	About 11.3 cc	1.45 (36)	1	
$(C_2H_5)_3P$		1.45 (35)		

Instability Constants for Complexes and the Polarized Ionic Model

In 1953 Irving and Williams[7b] completed a most thorough analysis of essentially all the data available on the instability constants of complexes of dipositive ions of the transition metals of the first period. The order Mn < Fe < Co < Ni < Cu > Zn was found to hold for the stability of nearly all such complexes irrespective of the nature of the coordinated ligand or the number of ligand molecules involved. They demonstrated the failure of an electrostatic model which neglects polarization terms and showed that Pauling's theory[39] (Chapter 4) fails to account even qualitatively for the order of stability of metal complexes. On the other hand, they showed in a most convincing manner that the above Irving-Williams order of the transition metal (II) cations follows logically from considerations of the reciprocal of the ionic radii and the second ionization potentials of the metals concerned. It is apparent that these are the very parameters which are indicative of the electrostatic field strength of the cations of the transition metals involved. They point out that if attempts are made to introduce other cations such as Cd^{++} into the sequence, difficulties arise. This is readily understood as they describe, and can also be correlated with the fact that the cation polarizabilities (deformabilities) of the transition metal and palladium type ions differ; thus the order of stability would be dependent upon the ligand selected [i.e., compare treatment of ammines and hydrates of Na^+ and Ag^+ in which cation polarizabilities differ.] As noted by these authors, other factors such as steric hindrance and entropy terms must also be considered for a thorough analysis of complex stability.

Physical Properties of Complex Compounds and the Ionic Model

Color and Structure. The remarkable colors commonly associated with coordination compounds were attributed by Fajans[41] to a strong deformation of the electron clouds of the coordinated groups. This concept was amplified by Pitzer and Hildebrand[42]. Orgel[43] has recently considered the similarity in the spectra of Cr^{+++} and Co^{+++} as a consequence of the Stark splitting of the d levels by the strong crystal field. The crystal field theory is discussed in connection with magnetism and may yet provide a sound interpretation of the color of complex ions.*

39. Pauling, *J. Chem. Soc.*, **1948**, 1461; "Valence Commemoratiff Victor Henri, Liege, 1947.

41. Fajans, *Naturwissenschaften*, **11**, 165 (1923); Remarks to this paper, circulated privately, 1946.

42. Pitzer and Hildebrand, *J. Am. Chem. Soc.*, **63**, 2472 (1941).

43. Orgel, *J. Chem. Soc.*, **1952**, 4756.

* Note added in proof: In a recent series of papers from J. Bjerrum's laboratory, Bjerrum, Jörgensen and others have treated the color of complexes of Cu^{++}, etc., using an electrostatic model. *Acta. Chem. Scand.*, **8**, 1289 (1954); **9**, 116, 1362 (1955).

Stereochemistry and the Polarized Ionic Model. The rigid ionic model of Kossel leads to a linear molecule for coordination number two, a planar structure for coordination number three, a tetrahedral molecule for coordination number four, and a regular octahedron for coordination number six. Deviations from these forms have been attributed to polarization[16, 18]. Because of the success of the polarization treatment in justifying the stereochemistry of the water molecule, several attempts have been made to justify the planar structure of platinum(II) complexes on the basis of the large polarizability of the central platinum(II) ion[27].* Nekrasov[44] used polarization and the radius ratio to justify the planar structure. Values of the radius ratio below 0.41 supposedly favor a tetrahedral arrangement, while high polarizability of the coordinated ligand and values of the radius ratio greater than 0.41 presumably favor a planar arrangement.†

Tsuchida[45] and co-workers developed a stereochemical theory which might be considered as a compromise between the ionic model and the electron pair bond model. They considered that all coordination compounds are built up from ions, polar molecules, and stereochemically active electron pairs (or odd electrons in some cases). The shape of a molecule would then be determined by the most symmetrical grouping of these ligands around a cation. Walsh[46] has recently given a molecular orbital treatment to simpler molecules which leads essentially to the rules of Tsuchida, but without the ionic implications. According to Tsuchida, the charge of the cation would be equal to its position in the periodic table except for the transition elements, whose charge would be equal to the accepted oxidation state of the ion under consideration (i.e., Fe^{+++}). In such a scheme molecular shape would be determined by the number of coordinating groups (including stereochemically active electron pairs). The shapes proposed for different numbers of groups are: linear for 2; planar for 3, tetrahedral for 4; octahedral for 6, and cubic for 8.

Special attention was given to transition elements with a coordination number of four in planar arrangement. It was noted that such metals con-

---

* Cases of planar coordination have been experimentally established only for complexes in the solid states or in solution. Fajans has raised the interesting possibility that the planar arrangement may be due in part to electric field effects in the crystal or in solution. If so, a planar structure might not appear in the vapor state.

† The conclusions regarding radius ratio are the same as those advanced by Straubel and Hüttig in 1925. (p. 143, ref. 75 and 76).

44. Nekrasov, *J. Gen. Chem. U.S.S.R.*, **16**, 341 (1946); cf. *Chem. Abs.*, **41**, 633 (1947).
45. Tsuchida, *Bull. Chem. Soc. Japan*, **14**, 101 (1939); *J. Chem. Soc. Japan*, **60**, 245 (1939); *Rev. Phys. Chem. Japan*, **13**, 31 (1939); Tsuchida and Kobayashi, *Rev. Phys. Chem. Japan*, **13**, 61 (1939); Tsuchida, Kobayashi, and Kuroya, *Rev. Phys. Chem. Japan*, **13**, 151 (1939); Tsuchida, *Collected Papers Faculty Sci., Osaka Imp. Univ.* [C] 6, No. 35 (1938).
46. Walsh, *J. Chem. Soc.*, **1953**, 2260, 2266, 2288, 2296, 2306.

tain nearly full d levels (i.e., 8 electrons); hence, two pairs of electrons could become stereochemically active, one above and one below the plane to give an octahedral configuration instead of the apparent planar structure.* If the d-level contains less than four electrons, such coordination would be impossible and a tetrahedral structure would be mandatory. The basis for determining which electron pairs would be stereochemically active in planar complexes was never clearly defined although one could now make reasonable decisions on the basis of the crystal field splitting of the d levels[44].

Tsuchida's theory† is interesting in that it provides a simple empirical scheme for many stereochemical predictions, but it is unrealistic in its chemical implications. For example, attributing hydridic character to the hydrogens of water and ammonia is obviously unreasonable in view of the latent acid character of these two solvents.

The fundamental stereochemical ideas of Tsuchida without the accompanying chemical objections are embodied in the modern quanticule theory of Fajans[49]. The electron pair is retained as a coordination group in certain formulations but chemical contradictions are avoided. For example, water is considered as a polarized oxide ion with two imbedded protons. Ammonia is considered as a nitride ion with three imbedded protons. In both cases the correct geometry can be obtained, if polarizability of the anion is considered in a quantitative fashion[18]. Fajans also differentiates certain chemically recognizable groups as a single "quanticule" or group of atoms with common quantization. For example, the peroxide ion would represent a quanticule composed of two oxygen atoms with essentially molecular quantization of the electrons between them. In this respect and others, it has much in common with the qualitative aspects of the molecular orbital theory. The CH_3^- quanticule (ion) would be considered as a starting point for a polarization treatment of $[Pt(CH_3)_4]_4$ in order to avoid the problem of hexacovalent carbon (see p. 165). More detailed examples are given by Fajans.

Magnetism and the Polarized Ionic Model. It is a well known fact, widely used in spectroscopy, that the energy levels in an atom or ion will be altered by the presence of a magnetic or electrostatic field [Zeeman effect and Stark effect]. If the magnetic field is very strong, the spin and orbital vectors of angular momentum can no longer be combined to give the quantum number J, but each vector is space quantized independently to give inde-

---

* Others[47] have also raised this possibility.

† A set of empirical structural rules which utilize a stereochemically active electron pair was also proposed by Helferich.[48]

47. Sidgwick, *J. Chem. Soc.*, **123**, 730 (1923); Fowler, *Trans. Faraday Soc.*, **19**, 468 (1923); Sidgwick and Powell, *Proc. Roy. Soc. London*, **176A**, 159 (1940).

48. Helferich, *Z. Naturforsch*, **1**, 666 (1946); cf. *Chem. Abs.*, **41**, 6086 (1947).

49. Fajans, *Chem. Eng. News*, **27**, 900 (1949).

pendent orbital and spin interactions with the field. This is known as the Paschen-Back effect and indicates that the field is stronger than the spin-orbit coupling. The uncoupling of the L and S vectors by a strong electrostatic field [i.e., an electrostatic Paschen-Back effect] is also possible though not as widely recognized. The electrostatic field in crystals is strong and it is, indeed, this resulting "electrostatic Paschen-Back effect" which makes the magnetic properties of the first transition elements differ from those of the rare earths.

If an even stronger field is imposed upon the d electrons of a cation, their interaction with the field becomes so strong that the ground state of the ion can no longer be obtained by using Hund's rules for electron distribution (i.e., rule of maximum multiplicity) and then combining individuals values by means of Russell-Saunders coupling. New formulas are then necessary to calculate the magnetic moment of the ion; the value is no longer determined by the procedures used for the simple ion. This situation is applicable to many complex compounds.

In recent years the powerful new tool of paramagnetic resonance absorption has been developed, permitting a much more detailed knowledge of the magnetic properties of complexes than has been possible heretofore.* Crystal field theory has frequently been applied to treat the detailed data.

The details of the crystal field theory may be outlined as follows. A central metal cation is surrounded by anions or dipoles, i.e. $[Ir^{4+} Cl_6^-]^=$ or $[Fe^{+++}(CN^-)_6]^=$, which set up a strong electrostatic or crystalline field. In this electrical field the normally degenerate d levels are split as in the familiar spectroscopic Stark effect, the extent of the splitting depending upon the central cation and upon the symmetry and strength of the applied field.† The behavior of the ion in this field is approximated by the methods of wave mechanics. The three cases of: (1) weak field as in the rare earths, (2) moderate field as in the so-called "ionic" complexes of transi-

---

* The paramagnetic resonance absorption phenomenon is a phase of microwave spectroscopy. It has been reviewed in masterful fashion by Bleaney[50], and Bleaney and Stevens[51].

† For example, changing the field by changing the ligand in a complex has a significant effect upon the moment, even when the same orbitals are ostensibly used. For example, in $[CoX_4]^-$ complexes, the moment along the sequence $\mu_{Cl} > \mu_{Br} > \mu_I > \mu_{CNS}$ falls[52]. Nyholm[53] has recently utilized the results of the crystal field treatment by Penney and Schlaap[54] and by Van Vleck[55] as a basis for suggesting that in "ionic" Co^{++} complexes a larger orbital contribution indicates octahedral coordination while the smaller orbital value indicates tetrahedral. A particularly large orbital contribution was reported empirically for planar Co^{++} complexes.

50. Bleaney, *J. Phys. Chem.*, **57**, 508 (1953).
51. Bleaney and Stevens, *Reports on Progress in Physics.*, **16**, 108 (1953).
52. Nyholm, *Quart. Revs.*, **7**, 404 (1953).
53. Nyholm, *J. Chem. Soc.*, **1954**, 12.

tion metals, and (3) strong field as in the so-called covalent complexes can be differentiated. Because of the importance of case three in the electrostatic theory of complexes, it will be considered more carefully.

In the presence of a strong field, the degenerate d levels are split into sublevels. If, then, the distribution of electrons in orbits is based on these sublevels rather than the original five degenerate d levels, the magnetic properties must follow. The manner in which the d levels are split is determined by the field geometry as shown in Fig. 3.2. For the case of K_2PtCl_6 (Fig. 3.2A) the normally degenerate d levels are split into three lower and two upper levels. Filling the lower triplet with six electrons as indicated gives the expected diamagnetic result. The cases of tetrahedral Ni^{II}, planar Ni^{II}, and duodecahedral Mo^{IV} are also worked out. In every case the qualitative agreement between predictions of the atomic orbital, molecular orbital, and crystal field theories is gratifying.

These ideas, which are an extension of generally applicable magnetic theory, were first used to explain the magnetism of complex compounds by Penney and Schlaap[54] by Van Vleck[55] and Van Vleck and Penney[57]. Howard[58] accounted for not only the gross magnetic moment of $K_3[Fe(CN)_6]$ by this method but accounted for the magnetic anisotropy and temperature dependence of the moment in the solid. Kotani[59] gave a more rigorous treatment of the temperature dependence for several transition complexes. The method has been applied extensively in recent years to the interpretation of paramagnetic resonance absorption data[50, 51, 60, 61] for complex ions, and appears to be more tractable than the orbital theories in the quantitative interpretation of modern detailed data.

The essential physical ideas of electron distribution according to the crystal field theory and their applications to magnetism, color, planar configuration, and heat of hydration of the transition metal cations have been considered in an outstanding paper by Orgel[43]. The electrons tend to avoid those regions where the field due to the attached negative ions and dipoles is largest, a fact which accounts for the field splitting of d levels. The two *high energy* orbitals correspond to a high electron density along the lines joining the central metal cation with the attached ligands, whereas the three low energy orbitals correspond to a high electron density *between* these

54. Penney and Schlapp, *Phys. Rev.*, **41**, 194 (1932).
55. Van Vleck, *J. Chem. Phys.*, **3**, 812 (1935).
56. Kimball, *J. Chem. Phys.*, **8**, 198 (1940).
57. Van Vleck and Penney, *Phil. Mag.*, **17**, 961 (1934).
58. Howard, *J. Chem. Phys.*, **3**, 813 (1935).
59. Kotani, *J. Phys. Soc. Japan*, **4**, 293 (1949).
60. Abragam and Pryce, *Proc. Roy. Soc. London*, **206A**, 164, 173 (1951).
61. Stevens, *Proc. Roy. Soc. London*, **219A**, 542 (1953); Griffiths, Owen, and Ward, *Proc. Roy. Soc. London*, **219A**, 526 (1953).

lines. In this sense the former doublet would be bonding for the ligands and the latter triplet would be nonbonding, as is also suggested by both atomic and molecular orbital theories. The separation between these levels can be found in some cases from the optical spectrum of the complex, a fact which indicates that it may be possible to correlate color as well as magnetism in more definite theoretical terms[43]. The relationship between these ideas and cation deformability (Fig. 3.1) is obvious.

Another way of viewing the transition from the paramagnetic to the di-

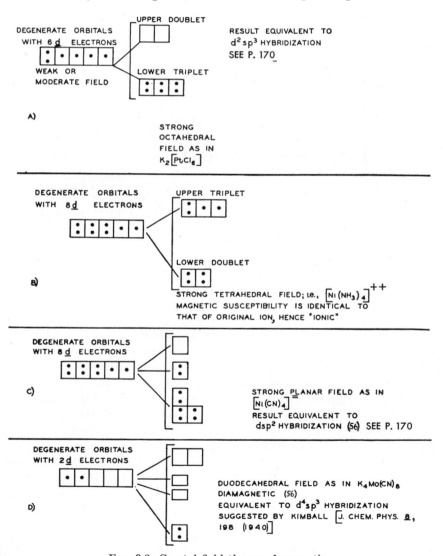

FIG. 3.2. Crystal field theory of magnetism

amagnetic state can be seen in Fig. 3.3. The case of cobalt(III) is taken as an illustrative example, although any other ion with paramagnetic and diamagnetic configurations could be used equally well. The ground state for the cobalt(III) ion is obtained by Hund's rules as the lower representation [5_D] on the left-hand side of Fig. 3.3. An excited state of this ion [I] is shown at a higher energy on the left-hand side. If now a crystalline field is applied to both states, the relative energies of each will undergo change dependent upon field direction and geometry. [Each state will be split into

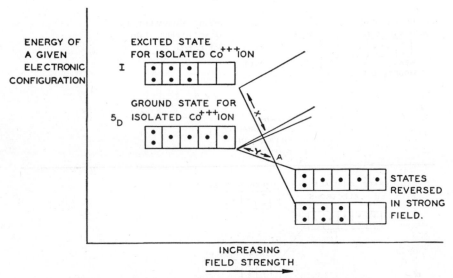

Fig. 3.3. Crystal field effects on cobalt(III)

different levels by the field]. If the excited state changes in energy more rapidly than does the ground state [i.e., slope of line X greater than line Y], the two configurations will reverse at the intersection of lines X and Y ("A" on the diagram). The point "A" then indicates the strength of the crystal field required to bring about the transition from the "ionic" to the "covalent" configuration. It is now immediately apparent that the location of A is dependent upon the original energy separation of the two levels and upon the slopes of lines X and Y, (i.e., upon electronic structure of cation).

It is interesting to note that no discontinuous energy change is involved in the transition from "ionic" to "covalent" configuration although the rate of change of energy with field strength is altered at this point. This fact justifies the observation of Orgel that "covalent" bonds in one system are not necessarily stronger than "ionic" bonds in another system (see also Taube[62]).

62. Taube, *Chem. Revs.*, **50**, 69 (1951).

Finally, a word should be said concerning the argument involving terminology which arose when the crystal field theory was first introduced[63]. Objections were raised to the crystal field treatment on the ground that $[FeF_6]^{\equiv}$, which is "ionic" according to magnetic measurements, should have a stronger crystal field than $[Fe(CN)_6]^{\equiv}$ which is "covalent." Such an argument involves a matter of definition of the terms "ionic" and "covalent" in relation to field strength[64]. If polarization is included, the cyanide crystal field is stronger than the fluoride (see, for example, Fig. 3.1) and the observed moments are in line with this expectation. One might argue that the polarization of the cyanide group is in itself indicative of covalent character in the bond. Such an argument is valid, however, solely because of the way chosen to define the term "covalent" and in no way alters the fundamental validity of the crystal field theory. In short, an approach involving polarization of ions leads to the same gross qualitative result as a model involving the perturbation of atoms by mutual interaction. The former approach is currently most useful for quantitative interpretation of detailed data on the magnetism of complexes.

THE THERMOCHEMICAL CYCLE IN COMPLEX FORMATION

The relationship between dipole moment and coordinating ability is not always as simple as the section on chemical properties would suggest. Hertel[26b] compared the stability of complexes formed between nickel(II) cyanide and methyl amine, ethyl amine, propyl amine, and butyl amine. Stability was determined by measuring and comparing the vapor pressures of the amines above the complexes. The complexes identified were $Ni(CN)_2 \cdot R$ and $Ni(CN)_2 \cdot 2R$ (R = the original amine). Though the size of the dipole increases slightly in the series $MeNH_2$, $EtNH_2$, $PrNH_2$, $BuNH_2$, the stability of the coordination compounds decreases markedly from methyl amine to butyl amine. Data are summarized in Table 3.3.

TABLE 3.3. DEPENDENCE OF DIPOLE MOMENT ON SIZE OF ALKYL GROUP IN PRIMARY AMINES

Amine	Permanent Dipole Moment[34] $\times 10^{18}$ e.s.u.	Relative Complex Stability
NH_3	1.46	1 Most stable
$MeNH_2$	1.23	2
$EtNH_2$	1.3	3
$PrNH_2$	about 1.3 to 1.4	4
$BuNH_2$	about 1.3	5 Least stable

63. Pauling, *J. Am. Chem. Soc.*, **54**, 988 (1932); Pauling and Huggins, *Z. Krist.*, **87**, 205 (1934); Van Vleck, *J. Chem. Phys.*, **3**, 807 (1935).
64. Moeller, "Inorganic Chemistry," p. 205, New York, John Wiley and Sons, Inc., 1952.

Obviously, some factor which was neglected in the simplified treatment is now of importance. The factors previously discussed (page 126) were restricted to the formation of a free gaseous complex ion from a gaseous metal ion and the gaseous amine. The energy released in this reaction is the *energy of coordination*. The actual process which is usually considered in the laboratory involves reaction between a solid metal salt and the amine to form the solid complex compound. In this process other energy terms may overshadow small differences in the coordination energy. The relative importance of each energy term may be illustrated by describing the laboratory process with a thermochemical cycle.

The simple crystalline salt is vaporized and ionized (if it is not already ionized); then the gaseous metal ions combine with the amine to give the complex cation, and finally the complex cation and the salt anion combine to give the solid complex compound. The process is represented in Fig. 3.4. All values are exothermic and positive in the direction of the arrows; then $Q = E + U_2 - U_1$. Since accurate entropy data are not available, the heat of formation, Q, (or $-\Delta H_{form}$), may be considered as an approximate measure of the relative stability of comparable complexes. Differences in the energies of coordination, E, are frequently sufficiently large to overshadow the effects of differences in the lattice energies, U_1 and U_2; i.e., $\Delta(U_1 - U_2)$, is small in comparison to ΔE (the differences in energies of coordination). In such a case the stability of the complex can be correlated with factors influencing only the energy of coordination, E. Such a situation is illustrated by the water, alcohol, ether, and hydrogen sulfide, mercaptan, thioether series discussed earlier. However, in the cases of the different primary alkyl amines, the differences in the lattice energy terms $\Delta(U_2 - U_1)$

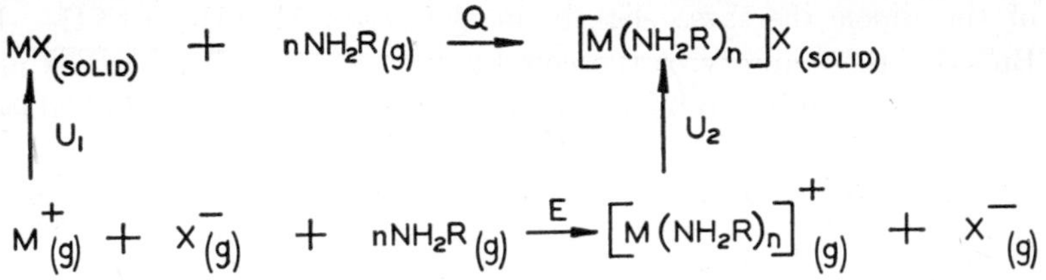

Fig. 3.4. Ammine formation as represented by a thermochemical cycle.

U_1 = lattice energy of solid "simple" salt.

U_2 = lattice energy of solid "complex" salt.

Q = heat evolved in formation of solid complex from solid salt and gaseous amine.
E = energy of coordination = heat evolved in reaction between gaseous metal ion and gaseous amine to give a gaseous complex ion.

---

* If stabilities are compared in solution, solvation energies for the simple cation, the complex cation, and the ligand replace the lattice energy terms U_1 and U_2.

TABLE 3.4. EXPANSION OF THE CRYSTAL LATTICE OF A COMPLEX SALT AS THE SIZE OF THE COORDINATED GROUP INCREASES

Complex	Length of One Edge of Cube of Unit Cell (Å.)	Metal-iodide Distance (Å.)
$[Ni(NH_3)_6]I_2$	10.88	4.71
$[Ni(MeNH_2)_6]I_2$	12.03	5.19
$[Co(NH_3)_6]I_2$	10.91	4.73
$[Co(MeNH_2)_6]I_2$	12.05	5.20

become of greater significance than the small differences in the coordination energy, ΔE. Differences in coordination energy, E, for the series methyl, ethyl, propyl, and butyl amine are not large because the dipole moments and polarizabilities do not change appreciably throughout the series. On the other hand, appreciable differences are observed in the lattice energy terms for the series. Going from ammonia successively to methyl amine, ethyl amine, propyl amine, and butyl amine brings about a progressive expansion in the size of the lattice. The larger distance between the complex cation and the salt anion reduces the electrostatic lattice energy, U_2. Since U_1 is the same as long as only a single simple salt is being considered and since differences in the energy of coordination are not particularly large for the primary amines, the differences in the values of Q and thus the differences in stability of the amine complexes can be attributed largely to differences in the lattice energy of the complex, U_2. As the size of the R group on the amine increases, the lattice energy, U_2, usually decreases. Since $Q = E + U_2 - U_1$, a decrease in lattice energy will bring about a decrease in Q and a lesser stability of the solid complex. This deduction is in agreement with the observations of Hertel.

The expansion of the complex lattice as the size of the R-group increases is indicated by x-ray data on hexammine-nickel(II) iodide and hexammine-cobalt(II) iodide and the corresponding methyl amine complexes[50]. All crystallize in the fluorite type lattice. The length of the unit cell, and the metal-halogen distances are as indicated in Table 3.4.

The Influence of Anions on the Stability of Solid Complex Compounds

The preceding discussion suggests that any factor which might influence the lattice energy of the simple salt or of the complex might influence the stability of the entire complex compound. Data of Ephraim, Biltz, and their co-workers on anion effects in complexes provide adequate support for such a conclusion. Biltz and Messerknecht[65] measured the heat evolved in the formation of a number of ammines of zinc chloride, zinc bromide, and zinc iodide (Fig. 3.5). Similar data[66] showing the heat evolved in the forma-

65. Biltz and Messerknecht, *Z. anorg. allgem. Chem.*, **129,** 161 (1923).
66. Biltz and Hansen, *Z. anorg. allgem. Chem.*, **127,** 1 (1923).

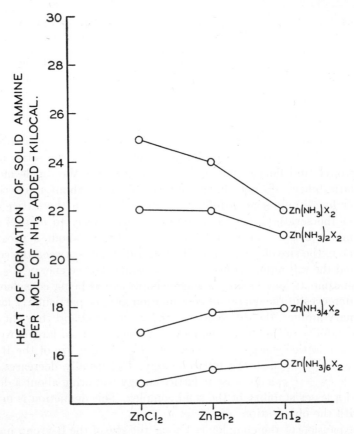

FIG. 3.5. Heats of formation of zinc ammine halides

tion of ammines of lithium chloride, lithium bromide, and lithium iodide are shown in Fig. 3.6. If one considers a simple salt such as zinc chloride, the energy of coordination per ammonia molecule falls sharply as the number of ammonia molecules increases. Such behavior is in agreement with qualitative predictions based on electrostatics. In this case, the only variables considered are the energy of coordination and the lattice energy of the solid complex crystal.

If one considers variations in any given set of ammines such as $[Zn(NH_3)_4]Br_2$ and $[Zn(NH_3)_4]I_2$, the energy of coordination, E, will be the same in each case (e.g., $Zn^{++}_{(g)} + 4NH_{3(g)} \rightarrow [Zn(NH_3)_4]^{++}_{(g)}$). The difference between lattice energies of the simple salt and the complex salt of each halide will account for the observed differences.

A similar treatment is useful in correlating other generalizations on anion effects in complex ammines. Ephraim[67] found that the nickel salts of strong

67. Ephraim, *Ber.*, **46**, 3103 (1913).

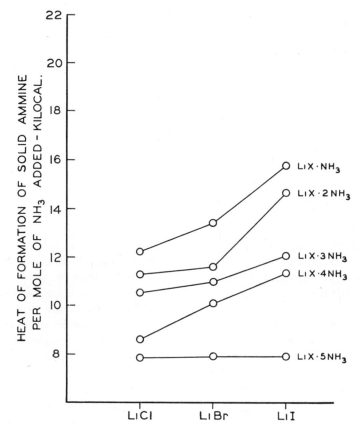

FIG. 3.6. Heats of formation of lithium ammine halides

acids have greater affinity for ammonia than nickel salts of weak acids, affinity being almost parallel to acid strength. Spacu and Voichescu[68] found that the stability of the solid ammines of copper salts of organic acids runs almost parallel to the strength of the organic parent acid. Shuttleworth[69] reports similar behavior for complexes of the chromium salts. If one makes the plausible assumption* that those anions which bind the proton strongly

---

* The correlation between the binding of a proton and the binding of a metal ion has received considerable experimental support. Calvin and Wilson[70], Bruehlman and Verhoeck[71], and others have noted an almost linear relationship between the ability of a coordinating group to bind a metal ion and its ability to bind an H^+ ion. Groups of comparable type must be considered.

68. Spacu and Voichescu, *Z. anorg. allgem. Chem.*, **226**, 273 (1936).
69. Shuttleworth, *J. Soc. Leather Trades Chem.*, **30**, 342 (1946); cf. *Chem. Abs.*, **41**, 1572 (1947).
70. Calvin and Wilson, *J. Am. Chem. Soc.*, **67**, 2003 (1945).
71. Bruehlman and Verhoek, *J. Am. Chem. Soc.*, **70**, 1401 (1948).

will also bind the nickel, copper, or chromium ion strongly, one can draw a parallel between low acid strength of the parent acid and high lattice energy for the simple salt, U_1. Since $Q = E + U_2 - U_1$, a high value for U_1, the lattice energy of the simple metal salt of the organic acid, will reduce Q and lower the stability of the ammine.

Quantitative Treatment of the Thermochemical Cycle

Biltz and Grimm[72] were the first to recognize and outline the importance of the various energy terms in complex formation. They attempted a quantitative treatment of the factors involved. From the expression $E = Q + (U_1 - U_2)$ they estimated E for the coordination of six ammonia molecules to calcium ion. Q was measured directly and $(U_1 - U_2)$ was estimated from electrostatics. Using an E value of 30 kcal per mole of ammonia as the average energy for the coordination of each of six ammonia molecules around a calcium ion, they predicted that the reaction between calcium fluoride and gaseous ammonia would be endothermic because of the very large amount of energy required to expand the calcium fluoride lattice. Subsequent attempts by Biltz and Rahlfs[73] to prepare ammoniates of the alkali and alkaline earth fluorides were unsuccessful, thus offering experimental support for the earlier theoretical predictions. Fluoride salts of more strongly polarizing metal cations such as silver(I), copper(II), manganese(II), iron(II), cobalt(II), and nickel(II) add ammonia to form complexes[73]. This fact may be correlated with the much larger amount of energy released in coordinating the polarizable ammonia molecules around the strongly polarizing cation. The large coordination energy overcomes the high fluoride lattice energy.

One of the most thorough and generally satisfactory electrostatic treatments of the coordination process was carried out by Garrick[28b]. He evaluated the energy of coordination, E, by two more or less independent methods. First, the coordination energy was estimated from a thermochemical cycle by the methods of Biltz and Grimm[72] and of Grimm and Herzfeld[74]. Then the coordination energy, E, was estimated directly from the electrostatic interaction between the cation and the coordinated dipoles in a manner similar to that of Van Arkel and de Boer[27]. Three ammines were considered: $[Zn(NH_3)_6]^{++}$, $[Fe(NH_3)_6]^{++}$, and $[Mn(NH_3)_6]^{++}$. The results appear in Table 3.5.

The agreement between values for E obtained by the two methods is fairly good, and suggests that for the so-called ionic or normal ammines the pure electrostatic model (E_B, Table 3.5) may be fairly reliable. It is signifi-

72. Biltz and Grimm, *Z. anorg. allgem. Chem.*, **145,** 63 (1925).
73. Biltz and Rahlfs, *Z. anorg. allgem. Chem.*, **166,** 351 (1927).
74. Grimm and Herzfeld, *Z. Phys.*, **19,** 141 (1923).

TABLE 3.5. ENERGY OF COORDINATION

Complex Compounds	U_1 Lattice Energy, U_1, Simple Salt Kcal/mole	U_2 Lattice Energy of Complex Salt U_2, Kcal/mole	Q Heat of Reaction Salt + NH$_3$ Kcal/mole	E_A Energy Co-ordination from Thermo-chem. Cycle Kcal/mole	E_B Energy Coordination from Electro-statics Kcal/mole
[Zn(NH$_3$)$_6$]Cl$_2$	676	327	89	438	439
[Fe(NH$_3$)$_6$]Cl$_2$	634	327	88	395	423
[Mn(NH$_3$)$_6$]Cl$_2$	615	323	82	374	391

TABLE 3.6. THE COORDINATION NUMBER AS DETERMINED BY THE RADIUS RATIO

Number of Coordinated Spheres	Radius Metal Ion / Radius Coordination Group (Radius Ratio)	Spatial Distribution of Coordinated Ions
3	.1548 to .2164	Equilateral triangle
4	.2165 to .4142	Tetrahedron
	.4143 to .5912	Plane
5	.4143 to .5912	Trigonal bipyramid
6	.4143 to .5912	Octahedron
8	.6455 to .7323	Cube or regular square prism

cant, however, that the two methods give values differing by as much as 28 kcal. This difference emphasizes the difficulty in quantitative correlation of chemical properties and electrostatic energy terms, since even one or two kcal. may be of great chemical significance.

The Coordination Number in Relation to the Thermochemical Cycle

Straubel[75] and Hüttig[76] considered the problem of predicting the coordination number* from the geometry of the packing of rigid spherical ions or molecules around a central spherical ion. Since the relative sizes of the ions will be of major importance in determining the packing, it is convenient to consider the radius ratio as a differentiating parameter[77]. The coordination numbers and the configurations are summarized in Table 3.6.

In many cases the radius ratio is not an adequate criterion for determining the coordination number of complex compounds. For example, the

* Sidgwick pointed out in 1928 that the maximum coordination number for elements of the first short period is usually 4; for elements of the second short period and first long period it is usually 6; while the maximum coordination number for the remaining elements is usually 8.

75. Straubel, *Z. anorg. allgem. Chem.*, **142**, 133 (1925).
76. Hüttig, *Z. anorg. allgem. Chem.*, **142**, 135 (1925).
77. Rice, "Electronic Structure and Chemical Binding," p. 317, New York, McGraw-Hill Book Co., 1940.

smaller ions of higher valence state almost invariably have a *greater* coordination number than the *larger* ions of *lower* valence state. Penney and Anderson[78] illustrated this point with the complexes of platinum.

Ion	Ionic Radius, A.	Coordination No.
Pt^{++}	0.93Å.	4
Pt^{4+}	0.69Å.	6

An alternative method for evaluating the number of coordinated groups was suggested by Kossel[3d]. It is possible, at least in principle, to estimate from electrostatics and polarization the amount of energy released by the grouping of negative ions or dipolar molecules around a central positive ion. It may then be assumed that the arrangement of coordinated groups which releases the most energy will give the most stable coordination compound. If two arrangements release about the same amount of energy, two forms may exist in equilibrium.

These ideas were used by a number of investigators[28c, 79] to calculate the most probable formulas for many compounds. The early investigators assumed rigid spherical ions and made no provision for lattice energy or hydration energy terms; however, Garrick[28a, 80] refined the methods by considering polarization of ions and by using a thermochemical cycle. Using the refined technique, he calculated the coordination number to be expected when water or ammonia is coordinated around a free gaseous metal ion. His calculated values* are in fair agreement with experimental results. A more complete treatment involving a thermochemical solution cycle was used to calculate coordination numbers and formulas of metal chloride and fluoride complexes in solution. In general his theoretical results were in striking agreement with experiment, indicating stable ions such as $[AlF_6]^=$ and $[BF_4]^-$. Similar calculations were carried out for the solid complexes. In view of the uncertainties of the calculations, the agreement must be regarded as rather fortuitous.

* Values obtained by Garrick for coordination of water molecules are:
    Coordination No. 4: Li^+, Be^{++}
    Coordination No. 6: Na^+, K^+, Mg^{++}
    Coordination No. 8: Cs^+, Ba^{++}
For ammonia:
    Coordination No. 4: Mg^{++}
    Coordination No. 6: Na^+, K^+, Ca^{++}, Sr^{++}
    Coordination No. 8: Rb^+, Cs^+, Ba^{++}
No coordination number of 2 was reported.

78. Penney and Anderson, *Trans. Faraday Soc.*, **33**, 1364 (1937).
79. Remy and Laves, *Ber.*, **66**, 401, 571 (1933); Remy and Pellens, *Ber.*, **61**, 862 (1928); Remy and Rothe, *Ber.*, **58**, 1565 (1925); Remy and Busch, *Ber.*, **66**, 961 (1933).
80. Garrick, *Phil. Mag.*, [7] **14**, 914 (1932).

Ablov[81] attempted to relate the coordination number to the nature of the anion in the simple salt. When the coordination of pyridine with nickel and copper salts of organic acids was investigated, he found an increase in coordination number as the acid strength of the parent organic acid was increased; these facts are readily understandable in view of the close relationship between the coordination number and the energy of the complete thermochemical cycle. Changing the anion of the nickel salt alters the lattice energy of both the simple and complex salts and thus brings about a change in the total energy released in the formation process. Also, the weak acid radical may fill a position in the coordination sphere.

Thermochemical considerations also suggest that the nature of the coordinated amine may be important and that different results may be found if different amines are used. In a separate study, Ablov[82] considered complexes between nickel trichloroacetate and a series of organic amines, mostly substituted anilines. He observed a rather indistinct relationship between the dipole moment of the amine and the coordination number of the nickel. A relatively large increase in dipole moment frequently increased the number of amine molecules bound to the nickel. Again, such factors are intelligible if the entire thermochemical cycle is considered, but consideration of a single factor such as the dipole moment is inadequate.

Much of the data in the literature on coordination number, such as that of Ablov and of Remy[79, 81, 82], assumes that the coordination number can be obtained from the empirical formula of the complex compound. Such evidence, however, is subject to the criticism that water molecules may coordinate in solution to give a coordination number of six for ions such as $[FeF_5]^=$ and that corners of the individual octahedra may be shared in the solid state to give coordination numbers which are larger than those indicated by the empirical formula. A coordination number which is smaller than that indicated by the empirical formula may also exist if extra molecules of the coordinated ligand can be packed into the lattice interstices. Ephraim and his co-workers[83] and Clark[84] observed that, when cations such as Ni^{++}, Co^{++}, and Fe^{++}, which normally show a coordination number of six, are associated with very large anions, such as the benzoate ion or $[Co(NH_3)_2(NO_2)_4]^-$, eight or ten ammonia molecules may appear to be coordinated to the central metal cation at room temperature. They suggested that the last two or four molecules of ammonia are probably trapped in the lattice interstices, since they differ appreciably from the first six ammonias

81. Ablov, *Bull. soc. chim.*, [5] **1**, 731, 1489 (1934).
82. Ablov, *Bull. soc. chim.*, [5] **2**, 1724 (1935); **3**, 1673 (1936).
83. Ephraim and Moser, *Ber.*, **53**, 548 (1920); Ephraim and Rosenberg, *Ber.*, **51**, 644 (1918).
84. Clark, Quick, and Harkins, *J. Am. Chem. Soc.*, **43**. 2496, 2488 (1920).

in their heats of coordination and in their effect on complex color. Somewhat more recently, Lamb and Mysels[85] have reported that the water in $[Co(NH_3)_5CO_3]NO_3 \cdot H_2O$ has no structural significance but may be considered as lattice water.

It may be concluded that the coordination number has been successfully estimated by the electrostatic treatment for the simplest cases involving normal or ionic type complexes. For the more polarized covalent or penetration* type compounds the electrostatic treatment is completely inadequate in its present state of development. In cases where the electrostatic treatment can be successfully applied, all the terms in the thermochemical cycle must be considered. In general, the interactions of such factors as appear in these cycles are too numerous and involved to permit close general correlation with any single molecular or ionic property, such as dipole moment, ion charge, or ionic potential.†

THE APPLICATION OF THE COMPLETE IONIC MODEL TO THE PROPERTIES AND STRUCTURES OF SELECTED COMPLEX COMPOUNDS

The Trans Effect

One of the useful concepts suggested by Werner in the development of his theory was the idea of "trans elimination" in substitution reactions. In brief, the rule of "trans elimination" suggests that the "reactivity" of a given group, A, in a coordination compound is dependent, in large measure, upon the nature of the group coordinated in the position trans to group A. (By "reactivity" we mean the ease with which the group A may be replaced in the coordination sphere by other donor molecules.) In general, acid anions and neutral groups which are easily polarized show a much greater trans effect than groups such as water or ammonia. Thus, a group which is trans to chloride or bromide is much more labile than a group trans to a neutral molecule such as water. The idea of trans elimination has been applied to compounds of platinum, cobalt, chromium, osmium, palladium, rhodium, and iridium. The principle has been widely used and developed by Tscherniaev[87], Grinberg[88] and their co-workers. A comprehensive review on the trans effect has been published by Quagliano and Schubert[89].

---

* For description of penetration complexes, see page 151.

† A most interesting treatment of the heats of formation in oxyacid salts in terms of an ionic model and lattice energies has been given by Ramberg[86].

85. Lamb and Mysels, *J. Am. Chem. Soc.*, **67**, 468 (1945).
86. Ramberg, *J. Chem. Phys.*, **20**, 1532 (1952).
87. Tscherniaev, *Ann. Inst. Platine, U.S.S.R.*, **4**, 261 (1926); **5**, 118, 134 (1927).
88. Grinberg, Shulman, and Khorunzhenkov, *Ann. Inst. Platine, U.S.S.R.*, **12**, 69, 119 (1935); cf. *Chem. Abs.*, **29**, 3253 (1935); *Ann. Inst. Platine, U.S.S.R.*, **11**, 17 (1933); *Ann. Inst. Platine, U.S.S.R.*, **10**, 58 (1932); cf. *Chem. Abs.*, **28**, 1447 (1934).
89. Quagliano and Schubert, *Chem. Revs.*, **50**, 201 (1952).

Grinberg[90] suggested the following explanation of the trans effect based on the ideas of electrostatics and polarization. If a central metal ion is surrounded by four identical groups, the cation is in a symmetrical field and all dipoles induced in the central ion are compensated by one another. Now, if one of the coordinated groups is replaced by a relatively more negative or more easily polarized group ("Y" in Fig. 3.7), the symmetry of the field around the central ion is destroyed and a noncompensated dipole is induced in the central metal ion. The group X2 which is adjacent to the negative end of the induced dipole is labilized, and trans elimination can easily occur.

On the basis of this explanation, the trans effect will be exhibited by any group which possesses mobile electrons that can be dislocated in the direc-

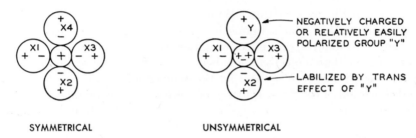

SYMMETRICAL   UNSYMMETRICAL

FIG. 3.7. The trans effect according to the electrostatic concept

tion of the central ion[91]. Tronev and Chulkov[92] report the decreasing efficacy of a substituent in labilizing the group trans to it, as:

$$CN^-, C_2H_4, NO_2^-, I^-, Br^-, Cl^-, NH_3, OH^-, H_2O$$
$$\underrightarrow{\text{Decreasing Trans Influence}}$$

Chatt and Williams[93] give the order: $CN^- > C_2H_4 > CO > NO_2^- > SC(NH_2)_2 > R_2S \sim PR_3 \sim I^- > Br^- > Cl^- > F^- \sim NH_3 > OH^- > H_2O$. This order is roughly that expected on the basis of the above treatment. Substituted phosphines have been reported to have a high trans influence[94], as would be predicted.

The above mechanism for the trans effect suggests that the effect will

90. Grinberg and Ryabchikov, *Acta Physicochim. U.R.S.S.*, **3**, 555, 573 (1935); cf. *Chem. Abs.*, **30**, 4074 (1936).

91. Grinberg, *Bull. acad. sci., U.R.S.S., Classe sci., chim.*, 350 (1943); cf. *Chem. Abs.*, **39**, 252 (1945).

92. Tronev and Chulkov, *Doklady Akad. Nauk. S.S.S.R.*, **63**, 545 (1948); cf. *Chem. Abs.*, **43**, 2854 (1949).

93. Chatt and Williams, *J. Chem. Soc.*, **1951**, 3061.

94. Grinberg, Razumova, and Troitskaya, *Bull. acad. sci., Classe sci., chim.*, **3**, 253 (1946); cf. *Chem. Abs.*, **43**, 4172 (1949); Grinberg and Razumova, *Zhur. Priklad. Khim.*, **27**, 105 (1954); cf. *Chem. Abs.*, **48**, 6308 (1954).

be promoted by:

(1) A central cation of high field strength which is itself easily deformed; both Pd++ and Pt++ meet this specification. Chatt and Hart[95] find some evidence to indicate that palladium(II) compounds are less influenced by trans directing groups than the corresponding platinum(II) compounds.

(2) A coordinated group which can release electrons toward the central cation; thus anions and easily polarized groups would be more effective than neutral molecules of low polarizability such as H_2O.

The two most serious* objections raised to the treatment of Grinberg are: (a) that the diamagnetism of the platinum(II) compounds indicates that the platinum cannot be present as the dipositive ion since platinum(II) should have two unpaired electrons and, (b) a high trans effect has been attributed to PF_3 by Chatt and Williams[93], though they assume that the polarizability of the attached phosphorus would be so reduced by attached fluorine atoms that its trans effect would be reduced rather strongly.

The first of these objections has been answered in the section on magnetism where it has been shown that the diamagnetism in the platinum(II) is a direct result of the Stark splitting of normally degenerate d levels in the crystal field. This cannot be considered as a valid objection. The second point raised by Chatt[93] cannot be accepted as unequivocal and must be regarded as an open question for the following reasons:

(1) The assumption that the attached fluorines on PF_3 reduce the polarizability of the free electron pair on phosphorus to a point where it would not be expected to be trans directing has no direct experimental support.

(2) *A strong trans effect for PF_3 has never been established.* Coordination compounds of PF_3 have been prepared such as $PtCl_2(PF_3)_2$ which are analogous to the corresponding carbonyl halides of platinum. Hel'man attributed a strong trans effect to CO since it directs pyridine trans when the pyridine replaces a chloride ion in $[COPtCl_3]^-$ and since it is analogous to C_2H_4 in many of its coordination compounds; C_2H_4 is reported to have a high trans effect (p. 490).

On the other hand, the only direct evidence available on the reactions of PF_3 which is comparable in nature to that used in establishing the trans series, would suggest that PF_3 is *not* highly trans directing. The complex solid (a) reacts with PF_3 to give the cis isomer (b) as indicated by dipole

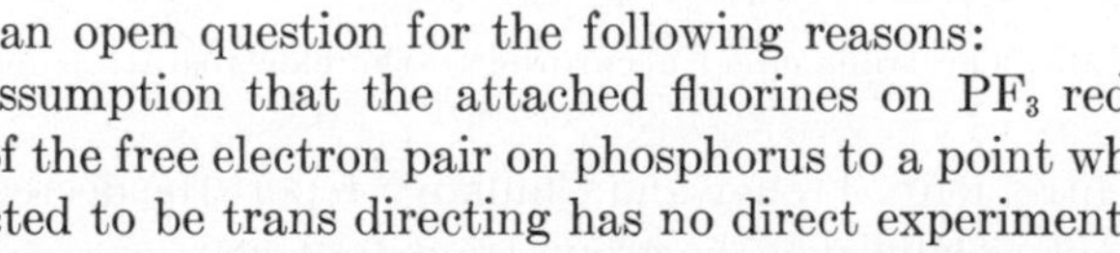

* Other objections cited[89] are trivial.

95. Chatt and Hart, *J. Chem. Soc.*, **1953**, 2367.

measurements[93, 97], yet on the basis of a high trans directing influence for PF_3 a trans isomer was predicted for the compound by Quagliano and Schubert[89]. Chatt and Wilkins[98] also suggested a trans structure for the product obtained by the analogous reaction between the strongly trans directing C_2H_4 and its comparable dimeric complex. Despite such predictions, the PF_3 product is *cis*. It has also been shown that CO gives the cis product, contrary to expectations for strong trans directing properties. Even the trans case for CO is established on very meager evidence as compared to that used by Werner in first elucidating the concept.

(3) Further, the nature and operational meaning of the trans effect are very uncertain. No definite quantitative method, free from objections, can be applied to place groups in the series. If the effect is considered to be one of thermodynamics involving bond stabilities, difficulties are legion. Chatt[99] tried to evaluate the relative coordinating affinity of a series of tertiary alkyls in Group V. He reported the order: $PR_3 > AsR_3 > SbR_3 > NR_3 > BiR_3$. Attempts to place ethylene in this series led to conflicting positions depending upon the experimental criterion selected, indicating that the relative coordinating ability is affected by many other variables, such as the groups already attached to the metal. Chatt and Wilkins[100] estimated certain of the thermodynamic constants for the metal–tertiary phosphine linkage and concluded: "This study also serves to emphasize the importance of the entropy term in determining the position of equilibrium in reactions involving the formation or destruction of highly polar molecules, and how completely erroneous conclusions regarding relative stability can be arrived at by consideration of *only equilibrium positions* or *decomposition temperatures* in coordination chemistry." Much of the trans effect series is based on relative yields obtained under different sets of conditions.

On the basis that such yields are determined by relative rates of reaction rather than complex stability, mechanisms have been suggested for various processes which are designed to show that even when using the trans effect, a result directly contrary to that normally expected can be obtained[101]. In view of this situation the trans effect must be considered, at the present time, as only a broad qualitative generalization covering a very complex process.

Application of the Polarization Theory to a Number of Unusual Compounds

The strength of any theory lies in its ability to adequately describe the unusual as well as the commonplace. In the following section, types of com-

97. Lutton and Parry, *J. Am. Chem. Soc.*, **76**, 4271 (1954).
98. Chatt and Wilkins, *J. Chem. Soc.*, **1952**, 2622.
99. Chatt, *J. Chem. Soc.*, **1951**, 652.
100. Chatt and Wilkins, *J. Chem. Soc.*, **1952**, 276.

plexes which differ from the classical Werner coordination compounds are discussed. The relationship of each complex to the polarization theory is noted. The customary successes and failures are observed.

"*Super Complexes.*" If one considers the positively or negatively charged complex ion as a unit, it becomes apparent that an electrostatic field exists around the complex ion just as a field exists around a simple ion. Because the complex is in general much larger than the simple ion[102], the attraction of the complex for the solvent or for ions of opposite charge in solution is significantly less than that exerted by the simple ion. Still, the fact that a complex ion may enter into an ionic crystal as a structural unit offers conclusive proof that the residual field is not negligible. The existence of this field would lead one to suspect that additional ions or dipolar molecules might be attracted to the complex ion to produce a second, a third, or perhaps even a fourth coordination sphere in solution. Obviously, groups held in these outer spheres will be held less tightly as their distance from the central ion increases. Such super complexes have been described by Brintzinger[103]. Definite formulas such as $[Fe(H_2O)_{18}]^{+++}$ and $[Co(NH_3)_6(SO_4)_4]^{5-}$ have been reported from diffusion studies. Such formulations are completely arbitrary and of little significance, since the formula is dependent upon the nature and the reliability of the method used to define the compound.* Laitinen, Bailar, Holtzclaw, and Quagliano[104] obtained polarographic evidence for such complexes and suggested that the super complexes formed between the hexamminecobalt(III) ion and acetate or sulfate ion may be strong enough to cause a measurable shift of the reduction potential for the hexammine ion and a lowering of the polarographic diffusion current. The existence of such super complexes can best be considered as an electrostatic phenomenon, probably more comparable to the Debye-Hückel ionic atmosphere than to true coordination compounds.

Ammoniates of the Alkaline Earth Metals. An interesting series of compounds is the alkaline earth metal ammines: $Ca(NH_3)_6$, $Sr(NH_3)_6$, and $Ba(NH_3)_6$. These compounds are formed by simple addition of ammonia to the *solid metal*. The stability decreases from calcium to barium. Measurements by Biltz[107] indicate that the metal-ammonia complex is almost

* Brintzinger's methods have been criticized by a number of investigators. See particularly J. Bjerrum[105].

101. Jonassen and Cull, *J. Am. Chem. Soc.*, **73**, 274 (1951); Jonassen, Sistrunk, Oliver, and Helfrich, *J. Am. Chem. Soc.*, **75**, 5216 (1953).
102. Bødtker-Naess and Hassel, *Z. anorg. Chem.*, **211**, 21 (1933); *Z. phys. Chem.*, **22B**, 471 (1933).
103. Brintzinger and Osswald, *Z. anorg. allgem. Chem.*, **223**, 253 (1935); **225**, 221 (1935).
104. Laitinen, Bailar, Holtzclaw, and Quagliano, *J. Am. Chem. Soc.*, **70**, 2999 (1948).
105. Reference 7a., p. 77.
107. Biltz, *Z. Elektrochem.*, **26**, 374 (1920); *Z. anorg. Chem.*, **114**, 241 (1920).

as stable as the ion-ammonia complex, $[Ca(NH_3)_6]^{++}$ or $[Ba(NH_3)_6]^{++}$. Since in the metal-ammonia complex there is no charged ion to attract the dipoles of the ammonia, any explanation based on electrostatics must assume an arbitrary reassignment of charge among components of the molecule, or it must assume that dipoles are induced in the central metal atom by the dipoles of the ammonia.

Watt[108] and his students have reported the analogous $Pt(NH_3)_4$ and $Ir(NH_3)_5$. Explanations of why dipoles or multipoles would arise in such compounds are inadequate at present.

Metal Carbonyls. The interesting coordination of compounds formed by the reaction between carbon monoxide and many metals, particularly those of Group VIII, are known as the metal carbonyls (Chapter 16). These compounds, of which $[Ni(CO)_4]$ and $[Fe(CO)_5]$ are typical, are particularly difficult to fit into the electrostatic polarization scheme since the central metal atom apparently bears no charge and the carbon monoxide has such a low dipole moment that bonding based on dipole-induced dipole interaction is completely unrealistic. The effective atomic number concept of Sidgwick (page 159) has been particularly fruitful in a consideration of the formulas and chemistry of these substances.

The interesting $[Ni(PF_3)_4]$ and $[Ni(PCl_3)_4]$ complexes[109], the compound $[NiH(CO)_3]_2$[110], as well as $Ni(N_4S_4)$[111] and the metal cyclopentadienes (Chapter 15) provide other examples of the same type of substance.

Types of Complexes: Normal (or Ionic) and Penetration (or Covalent) Complexes

The ammoniates of the alkali halides and of compounds such as $[Fe(NH_3)_6]Cl_2$ can be rather accurately described with a polarized electrostatic model. On the other hand, the carbonyls and alkaline earth and platinum *metal** ammoniates are not particularly well adapted to treatment by electrostatics. With many compounds, such as those just mentioned, the electron-pair bond or molecular orbital theory is more useful in correlating experimental facts. In between the typical electrostatic or ionic alkali halides on one hand and the strongly covalent metal carbonyls on the other, lie most of the common coordination compounds. Biltz[112], recognizing this

---

* One must differentiate metal-ammoniates, $Ca(NH_3)_6$, from ion-ammoniates $[Ca(NH_3)_6]^{++}$.

108. Watt, Walling, and Mayfield, *J. Am. Chem. Soc.*, **75,** 6175 (1953).
109. Irvine and Wilkinson, *Science*, **113,** 742 (1951); Wilkinson, *J. Am. Chem. Soc.*, **73,** 5501 (1951).
110. Brehrens and Lohöfer, *Z. Naturforsch*, **8b,** 691 (1953).
111. Goehring and Debo, *Z. anorg. allgem. Chem.*, **273,** 319 (1953).
112. Biltz, *Z. anorg. Chem.*, **164,** 245 (1927).

fact, attempted to set up a method of classifying compounds based on four experimental criteria. The properties selected and applied to the cobalt ammines were: (1) thermochemical and chemical data indicating the stability of the complex unit, (2) the molecular volume of the coordinated groups, (3) molecular distances as obtained from x-ray data, (4) magnetic susceptibility measurements. On the basis of the above factors it is possible to divide coordination compounds roughly into two general types, though, as Taube[62] and Orgel[43] have shown, the classification is not unequivocal.

The first group is characterized by a comparatively weak bond between the central group and the coordinating ligands. Members of this group can be readily and reversibly dissociated into their component parts, either in the solid phase or in solution; they show a comparatively large bond distance between the coordinated ligand and the central atom; and they show no deep-seated electronic rearrangement as measured by changes in the magnetic susceptibility of the central ion. These compounds were named *normal complexes* by Biltz[112]. The ammoniates of the alkali halides and of certain divalent metal halides such as cobalt(II) chloride represent typical examples of the normal complex. The term, normal complex, is often used synonymously with the term *ionic complex*, although the terms "ionic" and "covalent" as applied to complexes indicate different things to different workers.

Members of the second group are not in facile equilibrium with their components in either the solid state or solution. An unusually short bond distance between the coordinating group and the central ion is usually characteristic of this class of compounds, and a deep-seated electronic change is frequently indicated by a change in the magnetic susceptibility of the central ion. Such compounds were called *Werner complexes* by Biltz. Since the so-called normal complexes may also be called Werner complexes, Ray[113] introduced the term "Durchdringungskomplexe" or *penetration complex* for the second group because of the apparent penetration of the coordinating ligand into the central ion. The term, penetration complex, is frequently considered to be synonymous with the term, covalent complex.

The two types of compounds are illustrated by the hexamminecobalt(II) ion and the hexamminecobalt(III) ion. In the subsequent discussion experimental evidence for the classification will be reviewed.

Chemical Properties as a Basis for Classification

Thermal decomposition of $[Co(NH_3)_6]Cl_2$ is characterized by the reversible evolution of ammonia from the solid[114].

113. Ray, *Z. anorg. Chem.*, **174**, 189 (1928); *J. Indian Chem. Soc.*, **5**, 73 (1928).
114. Biltz, *Z. anorg. Chem.*, **89**, 97 (1914).

$$[Co(NH_3)_6]Cl_2 \underset{}{\overset{150°}{\rightleftharpoons}} Co(NH_3)_2Cl_2 + 4NH_3$$

$$\overset{below\ 200°}{\longrightarrow} CoCl_2 + 2NH_3$$

The hexammine can be easily reformed by exposing the anhydrous cobalt(II) chloride to ammonia vapors. The compound $CoCl_2 \cdot 6NH_3$ exists in aqueous solution in labile equilibrium with its components:

$$6H_2O + [Co(NH_3)_6]^{++} \rightleftharpoons [Co(H_2O)_6]^{++} + 6NH_3.$$

The solid hexammoniate may be crystallized from a concentrated solution as red octahedra. The moist complex is readily oxidized by air and is destroyed by acids. The dry ammoniate is fairly stable in air; in fact, ammonia replaces water from cobalt(II) chloride 6-hydrate when a stream of ammonia is passed over the solid compound[84]. These chemical properties are typical of normal complexes.

In sharp contrast to the ammoniates of the cobalt(II) salts, the hexamminecobalt(III) salts do not undergo reversible thermal decomposition. When $[Co(NH_3)_6]Cl_3$ is carefully heated, one molecule of ammonia is given off to produce chloropentamminecobalt(III) chloride[84].

$$[Co(NH_3)_6]Cl_3 \xrightarrow{175°\ to\ 180°} [Co(NH_3)_5Cl]Cl_2 + NH_3$$

The reaction is slow and not readily reversible. Further heating brings about complete decomposition of the chloro complex with reduction of the cobalt(III) ion by the ammonia[84, 115].

$$6\ [Co(NH_3)_5Cl]Cl_2 \xrightarrow{180°\ to\ 220°} 6CoCl_2 + 6NH_4Cl + 22NH_3 + N_2$$

The hexamminecobalt(III) phosphate undergoes immediate and complete decomposition on heating:

$$6\ [Co(NH_3)_6]PO_4 \rightarrow 3Co_2P_2O_7 + 34NH_3 + 3H_2O + N_2$$

In solution, the hexamminecobalt(III) ion does not undergo dissociation into its component parts, as is demonstrated by the fact that exchange studies on this and related complex ions have revealed no exchange between the central metal ion and radioactive metal ions in solution[116], and by the

115. Biltz, *Z. anorg. Chem.*, **83**, 190 (1913).
116. Lewis and Coryell, Brookhaven Conf. Rept. BNL-C-8, Isotopic Exchange Reactions and Chem. Kinetics, Chem. Conf., No. 2, 131 (1948); Lewis, Coryell and Irvine, *J. Chem. Soc.*, **1949**, S386; McCallom, Brookhaven Conf. Rept. BNL-C-8, Isotopic Exchange Reactions and Chem. Kinetics, Chem. Conf., No. 2, 120 (1948); McCallom and Hoshowsky, *J. Chem. Phys.*, **16**, 254 (1948); Hoshowsky, Holmes, and McCallom, *Can. J. Research*, **27B**, 258 (1949); Flagg, *J. Am. Chem. Soc.*, **63**, 557 (1941).

fact that the complex ion is stable even in strongly acid solutions where the cobalt(II) complex is rapidly decomposed. In many chemical reactions the complex hexamminecobalt(III) ion participates as a unit in a manner analogous to that of sulfate, phosphate, and other stable radicals:

$$2[Co(NH_3)_6]Cl_3 + 3H_2SO_4 \rightarrow [Co(NH_3)_6]_2(SO_4)_3 + 6HCl$$

These chemical properties are characteristic of penetration or covalent complexes. Chromium is similar to cobalt. Dipositive chromium forms normal complexes and tripositive chromium forms penetration complexes. It might appear that the greater charge and polarizing power of the tripositive ion could account for the differences in stability; however, as Klemm[117] points out, the higher charge on the central atom cannot explain the phenomenon by itself since ammines of iron(III) are apparently less stable than those of iron (II)[118].

Molecular Volume as a Criterion for Classification of Complexes

The chemical properties of the hexammine of tripositive cobalt suggest a much stronger bond between cobalt and nitrogen than is found in the hexammoniates of the cobalt(II) salts. One might logically expect the formation of the stronger cobalt-nitrogen bond to be accompanied by a decrease in the distance between the cobalt and nitrogen nuclei. Many of the early German workers reasoned that the decrease in the bond distances might become apparent if the molecular volumes of di- and tripositive metal ammine salts were compared. For this reason molecular volume was introduced as a criterion of bond type.

Biltz and his co-workers[119] applied Kopp's rule of additive volumes to coordination compounds. They were able to show that the molecular volumes of a number of hexammines of the divalent metal chlorides are roughly equal to the sums of the zero point volumes of the components. If the additivity relationship were applicable to the hexammines of the tripositive metal chlorides, one would expect the volumes of the compounds containing tripositive metal ions to exceed the volumes of the complexes containing divalent metal ions by an amount equal to the volume of the extra chloride ion (about 16 cc).

It is then somewhat surprising to find that the molecular volumes of the hexammines of di- and tripositive metal ions with any given anion are practically identical in a very large number of cases. The extra anion, in most

117. Klemm, Jacobi, and Tilk, *Z. anorg. Chem.*, **201**, 1 (1931).
118. Thorne and Roberts, "Fritz Ephraim's Inorganic Chemistry," pp. 252, 271, and 310, New York, Interscience Publishers, Inc., (1946).
119. Biltz and Birk, *Z. anorg. Chem.*, **134**, 125 (1924); Biltz, *Z. anorg. Chem.*, **130**, 116 (1923).

TABLE 3.7. A COMPARISON OF MOLECULAR VOLUMES FOR SELECTED NORMAL AND PENETRATION COMPLEXES SHOWING THE NEAR IDENTITY OF VOLUME IN COMPARABLE DI- AND TRIPOSITIVE AMMINES

Normal Complexes			Penetration Complexes		
Ammine	Apparent Mol. Vol. NH₃ (cc)	Mol. Vol. Ammine	Ammine	Apparent Mol. Vol. NH₃ (cc)	Mol. Vol. Ammine
$[Co(NH_3)_6]Cl_2$	20	156.9	$[Co(NH_3)_6]Cl_3$	17	156.4
$[Co(NH_3)_6](NO_3)_2$	22	193.2	$[Co(NH_3)_6](NO_3)_3$	17	192.5
$[Co(NH_3)_6](ClO_4)_2$	—	225.4	$[Co(NH_3)_6](ClO_4)_3$	—	
$[Co(NH_3)_6](CNS)_2$	21	217.3	$[Co(NH_3)_6](CNS)_3$	14.5	218.2
$[Co(NH_3)_6]Br_2$	21	171.6	$[Co(NH_3)_6]Br_3$	18	171.3
$[Co(NH_3)_6]I_2$	24	198.0	$[Co(NH_3)_6]I_3$	19	197.3
$[Cr(NH_3)_6]Br_2$	22	182.8	$[Cr(NH_3)_6]Br_3$	19	183.2
$[Cr(NH_3)_6]I_2$	27	220.3	$[Cr(NH_3)_6]I_3$	22	220.6

The Approximate Additivity Relationship in Certain Di- and Tripositive Hexamminecobalt Salts

$[Co(NH_3)_6]SO_4$	19.1	155.5	$[Co(NH_3)_6]_2(SO_4)_3$	18.7	339.8 (169.9)
$[Co(NH_3)_6]C_2O_4$	19.5	165.6	$[Co(NH_3)_6]_2(C_2O_4)_3$	19.1	368.1 (184.0)
$[Co(NH_3)_6](C_{10}H_7SO_3)_2$	18.3	408.7	$[Co(NH_3)_6](C_{10}H_7SO_3)_3$	18.0	553.4

cases, does not bring about a significant increase in the volume of the crystalline salt. Data illustrating this point are summarized in Table 3.7.

Biltz and other German workers of the early 1920's attributed this unusual situation to a compression of the coordinated ammonias during the formation of penetration complexes. In fact, it was from this apparent compression of the coordinated ammonias that the name "penetration complex" arose.

It has been shown, however[120], that the equal volume relationship is not due to the compression of the coordinated ammonias, but to the fact that many of the normal complexes such as $[Co(NH_3)_6]X_2$ crystallize in a lattice of the calcium fluoride type. This lattice contains holes into which four extra anions per unit cell may be packed without destroying the basic crystal pattern.

Magnetic Susceptibility Measurements and Other Data as Criteria for the Classification of Complexes

In his original discussion of penetration complexes, Biltz noted that the formation of such complexes is accompanied by profound changes in elec-

120. Parry, *Chem. Revs.*, **46**, 507 (1950).

tronic arrangement. The interpretation of these changes in terms of a highly polarized ionic model has been given in the section on magnetism. A comprehensive review of magnetic data in coordination compounds was published by Selwood[121] in 1943. This work and other work on bond type is most conveniently considered after a discussion of the electron-pair bond.

121. Selwood, "Magnetochemistry," New York, Interscience Publishers, Inc., 1943.

4. Modern Developments: The Electron Pair Bond and Structure of Coordination Compounds

Raymond N. Keller

University of Colorado, Boulder, Colorado

and

Robert W. Parry

University of Michigan, Ann Arbor, Michigan

EARLY TREATMENTS OF THE COVALENT BOND IN COORDINATION THEORY

Werner's Primary and Secondary Valences

The advent of electronic theories of valence made it possible to reconcile the coordination theory with the structural theory of organic chemistry. The key to the problem was found by G. N. Lewis[1] in a postulate to the effect that the covalent bond consists of a shared pair of electrons, this pair originating in one of two ways: each of the two atoms forming the bond can furnish one electron, or one atom can furnish both. In either case, the outer shells of both atoms will tend to be filled and covalent links will be formed. Because of its simplicity, this concept has served as the foundation upon which much of our present valence theory has been built.

An electronic picture of a chemical bond did much to make Werner's postulates of primary and secondary valences more acceptable. For example, in the ammonia molecule the nitrogen contributes one electron to each of the three hydrogen atoms to form three normal *covalent bonds.* These were Werner's "primary valences." In forming the ammonium ion the unshared electron pair on the nitrogen of the ammonia molecule binds a fourth proton to form a *coordinate covalent* bond or, a "secondary valence." Although the mode of forming the two types of bonds is different, the bonds to all hydrogens become identical once they are formed. On the other hand, when ammonia is coordinated to a metal ion, the metal-nitrogen bond will

1. Lewis, *J. Am. Chem. Soc.*, **38,** 778 (1916).

differ from the hydrogen-nitrogen bond, not because one bond is a normal covalent bond and one a coordinate covalent bond, but because the proton and the metal ion differ in their abilities to interact with the electrons of the nitrogen.

If the electronic interaction between two atoms, A and B, results in a complete transfer of an electron from A to B, the ions A^+ and B^- are produced to give the conventional *electrovalent* or *ionic* bond.

Recognition of these different modes of electron interaction did much to dispel one of the great objections to Werner's early theory—that some compounds of "first order" are ionic (e.g., NaCl) and others are not (e.g., CCl_4). It soon became apparent that Werner's compounds of the "first order" could be divided into two extreme groups, ionic and covalent, according to the extent of electron transfer and that the covalent group displayed many properties which were almost identical to those of Werner's compounds of the "second order." For instance, in the compound $[Co(NH_3)_5Cl]Cl_2$ the normal covalent cobalt-chlorine bond in

$$[Co(NH_3)_5Cl]^{++}$$

is quite similar to the coordinate covalent cobalt-nitrogen bond in terms of chemical behavior (i.e., slow reaction of Cl^- with Ag^+, etc.). On the other hand, the ionic bonds binding the two remaining chlorides to the cation are very different chemically from their covalent counterpart. In short, one form of Werner's primary valence appears to be quite similar to his secondary valence.

Early Theories of Electron Quantization

One of the important problems which followed the simple electronic interpretation of Werner's postulates involved the quantization of the electrons in a complex molecule in a manner comparable to that proposed by Bohr[2] for a simple atom. The problem is still an active one and many methods of approach are still being explored. Many early proposals associated with such names as Huggins[3], Sidgwick[4, 5], Lowry[6], Main-Smith[7], Pauling[8], Fowler[9], Butler[10, 11], and Bose[12] are of current interest in that they

2. Bohr, *Phil. Mag.* [6], **26**, 1, 476, 857 (1913).
3. Huggins, *Phys. Chem.*, **26**, 601 (1922); *Science*, **55**, 459 (1922).
4. Sidgwick, *J. Chem. Soc.*, **123**, 725 (1923); *Trans. Faraday Soc.*, **19**, 469 (1923); *Chemistry & Industry*, **42**, 901 (1923).
5. Sidgwick, *Chem. and Ind.*, **42**, 1203 (1923); "The Electronic Theory of Valency," pp. 100, 172, 124, Oxford, Clarendon Press, 1927.
6. Lowry, *Chemistry & Industry*, **42**, 316 (1923).
7. Main Smith, *Chemistry & Industry*, **42**, 1073 (1923); **44**, 944 (1925); *Trans. Faraday Soc.*, **21**, 356 (1925–26).
8. Pauling, *J. Am. Chem. Soc.*, **53**, 1367 (1931); **54**, 988 (1932).
9. Fowler, *Trans. Faraday Soc.*, **19**, 459 (1923).

suggest much of our modern theory. For example, the modern idea of double bonds between metal and ligand was implied in one of Sugden's early papers[13]. A number of early proposals involving single electron bonds[14] were severely criticized[5a, 15] and are of little present day value.

Sidgwick's Effective Atomic Number Concept

The apparent tendency of simple atoms to achieve an inert gas configuration in compound formation has been a helpful and much used concept. Sidgwick[4] extrapolated this idea in a somewhat modified form to the heavy metal atoms. He postulated that the central metal atom or cation of a complex will share electron pairs with coordinating groups (or triplets in some cases, as in coordination with NO) until the "effective atomic number" (EAN)[16] of the next higher inert gas is achieved.

In the case of $[PtCl_6]^=$, for example, the effective atomic number of the platinum atom is obtained by adding 74 electrons from the Pt^{4+} *ion* and 2 electrons from each of the six coordinated chloride *ions* to obtain a total of 86. This is the atomic number of the inert gas radon.

The scheme is applicable to such a large group of compounds that its validity can hardly be fortuitous. The metal carbonyls and nitrosyls are particularly susceptible to treatment by this scheme. For example, the formulas of the carbonyls and nitrosyls, and in some cases their substitution products, can usually be predicted by an application of the following relatively simple EAN rules:

(1) Carbon monoxide and electron pair donors such as pyridine etc., are assumed to donate an electron pair to the metal atom.

(2) Nitric oxide (NO) is assumed to donate three electrons to the metal atom, since the ion NO^+ is isoelectronic with CO.

(3) Hydrogen atoms, halogen atoms, and pseudo halogens such as CN are assumed to donate a single electron to the metal atom. (One can also look at this in an equivalent manner as the halide *ion* donating an electron *pair* to the metal *ion*.)

---

10. Butler, *Trans. Faraday Soc.*, **21**, 349 (1925–26).
11. Butler, *Trans. Faraday Soc.*, **21**, 359 (1925–26).
12. Bose, *Phil. Mag.*, [7], **5**, 1048 (1928).
13. Sugden, *J. Chem. Soc.*, **1927**, 1173.
14. Main Smith, *Chemistry & Industry*, **43**, 323 (1924); Sugden, "Parachor and Valency," Chapts. 6 and 7. Geo. Routledge and Sons, Ltd., 1930; Sugden, *J. Chem. Soc.*, **125**, 1177 (1924).
15. Samuel, *J. Chem. Phys.*, **12**, 167 (1944); Pauling, *J. Am. Chem. Soc.*, **53**, 3229 (1931); Emeleus and Anderson, "Modern Aspects of Inorganic Chemistry," 2nd Ed., p. 173, p. 169, New York, D. Van Nostrand Co., Inc., 1952; Lessheim and Samuel, *Nature*, **135**, 230 (1935).
16. Sidgwick, *Trans. Faraday Soc.*, **19**, 472 (1923).

TABLE 4.1. EFFECTIVE ATOMIC NUMBER CONCEPT AS APPLIED TO METAL
CARBONYLS, NITROSYLS, AND THEIR DERIVATIVES

Compound	Electrons From Central Atom	Electrons From Ligands	Effective Atomic Number	Deviation of E.A.N. from Inert Gas	Normal Degree of Association of Molecule
$Ni(CO)_4$	28	8	36	0	Monomer
$Fe(CO)_4I_2$	26	10	36	0	Monomer
$HCo(CO)_4$	28	9	36	0	Monomer
$Fe(NO)_2(CO)_2$	26	10	36	0	Monomer
$Co(CO)_4$	27	8	35	1	Dimer $[Co(CO)_4]_2$
$HNi(CO)_3$	28	7	35	1	Dimer
$Fe(CO)_4$	26	8	34	2	Trimer

(4) If the effective atomic number of the metal in the compound is that of an inert gas, the compound will be a monomer.

(5) If the effective atomic number of the metal in the compound is one short of that of an inert gas, the compound will be a dimer. This statement is equivalent to the hypothesis that the two metal atoms share their odd electrons to achieve the inert gas configuration. More sophisticated treatments of this problem in terms of molecular orbital theory have been given[17], and the postulated metal-metal bond seems reasonable. A short Fe-Fe distance in $Fe_2(CO)_9$ offers experimental support for the metal-metal bond[18].

(6) If the effective atomic number of the metal in the compound is *two* short of that of an inert gas, the compound will be a trimer.

(7) If the effective atomic number of the metal in the compound is *three* short of that of an inert gas, the compound will be a tetramer.

The formulas in Table 4.1 illustrate the application of these rules.

On the other hand, for non-carbonyl or nitrosyl compounds there are a number of exceptions to the rare gas generalization. These were clearly recognized by Sidgwick. The stable hexacoordinate chromium(III) and nickel(II) complexes (EAN = 33 and 38, respectively) and the stable tetracoordinate nickel(II), palladium(II), platinum(II), and gold(III) complexes (EAN = 34, 52, 84, and 84, respectively) are particularly striking examples.

Several well-known complexes of the alkali and alkaline earth metals are particularly damaging deviations from the rare gas rule. The rules on polymerization also seem to be violated in a number of cases involving normal covalent bonds, particularly where the halo carbonyls or thio carbonyls are concerned. In some cases these exceptions can be rationalized by assuming a bridged type of configuration and by using more than one pair of electrons per donor group, but some discrepancies still remain un-

17. Dunitz and Orgel, *J. Chem. Soc.*, **1953**, 2594.
18. Powell and Evans, *J. Chem. Soc.*, **1939**, 286.

explained. For example, the compounds $Fe(CO)_3SEt$ and $Fe(NO)_2SEt$ are dimeric in organic solvents whereas a strict application of the preceding rules would give an effective atomic number of 33 in each case with a resulting tetrameric structure. A rationalization of this apparent exception is obtained if a bridged structure is assumed involving the sulfides, the formulas becoming

Each iron atom in the above structures has thus achieved an EAN of 36 which is consistent with the dimeric formulation. It should be noted, however, that such an explanation begs the question since three of the CO groups in $Fe_2(CO)_9$ also serve to bridge the two iron atoms,

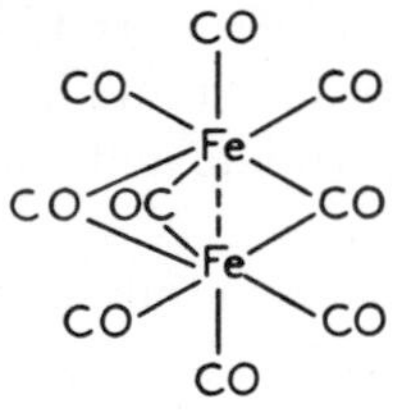

yet, in this case each bridge CO is still assumed to donate only two electrons to the metal atoms. The Fe-Fe distance and the possibility of forming a metal-metal bond is probably important in differentiating the two cases. Even more disturbing is the compound $Fe(CO)_3SC_6H_5$ which has an EAN of 33 yet is a monomer in organic solvents[20]. A similar type of problem arises in the case of the compounds $Pt(CO)_2Cl_2$ and $[Pt(CO)Cl_2]_2$ which give EAN values of 84 and 82, respectively. These compounds, which involve normal Pt—Cl bonds, are suggestive of the well-known compounds $[Pt(NH_3)_2Cl_2]$ and $[Pt(NH_3)_4]Cl_2$, which are well-recognized exceptions to the EAN generalization. R_3PAuCl (EAN = 82) is also monomeric[19], as is $Zn(en)_3^{++}$ (EAN = 40).

In short, the rules appear to be strictly applicable to the pure nitrosyls, carbonyls, and carbonyl hydrides, but their application becomes less reliable as other groups forming normal covalent bonds are attached to the metal atom. The compound $Fe(NO)_4$ might appear to be an exception to

19. Mann, Wells and Purdie, *J. Chem. Soc.*, **1937**, 1828.
20. Hieber and Scharfenberg, *Ber.*, **73**, 1012 (1940); Hieber and Spacu, *Z. anorg. Chem.*, **233**, 353 (1937).

this statement, but available information on its chemical properties indicates the structure can be regarded as NO^+, $[Fe(NO)_3]^-$ in which the EAN rules are strictly obeyed[21].

In some cases magnetic susceptibility measurements can be interpreted satisfactorily by the EAN concept. For example, the carbonyls, the nitrosyls, and compounds such as $K_3[Co(CN)_6]$, $[Co(NH_3)_6]Cl_3$, $[Co(NH_3)_3(NO_2)_2Cl]$, and $K_4[Fe(CN)_6]$ in which the metal has an EAN of 36 are diamagnetic. Moreover, many compounds in which the EAN of the central atom is not that of an inert gas are paramagnetic, and show susceptibilities which correspond closely to the deficiency or excess of electrons[22].

QUANTUM MECHANICAL THEORIES OF DIRECTED VALENCE

Inherent in the early Lewis concept of the shared electron pair and all other static models which arose as variants of Lewis' early picture of the chemical bond was the implication of stationary electrons and charges. Since Earnshaw's theorem of electrostatics states that no system of charges can be in stable equilibrium while at rest, such models did violence to established rules of electrical behavior and failed to describe obvious physical phenomenon such as absorption and radiation of energy by atomic systems.

Bohr's postulate of the planetary atom in which electrons rotate about a central positively charged nucleus obviated some of these difficulties, but the recognition of the Uncertainty Principle by Heisenberg in 1927 indicated that the idea of definite electron orbitals was likewise untenable. As Heisenberg showed, there is no way of measuring exactly the velocity of an electron at any given point; hence, a model describing the electron in such exact terms is unacceptable.*

From this background the modern discipline of wave mechanics developed. The theory introduced by Shrödinger rests upon two concepts: (1) the wave nature of the electron and (2) the statistical character of our knowledge concerning the position of the electron. The application of these ideas to general questions of valence is admirably done by Coulson[23] and his book should be consulted for any further background information.

The probability of finding the electron in any given direction from the nucleus can be obtained for different orbitals of the hydrogen atom by a

21. Sidgwick, "The Chemical Elements and Their Compounds," Vol. II, p. 1373. Oxford, Clarendon Press, 1950.
22. Selwood, "Magnetochemistry," (a) p. 174, (b) p. 161, New York, Interscience Publishers, Inc., 1943.
  * See References 23, 24, 25.
23. Coulson, "Valence," (a) p. 201, (b) p. 216, Oxford, Clarendon Press, 1952.

proper solution of the wave equation. The electron distribution associated with s, p, or d* electrons is indicated in Fig. 4.1. The electron can be found

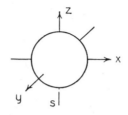

A. S-ORBITAL

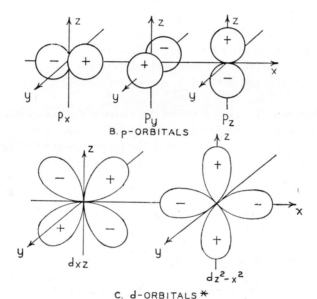

B. p-ORBITALS

C. d-ORBITALS *

FIG. 4.1. Shapes of atomic orbitals

inside the appropriate boundary surface any given percentage of the time, depending upon the absolute scale chosen for the drawing[23, 26].

* See: Ref. 26 for more general representation of d orbitals.

24. Lipscomb, "Atomic and Molecular Structure" in "Comprehensive Inorganic Chemistry," edited by Sneed, Maynard and Brasted. New York, D. Van Nostrand Co., Inc., 1953; Pitzer, "Quantum Chemistry," New York, Prentice-Hall, Inc., 1953.
25. Pauling and Wilson, "Introduction to Quantum Mechanics," New York, McGraw-Hill Book Co., 1935; Eyring, Walter and Kimball, "Quantum Chemistry," New York, John Wiley & Sons, Inc., 1944.
26. White, "Introduction to Atomic Spectra," p. 63, New York, McGraw-Hill Book Co., Inc., 1934.

Two well-established approximate methods for treating molecular structures are currently in use: (1) the atomic orbital approximation, and (2) the molecular orbital approximation. These two approaches to the structure of molecules differ in their basic philosophies and consequently in the mathematical apparatus used. It is gratifying, therefore, that the same ideas of stereochemistry and magnetism of coordination compounds can usually be obtained by the use of either method.

The Atomic Orbital Approximation

In principle, the atomic orbital approximation pictures the electron pair bond as arising when two atoms are brought together in a manner such that their appropriate electronic orbitals interact. As a first approximation, such interaction will lead to bonding if (a) the electrons in the two orbitals have opposite spin so that electron pairing may result, and (b) the orbitals of the two bonding electrons overlap. In fact, it is frequently assumed that the extent of the overlap will determine the covalent bond strength. Since the electron clouds are directed in space, the concept of directed valence follows.

Hybridization. A modification of the above theory of directed valence, based on the method of localized electron pairs[8b, 27], has been widely applied in the correlation and interpretation of the properties of coordination compounds. It recognizes the experimental facts that all coordinating groups in a complex ion such as $[PtCl_6]^=$ are bound to the central metal ion in exactly the same manner and occupy positions about the metal ion which are geometrically equivalent. It follows that the atomic orbitals involved in forming a number of equivalent covalent bonds must differ from each other only in direction.

In the formation of complex compounds there is usually an insufficient number of equivalent bonding orbitals available. It is postulated that with atoms or ions in which several of the outer electronic levels differ little in energy the normal quantization can be changed or broken down and new equivalent bonding orbitals can be formed. This is usually referred to as a "hybridization" process and the resultant equivalent bonding orbitals, as "hybridized" orbitals. In this manner, it is possible, for example, to get four equivalent orbitals directed toward the corners of a tetrahedron or square, or six toward the corners of an octahedron. The energy for this change in quantization comes from the interaction energy accompanying

27. Pauling, "The Nature of the Chemical Bond," 2nd Ed., Ithaca, New York, Cornell University Press, 1940; Heitler and London, *Z. Physik.*, **44**, 455 (1927); Heitler, *Z. Physik.*, **46**, 47 (1928); **47**, 836 (1928); **51**, 805 (1928); London, *Z. Physik.*, **46**, 455 (1928); **50**, 24 (1928); *Naturwissenschaften*, **16**, 58 (1928); *Physik. Z.*, **29**, 558 (1928); Eisenschatz and London, *Z. Physik.*, **60**, 491 (1930); Slater, *Phys. Rev.*, **37**, 481 (1931); **38**, 1109 (1931).

the formation of the electron-pair bonds. Calculations by Pauling indicate that this orbital hybridization process results in the formation of stronger bonds* than would result from bonding with pure unhybridized orbitals. In general, the bonds formed between atoms will be those with the greatest bond strength, i.e., the condition of minimum potential energy.

Coordination Number VI. Further insight into this theory can perhaps best be gained by considering the compounds and complex ions of coordination number six. As can be seen by reference to a table showing the electronic structure of the elements, there are no atoms or common ions which have as many as six equivalent peripheral orbitals.

For elements of the first short period of the periodic classification, the single $2s$ and the three $2p$ orbitals are available for bonding purposes. To obtain six equivalent orbitals for these elements, all or some of the four L ($n = 2$) orbitals must be combined or hybridized with orbitals of higher energy. Inasmuch as the L shell contains no d orbitals, use would have to be made of orbitals of the M ($n = 3$) shell. The large energy separation between the $n = 2$ and $n = 3$ levels evidently precludes this possibility, and no hexacoordinate derivatives of these elements are known.†

In the case of the elements of the second short period, the situation is somewhat different. The M shell contains five $3d$ orbitals along with one $3s$ and three $3p$ orbitals, but various lines of evidence indicate that the $3d$ orbitals lie considerably above the $3p$ orbitals in energy. Evidently for this reason s-p-d hybridization is not common among these elements, but it is not excluded and may be operative in hexacoordinate derivatives such as SF_6, $[PCl_6]^-$, $[SiF_6]^=$, and $[AlF_6]^=$. Pauling has suggested that these molecules may exist as partial ionic structures stabilized by considerable resonance energy or may involve essentially ionic rather than covalent bonds[30].

The electronic constitution of the elements of the first long period is different from that of either of the two short periods. In this period the elements of the first transition series occur. These elements are characterized by the building up of the $3d$ sublevel. Both spectroscopic and chemical evidence lead to the conclusion that the $3d$ electrons in these elements differ very little in energy from the $4s$ electrons. As Pauling pointed out, it is in

* Pauling's interpretation of bond strength as the product of the "strengths" of two separate orbitals, ψ_A and ψ_B, has been extensively criticized[23a, 28, 29]. Mulliken[29] suggests the overlap integral computed at the experimental bond distance, r, as a more satisfactory index of bond energy.

† The compound $[Pt(CH_3)_4]_4$ represents an exception to this statement, since one carbon in each methyl group actually appears to be hexacoordinate (Rundle and Sturdivant, *J. Am. Chem. Soc.*, **69**, 1561 (1947)); the higher hydrides of boron can also be classed as exceptions, requiring special treatment.

28. Craig, Maccoll, Nyholm, Orgel and Sutton, *J. Chem. Soc.*, **1954**, 332.
29. Mulliken, *J. Am. Chem. Soc.*, **72**, 4493 (1950); *J. Phys. Chem.*, **56**, 295 (1952).
30. Reference 27a, pp. 92 and 228.

elements of this very type—elements in which the energy of the inner d orbitals is quite similar to that of the s or p orbitals of the valence shell— that the d orbitals are most prone to play an important part in bond forma- tion, provided they are not fully occupied by electron pairs in the uncom- bined species. It has been shown[31] using the atomic orbital approximation that a set of six equivalent bonding orbitals can be obtained by d^2sp^3 hy- bridization, and that these hybridized orbitals are directed toward the corners of a regular octahedron.

These concepts can be illustrated by applying them to the cobalt(III) ion. The outer electron configuration for the ground state of the neutral cobalt atom is $3d^7 4s^2$, and for the cobalt(III) ion, $3d^6$. Application of Hund's rule of maximum multiplicity to obtain the ground state of the ion gives:

$$\text{Co}^{+++} \quad \underset{\displaystyle 3d}{\underline{\text{↑↓ ↑ ↑ ↑ ↑}}} \qquad \underset{\displaystyle 4s}{\underline{}} \qquad \underset{\displaystyle 4p}{\underline{}}$$

When this ion combines with six ammonia molecules, for example, six pairs of electrons are supplied by the ammonias to make the six bonds. To make six equivalent orbitals available for these electrons, a rearrangement of electrons and levels must occur. The electrons occupying orbitals singly pair up, thereby freeing two of the $3d$ levels for the hybridization process. The combination of two d, one s, and three p orbitals gives the six equiva- lent hybrid bonds; the resulting configuration is abbreviated as d^2sp^3. The final electron distribution is shown below. Since all the electrons are paired, the complex ion is diamagnetic.

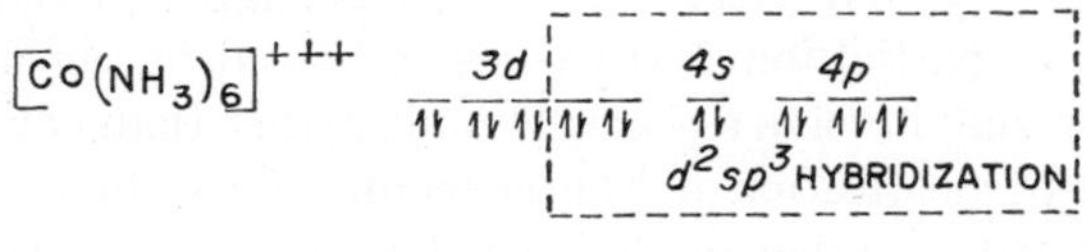

$$\left[\text{Co}(\text{NH}_3)_6\right]^{+++} \quad \underset{\displaystyle 3d}{\underline{\text{↑↓ ↑↓ ↑↓}}}\Big|\underset{}{\underline{\text{↑↓ ↑↓}}} \quad \underset{\displaystyle 4s}{\underline{\text{↑↓}}} \quad \underset{\displaystyle 4p}{\underline{\text{↑↓ ↑↓↑↓}}}$$
$$d^2sp^3 \text{ HYBRIDIZATION}$$

In some instances the total number of electrons involved is not sufficient to fill all the d orbitals after the hybridization process, and unpaired elec- trons are present in the complex. The electronic configurations for the iron(III) ion and the cyanide complex of this ion are given as:

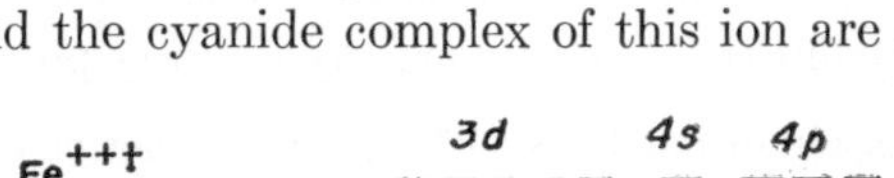

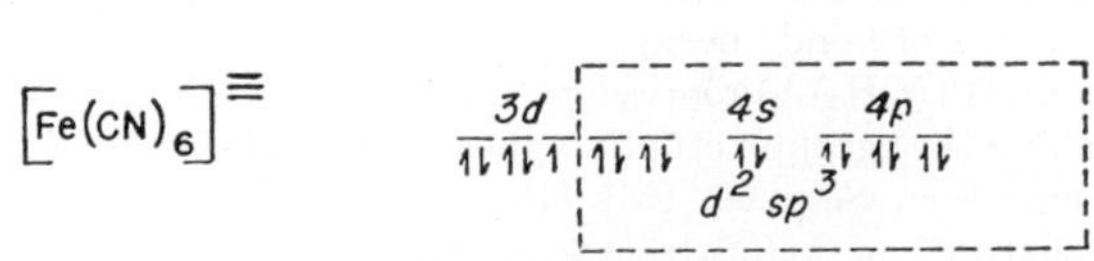

$$\text{Fe}^{+++} \qquad \underset{\displaystyle 3d}{\underline{\text{↑ ↑ ↑ ↑ ↑}}} \quad \underset{\displaystyle 4s}{\underline{}} \quad \underset{\displaystyle 4p}{\underline{}}$$

$$\left[\text{Fe}(\text{CN})_6\right]^{\equiv} \qquad \underset{\displaystyle 3d}{\underline{\text{↑↓ ↑↓ ↑}}}\Big|\underset{}{\underline{\text{↑↓ ↑↓}}} \quad \underset{\displaystyle 4s}{\underline{\text{↑↓}}} \quad \underset{\displaystyle 4p}{\underline{\text{↑↓ ↑↓ ↑↓}}}$$
$$d^2sp^3$$

31. Pauling, *J. Am. Chem. Soc.*, **53**, 1386 (1931); Mills, *J. Chem. Soc.*, **1942**, 465; Hultgren, *Phys. Rev.*, **40**, 891 (1932).

The presence of one unpaired electron in the cyanide complex is confirmed by magnetic susceptibility measurements[22].

In the case of $CoF_6^=$, in which the magnetic moment is the same as that of the Co^{+++} ion before hybridization, it is generally assumed that the six F^- ions are bound to the central Co^{+++} by electrostatic forces such that d^2sp^3 hybridization is not required. An alternative explanation would use $4d$ orbitals so that the $3d$ pattern would not be disturbed (see page 214).

In contrast to the cases just cited, in which the total number of electrons is insufficient to fill all of the orbitals remaining after hybridization, is the case in which the d sublevel in the simple ion already contains the maximum number of electrons allowable by the Pauli principle. Copper(I) serves as an illustration:

$$Cu^+ \qquad \underset{\uparrow\downarrow\;\;\uparrow\downarrow\;\;\uparrow\downarrow\;\;\uparrow\downarrow\;\;\uparrow\downarrow}{\underline{\quad\;\;3d\quad\;\;}\;\underline{\;\;}\;\underline{\;\;}\;\underline{\;\;}\;\underline{\;\;}} \qquad \underset{}{\underline{\;\;4s\;\;}} \quad \underset{}{\underline{\;\;4p\;\;}\;\underline{\;\;}\;\underline{\;\;}}$$

For this ion to form six covalent bonds involving d^2sp^3 hybridization, four electrons would have to be forced out of the $3d$ level and promoted to a higher state such as the $4d$; alternatively, $4s4p^34d^2$ hybridization might occur. However, with a nuclear charge of the order of that of copper, the energy difference between the $4p$ and $4d$ levels is considerable, and either of the possibilities for providing six equivalent bonding orbitals would require considerable energy. It is not surprising, therefore, that copper(I) shows a common coordination number of four rather than six.*

It is apparent that these principles apply equally well (with appropriate change in quantum numbers) to the $4d$ transition elements in the second long period and to the $5d$ transition elements in the third long period. The existence of complexes of some of the heavy metals in which the underlying d shell is already filled, as for example, $SnCl_6^=$ and $SnBr_6^=$, suggests that the d orbitals of the valence shell of the central atoms are utilized in these complexes, or that the complexes are essentially ionic in character.

Nearly every theoretical treatment in coordination chemistry has apparent exceptions which require alteration of the simple picture. In this respect, the atomic orbital approximation runs true to form since disturbing exceptions to the above treatment are known. The ion $[Ru_2Cl_{10}O]^{4-}$ has the hexacoordinate atomic arrangement shown in Fig. 4.2[32]. In this com-

---

* The question of electron promotion is discussed in more detail on pages 169 and 184.

32. Mathieson, Mellor and Stephenson, *Acta Cryst.*, **5**, 185 (1952).

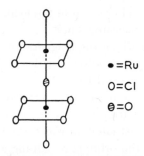

FIG. 4.2. The structure of $[Ru_2Cl_{10}O]^{4-}$

pound ruthenium has a formal oxidation state of $+4$ and the complex should be analogous to the well-known ion $RuCl_6^=$. The magnetic moment of the latter complex indicates two unpaired electrons per ruthenium atom:

$$[RuCl_6]^{=} \quad \underset{\uparrow\downarrow\ \uparrow\quad\uparrow}{\underline{4d}} \ \Big|\ \underset{\uparrow\downarrow\ \uparrow\downarrow}{\underline{}} \quad \underset{\uparrow\downarrow}{\underline{5s}} \quad \underset{\uparrow\downarrow\ \uparrow\downarrow\ \uparrow\downarrow}{\underline{5p}} \Big|$$
$$d^2sp^3 \text{ HYBRIDIZATION}$$

(μ for K_2RuCl_6 is 3.07 Bohr magnetons). However, the oxo-complex is diamagnetic. The obvious conclusion to be drawn from this is that seven orbitals of each ruthenium atom are being used for bond formation instead of six. Pauling[8a] suggested that two of the seven bonding orbitals are involved in double bond formation to the oxygen (page 202). Acceptance of such an explanation reduces the orbital treatment to a much less certain means of correlating structure and magnetism, since a decision cannot be made in advance as to when the d^2sp^3 hybridization will not correlate the facts associated with the octahedral configuration. Any explanation must do violence to the generally accepted d^2sp^3 hybridization for the octahedral structure. The problem has been treated by molecular orbital theory (page 201).

Tetrahedral Configuration. A tetrahedral arrangement of orbitals around a central ion may be obtained by sp^3 hybridization. Elements of the first short period exhibiting this type of symmetry are found in $Be(NH_3)_4^{++}$, BF_4^-, CCl_4, and NH_4^+.

Representative species of the first long period of elements presumably showing sp^3 hybridization are: $[Cu(CN)_4]^\equiv$, $[Zn(CN)_4]^=$, and $[Ni(CO)_4]$. Both $Cu(I)$ and $Zn(II)$ have completely filled $3d$ sublevels; hence, utilization of the d electrons in single bond formation is unlikely. The sp^3 hybridization appears possible for all the elements beyond and including zinc in the first long period. The tetrahedral configuration seems to be generally favored except in the cases of a relatively few hexacoordinate derivatives such as $[Zn\ en_3]^{++}$, $SeF_6^=$ and AsF_6^- which may involve predominantly ionic bonding or utilization of $4d$ levels.

Tetracoordinate derivatives of the transition elements may also attain a tetrahedral arrangement by hybridization of three of the penultimate d orbitals with the s orbitals of the valence shell. Such behavior is, of course, usually limited to the higher oxidation states of these elements as in $CrO_4^=$, MnO_4^-, $MoO_4^=$, and $WO_4^=$.

Planar Configuration. When only one d orbital of the penultimate major quantum shell is available, dsp^2 hybridization occurs, and the resulting equivalent hybridized orbitals are directed in space toward the corners of a square. It is remarkable that most of the planar molecules and ions so far discovered are compounds of nickel(II), palladium(II), platinum(II), and gold(III). It will be noticed that each of these ions has only eight d electrons, leaving one d orbital available for hybridization with s and p orbitals. It seems quite likely that all tetracovalent compounds of copper(II) are planar[33]. Since the copper(II) ion contains $9d$ electrons, dsp^2 hybridization can take place only if one d electron is promoted to a $4p$ or $4d$ level, a process requiring energy. However, if sufficient energy can be gained by the formation of dsp^2 hybrid bonds, the combination procedure of d-electron promotion plus dsp^2 hybridization is favored over the alternative of sp^3 hybridization.[*] On the basis of a limited amount of experimental evidence, silver(II) and silver(III) as well as copper(III) show a square configuration in covalent structures[33, 34].[†]

The original theory, as stated by Pauling, predicted a planar configuration for ions having one and only one d orbital available for bond formation, those with more than one d orbital forming either tetrahedral or octahedral compounds. However, there is some evidence for the planar configuration of cobalt(II) and manganese(II)[33a, 34, 35].

[*] Nyholm[34] has pointed out that there are serious objections to this hypothesis of electron promotion in copper(II) complexes. First, promotion of the electron to a $4p$ level should result in facile oxidation of square copper(II) complexes to the copper(III) state. This is not observed. Also, theoretical work[28] leads to the conclusion that fairly electronegative groups like H_2O and Cl^- (which do give square copper(II) complexes) are more likely to use $4d$ rather than $3d$ bond orbitals. In the case of Ni(II), groups of low electronegativity are required to form $3d4s4p^2$ bonds. Nyholm favors a $4s4p^24d$ configuration for square copper(II) complexes.

[†] The compound K_3CuF_6 containing copper(III) has a moment of 2.9 Bohr magnetons; hence the structure is probably ionic and octahedral (p. 172).

33. Mellor, *Chem. Rev.*, **33**, 137 (1943); Helmholz, *J. Am. Chem. Soc.*, **69**, 886 (1947).
34. Nyholm, *Quart. Revs.*, **7**, 392 (1953).
35. Calvin and Melchior, *J. Am. Chem. Soc.*, **70**, 3273 (1948); Biltz and Fetkenheur, *Z. anorg. Chem.*, **89**, 97 (1914); Cambi and Malatesta, *Gazz. chim. ital.*, **69**, 547 (1939); Mellor and Craig, *J. Proc. Roy. Soc.*, *N. S. Wales*, **74**, 495 (1940); Barkworth and Sugden, *Nature*, **139**, 374 (1937); Mellor and Coryell, *J. Am. Chem. Soc.*, **60**, 1786 (1938); Cox, Shorter, Wardlaw and Way, *J. Chem. Soc.*, **1937**, 1556; Figgis and Nyholm, *J. Chem. Soc.*, **1954**, 12.

TABLE 4.2. ORBITAL AND SPATIAL CONFIGURATIONS FOR COORDINATION NUMBERS TWO THROUGH EIGHT INCLUDING BOND STRENGTHS AND REPRESENTATIVE COMPOUNDS*

Coordination No.	Orbital Configuration	Spatial Configuration	Relative Bond Strengths*	Examples
2	p^2	angular	1.732	H_2O, H_2S, OF_2, SCl_2
	sp	linear	1.932	$Ag(CN)_2^-, Hg_2X_2$
3	p^3	trigonal pyramid	1.732	$NH_3, PH_3, AsCl_3$
	sp^2	trigonal plane	1.991	$B(CH_3)_3, NO_3^-$
4	sp^3	tetrahedron	2.000	$[B(CH_3)_3NH_3], Ni(CO)_4, [Cu(CN)_4]^=$
	dsp^2	tetragonal plane	2.694	$[Pt(NH_3)_4]^{++}, [AuCl_4]^= [Ni(CN)_4]^=$
	d^3s	tetrahedron	2.950	$CrO_4^=, MoO_4^=$
	d^2p^2	tetragonal plane	—	ICl_4^- †
5	dsp^3 or d^3sp	trigonal bipyramid	—	$PCl_5, MoCl_5, TaF_5$
	$d^2sp^2, d^4s, d^2p^3,$ or d^4p	tetragonal pyramid	—	$IF_5, [Ni(PEt_3)_2Br_3]$
6	d^2sp^3	octahedron	2.923	$[PdCl_6]^=, [Co(NH_3)_6]^{+++}$
	d^4sp	trigonal prism	2.983	MoS_2, WS_2
7	d^5sp or d^3sp^3	octahedron with an atom at the center of one face	—	$[ZrF_7]^{-3}$
	d^4sp^2 or d^5p^2	trigonal prism with an atom at center of one of the square faces.	—	$[TaF_7]^-, [NbF_7]^-$
8‡	d^4sp^3	dodecahedron	—	$[Mo(CN)_8]^{4-}$
	d^5p^3	antiprism	—	$[TaF_8]^=$
	d^5sp^2	face-centered prism	—	$[OsF_8]$

* For the special meaning of "bond strength" as used here, see references[28, 29, 37].

† The iodine atom in this compound is also considered to possess two stereochemically active unshared electron pairs in octahedral positions, a structure which at the present time appears to be unique[33a, 38].

‡ Van Vleck[39] has expressed the opinion that a complex with eight attached groups is unlikely to be stable unless f orbitals are available on the central atom. This may be one reason why relatively few atoms exhibit a coordination number of eight[40].

Other Coordination Numbers. A comprehensive treatment of coordination involving different modes of hybridization was carried out by Kimball[36] using both the atomic orbital and molecular orbital approximations. A summary of the stereochemical implications of his results for coordination numbers two through eight appears in Table 4.2.

36. Kimball, *J. Chem. Phys.*, **8**, 188 (1940).
37. Reference 27a, Chap. III; Pauling and Sherman, *J. Am. Chem. Soc.*, **59**, 1450 (1937); Ref. 23, p. 197.
38. Sidgwick and Powell, *Proc. Roy. Soc.* (*London*), **A176**, 153 (1940); Mooney, *Z. Krist.*, **98**, 377 (1938).
39. Van Vleck, *J. Chem. Phys.*, **3**, 805 (1935).
40. Penney and Anderson, *Trans. Faraday Soc.*, **33**, 1363 (1937).

Stereochemistry and the Nature of the Central Atom.* As has been indicated previously, the nickel(II) ion has an electronic structure which permits formation of diamagnetic square planar dsp^2 bonds, yet paramagnetic tetrahedral sp^3 nickel(II) complexes are also known. The nickel glyoximes and $Ni(CN)_4^=$, for example, have been shown to be diamagnetic and planar[41], whereas $[Ni(NH_3)_4]^{++}$ is paramagnetic and presumably tetrahedral.†

In a comprehensive review, Mellor[33a] considered which electronic configurations of a metal will favor octahedral, planar, or tetrahedral structures. After a very careful review of the data, he concluded that, "when a metal atom of the transition series forms a *covalent complex*, it tends to assume that configuration (tetrahedral, square, octahedral, etc.) which involves the least possible number of unpaired electrons."‡ This generalization appears to follow from an inspection of Table 4.3, which is reproduced from Mellor's paper. The relatively few ions for which a planar configuration has been reported are underlined. It is significant that the planar configuration is most common among the elements in those oxidation states for which the resulting complex contains no unpaired electrons (Ni^{++}, Pd^{++}, Pt^{++}, Au^{+++}) or one unpaired electron (Cu^{++}, Ag^{++}, Co^{++}); the planar configuration is much less common or even doubtful among those ions giving dsp^2 bonded complexes with two or three unpaired electrons (Fe^{++}, Mn^{++}), and is probably not existent among those containing the maximum of four unpaired electrons. The octahedral configuration is invariably associated with complexes of Co^{+++}, Rh^{+++}, Pd^{4+}, Ir^{+++}, and Pt^{4+}; and, with few exceptions, these complexes are diamagnetic.

According to the original criteria used to predict planar and tetrahedral configurations, a change in the oxidation state of a central metal ion can lead to a complete change in bond orientation (Table 4.3). This is confirmed by the existence of tetrahedral $Ni(CO)_4$ and planar $[Ni(CN)_4]^=$ which are derivatives of nickel(0) and nickel(II), respectively, and by diamagnetic

---

* See also Chapter 9.

† It is interesting that unequivocal experimental proof for the tetrahedral configuration for this ion is not yet available—more than twenty years after Pauling's suggestion—but Nyholm[42a] has summarized existing evidence for the tetrahedral form in a rather convincing fashion. The complexes assumed to be tetrahedral are generally green or blue in color as compared to the diamagnetic complexes which are usually red, brown, or yellow[42]. Mellor[43] and his co-workers have reported, however, that the correlation between configuration and color is not always clear-cut. Nyholm[42a] reports that a more reliable though not infallible criterion of diamagnetism is a sharp absorption band in the vicinity of 4,000 Å.

‡ Van Vleck[39] expressed about the same idea in calling attention to the fact that while a large spin (due to unpaired electrons) might be an advantage as far as a free atom is concerned, in an atomic system the interatomic energy may be decreased by a lowering of the total spin.

TABLE 4.3. PREDICTED MAGNETIC MOMENTS* OF COMPLEXES CONTAINING TRANSITION ELEMENTS

	The Iron Period (Period 4)	The Palladium Period (Period 5)	The Platinum Period (Period 6)	No. of Electrons in d Shell ($3d$, $4d$, or $5d$)	Magnetic Moment in Bohr Magnetons		
					For Ionic or sp^3 (tetrahedral) bonds	For Four dsp^2 (square) bonds	For Six d^2sp^3 (octahedral) bonds
1	K^+, Ca^{++}, Sc^{+++}, Ti^{4+}	Rb^+, Sr^{++}, Y^{+++}, Zr^{4+}, Nb^{5+}, Mo^{6+}	Cs^+, Ba^{++}, Hf^{4+}, Ta^{5+}, W^{6+}	0	0.00	0.00	0.00
2	V^{4+}	Nb^{4+}, Mo^{5+}	W^{5+}	1	1.73	1.73	1.73
3	V^{+++}, Cr^{4+}	Mo^{4+}, Ru^{6+}	W^{4+}, Os^{6+}	2	2.83	2.83	2.83
4	V^{++}, Cr^{+++}, Mn^{4+}	Mo^{+++}	Os^{4+}	3	3.88	3.88	3.88
5	Cr^{++}, Mn^{+++}, Fe^{4+}	Mo^{++}, Ru^{4+}	Os^{+++}, Ir^{4+}	4	4.90	4.90	2.83
6	Mn^{++}, Fe^{+++}, Co^{4+}	Ru^{+++}	Ir^{+++}, Pt^{4+}	5	5.91	3.88	1.73
7	Fe^{++}, Co^{+++}, Ni^{4+}	Ru^{++}, Rh^{+++}, Pd^{4+}	Ir^{++}	6	4.90	2.83	0.00
8	Co^{++}, Ni^{+++}	Rh^{++}	Pt^{++}, Au^{+++}	7	3.88	1.73	
9	Ni^{++}	Rh^+, Pd^{++}, Ag^{+++}		8	2.83	0.00	
10	Cu^{++}	Ag^{++}		9	1.73	1.73	
11	Cu^+, Zn^{++}, Ge^{4+}	Ag^+, Cd^{++}, In^{+++}	Au^+, Hg^{++}, Ti^{+++}, Pb^{4+}, Bi^{5+}	10	0.00		

* When number of unpaired electrons is 1, 2, 3, 4, or 5, the magnetic moment is equal respectively to 1.73, 2.83, 3.88, 4.90, and 5.91 Bohr magnetons.

tetrahedral complexes of copper(I) and silver(I) as opposed to the para-magnetic planar derivatives of copper(II) and silver(II).

The question as to which of *two possible* structures, square or tetrahedral, will be assumed by the nickel(II) compounds is more complex. One of the major factors determining the geometry appears to be the relative differences in the electronegativities of the nickel and of the atoms linked to it. Large differences appear to favor predominantly ionic bonds and the tetrahedral configuration, although the nature of the functional group in which the atom bonded to the nickel occurs may also be significant. Steric factors are sometimes of major importance[44].

In some instances the type of crystal lattice, the solvent, and the temperature appear to be important in determining which configuration will be assumed[42a, 45, 46]. For example, [Ni en$_2$] [AgIBr]$_2$ is diamagnetic in the solid state, whereas compounds of [Ni en$_2$]$^{++}$ with anions like ClO$_4^-$ are paramagnetic in the solid state. Similarly, dipole moment measurements and magnetic data indicate that [NiCl$_2 \cdot \{(C_2H_5)_3P\}_2$] and [NiBr$_2 \cdot \{(C_2H_5)_3P\}_2$] are trans-planar, but when the halogens are replaced by nitrate, both the dipole data and magnetic moments indicate a tetrahedral structure. Lattice factors are of importance in determining the reorientation of orbitals. The compound bis(salicylaldoxime) nickel(II) is diamagnetic both in the solid state and in benzene solution, but has a magnetic moment indicating two unpaired electrons in pyridine solution. This has been ascribed to octahedral coordination in pyridine solution. On the other hand, bis(N-methyl-salicylaldimine) nickel(II) is diamagnetic in the solid state but paramagnetic in benzene. Since benzene does not usually coordinate with nickel one might assume that the paramagnetic form represents a tetrahedral structure in benzene. Actually, Klemm and Raddatz[47] have reported the isolation of paramagnetic and diamagnetic forms of the solid salt; the paramagnetic form changes spontaneously to the diamagnetic form on standing. Recently Basolo and Matoush[46] reported that no direct correla-

41. Sugden, *J. Chem. Soc.*, **1932**, 246; Brasseur, de Rassenfosse and Pierard, *Compt. rend.*, **198**, 1048 (1934); Cambi and Szego, *Ber.*, **64**, 2591 (1931).
42. Nyholm, *Chem. Rev.*, **53**, 267 (1953); Lifschitz, Bos, and Dijkema, *Z. anorg. allgem. Chem.*, **242**, 97 (1939); Lifschitz and Bos, *Rec. trav. chim.*, **59**, 407 (1940); Lifschitz and Dijkema, *Rec. trav. chim.*, **60**, 581 (1941); Ref. 27a, p. 122.
43. Mills and Mellor, *J. Am. Chem. Soc.*, **64**, 181 (1942); Mellor, Mills and Short, *J. Proc. Roy. Soc.*, *N. S. Wales*, **78**, 70 (1944).
44. Reference 22, p. 180.
45. Willis and Mellor, *J. Am. Chem. Soc.*, **69**, 1237 (1947); French, Magee, and Sheffield, *J. Am. Chem. Soc.*, **64**, 1924 (1942); Johnson and Hall, *J. Am. Chem. Soc.*, **70**, 2347 (1948); Lifschitz, *Rec. trav. chim.*, **66**, 401 (1947).
46. Basolo and Matoush, *J. Am. Chem. Soc.*, **75**, 5663 (1953).
47. Klemm and Raddatz, *Z. anorg. allgem. Chem.*, **250**, 207 (1942).

tion exists between the magnetic susceptibility of solutions of bis(formyl-camphor)ethylenediamine nickel(II) in methylbenzenes and the base strength of the solvent. If the paramagnetic susceptibility were due to formation of octahedral complexes by expansion of the coordination shell of nickel, one might expect such a correlation. The data lead to the conclusion that tetrahedral nickel(II) compounds are formed in the solvent. Data delineating the effects of temperature on the conversion are sparse.

Sidgwick and Powell[38a] studied the *empirical* relationship between stereochemical types, the nature of the valence group of the central atom, and the number of shared electrons. Their scheme bears considerable resemblance to that of Tsuchida (page 131) in application, although the assumed charge distribution is quite different in the two cases. The results are empirically useful, although of doubtful theoretical interest at present.*

Stability of Complexes and the Atomic Orbital Theory. *The Role of the Metal.* The stability of complexes has been considered in terms of a thermochemical cycle on page 137. It is apparent that the ultimate stability of any given compound is dependent upon small differences between large energy terms (page 143); thus, the degree of precision required in making energy estimates for any given step in the cycle must be very high; otherwise the final energy of formation of a compound may even be reversed in sign as a result of relatively small errors in any one term. Fortunately, in many cases of complex formation, particularly in aqueous solution, the stabilities of compounds of similar type can be compared under such conditions that differences in the energy of coordination, E, for different metals will be relatively large compared to differences in other energy terms such as heats of hydration of the gaseous ions and the ligands involved. Under such conditions the stabilities of the complexes may be correlated with those factors influencing the energy of coordination:

$$M(g)^{++} + Ligand(g) \rightarrow M\,Ligand(g)^{++}$$

Since nitrogen, oxygen and sulfur serve as the actual bonding atoms in a large majority of complex compounds, Sidgwick[49] divided the metals into three categories on the basis of their relative abilities to combine with oxygen (usually through a normal covalent bond) or nitrogen (usually through

---

* Several general rules applying to molecular configurations and electronic constitution of simple molecules, which are almost identical to portions of the scheme of Sidgwick and Powell, were advanced more recently by Helferich[48].

48. Helferich, *Z. Naturforsch.*, **1**, 666 (1946).
49. Sidgwick: *J. Chem. Soc.*, **433** (1941); "The Electronic Theory of Valency," Oxford University Press, 1927.

a coordinate covalent bond). These categories are:

(1) Bond to oxygen stronger than to nitrogen:

$$Mg, Ca, Sr, Ba, Ga, In, Tl, Ti, Zr, Th, Si, Ge, Sn, V^V, V^{IV}, Nb^V,$$

$$Ta^V, Mo^V, U^{VI}, Fe^{III}, Co^{II}.$$

(2) Bond to oxygen and nitrogen with about equal strength:

$$Be, Cr^{III}, Fe^{II}, \text{platinum metals}$$

(3) Bond to nitrogen stronger than to oxygen:

$$Cu^I, Ag^I, Au^I, Cu^{II}, Cd, Hg, V^{III}, Co^{III}, Ni^{II}.$$

It will be noticed that nearly all of the ions of group (1) are of the inert gas type; those of group (3) are of the palladium type or are small and have a nearly full d level (i.e., Ni^{++}), whereas the intermediate ions are the very small beryllium ion and the larger transition ions. Some justification for this grouping has been given in Chapter 3.

It must be recognized that broad generalizations such as the above will have many exceptions, particularly in certain intermediate regions, but it is significant that in a recent survey of the coordinating ability of a number of different ligands VanUitert and Fernelius[50] reported that "compounds formed by chelating agents bonding through nitrogen show a greater dependency upon metal ion electronegativity than those bonding through oxygen," an observation which supports admirably the foregoing generalization. In particular it was found that Ca^{++} and Mg^{++} coordinate more effectively through oxygen whereas Cu^{++} and Ni^{++} coordinate best through nitrogen.

A number of investigators in recent years have attempted to list the metal cations on the basis of their ability to coordinate with one or two specific ligands. Using a chelating agent involving oxygen and nitrogen bonds, Pfeiffer, Thielert, and Glaser[51] obtained the following order of decreasing stability of complex: Cu^{++}, Ni^{++}, Fe^{++}, Zn^{++}, Mg^{++}. Mellor and Maley[52] studied the stability of salicylaldehyde complexes in 50 per cent water-dioxane solution using the method developed by Bjerrum[53]. Their order of decreasing stability was: Pd^{++}, Cu^{++}, Ni^{++}, Co^{++}, Zn^{++}, Cd^{++}, Fe^{++}, Mn^{++}, Mg^{++}. With minor exceptions the order is the same as that given by Pfeiffer and as that found when glycine, 8-hydroxyquinoline, or ethylenediamine is the chelating group in aqueous solution.

50. VanUitert and Fernelius: *J. Am. Chem. Soc.*, **76**, 375, 379 (1954).
51. Pfeiffer, Thielert, and Glaser: *J. prakt. Chem.*, **152**, 145 (1939).
52. Mellor and Maley: *Nature*, **159**, 370 (1947); **161**, 436 (1948).
53. Bjerrum: "Metal Ammine Formation in Aqueous Solution," Copenhagen, P. Haase and Son, 1941.

Calvin and Melchior[35a] used the method of Bjerrum to study the stability of the salicylaldehyde chelates in water solution, using a sulfonated salicylaldehyde to obtain water solubility. A similar set of data was accumulated for o-formylnaphthols. In all cases the stability of the series was:

$$Cu^{++}, Ni^{++}, Co^{++}, Zn^{++}$$

$$\underset{\text{of Chelate}}{\underline{\text{Decreasing Stability}}} \longrightarrow$$

Since the order is essentially the same as that of Mellor, the role of the solvent seems to be small.

VanUitert, Fernelius, and Douglas[56], using a modification of the Bjerrum titration method, studied the stabilities of the metal chelates of several substituted β-diketones. They found that the general order of stability in 75 per cent dioxane-water solution is:

$$Hg^{++}, (Cu^{++}, Be^{++})\ Fe^{++}, Ni^{++}, Co^{++}, Zn^{++}, Pb^{++}, Mn^{++}, Cd^{++}, Mg^{++}, Ca^{++}, Sr^{++}, Ba^{++}.$$

$$\overline{} \longrightarrow$$
Decreasing stability

Similar series using other ligands have also been given[54, 55, 56]. Results show some deviation from the above lists, but certain features are recurrent.

In general, the stability of the complexes of the alkali and alkaline earth metals decreases as the charge on the cation decreases or as the size of the cation increases. Lumb and Martell[57] found that the stabilities of alkaline earth complexes of glutamic and aspartic acids fall in the order $Mg^{++} > Ca^{++} > Sr^{++} > Ba^{++} > Ra^{++}$. The stability of the citric acid complexes of the alkaline earths falls in the order $Ca^{++} > Sr^{++} > Ba^{++}$[58]. A similar order has been reported for the complexes of a number of alkali and alkaline earth metal ions with N-acetic acid substituted amines and with polyamines.[59] All data on the complexes of the rare earth ions are also consistent in showing a decrease in complex stability with increasing size of the rare earth ion[60, 61, 62, 63, 64]. (See Fig. 4.4)

54. Merritt, "Frontiers of Science Outline," Wayne University, Spring, 1949;
55. Chabarek and Martell: *J. Am. Chem. Soc.*, **75**, 2888 (1953).
56. VanUitert, Fernelius, and Douglas: *J. Am. Chem. Soc.*, **75**, 457, 2736, 2739, 3577, (1953); VanUitert and Hass, *J. Am. Chem. Soc.*, **75**, 451 (1953); VanUitert, Hass, Fernelius, and Douglas, *J. Am. Chem. Soc.*, **75**, 455 (1953).
57. Lumb and Martell, *J. Am. Chem. Soc.*, **75**, 690 (1953).
58. Hennig, Schmahl, and Theopold, *Biochem. Z.*, **321**, 401 (1952).
59. Martell and Calvin, "Chemistry of the Metal Chelate Compounds," (a) p. 192; (b) p. 190, New York, Prentice-Hall, Inc., 1952.
60. Spedding and Powell, *J. Am. Chem. Soc.*, **76**, 2545, 2550 (1954) and earlier papers of Spedding on ion exchange separation of rare earths with citrate.
61. Fitch and Russell, *Can. J. Chem.*, **29**, 363 (1951); *Anal. Chem.*, **23**, 1469 (1951); Beck, *Chem. Acta*, **29**, 357 (1946).
62. Moeller, *Record Chem. Progress*, **14**, 69 (1953).

Irving and Williams[65] summarized the results of many investigators in an excellent review of available stability data. They recognized that comparisons of the stabilities of complexes of different ligands are most effective when metals of the same type are used. Reversals found in the earlier lists arise because comparisons were drawn between complexes of dissimilar metals. When comparisons were restricted to bivalent metals of the first transition series they found that the order Mn < (poorer than) Fe < Co < Ni < Cu > (better than) Zn is valid irrespective of the nature of the coordinated ligand or the number of ligands involved. Since the ability of metals to coordinate with nitrogen, oxygen or sulfur varies, depending upon the type of metal considered, no single series involving all metal ions with all ligands can ever be expected. Irving and Williams correlated their series with the reciprocal of the ionic radii and the second ionization potentials of the metals as suggested by Irving and Williams[65b] and by Calvin and Melchior[35a].

Such a correlation finds justification in that the second ionization potential for ions of comparable size can be used as an estimate of the strength of the σ bond between metal and ligand. The ion type is important in that it determines the extent of secondary interactions such as multiple bond formation (p. 191). The data for the alkaline earth, alkali metal, and rare earth metal ions can best be considered in terms of predominantly ionic bonds (Chapter 3).

Martell and Calvin[59b] indicated the general relationship between the formation constants of metal chelates and the second ionization potentials of the metals by means of the plot shown in Fig. 4.3. The relationship between the stability constants of the rare earth chelates of ethylenediamine tetraacetate and the reciprocal of the radius of the rare earth ions is shown in Fig. 4.4. In both of these cases the ions are sufficiently similar so that the method chosen to estimate the field strength around the ion is reasonably good for all members of the series.*

The Role of the Ligand. If one accepts the definition of G. N. Lewis that a base is an electron pair donor, the process of coordination is an acid-base phenomenon in which the coordinated ligand acts as a base and the metal ion acts as an acid. The point is illustrated by comparing the typical acid-

---

* Wheelwright, Spedding and Schwarzenbach[64b] suggested that the rare earth ethylenediaminetetraacetate complexes change from hexadentate to pentadentate structures at Gd^{+++} because of steric effects due to decreasing size of cation.

63. Dissertations, University of Illinois, Brantley (1949); Moss (1952).

64. Martell and Plumb, *J. Phys. Chem.*, **56**, 993 (1952); Wheelwright, Spedding, and Schwarzenbach, *J. Am. Chem. Soc.*, **75**, 4196 (1953); Spedding, Powell, and Wheelwright, *J. Am. Chem. Soc.*, **76**, 2557 (1954); Templeton and Dauben, *J. Am. Chem. Soc.* **76**, 5237 (1954).

65. Irving and Williams, *J. Chem. Soc.*, **1953**, 3192; *Nature* **162**, 746 (1948).

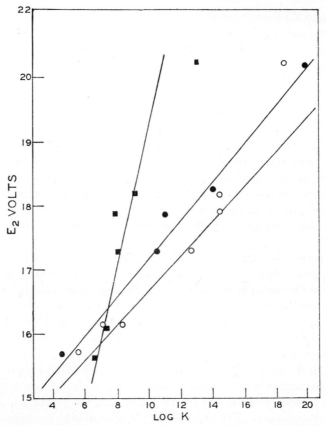

FIG. 4.3. Relationships between formation constants of metal chelates and the second ionization potentials of the metals. ● Ethylenediamine; ○ β, β', β" tri-aminotriethylamine; ■ salicylaldehyde.

base reaction between ammonia and hydrogen ion with the similar reaction between ammonia and copper(I) ion.

$$
\begin{matrix}
& \overset{\text{H}}{\underset{\text{H}}{\ddot{\text{N}}}} & & \overset{\text{H}}{\underset{\text{H}}{\ddot{\text{N}}}} & \\
\end{matrix}
$$

(1)   H⁺ + :N:H → H:N:H⁺   Acid-base process

    Acid   Base

(2)   Cu⁺ + :N:H → Cu:N:H⁺   Coordination process

    Acid   Base

The formal analogy is apparent, though even elementary considerations suggest that the ability of the positive ion to attract electrons will be influenced by many characteristics of the cation such as charge, size, polariza-

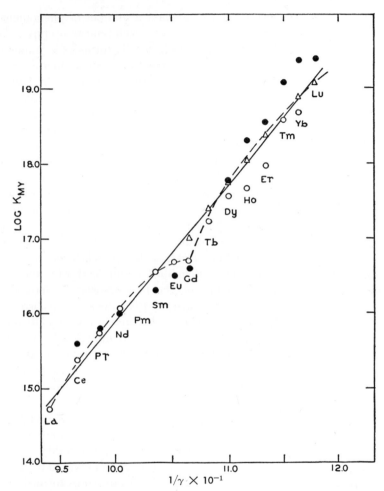

Fig. 4.4. Log of the Stability constants of the rare earth complexes of ethylene-diamine tetraacetate[64b] as a function of reciprocal of the empirical radius[64d].

○ — Potentiometric data

● — Polarographic data in KNO_3 $\mu = 0.1$

△ — Polarographic data in KCl $\mu = 0.1$

The potentiometric data are most accurate for the ions La-Eu.

The polarographic data are most accurate for the ions Gd-Lu.

bility, screening constants and other properties as well as by properties of the ligand. In view of the formal analogy, a correlation between the basic strength of a ligand and its coordinating ability is not unexpected, although one could hardly hope for a strict parallelism.

In 1928 Riley[66] suggested that any factor which increases the localization of negative charge in the base (coordinating ligand) makes the electrons more readily available and thus increases the ability of the base to coordinate. These ideas were used to explain a number of phenomena. It has been observed that sulfate and sulfite ions each tend to occupy a single coordination position while carbonate preferentially forms a four membered chelate ring involving two coordination positions. Steric factors cannot explain this difference. Riley attributed the difference to a tighter binding of the electrons on the sulfate because of the higher nuclear charge on the central sulfur atom. Carbonate ion with a lower nuclear charge on the central carbon atom supposedly can contribute the four electrons necessary to form *two coordinate* bonds more readily than can the sulfate ion.

Many attempts to establish a linear relationship between the basic strength of a ligand (as measured by its pK_{H^+} value) and the complex forming ability of the ligand (as measured by the logarithm of the formation constant of its metal complexes) have been recorded. One of the first attempts was that of Larsson[67]. The relationship was disputed by later workers[68, 69], but it now seems well established that when systems of *sufficient structural similarity* are compared, a linear relationship between $pK_{complex}$ and pK_{base} is obtained. Bruehlman and Verhoek[70] found, for example, that when the logarithm of the first association constants of silver-amine complexes are plotted against the pK values for the corresponding substituted ammonium ions, two straight lines are obtained: one for the pyridines and primary aliphatic amines and one for the secondary amines. Data from the literature indicate that tertiary aliphatic amines lie on a third curve. The slope of the curves (Fig. 4.5) is approximately one-fourth, indicating a much smaller range of basic strengths when measured against hydrogen ion, a not unexpected observation.

Bjerrum[71] confirmed the linear relationship for cyclic amines and primary amines and extended the data to include mercury(II) complexes as well. The data of Schwarzenbach and his co-workers on the stability constants of the complexes of the alkaline earths with aminopolycarboxylic acids show a similar relationship if the number of chelate rings formed in the structure is taken into account (page 229).

Calvin and Bailes[72] in 1946 studied polarographically the stability of copper chelates of the form

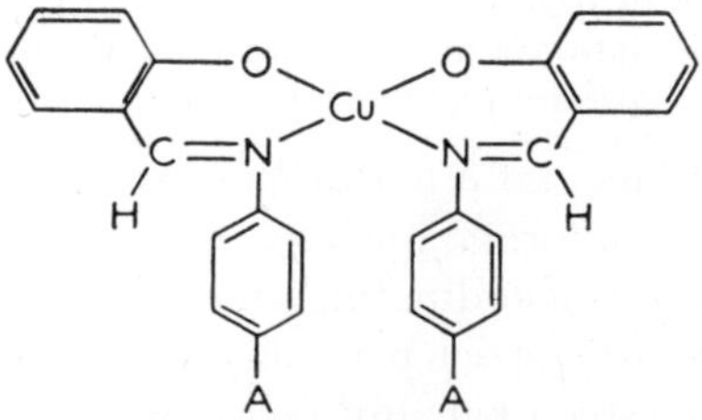

66. Riley, *J. Chem. Soc.*, **1928**, 2985; Ives and Riley, *J. Chem. Soc.*, **1931**, 1998.
67. Larsson, *Z. physik. Chem.*, **A169**, 215 (1934).

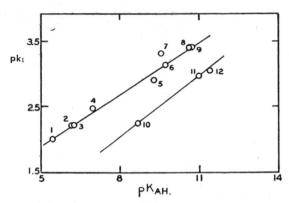

Fig. 4.5. Relationship between strength of the base and its ability to form co-ordination compounds with silver(I) ion (From Ref. 70).

(1) Pyridine
(2) α-Picoline
(3) γ-Picoline
(4) 2,4-Lutidine
(5) β-Methoxyethylamine
(6) Ethanolamine
(7) Benzylamine
(8) Isobutylamine
(9) Ethylamine
(10) Morpholine
(11) Diethylamine
(12) Piperidine

where A represents an electron attracting group. They found that, in general, the greater the electron attracting power of A the greater the tendency to remove electrons from the nitrogen and hence the lower the basic strength of the amine and the stability of the copper complex. The stability of the compounds varied as A was changed, the order being

$$-NO_2 < -SO_3Na < -\langle S \rangle < -H < -CH_3 < -OH < -OCH_3 .$$

More recently Fernelius and co-workers[56] have carried out intensive investigations on the coordinating ability of diketones of the type RCOCH$_2$-COR′ where the nature of the R groups was varied systematically. They report a linear relationship between the logarithm of the formation con-

68. Vosburgh and Cogswell, *J. Am. Chem. Soc.*, **65**, 2412 (1943).
69. Britton and Williams, *J. Chem. Soc.*, **1935**, 796.
70. Bruehlman and Verhoek, *J. Am. Chem. Soc.*, **70**, 1401 (1948).
71. Bjerrum, *Chem. Revs.*, **46**, 381 (1950).
72. Calvin and Bailes, *J. Am. Chem. Soc.*, **68**, 953 (1946).

stants of the sodium complexes of the β-diketones with aromatic R groups and the pK values of the diketones. If one assumes that the β-diketones are largely in the enol form, the following represents the influence of the aromatic R groups in decreasing the basic strength of the diketone ion.

DECREASING BASIC STRENGTH

It was found also that the relationship holds for many metals, the slope

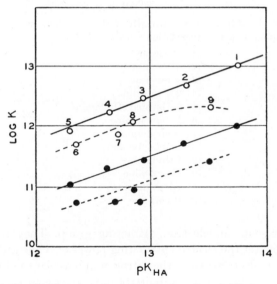

Fig. 4.6. Relationship between the acid pK of various β-diketones and the ability of the diketones to coordinate with copper(II). (Data from Ref. 56a)
○ log K_1 for process $M^{++} + Ke^- \rightarrow MKe^+$
● log K_2 for process $MKe^+ + Ke^- \rightarrow M(Ke)_2$
Solid lines represent ketones with two aromatic groups; dotted lines, those with one alkyl group.

Compound	R	R¹
1	phenyl	phenyl
2	2, thenyl	phenyl
3	2, furyl	phenyl
4	2, thenyl	2, thenyl
5	2, furyl	2, thenyl
6	2, thenyl	methyl
7	methyl	methyl
8	phenyl	methyl
9	silyl	methyl

TABLE 4.4. STABILITY CONSTANTS OF SUBSTITUTED
MALONATE COMPLEXES OF COPPER

R	R'	Acid Constants of Malonic Acids			$-\log$ $K_{complex\ dissoc.}$ (larger value = greater stability)
		pK_1	pK_2	$pK_1 + pK_2$	
H	H	2.75	5.36	8.11	8
Me	H	2.97	5.46	8.43	8
Et	H	2.90	5.55	8.45	8
n-Pr	H	2.97	5.68	8.65	8
i-Pr	H	2.93	5.80	8.73	9
Me	Me	3.08	5.82	8.90	5.4
Et	Et	2.24	7.23	9.47	5
n-Pr	n-Pr	2.06	7.48	9.54	5

A similar situation was observed qualitatively by Bailar and Work when they observed that neopentanediamine, $NH_2CH_2C(CH_3)_2CH_2NH_2$,[74] coordinates more readily and gives more stable compounds than its unsubstituted analog, trimethylenediamine.

of the line becoming greater with more electronegative metals. A second linear relationship was obtained for those ligands in which R is an aromatic group and R' an alkyl group. Representative data for their copper complexes are shown in Fig. 4.6. In general the β-diketones containing two aromatic rings form more stable chelate compounds than those containing one aliphatic group. This difference is greater for the second ligand than for the first. Among the alkyl groups studied were CH_3—, C_2H_5—, $(CH_3)_2CH$—, $(CH_3)_3SiCH_2CH_2$—, $(CH_3)_3C$—, and F_3C—. As might be expected from the inductive effect, the trifluoromethyl group reduces the basic strength of the ligand very markedly.

Two rather anomalous observations on electronic effects merit brief consideration. Riley[66] studied the stability of copper complexes of substituted malonic acids of the type $CHR(COOH)_2$. He found that if R is methyl, ethyl, or normal propyl, the resulting complex is slightly *less* stable than if R is hydrogen. On the other hand, if R is an isopropyl group the complex is reportedly much more stable than when R is hydrogen. For malonate ions of the type $RR'C(COO)_2^=$ the resulting complex is much less stable than when only a single group is present. Ethyl and propyl have a bigger effect than methyl in reducing stability, which implies steric factors or solvation factors with the disubstituted compound.

As the data in Table 4.4 show, the stability constants for the copper complexes do not parallel the pK values for these acids[73]. The role of the isopropyl group appears to be anomalous in this case.

73. Gane and Ingold, *J. Chem. Soc.*, **1929,** 1698.
74. Bailar and Work, *J. Am. Chem. Soc.*, **68,** 232 (1946).

Stabilization of Valence by Coordination.* A number of attempts have been made to justify by the atomic orbital theory the fact that coordination can stabilize both common and uncommon valence states of a metal. For example, the relative stabilities of the 2+ and 3+ states of cobalt have been explained repeatedly in terms of atomic orbital theory. The cobalt(II) cyanide complex is so unstable that it reduces water with the liberation of hydrogen, while the hydrated cobalt(III) ion is so unstable that it will liberate oxygen from water (see page 185). Pauling suggested[27a] that these facts may be explained from a consideration of orbitals available in the cobalt cyanide complexes. The hexacovalent cobalt(II) cyanide is represented as:

$$\left[Co(CN)_6 \right]^{4-}$$

In order to free two d orbitals for complex formation, the seventh d electron in the cobalt(II) ion is promoted to a higher energy level where it is easily lost to give the cobalt(III) complex. Two arguments may immediately be raised against such a simple explanation. First, it is known that the hydrated cobalt(III) ion is also diamagnetic; hence, it, like the cyanide, should have little tendency to pick up the electron in the excited level to permit reversion to cobalt(II). This is a contradiction of fact. Second, Adamson[77] has presented evidence to indicate that the cobalt(II) cyanide complex is actually pentacovalent $[Co(CN)_5]^{\equiv}$; hence, the necessity to free the sixth orbital by promotion of an electron is eliminated. Without the promoted electron, the argument loses its validity.

In general terms, one can say that the oxidation state which is lowest in energy will be most stable. Obviously, then, any comprehensive explanation must involve consideration of all of the terms which contribute to the energy of different oxidation states. Sufficient data to make such a study meaningful are not available, but a number of empirical rules which systematize many oxidation states can be employed. Usually, more than one factor must be considered because of the large number of energy terms involved in even the energy of coordination. For this reason the treatment is only an approximation.

The "anomalous" oxidation states of the rare earths can be systematized by assuming that certain electronic configurations such as an empty f level, a half full f level, or a full f level will be stable. The same type of argument is utilized here. The following postulates are made:†

* See also Chapter 2.

† The authors are indebted to Dr. Daryle Busch for many helpful suggestions in outlining this set of generalizations.

77. Adamson, *J. Am. Chem. Soc.*, **73**, 5710 (1951).

(1) Stable electronic configurations for the central metal ion are:

a. a half filled shell, as in the iron(III) ion.

b. a completely filled d level, as in covalent iron(II) and cobalt(III).

c. half filled, unused d orbitals which are left after hybridization to obtain the bonding orbitals (e.g., Cr^{+++} and V^{++}).

(2) If the electronegativity of the bonding atom in the ligand is high* so that ionic bonds are favored, that valence of the central metal which involves the half filled d shell (postulate 1a) or the ionic state of maximum multiplicity is usually favored.

(3) If the electronegativity of the bonding atom in the ligand is low† so that covalent bonds are favored, the valence with either completely filled d levels or half filled *unused* d levels is stabilized (postulate 1b or 1c).

A number of examples may be used to illustrate the applications of the above postulates:

(a) $Co(NH_3)_6^{++} \rightleftharpoons Co(NH_3)_6^{+++} + e^-$ $E^0 = -0.1$ v.

Since Co^{+++} cannot achieve a half filled d shell and since NH_3 forms bonds which are quite covalent in character, stable structure 1b (completely filled d levels) is obtained to stabilize the Co^{+++} state.

(b) $Co(H_2O)_6^{++} \rightleftharpoons Co(H_2O)_6^{+++} + e^-$ $E^0 = -1.84$ v.

Water has little tendency to enter the covalent state, so the ionic cobalt(II) state is obtained without achieving any of the preferred structures.

(c) $[CuI_2(H_2O)_2]^- \rightleftharpoons [CuI_2(H_2O)_2] + e^-$ $E^0 =$ LARGE NEGATIVE VALUE

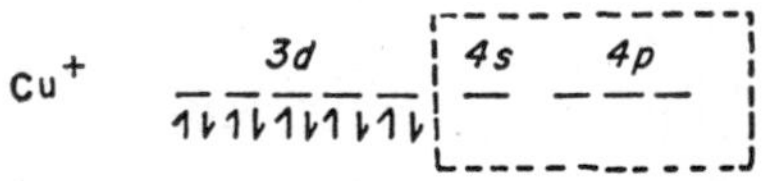

Since iodide forms strongly covalent bonds (easily polarized), the structure giving a full d shell or a Cu^+ state is favored.

(d) $[Cu(H_2O)_4]^+ \rightleftharpoons [Cu(H_2O)_4]^{++} + e^-$ $E^0 = -0.153$ v.

Water is too electronegative to form strongly covalent bonds; hence, Cu^{++} is more stable. The same appears to be true of ammonia and ethylenedi-

---

* An alternative statement is: "If the ligand is of low deformability . . ." See page 125 for discussion.

† An alternative statement is: "If the ligand is of high deformability . . ."

amine complexes, the Cu—NH_3 bond being less covalent than the Co—NH_3 bond.

$$(e) \quad [Cu(CN)_2]^- \rightleftharpoons Cu^{++} + 2CN^- + e^- \qquad E^0 = -1.1 \text{ v.}$$

Since cyanide prefers covalent bond formation, the Cu^+ state is favored. Coordination of nitrites or sulfur compounds appears to give a similar result.

$$(f) \quad [Cr(H_2O)_6]^{++} \rightleftharpoons [Cr(H_2O)_6]^{+++} + e^- \qquad E^0 = 0.414 \text{ v.}$$

Although water should not be expected to form strong covalent bonds on the basis of electronegativity, the strong covalent character of the water-Cr bond is indicated by the slow rate of exchange between coordinated and solvent water. On this basis the covalent state Cr^{+++} defined by 1c is favored.

$$(g) \quad [Cr(CN)_6]^{4-} \rightleftharpoons [Cr(CN)_6]^= + e^- \qquad E^0 = 1.28 \text{ v.}$$

Cr^{+++} should be stabilized here more than in the corresponding case of water since CN^- forms bonds of greater covalent character. This is observed.

$$(h) \quad [Cr(NH_3)_6]^{++} \rightleftharpoons [Cr(NH_3)_6]^{+++} + e^- \qquad E^0 = ?$$

Although the potential for this couple is not known, one would predict that it lies at about 0.7 v, between that for the aquated chromium system and the cyanide system.

$$(i) \quad V_{(H_2O)}{}^{++} \rightleftharpoons V_{(H_2O)}{}^{+++} + e^- \qquad E^0 = 0.255 \text{ v.}$$

The structure of V^{++} is:

Since water does not form strongly covalent bonds with V^{2+} there is no advantage to the 2+ state as opposed to the 3+ state.

$$(j) \quad [V(CN)_6]^{4-} \rightleftharpoons [V(CN)_6]^= + e^- \qquad E^0 = ?$$

The E value for this system is not known, but the possibility of stabilizing a half filled, unused d shell by covalent bond formation on V^{2+} would suggest that $[V(CN)_6]^{4-}$ should be stabilized with respect to the $[V(CN)_6]^=$ state. The above potential would be more negative than that for the aquated system; qualitative data indicate that such a potential is reasonable[78]. The ability of the vanadium(II) ion to form a stable complex, $[V(dipy)_3]^{++}$, as against a less pronounced tendency by the vanadium(III) ion would also be expected from the above treatment. King and Garner[79] report that this

78. Reference 21, p. 806; Taube, *Chem. Revs.*, **50**, 69 (1952).
79. King and Garner, *J. Am. Chem. Soc.*, **74**, 3709 (1952).

difference is so strong that V^{++} and V^{+++} can be separated quantitatively in aqueous solution by complexing the V^{++} and then precipitating the V^{+++}.

(k) Arguments similar to these have been employed quite successfully in correlating the oxidation states of nickel. Nickel is normally divalent, but Jensen[80] found that the complex [$NiBr_2 \cdot \{P(C_2H_5)_3\}_2$] can be oxidized to give pentacovalent nickel(III). The electronic configuration

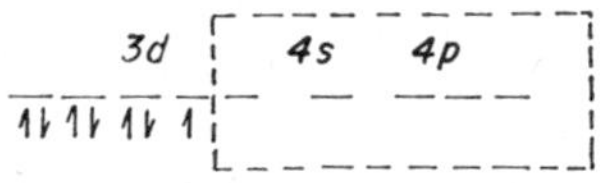

correlates with the observed paramagnetism equivalent to one unpaired electron.

To form hexacovalent nickel by d^2sp^3 hybridization, a d electron would have to be promoted to a $4d$ or $5s$ level. The $5s$ level has been suggested as the preferred lower energy level[42a, 81]. Such promotion would lead to easy oxidation of nickel to the $4+$ state if the six covalent bonds were very strong. Nyholm[42] reports the complex,

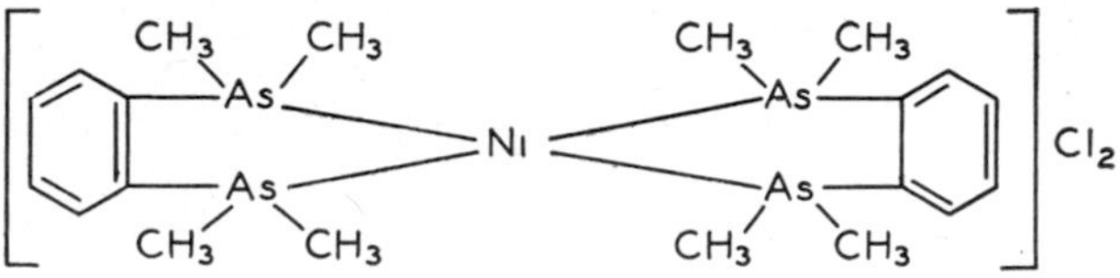

containing tetracoordinate nickel(II); this can be oxidized to $NiCl_3 \cdot$ 2 diarsine. The structure proposed for the latter compound is

$$[Ni(diarsine)_2Cl_2]Cl.$$

Since hexacoordinate covalent nickel is present, one d electron was probably promoted to a five s level and should be easily lost. Such a hypothesis receives support from the fact that the complex may be oxidized to nickel(IV) complexes; furthermore, the magnetic moment of the nickel(III) compound corresponds to one unpaired electron with little spin contribution, a fact expected from an odd electron in an s state. Nyholm[42a] has pointed out that if use is made of a ligand of low electronegativity which forms very stable covalent complexes and if the metal-ligand bonds are sufficiently strong, other examples of nickel(III) and nickel(IV) compounds might be observed, provided the coordination number is expanded to five or six.

It is evident that the metal is as important as the ligand in determining the degree of covalent character and the strength of the metal-ligand bond. (This is also evident from the field splitting treatment of magnetism using

80. Jensen, *Z. anorg. allgem. Chem.*, **229**, 265 (1936).
81. Burstall and Nyholm, *J. Chem. Soc.*, **1952**, 3570.

the ionic model, page 132.) For example, water is able to form stable covalent bonds with chromium, unstable covalent bonds with cobalt, and apparently very unstable bonds with copper(II). An even more striking example is found in the case of complex fluorides. Klemm and Huss[82] prepared the following complex fluorides: K_3FeF_6, K_3CoF_7, K_2NiF_6, and K_3CuF_6. The magnetic moments of the iron and cobalt complexes indicate an ionic type of bond, the ionic structure for the iron(III) and cobalt(IV) being particularly favored by the half filled d shell. It is surprising, however, that the nickel(IV) in K_2NiF_6 was found to be diamagnetic, indicating covalent Ni—F bonds.* The corresponding K_2PtF_6 is also diamagnetic. It is of interest that fluorine and oxygen can stabilize unusually high valence states such as Co^{4+}, Ni^{4+}, and Fe^{6+}.

As might be expected with a topic of this complexity, any set of valence generalizations is apt to produce inconsistencies. For example,

$$\text{(a)} \quad [FeF_6]^{4-} \rightleftharpoons [FeF_6]^{=} + e^- \qquad E^0 = > -0.4 \text{ v.}$$

The half filled d level in Fe(III) and the small tendency for covalent character in Fe—F bonds should stabilize the Fe^{+++} state. This is roughly true.

$$\text{(b)} \quad [Fe(H_2O)_6]^{++} \rightleftharpoons [Fe(H_2O)_6]^{+++} + e^- \qquad E^0 = -0.771 \text{ v·}$$

Water-metal bonds are likewise ionic but less so than fluorine-metal bonds; so the trivalent state here should be somewhat less stable than in the case of the fluoride complex. This is also roughly true; *but*

$$\text{(c)} \quad [Fe(CN)_6]^{4-} \rightleftharpoons [Fe(CN)_6]^{=} + e^- \qquad E^0 = -0.36 \text{ v.}$$

The metal-cyanide bonds should be strongly covalent and should favor the Fe(II) state with the structure

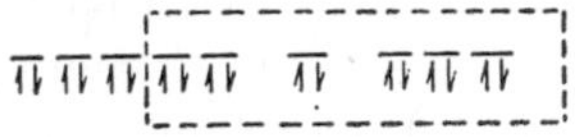

as compared to the Fe(III) state with the structure

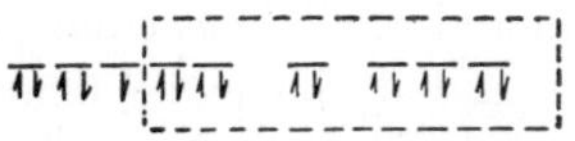

The electrode potential indicates that the ferricyanide is more stable (i.e., poorer oxidizing agent) than the corresponding $[Fe(H_2O)_6]^{+++}$ ion, in direct

---

82. Klemm and Huss, *Z. anorg. allgem. Chem.*, **258,** 221 (1949); **262,** 25 (1950); *Naturwissenschaften*, **37,** 175 (1950).

* An alternative treatment of these facts can be given by the crystal field splitting method described on page 132.

contradiction to theory:

$$[Fe(H_2O)_6]^{+++} + [Fe(CN)_6]^{4-} \rightleftharpoons [Fe(H_2O)_6]^{++} + [Fe(CN)_6]^{\equiv} \qquad E^0 = +.41 \text{ v.}$$

Pauling[83] has attempted to explain this, but he appears to have the facts reversed. He states, "The interesting fact that the ferrocyanide ion is *less* easily oxidized to the ferricyanide ion than is the hydrated ferrous ion to the hydrated ferric ion can now be explained." His explanation, based on double bonds, attributes enhanced stability to the ferrocyanide. From the potentials given by Latimer[84], it is apparent that ferrocyanide is *more* easily oxidized to ferricyanide than hydrated ferrous ion is to ferric ion.

$$(d) \quad [Fe(ophen)_3]^{++} \rightleftharpoons [Fe(ophen)_3]^{+++} + e^- \qquad E^0 = -1.12 \text{ v.}$$

If it is assumed, as seems logical, that the Fe—ophen bonds are strongly covalent, the iron(II) state would be expected. (See electron diagram above.) This is an agreement with fact. Similar arguments explain the system

$$[Fe(dipy)_3]^{++} \rightleftharpoons [Fe(dipy)_3]^{+++} + e^- \qquad E^0 = -1.096 \text{ v.}$$

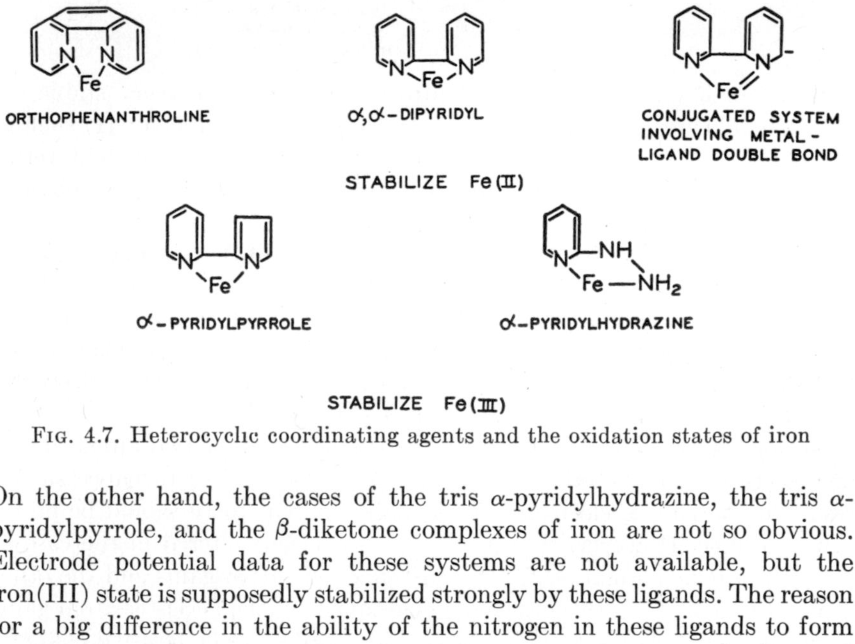

ORTHOPHENANTHROLINE α,α–DIPYRIDYL   CONJUGATED SYSTEM INVOLVING METAL – LIGAND DOUBLE BOND

STABILIZE Fe(II)

α–PYRIDYLPYRROLE α–PYRIDYLHYDRAZINE

STABILIZE Fe(III)

Fɪɢ. 4.7. Heterocyclic coordinating agents and the oxidation states of iron

On the other hand, the cases of the tris α-pyridylhydrazine, the tris α-pyridylpyrrole, and the β-diketone complexes of iron are not so obvious. Electrode potential data for these systems are not available, but the iron(III) state is supposedly stabilized strongly by these ligands. The reason for a big difference in the ability of the nitrogen in these ligands to form covalent bonds as compared to the nitrogen in orthophenanthroline and dipyridyl is not immediately obvious. The possibility of forming multiple metal-ligand bonds with the nitrogens of both aromatic rings is probably

83. Pauling, *J. Chem. Soc.*, **1948**, 1461.
84. Latimer, "Oxidation Potentials," 2nd Ed., New York, Prentice-Hall, 1952.

important in the orthophenanthroline and dipyridyl systems. In α-pyridyl-hydrazine and α-pyridylpyrrole only one nitrogen is part of an aromatic ring system, so the possibility of resonating metal-ligand double bonds on both nitrogens is reduced. This is seen by reference to the structural formulas in Fig. 4.7. On the other hand, the β-diketones might logically be expected to form more ionic bonds than orthophenanthroline since coordination is through the more electronegative oxygen atom and the complex is paramagnetic. The stability of the 3+ state here is not surprising.

(f) Several unusual oxidation states of silver pose rather vexing problems, particularly in view of the conclusions about the strong covalent bond-forming power of orthophenanthroline. Silver has an outer electronic structure similar to that of copper; hence, strongly covalent ligands might be expected to give a stable silver(I) state for tetracoordinate or bicoordinate covalent derivatives.

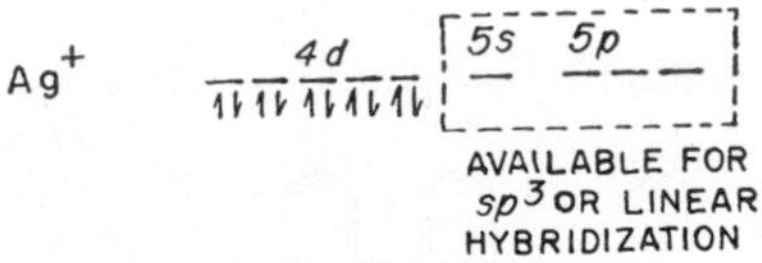

AVAILABLE FOR
sp^3 OR LINEAR
HYBRIDIZATION

Actually orthophenanthroline and dipyridyl, which form very stable covalent bonds in the iron system, give stable complexes of silver(II) such as $[Ag(ophen)_2]^{++}$ and $[Ag(dipy)_2]^{++}$. The reason why such divalent tetracoordinate silver complexes should be stable is not immediately obvious from the preceding set of rules.

Ionic and Multiple Bonds Between the Metal and the Ligand. *The Principle of Electroneutrality.* The concept of the coordinate bond appears simple enough, yet more careful scrutiny of the nature of these bonds from the standpoint of electron distribution and bond polarities led to difficulties[85, 86, 87, 88] in interpretation which are not yet entirely resolved.

In normal covalent bond formation in which each of two atoms shares one electron with the other, no considerable electrical disturbance should result; if the pair of electrons were equally shared, there should be no resulting dipole. However, the situation is somewhat altered in the case of coordinate bond formation. In this instance, one atom gains and the other atom loses a share in two electrons; consequently, the acceptor atom gains in net negative charge and the donor atom gains in net positive charge[85].

85. Sidgwick, *Chemistry & Industry*, **46**, 803 (1927). Reference 5b, pp. 71 and 122.
86. Lowry, *Chemistry & Industry*, **42**, 412 (1923).
87. Sidgwick, *Trans. Faraday Soc.*, **19**, 473 (1923).
88. Lowry, *Chemistry & Industry*, **42**, 715 (1923); Sidgwick, Ann. Reports, **1934**, 38; Hunter and Samuel, *Chemistry & Industry*, **1935**, 635; Mathieu, *Compt. rend.*, **215**, 325 (1942); Reference 5b, p. 121.

This is implied by Sidgwick's arrow, $A \rightarrow B$, where A is the donor atom and B is the acceptor. Lowry[89] indicated this by plus and minus signs, as
$$\overset{+}{A}—\overset{-}{B}.$$

Of direct interest is the fact that the above logic would seem to call for an accumulation of negative charges on the central atom of coordination compounds—an unaccustomed concept for metallic elements traditionally considered as electropositive in character.

In modern theory the problem has been considered in two more or less complementary ways: (1) by assuming the formation of double (or triple) bonds in which unused d electron pairs of the metal are donated back to the ligand, and (2) by assuming an ionic contribution to the bond such that the negative charge on the ion is reduced. Pauling has expressed the opinion that this charge transfer takes place until each atom has essentially zero residual charge. He has expressed this formally[83, 90] as the postulate of *the electrical neutrality of atoms*; namely, "that the electronic structure of substances is such as to cause each atom to have essentially zero resultant electrical charge, the amount of leeway being not greater than about $\pm \frac{1}{2}$, and these resultant charges are possessed mainly by the most electropositive and electronegative atoms, and are distributed in such a way as to correspond to electrostatic stability." Data on x-ray K absorption edges for complexes of Cr, Mn, Fe, and Ni[91] have been interpreted as supporting the principle of electrical neutrality.

Multiple Bonds. Multiple bonds can arise in those cases in which the entering ligand can act as an electron acceptor as well as an electron donor. Cyanides, carbonyls, and other groups containing first period elements joined to other atoms by multiple bonds can serve as such acceptors by virtue of their own double bonds. In addition, recent work suggests that second period elements such as phosphorus and sulfur may be joined to the metal by double bonds if $3d$ orbitals in these atoms are used to receive the electrons from the metal[92]. The carbonyls and cyanides have been extensively considered by many workers. On the basis of the hybridized orbital treatment as applied to $Ni(CO)_4$, the nickel atom contains 5 unshared $3d$ electron pairs:

$$\text{Ni in} \quad \text{Ni (CO)}_4 \qquad \overset{3d}{\underline{\uparrow\downarrow\,\uparrow\downarrow\,\uparrow\downarrow\,\uparrow\downarrow\,\uparrow\downarrow}} \quad \underset{sp^3 \text{ HYBRIDS}}{\overline{\underline{\big|\,4s \quad 4p\,\big|}}}$$

89. Lowry, *Trans. Faraday Soc.*, **19**, 488 (1923).
90. Pauling in Victor Henri Memorial Volume, "Contribution to the Study of Molecular Structure," p. 1. Liege, Desoer, 1947.
91. Mitchell and Beeman, *J. Chem. Phys.*, **20**, 1298 (1952).
92. Chatt and Williams, *J. Chem. Soc.*, **1951**, 3061; Chatt, *Nature*, **165**, 637 (1950); Syrkin and Dyatkina, *J. Gen. Chem.*, *U.S.S.R.*, **16**, 345 (1946).

It is assumed that these unshared electrons can be used to produce the following structure, which involves a double bond between the nickel and the carbon atoms:

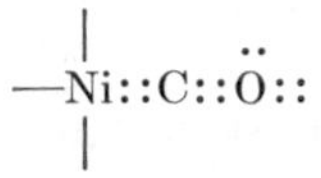

$$
\begin{array}{ccc}
& & O \qquad\qquad O \\
& & \diagdown\diagdown \quad \diagup\diagup \\
& & C \qquad\quad C \\
| & & \diagdown\diagdown \; \diagup\diagup \\
\mathrm{-Ni::C::\overset{..}{O}::} & \text{or} & \mathrm{Ni} \\
| & & \diagup\diagup \; \diagdown\diagdown \\
& & C \qquad\quad C \\
& & \diagup\diagup \quad \diagdown\diagdown \\
& & O \qquad\qquad O
\end{array}
$$

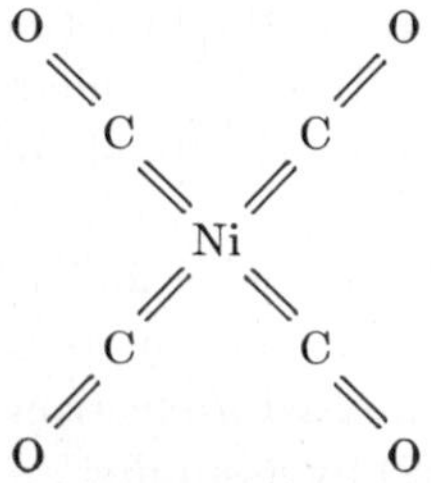

Pauling suggested that this double bonded structure, which produces an electrically neutral nickel atom, is in resonance with the single bonded sp^3 hybrid structure, the latter determining the stereochemistry of the molecule. In support of this double bond postulate, Pauling cited the fact that the metal-carbon distance is much shorter than the sum of the single bond radii. Wells[93] has criticized the use of interatomic distances as evidence for multiple bond formation on the grounds that for many complexes such as nickel carbonyl, the single bond lengths used as a standard have been obtained by dubious extrapolation procedures. A number of theoretical opinions have favored the double bond for nickel carbonyl[23b, 42a, 94]. In short, the experimental criteria for double bond character in nickel carbonyl are by no means unequivocal, but application of the principle of electroneutrality to remove the improbable negative charge from the central metal atom makes double bond formation seem entirely reasonable.

The same formal treatment can be given to other carbonyls with slight modification. For example, in chromium carbonyl six d electrons are available to form three double bonds after d^2sp^3 hybridization. The three chromium-carbon double bonds would then resonate among the six positions to give some double bond character to the metal-ligand linkages, although it is significant that such a procedure would not by itself give a neutral chromium atom. Syrkin and Dyatkina[95] favor the structure having chromium with three negative charges.

The theory of double bond formation* has often been invoked in the in-

93. Wells, *J. Chem. Soc.*, **1949**, 55.

94. Long and Walsh, *Trans. Faraday Soc.*, **43,** 348 (1947).

95. Syrkin and Dyatkina (translated by Partridge and Jordan), "Structure of Molecules and the Chemical Bond," pp. 346, 358, New York, Interscience Publishers, Inc., 1950.

* Several earlier references to double bond formation between metal and ligand appeared in the literature prior to its extensive development. Gapon[96] proposed a scheme utilizing double bonds; Blanchard and Gilliland[97] proposed a structure for $Ni(CO)_4$, containing essentially a double bond, and Kharasch and Ashford[98] in 1936

terpretation of the structures of metal cyanides. Pauling[99] considered three possible bond types as contributing to the final structure of the ferrocyanide, the electrostatic bond (A), the single covalent bond (B), and the double covalent bond (C), with the latter type being the most important.

$$\text{Fe}^+ \qquad (\text{CN})^- \qquad \bar{\text{Fe}}{:}\text{C}{:}{:}{:}\text{N}{:} \qquad \text{Fe}{:}{:}\text{C}{:}{:}\bar{\text{N}}{:}$$

$$\text{(A)} \qquad\qquad \text{(B)} \qquad\qquad \text{(C)}$$

There are more than enough unshared $3d$ electrons on the nickel atom in Ni(CO)_4 to formulate a structure in which all four carbonyl groups are held by double bonds, but this cannot be the situation in the case of iron in $[\text{Fe(CN)}_6]^{4-}$, as is apparent from the following:

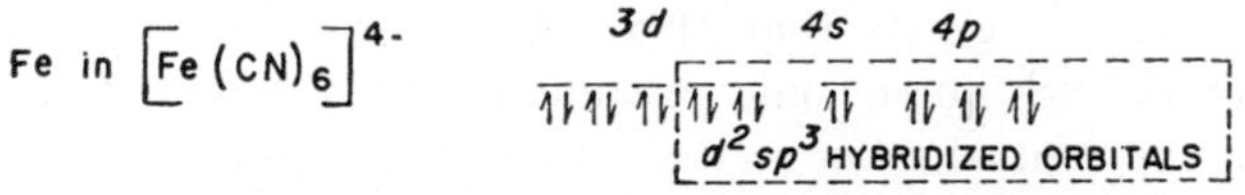

If all the $3d$, $4s$, and $4p$ orbitals of the iron atom are used in the sense proposed above, the following structure can be written for this ion:

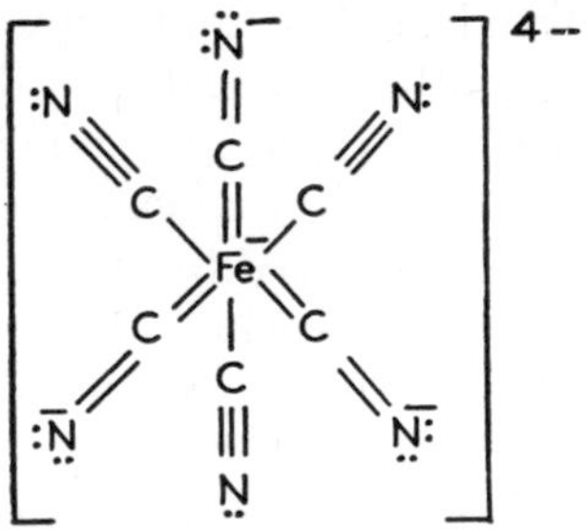

The effective charge on the iron atom in the above structure (or in any of the equivalent resonance structures obtained by redistributing the bonds) is negative one, with an average charge of negative one-half on each of the six nitrogen atoms. Pauling concluded that the ionic character of the bonds may be great enough to reduce further the negative charge on the iron atom, or even to make it positive.

Similar structures involving partial double bond character were proposed[99] for $\text{Fe(CN)}_6^\equiv$, $\text{Co(CN)}_6^\equiv$, Mn(CN)_6^{4-}, Cr(CN)_6^{4-}, $\text{Ni(CN)}_4^\equiv$, $\text{Zn(CN)}_4^\equiv$, Cu(CN)_2^-, and analogous systems involving palladium and

indicated bonds with partial double bond character in their discussion of platinum-olefin complexes.

96. Gapon, *Ukrain. Kem. Zhur.*, **1**, 595 (1925).
97. Blanchard and Gilliland, *J. Am. Chem. Soc.*, **48**, 872 (1926).
98. Kharasch and Ashford, *J. Am. Chem. Soc.*, **58**, 1733 (1936).
99. Ref. 27a, pp. 254–8.

platinum. The unusual stability of $Cr(CN)_6^{\equiv}$ (comparable to iron cyanides) is not amenable to such a treatment. Since the chromic ion has three unpaired electrons,

$$Cr^{+++} \quad \underset{\uparrow\;\uparrow\;\uparrow}{\underline{\quad 3d \quad}} \quad \underset{d^2sp^3}{\left[\,\underline{\quad}\;\underline{\quad}\; \underset{4s}{\underline{\quad}}\; \underset{4p}{\underline{\quad}\;\underline{\quad}\;\underline{\quad}}\,\right]}$$

the formation of double bonds is improbable, and the entire elimination of charge from the central metal is usually assumed to take place through resonance with ionic forms[100] (page 208). Similarly, the stability of the complex ions $Mo(CN)_8^{\equiv}$ and $Mo(CN)_8^{4-}$ and their tungsten analogs cannot be attributed to double bond formation because of the small number of d electrons. Pauling suggests that these complexes likewise involve single covalent bonds with some ionic character which transfers the negative charge from the central atom to the attached groups.

It is interesting that many of the donor atoms which show strong complexing tendencies and which stabilize unusual oxidation states are potential electron acceptors as well as electron donors. Among these are the tertiary phosphines and arsines, cyanide, nitrite, and molecules containing aromatic nitrogen such as orthophenanthroline and α,α'-dipyridyl. On the other hand, it is difficult to seriously attribute the stability and other properties of their complexes to double bond formation, since available data indicate that these same properties are displayed by structures such as the chromicyanide and molybdenum cyanide in which the possibility of double bond formation is absent. Further, electrode potential data indicate that the ferricyanide, in which only two double bonds are possible, is more stable than the corresponding ferrocyanide in which three double bonds can be formed. This lack of correlation between the properties of these complexes and the ability of the donor metal to form double bonds* must be regarded as a serious weakness in the concept.

* In this same connection Chatt[92b] has pointed out that boron, which can form no double bonds, gives much weaker complexes with carbon monoxide than does platinum, which can form double bonds. Qualitative data obtained by Lutton and Parry[101a] indicate that under comparable conditions this difference is not as large as usually assumed since even $[PtCl_2CO]_2$ will lose carbon monoxide under reduced pressure at room temperature to give black residues; hence apparent stability differences reflect only rates of decomposition. Further, the stable compound, $H_3BP(Me)_3$, has been reported[102] to melt at 106°C without decomposition and to withstand temperatures up to 200°C, indicating a stability comparable to that of the platinum phosphine complexes. On the other hand, Chatt points out that PF_3 will not form complexes with boron or aluminum compounds but will complex with platinum—a fact which is interpreted as offering strong support for his argument. Recently, however, the compound H_3BPF_3 has been prepared[101b].

100. Ref. 95, p. 375.

In a separate treatment of charge distribution in complexes, Syrkin and Dyatkina[103, 104, 105] started with somewhat different philosophical assumptions and arrived at the same picture as Pauling. It has been suggested that their ideas might be helpful in estimating electronic transitions in the molecule[23]. The concept has definite limitations.

Ionic Structure. For complexes containing ammonia, derivatives of ammonia, water, hydroxyl ion, and the like, it is not possible to invoke the double bond to reduce the negative charge on the metal ion and to explain complex stability, for these coordinating groups cannot act as acceptors of electrons. Here, the $2s$ and $2p$ orbitals are full, and the $3s$, $3p$, and $3d$ orbitals are of too high energy for bond formation. Pauling pointed out that the usual coordinating groups of this type which commonly form complexes with the iron group transition elements are in the main strongly electronegative in character, and suggested that, because of this property, they are able to remove most or all of the negative charge from the central atom and thus stabilize the complex without converting the essentially covalent structure to an essentially ionic structure. He has cited as possible evidence for this argument the fact that the iron group elements tend to form less stable halide complexes as the electronegativity of the halogen decreases. For example, the iodide complexes of the $3d$ elements are very unstable.

According to Pauling, the electropositive character of the $4d$ palladium and $5d$ platinum transition elements is less than that for the $3d$ series. This difference is reflected in the type of complexes they form. The metals of the palladium and platinum series not only enter into combination with all the coordinating groups mentioned in connection with the iron group elements, but they also form stable complexes with less electronegative groups such as iodide. Since it is assumed that the metals of these two groups have little or no tendency to form positive ions, but prefer to remain neutral or even become negative, some of the negative charge may actually be left on the central metal of the complex. It becomes less essential, therefore, according to Pauling, to search for conditions which can bring about reduction of the negative charge on the central atom.

The Trans Effect in Resonance Theory. An explanation of the trans effect (page 146) in terms of the ion-polarization theory was given in Chapter 3. It was noted that the magnitude of the trans effect in a series

101. Lutton and Parry, *J. Am. Chem. Soc.*, **76**, 4271 (1954); Bissot and Parry, unpublished results.
102. Burg and Wagner, *J. Am. Chem. Soc.*, **75**, 3872 (1953).
103. Syrkin and Dyatkina, *Acta Physicochim. U. R. S. S.*, **20**, 137, 273 (1945); Ref. 95, Chap. 14.
104. Van Vleck, *J. Chem. Phys.*, **1**, 177 (1933); **2**, 20 (1934); Mullikan, *J. Chem. Phys.*, **2**, 782 (1934); Moffitt, *Proc. Roy. Soc. (London)*, **A202**, 534, 548 (1950).
105. Ref. 95, (a) p. 371, (b) p. 383.

of donors increases in the direction of decreasing electronegativity[106], which parallels the direction of expected increase in covalent character of a bond. Syrkin[107] proposed an explanation of the phenomenon based on the concept of resonating ionic and covalent forms. In the case of platinum(II) complexes, Syrkin suggested that the actual state of the platinum might be intermediate between those represented by structures (A), (B), (C), and (D).

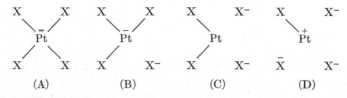

Structure (A) involves covalent dsp^2 hybridized bonds; structure (B) involves three covalent dsp bonds and a single ionic bond (four such structures would contribute toward the bonding in the resultant species); structure (C) represents two covalent ds hybridized bonds and two ionic bonds (four structures assumed); and (D) represents a single covalent d bond along with three ionic bonds (four structures). When all the coordinated groups are identical (as in this example) the various permutations of bonds for a single contributing structure, such as (B) are of equal weight. However, in the case where one of the groups, X, is replaced by a group Y, which forms bonds of a higher degree of covalent character, certain of the permutations are enhanced or minimized in importance. Thus, in the complex PtX₃Y, structure (B) has three of its forms approximately equivalent while the fourth, that involving covalent bonds to the three X groups and an ionic bond to the Y group, is minimized. Similarly, for structure (D), the form in which Y is bound covalently while the three X groups are ionic would be enhanced in its importance. According to the changes in importance of the canonical forms represented by structures (B) and (D), the effect of substituting Y for X to produce PtX₃Y is merely to weaken the bonds holding the X groups. However, similar treatment of the structure (C) indicates that the group trans to Y is weakened to a greater extent. The four forms of structure C considered are:

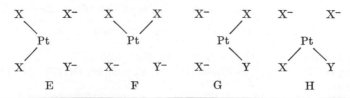

106. Quagliano and Schubert, *Chem. Rev.*, **50**, 246 (1950).
107. Syrkin, *Bull. acad. sci. U. R. S. S., Classe sci. chim.*, **1948**, 69.

Since Y tends to form covalent bonds to a greater extent than does X, forms G and H will be favored. From this picture, it is apparent that the bonds of the groups X which are cis to Y are strengthened by the presence of Y, while the group X which is trans to Y has lost in covalent character.

Such a model does not justify the strong trans effect attributed to PF₃ by Chatt[92], since three fluorines attached to the phosphorus might be expected to increase its electronegativity enough to minimize its strong covalent bond-forming tendencies. In addition, if such ionic resonance forms make a major contribution to the structure, the rationalization of the planar geometry becomes more difficult in atomic orbital theory. Finally the reason for neglecting *sp* hybridization and the contributing structure

is not obvious. Inclusion of this structure would invalidate the argument.

On the other hand, the general concept of charge distribution indicated by all structures does give an explanation of most cases of trans labilization and cis stabilization. The unexpected trans influence of PF₃ mentioned above has not been proved without question (see p. 148); hence, it cannot be cited as a completely valid objection. Furthermore, the ability of fluorine to reduce the covalent bond-forming power of phosphorus has not been considered on a quantitative basis, so such arguments are equivocal. This then represents an additional approach to the trans effect.

The Molecular Orbital Approximation

The method of molecular orbitals was conceived and developed in its early years largely by Hund, Mulliken, and Lennard-Jones. Though the method itself is as old as the Heitler-London-Pauling-Slater atomic orbital approximation, its extensive application to coordination compounds has occurred only in very recent years, largely as a result of the work of Lennard-Jones, Coulson, and their associates. From this work have emerged valuable ideas relative to such problems as the structure of the carbonyls (Chapter 16), coordination through the ethylenic double bond (Chapter 15), and the structure of the metal cyclopentadiene complexes.* An excellent non-mathematical resume of the results of the molecular orbital method up to 1947 was given by Coulson[108]. Other nonmathematical treat-

---

* The coordination number eight for Zr, Mo, Ru, Ce, Hf, W, Os, and Th has been treated by Penney and Anderson[40] using the method of molecular orbitals.

108. Coulson, *Quart. Revs.*, **1,** 144 (1947).

ments have been given by Palmer[109], Bowen[110], Walsh[111], Emeleus and Anderson[112],[114], and by later workers applying the ideas to specific problems[17, 28, 92, 113, 115].

Probably the best comparison of the two methods is in Coulson's outstanding book, "Valence"[23]. The essential mathematical methods as well as the chemical results of the theory are summarized in a fashion which can be understood by both the mathematical and non-mathematical reader. Mathematical methods are available in books on quantum mechanics[25].

In general, the atomic orbital theory assumes that through the hybridization of atomic orbitals a new set of directed orbitals is obtained (page 164). The bond between groups then arises from the overlap of one of the orbitals of this set and the *bonding orbital* of the coordinated ligand. In short, a highly localized bond is formed involving only a bonding function from each of the two groups which are joined. In the molecular orbital theory the situation is quite different. The bonding orbitals for the entire complex group (e.g., $Ni(CN)_4^=$) are involved in the formation of each bond. For instance, in the bonding of four cyanide ions to a central nickel(II) ion, a nonlocalized set of *molecular orbitals* may be obtained from the four nickel orbitals (dsp^2-hybridized, if necessary) and all *four* cyanide groups. It is true that usually the orbital of one cyanide group will contribute much more heavily to a given bond than the other three cyanides, but the important point is that provision is made for all to contribute. From the physical standpoint, the original atomic orbital theory* pictured the bond as being restricted to the interaction of a single electron pair; in contrast, the molecular orbital method assumes that a pair of bonding electrons is not confined to a single bond but participates in all bonds. A necessary consequence of the molecular orbital picture is that the bonds will all be interrelated and changes in one bond will be propagated to all other links in the compound. The effect produced by altering one bond in the complex is illustrated by "trans elimination" (page 204).

One may also consider that the simple atomic orbital representation and

---

* The above description of the Pauling theory is not representative of the present day version. More recent modifications introduce ionic contributions and resonance among several canonical structures to account for nonlocalization of electrons[27a, 83]. In this form, it approaches the original molecular orbital treatment. See the section on ionic structures and double bonds (pages 191 and 195).

109. Palmer, "Valency, Classical and Modern," pp. 179–196, London, Cambridge University Press, 1944.
110. Bowen, *Endeavor*, **4**, 75 (1945).
111. Walsh, *Quart. Revs.*, **2**, 73 (1948).
112. Ref. 15c, pp. 54–59.
113. Jaffe, *J. Phys. Chem.*, **58**, 185 (1954).
114. Van Vleck and Sherman, *Rev. Mod. Physics*, **7**, 167 (1935).
115. Lennard-Jones and Pople, *Proc. Roy. Soc. (London)*, **210**, 190 (1951).

the extreme ionic viewpoint are really special cases of the molecular orbital theory. For instance, the complex ion $[Fe(CN)_6]^=$ may be represented in molecular orbital theory as the ionic $[Fe^{+++}(CN^-)_6]^=$ or the covalent $[Fe^=(CN)_6]^=$ or as any structure in between, depending upon the relative sizes of three arbitrary coefficients in the wave equation. The intermediate state is achieved in the atomic orbital system by introducing the concept of "resonance." That is, the molecule may be represented by the super-position of a number of canonical structures, each of which corresponds to a chemical picture of localized bonds or ions. The state of the molecule has properties which are different from those of the individual canonical structures, but can be represented in terms of a set of structures. Ionic structures and double bonded structures are utilized to remove charge from the central metal (pages 191 and 195). The same end is achieved in the ionic model by the introduction of polarization terms and the concept of the crystal field splitting of the degenerate d levels in the central ion. (See Chapter 3.)

Coulson[108] has differentiated between "localized" molecular orbitals which resemble the atomic orbital picture, and the "nonlocalized" molecular orbitals described above. The nonlocalized orbitals have been particularly useful for simple systems such as the oxygen and nitrogen molecules and systems of conjugated double bonds such as benzene. On the other hand, most complex systems usually demand some bond localization as a simplifying approximation.

The σ, π, δ Designation of Molecular Orbitals. Bonding, Antibonding and Nonbonding Orbitals. The designation of molecular orbitals as σ, π, or δ has arisen in both atomic and molecular orbital theories. The symmetry of bonds with these designations is most easily seen from a brief consideration of the methods for combining atomic orbitals to give molecular levels. The symmetry of the individual s, p, and d orbitals has already been indicated (Fig. 4.1). It is usually assumed in molecular orbital theory that suitable localized molecular orbitals can be obtained by a combination of the appropriate atomic functions. Thus, two s orbital functions may be added to give a molecular orbital which is *symmetrical around the internuclear axis* and which concentrates the electronic charge between the two nuclei. Such an orbital is known as a σ bonding orbital, the σ designation indicating bond symmetry around the internuclear axis. Alternatively, two σ functions may be subtracted to give an orbital which is still symmetrical about the internuclear axis, but which concentrates the charge away from the space between the two nuclei (Fig. 4.8). This is known as a σ antibonding level.

In contrast to σ bonds, the combination of two p_x or two p_y orbitals to give a bonding molecular orbital results in a concentration of charge in ribbon-shaped streamers above and below the internuclear axis (Fig. 4.9).

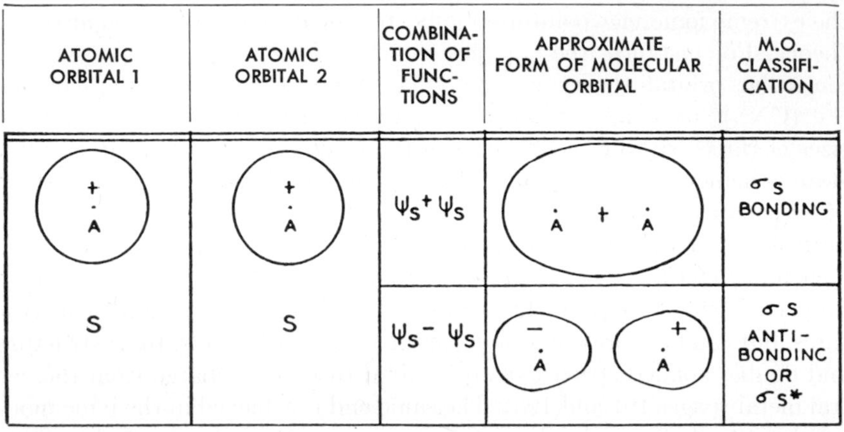

ATOMIC ORBITAL 1	ATOMIC ORBITAL 2	COMBINATION OF FUNCTIONS	APPROXIMATE FORM OF MOLECULAR ORBITAL	M.O. CLASSIFICATION
+ A S	+ A S	$\psi_S + \psi_S$	+ A A	σ s BONDING
		$\psi_S - \psi_S$	− A + A	σ s ANTI-BONDING OR σ s*

FIG. 4.8. Bonding and antibonding σ molecular orbitals between two atoms—localized bonds.

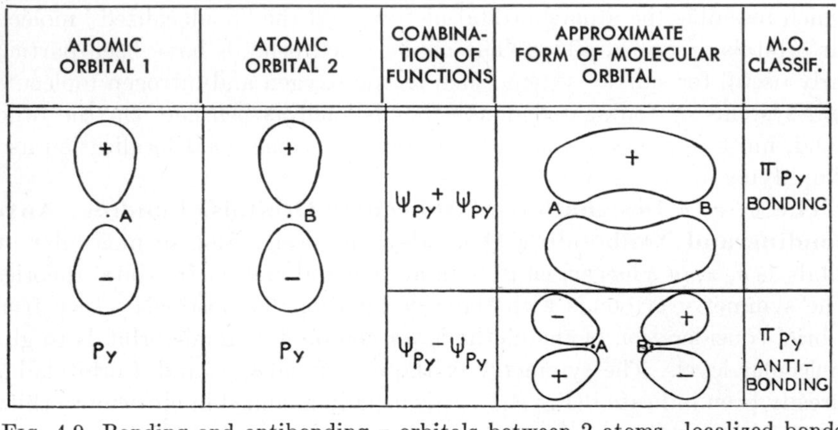

ATOMIC ORBITAL 1	ATOMIC ORBITAL 2	COMBINATION OF FUNCTIONS	APPROXIMATE FORM OF MOLECULAR ORBITAL	M.O. CLASSIF.
+ A − P$_y$	+ B − P$_y$	$\psi_{Py} + \psi_{Py}$	+ A B −	π P$_y$ BONDING
		$\psi_{Py} - \psi_{Py}$	− A B + + −	π P$_y$ ANTI-BONDING

FIG. 4.9. Bonding and antibonding π orbitals between 2 atoms—localized bonds

Since such an orbital is not symmetrical around the bond axis and since it represents a component of angular momentum around the bond direction equal to one, it is known as a π orbital. It is the molecular analog of the atomic p state. (See end view, Fig. 4.11, for analogy to atomic p orbital.) π bonds can also be of antibonding character as illustrated in Fig. 4.9.

δ orbitals are of relatively rare occurrence in most systems. The formation of a δ bond by combination of two d_{xy} bonds along the z axis is shown in Fig. 4.10. From the end-on view, Fig. 4.11, this orbital is seen to have symmetry similar to that of the atomic d_{xy} orbital, and hence, has a component of angular momentum equal to two around the bond direction. This then justifies the δ designation. In short, molecular orbitals are designated

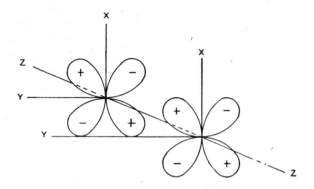

d$_{xy}$ & d$_{xy}$ ATOMIC ORBITALS IN POSITION TO FORM

δ MOLECULAR ORBITAL BY APPROACH DOWN Z AXIS

FIG. 4.10. δ Orbital formation

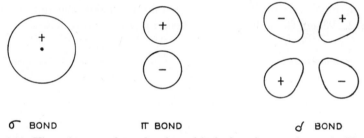

σ BOND   π BOND   δ BOND

FIG. 4.11. View of σ, π, and δ molecular orbitals *down* internuclear axis. Note similarity to atomic *s,p,d*.

as σ, π, δ, etc., accordingly as the component of angular momentum around the bond direction is 0, 1, 2, ... etc. If the electrons in a given orbital spend most of their time between the nuclei, the orbital is termed bonding; if the electron is restricted in its movement so that only a small percentage of its time is spent between the nuclei, the orbital is termed antibonding; and, finally, if the electron in an atom is not disturbed seriously by the presence of the second nucleus (i.e., inner core electrons), the orbital is termed nonbonding.

Application of Molecular Orbital Theory to Complex Compounds. *The Compound* $K_4Ru_2Cl_{10}O \cdot H_2O$. The diamagnetism of the compound $K_4Ru_2Cl_{10}O \cdot H_2O$ which contains two atoms of formally tetravalent ruthenium has already been mentioned as a point of difficulty in the atomic orbital interpretation (page 167 and Fig. 4.2). Dunitz and Orgel[17] showed by a molecular orbital treatment that an earlier suggestion of Pauling (mentioned in Ref. 32) to the effect that "seven orbitals of each ruthenium are used in bond formation of which two on each ruthenium are used in double bond formation with the central oxygen" can be understood from a molecular orbital treatment. Actually, however all available remaining *spd* orbitals of ruthenium must be considered rather then just seven. Dunitz and Orgel assumed, in essence, that each of the ten chlorine atoms is bound to the ruthenium ion by a σ bond. They then obtained non-localized molecular orbitals for the Ru—O—Ru system involving the π oxide levels and the remaining available orbitals of the ruthenium ion. The transformation of atomic orbitals into the appropriate molecular forms is indicated schematically in Fig. 4.12. Each molecular orbital may be made from half of two atomic orbitals (E_u from P_x and P_{xy}) or from a single atomic orbital (E_g from P_{yz}). The total number of molecular orbitals must be equal to the number of atomic orbitals used. (The symbolism of Eyring, Walter, and Kimball[25] is used.) After the five σ bonds to chlorine and one σ bond to oxygen are formed by each ruthenium ion, the four remaining electrons on each ruthenium ion and the four unused π electrons on the oxide must be placed in molecular orbitals which are shown inside the dotted line in Fig. 4.12. When these levels are filled by the twelve electrons in ac

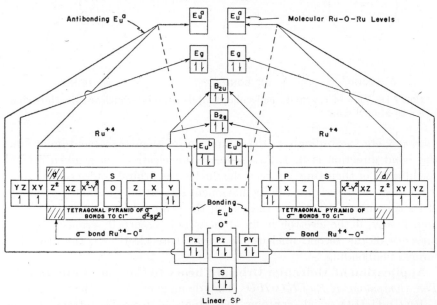

FIG. 4.12. Molecular orbital representation of diamagnetism in $K_2Ru_2Cl_{10}O \cdot H_2O$

cordance with the principle of maximum multiplicity, diamagnetism is obtained. The double bond to oxygen from each ruthenium is then contributed by a σ Ru—O bond and an $E_u{}^b$ molecular orbital level. The $E_u{}^b$

orbital may be described as a double degenerate bonding π orbital. The actual extent of the π bonding will be sensitive to the relative electronegativities of the atoms concerned, but the observed Ru—O distance, 1.80 Å, is close to the value 1.74 Å found in RuO_4, a fact which has been interpreted as indicating considerable double bond character in the Ru—O interaction. It is also clear that the degree of bonding and hence the stability of the anion would be diminished by any departure from linearity for the Ru—O—Ru system.

The molecular orbital explanation of diamagnetism in this case is reminiscent of its similar success in interpreting the paramagnetism of the oxygen molecule[116].

In Chapter 3 it was stated that the quanticule theory of Fajans (page 132) bears a resemblance to the molecular orbital interpretation. This can now be seen since in quanticule terms the $[Ru—O—Ru]^{6+}$ grouping would be considered as a quanticule to which ten Cl^- ions could be bound through the polarized ion concept. After considering appropriate polarization terms, the end result would approach quite closely the above molecular orbital treatment, even though the starting points are very different.

The Compounds $[(NH_3)_5Co—O_2—Co(NH_3)_5]X_5$ *and* $[(NH_3)_5Co—O_2—Co(NH_3)_5]X_4$. The linear Co—O$_2$—Co group can be treated analogously to the ruthenium compound except that the peroxide ion now has both internally bonding $E_u(w\pi)$ and antibonding $E_g(v\pi)$ orbitals which follow directly from the treatment for molecular oxygen. It follows that there are twenty electrons after σ bonding to place in molecular levels (i.e., six electrons from each cobalt and eight π electrons from $O_2^=$). The order of the molecular levels is:

$$(E_u^b)[(B_{2g})(B_{2u})(E_u^a)(E_g^b)](E_g^a)$$

The relative order of levels inside the square brackets is not known. The bonding E_g^b and antibonding E_g^a levels now arise from interaction of the previously described E_g metal levels (see the case of $[Ru—O—Ru]^{6+}$) with the extra π levels of the $O_2^=$ ion. The oxide ion had only two unused p levels for interaction with the metal, whereas the peroxide ion now has four unused π levels, giving additional interaction possibilities. Placing the twenty electrons in appropriate levels gives:

$$(E_u^b)^4[(B_{2g})^2(B_{2u})^2(E_u^a)^4(E_g^b)^4](E_g^a)^4$$

Since all orbitals are filled, diamagnetism follows. The filling of both the bonding and the corresponding antibonding levels indicates that the metal-O_2 bond and the O—O bond should have no double bond character.

The oxidation of $[(NH_3)_5Co—O_2—Co(NH_3)_5]X_4$ to the corresponding $[(NH_3)_5Co—O_2—Co(NH_3)_5]X_5$ must involve removal of an electron from

116. Lennard-Jones, *Trans. Faraday Soc.*, **25**, 668 (1929).

the least stable orbital, which is $E_g{}^a$, and presumably centered mainly on the —O_2— grouping. It is in this sense that one would attribute the electron loss to the $O_2{}^=$ rather than to cobalt(III). The O—O group would then resemble the superoxide ion, $O_2{}^-$; the preparation of the compound by means of alkali metal superoxides might be suggested.

The Fe—Fe interaction in metal carbonyls has also been justified by the molecular orbital theory[17].

The Paramagnetic Resonance of $IrCl_6{}^=$. Stevens[117] has recently applied the molecular orbital theory to a discussion of details in the paramagnetic resonance absorption spectrum of $IrCl_6{}^=$. The paramagnetic absorption data are usually interpreted in terms of an ionic model. His work represents an initial attempt to formulate orbitals that describe some deviations from an ionic model which seem to be required by details of the spectrum.

On an ionic model, the complex is considered to be a central iridium(IV) with five $5d$ orbital electrons, surrounded by a regular octahedron of Cl^- ions. The complex shows $s = \frac{1}{2}$ and $g = 1.8$ and is a typical $(d\epsilon)^5$ compound. According to the Stevens' modification, an electron which is on one of the chlorine ions migrates to the iridium. It will presumably go into the $(d\epsilon)^5$ shell which then has six electrons and is closed. The chloride ion becomes a chlorine atom with one unpaired spin, so that as far as the magnetic properties are concerned, the process looks like the transfer of a magnetic hole from the iridium to a chlorine. Adopting this sort of an approach, the next step was to fit it into the self-consistent field model and set up a wave function which has the required symmetry and allows the electron to spend part of its time near the chlorine. Such a molecular orbit was constructed from a d_{xy} type of metallic function and a p type function from the ligands.

Double Bonds and the Trans Effect. The possibility of double bond formation arising from the donation of central cation d electrons to acceptor levels in the coordinated ligand has been considered extensively in molecular orbital theory. Craig, Maccoll, Nyholm, Orgel, and Sutton[28] have summarized the evidence for the existence of d_π—p_π bonding using a penultimate d_π-orbital as follows:

(1) Complexes in which this could occur (i.e., cyanide, carbonyl, and nitrosyl) are formed with elements which have suitable penultimate d orbitals such as the transition metals, copper or silver, and even the group IIB elements. These compounds are not formed by elements which lack penultimate d orbitals such as aluminum.

(2) Such complexes are more stable than the corresponding ones formed with Cl^-, and Br^-, which have no p_π orbitals free to accept a bond from the metal atom.

117. Stevens, *Proc. Roy. Soc. (London)*, **A219,** 542 (1953).

(3) The bond lengths, where known, are less than would be expected for σ bonding alone.

All three of these points are subject to criticism. Points (1) and (2) become less impressive when the stabilities of $Mo(CN)_8^=$ and $Cr(CN)_6^=$ are recalled. The latter stable complex cannot be stabilized by d_π—p_π bonds unless one assumes the participation of unpaired electrons in such a bond. In the former case, no electrons are available. Further, the extreme stability of certain of the phosphorus-boron bonds in compounds between boron hydrides and the alkyl phosphines would require the postulation of a source of double bonding electrons other than the d orbitals[102]. In connection with point (3), Wells has criticized the use of bond lengths as a criterion of double bond character[93].

Additional evidence cited for double bond character is that for those metals in which no double bonding is possible the coordinating power for a series of amines runs parallel to the basic constants; so, if only σ bonds were formed, ethylenediamine would always be a stronger coordinating agent than dipyridyl. Since the reverse is true with the transition metals, it is concluded that double bonding occurs with the transition metal complexes. Since molecular orbital calculations[28, 113] indicate the theoretical feasibility of d_π-p_π bonds, the principal remaining problem is to obtain proof that such bonds produce the results attributed to them.

The stability of PF_3 complexes such as $(PF_3)_2PtCl_2$[92a] and $Ni(PF_3)_4$[118] has been attributed to d_π-p_π double bonding. Because the π bond would tend to neutralize the formal charges set up by the formation of the σ bond, the latter might be strengthened.

Since two of these π bonds could be formed at right angles, the cis form of compounds L_2MX_2 would be favored if only L could form such bonds with M. Such cis stabilization would then provide a reasonable basis for trans weakening and would thus explain the trans effect or trans elimination of PF_3. Chatt[92a] has treated the trans effect along these lines; his explanation of the trans effect for PF_3 is cited as one of the major advantages of his treatment as compared to the two previous explanations (pp. 147 and 195).

The argument can be illustrated by following the explanation of Chatt and Wilkins[119] for the cis-trans conversion of $\{P(Et)_3\}_2PtCl_2$. They estimated from a thermochemical study that the conversion of trans $\{P(Et)_3\}_2PtCl_2$ to the cis form results in an increase of about 12 kcal in bond energy. Since both phosphorus and chlorine have vacant d orbitals, d_π-d_π bonds could be expected for Pt—P and Pt—Cl. It is assumed that the

118. Irvine and Wilkinson, *Science*, **113**, 742 (1951).
119. Chatt and Wilkins, *J. Chem. Soc.*, **1952**, 273, 4300; **1953**, 70

Pt—P bond has greater double bond character than the Pt—Cl bond because P is higher in the trans influence series.

The dotted lines in Fig. 4.13 represent the π or other bond components in which electron pairs from the filled d orbitals of the metal atom contribute in some manner to the strength of the Pt—P and Pt—Cl bonds. The strengths of these components are represented by the size of the dots. In the trans complex (I) both the Pt—P bonds must use the same d orbitals in the π component; hence the π components are weaker than in the cis

(I)   (II)

Fig. 4.13. Bond components in Pt—P and Pt—Cl bonds

complex where each Pt—P bond has available a different d orbital. On the other hand, the chlorine atoms in the cis complex (II) are now competing with the phosphorus atoms for electrons from d orbitals of the platinum atom, so will get a smaller share than they had in the trans isomer. The chlorine bonds in the trans position are thus weakened, as the trans effect indicates.

The argument has an interesting application to complexes containing PF_3. Only the cis form of $PtCl_2(PF_3)_2$ is stable, as this argument suggests[92a]. Further, the weakening of the σ bond between phosphorus and platinum due to the inductive effect of the fluorine would be partially compensated by the increased strength of the π bond, since the electronegative fluorine attached to phosphorus should make the phosphorus d levels contract to a point where they would be more capable of π bond formation[28]. This line of argument would then suggest that in $(C_2H_5)_3P$—Pt bonds, where π bonds are somewhat less effective* than in F_3P—Pt, one might expect a more polar bond than in the latter case. Estimates of bond dipole moments by Chatt and Williams[92a] bear out this prediction. In such a circumstance, strong B—$P(C_2H_5)_3$ bonds might occur with less π bonding contribution than would be required to stabilize the B—PF_3 bond. Hence, Chatt[92a] cites the nonexistence of X_3B—PF_3 complexes as strong support for his double bond postulate since boron does not have d electrons available for donation to the phosphorus in PF_3. The compound H_3B—PF_3 is now known, however[101b].

A variation of this d_π-d_π treatment of the trans effect using d_π and dp_π hybrid orbitals has been given by Jaffe[113].

* The less electronegative (C_2H_5) groups would not be as effective as F in making the phosphorus orbitals contract to a point where strong π bonds could form[28].

Bonding of Metals to Double Bonds in Terms of the Molecular Orbital Theory. Coordination of metals to the double bond of ethylene and related olefins has been treated by several investigators (e.g., Ref. [120]) using the molecular orbital theory and is discussed elsewhere (page 506). A. E. A. Werner[121] postulated a π electron bond between carbon and nitrogen in the azobenzene platinum(IV) chloride described by Kharasch and Ashford[98]:

$$
\begin{array}{ccc}
& \mathrm{Cl} \quad\quad \mathrm{Cl} & \\
\mathrm{C_6H_5-N} & \diagdown \quad \diagup & \mathrm{N-C_6H_5} \\
\| & {-\!-\!-\mathrm{Pt}\!-\!-\!-} & \| \\
\mathrm{C_6H_5-N} & \diagup \quad \diagdown & \mathrm{N-C_6H_5} \\
& \mathrm{Cl} \quad\quad \mathrm{Cl} &
\end{array}
$$

In order to represent the difference between the π and σ electrons of the double bond, he suggested that the bond might be formulated as

$$
\diagdown \quad\quad \diagup \\
\mathrm{N} \overset{xx}{-\!-\!-} \mathrm{N} \\
\diagup \quad\quad \diagdown
$$

where xx represents the electrons in the π orbital. However, it is quite possible that the unshared pair of electrons of one or both of the nitrogen atoms[122] in the azo group contributes to the bonding.

The metal cyclopentadiene complexes such as M(cyclopentadiene)$_2$ with their interesting sandwich structure are obvious compounds for a molecular orbital treatment. Such treatments have been given by Dunitz and Orgel[123], Jaffe[124], and Moffitt[125].

BOND CLASSIFICATION—IONIC AND COVALENT BONDS—INNER AND OUTER ORBITAL COMPLEXES

Throughout this and the preceding chapter the idea that there are two limiting types of complexes has been recurrent. The discussions based on the electron-pair bond have dealt with complexes of the type which might most unambiguously be called penetration complexes. They are distinguished from the normal or "ionic" complexes by gross properties such as stability in the solid state, slow rates of reaction and dissociation, irreversible electrode and dissociation behavior, and almost complete masking

120. Dewar, *Bull. Soc. chim.*, **18**, C79 (1951); Chatt and Duncanson, *J. Chem. Soc.*, **1949**, 3340; **1952**, 2622; **1953**, 2939.
121. Werner, *Nature*, **160**, 644 (1947).
122. Callis, Nielsen, and Bailar, *J. Am. Chem. Soc.*, **74**, 3461 (1952); Bailar and Callis, *J. Am. Chem. Soc.*, **74**, 6018 (1952); Liu, Thesis, University of Illinois, 1951.
123. Dunitz and Orgel, *Nature*, **171**, 121 (1953).
124. Jaffe, *J. Chem. Phys.*, **21**, 156 (1953).
125. Moffitt, *J. Am. Chem. Soc.*, **76**, 3386 (1954).

of the constituent groups. The marked differences in the properties of the two types of complexes have commonly been attributed to a distinct difference in their bond types. The penetration complexes are often tacitly assumed to be predominately covalent while the normal complexes are considered to be ionic. The designations covalent and ionic, however, appear to depend in large measure upon the individual using the terms, since no unequivocal experimental test is available as a means of classification. With this in mind it appears to be profitable to review the experimental parameters considered in the classification and then to try to relate these parameters to electronic structure or other fundamental characteristics of the complex.

The Magnetic Criterion for Bond Type

Reference has already been made to the interesting observation that in the formation of typical coordination compounds from paramagnetic metal ions the magnetic susceptibility of the resulting complexes is frequently changed from that of the simple ions. This is usually interpreted in terms of the atomic or hybridized orbital theory as meaning that unpaired d electrons in the simple ion have become paired in the complex and that the d orbits thus made available have formed covalent bonds with the coordinated groups or ions. In some cases, however, the full paramagnetism of the central ion is unchanged when this ion is made part of a complex. For example, the compounds $[Fe(NH_3)_6]Cl_2$, $[Co(N_2H_4)_2]Cl_2$, $(NH_4)_3[FeF_6]$, and $K_3[CoF_6]$ appear to possess, respectively, the same number of unpaired electrons as the gaseous metal ions in the ground state. It would seem that in these instances there has been no fundamental reorganization of the electrons about each component of the complex.

Pauling, following the lead of earlier workers, considered the bonding forces in the "ionic" [126, 127] * or normal complexes to be essentially electrostatic in character. He did not believe, however, that a complex ion, such as $[FeF_6]^{\equiv}$, which contains five unpaired electrons, should be considered to be of the extreme ionic type[127]. Use could be made of the $4s$ and $4p$ orbitals to form as many as four covalent bonds without disturbing the $3d$ shell, the magnetic moment of the complex being unchanged by this amount of covalent character of the bonds.

In considering resonance possibilities it is important to realize that the ion $[FeF_6]^{\equiv}$ cannot have an intermediate structure corresponding to reso-

---

* The terms "covalent" and "ionic" are purely comparative, but their use in this connection is somewhat confusing. For example, the fluoride complex $[FeF_6]^{\equiv}$ is not ionized in water and the Fe—F bond is not at all "ionic" as compared with the Na—F bond in sodium fluoride.

126. Pauling, J. Am. Chem. Soc., 54, 1002 (1932).
127. Ref. 27a, pp. 37, 38 and 115.

nance between the ionic type (containing five unpaired electrons) and the d^2sp^3 covalent type (containing one unpaired electron)* since the conditions for resonance require that the resonating structures have the same number of unpaired electrons[127]. Since there can be no intermediate type, the magnetic criterion should be capable of distinguishing between the predominantly covalent and predominantly ionic complexes as defined above. In each of the examples cited above, the number of unpaired electrons for the covalent type of structure is different from that for the ionic type, and measurements of magnetic moments can be used conveniently to determine which type exists. This criterion fails, however, in those cases where the number of unpaired electrons is the same for either extreme structural type. For example, the number of unpaired electrons is three in a complex of chromium(III) of coordination number six, assuming either a covalent d^2sp^3 structure or an essentially ionic structure. Similarly, it has been suggested[35a, 128] that a complex of cobalt(II) and four associated groups may contain three unpaired electrons for an ionic structure or a covalent tetrahedral configuration.

No distinction can be made by means of magnetic moment measurements between covalent tetrahedral (sp^3 hybridization) and ionic structures for complexes of copper(I), silver(I), and gold(I); nor between covalent planar (dsp^2 hybridization with promotion of one d electron to a p orbital), covalent tetrahedral (sp^3 hybridization), and ionic structures for copper(II) and silver(II).

In a similar manner, magnetic susceptibility measurements fail to serve as a criterion for distinguishing between bond character in the compounds of the nontransition elements, all of the simple ions of these elements—as well as their complex ions—being uniformly diamagnetic.

The outstanding example in which measurements of magnetic susceptibility have been of value in assigning stereochemical configurations is in connection with the complexes of tetracoordinate nickel(II). This case has been discussed on page 171. Figgis and Nyholm[35h] have also considered the case for cobalt(II) complexes and have suggested the size of the orbital component as an additional variable with stereochemical significance.

Resolution of Optical Isomers as a Criterion for Bond Type

Some attempts have been made to employ the results of resolution studies as an additional key to the character of bonds in compounds. Mann[129], for example, considered his isolation of the dextro form of tetra-

---

* See Table 4.3.

128. Calvin and Barkelew, *J. Am. Chem. Soc.*, **68**, 2267 (1946).

129. Mann, *J. Chem. Soc.*, **1930**, 1745.

chloro $(\beta,\beta'$-diaminodiethylsulfide monohydrochloride) platinum(IV),

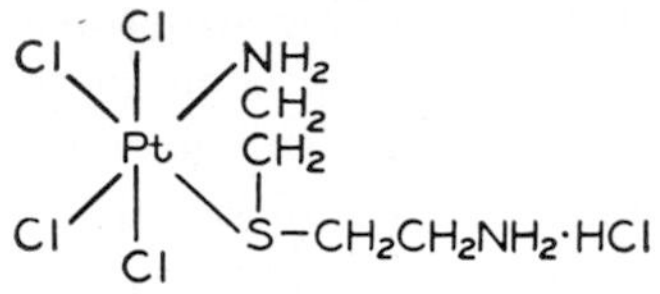

as decisive evidence for the presence of a coordinate bond between the sulfur and platinum atoms. In this compound the valence bonds of the sulfur atom, which has apparently become asymmetric by the process of coordination, presumably possess space directions similar to those of the sulfur atom in the asymmetric sulfoxides[130] and sulfinates[131]. Johnson[132] went so far as to propose a connection between the existence or nonexistence of stable optical isomers and the bond character of the coordination compounds. He indicated that stable optical isomers are possible only in those cases in which the coordinated groups are attached to the central metal ion by covalent bonds.*

Johnson[132] cited the apparently good correlation between resolvability of complexes and the magnetic criterion for bond type. The following diamagnetic ions, for example,

$$[Co(C_2O_4)_3]^{\equiv}\ ^{136},\ [Rh(C_2O_4)_3]^{\equiv}\ ^{137},\ [Co(en)_3]^{+++}\ ^{138},\ \text{and}\ [Rh(en)_3]^{+++}\ ^{139}$$

have been resolved into stable optical isomers, whereas $[Mn(C_2O_4)_3]^{\equiv}$ and $[Fe(C_2O_4)_3]^{\equiv}$, which contain four and five unpaired electrons, respectively, have resisted all attempts at unequivocal resolution[132, 140]. Failure to resolve complexes of this type, in which configurational dissymmetry almost certainly exists, is probably due to a rapid rate of racemization of the optical isomers. The assumption made by Johnson implies that this rate is too rapid to allow separation and identification of the isomers when the bonds between the central metal atom and the attached groups are essentially ionic, but is sufficiently slow for resolution to be effected when the attached

130. Harrison, Kenyon, and Phillips, J. Chem. Soc., **1926**, 2079.
131. Phillips, J. Chem. Soc., **127**, 2552 (1925).
132. Johnson, Trans. Faraday Soc., **28**, 845 (1932).
    * Essentially the same suggestion had been made earlier by Sidgwick[133].
133. Ref. 5b, p. 86.
134. Hunter and Samuel, Chemistry and Industry, **1935**, 34.
135. Orgel, J. Chem. Soc., **1952**, 4756.
136. Jaeger and Thomas, Proc. Acad. Sci. Amsterdam, **21**, 693 (1919); Johnson and Mead, Trans. Faraday Soc., **29**, 626 (1933).
137. Werner, Ber., **47**, 1954 (1914); Jaeger, Rec. Trav. Chim., **38**, 256 (1919).
138. Werner, Ber., **45**, 121 (1912).
139. Werner, Ber., **45**, 1228 (1912).
140. Thomas, J. Chem. Soc., **119**, 1140 (1921); Jaeger, Rec. Trav. Chim., **36**, 242 (1919).

groups are bound by covalent bonds. Inherent in all of the foregoing arguments is the assumption that a covalent bond is of necessity stronger than an ionic one or is slower in reaction. This point has been justly criticized[134, 135].

It is significant in support of Johnson's arguments that $Cr(C_2O_4)_3^{\equiv}$ has been resolved[141] while $Al(C_2O_4)_3^{\equiv}$ could not be resolved[132, 143] despite earlier claims for resolution[142].

Exchange Studies as a Criterion for Bond Type. There appears to be a rough parallelism between the conclusions obtainable from exchange experiments, magnetic susceptibility data, and studies involving the isolation of stable isomers. That is to say, those complexes which, on the basis of magnetic moment measurements, appear to satisfy the criterion for covalent binding are also usually resolvable into optical isomers or separable into cis and trans isomers and do not undergo rapid exchange between the central metal atom of the complex and a radioactive isotopic ion of this metal[78b, 144, 145]. To illustrate, bis(methylbenzylglyoxime)nickel(II) is diamagnetic, has been separated into two stable geometric isomers[41a], and does not exchange with radioactive nickel(II) ions[144a]. Similarly, the diamagnetic ion $[Copn_2Cl_2]^+$ was found not to exchange with radioactive cobalt(II) ions[146]. Further, the diamagnetic ion $[Co(C_2O_4)_3]^{\equiv}$, which has been resolved[136] into stable d and l forms, does not exchange[147] its bonded oxalate radicals with uncombined oxalate ions containing radioactive carbon.

Exchange experiments carried out by Long[147, 148] between uncombined oxalate ions containing radioactive carbon and the complex oxalato ions of aluminum(III), iron(III), cobalt(III), and chromium(III) appear to be in agreement with the resolution studies. The oxalate complexes of aluminum(III) and iron(III) undergo rapid interchange while those of cobalt(III) and chromium(III) show none.

The results of exchange experiments between radioactive cobalt and complexes of cobalt(II) and cobalt(III) containing bidentate ligands led West[144c] to the general conclusion that slow exchange can be associated with strong covalent bonds in the complex and rapid exchange with weak

141. Werner, *Ber.*, **45**, 3061 (1912).
142. Wahl, *Ber.*, **60**, 399 (1927); Burrows and Lauder, *J. Am. Chem. Soc.*, **53**, 3600 (1931).
143. Johnson, *Trans. Faraday Soc.*, **31**, 1612 (1935).
144. Johnson and Hall, *J. Am. Chem. Soc.*, **70**, 2344 (1948); Hall and Willeford, *J. Am. Chem. Soc.*, **73**, 5419 (1951); West, *J. Chem. Soc.*, **1952**, 3115; Libby, "Theory of Electron Exchange Reactions in Aqueous Solutions," p. 39, Preprint, Symposium on Electron Transfer and Isotopic Reactions, Division of Physical and Inorganic Chemistry, American Chemical Society, and Division of Chemical Physics, American Physical Society, Notre Dame, June 11–13, 1952.
145. Adamson, Welker, and Volpe, *J. Am. Chem. Soc.*, **72**, 4030 (1950).
146. Flagg, *J. Am. Chem. Soc.*, **63**, 557 (1941).
147. Long, *J. Am. Chem. Soc.*, **63**, 1353 (1941).
148. Long, *J. Am. Chem. Soc.*, **61**, 570 (1939).

covalent or ionic bonds. Oxalato and malonato complexes of iron(III) which have magnetic susceptibilities corresponding to five unpaired electrons are reported to exchange rapidly with carbon-14 labeled ligands, whereas $K_3Fe(CN)_6$, which has a moment corresponding to one unpaired electron, shows negligible exchange[149].

The above facts support the general consistency of the three experimental criteria used for bond classification (i.e., magnetic moment, resolution, exchange); however, some cases of apparent disagreement have been reported and should be considered. According to Johnson[150], the ion [Ni en$_3$]$^{++}$ could not be resolved into its optical iosmers, and on this basis the bonds between the nickel and nitrogen atoms would be termed ionic in character. In the case of [Ni dipy$_3$]$^{++}$, there seems no obvious reason for expecting a fundamentally different type of binding between nickel and the nitrogen atoms, yet this complex ion has been resolved[151] and so would be classed as covalent in character. Claims[152] have also been made for the resolution of [Ni en$_2$(H$_2$O)$_2$]$^{++}$. This would require the highly improbable conclusion that the binding in [Ni en$_2$(H$_2$O)$_2$]$^{++}$ is covalent in character, whereas the tris-(ethylenediamine) complex is ionic. Magnetic moment measurements obviously can supply no clue in these cases inasmuch as both the ionic and covalent structures involve two unpaired electrons.

Further disagreement in classification is observed between the resolution method and the exchange method[78b]. Neogi and Dutt[153] have reported the resolution of [Ga(C$_2$O$_4$)$_3$]$^{\equiv}$; however, the general exchange behavior of gallium(III) makes it seem almost certain that the complex would exchange oxalate rapidly. Resolution of [Zn en$_3$]$^{++}$ and [Cd en$_3$]$^{++}$ has been reported[154], yet formation and dissociation of these complexes is instantaneous. Such resolution seems improbable.

The complexes of iron(II) with o-phenanthroline and α,α'-dipyridyl are diamagnetic[155] and the tris complex of the latter coordinating molecule has been resolved into its stable optical isomers[156]. Accordingly, the iron-nitrogen bonds in these complexes are generally conceded to be mainly covalent in character[157]. Thus, exchange between radioactive iron(II) and these complex ions might not be anticipated. However, Ruben and coworkers[158] demonstrated that these ions experience exchange at a slow but

149. Clark, Curtis and Odell, J. Chem. Soc., **1954**, 63.
150. Johnson, Trans. Faraday Soc., **28**, 854 (1932).
151. Morgan and Burstall, J. Chem. Soc., **1931**, 2213; Nature, **127**, 854 (1931).
152. Wahl, Acta Sci. Fennicae, Comm. Phys. Math. **4**, 1 (1927).
153. Neogi and Dutt, J. Indian Chem. Soc., **15**, 83 (1938).
154. Neogi and Mukherjee, J. Indian Chem. Soc., **11**, 225 (1934).
155. Ref. 22b.
156. Werner, Ber., **45**, 433 (1912).
157. Ref. 27a, p. 117.
158. Ruben, Kamen, Allen, and Nahinsky, J. Am. Chem. Soc., **64**, 2297 (1942).

easily measurable rate in aqueous solution. On the contrary, the iron(III) in ferrihemoglobin and ferriheme, which is considered to be held by ionic or electrostatic forces on the basis of magnetic data[159], did not exchange with radioactive iron(III) ions after two months. These workers concluded that the rate of exchange appears to depend more on the structural features of the complex ion than on bond type. It has been suggested[158, 160] that in those complexes with a fused ring structure, such as ferrihemoglobin, there may be considerably greater stereochemical resistance to exchange than in the case of dipyridyl and similar complexes simply because of the necessity of breaking the four metal-nitrogen bonds without bond reformation in the former as against a "stepwise" exchange in the latter. On the basis of probability considerations, then, exchange in the dipyridyl type complexes may be favored over that in the fused ring type in spite of predictions to the contrary based on magnetic data.

The diamagnetic $Ni(CN)_4^=$ undergoes rapid exchange in direct contradiction to the expected result.

Other Criteria for Bond Type

X-ray analyses, electron diffraction studies, and optical methods have supplied extremely useful information[161, 162] regarding complex molecules and ions, but such information usually yields clues as to the nature of the bonds between the constituent parts of these complexes only as it can be interpreted in the light of other data and current theories of binding. Some information regarding the force constants of the bonds in coordination compounds has been obtained from a study of the Raman spectra of these substances. From these studies has come the rather unexpected result[15c] that the force constants for typical coordinate bonds are of the same order of magnitude though somewhat smaller than that for ordinary single bonds.

The "Inner and Outer Orbital" Complexes of Taube

The entire field of substitution reactions in complex ions, including both radioactive exchange, racemization, and chemical substitution reactions was considered in an excellent review by Taube[78b]. He pointed out that a useful classification of complexes can be based on differences in their adjustment to equilibrium with respect to substitution reactions (chemical basis of bond type). On the other hand, he emphasized that a slower rate for substitution does not necessarily mean greater bond stability and that rates of reaction will not, of necessity, correlate with factors related to bond

159. Pauling and Coryell, *Proc. Natl. Acad. Sci.*, **22**, 159, 210 (1936).
160. Ikler, *J. Am. Chem. Soc.*, **69**, 724 (1947); Reference 22, p. 171.
161. Fernelius, "Chemical Architecture" (Burk and Grummitt, Eds.), Chap. III. New York, Interscience Publishers, Inc., 1948; Ref. 15c, p. 167; Chap. V.
162. Szabo, *Acta Univ. Szegediensis, Acta Chem. et Phys. (N. S.)*, **1**, 52 (1942).

strength. (On this basis Bjerrum's term "robust" complexes was criticized, since it implies greater stability.) As a case in point, Taube noted that the complex $CrCl^{++}$ is more dissociated at equilibrium than the corresponding $FeCl^{++}$ ion, yet the iron(III) complex is in labile equilibrium with its surroundings while the chromium(III) ion is not.

Taube's summary of the data relative to the lability of various complexes with respect to substitution reactions is made in Table 4.5. *Inert* and *labile* groups may be readily distinguished.

The *electron structures* for the complexes of coordination number six fall quite naturally into two classes: in one class, which will be designated as the "inner orbital" type, relatively stable d orbitals of lower principal quantum number are combined with the sp^3 set of orbitals of higher quantum number; in the other, designated as the "outer orbital" type, the d orbitals have a considerably lower stability, since they are of the same principal quantum number as the s and p orbitals with which they are hybridized.* The subdivision of the inner and outer orbital complexes into the labile and inert classifications is indicated in Table 4.6. The important point indicated by the classification is the discontinuity in rates which appears at the point at which the last available inner d orbital is occupied by an unshared electron. For example, reactions of

$$V^{+++} \quad \frac{3d}{\uparrow\uparrow} \begin{array}{|ccc|} \hline & 4s & 4p \\ \hline \end{array}$$

are rapid, while those of

$$Cr^{+++} \quad \frac{3d}{\uparrow\uparrow\uparrow} \begin{array}{|ccc|} \hline & 4s & 4p \\ \hline \end{array}$$

are slow.

Mo^{5+} ($d^1d^0d^0D^2SP^3$) complexes are labile; those of Mo^{+++} ($d^1d^1d^1D^2SP^3$) are relatively inert.

Taube pointed out that this factor appears to be of major significance, and it cannot be attributed to a sudden change in degree of covalent character of the bonding since evaluation of degree of covalent bond character by independent means shows no sudden discontinuity at the appearance of this particular configuration. As independent indices of covalent character

---

* Huggins[163] first proposed the use of inner and outer orbitals for coordinate bond formation. Pauling rejected[164] the idea on the grounds that such bonds are too weak to be of importance. More recent calculations[28] of bond strength from the overlap integral indicate that such outer orbital complexes are justifiable, particularly under the conditions outlined by Huggins (i.e., with groups of high electronegativity).

163. Huggins, *J. Chem. Phys.*, **5**, 527 (1937).
164. Ref. 27a, p. 115.

TABLE 4.5. LABILITY OF HEXACOORDINATED COMPLEX IONS
(From Reference 78b)

Complex ions of the following are labile with respect to simple substitution aluminum(III), scandium(III), yttrium(III), tripositive rare earth ions, titanium(IV), zirconium(IV), thorium(IV), UO_2^{++}, plutonium(III), plutonium(IV) PuO_2^{++}.

Element	Lability of Complex Ions
V(II)	$V(CN)_6^{4-}$ is inert; no definite evidence on other complex ions
V(III)	F^-, CNS^-, CN^-, $SO_4^=$, $C_2O_4^=$, citrate, and pyrophosphate complex ions are "labile"; $V(CN)_6^=$ appears to be more labile than $V(CN)_6^{4-}$
Nb(II)	Only polynuclear complexes known in solution
Nb(III)	$SO_4^=$ complex probably labile
Nb(V)	Cl^-, Br^-, and H_2O complexes labile
Ta(II)	Only polynuclear complexes known in solution
Ta(III)	No definite information; CN^- complex probably labile
Ta(V)	CN^- complex labile; F^- and $C_2O_4^=$ complexes probably labile
Cr(II)	Cl^- complex reported inert
Cr(III)	H_2O, F^-, Cl^-, CN^-, CNS^-, NH_3, etc. complexes inert
Mo(II)	Only polynuclear complexes known in solution
Mo(III)	Cl^-, Br^-, and CNS^- complexes inert; replacement of NH_3 slow in acid
Mo(IV)	$Mo(CN)_8^{4-}$ inert
Mo(V)	Cl^- and Br^- complexes labile; CNS^- complex may be measurably slow in substitution; $Mo(CN)_8^=$ inert
Mo(VI)	F^-, Cl^-, and HOO^- complexes labile
W(II)	Only polynuclear complexes in solution
W(III)	$W_2Cl_9^=$ characterized as inert
W(IV)	Cl^- complex probably labile; $W(CN)_8^{4-}$ inert
W(V)	Cl^- and $C_2O_4^=$ complexes probably labile; $W(CN)_8^=$ inert
W(VI)	F^- and Br^- complexes labile; Cl^- complex doubtful
Mn(II)	En and pyrophosphate complexes labile; $Mn(CN)_6^=$ inert
Mn(III)	F^-, Cl^-, $C_2O_4^=$, and pyrophosphate complexes labile; $Mn(CN)_6^=$ inert
Mn(IV)	F^- and $C_2O_4^=$ complexes inert
Re(III)	Cl^- complex inert; NH_3 complex probably inert
Re(IV)	Cl^-, Br^-, and I^- complexes inert
Re(V)	Cl^- and CNS^- complexes labile; $ReO_2(CN)_4^=$ indeterminate, may be inert
Re(VI)	F^- complex labile
Fe(II)	En and $C_2O_4^=$ complexes labile; $Fe(CN)_6^{4-}$ (and substitution derivatives), $Fe(ophen)_3^{++}$, and $Fe(dipy)_3^{++}$ inert
Fe(III)	F^-, Cl^-, Br^-, CNS^-, NH_3, $S_2O_3^=$, $SO_3^=$, and $C_2O_4^=$ complexes labile; $Fe(CN)_6^=$ (and substitution derivatives) and $Fe(ophen)_3^{+++}$ inert

TABLE 4.5—*Continued*

Element	Lability of Complex Ions
Ru(II)	Cl^-, CN^-, and NH_3 complexes inert
Ru(III)	Cl^-, Br^-, and $C_2O_4^-$ complexes inert; complex ammines and derivatives inert
Ru(IV)	Cl^- complex inert
Ru(VI)	Cl^- complex labile
Os(II)	Cl^- complex inert; CN^- complex probably inert
Os(III)	Cl^- complex inert
Os(IV)	Cl^- complex inert
Os(VI)	F^- complex labile; $C_2O_4^-$, NO_2^-, and Cl^- complex on OsO_2^{++} undergo rapid substitution
Co(II)	Cl^-, Br^-, I^-, CNS^-, and NH_3 complexes labile; $Co(CN)_6^{4-}$ may be inert
Co(III)	H_2O in presence of Co^{++} labile; CN^-, SO_3^-, NO_2^-, and $C_2O_4^-$ complexes inert; complex ammines and derivatives inert
Rh(II)	Br^- in $Rhpy_5Br^+$ slow in substitution
Rh(III)	Cl^-, CN^-, SO_4^-, and NH_3 complexes inert
Ir(III)	Cl^-, Br^- probably, and CN^- complexes inert; complex ammines and derivatives inert; SO_4^- and $C_2O_4^-$ complexes inert
Ir(IV)	Cl^- and py complexes inert
Ni(II)	NH_3, en, $C_2O_4^-$, tartrate, and CN^- complexes labile dipyridyl complex inert
Pd(II)	Coordination number 4 only in complex ions and derivatives; some reactions measurably slow
Pd(IV)	No definite conclusions
Pt(II)	Coordination number 4 only; Cl^- and NO_2^- complexes inert; ammines and derivatives inert; complexes less labile than those of palladium(II)
Pt(IV)	Halide and CNS^- complexes inert; ammines and derivatives inert
Cu(I), Cu(II)	Cl^-, Br^-, NH_3, and SO_3^- complexes labile
Ag(I)	NH_3, CN^-, and SO_3^- complexes labile
Au(I)	Cl^-, Br^-, CN^- and CNS^- complexes probably labile
Au(III)	SO_4^-, Cl^-, and NH_3 complexes inert; NO_3^- complex hydrolyzed rapidly
Zn(II), Cd(II), Hg(II)	Labile
Ga(III)	F^-, Cl^-, and $C_2O_4^-$ complexes labile
In(III)	Probably labile
Tl(III)	$C_2O_4^-$ complex labile; Cl^- and Br^- complexes not certain
Si(IV)	F^- in SiF_6^- measurably slow in substitution
Ge(IV)	No conclusions for coordination number 6
Sn(IV)	No conclusions for coordination number 6
P(V)	PF_6^- inert
As(V)	AsF_6^- and $As(C_6H_4O_2)_3^-$ inert
Sb(V)	SbF_6^- and $SbCl_6^-$ inert
SF_6, SeF_6, TeF_6	Inert

TABLE 4.6. INNER AND OUTER ORBITAL COMPLEXES INERT AND LABILE FORMS
(From Reference 78b)

I. Inner orbital complexes
  A. Labile members
    (1) $d^0d^0d^0D^2SP^3$ Sc(III), Y(III), rare earths(III), Ti(IV), Zr(IV), Hf(IV), Ce(IV), Th(IV), Nb(V), Ta(V), Mo(VI), W(VI), Np(III), Np(IV), Pu(III), Pu(IV).
    (2) $d^1d^0d^0D^2SP^3$ Ti(III), V(IV), Mo(V), W(V), Re(VI).
    (3) $d^1d^1d^0D^2SP^3$ Ti(II), V(III), Nb(III), Ta(III), W(IV), Re(V), Ru(VI).
  B. Inert members
    (1) $d^1d^1d^1D^2SP^3$ V(II), Cr(III), Mo(III), W(III), Mn(IV), Re(IV).
    (2) $d^2d^1d^1D^2SP^3$ $Cr(CN)_6^{4-}$, $Mn(CN)_6^{=}$, Re(III), Ru(IV), Os(IV).
    (3) $d^2d^2d^1D^2SP^3$ $Mn(CN)_6^{=}$, Re(II), $Fe(CN)_6^{=}$, $Fe(ophen)_3^{+++}$, $Fe(dipy)_3^{+++}$ Ru(III), Os(III), Ir(IV).
    (4) $d^2d^2d^2D^2SP^3$ $Fe(CN)_6^{4-}$, $Fe(ophen)_3^{++}$, $Fe(dipy)_3^{++}$, Ru(II), Os(II), Co(III) in all but F complexes, Rh(III), Ir(III), Pd(IV), Pt(IV).
II. Outer orbital complexes
  Lability tends to decrease slowly as charge on central cation increases. Typical "outer orbital ions": Al^{+++}, Mn^{++}, Fe^{++}, Fe^{+++}, Co^{++}, Ni^{++}, Zn^{++}, Cd^{++}, Hg^{++}, Ga^{+++}, In^{+++}, and Tl^{+++}.

he used the acid dissociation constants of the hydrated ions, the hydration energies of the metal ions, and theoretical arguments from size and charge of the ion.

This is not to imply that the degree of covalent character in the bond may not exercise an influence on the rate of substitution reactions; on the contrary, the variation in the degree of covalent character is an important factor in determining, for those ions for which both possibilities exist, whether the complex ion will be of the inner orbital or outer orbital electronic type. But it is particularly significant that under some circumstances, complexes of the outer orbital type which are described as "ionic" may have bonds of more covalent character than some of the inner orbital complexes which are classified as "covalent". For example, there is reason to believe that $[Ga(H_2O)_6]^{+++}$ is more covalent in its bonds than is $[Cr(H_2O)_6]^{+++}$, yet from exchange studies $[Ga(H_2O)_6]^{+++}$ is classed as "ionic" while $[Cr(H_2O)_6]^{+++}$ is classed as "covalent". It is in this sense that Taube's classification seems much superior to the conventional ionic-covalent description. The terms "ionic" and "covalent" must remain indefinite because they are not defined unambiguously.

On the other hand, the experimental classification of complexes into inert and labile compounds is usually definite and the theoretical description of these complexes is quite unambiguous except in a relatively small number of cases where either the inner or outer orbital designation may apply (i.e., Cu^{++}, $Ni(A)_6^{++}$, etc.).

The implication that all bonds involving a change in magnetic moment are stronger than bonds in which no such change is observed (i.e., "covalent" bonds by magnetic criterion are stronger than "ionic") has been shown to be untrue in an earlier discussion (Chapter 3, p. 136). One then looks to a factor other than "bond strength" to explain the rapid exchange in the labile complexes and the slow exchange in the inert complexes. Since one is dealing with a problem in kinetics in all exchange and racemization studies, it would appear that there is a sharp discontinuity in the energy required to form the activated complex as soon as the last d orbital gets at least one electron.

Taube interpreted these facts as indicating that substitution proceeds by an intermediate species of coordination number seven which can be stabilized through utilization of the empty d orbital on the central metal ion. If the inner d orbitals are completely occupied, electrons must be promoted or paired to make a d level available. Either process would require energy which would appear as an activation energy. The alternative path, in which a ligand is lost in the rate determining steps, can also be supposed to require a high activation energy, since there is no factor which compensates effectively for the energy required to remove the group.

In outer orbital complexes lability is observed if the central ion has low charge, while increasingly inert character is observed as the charge on the central ion builds up. Substitution by dissociation mechanism seems reasonable when the charge is low (i.e., 1, 2, or 3). It has been suggested that the energy required to remove one of the groups is compensated in part by rehybridization of the lower orbitals (i.e., sp^3 or sp^2d to a lower coordination number). The observation that many of the metals of these complexes readily assume a coordination number of four was cited in support of such an argument. Increasing charge on the central ion is bound to produce bonds of more covalent character which are stronger and harder to dissociate or substitute by any mechanism. This is illustrated by the fact that the rate of hydrolysis decreases in the series of the hexafluoro complexes: $AlF_6^= > SiF_6^= > PF_6^- \gg SF_6$.

An exception to the above rules is found in the case of $[Co(H_2O)_6]^{+++}$. This ion exchanges water rapidly, much more rapidly than replacement of NH_3 by H_2O in $[Co(NH_3)_6]^{+++}$. The electronic structure as determined by its diamagnetism is $d^2d^2d^2D^2SP^3$, which should lead to slow exchange on the basis of the above considerations for inner orbital complexes. It is probable, however, that the paramagnetic labile state for Co^{+++} ($d^2d^1d^1d^1SP^3D^2$) is only slightly above the diamagnetic ground state in energy. This relation is expected from the fact that in the complex with fluoride the paramagnetic state is lowest while in the hexammine the diamagnetic state is lowest. Since water is intermediate between fluoride and ammonia in polarizability, one might expect on the basis of crystal field splitting arguments (Chapter

3) that the two states, paramagnetic and diamagnetic, would lie close together in the water complex (i.e., near to the point (A) of intersection of the two lines in Fig. 3.3 (p. 136)). On this basis a small activation energy would suffice to give the outer orbital paramagnetic structure, which could undergo exchange more readily than the closed shell type of structure.

Taube's work emphasizes a point which should be obvious but which none the less results in much confusion. Criteria based on rate are dependent upon mechanism and as such are frequently much less dependent upon bond strength than is commonly supposed. In this sense all explanations of the trans effect are inadequate, since it has never been fully established that the result is due to bond strength rather than rate and mechanism. Taube's postulates would suggest that mechanism might be of major importance in explaining these substitution processes, yet all explanations of the effect are based on the concept of bond strength. In fact, one must conclude with Taube that our knowledge of reaction mechanisms of coordination compounds is still very meager.

5. Chelation and the Theory of Heterocyclic Ring Formation Involving Metal Ions

Robert W. Parry

University of Michigan, Ann Arbor, Michigan

The term "chelate" was proposed by Morgan[1] to designate those *cyclic* structures which arise from the union of metallic atoms with organic or inorganic molecules or ions. The name is derived from the Greek word *chela* which means the claw of a lobster or crab. Chelate ring systems can be formed only by ligands which have more than one point of attachment to the metal. For example, *unidentate* NH_3 cannot form a ring, but *bidentate* ethylenediamine can form chelate structures. Ligands with three points of attachment are known as tridentate, those with four, as tetradentate, and so on:

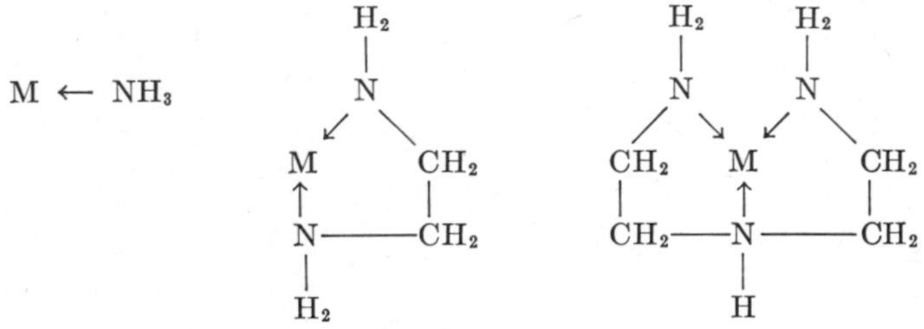

$$M \leftarrow NH_3$$

Monodentate Ligand No Chelation	Bidentate Ligand One Chelate Ring

Tridentate Ligand
Two Interlocked
Chelate Rings

A comprehensive review of the chelate rings was given by Diehl[2] in 1937 and a more recent treatment by Martell and Calvin[3] in their book, "The Chemistry of the Metal Chelate Compounds."

Many widely divergent chemical and biological problems are intimately related to the formation of chelate rings. For example, metals which are

1. Morgan and Drew, *J. Chem. Soc.*, **117**, 1456 (1920).
2. Diehl, *Chem. Rev.*, **21**, 39 (1937); (a) p. 84.
3. Martell and Calvin, "Chemistry of the Metal Chelate Compounds," New York, Prentice-Hall, Inc. 1952.

essential for plant and animal nutrition form chelate rings in the organism (Chapter 21). Thus, hemin is an iron chelate and chlorophyll is a magnesium ring compound. Also, metals play an important role in the functioning of enzymes—apparently through chelate ring formation in the intermediates.

Another point of biological interest is the use of metal ion buffers. By selecting a proper complexing agent, free metal ion concentration can be maintained at a relatively constant level in a predetermined range just as a constant hydrogen ion concentration is maintained in conventional buffer systems.

A novel use of chelating agents for the direct titration of metals has been suggested by Schwarzenbach[4]. He points out that many chelating agents change color according to the metal ion concentration in a manner completely analogous to the pH dependent color changes observed with acid-base indicators. This makes direct metal titrations possible.

THE STABILITY OF CHELATE STRUCTURES

Extra Stability Due to Chelation—The "Chelate Effect"

One of the most striking properties of chelate ring compounds is their unusual stability. In this respect they resemble the aromatic rings of organic chemistry. As an illustration, one may compare the relatively stable chelate $[Ni(en)_3]^{++}$ with the analogous, but less stable non-chelate compound $[Ni(NH_2CH_3)_6]^{++}$. The ethylenediamine complex is stable in solution at high dilution, but the methylamine compound dissociates under the same conditions to precipitate nickel hydroxide[2a]. Data on formation constants in solution[5] indicate that the chelate complexes of ethylenediamine and other polydentate amines are usually much more stable than the corresponding ammonia complexes.

An illustration involving compounds of a different type is found in the β-diketones which may enolize and form stable six-membered rings with metal atoms. Representative acetylacetonates are shown in Fig. 5.1. The stability of the metal acetylacetonates is indicated by the fact that they may be heated without decomposition to temperatures well above that at which acetylacetone itself is decomposed[2]. This remarkable stability contrasts sharply with the low stability of coordination compounds containing simple ketones such as acetone.

The formation of fused rings around the metal seems to confer an even

4. Schwarzenbach, *Chimia*, **3**, 1 (1949); Schwarzenbach and Gysling, *Helv. Chim. Acta*, **32**, 1314 (1949); Schwarzenbach and Willi, *Helv. Chim. Acta*, **34**, 528 (1951); and other papers in the series on metal indicators.
5. Schwarzenbach, *Helv. Chim. Acta*, **35**, 2344 (1952).

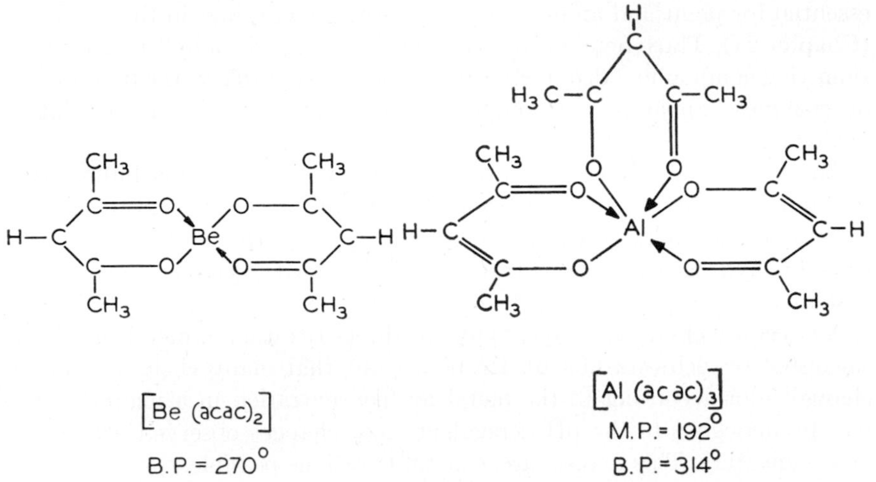

FIG. 5.1. Acetylacetone complexes of beryllium and aluminum

greater stability than the formation of single rings. For instance, copper(II) ethylenediamine-bis-acetylacetone, which contains three interlocked rings,

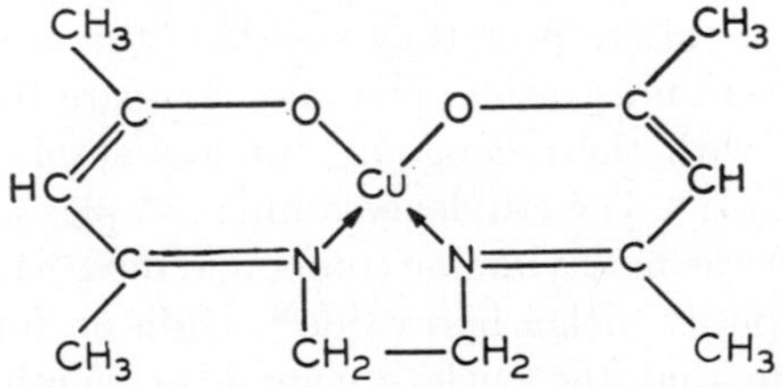

may be heated nearly to redness without suffering decomposition[6]. Calvin and Bailes[7] made a polarographic study of the compounds (A) and (B) (Fig. 5.2) and reported that the reduction potentials indicate much greater

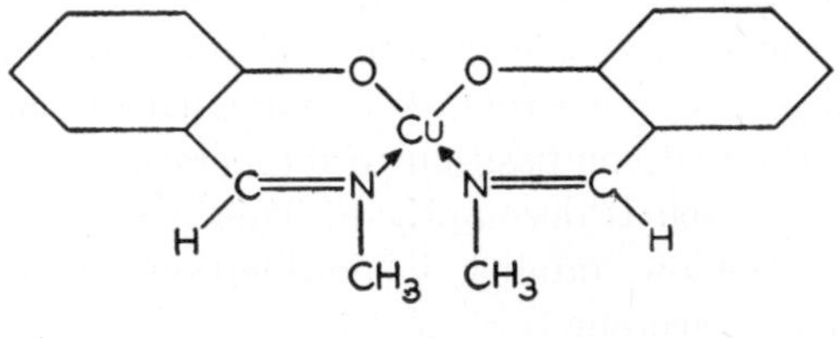

A

$$E_{\frac{1}{2}} = +0.02 \ \left(\text{REDUCTION}\right)$$

6. Morgan and Smith, *J. Chem. Soc.*, **127**, 2030 (1925).
7. Calvin and Bailes, *J. Am. Chem. Soc.*, **68**, 953 (1946).

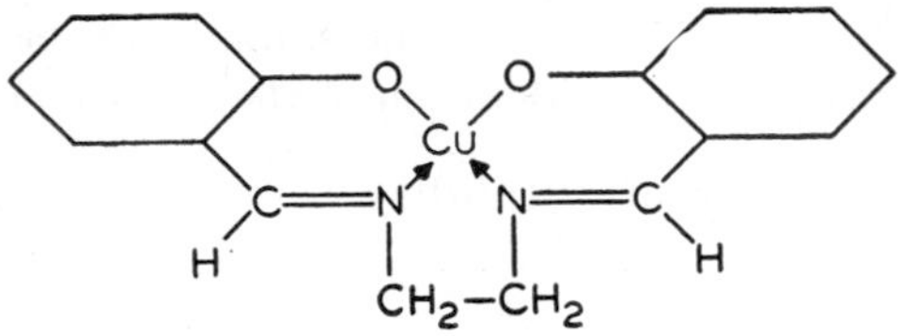

$$B$$

$$E_{\frac{1}{2}} = -0.75$$

Fig. 5.2. Polarographic comparison of chelated and nonchelated structures

stability for the interlocked three ring system, (B), than for the comparable two ring system, (A). Other examples have also been cited.

Of even more interest are the biologically important metal porphyrin derivatives which are constituents of chlorophyll X and hemin (Chapter 21). These have completely interlocked ring systems (Fig. 5.3). Such materials and the structurally similar phthalocyanines (Chapter 22)

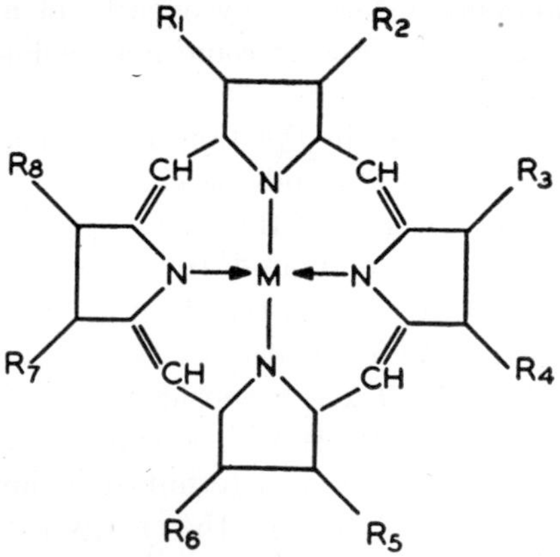

Fig. 5.3. The porphyrin ring system

are very stable in acid solution. In fact, the copper phthalocyanine complex is reported to be stable in the vapor phase at 500°C.

The stability of multiple ring systems has been utilized extensively in the commercial applications of ethylenediaminetetraacetic acid, salts of which are sold under such trade names as "Versene," "Sequestrene," and "Nullapon." Schwarzenbach has published an outstanding series of papers on the stability of such systems, varying a number of structural factors in the ligand. The enhanced stability conferred on a complex as a result of ring formation has been termed the "chelate effect" by Schwarzenbach[5]. A review of the factors contributing to the stability of complexes will be a useful starting point in the consideration of the chelate effect.

Factors Involved in Chelate Stability

Since chelate compounds are merely a special class of coordination compounds, all factors outlined in Chapters 3 and 4 are important in determining their stability. In addition, a few factors assume special importance as a result of ring formation and will be considered specifically here. The question of solvation effects is of particular importance in the study of chelate compounds since many of the large organic ligands are only very slightly soluble in water so their complexes have been studied in mixed solvents[11], or in organic solvents[9, 12]. If solvation terms (p. 138) were truly negligible, the choice of solvent would be of minor importance. That such is not always the case is shown by a number of investigations (e.g., Refs. 12, 13). In fact, in organic solvents, a metal cation and its anion are usually associated. An interesting correlation of observations in mixed solvents and in water was given by Van Uitert and Haas[12b]. Van Uitert, Fernelius, Douglas, and their co-workers[12, 13] have applied data from mixed solvents to the study of many different chelate systems. Trotman and Dickenson[10] suggest that solvation energy terms may even be of major importance in determining the relative stabilities of some non-chelated complexes, such as the silver ammines.

It is important to note that in the thermochemical (p. 138) cycle entropy effects have been neglected and the change in heat content, ΔH, is taken as an approximate measure of the change in free energy, ΔF, which determines the stability of the compound. In a consideration of the "chelate effect" the entropy terms are so large that they can't be neglected, even as a first approximation. These effects are discussed in more detail in a later section. Since $\Delta F = \Delta H - T\Delta S$, a consideration of factors influencing both ΔH and ΔS is appropriate. It will be convenient as a conventional simplification to *assume* that ΔH is determined in large measure by the energy of coordination (see p. 138) (i.e., the energy for the processes):

$$M_{(o)}{}^h + yAB_{(o)}{}^z \rightarrow [M(AB)_y]_{(o)}{}^{h-yz}$$

8. Bjerrum, *Chem. Revs.*, **46**, 381 (1950).
9. Burkin, *J. Chem. Soc.*, **1954**, 71; Jonassen, Fagley, Rolland, and Yates, *J. Phys. Chem.*, **58**, 286 (1954).
10. Trotman and Dickenson, *J. Chem. Soc.*, **1949**, 1293.
11. Calvin and Wilson, *J. Am. Chem. Soc.*, **67**, 2003 (1945).
12. VanUitert, Fernelius, and Douglas, *J. Am. Chem. Soc.*, **75**, 3577 (1953); VanUitert and Haas, *J. Am. Chem. Soc.*, **75**, 451 (1953); VanUitert, Fernelius, and Douglas; *J. Am. Chem. Soc.*, **75**, 457 (1953); VanUitert, Haas, Fernelius, and Douglas, *J. Am. Chem. Soc.*, **75**, 455 (1953).
13. VanUitert, Fernelius, and Douglas, *J. Am. Chem. Soc.*, **75**, 2736, 2739 (1953).

The energy of coordination may then be considered in terms of steric factors for both the central ion and the ligand which arise from chelation and electronic factors for both components of the complex, which are peculiar to chelate systems.

Steric Factors in Chelate Ring Formation

Ring Size

Bonds in coordination compounds may arise from two general types of groups: (1) primary acid groups in which the metal ion replaces an acid hydrogen and, (2) neutral groups which contain an atom with a free electron pair suitable for bond formation. If two groups from either class 1 or 2 or from classes 1 *and* 2 are present in the same molecule in such positions that both groups can form bonds with the same metal ion, a chelate ring may be formed. When the groups are present in such positions as to form a five- or six-membered ring, the resulting complex is most stable, although 4-, 7-, 8- and even larger rings are known (Chapter 6). The existence of three-membered rings has not been established.

Evidence on Three-Membered Rings

In a review of the coordination compounds of hydrazine, Audrieth and Ogg[14] point out the interesting fact that in a surprisingly large number of cases, the number of hydrazine groups coordinated to a metal ion is one-half the normal coordination number of the metal. Since no structural determinations have been made, the possibility of a three-membered chelate ring cannot be definitely eliminated; however, the low solubilities of most of these compounds suggest polynuclear structures involving hydrazine bridges rather than chelate structures. The complexes $[PtCl_2(N_2H_4)]$ and $[PdBr_2(N_2H_4)]$[15] are probably dimers of the type:

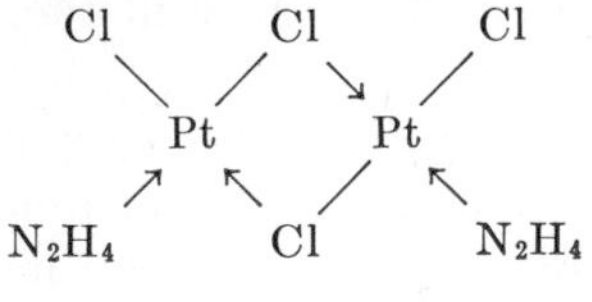

In one of the few cases in which hydrazine complexes have been studied in solution, Rebertus, Laitinen, and Bailar[16] found that the zinc(II) ion will coordinate four hydrazine molecules with only small differences between the separate dissociation constants; this indicates strongly that hydrazine is

14. Audrieth and Ogg "The Chemistry of Hydrazine," p. 181, New York, John Wiley & Sons, Inc., 1951.
15. Goremykin and Gladyshevskaya, *J. Gen. Chem. (U.S.S.R.)* **13**, 762 (1943); **14**, 13 (1944).
16. Rebertus, Laitinen, and Bailar, *J. Am. Chem. Soc.*, **75**, 3051 (1953).

monodentate with the normally four coordinate zinc(II) ion. A similar study conducted by Schwarzenbach and Zobrist[17] indicated that four hydrazine molecules are bound to zinc(II) and six to nickel(II) in a manner comparable to the binding of ammonia to these metals. They concluded that no three-membered chelate rings were ever formed.

Finally, no well authenticated case of optical isomerism which might be used as evidence for a chelate ring structure has been observed with hydrazine complexes.*

Four-Membered Rings

The stereochemistry of metal chelate rings differs from that of carbon ring systems in that all of the atoms in the ring are not the same size and some of the bond angles normally vary from 109° (or 120°) as a result of the directed valences of the metal ion. These two factors may relieve the instability of four-membered ring systems. For example, the carbonate group in $[Co \ en_2 \ CO_3]^+$ occupies two positions to give a rather stable four-membered ring. Scale drawings of this ring, using Pauling's covalent radii, indicate that the steric strain is much less than in a corresponding four-membered carbon system. Similarly, sulfate, sulfite, thiosulfate, thiocarbonate, selenate, selenite, molybdate, and chromate can each occupy two positions in the coordination sphere[2, 18a, 19]. (See also p. 180 for electronic interpretations.) Four-membered rings are very common in bridged molecules such as:

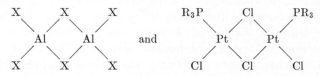

(p. 18 and 22). The formation of four-membered oxo-bridges in basic solutions of chromium(III) is of great importance in the leather tanning industry (Chapter 13).

Unusual four-membered rings have been reported by Dwyer and Mellor[21, 22], who found that copper, nickel, palladium, and silver ions form complexes with triazene derivatives which are much more stable than the

---

* A report that $[Co(N_2H_4)_3]Br_3$ has been resolved into optical isomers is a typographical error. The ligand should be ethylenediamine, not hydrazine. (Wells, "Structural Inorganic Chemistry," p. 530).

17. Schwarzenbach and Zobrist, *Helv. Chim. Acta*, **35**, 1291 (1952).
18. Riley, *J. Chem. Soc.*, **1928**, 2985; **1929**, 1307; **1930**, 1642.
19. Briggs, *J. Chem. Soc.*, **1929**, 685.
20. Yoe and Sarver, "Organic Analytical Reagents," New York, John Wiley & Sons, Inc., 1941.
21. Dwyer, *J. Am. Chem. Soc.*, **63**, 78 (1941).
22. Dwyer and Mellor, *J. Am. Chem. Soc.*, **63**, 81 (1941); Dwyer, *J. Am. Chem. Soc.*, **63**, 78 (1951).

parent triazene. They withstand the action of boiling hydrochloric acid and concentrated alkali; some of them are stable at temperatures above 300°C. The following structure has been suggested:

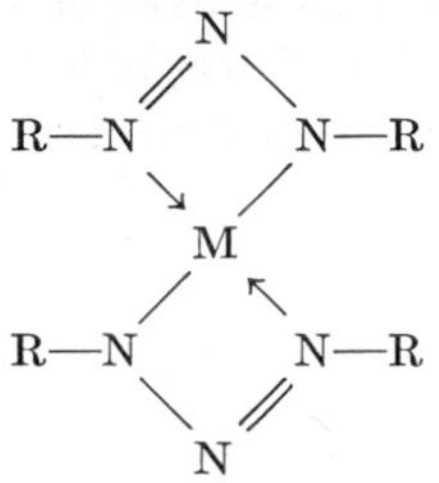

$$
\begin{array}{c}
N \\
\diagup\!\!\diagup \quad \diagdown \\
R\!-\!N \qquad N\!-\!R \\
\diagdown \qquad \diagup \\
M \\
\diagup \qquad \diagdown \\
R\!-\!N \qquad N\!-\!R \\
\diagdown \qquad \diagup\!\!\diagup \\
N
\end{array}
$$

One would expect a ring of this type to be somewhat strained, but the unusual stability of the compounds gives no indication of this. It is observed, however, that at low temperatures the compound dimerizes, a process which could relieve strain by opening the rings and crosslinking the metal atoms. Four-membered diamagnetic nickel chelate rings of ethylxanthogenate

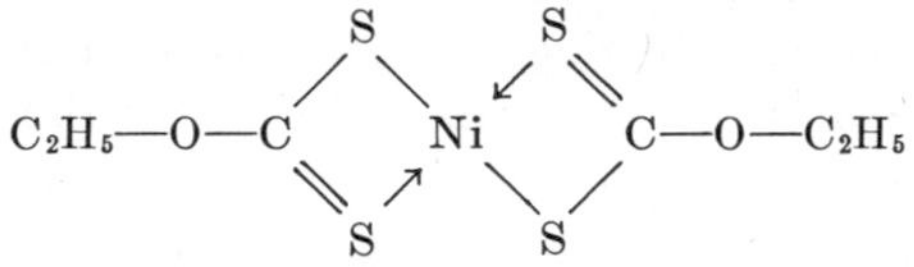

$$
C_2H_5\!-\!O\!-\!C
\begin{array}{c}
S \\
\diagup \quad \diagdown \\
\\
\diagdown \quad \diagup \\
S
\end{array}
Ni
\begin{array}{c}
S \\
\diagdown \quad \diagup\!\!\diagup \\
\\
\diagup \quad \diagdown \\
S
\end{array}
C\!-\!O\!-\!C_2H_5
$$

and nickel ethyl dithiocarbamate,

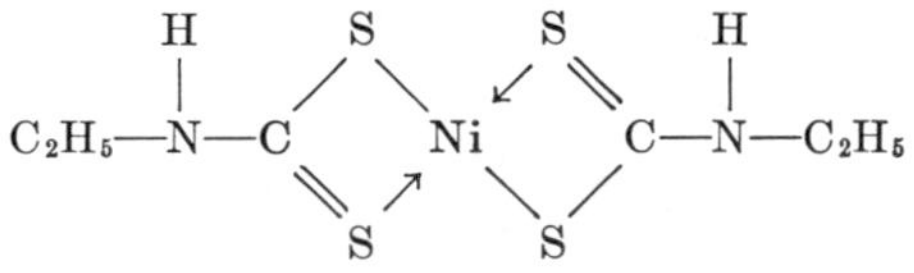

$$
C_2H_5\!-\!N\!-\!C
\begin{array}{c}
H \qquad S \\
| \qquad \diagup \quad \diagdown \\
\\
\diagdown \quad \diagup \\
S
\end{array}
Ni
\begin{array}{c}
S \qquad H \\
\diagdown \quad \diagup\!\!\diagup \qquad | \\
\\
\diagup \quad \diagdown \\
S
\end{array}
C\!-\!N\!-\!C_2H_5
$$

have been described[23].

Five-Membered Rings

Five- and six-membered rings are very common. Hundreds of examples of each type have been described[2, 20, 24, 25, 26]. In general, it is observed that saturated compounds tend to form five-membered structures whereas those ligands which give rings with two double bonds tend to form six-membered rings. The evidence for a five-membered saturated ring arises from several unrelated types of experiments. For example, 1,2,3-triaminopropane,

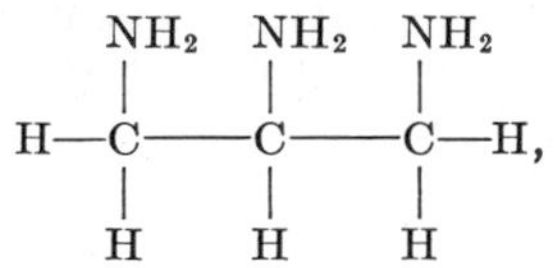

$$
\begin{array}{ccc}
NH_2 & NH_2 & NH_2 \\
| & | & | \\
H\!-\!C\!\!-\!\!-\!\!-\!C\!\!-\!\!-\!\!-\!C\!-\!H, \\
| & | & | \\
H & H & H
\end{array}
$$

23. Cambi and Szego, *Ber.*, **64**, 2591 (1931).

can react with a metal so as to occupy only two coordination positions, the third amine group then being capable of salt formation. The compound of this type formed with platinic chloride will then be either disymmetric (A) or symmetrical (B), according as a five- or six-membered ring is formed preferentially by chelation. Mann[27] was able to resolve the complex, establishing the existence of the five-membered ring A.

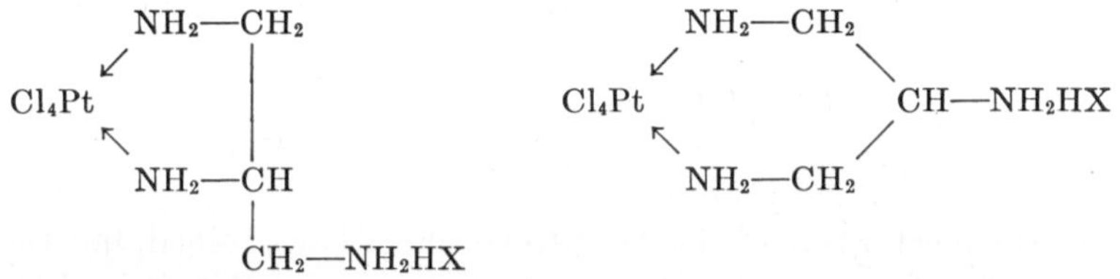

$$
\begin{array}{cc}
\text{NH}_2\text{—CH}_2 & \text{NH}_2\text{—CH}_2 \\
\text{Cl}_4\text{Pt} \quad\quad | & \text{Cl}_4\text{Pt} \quad\quad\quad \text{CH—NH}_2\text{HX} \\
\text{NH}_2\text{—CH} & \text{NH}_2\text{—CH}_2 \\
| & \\
\text{CH}_2\text{—NH}_2\text{HX} &
\end{array}
$$

A. Resolvable   B. Nonresolvable
Five-membered Ring   Six-membered Ring

FIG. 5.4. Chelation of 1,2,3-triaminopropane

Another example is found in the fact that ethylenediamine forms very stable five-membered chelate rings. The presence of substituents on the carbon does not disturb the five-membered ring and thus has only a minor effect on the color and stability of the coordination compound. The cobalt(III) compounds containing propylenediamine and 2,3-butylenediamine are similar to their ethylenediamine homologs in ease of formation, stability and color. Other substituted ethylenediamines such as *meso*-stilbenediamine, isobutylenediamine[28], cyclopentanediamine[29], and cyclohexanediamine[29] form very stable coordination compounds comparable to their ethylenediamine parent. On the other hand, a very different effect is produced by increasing the number of carbon atoms between the amine groups, since this expands the ring. Trimethylenediamine forms six-membered chelate rings with cobalt[30], nickel[31], platinum[31, 32], and iron[33];

24. Flagg, "Organic Reagents in Gravimetric and Volumetric Analysis," New York, Interscience Publishers, Inc., 1948.
26. Mellan, "Organic Reagents in Inorganic Analysis," p. 53, Philadelphia, The Blakiston Co., 1941; Freudenberg, "Stereochemie," Vol. 3, p. 1200, Franz Deuticke, Leipzig and Wien, 1932.
27. Mann, *J. Chem. Soc.*, **129**, 2681 (1926).
28. Mills and Quibbell, *J. Chem. Soc.*, **1935**, 839; Lidstone and Mills, *J. Chem. Soc.*, **1939**, 1754.
29. Jaeger and terBerg, *Proc. Acad. Sci. Amsterdam*, **40**, 490 (1937); Jaeger and Bijerk, *Proc. Acad. Sci. Amsterdam*, **40**, 12, 116, 316 (1937); *Z. anorg. allgem. Chem.*, **233**, 97 (1937); earlier articles by Jaeger.
30. Werner, *Ber.*, **40**, 61 (1907).
31. Tschugaeff, *Ber.*, **39**, 3190 (1906); *J. prakt. Chem.* [2] **75**, 159 (1907); [2] **76**, 89 (1907).

available evidence indicates that such compounds are less stable and more difficult to prepare than the analogous propylenediamine compounds containing five-membered rings. Bailar and Work[36] found that neopentanediamine, $NH_2CH_2C(CH_3)_2CH_2NH_2$, coordinates more readily and gives more stable compounds than does trimethylenediamine, $H_2N—CH_2—CH_2—CH_2—NH_2$. This unexplained observation contrasts sharply with the fact that propylenediamine, 2,3-butylenediamine and many other 2,3-diamines strongly resemble ethylenediamine in their complexing behavior. In the latter case, substitution on the carbon does not greatly alter the complexing properties.

A second line of evidence has been obtained by Schwarzenbach[5] from a consideration of the formation constants of metal complexes related to ethylenediaminetetraacetates, and of the general type:

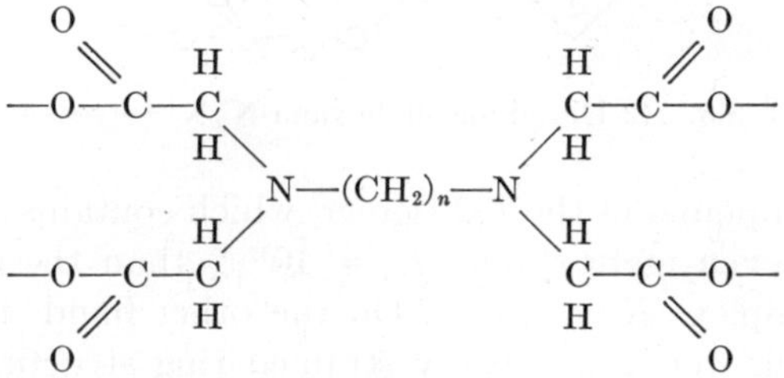

$$\begin{array}{ccccccc}
O & & & & & & O \\
\diagdown & H & & H & & \diagup \\
—O—C—C & & & & C—C—O— \\
& H\diagdown & & \diagup H & \\
& & N—(CH_2)_n—N & & & & \text{(I)}\\
& H\diagup & & \diagdown H & \\
—O—C—C & & & & C—C—O— \\
\diagup & H & & H & & \diagdown \\
O & & & & & & O
\end{array}$$

The value of n varied from 2 to 5, giving five-, six-, seven-, and eight-membered chelate rings involving the nitrogen atoms. The corresponding imino diacetate complexes

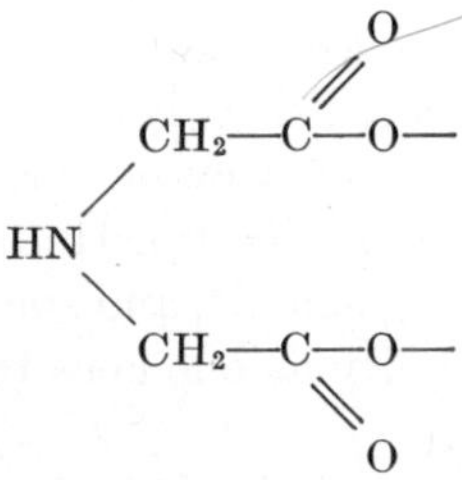

$$\begin{array}{cc}
& O \\
& \diagup\!\!\diagup \\
CH_2—C—O— \\
\diagup \\
HN & \text{(II)}\\
\diagdown \\
CH_2—C—O— \\
& \diagdown \\
& O
\end{array}$$

were studied as standards in which no chelate ring formation involving only nitrogen atoms was possible. Data indicate that when $n = 2$ the stabilization due to the chelate ring formation is a maximum. As the chain length (value of n) increases, the stabilizing effect due to chelation disappears and is even replaced by a slight destabilizing effect. It was also observed that

32. Drew and Tress, *J. Chem. Soc.*, **1933**, 1335.
33. Breuil, *Compt. rend.*, **199**, 298 (1934).
34. Pfeiffer and Hainmann, *Ber.*, **36**, 1064 (1903).
35. Bailar and Work, *J. Am. Chem. Soc.*, **68**, 232 (1946).
36. Schwarzenbach and Ackerman, *Helv. Chim. Acta*, **32**, 1682 (1949).

as the chain length is increased the tendency of the ligand to bind two separate metal ions increases rapidly so the formation of polynuclear complexes takes place. Similar results were reported by Schwarzenbach and Ackerman[36] from their study of the isomeric diaminocyclohexane-N,N'-tetraacetates (Fig. 5.5) coordinated with the alkaline earth ions. The cal-

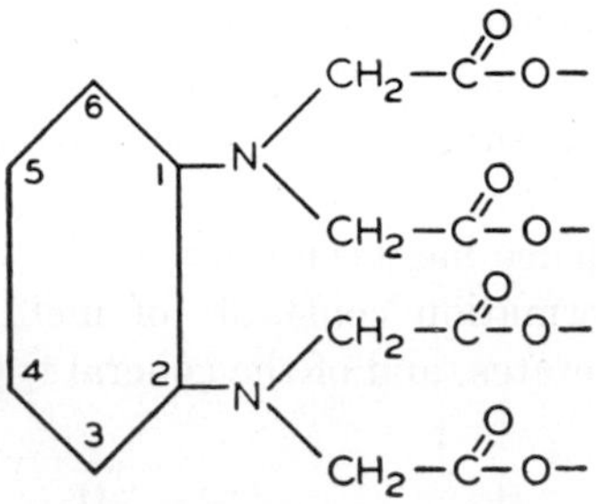

Fig. 5.5. 1,2-Diaminocyclohexane-N,N' tetraacetate

cium chelate compound of the 1,2 isomer, which contains a five-membered chelate ring, is even more stable ($K = 10^{12.5}$) than the ethylenediamine tetraacetate complex ($K = 10^{10.5}$). On the other hand, the 1,3 and 1,4 derivatives which would give badly strained ring structures in the metal complexes are much less stable and show a strong tendency to coordinate with two metal cations rather than to form a ring.

Schwarzenbach[5] also reports formation constants for complexes of ethylenediamine and trimethylenediamine which confirm the greater stability of the five-membered metal-nitrogen ring.

The stability of five-membered rings is not restricted to the coordination of amines. Dey[37] compared the efficacy of dicarboxylic acids in the formation of coordination compounds with tin. He found the order of *decreasing* complexing power to be oxalic, malonic, and succinic acids. This corresponds to a decrease in chelate stability as one goes from a five- to a seven-membered ring.

Similar observations were made by Riley[18]. He found that the stability of complexes formed between the Cu^{+2} ion and the oxalate, malonate, and succinate ions *decreased* in the order listed. Electronic effects cannot justify this observation since succinate ion is a stronger base than oxalate[38]. Recently Courtney, Chabarek, and Martell[39] found that if the acetate groups of ethylenediaminetetraacetate are replaced by propionate groups to give terminal rings of six rather than five members, the stability of the chelate is reduced.

37. Dey, *Univ. Allahabad Studies, Chem. Sect.*, **1946**, 7; [*Chem. Abs.*, **41**, 6169 (1947)].
38. Hixon and Johns, *J. Am. Chem. Soc.*, **49**, 1786 (1927).
39. Courtney, Chaberek, and Martell, *J. Am. Chem. Soc.*, **75**, 4814 (1953).

Rings of Six or More Members

In general it is found that stable chelate rings involving *two double bonds* are usually six-membered structures. Thus acetylacetone and salicylaldehyde and their derivatives coordinate readily to give very stable six-membered chelate complexes:

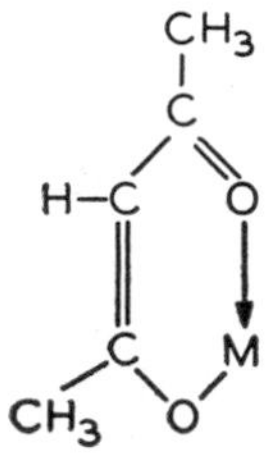

ACETYLACETONE CHELATE

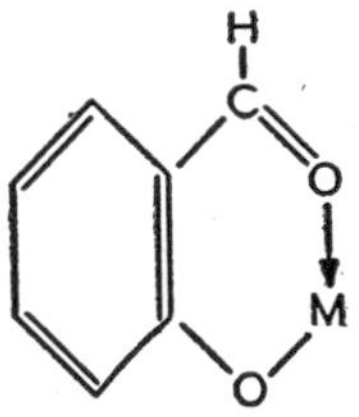

SALICYLALDEHYDE
CHELATE

If only one double bond is present in the ring, both five- and six-membered structures are common, with the five-membered unit appearing somewhat more frequently in the usual descriptions.*† Heller and Schwarzenbach[40] examined iron(III) complexes of pyrocatechindisulpho acid and chromotropic acid. In the former case (A) a five-membered ring involving one resonating double bond is formed and in the latter case (B) a comparable

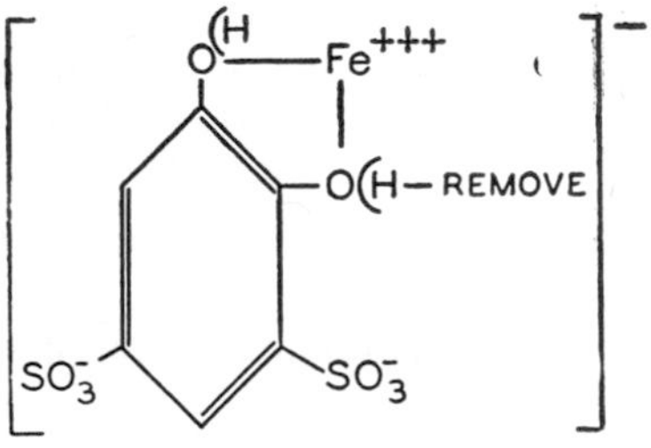

PYROCATECHIN COMPLEX
OF Fe^{+++}
A

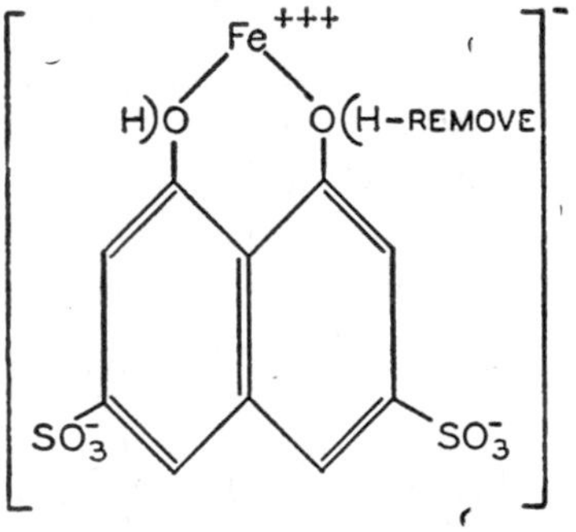

CHROMOTROPIC ACID
COMPLEX OF Fe^{+++}
B

FIG. 5.6

---

* Lowry[41] attempted to justify the stability of six-membered rings on the basis of alternating polarity with the metal atom as a negative group. Using this hypothesis, he concluded that six-membered rings are more stable than those containing five members. The limitations of this concept are obvious from the discussion on ring size.

† Bobtelsky and Bar-Gadda[42] conclude that a double bond in a ring is apparently effective in stabilizing even a seven-membered ring.

40. Heller and Schwarzenbach, *Helv. Chim. Acta,* **34,** 1876 (1951).

six-membered ring is produced. The values of the formation constants were given as:

$$FeX + A^{-4} \rightarrow [FeXA]^{-4} \qquad \log K = 15.7 \pm 0.4$$

$$FeX + B^{-4} \rightarrow [FeXB]^{-4} \qquad \log K = 17.0 \pm 0.5$$

where X = anion of nitrilotriacetic acid. The differences in the formation constants are smaller than the differences in the acid constants of the parent compounds, thus indicating little influence due to ring size.

The problem of ring size also arises in the discussion of citrate and tartrate complexes. A variety of formulas has been proposed which involve rings of various sizes[20, 43, 44, 45, 46]. It has been established that the citrate ion can lose its hydroxyl hydrogen as well as the carboxyl hydrogens and can coordinate with a bivalent metal such as copper even in acid solution[46, 47]. This suggests the possibility of the formation of both six- and seven-membered rings in the citrate complexes, the six-membered ring probably forming preferentially[46, 47]:

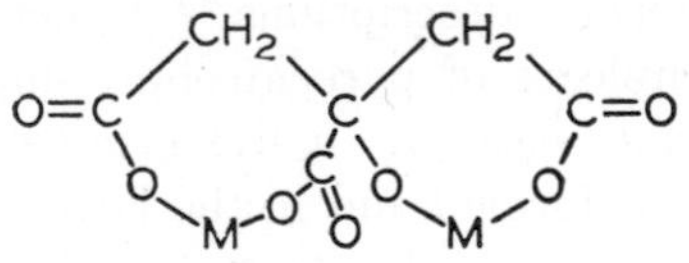

The fact that tartrate complexes are in general more stable than the analogous succinate complexes and that citrate complexes are more stable than tricarballylate complexes also indicates the involvement of the OH groups in the chelation process.

Rings of seven or more members are comparatively uncommon, but are well established (Chapter 6). As the length of the chain between the two donor atoms increases, so does the tendency to form polymetallic complexes.

A few interesting exceptions to the foregoing generalizations are known. Thus, the dimethyl glyoxime chelate ring with nickel involves two double

---

* Alternatively both rings may form on the same metal to give the ion [MCi]⁻.

41. Lowry, *Chemical & Industrial*, **42**, 715 (1923).
42. Bobtelsky and Bor-Gadda, *Bull. soc. chim. France*, **1953**, 382.
43. Paulinova, *J. Gen. Chem. (U.S.S.R.)* **17**, 3 (1947); [*Chem. Abst.*, **42**, 53 (1948)].
44. Bobtelsky and Jordan, *J. Am. Chem. Soc.*, **67**, 1824 (1945); **69**, 2286 (1947); **75**, 4172 (1953).
45. Harada, *Sci. Papers Inst. Phys. Chem. Research (Tokyo)* **41**, 68 (1943), [*Chem. Abs.*, **41**, 6206 (1947)].
46. Parry and DuBois, *J. Am. Chem. Soc.*, **74**, 3752 (1952).
47. Warner and Weber, *J. Am. Chem. Soc.*, **75**, 5086 (1953).

bonds and may be formulated as a five- or six-membered structure:

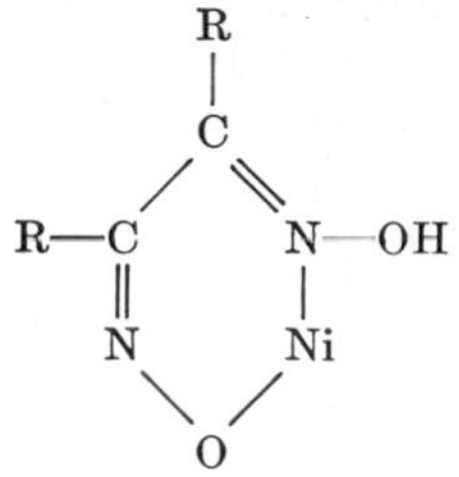

Six-membered ring 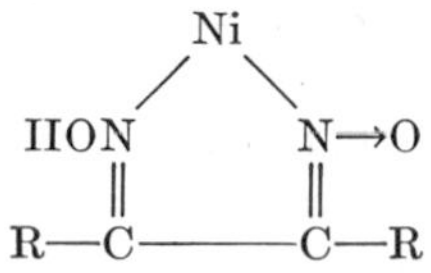   Five-membered ring

The original formulation[48] of the structure as a five-membered ring was based on the fact that the anti-glyoxime is the only isomer which gives the characteristic red nickel salt.

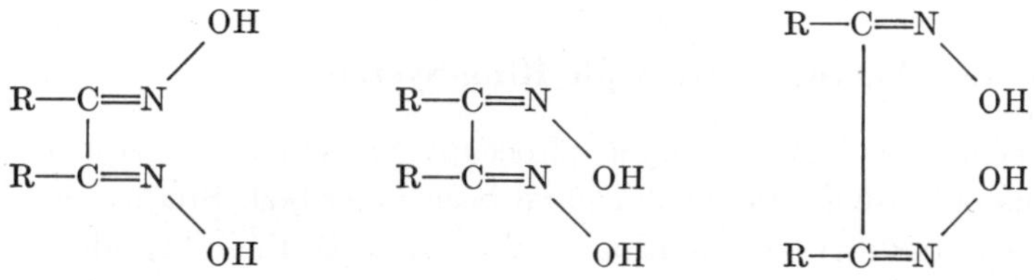

anti   *amphi*   *syn*

These stereochemical deductions have been supported completely by recent x-ray data[49]. Examination of the structure of the entire molecule makes the choice of five-membered rings reasonable even though two double bonds are involved. As Fig. 5.6 shows, the formation of five-membered rings gives

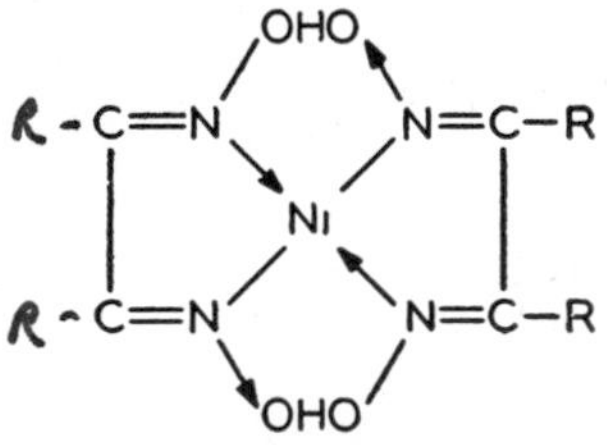

Multiple ring formation with five-membered ring and hydrogen bonds.

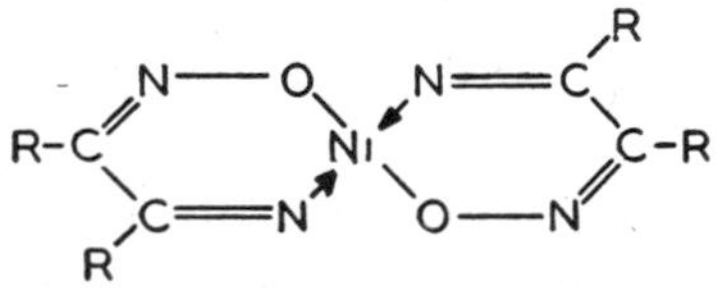

Only two possible rings if ring is six-membered.

Fig. 5.7. Possible structures of nickel dimethylglyoxime

the possibility of multiple ring formation through hydrogen bonding. Evi-

48. Pfeiffer, *Ber.*, **63**, 1811 (1930).

dence cited earlier indicates a marked increase in stability arising from the presence of multiple, interlocked rings. It is of some interest to note that the hydrogen bond in this complex is the shortest yet reported[49].

Another interesting exception is found in the complexes of silver. Schwarzenbach and his co-workers[50] report that the complexes of silver(I) with trimethylenediamine, tetramethylenediamine, and pentamethylene-diamine (six-, seven-, and eight-membered rings) are all more stable (log K = 5.85, 5.90, 5.95, respectively) than the corresponding silver complex with ethylenediamine (log K = 4.7). This is attributed to the fact that the two bonds of silver are linear and the longer membered chains are better able to form rings than are the shorter chains. Such an interpretation receives further support from the fact that the complex [Ag_2 en_2]$^{+2}$ is formed and was isolated as the crystalline sulfate. The molecular weight was confirmed by cryoscopic measurements.

Polydentate Ligands—Multiple Ring Systems

In recent years ligands capable of occupying as many as six coordination positions on a single metal ion have been described. Studies on the formation constants of coordination compounds with these ligands have been reported[39, 50, 51, 52, 53]. In general it is observed that the stability of the complex goes up with an increase in the number of groups available for coordination. Other studies, particularly those involving the preparation of penetration complexes of cobalt, are of considerable interest. Three types of chelating agents have been placed around all six of the coordination positions of cobalt(III). They are:

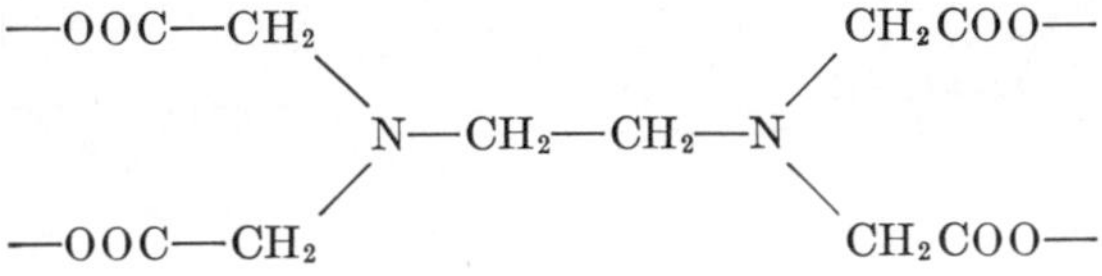

$$-OOC-CH_2 \diagdown \qquad\qquad CH_2COO- \diagup$$
$$N-CH_2-CH_2-N$$
$$-OOC-CH_2 \diagup \qquad\qquad CH_2COO- \diagdown$$

(A)

49. Godycki and Rundle, *Acta Cryst.*, **6**, 487 (1953).
50. Schwarzenbach, Maissen, and Ackermann, *Helv. Chim. Acta*, **35**, 2333 (1952); Schwarzenbach, Ackermann, Maissen, and Anderegg, *Helv. Chim. Acta*, **35**, 2337 (1952).
51. Jonassen, LeBlanc, and Rogan, *J. Am. Chem. Soc.*, **72**, 4968 (1950).
52. Chaberek and Martell, *J. Am. Chem. Soc.*, **75**, 2888 (1953); Lumb and Martell, *J. Am. Chem. Soc.*, **75**, 690 (1953).
53. Chaberek, Courtney, and Martell, *J. Am. Chem. Soc.*, **74**, 5052 (1952); **75**, 2185 (1953); Courtney and Martell, *J. Am. Chem. Soc.*, **74**, 5057 (1952); Chaberek and Martell, *J. Am. Chem. Soc.*, **74**, 6021, 6228 (1952).

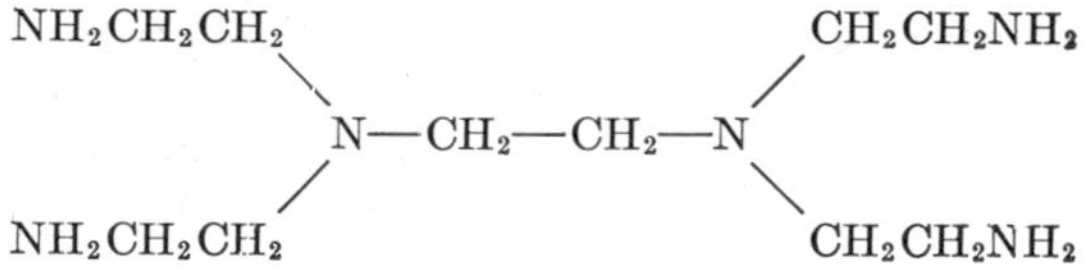

$$NH_2CH_2CH_2 \diagdown \quad \diagup CH_2CH_2NH_2$$
$$N—CH_2—CH_2—N$$
$$NH_2CH_2CH_2 \diagup \quad \diagdown CH_2CH_2NH_2$$

(B)

ethylenediaminetetraacetate (A), tetrakis(2-aminoethyl)ethylenediamine (B), and compounds of the general form:

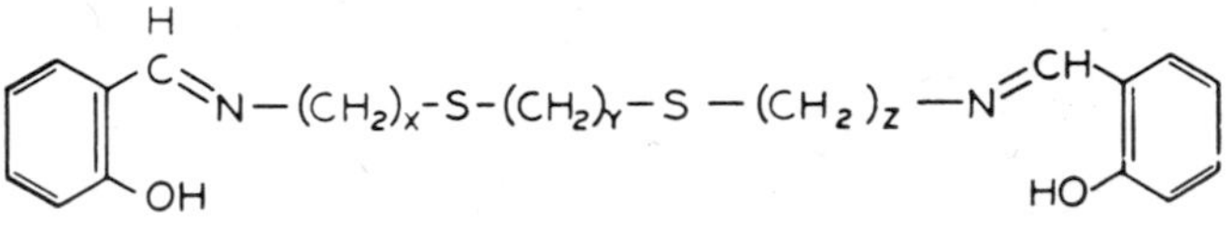

(C)

(X, Y, AND Z HAVE BEEN 2 OR 3)

of which 3,6-dithia,1,8-bis(salicylideneamino)octane, (C), is an example. Schwarzenbach[54] showed that cobalt(II) may fill only five of its coordination positions with ethylenediaminetetraacetate and the sixth with an auxiliary ligand such as Br^-, H_2O, or CNS^-. The stable penetration complex of cobalt(III), $[Co(Y)Br]^=$, can be prepared from the cobalt(II) salt by oxidation. On the other hand, the cobalt(III) ion can satisfy all of its coordination positions with ethylenediaminetetraacetate to give the sexicovalent complex, $[Co(Y)]^-$. This ion can be produced by complete substitution of the ligands from other cobalt(III) complexes: $[Co(NH_3)_6]^{+++}$ + $H_4Y \rightarrow 4NH_4^+ + 2NH_3 + [CoY]^-$. *Cis-* and *trans*-$[Co\ en_2Cl_2]^+$ and $[Co(ox)_3]^=$ behave in the same way. No intermediates have yet been identified. Bailar and Busch[55] confirmed the sexidentate character of the salt by examination of its infrared spectrum and by the resolution of the complex into optical isomers. They also reported that the elimination of the extra substituent (i.e., Br) in the pentadentate complex $[Co(Y)Br]^=$ proceeds without complete loss of optical activity.

Schwarzenbach and Moser[56] have also prepared complexes of Fe^{+++}, Co^{+++}, and Ni^{++} with the amine analog (B) of ethylenediaminetetraacetic acid; these appear to be sexidentate structures.

Dwyer, Lions, Gill, and Gyarfas[57] have synthesized many ligands of the third type (C), and have formed sexidentate complexes using Co(III). Such complexes have been resolved and show the highest optical activity

54. Schwarzenbach, *Helv. Chim. Acta*, **32**, 841 (1949).
55. Bailar and Busch, *J. Am. Chem. Soc.*, **75**, 4574 (1953).
56. Schwarzenbach and Moser, *Helv. Chim. Acta*, **36**, 581 (1953).
57. Dwyer, Lions, Gill, and Gyarfas, *Nature*, **168**, 29 (1951); *J. Am. Chem. Soc.*, **69**, 2917 (1947); **72**, 1545, 5037 (1950); **74**, 4188 (1952); **75**, 2443 (1953); **76**, 383 (1954).

yet recorded. They can be represented schematically as:

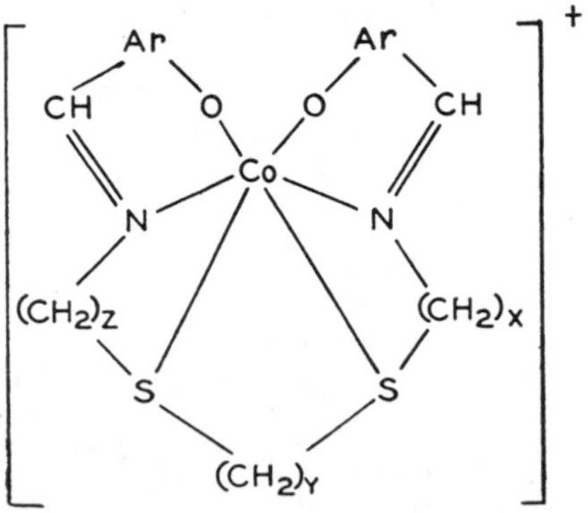

A ligand containing one oxygen in place of a sulfur also serves as a sexidentate group; this is most remarkable in that an ethereal oxygen is coordinated firmly to cobalt in a penetration complex. This ability of stable terminal groups to stabilize unstable ring arrangements in the complex is interesting but not unique (Ref. 3 p. 142).

Steric Factors Within the Complex. Interference by Attached Groups: F-Strain

In some cases the clashing of groups on two coordinated ligands will result in a distortion of bond angles and a decrease in stability. This is the phenomenon of F-strain, described by Brown[58], as applied to coordination compounds. A number of experimental observations on complex compounds can be reasonably interpreted in terms of steric strain. The thermodynamic stability of N and N,N'-alkyl substituted ethylenediamines has been studied by a number of investigators[59, 60, 61, 62]. The data clearly show reduction in the stability of the complex with substitution of alkyl groups for hydrogen atoms on the nitrogen. This is indicated by the instability constants for the nickel complexes in Table 5.1 and the thermodynamic values in Table 5.2. Steric strain or F strain appears to offer a logical though not unique interpretation of these data.

Data of Smirnoff[63] and Willink and Wibaut[64] on complexes of iron (II) sug-

58. Brown, Bartholomay, and Taylor, *J. Am. Chem. Soc.*, **66,** 435 (1944); Brown and Barbaras, *J. Am. Chem. Soc.*, **69,** 1137 (1947), and other papers, H. C. Brown.
59. Keller and Edwards, *J. Am. Chem. Soc.*, **74,** 215 (1952); **74,** 2931 (1952); Edwards dissertation, University of Michigan, 1950.
60. Irving and Griffiths, *J. Chem. Soc.*, **1954,** 213.
61. Basolo and Murmann, *J. Am. Chem. Soc.*, **74,** 5243 (1952); **76,** 211 (1954).
62. McIntyre, dissertation, Pennsylvania State College, 1953.
63. Smirnoff, *Helv. Chim. acta*, **4,** 802 (1921).
64. Willink and Wibaut, *Rec. Trav. Chim.*, **54,** 275 (1935).

TABLE 5.1. STABILITY CONSTANTS AT 25° OF THE NICKEL COMPLEXES OF SOME
DIAMINES OF THE TYPE $NRR'CH_2CH_2NHR''$
(Collected by Irving and Griffiths[60])

R	R'	R''		$\log K_1$	$\log K_2$	$\log K_1/K_2$	pK_{BH}^+
H	H	H	Decreasing Complex Stability	7.60	6.48	1.12	10.18
Me	H	H		7.36	5.74	1.62	10.40
Et	H	H		6.78	5.30	1.48	10.56
Pr	H	H		5.17	3.47	1.70	10.62
Me	H	Me		6.65	3.85	2.80	10.16

TABLE 5.2. THERMODYNAMIC DATA (0°)
$$[M(H_2O)_x]_{aq}^{+2} + n(AA)_{aq} \leftrightharpoons [M(AA)_n]_{aq}^{+2} + xH_2O$$
(Collected by Basolo and Murmann[61])

Amine	Nickel(II)				Copper(II)			
	n	ΔF^0	ΔH^0	ΔS^0	n	ΔF^0	ΔH^0	ΔS^0
Ethylenediamine	3	−25.1	−24.9	+1	2	−26.6	−24.6	+7
Ethylenediamine	2	−18.1	−16.3	+7				
N-Methylethylenediamine	2	−17.2	−17.0	+1	2	−25.3	−23.0	+8
N,N'-Diethylethylenediamine	2	−15.3	−7.8	+27	2	−23.3	−17.5	+21

gest reduced stability when interference of groups arises. It is reported
that α,α-dipyridyl coordinates with iron whereas the 6,6-disubstituted
dipyridyl does not. The low coordinating ability is attributed to clashing
of the methyl or amino groups in the 6,6-substituted complex. Merritt[65]
reports an analogous case with 8-hydroxyquinoline and its derivatives

A
COORDINATES WITH Fe^{+2}

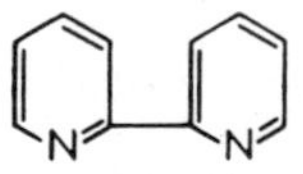

B
DOES NOT COORDINATE WITH Fe^{+2}

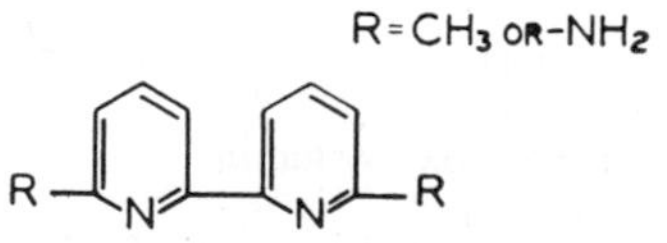

$R = CH_3$ OR $-NH_2$

$\alpha-\alpha'$ - DIPYRIDYL

6,6'- SUBSTITUTED DIPYRIDYL

and has proposed the use of selected steric factors to obtain selective or
specific analytical reagents. His work is described in more detail under
the use of coordination compounds in analytical chemistry (see p. 678).

65. Merritt, "Frontiers of Science Outline," Lecture Wayne University, Spring 1949;
    Merritt and Walker, *Ind. Eng. Chem., Anal. Ed.*, **16**, 387 (1944); Phillips, El-
    binger, and Merritt, *J. Am. Chem. Soc.*, **71**, 3986 (1949); Phillips, Huber, Chung,
    and Merritt, *J. Am. Chem. Soc.*, **73**, 630 (1951).

Irving, Cabell, and Mellor[66] have used the same type of arguments to justify reduced stability of the copper(II) and iron(II) complexes of 2,9-dimethyl-1,10-phenanthroline.

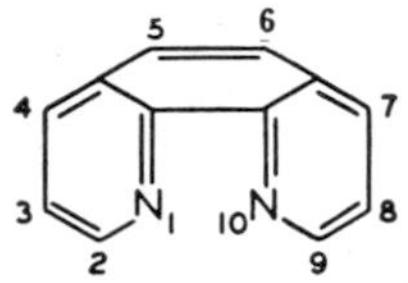

1, 10 - PHENANTHROLINE

As noted in Chapter 3, the coordination number is inadequately treated if size alone is considered, but size factors can be understood if the interaction energy or bond energy at a permitted distance of approach is taken into account. It is thus apparent that the interaction energy of metal and ligand at the permitted distance is important in determining compound stability. Recognizing this important restriction, Irving and his co-workers justified the fact that ions only slightly larger than aluminum(III), such as gallium(III) and iron(III), can give precipitates while aluminum(III) cannot. In view of such differences, Irving and his co-workers[66], as well as Berg[67], have also suggested the possibility of designing selective chelating agents based on stereochemical differences. Irving, Butler, and Ring[66a] have prepared a number of methyl and phenyl substituted 8-hydroxyquinolines. They found that substitution only in the 2 position always prevented formation of the Al^{+++} complex, but permitted chelation with chromium(III), iron(III), gallium(III), copper(II), and zinc(II) and that the acridines, which involve ring formation on the 2 position, also fail to yield complexes with aluminum(III), but give precipitates with the other cations listed.

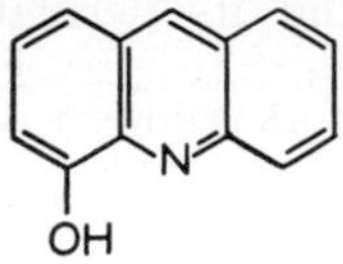

I - HYDROXY ACRIDINE 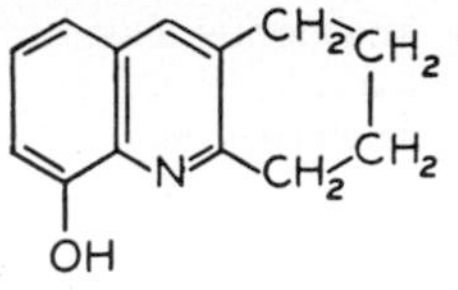   9 - HYDROXY - 1:2:3:4 - TETRAHYDRO ACRIDINE

Figure 5.8, taken from Irving, Butler, and Ring, shows the interference of the 2-methyl groups with the oxygen and nitrogen atoms in the chelate rings of the tris-2-methyl-8-hydroxyquinoline complex of aluminum(III). Phillips, Huber, Chung and Merritt[65d] report that the ultraviolet absorption spectrum of the copper chelate of 2-methyl-8-hydroxyquinoline gives no evidence of steric hindrance and that the unhindered aluminum complex

66. Irving, Butler, and Ring, *J. Chem. Soc.*, **1949**, 1489; Irving, Cabell, and Mellor, *J. Chem. Soc.*, **1953**, 3417.
67. Berg, *Z. anorg. Chem.*, **204**, 208 (1932).

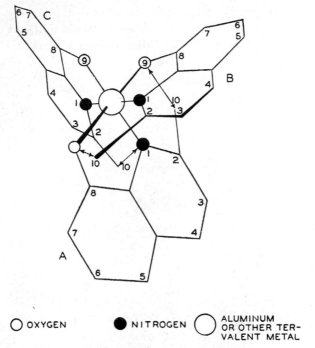

○ OXYGEN   ● NITROGEN   ○ ALUMINUM OR OTHER TER-VALENT METAL

Fig. 5.8. Steric hindrance in the tris-2-methyl-8-hydroxyquinoline chelate of aluminum. Points of interference are indicated by double arrows.

involving only one 2-methyl-8-hydroxyquinoline could be identified in solution by the method of continuous variations, yet no hindered bis- or tris-complexes of aluminum could be found. These facts are consistent with the proposed steric effect.

Steric Factors Determined by the Metal Ion

Elementary theory indicates that the most stable structures arise when the bonds of the metal are so directed in space that they overlap the orbitals of the ligand without serious distortion of either set of orbitals.

An interesting problem arises when the bonds of the metal ion and the bonds of the coordinating group do not have the same basic geometry. A case of this type is the divalent platinum complex of β,β',β''-triaminotriethylamine which was studied by Mann[68]. The base is a quadridentate molecule in which the four nitrogen atoms can be expected to occupy the corners of a tetrahedron but not the corners of a square. The bonds of the platinum(II) are normally directed to the corners of a square, but they are apparently forced into the tetrahedral configuration in

68. Mann, *J. Chem. Soc.*, **1926**, 482; Mann and Pope, *J. Chem. Soc.*, **1926**, 2675.

[PtN(CH₂CH₂NH₂)₃]⁺⁺ (p. 363). The complex could also be octahedral if the two anion groups were coordinated to the platinum (see Figs. 5.9 and 5.10). A crystal structure analysis of this complex is needed. There are no

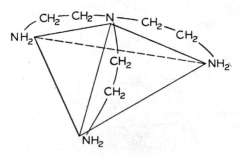

FIG. 5.9. Tetrahedral coordination of β,β',β triaminotriethylamine

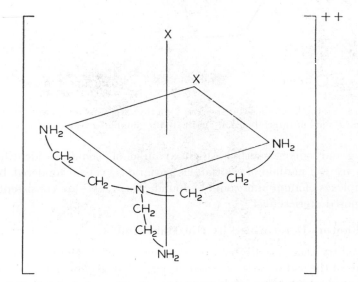

FIG. 5.10. Octahedral coordination of β,β',β triaminotriethylamine and two other groups.

data to indicate that this complex is any less stable because of the steric strain. Data are available, however, for the copper(II) complex which should also be planar, and it is indeed less stable than one would expect from trends in the periodic table. In Fig. 5.11 the log of the formation constants for a number of metal amines are plotted for the metals from manganese to zinc.

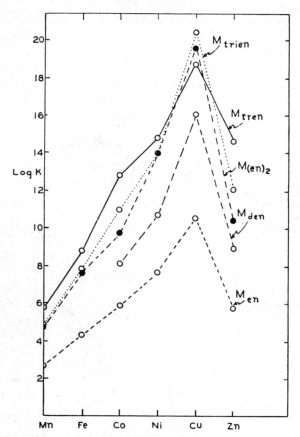

FIG. 5.11. Logarithms of the formation constants for complexes of polyamines with transition metals. (Data from Ref. 5).

en = ethylenediamine $NH_2CH_2CH_2NH_2$
dien = β,β'diaminodiethylamine $NH(CH_2CH_2NH_2)_2$
trien = triethylenetetraamine $NH_2CH_2CH_2NHCH_2CH_2NHCH_2CH_2NH_2$
tren = β,β',β''triaminotriethylamine $N(CH_2CH_2NH_2)_3$ (forced tetrahedral configuration)

For those metals which have no strong planar preference, the β,β',β''-triaminotriethylamine complex (M-tren) is more stable than the bis-ethylenediamine complexes because of the entropy associated with the completely interlocked ring system. On the other hand, the copper(II) complex, [Cu-tren], is less stable than the bis-ethylenediamine complex [Cu(en)$_2$]. This phenomenon has been associated with the steric strain arising from the tetrahedral structure around the normally planar copper(II) ion[5]. It is interesting to note that the nickel complex [Ni-tren] shows no reduced stability as a result of the tetrahedral configuration, but this is not unexpected since even the $Ni(NH_3)_4^{++}$ ion is normally tetrahedral rather than planar.

Another much quoted though unproved case of steric hindrance is that cited by Porter[69], who has shown with molecular models, that when bis-3,3′,5,5′-tetramethyl-4,4′-dicarbethoxypyrromethene (Fig. 5.12) func-

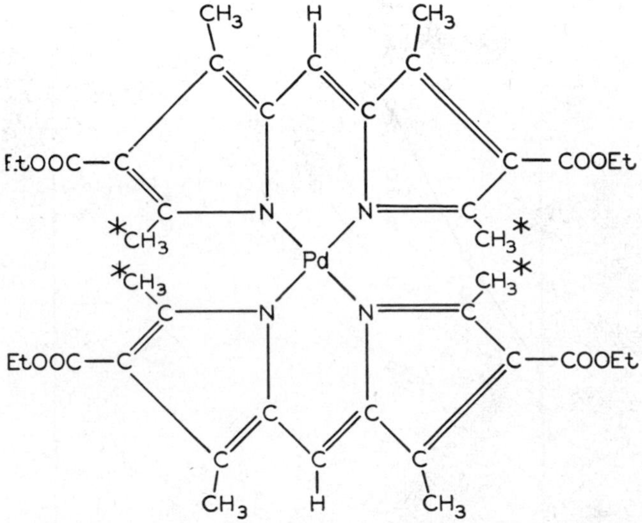

FIG. 5.12. Overlapping of 3,3′,5,5′-tetramethyl-4,4′-dicarbethoxypyromethane groups[58].

tions as a bidentate chelate group, the chelate is prevented from assuming a planar configuration by steric hindrance. The α methyl groups (marked by asterisks) overlap seriously as is seen in Fig 5.12. Complexes with Fe^{+2}, Ni^{+2}, Co^{+2}, Cu^{+2}, Zn^{+2}, Cd^{+2}, Pd^{+2} [69] and Pt^{+2} [70] have been prepared. Both the palladium[71] and platinum[70] complexes are diamagnetic, indicating "covalent" bonding; the nickel complex is paramagnetic indicating an "ionic" bond[71]. Since the normal covalent bonds of palladium(II) and platinum(II) are planar, one would expect that steric inhibition to the planar arrangement would lower the complex stability. Actually, little evidence is available to indicate that such is the case. In fact, limited data on complexes of 3,3′-dimethyl-4,4′-dicarbethoxydipyrromethene, in which there are no α methyl groups to overlap, indicate that the metal complexes are

69. Porter, *J. Chem. Soc.*, **1938**, 368; Mellor, *Chem. Revs.*, **33**, 171, 175 (1943).
70. Mellor and Willis, *J. Proc. Roy. Soc. N. S. Wales*, **79**, 141 (1945).
71. Mellor and Lockwood, *J. Proc. Roy. Soc. N. S. Wales*, **74**, 141 (1940).

TABLE 5.3. MAGNETIC MOMENTS OF PHTHALOCYANINE COMPLEXES

Metal in Complex	Obs. Mag. Moment in Bohr Magnetons	Theoretical Moment for dsp^2 Bonds	Theoretical Moment for Planar p^2d^2 Bonds	Theoretical Moment for Ionic Binding
Cu^{+2}	1.73	1.73	3.87	1.73
Ni^{+2}	0	0	2.83	2.83
Co^{+2}	2.16	1.73	1.73	3.87
Fe^{+2}	3.96	2.83	0	4.90
Mn^{+2}	4.55	3.87	1.73	5.92

actually less stable than the fully methylated compound[69] in which steric hindrance supposedly occurs.*

The converse problem of fitting a normally tetrahedral ion to a planar quadridentate molecule has also received attention. The phthalocyanine molecule (p. 73) is rigidly coplanar, and its complexes with the divalent ions of copper, nickel, platinum, cobalt, iron, manganese, magnesium and beryllium have been shown by x-ray studies to be planar[72]. The appearance of magnesium and beryllium with planar coordination is indeed surprising, since these metals normally assume a tetrahedral structure. It is noteworthy that both beryllium and magnesium phthalocyanins readily form hydrates; such behavior may be indicative of lower stability in the forced configuration. Two molecules of water would allow octahedral coordination.

The magnetic properties of the remaining phthalocyanines have been studied by Klemm and his students[73, 74]. Their data permit an answer to the problem: "Does assumption of a forced planar configuration by the metal ion require the use of planar dsp^2 or d^2p^2 bonds?" Data in Table 5.3 indicate that it does not, since the observed moments do not correspond to those expected for dsp^2 bonds. Selwood[75] suggested that the magnetic data actually indicate a transition from covalent to ionic bonds in the iron and manganese complexes with forced configurations.

Schwarzenbach and Ackerman[5] have invoked favorable steric and entropy factors as an argument to justify their observation that 1,2-cyclohexanediamine-N,N'-tetraacetate forms a more stable chelate with

---

* It is interesting that none of the pyrromethene complexes even approach the analogous porphyrins or phthaloyamins in stability, because of multiple ring effects in the latter[69].

72. Robertson, *J. Chem. Soc.*, **1935**, 615; **1936**, 1195; Linstead and Robertson, *J. Chem. Soc.*, **1936**, 1736.
73. Klemm and Klemm, *J. prakt. Chem.*, **143**, 82 (1935).
74. Senff and Klemm, *J. prakt. Chem.*, **154**, 73 (1939).
75. Selwood, "Magnetochemistry," p. 163, New York, Interscience Publishers, Inc., 1943.

Ca^{++} ($K = 10^{12.5}$) than does the related ethylenediaminetetraacetate ($K = 10^{10.5}$). It is assumed that this difference exists because the coordinating groups in the cyclohexanediamine derivative are fixed in position while those in the ethylenediamine derivative are free to rotate about the ethylene group. The smaller magnesium ion and the larger barium ion are less able to utilize this stereochemical advantage, so there are smaller differences for these ions between the complexes of the cyclohexanediamine and ethylenediamine derivatives.

Irving, Cabell, and Mellor[66] also suggest that the apparent relative stability of the ferrous tris-orthophenanthroline complex may be due in part to the fact that the ferric tris-orthophenanthroline structure is destabilized by steric hindrance. Evidence for this is obtained from the observation that when iron(III) ions react with orthophenanthroline directly, the binuclear complex

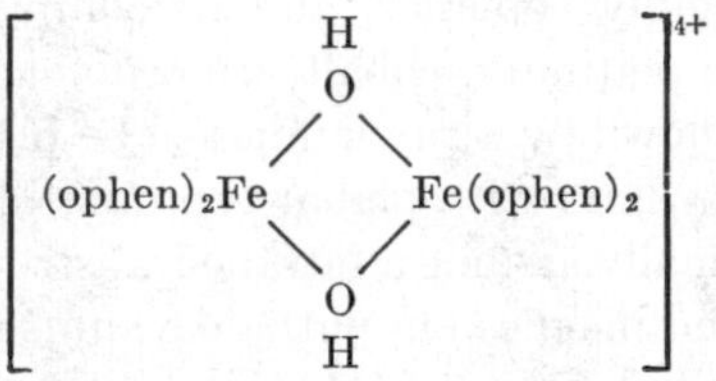

$$
\begin{bmatrix} & & \overset{\displaystyle H}{\underset{\displaystyle O}{}} & & \\ & & \diagup \quad \diagdown & & \\ (ophen)_2Fe & & & Fe(ophen)_2 \\ & & \diagdown \quad \diagup & & \\ & & \underset{\displaystyle H}{\overset{\displaystyle O}{}} & & \end{bmatrix}^{4+}
$$

is formed, rather than the tris-complex.

In summary, there is some evidence to indicate that the stereochemistry of metal cations is important in determining the stability and type of complex formed. However, exceptions are known. Present data indicate that the stereochemical properties of the metal ion are much more flexible in chelate ring formation than the stereochemical properties of the ligand.

ELECTRONIC EFFECTS PECULIAR TO CHELATE RINGS

Effects Due to Ring Closure

A few unusual electronic effects seem to arise in chelate systems as a result of ring formation. Such effects are as yet incompletely understood. Spike and Parry[77] measured indirectly the enthalpy and entropy associated with reactions of the type

$$M(NH_3)_2{}^+ \, en \rightarrow Men + 2NH_3$$

In some cases similar studies were made using methylamine in place of ammonia. If the formation of chelate rings produced no increase in the

76. Sidgwick, *J. Chem. Soc.*, 433 (1941); "The Electronic Theory of Valency," Oxford Univ. Press, 1927.
77. Spike and Parry, *J. Am. Chem. Soc.*, **75**, 2726, 3770 (1953); Spike, PhD Dissertation, University of Michigan, 1952.

stability of the metal-ligand bond, ΔH for the above process should be essentially zero and the increased stability of the chelated system should arise as a result of entropy factors. If, however, ring formation results in a stronger metal ligand bond, ΔH for the above process should be negative. When zinc and cadmium were used, ΔH for the process was found to be essentially zero, but when copper(II) was the metal ion the ΔH term was as large as the entropy term, indicating a much stronger metal-ligand bond as a result of ring formation. The absence of double bonds in the ethylene-diamine makes the usual resonance interpretations (see below) difficult.

Resonance Effects

In 1945 Calvin and Wilson[11], using the method of Bjerrum[82], found a straight line relationship between the basic strength of enolate β-diketones and the stability of copper(II) complexes (see also p. 178). Their work also indicated the necessity for subdividing the ligands into similar groups in order to establish a correlation. The data shown in Fig. 5.13 were classified into four groups (A), (B), (C), and (D), A and C giving linear plots with considerable scatter, and B and D giving one point lines. The structural types associated with the four lines are:

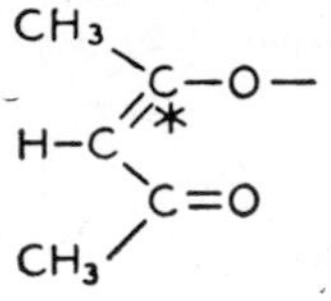

A

ENOLATE TYPE OF
ACETYLACETONE

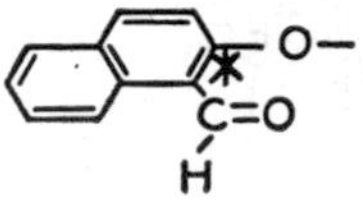

B

NAPTHOLATE ION OF
2-HYDROXYNAPTHALDEHYDE-I

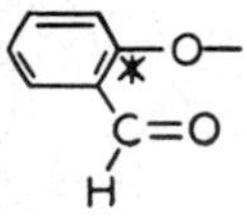

C

PHENOLATE ION
OF SALICYLALDEHYDE

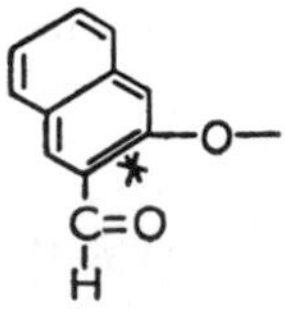

D

NAPTHOLATE ION OF
2-HYDROXYNAPTHALDEHYDE-3

According to Calvin and Wilson, the most important difference in these structures is the nature of the double bond between the two carbon atoms of the three carbon system which forms the conjugated chain between the two oxygen atoms. These bonds are marked with asterisks in the above formulas. In structure (A) only a methyl group and a hydrogen are at-

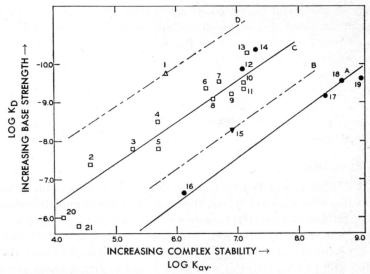

Fɪɢ. 5.13. Relationship between the basic strength of enolate β-diketones and the stability of their copper(II) complexes. (From Ref. 11).

Line A: β-Diketones and β-keto ester: (16) trifluoro acetylacetone (17) furoylacetone; (18) acetylacetone; (19) benzoylacetone; (12) acetoacetic ester; (14) C-Methyl acetylacetone

Line B: 2-hydroxynaphthaldehyde-1

Line C: Substituted salicylaldehydes: (2) 4-Nitro; (3) 3-Chloro; (4) 5-Chloro; (5) 3-Fluoro; (6) Salicylaldehyde; (7) 5-Methyl; (8) 3-Methoxy; (9) 4-Methoxy; (10) 3-n-Propyl; (11) 3-Ethoxy; (13) 4,6 Dimethyl; (20) 3-Nitro; (21) 5-Nitro

Line D: 2-hydroxynaphthaldehyde-3

K_{av} = equilibrium constant for:

$$\text{—C}\begin{array}{c}\text{C—O}^-\\[6pt]\text{C=O}\end{array} + \tfrac{1}{2}\,Cu^{++} \rightleftharpoons \text{—C}\begin{array}{c}\text{C—O}\\[6pt]\text{C=O}\end{array}Cu$$

K_D = equilibrium constant for:

$$\text{—C}\begin{array}{c}\text{O—O}\\[6pt]\text{H}\\[6pt]\text{C=O}\end{array} \rightleftharpoons \text{—C}\begin{array}{c}\text{C—O}^-\\[6pt]\text{C=O}\end{array} + H^+$$

tached to this bond. In structures (B), (C), and (D) the double bond is also part of a resonating aromatic ring. According to the method used by Pauling[78] and by Branch and Calvin[79], the double bond A which does not resonate with any single bonds in attached rings is given an arbitrary bond order of 2. In the case of structure (C) the double bond must resonate in the benzene ring, hence it may be regarded as only half of a double bond for the enolate system. It is assigned the value 1.5. Similarly, structure (B) is assigned the double bond order 1.67 and (D), 1.33. It can be seen from Fig. 5.12 that the stability of the copper complex at constant acidity of the chelating agent decreases in the same order as the decrease in this double bond character. In short, the greater the double bond character of the bond in the enolate system, the more stable is the complex. It is reported that these observations on stability of complexes of different types have also been supported by polarographic studies[7] and by exchange studies involving radioactive copper(II) ions[80].

The observations led to the following conclusion, "Resonance in the enolate (or chelate) ring plays a far greater part in the bonding of copper than it does in the bonding of hydrogen." Calvin suggested two possible explanations for this. The first is represented electronically as follows:

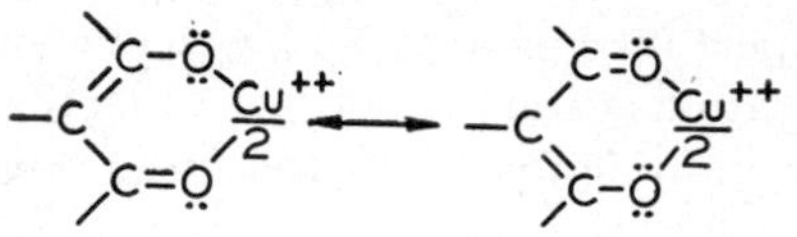

$$\begin{array}{ccc} \text{structure 1} & \longleftrightarrow & \text{structure 2} \end{array}$$

According to the second suggestion, a completely conjugated six-membered chelate ring analogous to pyridine is formed:

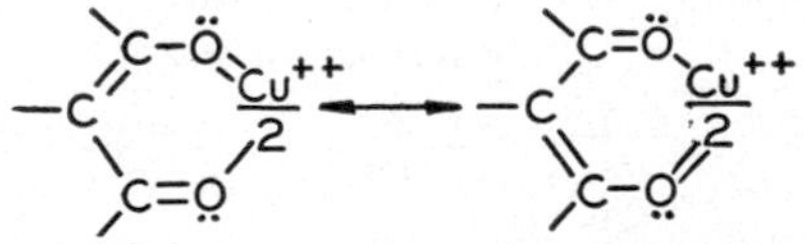

$$\begin{array}{ccc} \text{structure 1} & \longleftrightarrow & \text{structure 2} \end{array}$$

The second hypothesis assumes considerable double bond character for the metal-oxygen bond. Although double bonds between metal and ligand have been extensively postulated (see p. 191, Chapter 4) the suggestion in this case runs into rather serious difficulty. An electron balance shows that the electron pair used to form the metal-oxygen double bond came from the oxygen rather than from the metal ion as is normally postulated. A double

78. Pauling, "Nature of the Chemical Bond," pp. 179, 182, 187, 139, Cornell University Press, 1942.
79. Branch and Calvin, "The Theory of Organic Chemistry," p. 113, New York, Prentice-Hall, Inc. 1941.
80. Duffield and Calvin, *J. Am. Chem. Soc.*, **68,** 557 (1946).

bond of this type is diametrically opposed to the usual assumption that the metal ion donates the electrons and the ligand accepts them (see p. 191). Such a double bond would increase the residual negative charge on the copper rather than decrease it as is normally postulated. To assume that the copper(II) ion behaves in a normal fashion and uses d electrons to form a double bond with the oxygen is equally distasteful since oxygen has no low level orbitals which permit it to serve as an acceptor without destroying the conjugated double bond system in other parts of the ring.

Marked deviations between fact and prediction have been attributed to steric inhibition of resonance[11] although the supporting evidence for this postulate is still extremely sketchy in many cases. One of the more convincing illustrations is the copper complex derived from salicylaldehyde and 1,8-diaminonaphthalene

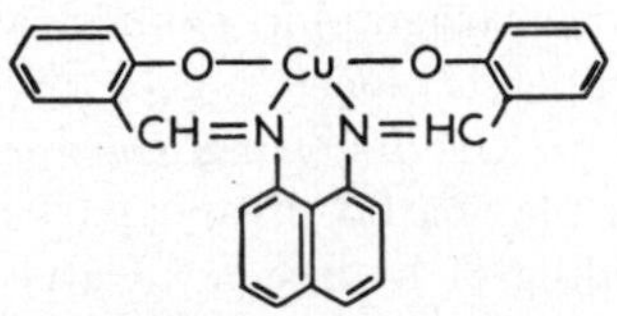

Since this complex is a multiple ring type involving a highly conjugated system, we would expect it to be more stable than comparable complexes in which the entire chelating system is not fused together. Actually, the complex is only slightly more stable than the open ring structures. Duffield and Calvin[80] attributed this unexpected behavior to the fact that steric factors prevent the complex from assuming a coplanar structure about the copper atom. It is suggested that such nonplanarity prevents or reduces the benzenoid chelate resonance and thus, the stability of the complex. It is possible that steric factors, independent of resonance effects, could also account for the reduced stability since Cu^{++} is normally a planar ion.

The opposite situation, in which *stability* of a strained structure is attributed to resonance has been described by Dwyer and Mellor[22]. A metallic triazine complex such as

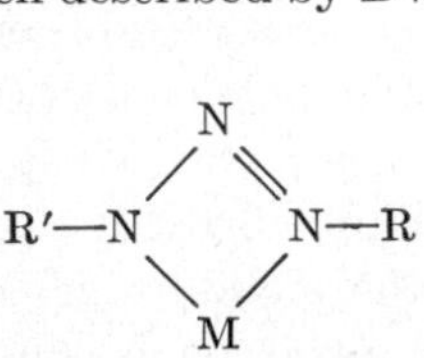

forms a four-membered ring which is unexpectedly stable. This stability has been attributed to resonance of the following type.

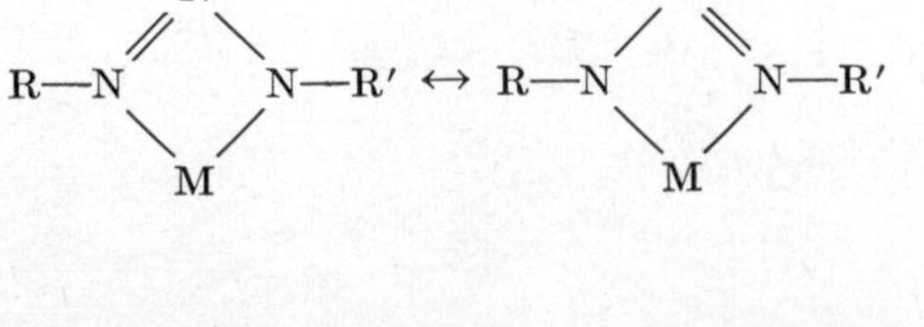

Chelates Involving Conjugated Double Bonds

Finally, an interesting compound described by Chatt and Wilkins[81] should be mentioned. This stable complex appears to be a chelate structure involving coordination to two double bonds of pentadiene. The molecular formula of the complex is $PtCl_2(C_5H_8)_2$, the monomeric nature of the compound having been established by molecular weight measurements. Butadiene, which would make a small and highly strained ring, does not chelate under the conditions used by Chatt and Wilkins but reacts independently with different platinum atoms.

ENTROPY EFFECTS IN CHELATION

Sidgwick[76] suggested in 1941 that the stability of chelate systems as compared to similar nonchelate structures may be due to a statistical factor which he pictured as follows. If one of the two metal-ligand bonds of a chelate system is broken, the remaining bond will hold the molecule in place so that the broken link can be reformed, whereas an atom or group that is bound by a single link will drift away if the bond is broken. Since this is a question of probability, it should appear in the entropy term. The relationship is somewhat more apparent if one writes a typical equation defining the chelate effect:

$$M(NH_2Me)_2{}^{++} + en \rightarrow Men^{++} + 2NH_2Me$$

The equation suggests an increase in the disorder of the system on chelation or an increase in the translational entropy of the system.

Concurrent with Sidgwick's 1941 paper, J. Bjerrum[82] published one of the most important experimental papers to appear in the field of coordination chemistry since the early work of Werner. In a classical theoretical and experimental analysis of metal ammine formation, he considered two factors which are important in determining the ratio between successive dissociation constants for a metal ammine such as the ethylenediamine complex of a metal. These are: (1) a statistical effect, and (2) a ligand effect. The statistical effect is defined as the joint contribution to the ratio of the dissociation constants which is attributable to purely statistical causes plus the stereochemical effects of dissimilar coordination positions. For example, if a given metal can coordinate a maximum of N ligands and at a particular time has bound only n ligands, then the statistical probability that the complex will lose a ligand should be proportional to n whereas the probability that it can pick up another ligand should be proportional to the number of stereochemically satisfactory sites remaining in the coordination sphere, or for a nonchelate ligand, $(N-n)$. For a chelate ligand the two sites

81. Chatt and Wilkins, *J. Chem. Soc.*, **1952**, 2622.
82. Bjerrum, J., "Metal Ammine Formation in Aqueous Solution," Copenhagen, P. Haase and Son, 1941.

must be adjacent in order to meet the sterochemical requirements of the donor molecule. It is apparent that this factor should appear in entropy terms. The ligand effect includes the joint contribution to the ratio of the dissociation constants which is attributable directly or indirectly to the ligands taken up. This would be an enthalpy term. The work of Bjerrum and others was admirably summarized by Burkin[83].

In 1952, Schwarzenbach[5] and Spike[77] utilized the model suggested by Sidgwick as the basis for independent kinetic treatments of the chelate effect. Following the suggestion of Bjerrum[82], the formation and dissociation of the nonchelated complex MA_2 and the chelated complex $M(AA)$ are considered to be step processes. It is then logical to assume that the chelate molecule (AA) reacts with or dissociates from the metal ion in two steps. The intermediate form is a complex in which the chelating ligand is bound by only one donor atom. By application of simple collision theory of reaction rates, by assuming a comparable energy of activation for the reaction of chelate and nonchelate structures, and by using the best available data on sizes of molecules, one can estimate the order of magnitude of the entropy term in the chelate effect[77b]. It appears from the above models that the rate of the reaction

$$MA^{++} + A \rightarrow MA_2{}^{++}$$

can be related to the size of the volume element containing one free amine molecule and the rate of the comparable reaction

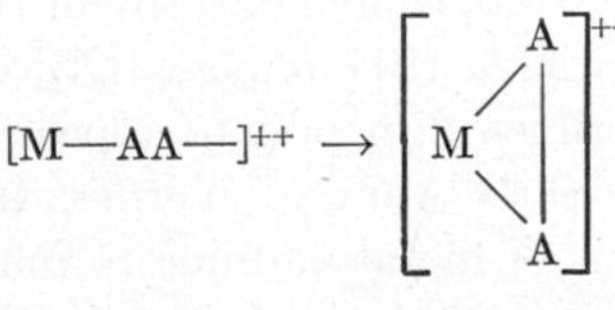

$$[M\text{—}AA\text{—}]^{++} \rightarrow \begin{bmatrix} M \diagup_{\diagdown} \begin{smallmatrix} A \\ \\ A \end{smallmatrix} \end{bmatrix}^{++}$$

can be related to that volume inside the sphere of radius r' which is available to the second end of the chelating ligand.

The above model suggests that the stabilization due to chelation should decrease rapidly as the chain of the ligand is lengthened. Schwarzenbach has shown that the difference in free energy of formation between chelate and nonchelate structures decreases rapidly and even reverses in sign as the chain is lengthened. One also arrives at a justification for the stability of five-membered rings. As a result of steric strain the energy of bond formation is low for small rings but increases as increasing size of the ring relieves strain. On the other hand, the stabilizing influence of chelation, which appears in the entropy term, is greatest for small rings. These two terms, working in opposite directions, produce a stability maximum in a five-

83. Burkin, *Quarterly Revs.*, **5**, 1 (1951).

TABLE 5.4. THERMODYNAMIC CONSTANTS IN 2M UNIVALENT SALT SOLUTION AT 25°C FOR REACTION MA_2^{++} + en → Men^{++} + 2A

	ΔF	ΔH	ΔS
$Cd(NH_2CH_3)_2^{++}$—$Cd(en)^{++}$	-1.40	0.0	4.7
$Cd(NH_3)_2^{++}$—$Cd(en)^{++}$	-1.20	$+.1$	4.3
$Zn(NH_3)_2^{++}$—$Zn(en)^{++}$	-1.55	$+.1$	5.3
$Cu(NH_3)_2^{++}$—$Cu(en)^{++}$	-4.30	-2.6	5.7

membered saturated ring and in a six-membered unsaturated ring, the stereochemistry of which is further restricted by double bond formation.

The model also indicates that further restriction on the mobility of the second ligand should enhance the stability of the complex if the size of the metal ion is such as to fit into the space between the binding atoms. Schwarzenbach and Ackerman[37] found that 1,2-cyclohexanediamine tetraacetate forms a more stable chelate with calcium(II) than does ethylenediamine tetraacetate. They attribute this to such steric stabilization.

The model also suggests that multiple ring formation should result in enhanced chelate stability, a fact which has already been well established. Schwarzenbach[5] reports that the chelate effect in a bidentate ligand is about half of that in a tridentate ligand which can form two interlocking rings and is about one third of that in a tetrafunctional ligand which can form three rings.

The preceding model would indicate that the chelate effect should be quite independent of the metal except insofar as special steric requirements of the metal are concerned (e.g., a linear structure of silver). Schwarzenbach[5] noted the low chelate effect for the $[Zn(en)]^{++}$ complex and suggested that this may indicate a tendency of the zinc(II) ion toward linearity. He interpreted the data on copper(II) complexes as being more representative of the chelate effect.

Spike and Parry[77] measured the entropy and enthalpy changes for reactions of the type $M(NH_3)_2$ + en → Men + $2NH_3$. Their data for the changes at 25° in a solution of 2 molar univalent nitrate salt (i.e., KNO_3 or NH_4NO_3) are summarized in Table 5.4.

All entropy differences are roughly of the same size, as might be expected, and the chelate effect for zinc(II) and cadmium(II) is definitely an entropy effect. On the other hand, it is significant that in the case of copper there is a marked enthalpy contribution to the chelate effect (i.e., bonds are stronger in the chelate structure.) The basis for this effect is still obscure. Irving[84] has confirmed the enthalpy contribution for the copper system by calorimetric measurements.

84. Irving, private communication.

The entropy term in chelate formation can also be considered qualitatively in terms of the number of particles on each side of the equation. For the reaction $Ni(NH_3)_6^{++} + 3en(aq) \rightarrow [Ni(en)_3]^{++} + 6NH_3$, Calvin and Bailes[7] reported the thermodynamic values: $\Delta F = -13.2$; $\Delta H = -6$; $\Delta S = 24$. Another factor of importance is the relative orientation of water molecules around the simple and chelated ions. Such a factor is of major importance when large organic ligands serve as the chelating ligands. The importance of such hydration effects has been considered by Cobble[85] in a series of useful empirical relationships.

Adamson[86] has recently suggested a new approach to the chelate effect in which the standard state of the ligand is changed to give a condition of minimum translation entropy. He proposes to use mole fraction unity as the standard for the ligands rather than the conventional molarity unity. Using this approach, the data are comparable to those using the conventional standard states if a comparable series of reactions is considered; however, comparisons between reactions involving different numbers of ligands will be altered.

85. Cobble, *J. Chem. Phys.*, **21**, 1443 (1953).
86. Adamson, *J. Am. Chem. Soc.*, **76**, 1578 (1954).

6. Large Rings

Thomas D. O'Brien*

University of Minnesota, Minneapolis, Minnesota

The more stable ring sizes among coordination compounds are analogous to those occurring among organic compounds. The coplanar five- and six-membered carbon rings are the most stable, according to the Baeyer strain theory, because of the smaller requisite deviation from the natural tetrahedral bond angle of 109° 28′. However, organic ring compounds which are thought to be strainless and which contain more than thirty members have been prepared. These compounds are quite possible if the atoms are not forced to be coplanar.

Stable chelate rings of five and six members containing metallic atoms are numerous and well known, but rings of seven or more members are comparatively uncommon. This is illustrated by early failures to prepare chelate rings with polymethylenediamines[1, 2, 3, 4, 5]. Only recently has Pfeiffer[6] reported the preparation of seven-membered chelates of tetramethylenediamine and nine-membered chelates of hexamethylenediamine. These were prepared in alcohol or ether solution, and are immediately hydrolyzed by water. The studies of Schwarzenbach (p. 229) on tetraacetic acid derivatives of such amines indicate that polymetallic complexes are to be expected as chain length increases. Duff[7] prepared complexes such as $[(NH_3)_5CoOOCRCOOCo(NH_3)_5]^{4+}$ and Macarovici[8] reported

* Now at Kansas State College, Manhattan, Kansas.

1. Werner, *Ber.*, **40**, 61 (1907).
2. Tschugaeff, *Ber.*, **39**, 3190 (1906); *J. prakt. Chem.* [*2*], **75**, 159 (1907).
3. Drew and Tress, *J. Chem. Soc.*, **1933**, 1335.
4. Pfeiffer and Haimann, *Ber.*, **36**, 1064 (1903).
5. Pfeiffer and Lübbe, *J. prakt. Chem.* [*2*], **136**, 321 (1933).
6. Pfeiffer, Böhm and Schmitz, *Naturwissenschaften*, **35**, 190 (1948).
7. Duff, *J. Chem. Soc.*, **1923**, 560.
8. Macarovici, *Bull sect. sci. acad. roumaine*, **23**, 61 (1940); *Chem. Abs.*, **37**, 6642 (1943).

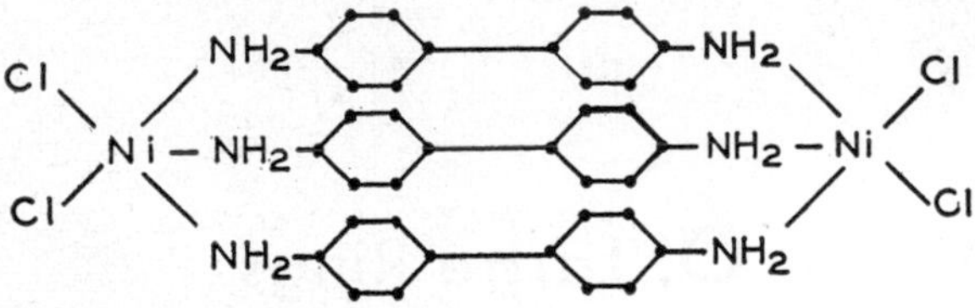

(Water may complete the coordination sphere.)

This structure, however, is based only on analysis. Dwyer and Mellor[9] formulated the nickel triazine complex as a dimer

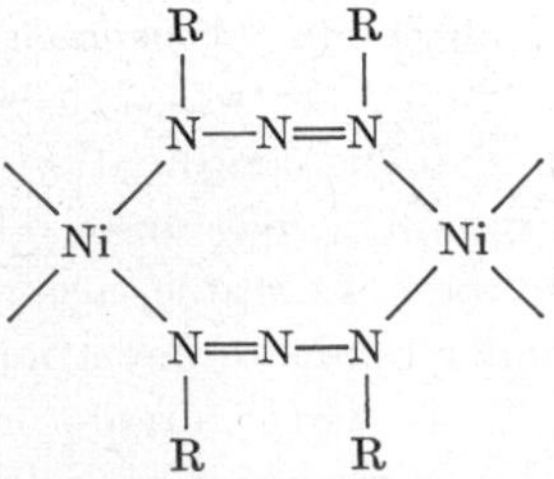

This raises an interesting question about the benzidine complexes of divalent metals, the formulas of which are frequently written

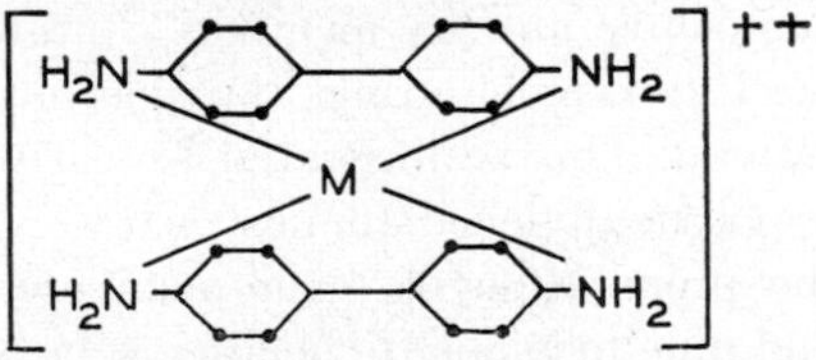

Such complexes are possibly polymeric, since benzidine does not chelate with cobalt in [Co en₂ benzidine Br]Br₂ but is monodentate[10].

SEVEN-MEMBERED RINGS

Duff[11] found that the dibasic acids *meso*-tartaric, maleic, dibromsuccinic, itaconic and citraconic, when added to carbonatobis(ethylenediamine)cobalt(III) bromide yielded crystalline compounds, which he supposed contained the ion

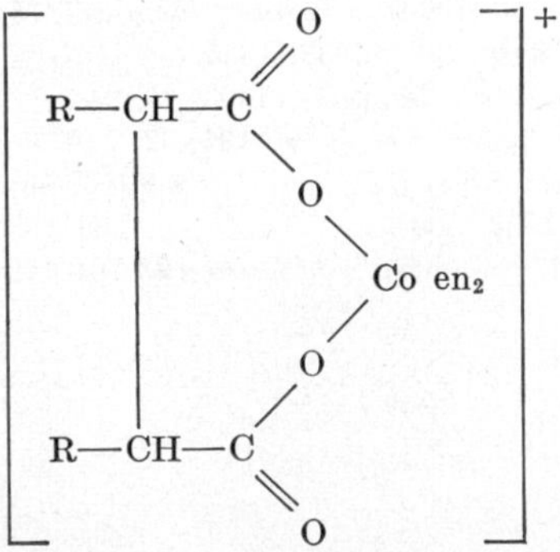

It is possible that the α-hydroxy acids form five-membered rings involving the metal, the carboxy and the hydroxy groups. A series of related dibasic acids in which the carbonyl groups are in the trans positions give only viscous syrups which have not been identified. It is possible that the acid molecules serve as bridge groups in building polymers. Several analogous compounds between cobalt and phthalic acid and some sulfur derivatives of phthalic acid were also reported by Duff[12]. He assigned the following structures on the basis of analytical data alone:

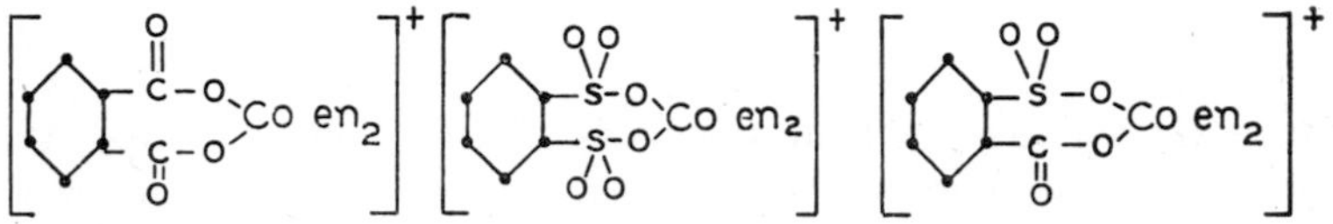

Tetrachlorodimethylphthalatotitanium(IV) has been reported by Scagliarini and Tartarini[13] who proposed the following structure, again on the basis of analytical data alone:

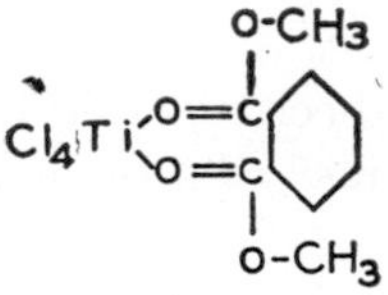

Shuttleworth[14] states that for the chromium chelate derivatives of dibasic acids, seven-membered ring structures are intermediate in stability between four- and six-membered rings. He reports complexes of the type $Cr(AA)_3$ with maleic, malonic, glutaric, adipic, suberic, phthalic and azelaic acids, remarking that the acids which do not form five-, six- or seven-membered rings tend to form polymers.

Brady and Hughes[15] investigated the reaction of 2,2'-biphenol with a number of metallic ions and complexes, and proposed seven-membered ring structures for two of the compounds prepared. When thallium(I) acetate, in ammoniacal methanol solution, was treated with 2,2'-biphenol, a precipitate was formed, which, from analysis, was assigned the structure

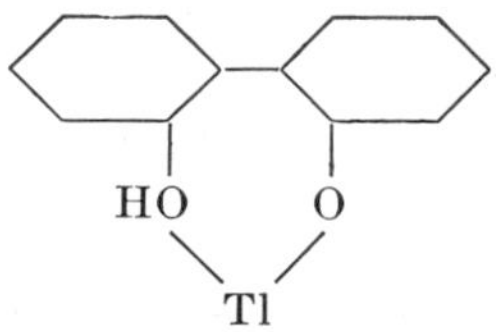

9. Dwyer and Mellor, *J. Am. Chem. Soc.*, **63**, 81 (1941).
10. Spacu, *Bull. sect. sci. acad. roumaine*, **23**, 181 (1940); *Chem. Abs.*, **37** 2291⁹ (1943).
11. Duff, *J. Chem. Soc.*, **119**, 385 (1921).
12. Duff, *J. Chem. Soc.*, **119**, 1982 (1921).
13. Scagliarini and Tartarini, *Atti accad. Lincei*, **4**, 318 (1926).
14. Shuttleworth, *J. Am. Leather Chemists Assoc.*, **45**, 169 (1950).
15. Brady and Hughes, *J. Chem. Soc.*, **1933**, 1227.

When this substance was treated with aqueous alkali, a less soluble compound was formed along with the liberation of an equivalent amount of biphenol.

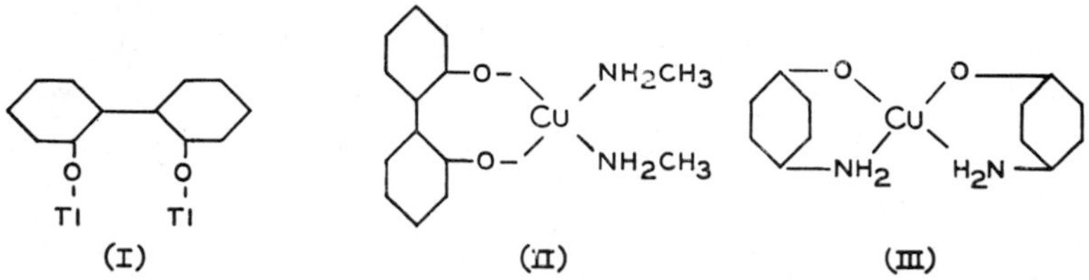

(I)   (II)   (III)

Structure (I) was assigned on the basis of these observations. Another seven-membered ring structure proposed by the same authors was that of the copper complex shown in (II).

Para-aminophenol yields blue-violet insoluble compounds with copper(II) and iron(II). From the composition of the compounds and their insolubility in water, Augusti[16] proposed the unlikely structure (III) for the copper complex.

Seven-membered rings have been reported in which the central atom coordinates to two nitrogen atoms[17] of a diamine. Middleton reports cobalt complexes with the structures

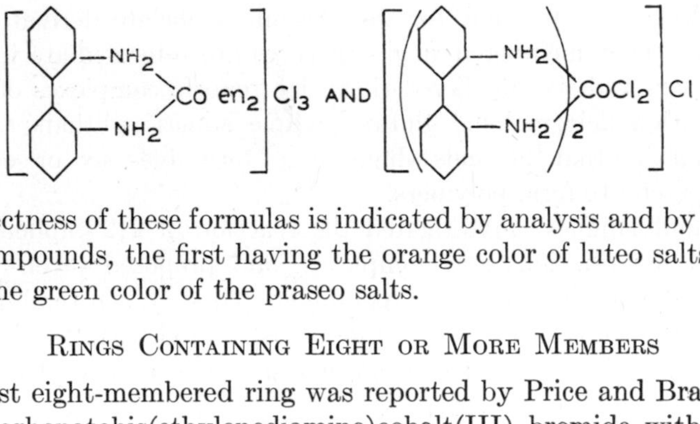

The correctness of these formulas is indicated by analysis and by the colors of the compounds, the first having the orange color of luteo salts, and the second, the green color of the praseo salts.

RINGS CONTAINING EIGHT OR MORE MEMBERS

The first eight-membered ring was reported by Price and Brazier[18] who treated carbonatobis(ethylenediamine)cobalt(III) bromide with sulfonyl-diacetic acid. They assigned the structure

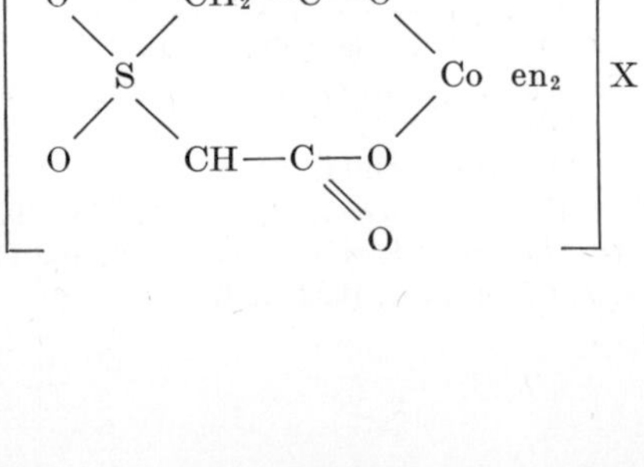

Under different conditions the two carboxyl groups are attached to two different cobalt atoms, giving rise to polynuclear structures. Moreover, if the sulfone group is replaced by sulfide, no compounds are obtained analogous to those for which the eight-membered ring structure was proposed. This suggests that the chelation may involve the oxygen atoms of the sulfone group rather than the carboxyl groups.

Schmitz-Dumont and Motzkus[19] obtained an insoluble compound when copper(I) ion was treated with bis-α-methyl-β-indyl methene, to which they assigned the structure

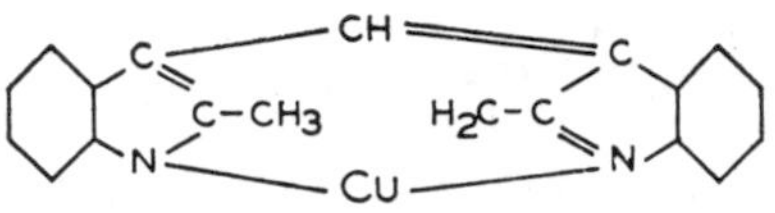

Triethanolamine has been used as a coordinating agent with a number of metallic ions. Tettamanzi and Carli[20] found that coordination compounds rather than basic salts are formed with nickel, cadmium, calcium and magnesium. They proposed the alternative structures (IV) and (V).

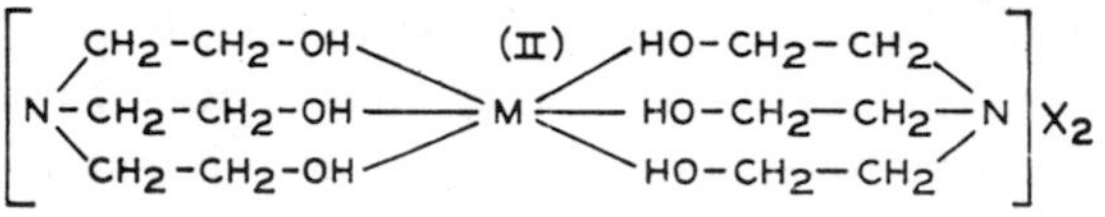

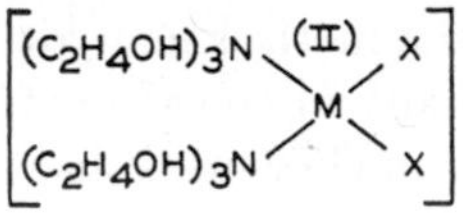

The blue color of the nickel salt furnishes evidence for structure (V). Since magnesium does not form stable magnesium to nitrogen coordinate bonds with other amines, structure (IV) is favored for the magnesium salt. Further work by Tettamanzi and Garelli[21] showed that when cobalt, copper, or zinc was used as the central atom, a hydrogen of one hydroxyl group was replaced by the metal giving a compound which they formulated as

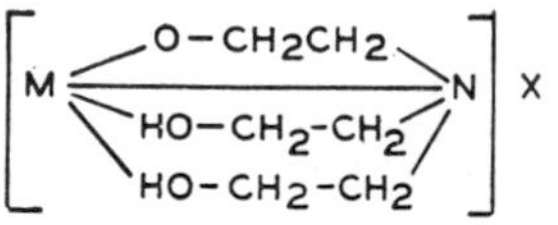

Miller[22] has prepared some crystalline derivatives of bismuth triethanol-

---

16. Augusti, *Mikrochemie*, **17**, 118 (1935).
17. Middleton, Thesis, University of Illinois, 1938.
18. Price and Brazier, *J. Chem. Soc.*, **107**, 1367 (1915).
19. Schmitz-Dumont and Motzkus, *Ber.*, **61**, 581 (1928).
20. Tettamanzi and Carli, *Gazz. chim. ital.*, **63**, 566 (1933).
21. Tettamanzi and Garelli, *Gazz. chim. ital.*, **63**, 570 (1933).
22. Miller, *J. Am. Chem. Soc.*, **62**, 2707 (1940).

amine and, from analytical data, has assigned the formulas

$$
\text{Na—O—Bi} \underset{O—CH_2—CH_2}{\overset{O—CH_2—CH_2}{\big\langle}} \text{N—CH}_2\text{—CH}_2\text{OH} \quad \text{and} \quad \text{Bi} \overset{O—CH_2—CH_2}{\underset{O—CH_2—CH_2}{\big\langle}} \text{O—CH}_2\text{—CH}_2\text{—N}
$$

A rather odd addition compound of thallium acetoacetic ester and carbon disulfide has been reported by Feigl and Bäcker[23]. Because of the color, insolubility, and stability (even toward acids and bases) the authors have proposed the following eight-membered ring structure:

$$
\begin{array}{c}
\text{CH}_3\text{—C=C=C—O C}_2\text{H}_5 \\
\quad | \qquad | \\
\quad \text{O} \qquad \text{O} \\
\quad | \qquad | \\
\quad \text{Tl} \qquad \text{Tl} \\
\qquad \diagdown \diagup \\
\qquad \text{CS}_2
\end{array}
$$

The double enolization of the methylene group is experimentally indicated by the fact that compounds of this type are not formed if one or both of the methylene hydrogens are replaced by an alkyl or aryl radical. It seems hard to conceive of the carbon atom in the carbon disulfide as the donor atom because it has no available electrons; however, each of the sulfur atoms has electron pairs available, so it seems more logical for the structure to be

$$
\begin{array}{c}
\text{CH}_3\text{—C=C=C—O C}_2\text{H}_5 \text{ ,} \\
\quad | \qquad\quad | \\
\quad \text{O} \qquad\quad \text{O} \\
\quad | \qquad\quad | \\
\quad \text{Tl} \qquad\quad \text{Tl} \\
\quad | \qquad\quad | \\
\quad \text{S=C=S}
\end{array}
$$

thus giving rise to a ten-membered ring.

Some early work by Schlesinger[24], who was attempting to span trans positions with a bidentate group, resulted in the preparation of a number of complexes of copper with polymethylene bis-α-amino acids:

$$
\begin{array}{c}
\text{O=C—O} \qquad\qquad \text{O—C=O} \\
\quad | \qquad \diagdown \text{Cu} \diagup \qquad | \\
\text{R'—C—N} \diagdown \qquad \diagup \text{N—C=R'} \\
\quad | \quad \text{H} \quad (\text{CH}_2)_n \quad \text{H} \quad | \\
\quad \text{R} \qquad\qquad\qquad \text{R}
\end{array}
$$

Compounds were prepared in which n has the values 2, 3, 5, 7, and 10; thus, if these structures are correct, the rings contain 5, 6, 8, 10, and 13

23. Feigl and Backer, *Monatsh.*, **49**, 401 (1928).
24. Schlesinger, *Ber.*, **58**, 1877 (1925).

members. For $n = 2$ or 3, deep blue compounds are formed, for $n = 10$, the product is red-violet, and for $n = 5$ or 7, both the blue and violet forms are obtained. These products are nonelectrolytes and monomolecular so that cis-trans isomerism was suspected, with the methylene groups spanning trans positions in the red-violet compound

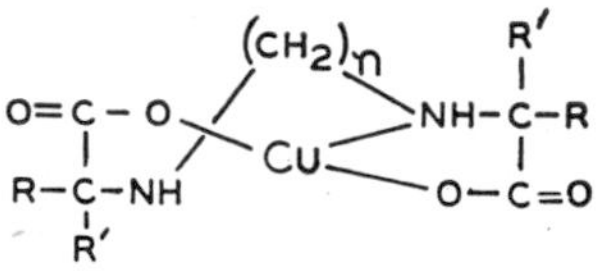

Mattern[25] prepared an interesting compound in which an eight-membered ring apparently spans the trans positions in the coordination sphere of a platinum(II) ion. The substance was produced by the series of reactions shown below.

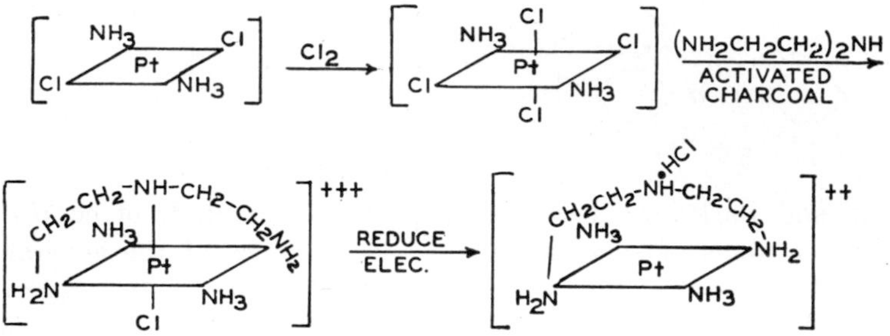

The structure of the end product was deduced from the mode of preparation, analysis, titration of available chlorine, and preparation of the dichloro-diammineplatinum(II) complex as a derivative. This dichloro derivative was shown to be the trans isomer, indicating that the original ion, containing diethylenetriamine hydrochloride, was also trans in configuration. When recrystallized from water, the compound tended to rearrange, liberating ammonium chloride according to the equation

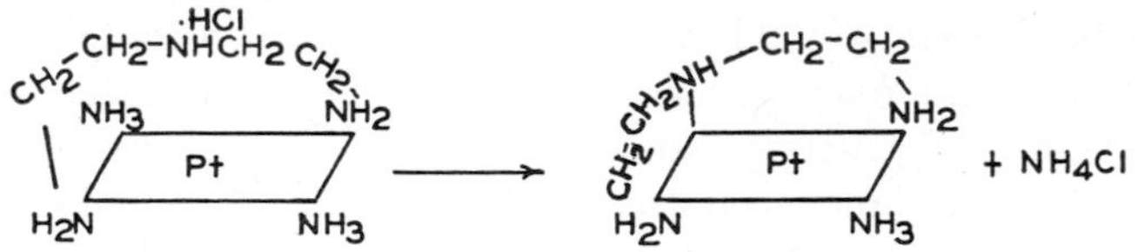

Pfeiffer and co-workers[26] have investigated the reactions of various metal ions with condensed systems of salicylaldehyde and several diamines. With decamethylenediamine salicylaldehyde and copper(II) ion they obtained a compound to which they assigned a thirteen-membered ring structure,

25. Mattern, thesis, University of Illinois, 1946.
26. Pfeiffer, *et al.*, *Ann.*, **503**, 84 (1933); *J. prakt. Chem.* [2] **145**, 243 (1936).

(structure (VI) with $n = 10$)

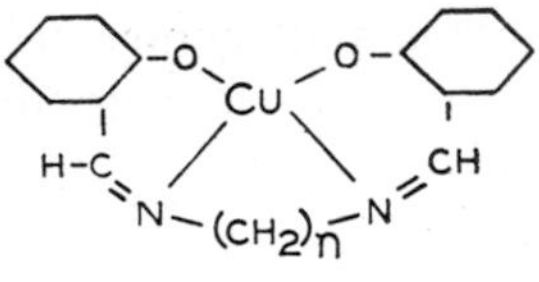

(VI)

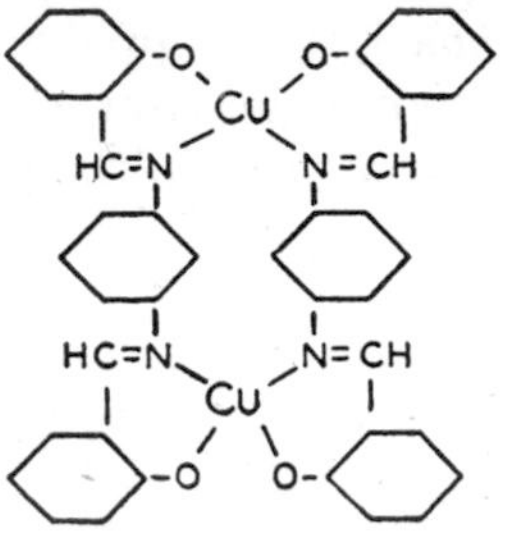

VII

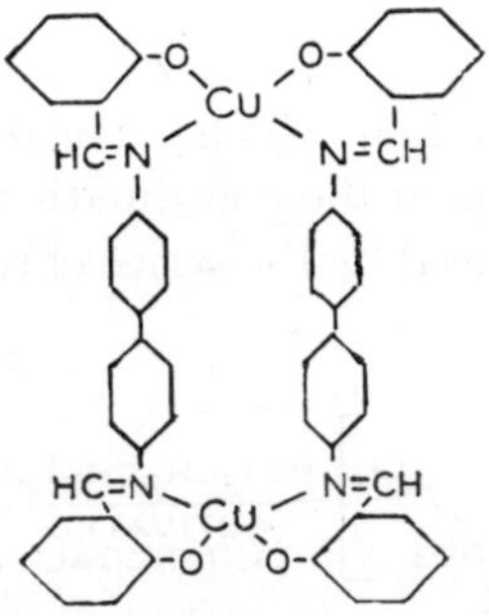

VIII

Calvin and Barkelew[27] have also reported compounds of copper with condensed systems of salicylaldehyde and diamines of the general type shown in structure (VI). Penta-, hexa-, and heptaamines were prepared giving rings of eight, nine and ten members respectively. As shown in the structural formulas, these molecules also involve two six-membered rings. The stability of these smaller rings and the flexibility of the di-, tri-, penta-, hexa-, hepta-, and decamethylene groups probably account for the formation of these complexes. The latter factor is emphasized in the cases where ortho-, meta-, and paradiamino benzene and benzidine[26] were substituted for the decamethylenediamine in the condensed ring system. Monomeric compounds were first reported. However, Pfeiffer later showed, on the basis of cryoscopic measurements, that these were actually dimers, so the meta phenylenediamine salt would have structure (VII) which contains a twelve-membered ring and four six-membered rings. The corresponding para-phenylenediamine derivative would contain a fourteen-membered ring, while the benzidine dimer would contain a twenty-two-membered ring as shown in (VIII).

It is quite evident that the proposed structures of complexes with chelate rings containing more than six atoms are not firmly established. Lack of x-ray and other conclusive data, the several possible linkages, and the possibility of polymerization, all tend to make the proposed structures highly speculative.

27. Calvin and Barkelew, *J. Am. Chem. Soc.*, **68**, 2267 (1946).

7. General Isomerism of Complex Compounds

Thomas D. O'Brien*

University of Minnesota, Minneapolis, Minnesota

A consideration of the number of different isomeric forms in which a relatively simple inorganic coordination compound can exist makes it apparent that the study of the isomerism of coordination compounds may become extremely complicated. As simple a compound as $Co(en)_2(H_2O)(NO_2)Cl_2$ can exist in eighteen different isomeric forms, twelve of which are optically active. Whereas stereoisomerism has probably been the most widely investigated of the different types of isomerism, the others are equally important.

Solvate Isomerism

The classic example of solvate isomerism is concerned with the three hydrate isomers of the compound, $CrCl_3 \cdot 6H_2O$. The green form, which is obtained from fairly concentrated solutions of hydrochloric acid, has been assigned the formula $[Cr(H_2O)_4Cl_2]Cl \cdot 2H_2O$ on the basis of conductivity measurements and relative ease of precipitation of the chlorides with silver(I) ion[1]. Upon dilution, stepwise aquation takes place. The resulting solutions yield the blue-green $[Cr(H_2O)_5Cl]Cl_2 \cdot H_2O$ and the violet $[Cr(H_2O)_6]Cl_3$.

Britton[2] reports that the decrease in conductivity and the decrease in the amount of chloride precipitated with silver nitrate, in going from the violet to the green form, are due, not to the transition between the two forms proposed by Werner[1], but to the formation of a green, highly aggregated, basic chromium(III) chloride which is virtually a colloidal electrolyte. If this explanation were correct, the green solutions should be more viscous than those containing the violet form of the chromium compound. However, Partington and Tweedy[3] measured the viscosities and found that

---

* Now at Kansas State College, Manhattan, Kansas.
1. Werner and Gubser, *Ber.*, **34**, 1601 (1901); Bjerrum, *Ber.*, **39**,, 1599 (1906); Bjerrum: "Studier over Kromiklorid," Kopenhagen, 1907; Bjerrum, *Z. phys. Chem.* **59**, 336, 581 (1907).
2. Britton, *J. Chem. Soc.*, **127**, 2128 (1925).
3. Partington and Tweedy, *Nature*, **117**, 415 (1926).

the violet solutions are more viscous than the green. This is in agreement with Werner's postulate since the tervalent hexaquochromium(III) ion should form solutions in which the pseudolattice is more stable than would be the case with the singly charged dichlorotetraquo ion.

Some doubt has been cast on the simple interpretation of Werner by the results[4] obtained in the preparation of tris(ethylenediamine)chromium(III) chloride. The reaction of hexaquochromium(III) chloride, $[Cr(H_2O)_6]Cl_3$, with anhydrous ethylenedimaine in toluene solution gives a yield of about 25 per cent of yellow tris(ethylenediamine)chromium(III) chloride. Similar treatment of ordinary hydrated chromium(III) chloride, which contains $[Cr(H_2O)_4Cl_2]Cl \cdot 2H_2O$ and $[Cr(H_2O)_5Cl]Cl_2 \cdot H_2O$, yields none of the tris-(ethylenediamine) complex. Normally, ethylenediamine replaces coordinated chlorides more easily than it replaces coordinated water. Marchi and McReynolds[4] state that $[Cr(H_2O)_4Cl_2]Cl \cdot 2H_2O$ should not result in a different product than that obtained with $[Cr(H_2O)_6]Cl_3$, and that the system is more complex than is implied by Werner.

Further evidence that the equilibria are complex has been reported in connection with the study of the transformation of $[Cr(H_2O)_4Cl_2]Cl \cdot 2H_2O$ to $[Cr(H_2O)_6]Cl_3$ by warming in dilute solutions[5a] and by conductometric titration[5b]. In the dark, equilibrium was reached in six and one-half hours, but in ultraviolet light the reaction was much faster. Also, if the equilibrium mixture obtained in the dark was subsequently exposed to ultraviolet light, there was a considerable shift in the equilibrium point. After measuring the pH, conductance, and extinction coefficient, the authors concluded that the equilibrium is very complex, that the conversions take place in steps and that each isomeric change is preceded by hydrolysis. This evidence does not appear to show anything about the nature of the isomerism. The shift in equilibrium simply indicates that the different compounds contain different amounts of energy. Conductometric titration of chromium(III) solutions shows nonstoichiometric ratios of bound chloride, the breaks occurring at 1.54, 2.1, and 3.0 equivalents of silver ion.

The equilibria are probably still best represented by the simple explanations given above. Recent kinetic studies support this conclusion[5c]. As in any other chemical reaction, the equation is not intended to represent a mechanism, but only the starting materials and final products.

Fremy[6] first prepared nitratopentamminecobalt(III) nitrate 1-hydrate, and converted it to the solvate isomer, aquopentamminecobalt(III) nitrate. The reverse reaction was carried out by Benrath and Mienes[7].

4. Marchi and McReynolds, *J. Am. Chem. Soc.*, **65**, 481 (1943).
5. Datar and Quershi, *J. Osmania Univ.*, **8**, 6 (1940); Law, *Trans. Faraday Soc.*, **32**, 1461 (1936); Hamm, *J. Am. Chem. Soc.*, **73**, 1240 (1951).
6. Fremy, *Ann. chim. phys.*, [3] **25**, 296 (1852).
7. Benrath and Mienes, *Z. anorg. Chem.*, **177**, 289 (1929).

When a solution of sulfatopentamminecobalt(III) hydrogen sulfate 2-hydrate, $[Co(NH_3)_5SO_4]HSO_4 \cdot 2H_2O$, is treated with chloroplatinic acid, orange-red crystals of sulfatopentamminecobalt(III) chloroplatinate 2-hydrate precipitate. An isomeric red-yellow aquopentammine complex, $[Co(NH_3)_5H_2O]_2(SO_4)_2[PtCl_6]$, is obtained when sulfuric acid and chloroplatinic acid are added to an aqueous solution of sulfatopentamminecobalt(III) sulfate[8].

Because water is by far the most widely used solvent, the above examples show hydrate isomerism, but this by no means precludes the possibility of other solvate isomers such as might be formed by alcohols, amines, or ammonia.

COORDINATION ISOMERISM

Two salts with the empirical formula $CoCr(NH_3)_6(CN)_6$ are known. Both are yellow and relatively insoluble in water. One is prepared by treating aqueous hexamminecobalt(III) chloride, $[Co(NH_3)_6]Cl_3$, with potassium hexacyanochromate(III),[9] $K_3[Cr(CN)_6]$, while the other is prepared by treating aqueous hexamminechromium(III) chloride, $[Cr(NH_3)_6]Cl_3$, with potassium hexacyanocobaltate(III), $K_3[Co(CN)_6]$.[10] The differences between them can easily be shown by treating solutions of each with silver nitrate. In each case an insoluble silver salt is obtained, but hexamminecobalt(III) nitrate is present in one filtrate and hexamminechromium(III) nitrate in the other. It follows that the formulas of the original compounds are $[Co(NH_3)_6]$ $[Cr(CN)_6]$ and $[Cr(NH_3)_6]$ $[Co(CN)_6]$. Another example is found in the isomerism of the violet tetramminecopper(II) tetrachloroplatinate(II) $[Cu(NH_3)_4]$ $[PtCl_4]$, and the green tetrammineplatinum(II) tetrachlorocuprate(II), $[Pt(NH_3)_4]$ $[CuCl_4]$.

It is not necessary that coordination isomers contain two different central atoms, as in the examples above. Atoms of the same metal can appear in both the cation and the anion as in $[Co(NH_3)_4(NO_2)_2]$ $[Co(NH_3)_2(NO_2)_4]$ and $[Co(NH_3)_6]$ $[Co(NO_2)_6]$.[11] A similar example of this type of isomerism is found in the orange-yellow $[Co(NH_3)_6]$ $[Co(NH_3)_2(NO_2)_4]_3$ which is isomeric with the orange-red salt $[Co(NH_3)_4(NO_2)_2]_3[Co(NO_2)_6]$.[11]

The reversible transformation at 45° of a double silver-mercury iodide from a red to a yellow form[12] has been explained by the hypothesis that the change is due to a change in function of the metal atoms according to the equation $AgHg[AgI_4] \rightleftharpoons Ag_2[HgI_4]$. The crystal structures are shown in

8. Jorgensen, *J. prakt. Chem.*, **31**, 271 (1885).

9. Braun, *Ann.*, **125, 183** (1863).

10. Jorgensen, *J. prakt. Chem.*, [*2*] **30**, 31 (1884); Pfeiffer, *Ann.*, **346**, 42 (1906).

11. Jorgensen, *Z. anorg. Chem.*, **5**, 177 (1894); *ibid.*, **5**, 182 (1894); *ibid.*, **7**, 287 (1894); *ibid.*, **13**, 183 (1897); Werner and Miolati, *Z. physik. Chem.*, **14**, 514 (1894).

12. Roozeboom, *Proc. K. Akad. Wetensch. Amsterdam*, **3**, 84 (1900).

Fig. 7.1[13]. X-ray and conductivity measurements show that in the alpha form the mercury and silver atoms statistically fill three out of the four equivalent positions in the crystal lattice.

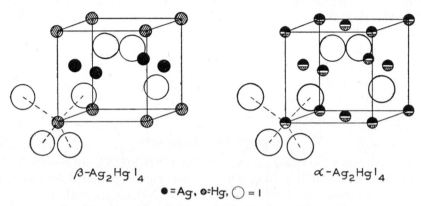

β-Ag$_2$Hg I$_4$ α-Ag$_2$HgI$_4$

● = Ag, ◐ = Hg, ◯ = I

Fig. 7.1. Crystal structures of the two forms of Ag$_2$HgI$_4$

POLYMERIZATION ISOMERISM

The word "polymerization" as applied to polymerization isomerism in coordination chemistry has a different connotation from that in modern usage in organic chemistry. In organic chemistry, polymerization denotes

TABLE 7.1

Formula	Molecular Weight	Properties[11]
[Co(NH$_3$)$_6$] [Co(NO$_2$)$_6$]	Double	Yellow. Insoluble in water.
[Co(NH$_3$)$_4$(NO$_2$)$_2$] [Co(NH$_3$)$_2$(NO$_2$)$_4$]	Double	Yellow-brown. Four forms possible; cis-cis, trans-trans, cis-trans, trans-cis.
[Co(NH$_3$)$_5$NO$_2$] [Co(NH$_3$)$_2$(NO$_2$)$_4$]$_2$	Triple	Orange. Difficulty soluble. Anion can exist in cis or trans form.
[Co(NH$_3$)$_6$] [Co(NH$_3$)$_2$(NO$_2$)$_4$]$_3$	Quadruple	Yellow-orange. Anion can exist in cis or trans form.
[Co(NH$_3$)$_4$(NO$_2$)$_2$]$_3$[Co(NO$_2$)$_6$]	Quadruple	Orange-red. Cation can be either cis or trans.
[Co(NH$_3$)$_5$NO$_2$]$_3$[Co(NO$_2$)$_6$]$_2$	Quintuple	Brown-yellow.

13. Ketelaar, Z. *Krist.*, **87**, 436 (1934) Fig. 7.1 is taken from Clark, Applied X-rays. 3rd Edition, p. 364. McGraw-Hill Book Co., New York, 1940.

TABLE 7.2

Formula	Molecular Weight	Comments
$[Pt(NH_3)_2Cl_2]$[16]	Single	Yellow. The cis isomer is commonly called Peyrone's chloride, while the trans is known as Reiset's chloride.
$[Pt(NH_3)_4]$ $[PtCl_4]$[17]	Double	Green. Known as Magnus' salt.
$[Pt(NH_3)_3Cl]$ $[Pt(NH_3)Cl_3]$	Double	
$[Pt(NH_3)_4]$ $[Pt(NH_3)Cl_3]_2$[18]	Triple	Orange-yellow.
$[Pt(NH_3)_3Cl]_2[PtCl_4]$[19]	Triple	

the union of a large number of separate units. The implications associated with the term in coordination chemistry can probably best be illustrated by the following examples, which were originally reported by Werner. Six polymerization isomers of trinitrotriammine-cobalt(III), $[Co(NH_3)_3(NO_2)_3]$, are shown in Table 7.1. Examples are known in the chromium series, also[14, 15] and a platinum series is included in Table 7.2.

There are two salts, one green and the other red, with the empirical formula $(CH_3)_2TeI_2$. For some time it was thought that the compound had a planar configuration and that these two were the cis and trans forms[20]. It is now believed that the green salt has a molecular weight double that of the red one, and that, in the green isomer, one tellurium atom is associated with a cation while a second is a part of an anion; the true formula is $[(CH_3)_3TeI]$ $[CH_3TeI_3]$[21].

Polymerization isomers of complex ions in which diallylamine behaves as a bidentate group have been prepared[22], $[Pt\{(CH_2=CHCH_2)_2NH\}Cl_2]$ $[Pt\{(CH_2=CHCH_2)_2NH\}_2]$ $[PtCl_4]$.

This type of isomerism is also known in cases where bridging occurs. Octammine-μ-diol-dicobalt(III) bromide 2-hydrate is a polymerization isomer of hydroxyaquotetramminecobalt(III) bromide. The formulas of

14. Werner and Jovanovits, unpublished work; cf. Werner: "New Ideas on Inorganic Chemistry," 2nd Ed., p. 232, New York, Longmans, 1911.
15. Christensen, *J. prakt. Chem.*, **45**, 371 (1892).
16. Peyrone, *Ann.*, **51**, 1 (1844), **55**, 205 (1845), **61**, 178 (1847). Gerstl, *Ber.*, **3**, 682 (1870); Odling, *Phil. Mag.*, **4**, No. 38, 455 (1870).
17. Magnus, *Pogg. Ann.*, **14**, 242 (1828).
18. Cossa, *Ber.*, **23**, 2503 (1890).
19. King, *J. Chem. Soc.*, **1948**, 1912.
20. Vernon, *J. Chem. Soc.*, **117**, 86, 889 (1920); **119**, 687 (1921); Knaggs and Vernon, *J. Chem. Soc.*, **119**, 105 (1921).
21. Drew, *J. Chem. Soc.*, **1929**, 560.
22. Rubinstein and Derbisher, *Doklady Akad. Nauk S.S.S.R.*, **74**, 283 (1950).

these compounds are

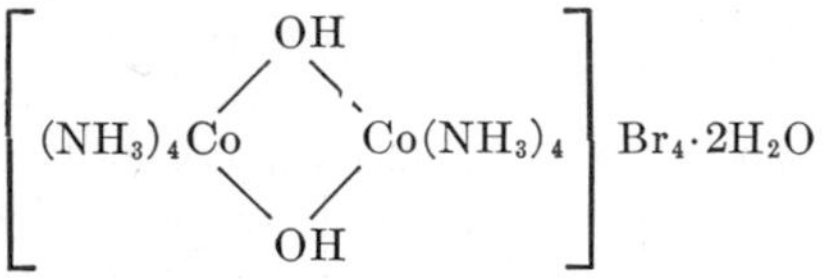

$$
\left[(NH_3)_4Co \underset{OH}{\overset{OH}{\diagup\diagdown}} Co(NH_3)_4 \right] Br_4 \cdot 2H_2O \quad \text{and} \quad \left[Co(NH_3)_4 \overset{H_2O}{\underset{OH}{}} \right] Br_2 ,
$$

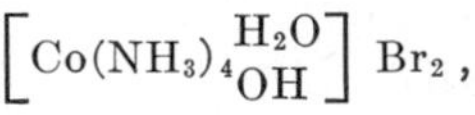

respectively[23]. Another interesting example is to be found in the isomeric hexammine-μ-triol-dicobalt(III),

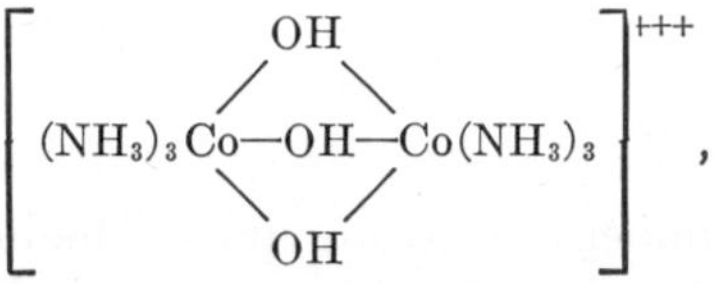

$$
\left[(NH_3)_3Co \overset{OH}{\underset{OH}{\diagup\diagdown}} OH \overset{}{\diagdown\diagup} Co(NH_3)_3 \right]^{+++} ,
$$

and dodecammine-μ-hexol-tetracobalt(III),

$$
\left[Co \left\{ \underset{HO}{\overset{HO}{\diagup\diagdown}} Co(NH_3)_4 \right\}_3 \right]^{6+}
$$

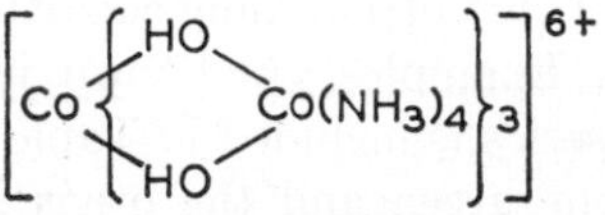

ions[24]. The second compound may be considered to be a dimer of the first, though its structure is quite different. The structure of this tetracobalt complex was proven by resolution into optical enantiomers[25]. The structural formula of another dodecammine-μ-hexol-tetracobalt(III) ion may be written[26]

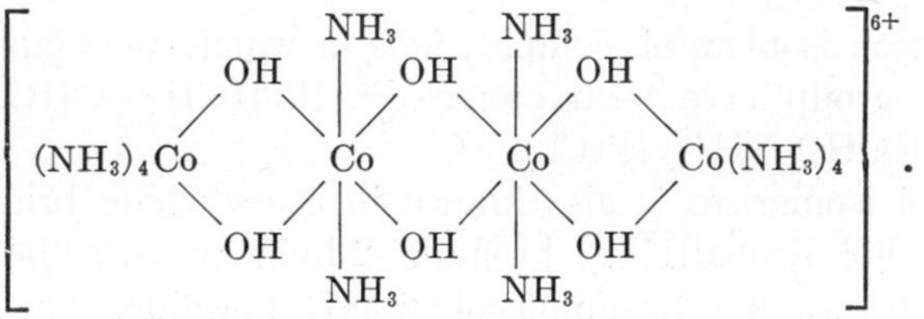

$$
\left[(NH_3)_4Co \underset{\underset{NH_3}{OH}}{\overset{\overset{NH_3}{OH}}{\diagup\diagdown}} Co \underset{\underset{NH_3}{OH}}{\overset{\overset{NH_3}{OH}}{\diagup\diagdown}} Co \underset{OH}{\overset{OH}{\diagup\diagdown}} Co(NH_3)_4 \right]^{6+} .
$$

However, there is no indication that this compound has been prepared.

An odd type of polymerization isomerization is implicit in the work of Rubinstein[27], who reports the formation of a new compound by the following reaction:

$[(NH_3)_4NH_2ClPt]Cl_2 + [Pt(NH_3)_4Cl_2]Cl_2 \rightarrow [(NH_3)_4NH_2ClPtCl_2] [(NH_3)_4Cl_2PtCl_2]$

23. Werner, *Ber.*, **40**, 4434 (1907).
24. Birk, *Z. anorg. allgem. Chem.*, **175**, 405 (1928); Werner, *Ber.*, **40**, 4836 (1907).
25. Werner, *Ber.*, **47**, 3087 (1914).
26. Hückel, "Structural Chemistry of Inorganic Compounds," Vol. I, p. 166, New York, Elsevier Publishing Co., 1950.
27. Rubinstein, *Izvest. Sektora Platini i Drug, Blagorod Metal. Inst. Obschei i Neorg. Khim. Akad. Nauk. S.S.S.R.*, **20**, 53 (1947).

According to Rubinstein, the new compound is characterized by the differences in its chemical and physical properties as compared to those associated with mixtures of the reactants. The author did not indicate any probable structure for this new compound, but it might be formulated as a dinuclear complex:

$$\left[(NH_3)_4Pt \begin{array}{c} NH_2 \\ \diagup \diagdown \\ \diagdown \diagup \\ Cl \end{array} Pt(NH_3)_4 \right] Cl_6 \quad \text{or} \quad \left[(NH_3)_4Pt \begin{array}{c} Cl \\ | \\ \end{array} NH_2 \begin{array}{c} Cl \\ | \\ \end{array} Pt(NH_3)_4 \right] Cl_5$$

Ionization Isomerism

Bromopentamminecobalt(III) sulfate[28] is dark violet in color; its solutions give no precipitate upon the addition of silver nitrate but give a precipitate immediately when barium chloride is added. If this dark-violet salt is heated with concentrated sulfuric acid and then cooled, the addition of dilute hydrogen bromide produces a violet-red compound of the same empirical formula[29]. This violet-red salt, however, gives no precipitate when barium chloride is added but silver bromide precipitates immediately with silver nitrate. From these experimental facts it is concluded that the isomers are bromopentamminecobalt(III) sulfate, $[Co(NH_3)_5Br]SO_4$, and sulfatopentamminecobalt(III) bromide, $[Co(NH_3)_5SO_4]Br$.

A similar set of isomers consists of the green *trans*-dichlorobis(ethylenediamine)cobalt(III) nitrite[30], *trans*-$[Co\ en_2\ Cl_2]NO_2$, and the red *trans*-nitrochlorobis(ethylenediamine)cobalt(III) chloride[31], $[Co\ en_2\ ClNO_2]Cl$. Still another example is furnished by dihydroxytetrammineplatinum(IV) sulfate[32], $[Pt(NH_3)_4(OH)_2]SO_4$, which yields neutral solutions, and sulfatotetrammineplatinum(II) hydroxide, $[Pt(NH_3)_4SO_4](OH)_2$,[32] solutions of which are strongly basic.

Nyholm[33] has reported a compound having the formula

$$PdBr_2\{As(C_2H_5)\ (C_6H_5)_2\}_3 ,$$

that exists in two forms which *might* be considered to be ionization isomers. The compound is soluble in organic solvents both at room temperature and at low temperatures. Molecular weight determinations indicate that it is dissociated over the entire temperature range studied. However, it under-

28. Jorgensen, *J. prakt. Chem.*, [2] **19**, 49 (1879); *Z. anorg. Chem.*, **17**, 463 (1898); Diehl, Clark, and Willard, *Inorganic Syntheses.* **1.** 186 (1939).
29. Jorgensen, *J. prakt. Chem.*, [2] **31**, 262 (1885).
30. Jorgensen, *J. prakt. Chem.*, [2] **39**, 1 (1889).
31. Werner, *Ber.*, **34**, 1773 (1901).
32. Cleve, *K. Sv. Vet. Akad. Handl.*, **10**, No. 9 (1871).
33. Nyholm, *J. Chem. Soc.*, **1950**, 848.

goes a change in character as the temperature is lowered considerably below zero. The color of the solutions changes at $-78°C$, and a distinct increase in the conductivity is observed. The equilibria proposed to explain this behavior are shown below.

$$(\text{solid}) \ [PdBr(AsR_3)_3]Br \xrightarrow[\text{benzene (25°)}]{\text{dissolve in}} [PdBr_2(AsR_3)_2] + AsR_3$$

$$[PdBr_2(AsR_3)_2] + AsR_3 \xrightarrow{-78°} [PdBr(AsR_3)_3]^+ + Br^-$$

STRUCTURAL ISOMERISM

The existence of this type of isomerism is based almost exclusively on the nitro and nitrito compounds. Jorgensen[34] prepared two compounds in the following manner:

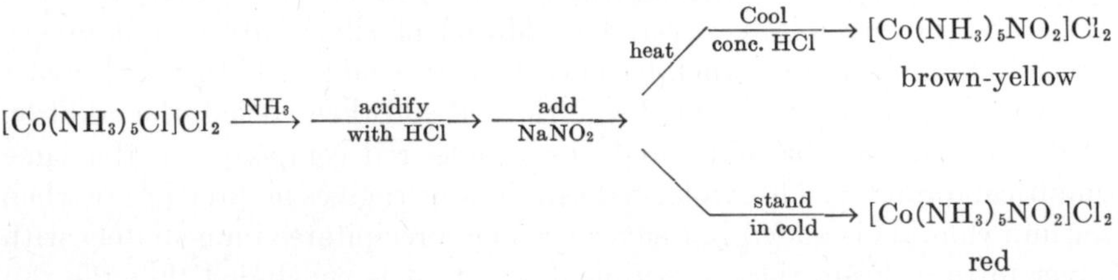

$$[Co(NH_3)_5Cl]Cl_2 \xrightarrow{NH_3} \xrightarrow[\text{with HCl}]{\text{acidify}} \xrightarrow[\text{NaNO}_2]{\text{add}}$$

heat / Cool conc. HCl $\rightarrow [Co(NH_3)_5NO_2]Cl_2$ brown-yellow

stand in cold $\rightarrow [Co(NH_3)_5NO_2]Cl_2$ red

The red form, believed to contain the nitrito group, is converted to the brown-yellow nitro form quite rapidly by heating in solution or by adding concentrated hydrochloric acid. It changes slowly even in the solid state.

Lecompte and Duval[35] prepared these two salts according to the method of Jorgensen[34] and determined the Debye-Scherrer patterns, the infrared absorption, and the ultraviolet absorption bands. The Debye-Scherrer patterns were "rigorously identical." By comparison with organic nitro and nitrito compounds, Lecompte and Duval concluded that there were no $-O-N=O$ links in the red cobalt compound, but only those of the

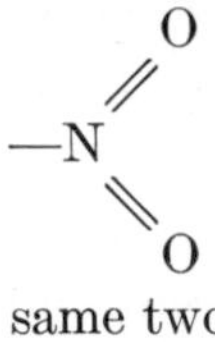

$$-N \overset{\displaystyle O}{\underset{\displaystyle O}{\big\langle}}$$

type. The isoxantho or red compound, in addition to having the same two strong absorption bands at 6.5 and 7.5 μ as the xantho or yellow salt, showed an additional band at 7.65 μ. This was shown to be the same as the maximum absorption band of chloropentamminecobalt(III) chloride, the starting material in the preparation of the nitro complex. Lecomte and Duval conclude that the red color is due to the presence of some unreacted starting material. These results are in accord with the earlier work of Piutti[36] who reported that the absorption spectra of the two forms are

34. Jorgensen, *Z. anorg. Chem.*, **5**, 168 (1894).
35. Lecompte and Duval, *Bull. soc. chim.*, **12**, 678 (1945).
36. Piutti, *Ber.*, **45**, 1832 (1912).

identical. Shibata[37], however, claimed that the two forms had quite different absorption spectra.

Adell[38] measured the rate of conversion of the "nitrito" to the nitro form photometrically and concluded that it followed the law for a first order reaction. These results can be considered to be only indirect structural evidence; however, it should be pointed out that the conversion of the highly ionized salt, chloropentamminecobalt(III) chloride-nitrite, $[Co(NH_3)_5Cl]ClNO_2$, to the nitro complex (assuming the conclusion of Lecomte and Duval to be correct) in solution should follow a second order rate law, unless the rate-determining step is a slow rearrangement which takes place subsequent to the collision of a chloropentamminecobalt(III) ion and a nitrite ion. This would imply a mechanism of substitution involving a temporary coordination number of seven for the cobalt ion.

Yalman and Kuwana[38b] have confirmed the results of Adell[38] and have shown that the conversion of the cis dinitritotetrammine salt to the corresponding cis dinitro salt is also first order. However, they were unable to show by spectrophotometric means, the existence of the cis nitritonitro-tetramminecobalt(III) salt, a logical intermediate in the isomeric transformation. Neither were they able to synthesize the cis nitritonitro salt from the corresponding cis nitroaquo salt.

Basolo, Stone, Bergman, and Pearson[38c], however, report the existence of the analogous *cis* nitritonitro-bis (ethylenediamine) cobalt(III) compound, but state that it is relatively unstable and undergoes an intramolecular rearrangement to the stable cis dinitro compound. The nitritonitro isomer could be isolated only when stabilized by high concentrations of nitrite ion.

The strongest evidence for the existence of the two structural isomers comes from the work of Taube and Murmann (private communication), who studied the reaction

$$[Co(NH_3)_5O^*H]^{++} + HONO \rightarrow [Co(NH_3)_5O^*NO]^{++} + H_2O,$$

(where 0^* is oxygen enriched with O^{18}). Their results show all of the heavy oxygen isotope is retained in the nitritopentamminecobalt ion, indicating no rupture of the cobalt-oxygen bond in the transformation. When the pink nitrito salt was heated either in the solid state or in solution, the yellow nitro isomer was formed. This, when treated with excess NaOH to reform the hydroxypentammine cobalt salt, released all the heavy oxygen in the nitrite ion.

37. Shibata, *J. Coll. Sci. Imp. Univ. Tokyo*, **37**, 15 (1915).

38. Adell, *Svensk. Kem. Tid.*, **56**, 318 (1944); *Z. anorg. Chem.*, **252**, 272 (1944).

38b. Yalman and Kuwana, paper presented before Physical and Inorganic Division, American Chemical Society, Kansas City, April, 1954.

38c. Basolo, Stone, Bergman, and Pearson, *J. Am. Chem. Soc.*, **76**, 3079, 5920 (1954).

Aquopentamminecobalt salts gave the same results when treated with nitrite ion, as did diaquotetramminecobalt ion.

Tracer experiments further showed that in going from the nitrito to the nitro isomer, there was no oxygen exchange of the coordinated nitrite with the solvent water or with nitrite ions. After isomerization was completed there was no exchange of the nitro-oxygen with nitrite ion.

These results indicate that the isomerization must occur by an intra-molecular rearrangement in which the nitrite ion is never free and in which the oxygen first linked to the cobalt is completely transferred to the nitrogen : $Co\underset{N-O}{\overset{O}{<}}$.

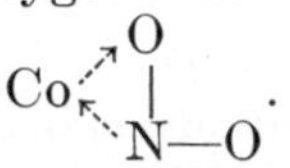

The dithiocyanatobis(ethylenediamine)cobalt(III) halides were reported by Werner to exist in two forms[39], one red and the other blue-red. These two forms were thought to differ in the manner in which the thiocyanate groups are linked to the central atom. However, Werner[40] later showed that in both forms the thiocyanate group is attached to the cobalt through the nitrogen and so concluded that these are *cis-trans*, rather than structural isomers.

Ray and Maulik[41] report isomerism associated with the compound $H_4[(CN)_5Co(S_2O_3)]$. These investigators suggested that it is possible that coordination takes place through oxygen in one case and through sulfur in the other, thus giving rise to structural isomerism. This suggestion is supported by the fact that the solid salts of the normal form are gold in color while those in which the thiosulfate ion is supposedly coordinated through a sulfur atom are brown.

OTHER TYPES OF ISOMERISM

Coordination Position Isomerism

Another type of isomerism is encountered in the polynuclear compounds. Werner[42] calls this "Coordination Position Isomerism"; it is illustrated by symmetrical dichlorohexammine-μ-diol-dicobalt(III) chloride

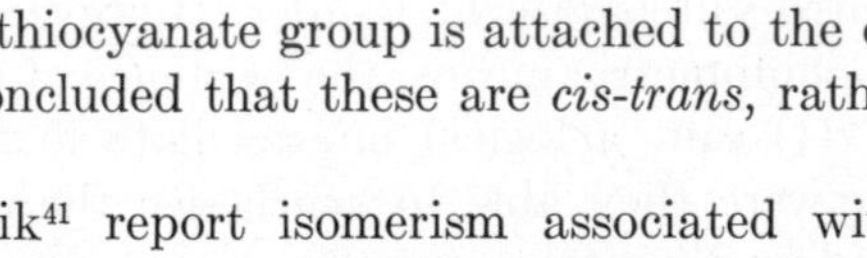

and the unsymmetrical

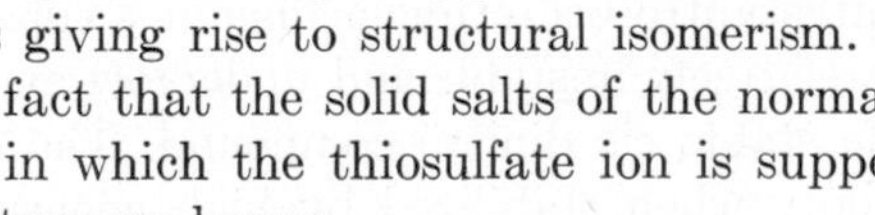

39. Werner and Braunlich, *Z. anorg. Chem.*, **22**, 127, 141 (1899).
40. Werner, *Ann.*, **386**, 22, 41, 192 (1912).
41. Ray and Maulik, *Z. anorg. Chem.*, **199**, 353 (1931).
42. Werner, *Ann.*, **375**, 7, 30, 32, 107, 111 (1910).

Werner[42] also studied salts containing the symmetrical and unsymmetrical forms of dichlorohexammine-μ-amino-peroxo-cobalt(III)-cobalt(IV) ions,

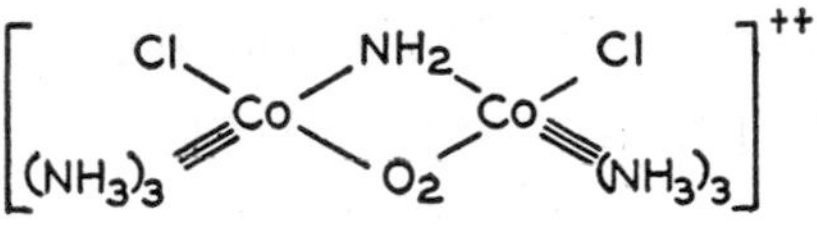

$$\left[\begin{array}{c} \text{Cl} \diagdown \quad \diagup \text{NH}_2 \diagdown \quad \diagup \text{Cl} \\ \text{(NH}_3)_3 {=\!\!=\!\!=} \text{Co} \qquad \text{Co} {=\!\!=\!\!=} \text{(NH}_3)_3 \\ \diagdown \text{O}_2 \diagup \end{array} \right]^{++} \quad \text{AND}$$

and

$$\left[\begin{array}{c} \text{Cl}_2 \diagdown \quad \diagup \text{NH}_2 \\ \text{(NH}_3)_2 {=\!\!=} \text{Co} \qquad \text{Co} {\equiv} \text{(NH}_3)_4 \\ \diagdown \text{O}_2 \diagup \end{array} \right]^{++}$$

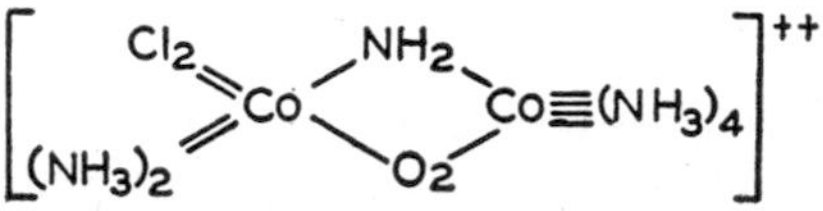

The first isomer forms gray-black salts which are difficulty soluble in water, while the second is green-brown in color and is easily soluble in water.

Jensen[43] described a second type of coordination position isomerism in the rhodo and erythrochromic complex ions. The two isomers differ in the nature of the bridge group connecting the two cobalt atoms. The rhodo and erythro complex ions are reported by Jensen to have the formulas,

$$[(\text{NH}_3)_5\text{CrOHCr(NH}_3)_5]^{5+} \quad \text{and} \quad \left[(\text{NH}_3)_5\text{CrNH}_2\text{Cr}^{\text{H}_2\text{O}}_{(\text{NH}_3)_4} \right]^{5+},$$

respectively. Recent work[44] indicates that these ions are not isomeric but that they have the formulas, rhodochromic,

$$[(\text{NH}_3)_5\text{CrOHCr(NH}_3)_5]^{5+}; \text{ erythrochromic, } \left[(\text{NH}_3)_5\text{CrOHCr}^{(\text{NH}_3)_4}_{\text{H}_2\text{O}} \right]^{5+},$$

Isomers Resulting from Isomerism of Ligands

Several types of isomerism met in organic chemistry are also found in the inorganic field. For example, Ablov[45] has studied the reaction of chloro-aniline with *trans*-dichlorobis(ethylenediamine)cobalt(III) chloride and found that the reaction involves only rearrangement to the cis form. However, under the proper conditions, it is entirely possible that chloroaniline could replace a coordinated chloride to give

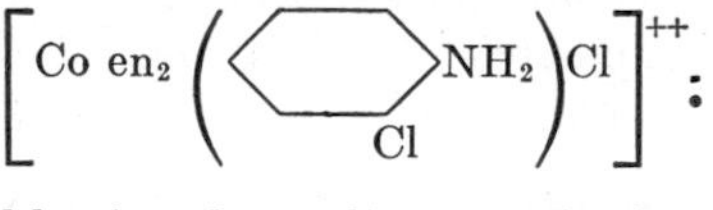

$$\left[\text{Co en}_2 \left(\bigcirc\text{-NH}_2 \right) \text{Cl} \right]^{++}:$$

Isomers of this ion could exist, depending on whether the chloroaniline were ortho, meta, or para. The action of toluidine on dichlorobis(ethylenedi-

43. Jensen, *Z. anorg. Chem.*, **232**, 257 (1937).
44. Wilmarth, Graff, Gustin, and Dharmatti, "The Structure and Properties of the Rhodo and Erythro Complex Compounds," preprint, Symposium, Division of Physical and Inorganic Chemistry, American Chemical Society, 1952.
45. Ablov, *Bull. soc. chim.* [5] **3**, 2270 (1936).

amine)cobalt(III) chloride has been reported to result in the compound, [Co en$_2$(CH$_3$C$_6$H$_4$NH$_2$)Cl]Cl$_2$,[46] which can exist in forms containing either ortho, meta, or para toluidine. Similarly, Kats[47] and Grünberg have reported dichlorobis(aminobenzoic acid)platinum(II),

$$[Pt(NH_2C_6H_4COOH)_2Cl_2],$$

in which *ortho*, *meta*, or *para*-aminobenzoic acid is present in the coordination sphere.

Ring Size Isomerism

The isomerism of the many diamines used as coordinating groups may lead to different types of isomerism in the coordination compounds formed. One of these is dependent on ring size. Tris(propylenediamine)cobalt(III) chloride and tris(trimethylenediamine)cobalt(III) chloride illustrate this phenomenon[48]. The trimethylenediamine compound is less stable, more soluble, and different in color from the propylenediamine complex.

Summation Isomerism

Another type of isomerism which might, for want of a better name, be called "summation isomerism" includes those instances in which entirely different groups are coordinated to the central atom, but the sum of all the atoms is constant. An example is to be found in the identical empirical formulas of the complex ions, dichloro(tetramethylenediamine) (ethylenediamine)cobalt(III) and dichlorobis(trimethylenediamine)cobalt(III). Although the following pairs of complexes have not actually been prepared, they serve to exemplify the type of isomerism under consideration:

$$[Co(NH_3)_4Cl(BrO_3)]^+, \quad [Co(NH_3)_4(ClO_3)Br]^+;$$

$$[Co(NH_3)_4(SO_3)(SCN)], \quad [Co(NH_3)_4(S_2O_3)(CN)];$$

$$[Co(NH_3)_4(ClO_3)(NO_3)]^+, \quad [Co(NH_3)_4(ClO_4)(NO_2)]^+.$$

Electronic Isomerism

The cations of nitrosylpentamminecobalt salts[49] may be obtained in two forms which are strikingly different in their physical and chemical properties, though their stoichiometries and structural formulas are identical, [Co(NH$_3$)$_5$NO]$^{++}$.[50] The chloride of one series is black and paramagnetic

46. Bailar and Clapp, *J. Am. Chem. Soc.*, **67**, 171 (1945).
47. Kats and Grünberg, *Zhur. Obshchei Khim.*, **20**, 248 (1950).
48. Bailar and Work, *J. Am. Chem. Soc.*, **68**, 232 (1946).
49. Moeller, *J. Chem. Ed.*, **23**, 542 (1946).
50. Sand and Genssler, *Ber.*, **36**, 2083 (1903); Werner and Karrer, *Helv. chim. acta.*, **1**, 54 (1918); Milward, Wardlaw, and Way, *J. Chem. Soc.*, **1938**, 233; Ghosh and Ray, *J. Indian Chem. Soc.*, **20**, 409 (1943).

while the corresponding salt of the second series is pink and dia-magnetic[50c, 50d, 51]. It is believed that dipositive cobalt and neutral nitro-gen(II) oxide are present in the black salt and that tripositive cobalt and NO^- ions are present in the pink complex[50, 51a].

51. Frazer and Long, *J. Chem. Phys.*, **6**, 462 (1938); Mellor and Craig, *J. Proc. Roy. Soc.*, *N.S. Wales*, **78**, 25 (1944); Ray and Bhar, *J. Indian Chem. Soc.*, **5**, 497 (1928).

8. Stereoisomerism of Hexacovalent Atoms

Fred Basolo

Northwestern University, Evanston, Illinois

INTRODUCTION

Werner's Coordination Theory

Shortly after Tassaert[1] discovered the compound $CoCl_3 \cdot 6NH_3$, it was noticed that some of the complex compounds with the same chemical composition had very markedly different properties. It was known, for instance, that $CoCl_3 \cdot 4NH_3$ could exist as a dark purple or a bright green crystalline salt. In terms of the structure of the molecule, this implies that the two forms differ in the arrangement of the atoms in the molecule. Numerous theories (Chapter 2) were proposed in an attempt to explain the experimental facts; at the turn of the century there were three popular theories. Jorgensen[2] modified the chain theory of Blomstrand[3] and represented what we now call the cis and trans isomers of [Co en₂ Cl₂]Cl as shown in Fig. 8.1. Friend[4] designated the structures by means of a "shell"

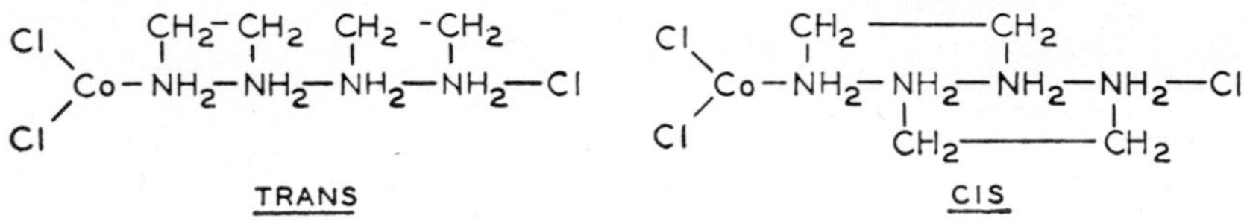

FIG. 8.1

surrounding the central atom (Fig. 8.2). In his coordination theory, Werner

1. Tassaert, *Ann. chim. phys.*, **28**, 92 (1798).
2. Jorgensen, *Z. anorg. Chem.*, **5**, 147 (1894).
3. Blomstrand, *Ber.*, **4**, 40 (1871).
4. Friend, *Trans. Chem. Soc.*, **93**, 260 (1908).

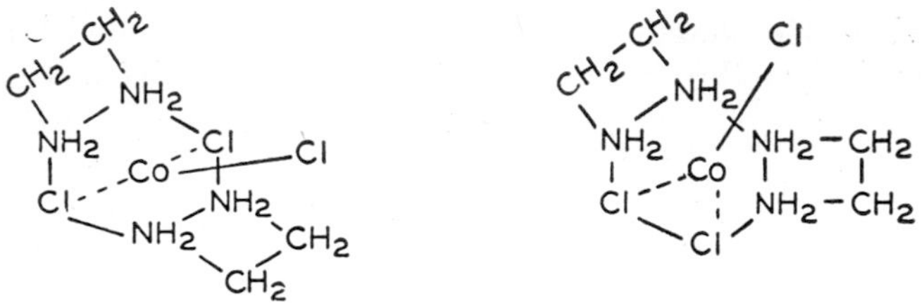

TRANS   CIS

FIG. 8.2

postulated that there must be, in addition to the primary valence bond, a secondary valence bond. Unlike Friend, he said the coordination groups are connected to the metal and not to each other (Fig. 8.3).

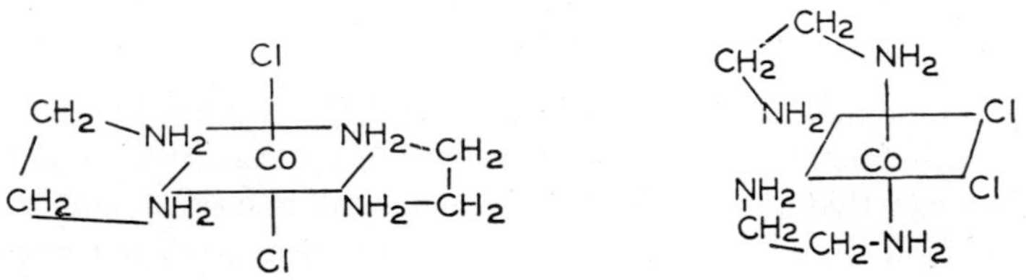

TRANS   CIS

FIG. 8.3

Werner predicted that *cis*-[Co en$_2$ Cl$_2$]Cl would be found to be optically active; this could be accounted for on the basis of the octahedral structure which he proposed. Jorgensen mentioned, however, that his structure likewise permitted a symmetrical trans form and an asymmetrical cis form. After the accumulation of more experimental data, Werner was able to convince his contemporaries that the structure he had proposed was correct. Of course, with the present-day knowledge of atomic structure, the configuration proposed by Jorgensen can be ruled out immediately, since it involves five covalent bonds attached to one nitrogen atom.

Proof of Octahedral Structure of Hexacovalent Elements

Three of the more symmetrical arrangements of six equivalent groups about a common center are: (a) plane hexagonal, (b) trigonal prismatic and (c) octahedral (Fig. 8.4). If these groups differ in composition they can be arranged in different ways depending on the structure or spatial arrangement of the system. The number of possible arrangements, or of stereoisomers, will suggest the geometric configuration involved. Each of the three models under consideration allows only one possible form for the compound [Ma$_5$b]; for the compound [Ma$_4$b$_2$], (A) and (B) lead to three isomers while (C) allows only two forms; for the compound [Ma₃b₃], (A) and (B) again give three forms while (C) gives only two isomers.

STEREOISOMERS THEORETICALLY POSSIBLE

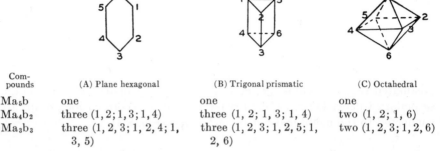

Com- pounds	(A) Plane hexagonal	(B) Trigonal prismatic	(C) Octahedral
Ma₅b	one	one	one
Ma₄b₂	three (1, 2; 1, 3; 1, 4)	three (1, 2; 1, 3; 1, 4)	two (1, 2; 1, 6)
Ma₃b₃	three (1, 2, 3; 1, 2, 4; 1, 3, 5)	three (1, 2, 3; 1, 2, 5; 1, 2, 6)	two (1, 2, 3; 1, 2, 6)

Fig. 8.4

Many compounds of the types [Ma₄b₂] and [Ma₃b₃] have been prepared and in no case has it been possible to isolate more than two isomers. This would indicate that the octahedral arrangement is correct, but it should be remembered that failure to isolate a third form does not necessarily prove its nonexistence.

Much more conclusive evidence on the spatial arrangement of the groups can be obtained by considering the symmetry of the entire complex. If it is assumed that bidentate groups span only adjacent positions, then the compound [M(AA)₃] may exist in one form if the structure is plane hexagonal and two forms if it is either trigonal prismatic or octahedral (Fig. 8.5). The trigonal prismatic arrangement yields two geometrical isomers,

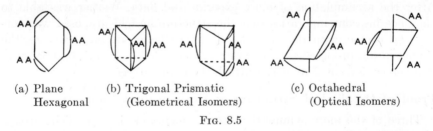

| (a) Plane Hexagonal | (b) Trigonal Prismatic (Geometrical Isomers) | (c) Octahedral (Optical Isomers) |

Fig. 8.5

each of which has a plane of symmetry, but an asymmetric molecule results if the arrangement is octahedral. Werner[5] prepared the purely inorganic compound [Co(AA)₃]⁶⁺, in which AA = $\left((NH_3)_4Co \begin{array}{c} OH \\ \\ OH \end{array} \right)^+$, and

5. Werner, *Ber.*, **47**, 3087 (1914).

resolved it by means of the dextro-α-bromocamphor-π-sulfonate into dextro and levo forms (see page 323). This proved conclusively the octahedral structure of hexacovalent cobalt(III) and it is now realized that, almost without exception, this is the correct structure for compounds containing atoms which are hexacovalent.

The Stereochemistry of Inorganic Complex Compounds Compared to That of Organic Compounds

The octahedral configuration of hexacovalent metals is now as generally accepted as the tetrahedral configuration of carbon. It presents many more possibilities for isomerism and intramolecular rearrangement than does the tetrahedral configuration of carbon. There are numerous questions which have not yet been answered, largely because the syntheses for these complex compounds are often based on empirical knowledge alone and it is frequently impossible to make a molecule of known configuration. The number of possible isomers becomes extremely large as the degree of complexity of the molecule increases; a compound of the type [Mabcdef] may exist in thirty different forms (fifteen pairs of mirror images). It is not surprising, therefore, that very little is known of compounds more complex than [M(AA)a_2b_2].

Geometrical Isomerism (cis-trans Isomerism)

The octahedral structure of hexacovalent atoms was first indicated by the fact that only two stereoisomers could be isolated for compounds of the types [Ma$_4$b$_2$] and [Ma$_3$b$_3$]. On the basis of this structure, the number of position isomers theoretically possible for any complex can be easily determined; in some cases all of the predicted isomers have been isolated, but many instances are known in which only the most stable form has been obtained.

Chelating Molecules Occupy cis-Positions

The principle that chelating groups span adjacent cis and not remote trans valence bonds of the central atom has been widely used to determine the configuration of complex compounds and to prepare compounds of known configuration. This principle was derived by comparing chelate ring formation with the formation of maleic, but not fumaric anhydride, and from the similarity of metal and carbon atoms in forming five- and six-membered rings more readily than those containing larger numbers of atoms.[6] Tress[7] points out that this principle can also be deduced from the isomerism of certain types of complex compounds. In the complex [M(AA)$_2$b$_2$], if the chelating group spans only cis positions the compound

6. Werner, *Ber.*, **40**, 61 (1907).
7. Tress, Chemistry & Industry, **1938**, 1234.

can exist in a racemic mixture and one inactive trans form; however, if it spans trans positions, only a racemate is possible (Fig. 8.6). A point which

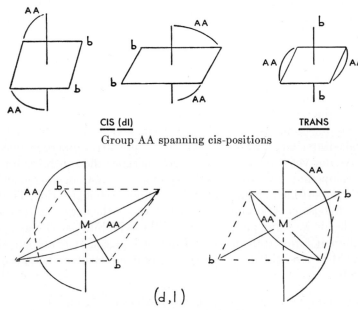

CIS (dl)   TRANS

Group AA spanning cis-positions

(d,l)

Group AA spanning trans-positions

Fɪɢ. 8.6

was not mentioned by Tress is that this assumes the trans spanning groups are not free to rotate around the corners. If this rotation were possible then only one optically inactive form would exist. Numerous compounds of this type, which exist in racemic and inactive forms, are known. In addition, several compounds of the type [M(AA)a$_2$b$_2$] have been resolved into their optically active antipodes. Optical activity can exist in these compounds only if the chelate ring spans cis positions; (Fig. 8.7).

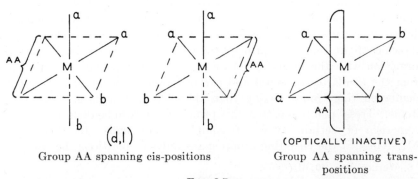

(d,l)   (OPTICALLY INACTIVE)

Group AA spanning cis-positions   Group AA spanning trans-positions

Fɪɢ. 8.7

Although it is generally agreed that chelating groups such as ethylenediamine are sterically incapable of spanning trans positions in the coordination sphere of a metal, there is no reason to suppose that a chelating group of sufficient size cannot do so under the proper conditions. However, except for recent work by Pfeiffer[8], all attempts to prepare simple chelate rings of seven or more members have given inconclusive or negative results (Chapter 6). A new approach has been studied[9] using 2-chloro-1,6-diammine-3,4,5-diethylenetriamineplatinum(IV) chloride (see page 259).

Various Types of Cis-trans Isomers

Cationic Complex Compounds. The method of preparation of both the cis and trans isomers of a complex depends upon the compound in question and no general rules for the preparation of these isomers can be laid down. It must also be remembered that molecular rearrangements are common in reactions of coordination compounds and that the expected isomer may not always be the one isolated. The fact that bidentate groups span cis positions suggests the possibility of preparing a cis salt by the displacement of groups occupying cis positions. This technique has been employed.

A very common starting material for the preparation of diacidotetramminecobalt(III) complexes is carbonatotetramminecobalt(III) nitrate[10]. The carbonate radical is coordinated firmly to the cobalt as is illustrated by the fact that it does not precipitate upon the addition of barium chloride. However, it does liberate carbon dioxide when acid is added (Fig. 8.8).

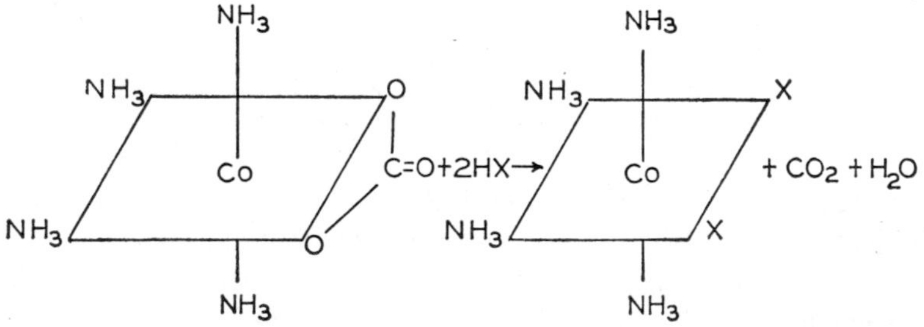

FIG. 8.8

Assuming that no rearrangement takes place during this reaction, one can expect to obtain the corresponding *cis*-diacido compound. Rearrangement to the trans salt can be kept at a minimum, if the solid complex is allowed to react with an alcoholic solution of the desired acid.

8. Pfeiffer, Böhn, and Schmitz, *Naturwissenschaften*, **35**, 190 (1948).
9. Mattern, thesis, University of Illinois, 1947.
10. Biltz and Biltz, "Laboratory Methods of Inorganic Chemistry," translated by Hall and Blanchard, p. 171., New York, John Wiley & Sons, Inc., 1909.

The procedure described above is adaptable to the preparation of *cis*-[Co(NH₃)₄(NO₂)₂]⁺, which is yellow-brown. The orange-yellow isomeric ion, *trans*-[Co(NH₃)₄(NO₂)₂]⁺, is readily obtained by the oxidation of cobalt(II) chloride 6-hydrate in the presence of ammonium chloride, ammonia and sodium nitrite[11]. These stereoisomers react differently with concentrated hydrochloric acid; the cis salt dissolves completely in the boiling acid, forming the green, crystalline *trans*-[Co(NH₃)₄Cl₂]Cl, whereas the trans salt forms a red precipitate of *trans*-[Co(NH₃)₄NO₂Cl]Cl.

The analogous compound containing ethylenediamine has been thoroughly studied by Werner[12] and his findings are illustrated by means of a flow sheet (Fig. 8.9).

$$Co\ en_2\ (NO_2)_2]^+$$

concentrated HNO₃

$$[Co\ en_2\ (NO_3)_2]^+$$

H₂O

$$[Co\ en_2\ (H_2O)_2]^{+++} \xrightarrow{KOH} [Co\ en_2\ (H_2O)OH]^{++} \xrightarrow{dilute\ HNO_3} [Co\ en_2\ (H_2O)_2]^{+++}$$

NaNO₂ + HC₂H₃O₂ · NaNO₂ HC₂H₃O₂

$$*[Co\ en_2\ (ONO)_2]^+ \qquad\qquad\qquad\qquad\qquad *[Co\ en_2\ (ONO)_2]^+$$

stand (warm) · stand (warm)

$$[Co\ en_2\ (NO_2)_2]^+ \qquad\qquad\qquad\qquad\qquad [Co\ en_2\ (NO_2)_2]^+$$

Cis-Series   *Trans*-Series

FIG. 8.9

* Recently, some conflicting reports have appeared in the literature with regard to the actual existence of nitrito complexes (page 268).

Although the cis isomer can sometimes be obtained by the displacement of a bidentate group, the procedures employed to produce the trans isomer are almost entirely empirical. There is some reason to believe, however, that when a planar tetracovalent compound changes to an octahedral structure, the two groups added occupy trans positions[13]. This procedure

11. Biltz and Biltz, *ibid.*, p. 178.
12. Werner, *Ber.*, **44**, 2445 (1911).
13. Werner, "New Ideas on Inorganic Chemistry," translated by Hedley, p. 261, London, Longmans, Green and Co., 1911; Jorgensen, *Z. anorg. Chem.*, **25**, 353 (1900).
14. Basolo, Bailar, and Tarr, *J. Am. Chem. Soc.*, **72**, 2433 (1950); Heneghan and Bailar, *J. Am. Chem. Soc.*, **75**, 1840 (1953)

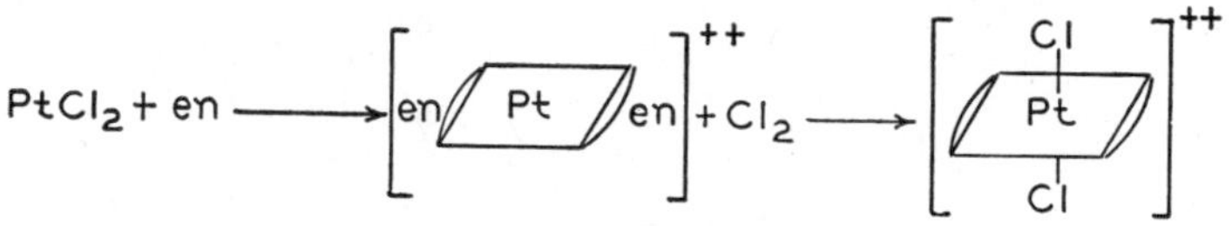

FIG. 8.10

was recently applied[14] in the preparation of *trans*-dichlorobis(ethylene-diamine)platinum(IV) chloride (Fig. 8.10).

Anionic Complex Compounds. There are fewer examples of cis-trans isomerism in anionic complexes and these have not been studied as extensively as the corresponding cationic compounds. The ion[15] $[Co(NH_3)_2(NO_2)_4]^-$ should exist in cis and trans forms, but only one isomer is known and there are conflicting reports as to its structure (page 292).

Delépine[16] has shown that potassium hexachloroiridate(III), $K_3[IrCl_6]$, and potassium oxalate react to form potassium *cis*-dichlorobis(oxalato)iridate(III), $K_3[Ir(C_2O_4)_2Cl_2]$. The cis configuration of this complex was established by its resolution, using strychnine. Prolonged boiling of a solution of the potassium salt yielded the corresponding trans isomer. The complex, $K[Ir\ py_2\ (C_2O_4)_2]$, (and its rhodium(III) analog[17]) was prepared by various methods and in every case the trans salt was isolated.

Ammonium disulfitotetramminecobaltate(III), $NH_4[Co(NH_3)_4(SO_3)_2]$, was first prepared[18] by the reaction of carbonatotetramminecobalt(III) chloride and ammonium sulfite. The cis configuration was assigned to this salt[19] on the basis of the fact that ethylenediamine replaces two of the ammonia molecules much more readily than the other two. If the sulfite groups are trans to each other, the four ammonia molecules are equivalent, and all of them would be replaced by ethylenediamine with equal ease. However, if the sulfite groups are cis to each other, the introduction of ethylenediamine may follow either of two paths; the path which allows the replacement of only two ammonia molecules would be expected because, according to the principle of trans elimination, the two ammonia molecules which are trans to the negative sulfite groups should be labilized (Fig. 8.11).

15. Erdmann, *J. prakt. Chem.*, **97**, 385 (1866); Biltz and Biltz, "Laboratory Methods of Inorganic Chemistry," translated by Hall and Blanchard, p. 150, New York, John Wiley & Sons, Inc., 1909.
16. Delépine, *Ann. chim.*, **19**, 149 (1923).
17. Delépine, *Anales, Soc. Espanola Fis. y Quim*, **27**, 485 (1929).
18. Hofmann and Jenny, *Ber.*, **34**, 3855 (1901).
19. Klement, *Z. anorg. allgem. Chem.*, **150**, 117 (1925); Bailar and Peppard, *J. Am. Chem. Soc.*, **62**, 105 (1940).

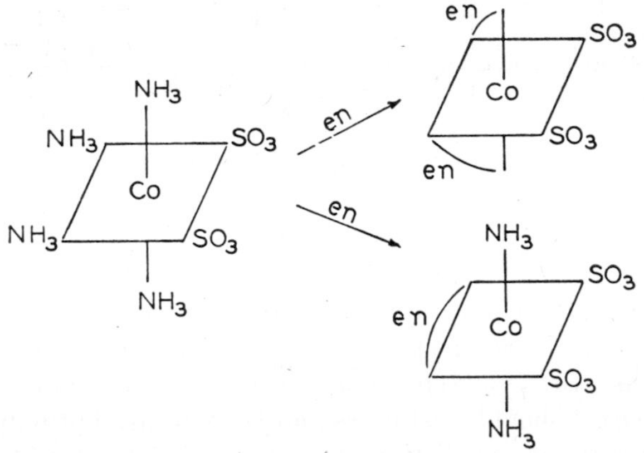

FIG. 8.11

Nonionic Complex Compounds. Complex compounds in which the charge on the central atom is neutralized by the coordinating groups are nonionic. Compounds of this type are usually capable of existing in stereoisomeric modifications, and, in some cases both isomers have been obtained. However, satisfactory proofs of their structures have not been possible. Much of the difficulty encountered results from the fact that suitable solvents are not known for some of these substances.

A very strong argument against the Blomstrand-Jorgensen chain theory and in favor of Werner's coordination theory was the fact that $[Co(NH_3)_3Cl_3]$ did not give a silver chloride precipitate readily. Werner interpreted this to mean that all of the chlorine was held firmly by the central metal atom. The analogous nitro compound[20], $[Co(NH_3)_3(NO_2)_3]$, is believed to have the trans, $(1,2,6)$ configuration. Duval[21] has prepared $[Co(NH_3)_3(NO_2)_3]$ by five different methods and the five products showed identical absorption spectra and similar electrical conductivities, but the x-ray diagrams of some of the powders differed slightly. It was concluded that this evidence was insufficient to establish the existence of different geometric structures for any of the five products. On the other hand, Sueda[22] claims to have prepared cis, $(1,2,3)$-$[Co(NH_3)_3(NO_2)_3]$ by starting with cis-$[Co(NH_3)_3(H_2O)_3]^{+++}$[22, 23, 24].

20. Biltz and Biltz, "Laboratory Methods of Inorganic Chemistry," translated by Hall and Blanchard, p. 182, New York, John Wiley & Sons, Inc., 1909.
21. Duval, *Compt. rend.*, **206**, 1652 (1938).
22. Sueda, *Bull. Chem. Soc., Japan*, **13**, 450 (1938).
23. Matsuno, *J. Coll. Sci. Imp. Univ. Tokyo*, **41**, 10 (1921).
24. Sueda, *Bull. Chem. Soc., Japan*, **12**, 188 (1937).

The nonelectrolyte complexes do not necessarily have to contain equal numbers of neutral groups and anions [Ma_3b_3], but may also be of the type [Ma_4b_2]. This particular type is realized with hexacovalent metals having oxidation states of two or four. A good example is shown by cis and trans isomers of [$Pt(NH_3)_2Cl_4$], which may be obtained by the oxidation of the corresponding dichlorodiammine platinum(II) compounds[13]; this also illustrates that the two groups added to the planar tetracovalent compound occupy trans positions in the resulting octahedron (Fig. 8.12).

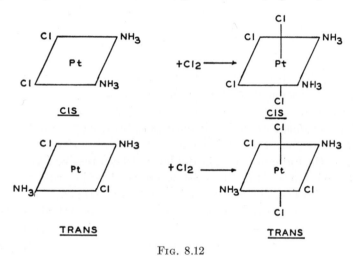

Fɪɢ. 8.12

Still another type of nonelectrolyte complex is possible if the neutral group and acid radical are united in the same molecule, as is the case in the amino acid, glycine, NH_2CH_2COOH. These are termed *inner complexes* and are important in analytical chemistry and mordant dyeing. Cobalt(III) oxide reacts with a solution of glycine to form a mixture of two compounds, both of which have the composition [$Co(NH_2CH_2COO)_3$], and which can be separated because of a slight difference in their solubilities[25]. They are extremely stable and may be dissolved without change in concentrated sulfuric acid; their aqueous solutions have practically no electrical conductivity; cryoscopic measurements show that they are undissociated in solution. They are believed to represent geometrical isomers in which all of the same groups (—NH_2 or —$CO\bar{O}$) of the glycine molecules occupy adjacent positions, or in which two of these are opposite to each other (Fig. 8.13).

25. Ley and Winkler, *Ber.*, **42**, 3894 (1909).

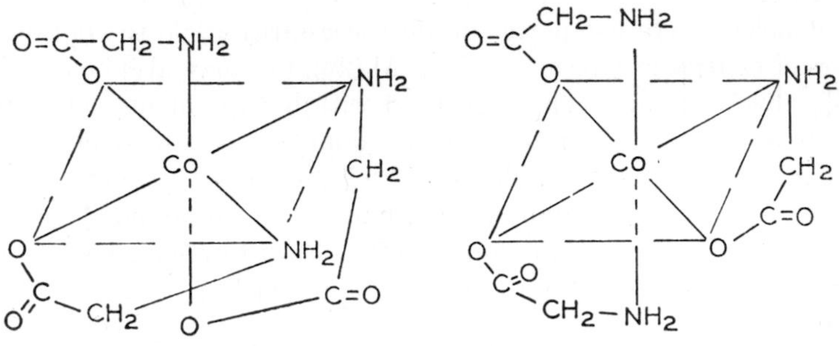
O=C—CH2—NH2
O
NH2
Co
CH2
O
NH2
C
O
CH2
O
C=O
CIS OR 1,2,3
CH2—NH2
O=C
O
NH2
Co
CH2
C=O
O
O
C=O
CH2—NH2
TRANS OR 1,2,6

Fig. 8.13

The absorption spectra suggest that the more soluble form is the trans isomer[26]. Examination of the diagrams will reveal that in neither case does the compound possess a plane of symmetry, so there exists the possibility of mirror image isomerism in each case, bringing the total number of stereoisomers to four. Since this compound is a nonelectrolyte it does not lend itself to the formation of salts and has not been resolved. Evidence has been obtained, however, for the existence of the four isomers of the analogous complex formed between *d*-alanine and cobalt(III)[27].

Complex Compounds Containing Unsymmetrical Bidentate Donor Molecules. The same type of isomerism which has just been discussed can also be realized when only one or two unsymmetrical molecules are introduced into the coordination sphere of a complex. The compound $[Co(DMG)_2\ NH_3Cl]$ has been resolved (page 313) by Tsuchida, Koboyaski, and Nakamura[28]. They said this means the ammonia and chloro groups occupied cis positions. If this is true, the two molecules of dimethylglyoxime are in different planes, which is contrary to the structure of analogous compounds of the types $[Co(DMG)_2A_2]X$ and $[Co(DMG)_2X_2]^-$ [29]. A more recent study of the ultraviolet absorption spectrum of this complex indicates that the negative portions of the dimethylglyoxime ions,

26. Kuroya and Tsuchida, *Bull. Chem. Soc., Japan*, **15**, 429 (1940); Basolo, Ballhausen, and Bjerrum, *Acta. Chem. Scand.*, **9**, 810 (1955).
27. Lifschitz, *Z. physik. Chem.*, **114**, 485 (1925).
28. Tsuchida, Kobayoski and Nakamura, *Bull. Chem. Soc., Japan*, **11**, 38 (1936).
29. Nakatsuka, *Bull. Chem. Soc., Japan*, **11**, 48 (1936); Thilo and Heilborn, *Ber.*, **64**, 1441 (1931).

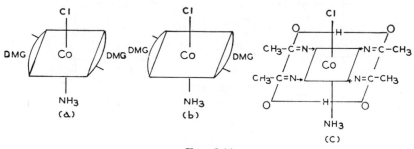

occupy trans positions (page 295). It is therefore suggested by Tsuchida and Koboyashi[30] that the dimethylgloximes may be in the same plane and the optical activity of the compound [Co(DMG)$_2$NH$_3$Cl] is caused by the unsymmetrical oximes (Fig. 8.14). No case of optical isomerism of this type has been definitely established. Furthermore, there is reason to believe that hydrogen bonding would occur[31] and that the trans complex is not optically active as represented in Fig. 8.14(a and b) but is instead symmetrical, as shown in Fig. 8.14c.

Fig. 8.14

A very striking example of isomerism resulting from the coordination of an unsymmetrical molecule has been clearly demonstrated with the compound dinitro(ethylenediamine)(propylenediamine)cobalt(III) bromide[32]. Since propylenediamine, NH$_2$(CH$_3$)CHCH$_2$NH$_2$, is not symmetrical, the methyl group (represented in Fig. 8.15 by the symbol) can be placed in the cis complex ions either near to the plane of the two nitro groups, or far from this plane.

30. Tsuchida, and Kobayoski, *Bull. Chem. Soc., Japan,* **12,** 83 (1937).
31. Rundle and Parasol, *J. Chem. Phys.,* **20,** 1489 (1952).
32. Werner and Smirnoff, *Helv. chim. Acta.,* **1,** 5 (1918).

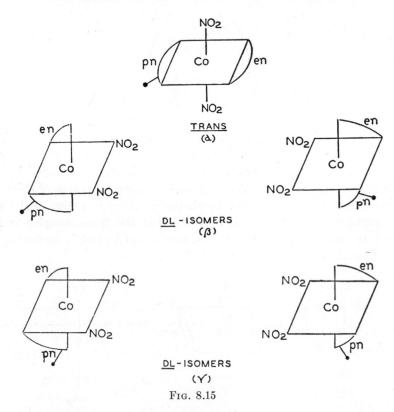

FIG. 8.15

These geometrical isomers will be distinguished as α, β, and γ compounds. In addition to being unsymmetrical, propylenediamine contains an asymmetric carbon atom and may exist in both the dextro and levo modifications; therefore, the total number of isomers possible is twice that shown in Fig. 8.15.

$$(\alpha)\ \begin{cases} [d\text{-pn}] \\ [l\text{-pn}] \end{cases} \qquad (\beta)\ \begin{cases} [d\text{-pn}]_D \\ [l\text{-pn}]_D \\ [d\text{-pn}]_L \\ [l\text{-pn}]_L \end{cases} \qquad (\gamma)\ \begin{cases} [d\text{-pn}]_D \\ [l\text{-pn}]_D \\ [d\text{-pn}]_L \\ [l\text{-pn}]_L \end{cases}$$

All of the predicted isomers were isolated.

Complex Compounds Containing Polydentate Donor Molecules. The most extensively studied chelate groups attached to a central atom are bidentate, but compounds are known which can fill three (tridentate), four (tetradentate), five (pentadentate) or six (hexadentate) positions in the coordination shell. The presence of six functional groups in the ethylenediaminetetraacetic acid (EDTA) molecule first provided the possibility of forming compounds in which a substance acts as a hexadentate chelating agent. The salts of the complex ions formed by this substance are usually hydrated; however, Brintzinger, Thiele and Müller[33] prepared anhydrous Na[Co(EDTA)] by drying the 4-hydrate at 150°. Schwarzenbach[34] prepared the anhydrous salt [Co en$_2$ Cl$_2$][Co(EDTA)]. Complex ions containing pentadentate ethylenediaminetetracetic acid have also been prepared. Schwarzenbach reports several salts of the ions [Co(HY)Br]$^-$ and [Co(HY)NO$_2$]$^-$ (Y represents the EDTA^{4-} ion). The pK of the free carboxyl group is approximately 3 in both cases. The infrared studies of Busch and Bailar confirm the hypothesis that EDTA may behave as either a pentadentate or hexadentate donor[35]. The hexadentate Co(III) complex has been resolved into optical isomers[35, 36]. Recently, Dwyer and Lions[37] have reported a cobalt(III) complex cation containing a new hexadentate chelate (Fig. 8.16); they report[37b] the extremely high molecular rotation for this compound of over 50,000° at the mercury green line (5461Å.). Models

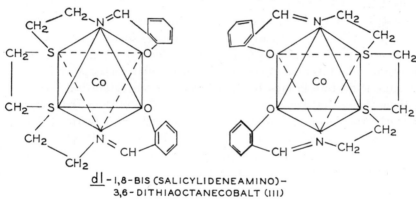

<u>dl</u> - 1,8-BIS (SALICYLIDENEAMINO)-
3,6- DITHIAOCTANECOBALT (III)

FIG. 8.16

show that this compound can exist in only one strainless geometrical form in which the nitrogen atoms are in trans positions and the sulfur atoms and oxygen atoms are in cis positions to each other. The resulting compound is asymmetric and the two enantiomorphs of the cobalt(III) complex were isolated. These investigators[38] have successfully extended the group of hexadentate compounds to several analogs of 1,8 bis-(salicylideneamino) 3,6 dithiaoctane cobalt(III). Dwyer and his co-workers[37b, 39] have continued

33. Brintzinger, Thiele, and Müller, Z. anorg. allgem. Chem., **251**, 285 (1943).
34. Schwarzenbach, Helv. chim. Acta, **32**, 839 (1949).
35. Busch and Bailar, J. Am. Chem. Soc., **75**, 4574 (1953).
36. Dwyer, Gyarfas, and Mellor, J. Phys. Chem., **59**, 296 (1955).
37. Dwyer and Lions, J. Am. Chem. Soc., **69**, 2917 (1947); **72**, 1545 (1950).
38. Dwyer and Gyarfas, J. Proc. Roy. Soc. N. S. Wales, **83**, 170 (1949).
39. Dwyer, Lions and Mellor, J. Am. Chem. Soc., **72**, 5037 (1950). Dwyer, Gill, Gyarfas and Lions, ibid., **74**, 4188 (1952). Collins, Dwyer, and Lions, ibid., **74,** 3134 (1952). Dwyer, Gill, Gyarfas and Lions, J. Am. Chem. Soc., **75**, 1526, 2443 (1953).

their investigations of these hexadentate chelate compounds utilizing different central metal atoms and different ligands. Other hexadentate chelates were prepared in which one and then both of the sulfur atoms in some of the above ligands were replaced by oxygen atoms[39b]. The authors also reported a resolution of the cobalt(III) complex containing the hexadentate chelate in which one sulfur was replaced by an oxygen atom. Magnetic studies[39a] supported their conclusions that the central atom is octahedral in configuration and that the bonds are of the hybridized d^2sp^3 type.

Tridentate groups, such as tripyridyl[41b] and α,β,γ-triamino propane[41c], form very stable compounds with hexacovalent metals of the types [M(tripy)$_2$] and [M{NH$_2$CH$_2$CH(NH$_2$)CH$_2$NH$_2$}$_2$], respectively. It is believed that in some of these compounds the coordinated group is attached in the 1,2,6 positions along an edge of the octahedron and not solely in the 1,2,3 positions bounding an octahedral face. That this is probably correct is indicated by the ease with which these tridentate groups fill three coordination positions in the planar tetracovalent complex, [Pt tripy Cl] Cl. This cannot be taken as conclusive evidence and certainly it is possible for some tridentate groups to be attached on an octahedral face as well as along the central plane of an octahedron. Models show that complexes in which triaminopropane is tridentate should have only the 1,2,3 configuration. Diethylenetriamine, NH$_2$CH$_2$CH$_2$NHCH$_2$CH$_2$NH$_2$, is also known to behave as a tridentate donor molecule[40] and should be capable of forming three geometrical isomers with a hexacovalent atom (Fig. 8.17).

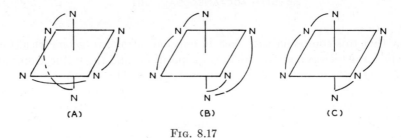

(A)   (B)   (C)

Fig. 8.17

The two 1,2,3 isomers, (B) and (C) would form optical isomers. Only one isomer of this type has been isolated and its configuration has not been definitely established.

Tetradentate donors are known to be possible and, recently, numerous

40. Mann, *J. Chem. Soc.*, **1934**, 466; **1930**, 1745.

coordination compounds of this type have been prepared[41]. Mann used β,β',β''-triaminotriethylamine and obtained *cis*-[Co trin (NCS)$_2$]NCS. Because of the structure of this amine, the corresponding trans salt does not exist. Morgan and Burstall investigated 2,2',2'',2'''-tetrapyridyl and reported it to yield *trans*-[Co tetrpy Cl$_2$]Cl. The salt had the characteristic green color of *trans*-dichlorotetraminecobalt(III) cations (p. 294).

Basolo[41e] has isolated coordination compounds of cobalt(III) with triethylenetetramine, NH$_2$CH$_2$CH$_2$NHCH$_2$CH$_2$NHCH$_2$CH$_2$NH$_2$, behaving as a tetradentate group. The complex [Co trien Cl$_2$]Cl was isolated; theoretically, it can exist in three geometrical forms (Fig. 8.18): one isomer in which the chloro groups occupy trans positions, and two isomers, both optically active, with the chloro groups adjacent to each other. Only one isomer was obtained and the cis configuration of this salt was established.

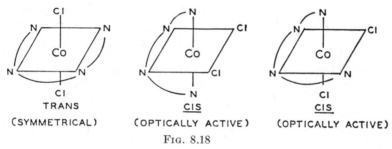

TRANS   CIS   CIS
(SYMMETRICAL)   (OPTICALLY ACTIVE)   (OPTICALLY ACTIVE)
FIG. 8.18

Since *cis-trans* rearrangements are known to occur readily in cobalt complexes, it may be that such a change in configuration always resulted in favor of a more stable cis modification. However, the fact that geometrical isomers are possible for coordination compounds containing certain polydentate groups has been demonstrated[39d].

Polynuclear Complex Compounds. Numerous polynuclear complexes of hexacovalent elements have been isolated and properly identified. The majority of these compounds are binuclear and result from the fact that some groups are capable of donating two pairs of electrons and, in so doing, can form a *bridge* between two metal atoms. A consideration of the octahedral structure reveals that this bridge can be formed in three different ways: (1) one donor group joining two corners of the octahedron, (2) two donor groups occupying one edge of each octahedron or (3) three donor groups occupying one face of each octahedron (Fig. 8.19).

41. Bailes and Calvin, *J. Am. Chem. Soc.*, **69**, 1886 (1947); Morgan and Burstall, *J. Chem. Soc.*, **1934**, 1498; Pope and Mann, *ibid.*, **1926**, 2675, 2681; *ibid.*, **1927**, 1224; Basolo, *J. Am. Chem. Soc.*, **70**, 2634 (1948); Morgan and Burstall, *J. Chem. Soc.*, **1938**, 1672; Mann, *J. Chem. Soc.*, **1929**, 409.

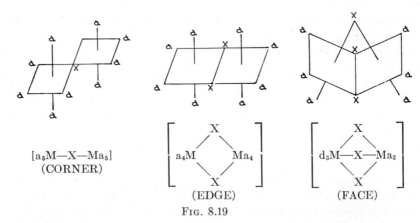

[a₅M—X—Ma₅] $\left[\; a_4M \begin{smallmatrix} X \\ \diagup\;\diagdown \\ \diagdown\;\diagup \\ X \end{smallmatrix} Ma_4 \;\right]$ $\left[\; d_3M—X—Ma_3 \;\right]$

(CORNER)   (EDGE)   (FACE)

$$[a_5M\!-\!X\!-\!Ma_5]\quad \left[\,a_4M\ \substack{X\\\diagup\diagdown\\\diagdown\diagup\\X}\ Ma_4\right]\quad \left[\,d_3M\!-\!X\!-\!Ma_3\right]$$

Fig. 8.19

The number of possible geometrical isomers of these polynuclear hexa-covalent complex compounds is extremely large. Even the very simplest compounds of the types [ba₄M—X—Ma₄b] and [ba₃M $\begin{smallmatrix}X\\\diagup\;\diagdown\\\diagdown\;\diagup\\X\end{smallmatrix}$ Ma₃b] may exist in three and five different geometric forms, respectively (Fig. 8.20). One of the latter (E and F) is optically active.

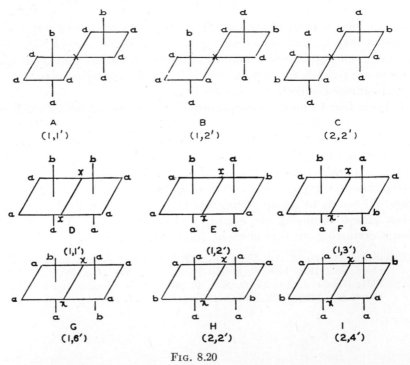

Fig. 8.20

The rather involved stereochemistry of the polynuclear cobalt(III) and chromium(III) ammines was investigated extensively by Werner[42]. His study was undertaken for the purpose of preparing mononuclear compounds of known structure and to "establish" the configuration of mononuclear complexes.

Determination of Configuration

Chemical Methods. *Bidentate Group.* The most commonly used method of determining configurations depends on the fact that bifunctional groups can span only coordination positions which are adjacent to each other. Hence, provided that no rearrangement of configuration occurs during the reaction, the isomer which is capable of combining with one mole of a chelate group, or which is formed whenever such a group is displaced, must belong to the cis series. The application of this type of reasoning to the geometrical isomers of $[Co(NH_3)_4Cl_2]Cl$ is summarized in Fig. 8.21. The

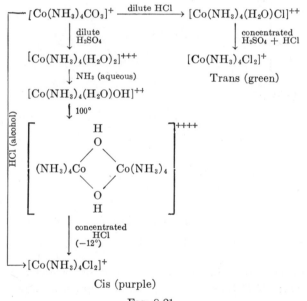

FIG. 8.21

determination of configuration involves the reaction of the binuclear complex,

$$\left[\begin{array}{c} H \\ O \\ \diagup\;\diagdown \\ (NH_3)_4Co \qquad Co(NH_3)_4 \\ \diagdown\;\diagup \\ O \\ H \end{array}\right](SO_4)_2$$

42. Werner, *Ann.*, **375**, 1 (1910).

with concentrated hydrochloric acid to give one mole of the dichloro complex and one of the diaquo complex. Assuming that no rearrangement takes place, the chloro groups must occupy adjacent positions and the salt must be cis-[Co(NH₃)₄Cl₂]Cl. It is important to observe, however, that, in this same series of reactions, a similar displacement of a bidentate group (carbonato) with hydrochloric acid, leads to a change of configuration.

Another example of this type is the "proof" of structure of $NH_4[Co(NH_3)_2(NO_2)_4]$, which has been obtained in only one form. Whenever the complex reacts with oxalic acid, two nitro groups are replaced by one oxalate group. If the original complex has the trans configuration, only one oxalate complex is to be expected, but if the ammonia groups are adjacent to one another, two oxalato derivatives may result and one of them should be enantiomorphous (Fig. 8.22).

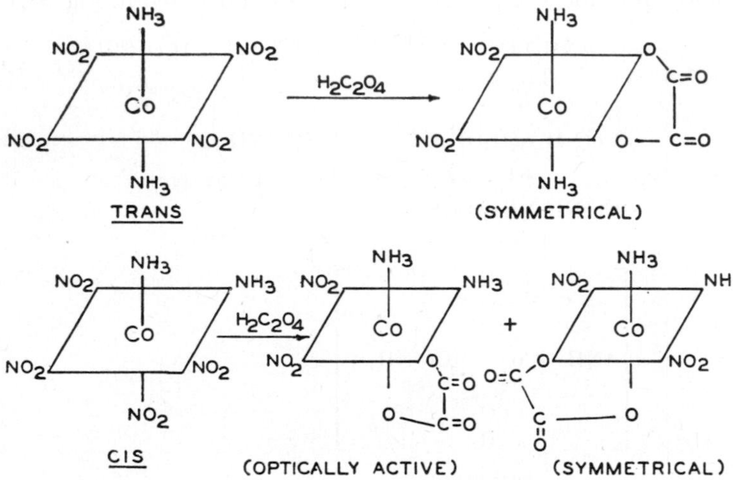

FIG. 8.22

Two products were isolated from the reaction between Erdman's salt and oxalic acid; one of these was resolved into optical antimers[43]. Although there are many instances in which structures determined by this method have been proven to be correct, one cannot disregard the fact that complex cobalt compounds are known to rearrange very readily, and, therefore, the assumption that a molecule retains its configuration as groups or atoms are replaced is not entirely reliable. This particular case may serve as a good illustration of this factor since the results obtained by the oxalate method

43. Shibata and Maruki, J. Coll. Sci. Imp. Univ., Tokyo, **41**, 2 (1917); Thomas, J. Chem. Soc., **121**, 2069 (1922); Thomas, ibid., **123**, 617 (1923).

do not agree with the findings of Riesenfeld and Klement[44], nor with x-ray studies which were made on the silver salt[45].

Optical Activity. In certain cases it is possible to establish the configurations of these isomers by showing that one is optically active and the other is inactive. This procedure offers conclusive proof except in examples where only one form is known and this cannot be resolved; failure to resolve the compound does not necessarily mean that the complex is symmetrical. A familiar example of this method is the proof that the purple salt, [Co en$_2$ Cl$_2$]Cl, which is optically active, has a cis configuration; the green inactive isomer must therefore have the trans configuration.

Bailar and Peppard[19b] used this method to determine the structures of the three stereoisomeric forms of dichlorodiammine(ethylenediamine)cobalt(III) ion. (I, III, and VI, Fig. 8.23). Salts of two of these were prepared by Chaussy[46] who designated them as *cis* and *trans* (referring to the relative positions of the chloro groups). Chaussy made no mention of the fact that two cis ions are possible. The colors of these ions enable one to determine the relative positions of the chloride groups with certainty, but do not distinguish between the two *cis*-dichloro configurations. The assignment of configurations, in this case, was based upon the fact that the *cis*-dichloro-*cis*-diammine ion (III) is asymmetric while the *cis*-dichloro-*trans*-diammine ion (VI) is not.

The methods employed to prepare the two cis isomers are of interest. (Fig. 8.23). The preparation of the *cis*-dichloro-*cis*-diammine salt (III) is

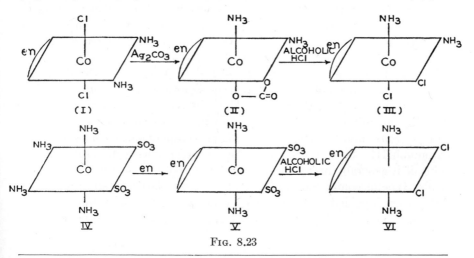

Fig. 8.23

44. Riesenfield and Klement, *Z. anorg. allgem. Chem.*, **124,** 1 (1922).
45. Wells, *Kristallogr., Z.*, **95A,** 74 (1936).
46. Chaussey, "Dissertation," Zurich, 1909.

based upon the fact that chelate groups can span only adjacent positions and, therefore, the dichloro salt (I) undergoes a rearrangement to produce the carbonato compound (II). The preparation of the *cis*-disulfito-*trans*-diammine salt (V) is a good illustration of a phenomenon known as the *trans effect* which has been studied in some detail by Chernyaev[47]. Bailar and Peppard[19b] have also found this principle of trans elimination to be useful in the synthesis of the *cis*-dichloro-*trans*-diammine salt (VI). The *cis*-disulfitotetrammine salt (IV) was used so that the NH_3 groups trans to the sulfite groups would be labilized and the ethylenediamine would enter in the 2,3 positions, to yield (V).

Chemical Behavior. The possibility of distinguishing between geometric isomers by means of their reactions has been considered. It is known, for instance, that *cis*- and *trans*-dinitrotetrammine, and *cis*- and *trans*-dinitro-bis(ethylenediamine) compounds react differently toward boiling hydrochloric acid[48]. The cis isomer is dissolved and, upon standing, a green crystalline salt separates from the purple solution; the trans isomer forms a red precipitate of the *trans*-nitrochloro complex. Although this qualitative test can be conveniently used for these particular dinitro complexes, it does not necessarily apply to all analogous compounds. A typical discrepancy is found in the work of Hurlimann[49], who was of the opinion that the product, [Co (*l*-pn)₂ (NO₂)₂] Br, obtained from the reaction of trinitrotriammine-cobalt(III) and *levo*-propylenediamine was the pure cis isomer, since no red precipitate formed when the complex was heated with concentrated hydrochloric acid. However, it has been shown by rotatory dispersion curves that the salt obtained was a mixture of the cis and trans isomers[50], and, furthermore, that *trans*-[Co (*l*-pn)₂ (NO₂)₂]⁺ does not give a red precipitate when boiled with concentrated hydrochloric acid.

Physical Methods. *Absorption Spectra.* In some cases the dissimilar spatial arrangements of the same ligands about a central atom results in a very noticeable difference in color. This difference is particularly obvious with the *praseo* (green) and *violeo* (blue-violet) series of isomers, characteristic of *trans*- and *cis*-dichlorotetrammine compounds of cobalt(III) and chromium(III). Since there are no known exceptions to this difference in color, it is generally accepted as conclusive proof of structure for this particular type of compound. Unfortunately, dissimilarity in structure is not always accompanied by such a vast color difference, as is shown by the fact that the corresponding dinitro complexes differ only slightly in appearance.

47. Chernyaev, *Ann. inst. platine*, **4**, 243 (1936).
48. Jorgensen, *Z. anorg. Chem.*, **17**, 468, 472 (1898); Klement, *Z. anorg. allgem. Chem.*, **150**, 117 (1925).
49. Hurlimann, "Dissertation," Zurich, 1918.
50. O'Brien, McReynolds, and Bailar, *J. Am. Chem. Soc.*, **70**, 749 (1948).

In this same connection the absorption spectra of coordination compounds have been thoroughly studied by numerous investigators. Shibata and Urbain[51] worked with cobalt complexes and noticed that there were always two bands of maximum absorption, one of which occurs in the visible while the other is found in the near ultraviolet. It was also observed that when two nitro groups are substituted for ammonia in the trans positions, a third absorption band occurs in the short ultraviolet[52]. Shibata made the following generalizations from his studies:

(1) Complexes of analogous constitution absorb similarly;

(2) Ligands of analogous chemical structure absorb similarly;

(3) Optical isomers absorb similarly;

(4) Geometric isomers in general absorb differently;

(5) Sign and magnitude of charge on the complex ion do not affect the absorption;

(6) The anion has no appreciable effect.

Generalization (4) is of interest in our discussion, because it may offer a possible method for distinguishing among stereoisomers.

Tsuchida[53] formulated some relatively simple theories to explain many of the complexities of the spectra. He proposed that the first absorption band (visible zone) is due to electronic transitions within the inner electron rings of the transition element which is the nucleus of the complex. He attributed the second band to the electrons linking the ligands with the central ion, and the third band (short ultraviolet region) to a special type of linking of ligands, e.g., two negative groups in trans positions. Kuroya and Tsuchida[26] obtained the absorption spectra of several carefully chosen complex cobalt compounds to show that the third absorption band is present in compounds which contain at least two negative ligands in trans positions, but is absent if the negative ligands are adjacent to each other (Table 8.1).

They say that the appearance of the third band is independent of (1) the nature and valency of the central ion, (2) the ligand in question, provided that it is of negative character, (3) the charge of the complex radical, and (4) the configuration, so long as the trans-pairing condition is fulfilled. Some question has recently[54, 55] been raised as to whether the presence or absence of this third absorption band for a complex with two or more negative ligands can be taken as absolute proof of geometric structure. However it does appear that in general the absorption bands in the ultraviolet region

51. Shibata and Urbain, *Compt. rend.*, **157**, 593 (1914).

52. Shibata, *J. Coll. Sci. Imp. Univ., Tokyo*, **37**, 1 (1915).

53. Tsuchida, *Bull. Chem. Soc., Japan*, **11**, 785 (1936); Tsuchida, *ibid.*, **13**, 388, 436, 471 (1938).

54. Basolo, *J. Am. Chem. Soc.*, **72**, 4393 (1950).

55. Shimura, *J. Am. Chem. Soc.*, **73**, 5079 (1951).

TABLE 8.1. ABSORPTION SPECTRA OF SOME GEOMETRICAL ISOMERS

Complex Salt	First Band		Second Band		Third Band	
	Å	log ε	Å	log ε	Å	log ε
cis-[Co(NH₃)₄(NO₂)₂]Cl	4580	1.99	3250	3.10		
trans-[Co(NH₃)₄(NO₂)₂]Cl	4490	2.32	3450	3.54	2500	4.08
cis-[Co en₂ (NO₂)₂]NO₃	4350	2.10	3250	3.68		
trans-[Co en₂ (NO₂)₂]NO₃	4300	2.20	3380	3.44	2490	4.37
trans-[Co(NH₃)₄ClNO₂]Cl	4750	1.87	3380	3.13	2440	4.07
trans-[Co en₂ ClNO₂]Cl	4350	2.00	3340	3.37	2410	4.35
cis-[Co en₂ Cl(NCS)]Cl	5030	2.18	3570	2.75		
trans-[Co en₂ Cl(NCS)]Br	5550	2.10	3460	2.93	2720	3.43

occur at the shorter wave length for the cis isomer than for the analogous trans compound.

A somewhat different observation has been reported by Sueda[22, 24], who studied the characteristic second absorption band of several nitroammine-cobalt(III) complexes and concluded that this band can be accounted for by an additive effect of groups in trans positions. The absorption (Fig. 8.24) of *cis*-[Co(NH₃)₄(NO₂)₂]Cl is assumed as a sum of three characteristic

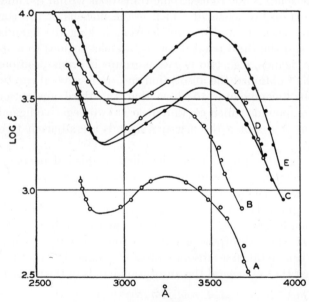

FIG. 8.24. Absorption spectra of some cobalt complexes.

    A. [Co(NH₃)₅NO₂]Cl₂
    B. *cis*-[Co(NH₃)₄(NO₂)₂]Cl
    C. *trans*-[Co(NH₃)₄(NO₂)₂]Cl
    D. [Co(NH₃)₃(NO₂)₃]
    E. K[Co(NH₃)₂(NO₂)₄]

absorptions, i.e., $(NH_3—Co—NH_3)$* and $2(NH_3—Co—NO_2)$. The absorption of $[Co(NH_3)_5NO_2]Cl_2$ can also be resolved into $2(NH_3—Co—NH_3)$ and $(NH_3—Co—NO_2)$. Since the absorption of $(NH_3—Co—NH_3)$ can be neglected† in comparison with that of $(NH_3—Co—NO_2)$, the absorption given by both salts shows that, due to the number of $(NH_3—Co—NO_2)$ groups contained, the former, the cis compound, has double the absorption intensity of the latter pentammine complex showing similar curves. With regard to the *trans*-$[Co(NH_3)_4(NO_2)_2]Cl$, its absorption may be considered to be the sum produced by $2(NH_3—Co—NH_3)$ and $(NO_2—Co—NO_2)$ and it is almost the same as that of $(NO_2—Co—NO_2)$, since the absorption of $(NH_3—Co—NH_3)$ is relatively small. The absorption of $[Co(NH_3)_3(NO_2)_3]$ can be resolved into $(NH_3—Co—NH_3)$, $(NH_3—Co—NO_2)$ and $(NO_2—Co—NO_2)$ and, as is expected, the absorption is represented as a sum of those given by $[Co(NH_3)_5NO_2]Cl_2$ and *trans*-$[Co(NH_3)_4(NO_2)_2]Cl$. The absorption intensity due to the complex $K[Co(NH_3)_2(NO_2)_4]$ is nearly twice that of the *trans*-$[Co(NH_3)_4(NO_2)_2]Cl$ and it is therefore assumed that the complex has a trans configuration and that its absorption results from $2(NO_2—Co—NO_2)$.

Sueda has applied his reasoning to a study of the structures of several aquochloroammines of cobalt(III) and chromium(III)[24], and also in establishing the cis configuration of $[Co(NH_3)_3(NO_2)_3]$ which he prepared from *cis*-$[Co(NH_3)_3(H_2O)_3]^{+++}$ [22].

Recent application of the crystal field theory to complex compounds[56] permits a better interpretation of the absorption spectra of these compounds. This theoretical treatment predicts differences in the absorption spectra of *cis* and *trans* isomers of hexacoordinated complexes[57], in good accord with experimental observations[58, 26b]. However, one immediate limitation is that for complexes containing ligands of approximately the same crystal field strength the differences predicted may be too small to observe experimentally.

X-ray Diffraction. The final result of a complete x-ray analysis of a substance is the determination of the relative positions of all the constituent atoms. As a rule this becomes increasingly difficult as the number of pa-

---

* This represents the characteristic absorption assumed to be produced by two ammonia molecules in trans positions having cobalt(III) as the central ion.

† It is convenient to say that the absorption capacity due to the $(NH_3—Co—NH_3)$ is weak compared to that of $(NH_3—Co—NO_2)$, since the extinction coefficient of the maximum absorption given by $[Co(NH_3)_6]Cl_3$ is only about 40 (at 336 Å), while that given by $[Co(NH_3)_5NO_2]Cl_2$, the weakest absorbent containing the group, $(NH_3—Co—NO_2)$, is about 1260 (at 325 Å).

56. Orgel, *J. Chem. Soc.*, 4756 (1952).
57. Ballhausen and Jørgensen, Kgl. Danske Videnskab. Selskab, Mat. fys. Medd., **29**, No. 14 (1955).
58. Linhard and Weigel, *Z. anorg. Chem.*, **271**, 101 (1952).

rameters required to fix these positions increases, and relatively few complete structure determinations of hexacovalent complex compounds have been made. Theoretically, however, it should be possible to establish the configuration of a stereoisomer by a careful x-ray study of the crystalline compound.

A large number of geometric isomers of the type $[Ma_4YCl]X$, where M is cobalt(III) or chromium(III), have been investigated by means of x-rays[59]. It was shown that if Y is a chloro or bromo group, the spectra for the cis and trans forms are different, but if Y is a group coordinated through nitrogen (NH_3, NO_2^- or NCS^-), the spectra are the same. The method was employed to show that the isomers were different, but not to establish which was cis and which trans.

A complete x-ray analysis of the crystal structure of $Ag[Co(NH_3)_2(NO_2)_4]$ indicates that the ammonia groups are in trans positions[45]. The crystals are tetragonal, $a = 6.97$, $c = 10.43$ Å, and the space group is $P4/nnc$-(D_{4h}^4). There are two molecules in the unit cell. This result differs from that obtained from chemical evidence, which assigns the cis configuration to the complex ion[43], but agrees with the results of Sueda.[22]

Rotatory Dispersion. The fact that trans complexes are not ordinarily resolvable while those of the cis configuration are, is commonly used to distinguish between geometrical isomers of the type $[Co(AA)_2a_2]$. If, however, the coordinating groups are optically active, both isomers of the complex will rotate the plane of polarized light, so that the presence of optical activity does not serve to distinguish one isomer from the other. O'Brien, McReynolds and Bailar[50] have shown that the configurations of such compounds can be conveniently determined by means of rotatory dispersion curves. The success of this method depends upon the fact that complex compounds containing optically active donor molecules normally exist only in certain preferred configurations (page 313). The optical activity of these compounds is due largely to the configurational asymmetry of the complex as a whole, so the rotatory dispersion curves of complexes having similar configuration should exhibit the same characteristics, whether a certain type of ligand is optically active or not. Thus, the rotatory dispersion curves of *cis*-$[Co\ en_2\ Cl_2]^+$ and *cis*-$[Co\ (l\text{-}pn)_2\ Cl_2]^+$ should be quite similar. It is also assumed that in a compound of the type $[M(AA)_2X_2]^+$ if the non-basic constituents (X) are in trans positions there can be no optical activity attributable to the asymmetry of the complex, and therefore the rotatory dispersion characteristics should be similar to those of the optically active base (AA). If, on the other hand, the complex has a cis configuration, there should be an induced activity and the rotatory dispersion of the complex should resemble that of a similar optically active ion and not that of the

59. Stelling, *Z. physik. Chem.*, **B33**, 338 (1933).

TABLE 8.2. EXAMPLES OF *cis-trans* CONVERSIONS

Starting Material	Reagent	Product
[Co(NH$_3$)$_3$(NO$_2$)$_3$]	propylenediamine	*cis* and *trans*-[Co pn$_2$ (NO$_2$)$_2$]NO$_2$
cis-[Co pn$_2$ Cl$_2$]Cl	KCNS	*trans*-[Co pn$_2$ (NCS)$_2$]NCS
trans-[Co pn$_2$ Cl$_2$]Cl	KCNS	*trans*-[Co pn$_2$ (NCS)$_2$]NCS
cis-[Co pn$_2$ Cl$_2$]Cl	NH$_3$ (aqueous)	*trans*-[Co pn$_2$ NH$_3$Cl]Cl$_2$
trans-[Co pn$_2$ Cl$_2$]Cl	NH$_3$ (aqueous)	*trans*-[Co pn$_2$ NH$_3$Cl]Cl$_2$
cis-[Co pn$_2$ Cl$_2$]Cl	NH$_3$ (anhydrous)	*trans*-[Co pn$_2$ (NH$_3$)$_2$]Cl$_3$
trans-[Co pn$_2$ Cl$_2$]Cl	NH$_3$ (anhydrous)	*trans*-[Co pn$_2$ (NH$_3$)$_2$]Cl$_3$
trans-[Co pn$_2$ Cl$_2$]Cl	Na$_2$SO$_3$	*cis*-[Co pn$_2$ SO$_3$]Cl

active base. The fact that this is true was shown by the rotatory dispersion curves of several ethylenediamine and *active*-propylenediamine cobalt(III) complexes of the types [Co(AA)$_2$a$_2$]$^+$ and [Co(AA)$_2$(BB)]$^+$ [50].

This technique was applied to the study of *cis-trans* conversion[50] in the reactions of coordination compounds containing optically active propylenediamine (Table 8.2).

Dipole Moment. The chemical bond between two atoms of the same or similar electronegativity is nonpolar, and a molecule such as A$_2$ has little tendency to orient itself when placed in an electric or magnetic field. If, on the other hand, the two atoms do not have similar electronegativities (such as AB) then the molecule will orient itself in such a field because it contains a permanent dipole. In much the same way, it is possible to distinguish complex molecules on the basis of their electrical symmetry. It would therefore appear that measurements of dipole moments could be used to distinguish between the cis and trans isomers of coordination compounds. Numerous studies of tetracovalent complexes of the type [Pta$_2$X$_2$][60] have been made by this method, but it has not been used for hexacovalent compounds. This is due largely to the fact that dipole moments are usually derived from measurements of dielectric constants; such measurements are difficult to make in polar solvents. Since most of the geometric isomers of hexacovalent compounds are salts, they are not soluble in nonpolar solvents. Perhaps some inner complexes such as [Co(NH$_3$)$_3$(NO$_2$)$_3$] and [Co(gly)$_3$] might be studied by this method.

Although it is difficult to measure the dipole moments of complex salts, polarographic measurements of the limiting currents for stereoisomers indicate differences which can be attributed to a variation in electrical symmetry[61]. It was found that the cations, *cis*-[Co(NH$_3$)$_4$(NO$_2$)$_2$]$^+$ and *cis*-[Co pn$_2$ Cl$_2$]$^+$ produce larger limiting currents than the corresponding trans isomers. This was attributed to their nonhomogeneous internal electric fields which cause the ions to orient with respect to an electrode and move toward it under the influence of this force as well as by diffusion. Since this

60. Jensen, *Z. anorg. Chem.*, **225**, 97 (1935); Jensen, *ibid.*, **229**, 225 (1936).
61. Holtzclaw, thesis, University of Illinois, 1947.

orientation effect is not present in the case of the trans isomers, the cis cation moves faster and carries more current.

Recent studies[62] on the separation of *cis*- and *trans*- $[Co(NH_3)_4(NO_2)_2]^+$ using a cation exchanger show that the trans isomer is more readily removed from the resin. Since the charge and size of these isomeric complexes are the same, it would appear that the cis form is more firmly held because of its larger dipole moment.

Raman Spectra. The Raman spectra, in principle, should be applicable to the determination of the configuration of geometric isomers in coordination compounds. In actual practice, it is often not possible to obtain sufficient information by this method to make any structural conclusion. The Raman spectra of coordination compounds are also rather difficult to obtain, because the solutions of many of these compounds are highly colored. Some studies have been made with tetracovalent compounds[63] but, as yet, very little[64] has been done with hexacovalent compounds.

Infrared Spectra. Recent studies[65] on the infrared spectra of complex compounds show that this method can be used to distinguish between *cis* and *trans* isomers. For example, fewer absorption peaks are present in the spectrum of *trans*-$[Co(NH_3)_4(NO_2)_2]Cl$ than in that of the *cis* isomer. This is the natural consequence of the selection rule, since the *trans* complex has a center of symmetry whereas the *cis* isomer does not.

Magnetic Susceptibility. The magnetic susceptibilities of a large number of metallic ammines have been determined by Rosenbohm[66]. He observed that the diamagnetism is greatest for the hexammines of cobalt(III), less for the pentammines, and still less for the tetrammines of this metal. The triammines of cobalt(III) are very weakly diamagnetic; some compounds of this type exhibit paramagnetism. It is evident, therefore, that the magnetism is largely influenced by the constitution of the molecule. However, an examination of the geometrical isomerides of cobalt(III), chromium(III), and platinum(IV) complexes indicates that the magnetic susceptibilities of the cis and trans forms are indistinguishable. This is also true of the respective optical isomers.

Solubility. The difference in the solubilities of the stereoisomers cannot be used to determine their structures. Perhaps, in most instances, it can be said that the cis isomer is more soluble than the corresponding trans salt, but there are numerous exceptions to this statement and it should certainly not be taken as a general rule.

62. King and Walters, *J. Am. Chem. Soc.*, **74**, 4471 (1952).
63. Mathieu, *J. chim. phys.*, **36**, 271, 308 (1939).
64. Mathieu, *Compt. rend.*, **204**, 682 (1937).
65. Quagliano and Faust, *J. Am. Chem. Soc.*, **76**, 5346 (1954).
66. Rosenbohm, *Z. physik. Chem.*, **93**, 693 (1919).

Some Properties of Cis-trans Isomers

Interconversion of cis-trans Isomers. It has already been mentioned that the preparation of a cis compound by the displacement of a chelate group, or the proof of structure by the replacement of singly bound groups with a chelate, is not reliable. This is largely because of the ease with which some geometric isomers are known to rearrange when in solution. In many instances, the trans isomers can be obtained by prolonged boiling of solutions of the cis salts, e.g., $K_3[Ir\ ox_2\ Cl_2]$[16], $K_3[Rh\ ox_2\ Cl_2]$[17] and $[Co\ en_2 (NO_2)_2]NO_3$[67].

The best known example is the transformation of green *trans*-$[Co\ en_2\ Cl_2]Cl$ into violet *cis*-$[Co\ en_2\ Cl_2]Cl$ and *vice versa*. Jorgensen[68] discovered that the trans to cis conversion is brought about by evaporation of the aqueous solution to dryness, and that the reverse process occurs in the presence of hydrochloric acid. Drew and Pratt[69] have suggested a mechanism for these changes which involves the rupture of a chelate link between ethylenediamine and the cobalt(III) (Fig. 8.25).

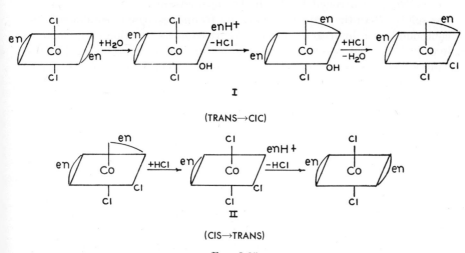

I

(TRANS→CIC)

II

(CIS→TRANS)

FIG. 8.25

This mechanism was proposed without any direct evidence but primarily on the analogy that ethylenediamine chelate rings in platinum(II) complexes have been opened by digestion with hydrochloric acid[70]. There is, in fact, little justification for the assignment of structures I and II to the

67. Werner, *Ann.*, **386**, 1 (1912).
68. Jorgensen, *J. prakt. Chem.*, **39**, 1 (1889).
69. Drew and Pratt, *J. Chem. Soc.*, **1937**, 506.
70. Drew and Tress, *J. Chem. Soc.*, **1932**, 2328; **1933**, 1335.

complexes generally represented as [Co en$_2$ Cl$_2$]Cl·H$_2$O and [Co en$_2$ Cl$_2$]Cl· HCl respectively. The cis hydrate is purple and the trans hydrochloride is green; that is, the colors are not markedly altered by the presence of either water or hydrogen chloride. Structure (I) would also suggest a similar mechanism for the aquation of the cis isomer, which leads to the racemization of optically active [Co en$_2$ Cl$_2$]$^+$ during aquation. However, Mathieu[71] has shown that instead of racemizing, the complex mutorotates to [Co en$_2$ H$_2$O Cl]$^{++}$ at a rate equal to that of chloride ion formation, and with essentially complete retention of configuration. The mechanism of this interconversion has been investigated using radioactive chlorine to determine the exchange that takes place during isomerization[72]. No evidence was found for any direct exchange of the coordinated chloro groups with the chloride ion. This suggests that the following equilibria exist in solution:

$$cis\text{- and } trans\text{-[Co en}_2 \text{ Cl}_2]^+ \rightleftharpoons \text{[Co en}_2 \text{ (H}_2\text{O)Cl]}^{++} \rightleftharpoons \text{[Co en}_2 \text{ (H}_2\text{O)}_2]^{+++}$$

The relative amounts of the isomeric chlorides in the solid residue appear to be largely controlled by solubility considerations[72]. The cis chloride is less soluble than the trans but the latter forms a sparingly soluble addition compound with hydrogen chloride. Apart from its function as precipitant, hydrochloric acid plays no essential role in the changing of cis to trans. This was shown using the complex nitrate instead of the chloride. A solution of trans-[Co en$_2$ Cl$_2$]NO$_3$ can be evaporated to dryness without isomerization taking place; conversely, cis-[Co en$_2$ Cl$_2$]NO$_3$ is, by the same procedure, converted quantitatively into the trans salt. In the case of the nitrate, the trans isomeride is only slightly soluble in water and is always the first to precipitate.

Ettle and Johnson[72] have suggested that the interconversion may occur by the following mechanism:

$$cis\text{-[Co en}_2 \text{ Cl}_2]^+ + \text{H}_2\text{O} \rightleftharpoons cis\text{-[Co en}_2 \text{ H}_2\text{O Cl]}^{++} + \text{Cl}^-$$
$$\Updownarrow$$
$$trans\text{-[Co en}_2 \text{ Cl}_2]^+ + \text{H}_2\text{O} \rightleftharpoons trans\text{-[Co en}_2 \text{ H}_2\text{O Cl]}^{++} + \text{Cl}^-$$

However, they do not describe how the rearrangement between the cis- and trans-chloroaquo complexes takes place. Mathieu[71] has observed that the rate of racemization of [Co en$_2$ H$_2$O Cl]$^{+2}$ is independent of the rate of chloride ion formation and suggests that this may occur as a result of the dissociation of the coordinated water. This explanation may be used also to account for the cis-trans interconversion of the chloroaquo complexes.

71. Mathieu, *Bull. soc. chim.*, [5] **4**, 687 (1937).
72. Ettle and Johnson, *J. Chem. Soc.*, **1939**, 1490.

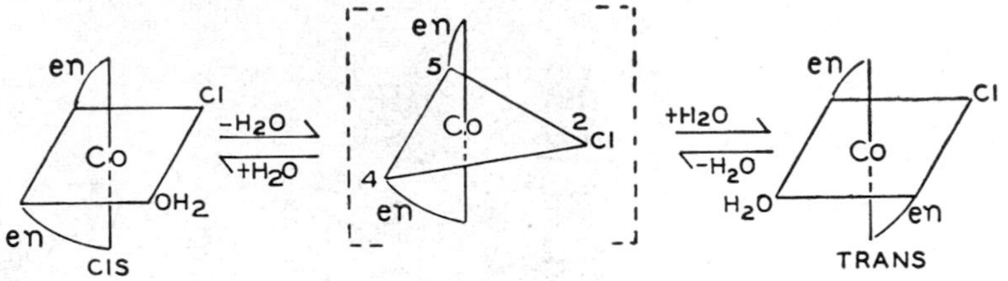

ACTIVATED INTERMEDIATE
FIG. 8.26

It is apparent from the trigonal bipyramid structure for the activated intermediate that an approach by water between positions 4 and 5 would yield the *trans*-chloroaquo complex whereas attack between 2 and 4 or between 2 and 5 would yield the cis isomer.

There is some evidence that the first steps in this interconversion (aquation of the dichloro complex) takes place without inversion of configuration. For example Mathieu[71] has observed that the reaction

$$d\text{-}[Co\ en_2\ Cl_2]^+ + H_2O \rightarrow l\text{-}[Co\ en_2\ H_2O\ Cl]^{++} + Cl^-$$

occurs with retention of configuration. Direct proof that the trans isomer behaves similarly is not available. However, since the rate of aquation of *cis*- and *trans*-[Co en$_2$ NO$_2$ Cl]$^+$ is rapid as compared to the rate of rearrangement of the isomers of [Co en$_2$ H$_2$O NO$_2$]$^{++}$, it has been possible to show that both of the chloronitro complexes aquate with retention of configuration. Furthermore, the suggestion that the interconversion actually occurs via the [Co en$_2$ H$_2$O Cl]$^{++}$ ions instead of the dichloro complexes is in accord with the numerous observations[54, 74-77] that aquo complexes generally rearrange more rapidly than the corresponding acido compounds.

Chemical Behavior of Cis-Trans Isomers. Closely related to the interconversion within an individual molecule are the conversions that may occur during reactions in which coordinated groups are displaced. Werner[67] made an extensive study of such reactions and some of the results obtained are given in Table 8.3.

It becomes immediately apparent that no conclusions can be drawn from these results. Reactions 1 and 2, 6 and 7, 8 and 9, and 12 and 13 show that the configuration of the product bears no relation to the configuration of the original material. Perhaps the most striking pair is 12 and 13, for a change of configuration takes place in each of these reactions. A thorough study was made of this case under various conditions, but the result was

74. Basolo, Stone, and Pearson, *J. Am. Chem. Soc.*, **75**, 819 (1953).
75. Uspensky and Tschibisoff, *Z. anorg. Chem.*, **164**, 326 (1927).
76. Cunningham, Burley, and Friend, *Nature*, **169**, 1103 (1952).
77. Hamm, *J. Am. Chem. Soc.*, **75**, 609 (1953).

TABLE 8.3. STEREOCHEMICAL CHANGES ACCOMPANYING THE REACTION OF SOME COBALT(III) COMPLEXES

Reaction	Starting Material cis	Starting Material trans	Starting Material	Reagent	Product	Ratio of cis	Ratio of trans
1	+	+	[Co en$_2$ Br$_2$]Br	NH$_3$ (liquid)	[Co en$_2$ (NH$_3$)$_2$]Br$_3$	20	1
2		+	[Co en$_2$ Br$_2$]Br	NH$_3$ (liquid)	[Co en$_2$ (NH$_3$)$_2$]Br$_3$	6	1
3	+	+	[Co en$_2$ SCN Cl]SCN	NH$_3$ (liquid)	[Co en$_2$ NH$_3$ SCN]ClSCN	2	1
4	+	+	[Co en$_2$ SCN Cl]SCN	NH$_3$ (liquid)	[Co en$_2$ NH$_3$ SCN]ClSCN	1	1
5	+	+	[Co en$_2$ SCN Br]ClO$_4$	NH$_3$ (liquid)	[Co en$_2$ NH$_3$ SCN]BrClO$_4$	2	1
6	+		[Co en$_2$ NH$_3$ SCN]X$_2$	KSCN	[Co en$_2$ (SCN)$_2$]SCN	*	*
7	+	+	[Co en$_2$ NH$_3$ SCN]X$_2$	KSCN	[Co en$_2$ (SCN)$_2$]SCN	*	*
8	+	++	[Co en$_2$ NH$_3$ Cl]X$_2$	Ag$_2$O	[Co en$_2$ NH$_3$ OH]X$_2$	†	
9			[Co en$_2$ NH$_3$ Cl]X$_2$	Ag$_2$O	[Co en$_2$ NH$_3$ OH]X$_2$	*	*
10	+		[Co en$_2$ SCN Cl]Cl	NH$_4$OH	[Co en$_2$ SCN OH]Cl		
11	+		[Co en$_2$ SCN Cl]Cl	KSCN	[Co en$_2$ (SCN)$_2$]SCN	*	*
12			[Co en$_2$ Cl$_2$]Cl	KOH	[Co en$_2$ H$_2$O OH]Cl$_2$	*	
13			[Co en$_2$ Cl$_2$]Cl	NH$_4$OH	[Co en$_2$ H$_2$O OH]Cl$_2$		*

* Chiefly.
† Quantitatively.

always the same as Werner had reported[78]. Werner isolated the reaction product and separated the two isomers in order to determine the relative amounts in which they were formed. However, these compounds are known to undergo isomeric rearrangements, so the observed isomeric ratio may not be a direct consequence of the reaction in question. However, some of the reactions studied by Werner have recently been reinvestigated[74] using a spectrophotometric technique to determine the ratio of cis and trans isomers *in situ* immediately following the substitution reactions. The results obtained by this method were generally in good accord with the earlier observations reported by Werner.

Werner at first believed that substitution normally takes place with retention of configuration, and that, whenever this is not the case, rearrangement takes place in order to form the more stable isomer. However, it soon became apparent to Werner that this interpretation was not compatible with the experimental facts. For example, reactions 3 and 4 in Table 8.3 show that *trans*-[Co en$_2$ NCS Cl]$^+$ reacts with liquid ammonia to yield two parts of *cis*- and one part of *trans*-[Co en$_2$ NH$_3$ NCS]$^{++}$; therefore the cis isomer is expected to be more stable than the trans complex. However, the reaction of *cis*[Co en$_2$ NCS Cl]$^+$ with liquid ammonia does not yield exclusively *cis*-[Co en$_2$ NH$_3$ NCS]$^{++}$, but equimolar quantities of the cis and trans isomers.

Werner attempted to explain these results by assuming that the complex is surrounded by an outer sphere of more loosely held groups. If the incoming group (c) is oriented in this outer complex in a position adjacent to the group that is to be replaced (b), there will be no change in configuration during the substitution (Fig. 8.27). However, if (c) is in a position opposite to (b), the reaction is accompanied by change in configuration.

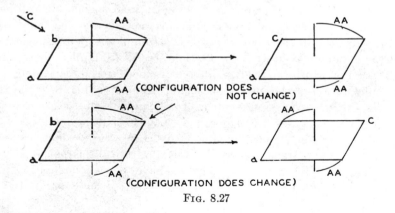

FIG. 8.27

---

78. Becker, thesis, University of Illinois, 1935.

The possibility of predicting the position of the incoming group on the basis of electrostatic forces has been suggested[79]. An explanation of this type might be used to interpret the fact that *cis*-[Co en$_2$ NH$_3$ Cl]Cl$_2$ is produced by the reaction of *trans*-[Co en$_2$ Cl$_2$]Cl and aqueous ammonia. If it is assumed that the negative nitrogen atom of ammonia approaches the octahedron in such a way as to maintain a maximum distance from the negative chloro groups, then the ammonia would be in the plane of the ethylenediamine molecules and it could be attached to positions 2, 3, 4 or 5 which would account for the formation of *cis*-[Co en$_2$ NH$_3$ Cl]Cl$_2$ (Fig. 8.28).

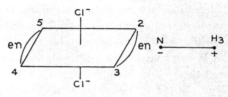

FIG. 8.28

Although this explanation appears to account satisfactorily for the reaction cited, it cannot be used as a general interpretation. For example, it would suggest that the analogous propylenediamine complex, *trans*-[Co pn$_2$ Cl$_2$]$^+$, should react with ammonia to yield the *cis*-chloroammine derivative; however, the product of this reaction is the trans isomer[50]. Furthermore, it is expected on the basis of such an approach that *cis*-[Co en$_2$ Cl$_2$]$^+$ would react to yield *trans*-[Co en$_2$ NH$_3$Cl]$^{++}$ but the product is known to be the cis complex. These results indicate that the electrostatic effect cannot be the sole factor responsible in determining the course of these reactions.

Basolo, Stone, and Pearson[74] have recently used a somewhat different approach to the problem of molecular rearrangements that may occur during substitution reactions in octahedral complexes. They suggest that the reaction involves either a dissociation process (S$_N$1) or a displacement (S$_N$2) reaction which can lead to different isomeric forms depending upon the configuration of the intermediate. For example in Fig. 8.29 the trans complex [M(AA)$_2$ax] is represented as undergoing a dissociation process (S$_N$1) by way of a tetragonal pyramid, to yield a trans product; if the intermediate has a trigonal bipyramid structure, the product may be a mixture of cis and trans isomers. However, with a displacement reaction (S$_N$2) as shown in Fig. 8.30 the product will have the cis configuration, if the attack of the incoming group is from the "back", but trans if the ap-

79. Mathieu, *Bull. soc. chim.*, [5] **5**, 783 (1938).

proach is from the "front" of the complex. Molecular rearrangements during substitutions have been discussed in terms of "edge" and "non-edge" displacements[79a]. It therefore becomes apparent that stereochemical studies alone will not elucidate a detailed mechanism of substitution reactions in octahedral complexes. However, some progress has already been made[80-82] toward the determination of the molecularity of these reactions. For the reaction [Co en$_2$ NO$_2$ Cl]$^+$ + H$_2$O → [Co en$_2$ H$_2$O NO$_2$]$^{++}$ + Cl$^-$ the experimental evidence supports a dissociation mechanism involving a tetragonal pyramid intermediate[71, 83, 84].

The observation that increased steric hindrance in a series of trans-[Co(AA)$_2$Cl$_2$]$^+$ compounds is accompanied by increased rates of aquation has been cited in support of an S$_N$1 mechanism[81]. Substitution reactions of cis-[Co en$_2$ Cl$_2$]$^+$ in methanol involve either an S$_N$1 or S$_N$2 process depending upon the nucleophilic character of the reactant[85].

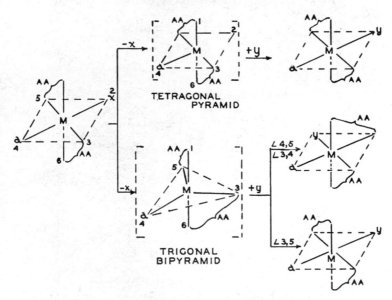

TETRAGONAL PYRAMID

TRIGONAL BIPYRAMID

FIG. 8.29. Dissociation process (S$_N$1) for trans-[M(AA)$_2$ax]

79a. Brown, Ingold, and Nyholm, *J. Chem. Soc.*, **1953**, 2674.
80. Basolo, Bergmann, and Pearson, *J. Phys. Chem.*, **56**, 22 (1952).
81. Pearson, Boston, and Basolo, *J. Am. Chem. Soc.*, **74**, 2943 (1952); **75**, 3089 (1953).
82. Rutenberg and Taube, *J. Chem. Phys.*, **20**, 823 (1952).
83. Werner, *Ber.*, **45**, 121 (1912).
84. Pfeiffer, Golther, and Angern, *Ber.*, **60**, 305 (1927)
85. Brown and Ingold, *J. Chem. Soc.*, 2680 (1953).

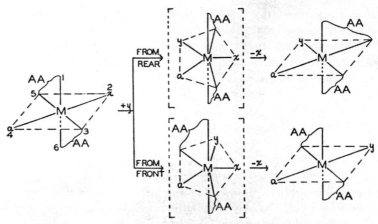

FIG. 8.30. Displacement (S_N2) process for trans-[M(AA)$_2$ax]

TABLE 8.4. RELATIVE AMOUNTS OF GEOMETRICAL ISOMERS ANTICIPATED ON THE BASIS OF VARIOUS REACTION MECHANISMS FOR SUBSTITUTIONS IN OCTAHEDRAL COMPLEXES OF THE TYPE [M(AA)$_2$ax]

[M(AA)$_2$ax]	Dissociation (S_N1)				Displacement (S_N2)			
	Tetragonal Pyramid		Trigonal Bipyramid		Rear		Front	
	cis	*trans*	*cis*	*trans*	*cis*	*trans*	*cis*	*trans*
	per cent	*per cent*	*per cent*	*per cent*	*per cent*	*per cent*	*per cent*	*per cent*
Trans	0	100	66.6	33.3	100	0	0	100
Cis	100	0	80	20	66.6	33.3	100	0

OPTICAL ISOMERISM

Numerous coordination compounds have been resolved into their enantiomorphs and some of the problems in this connection will be discussed.

The optical activity found in coordination compounds is not always caused by the presence of an asymmetric atom. Experiments have shown that molecules or ions in which the entire configuration possess only axial symmetry may exist in enantiomorphously related forms. Coordination compounds are of this general type and many are known to have high optical activity, i.e. [Co en$_3$]Br$_3$, [M]$_D$ = ± 602°. As is shown in Fig. 8.31,

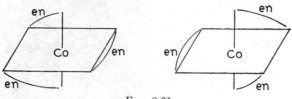

F<small>IG</small>. 8.31

there is no chemical contrast whatsoever between the three substituents attached to the central atom, and the optical activity results from the dissymmetrical spatial disposition of these identical substituents. There is no "asymmetric atom" in the sense of the Le Bel-Van't Hoff theory, but, in contrast, the division of space about the central atom is a decidedly symmetrical one. The fact that the only prerequisite for optical isomerism is an asymmetric molecule or ion can also be extended to certain carbon compounds which contain no asymmetric carbon atom. A good example of such a compound is the dilactone, Fig. 8.32, which was resolved by Mills

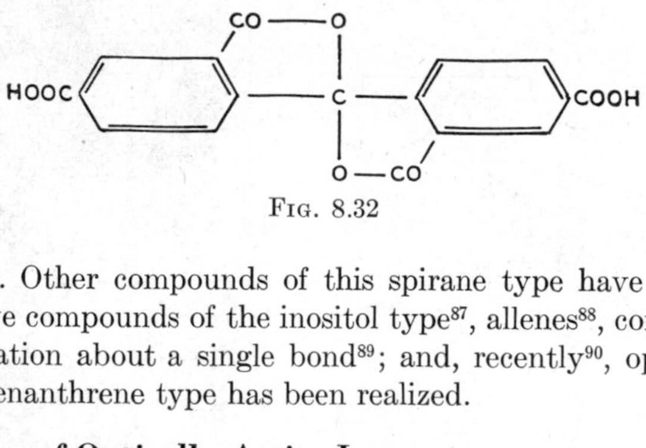

F<small>IG</small>. 8.32

and Nodder[86]. Other compounds of this spirane type have also been resolved, as have compounds of the inositol type[87], allenes[88], compounds with restricted rotation about a single bond[89]; and, recently[90], optical activity of the 4,5-phenanthrene type has been realized.

Various Types of Optically-Active Isomers

Cationic Complex Compounds. Numerous complex cations have been resolved into their optically-active antipodes. No attempt will be made to discuss the preparation and resolution of all of these compounds but the general types which have been resolved will be mentioned and some examples of each given. Complex cations with general formulas of $[M(AA)_3]$, $[M(AA)_2(BB)]$, $[M(AA)_2a_2]$, $[M(AA)_2ab]$, $[M(AA)a_2b_2]$, $[M(AA)(BB)a_2]$, $[M(AA'A)_2]$ and $[M(ABCCBA)]$ have been separated into their optically

86. Mills and Nodder, *J. Chem. Soc.*, **117**, 1407 (1920).
87. Mohr, *J. prakt. Chem.*, [27] **68**, 369 (1903).
88. Pope, Perkin, and Wallach, *Ann.*, **371**, 180 (1909).
89. Adams and Yuan, *Chem. Revs.*, **12**, 262 (1933).
90. Newman and Hussey, *J. Am. Chem. Soc.*, **69**, 3023 (1947).

TABLE 8.5. SOME ASYMMETRIC CATIONS WHICH ARE REPORTED TO HAVE BEEN RESOLVED

$[M(AA)_3]$	$[M(AA)_2(BB)]$	$[M(AA)_2a_2]$	$[M(AA)_2ab]$	$[M(AA)_2a_2b_2]$	$[M(AA)(BB)a_2]$	$[M(AA'A)_2]$	$[M(ABCCBA)]$
$[Co\ en_3]^{+++}$ [91]	$[Co\ en_2\ CO_3]^+$ [104]	$[Co\ en_2\ Cl_2]^+$ [106]	$[Co\ en_2\ xy]^+$ [104, 111]	$[Co\ en\ (NH_3)_2Cl_2]^+$ [19b]	$[Co\ en\ pn\ (NO_2)_2]^+$ [32]	$[Co(NH_2CH_2CH(NH_2)CH_2NH_2)_2]^{+++}$ [112]	$[Co(C_{22}H_{22}N_2O_2S_2)]^+$ [36b]
$[Co\ pn_3]^{+++}$ [92]	$[Co\ en_2\ C_2O_4]^+$ [105]	$[Co\ en_2\ (NO_2)_2]^+$ [12]					
$[Co\ cptn_3]^{+++}$ [93]		$[Co\ pn_2\ (NO_2)_2]^+$ [49, 107]					
		$[Co\ en_2\ (NH_3)_2]^{+++}$ [108]					
$[Co\ chxn_2]^{+++}$ [94]		$[Cr\ en_2\ Cl_2]^+$ [109]					
$[Cr\ en_3]^{+++}$ [95]		$[Ir\ en_2\ (NO_2)_2]^+$ [110]					
$[[Cd\ pn_3]^{++}$ [96]							
$[Fe\ dipy_3]^{++}$ [97]							
$[Fe\ dipy_3]^{+++}$ [8]							
$[Pt\ en_3]^{4+}$ [98]							
$[Pt\ pn_3]^{4+}$ [92]							
$[Rh\ en_3]^{+++}$ [99]							
$[Rh\ cptn_3]^{+++}$ [100]							
$[Ir\ en_3]^{+++}$ [101]							
$[Zn\ en_3]^{++}$ [102]							
$[Zn\ pn_3]^{++}$ [103]							

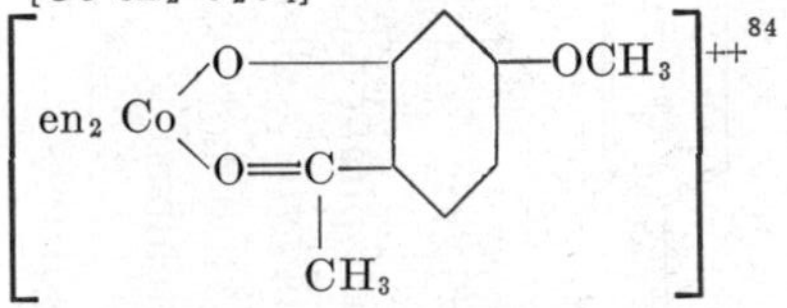

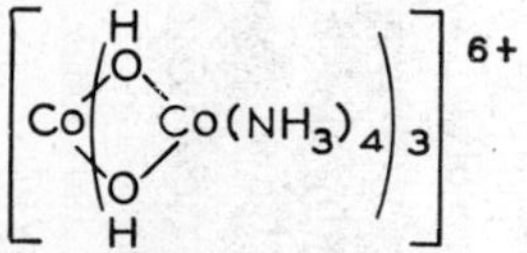

Structure under $[M(AA)_3]$ (footnote [5]): $\left[Co\{Co(NH_3)_4\}_3\right]^{6+}$

Structure under $[M(AA)_2(BB)]$ (footnote [84]): en_2Co coordinated to an ortho-disubstituted benzene ligand bearing an OCH_3 group and an acetate ($\overset{O}{\underset{O}{C}}CH_3$) group, charge $^{++}$.

active antipodes. Spatial arrangements for these enantiomorphs are shown in Fig. 8.33. For the last two, other arrangements are also possible. Some

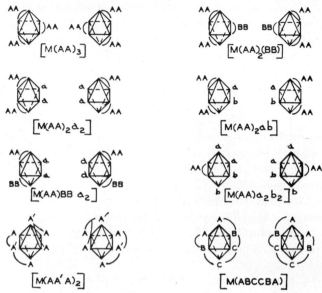

FIG. 8.33. Possible forms of some chelate complexes

specific examples of these compounds which have been resolved are listed in Table 8.5.

91. Werner, *Ber.*, **45**, 121 (1912).
92. Smirnoff, *Helv. chim. Acta.*, **3**, 177 (1920).
93. Jaeger and Blumendal, *Z. anorg. allgem. Chem.*, **175**, 161 (1928).
94. Jaeger and Bijkerk, *Proc. Acad. Sci. Amsterdam*, **40**, 116 (1937).
95. Werner, *Ber.*, **45**, 865 (1912).
96. Neogi and Mandal, *J. Indian Chem. Soc.*, **13**, 224 (1936).
97. Werner, *Ber.*, **45**, 433 (1912).
98. Jaeger, *Kristallogr., Z.*, **58**, 172 (1923).
99. Werner, *Ber.*, **45**, 1228 (1912).
100. Jaeger, "Spatial Arrangements of Atomic Systems and Optical Activity," p. 92, New York, McGraw-Hill Book Co., 1930.
101. Werner and Smirnoff, *Helv. chim. Acta.*, **3**, 476, 483 (1920).
102. Neogi and Mukherjee, *J. Indian Chem. Soc.*, **11**, 681 (1934).
103. Neogi and Mandal, *J. Indian Chem. Soc.*, **14**, 653 (1937).
104. Werner, *Ber.*, **44**, 1887 (1911).
105. Werner and McCutcheon, *Ber.*, **45**, 3281 (1912); **47**, 2171 (1914).
106. Bailar and Auten, *J. Am. Chem. Soc.*, **56**, 774 (1934).
107. Watts, "Dissertation," Zurich, 1912.
108. Bailar, Halsam and Jones, *J. Am. Chem. Soc.*, **58**, 2226 (1936).
109. Werner, *Ber.*, **44**, 3132 (1911).
100. Werner and Smirnoff, *Helv. chim. Acta.*, **3**, 472 (1920).
111. Werner, *Ber.*, **44**, 3272 (1911).
112. Mann and Pope, *J. Proc. Roy. Soc.*, *London*, **107A**, 80 (1925).

The usual method employed for the separation of these enantiomorphous cations may be illustrated with the racemate, [Co en$_3$]Cl$_3 \cdot$3H$_2$O. If a solution containing one mole of this salt is treated with one mole of silver *dextro*-tartrate, there is formed a chlorotartrate, [Co en$_3$]Cl(d-C$_4$H$_4$O$_6$). Slow evaporation of this solution causes the gradual deposition of triclinic crystals of *dextro*-[Co en$_3$]Cl(d-C$_4$O$_6$H$_4$) $\cdot$5H$_2$O. These crystals are removed as completely as possible; additional concentration of the mother liquor gives a viscous residue. Solutions of the triclinic crystals and of the viscous residue when treated with solutions of sodium iodide precipitate the crystalline iodides respectively: d-[Co en$_3$]I$_3 \cdot$H$_2$O and l-[Co en$_3$]I$_3 \cdot$H$_2$O. Although this procedure gives satisfactory results for [Co en$_3$]$^{+++}$, the task of separating enantiomers is often very tedious and the most suitable resolving agent and conditions must be found by trial and error for each particular complex cation (page 332).

Anionic Complex Compounds. The number of anionic complexes which have been obtained in optically-active form is considerably less than that for cationic complexes. The spatial arrangements are the same as illustrated in Fig. 8.33 and specific examples are given in Table 8.6.

TABLE 8.6. SOME ASYMMETRIC ANIONS WHICH ARE REPORTED TO HAVE BEEN RESOLVED

[M(AA)$_3$]

[Al(C$_2$O$_4$)$_3$]$^{\equiv 113}$

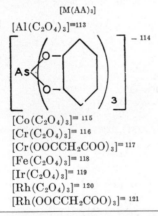

[Co(C$_2$O$_4$)$_3$]$^{\equiv}$ [115]
[Cr(C$_2$O$_4$)$_3$]$^{\equiv}$ [116]
[Cr(OOCCH$_2$COO)$_3$]$^{\equiv}$ [117]
[Fe(C$_2$O$_4$)$_3$]$^{\equiv}$ [118]
[Ir(C$_2$O$_4$)$_3$]$^{\equiv}$ [119]
[Rh(C$_2$O$_4$)$_3$]$^{\equiv}$ [120]
[Rh(OOCCH$_2$COO)$_3$]$^{\equiv}$ [121]

[M(AA)$_2$a$_2$]

[Ir(C$_2$O$_4$)$_2$Cl$_2$]$^{\equiv}$ [16]
[Rh(NHSO$_2$NH)$_2$(H$_2$O)$_2$]$^-$ [122]
[Rh(C$_2$O$_4$)$_2$Cl$_2$]$^{\equiv}$ [17]

[M(AA)$_2$ab]

[Ru py(C$_2$O$_4$)$_2$NO]$^-$ [123]

[M(AA)a$_2$b$_2$]

[Co(NH$_3$)$_2$C$_2$O$_4$(NO$_2$)$_2$]$^-$ [43]

113. Burrows and Lauder, *J. Am. Chem. Soc.*, **52**, 2600 (1931); Treadwell, Szabados, and Haimann, *Helv. chim. Acta.*, **15**, 1049 (1932); Wahli, *Ber.*, **60**, 399 (1927).
114. Rosenheim and Plato, *Ber.*, **58**, 2000 (1925); Weinland and Heinzler, *Ber.*, **52**, 1322 (1919).
115. Jaeger, *Rec. trav. chim.*, **38**, 247 (1919).
116. Jaeger, *ibid.*, **38**, 243 (1919); Werner, *Ber.*, **45**, 3061 (1912).
117. Jaeger, *Rec. trav. chim.*, **38**, 294 (1919).
118. Thomas, *J. Chem. Soc.*, **119**, 1140 (1921).
119. Delepine, *Compt. rend.*, **159**, 239 (1914); Delepine, *Bull. Soc. chim.*, [4] **21**, 161 (1917).

In general, the methods used to resolve complex anions are based on the same principles as those used with the cations, that is, the combination with an easily removable optically-active substance. Since the complexes are anions in this case, the cations to which they are linked must be replaced by optically-active bases. Strychnine has been used to resolve the trioxalatocobaltate(III), chromate(III), rhodate(III), and iridate(III) salts[124]. The strychnine can easily be removed by precipitation as the iodide with potassium iodide, the potassium salt of the optically active anion remaining in solution.

Nonionic Complex Compounds. Asymmetric inner-complex compounds are known to exist and, theoretically these can be resolved into their optically-active antipodes. The ordinary technique is not applicable to the resolution of these compounds because they do not form salts. Very few complexes of this type have been obtained in their optically-active forms. Lifschitz[27] did obtain some evidence for the existence of the four possible isomers of tris(d-alanine)cobalt(III). The resolution of a complex of the type, $[Co(DMG)_2 NH_3 Cl]$, has been accomplished by the preferential adsorption of an antipode on optically-active quartz[28, 125]. Dwyer and his co-workers have recently had some success with the resolution of nonionic complexes by applying their method of "configurational activity" (page 335).

Complex Compounds Containing Optically-active Donor Molecules. Optically-active bidentate molecules or ions have been made to coordinate with hexacovalent metals and the stereochemistry of some of these complex compounds has been investigated. Complexes of this type are of interest because they offer problems for which there are no counterparts in the stereochemistry of carbon compounds.

Limited Number of Isomers. An octahedral complex containing three molecules of an optically-active bidentate coordinating agent would be expected to exist in a large number of stereoisomeric forms. Taking D and L to represent the signs of rotation of the complex as a whole; and d and l, the signs of rotation of the bidentate molecule, there are eight possible combinations: D[lll], D[lld], D[ldd], D[ddd], L[lll], L[lld], L[ldd] and L[ddd]. Moreover, since these eight cases, when taken in pairs represent each other's mirror images (D[ddd] and L[lll], D[ldd] and L[dll], etc.) they may be combined pair-wise in equimolecular quantities to yield four racemoids and twenty-four partial racemoids. Experiment has shown, however, that these

120. Werner, *Ber.*, **47,** 1954 (1914).
121. Jaeger, *Rec. trav. chim.*, **38,** 300 (1919).
122. Mann, *J. Chem. Soc.*, **1933,** 412.
123. Charonnat, *Compt. rend.*, **178,** 1423 (1924).
124. Jaeger, *Rec. trav. chim.*, **38,** 245, 251, 263, 265 (1919).
125. Kuroya, Aimi, and Tsuchida, *J. Chem. Soc., Japan*, **64,** 995 (1943).

combinations are not all of equal stability; in fact, for octahedral complexes containing optically-active propylenediamine[92, 126], 1,2-cyclopentanediamine[93] and 1,2-cyclohexanediamine[94] only the L[*lll*] and D[*ddd*] (or, in other cases, L[*ddd*] and D[*lll*]) isomeric ions are stable enough to be isolated. A similar effect is observed if the complex contains only two optically-active coordinating groups. It has been shown that ions such as *cis*-[Co pn₂ Cl₂]⁺ and *cis*[Co cptn₂ Cl₂]⁺ exist in only two of the six possible forms-D[*ll*Cl₂] and L[*dd*Cl₂][127]*. If the dichlorobis(*levo*-propylenediamine)cobalt(III) ion, [Co *l*-pn₂ Cl₂]⁺, is treated with *dextro*-propylenediamine, the ion [Co *l*-pn₂ *d*-pn]⁺⁺⁺ apparently forms, but immediately rearranges to a mixture of the more stable L[Co *d*-pn₃]⁺⁺⁺ and D[Co *l*-pn₃]⁺⁺⁺ [92, 128]. Analogous results have been obtained with optically-active cyclopentanediamine and the reactions which occur are summarized by Jaeger[100] as:

$$[ddCl_2] \xrightarrow{l} [ddl] \rightarrow 2[ddd] + [lll], \quad \text{or } [ddd] + \text{racemoid}$$

$$[llCl_2] \xrightarrow{d} [lld] \rightarrow 2[lll] + [ddd], \quad \text{or } [lll] + \text{racemoid}$$

These selective effects, while pronounced, are not absolute, but relative. Lifschitz[27] found evidence that tris(*d*-alanine)cobalt(III) and chromium(III) exist in D[*ddd*] and L[*ddd*] forms. It has likewise been shown by Bailar and McReynolds[129] that the ion [Co *l*-pn₂ CO₃]⁺ exists in both D[*ll*CO₃] and L[*ll*CO₃] forms; they believed that the latter is unstable, rearranging to the former when warmed gently. Recent studies[130] indicate that these two forms are present in a state of equilibrium which shifts predominantly towards D[*ll*CO₃] upon standing in solution; however, if this solution is evaporated to dryness, the residue obtained is largely L[*ll*CO₃].

When only one molecule of the optically-active base is present in the coordination sphere, there is some tendency toward the formation of preferred orientations, but not enough to fix completely the configurations. Thus, when Jaeger and Blumendal[93] allowed racemic *trans*-1,2-cyclopentanediamine to react with racemic [Co en₂ Cl₂]⁺, they obtained a true racemic mixture of D-[Co en₂ *l*-cptn]⁺⁺⁺ and L-[Co en₂ *d*-cptn]⁺⁺⁺ without detecting any of the other two possible forms. When, however, they used *levo*-cyclopentanediamine, they observed that the base entered both the D and L forms of the complex, yielding D and L-[Co en₂ *l*-cptn]⁺⁺⁺. A comparable system, studied by Jonassen, Bailar and Huffman[131], reveals that *dextro*-tartaric acid reacts readily with [Co en₂ CO₃]⁺ to give the two di-

126. Tschugaeff and Sokoloff, *Ber.*, **40**, 177 (1907); *Ibid.*, **42**, 55 (1909).

* This disregards the possibility of position isomers (page 286).

127. Lifschitz, *Z. physik. Chem.*, **114**, 493 (1925).
128. Bailar, Stiegman, Balthis, and Huffman, *J. Am. Chem. Soc.*, **61**, 2402 (1939).
129. Bailar and McReynolds, *ibid.*, **61**, 3199 (1939).
130. Martinette and Bailar, *J. Am. Chem. Soc.*, **74**, 1054 (1952).
131. Jonassen, Bailar, and Huffman, *J. Am. Chem. Soc.*, **70**, 756 (1948).

astereoisomers D-[Co en$_2$ d-tart]$^+$ and L-[Co en$_2$ d-tart]$^+$, which differ strikingly in stability, reactivity, and solubility. It has recently been shown that the equilibrium mixture of the two diastereoisomers when heated to 150° changes to L-[Co en$_2$ d-tart]$^+$ [132].

These experiments with salts of the type [Co en$_2$ Cl$_2$]Cl show that a molecule of an optically-active base, such as *levo*-cyclopentanediamine, may be introduced into either the D or L antipode. Such an introduction is more difficult if two molecules of the optically-active antipode of the substitute are originally present, instead of two molecules of ethylenediamine. It would appear from this that there is a more pronounced contrast between a dextro and levo isomer of the same compound than exists between an optically-active molecule and a totally different substance. The presence of such nonrelated molecules in a coordination sphere appears to be a less serious hindrance to the entrance of an optically-active substitute than is the presence of similar molecules having opposed enantiomorphous arrangements.

Complex Compound as a Possible Resolving Agent. The results obtained with optically-active coordinating agents suggest that in the reaction between an optically-active complex and an excess of a racemic coordinating substance the complex may accept one antipode of the coordinating agent preferentially, thus effecting a resolution. Investigations of this possibility have been made[128, 133].

Although the presence of two or three optically-active chelate groups in an octahedral complex tends to fix a definite configuration upon the complex as a whole, and limits the number of stereoisomers which can be isolated to a small fraction of those theoretically possible, this effect is considerably less noticeable in complex ions containing only one asymmetric chelate group. As has already been indicated, however, while both the D and L forms of *dextro*-tartratobis(ethylenediamine)cobalt(III) ion, [Co en$_2$ d-tart]$^+$, exist, they differ greatly in reactivity[131]. When the mixture of the two is shaken with ethylenediamine at room temperature, part of the material reacts within two hours, giving D-[Co en$_3$]$^{+++}$, and the remainder does not react even in twelve hours. This indicates that if the complex were prepared from racemic tartaric acid, the active antipodes would be displaced at different rates. This effect has been considerably enhanced by using *levo*-propylenediamine in place of ethylenediamine. Racemic tartaric acid has been partially resolved by treating *dl*-tartratobis-(*l*-propylenediamine)cobalt(III) chloride with *l*-propylenediamine[133a, 134]. The first ion removed from the complex was largely the *l*-tartrate. Resolu-

132. Johnson, thesis, University of Illinois, 1948.
133. Jonassen, Bailar, and Gott, *J. Am. Chem. Soc.*, **74**, 3131 (1952); Hamilton, thesis, University of Illinois, 1947.
134. Gott and Bailar, *J. Am. Chem. Soc.*, **74**, 4820 (1952).

tion of this acid is also achieved when dl-tartratobis(l-propylenediamine)-cobalt(III) chloride is made to react with racemic tartrate[133b]. The l-tartrato group is displaced from the complex ion by d-tartrate and, consequently, the final reaction mixture contains largely l-tartrate ion and the d-tartrato complex. In the same manner, l-propylenediamine is obtained from the reaction of a mixture of d-tartratobis(l-propylenediamine)cobalt(III) chloride and d-tartratobis(d-propylenediamine)cobalt(III) chloride with racemic propylenediamine[132].

It may be mentioned in conclusion that many optically-active complex salts have been shown by Shibata to exhibit a catalytic oxidizing effect, analogous to the enzymic action of oxidases[135]. When, for example, $racemic$-3,4-dihydroxy-phenylalanine was oxidized under the catalytic influence of $levo$-chloroamminebis(ethylenediamine)cobalt(III) bromide, l-[Co en$_2$ NH$_3$ Cl]Br$_2$, the levo amino acid was preferentially destroyed. Although this has been attributed to an "enzyme-like action" by the inorganic complex, Bailar[136] has suggested as an additional explanation, that one form of the amino acid becomes part of the complex, while the other does not, and subsequent oxidation merely destroys one or the other. Studies of this type have likewise been carried out by Pugh[137] whose results are not entirely in accord with those of Shibata.

Partial Asymmetric Synthesis. The fact that hexacovalent complexes containing optically-active groups do not exist in all the possible stereochemical forms, but only in certain preferred configurations, suggests that these groups exert a steric effect on the coordination sphere of the central metal ion which hinders the formation of the other isomers. Thus, existence of only D[lll] and L[ddd] isomers indicates that the addition of l antipodes to a complex always gives rise to a DEXTRO configuration of the octahedron and, likewise, a d antipode always causes the formation of a LEVO structure. In other words, a preferred configuration is induced by optically-active coordinating groups, and reactions which introduce such groups give rise to an asymmetric octahedron.

Evidence that such partial asymmetric syntheses take place was obtained by a study of the molecular rotation of various platinum complexes containing different numbers of coordinated $levo$-propylenediamine molecules. It was shown[126b] that the molecular rotation caused by each molecule of $levo$-propylenediamine introduced into various platinum(II) complexes is about 96 degrees (Table 8.7). Since the presence of two molecules of active propylenediamine results in a molecular rotation of 192°, it might be expected that the addition of a third active molecule would give a com-

135. Shibata and Tsuchida, *Bull. Chem. Soc., Japan,* **4,** 142 (1929); Shibata, Tonaka, and Goda, *ibid.,* **6,** 210 (1931).
136. Bailar, *Chem. Revs.,* **19,** 67 (1938).
137. Pugh, *Biochem. J.,* **27,** 480 (1933).

TABLE 8.7. OPTICAL ROTATION OF PLATINUM(II) COMPLEXES CONTAINING
levo-PROPYLENEDIAMINE

Substance	$[\alpha]_D^{25°}$	$[M]_D^{25°}$
[Pt *l*-pn $(NH_3)_2$]Cl_2	+25.17	+94.14
[Pt *l*-pn en]Cl_2	+24.07	+96.28
[Pt *l*-pn tn]Cl_2	+23.60	+97.70
[Pt *l*-pn$_2$]Cl_2	+46.37	+192.0

pound with a molecular rotation of $+288°$. However, it was observed by Smirnoff[92] that the compounds formed by addition of this third base molecule were L-[Pt *d*-pn$_3$]X_4 and D-[Pt *l*-pn$_3$]X_4, with values of $[M]_D$ equal to $-1027°$ and $+1025°$, respectively. If it is assumed that only $288°$ of the total is due to the three active propylenediamine groups, the excess must be a result of the asymmetry of the cation.

A similar asymmetric effect is observed when only two optically-active bidentates are coordinated to the hexacovalent central ion. This is clearly demonstrated by the similar rotatory dispersion curves of numerous bis-(ethylenediamine)cobalt(III) ions and analogous *cis*-bis(*active*-propylene-diamine)cobalt(III) ions[50]. The rotatory dispersion curves of the corresponding trans isomers resemble that of active propylenediamine because the complex is symmetrical and therefore cannot contribute to the optical activity.

Complex Compounds Containing Optically-active Unsymmetrical Donor Molecules. The most extensively studied asymmetric bidentate molecule which has been used as a coordinating group is propylenediamine. The number of theoretically possible isomers of complexes of the type [M pn$_3$] is greatly increased due to the existence of position isomers as well as the optical isomers (Fig. 8.34).

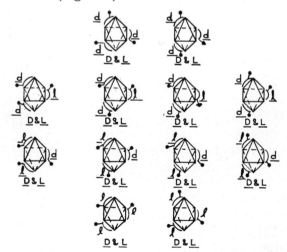

FIG. 8.34. Possible forms of some complexes containing optically active ligands.

If all of the predicted isomers and all the total and partial racemates were found, the chemistry of these complexes would be hopelessly complicated, but that is not the case. For example, the only isomers which were isolated or identified for cobalt(III) were D-[Co d-pn$_3$]Cl$_3$ and L-[Co l-pn$_3$]Cl$_3$ and the totally inactive racemic mixture of these two[138]. No effect of the position of the methyl groups could be detected. Here again the asymmetry of the coordinating group exerts an effect, presumably steric, on the complex formed by cobalt(III) ion. It was shown (Fig. 8.35) that theoretically there are two stereoisomers for each of the complexes [M-lll] and [M-ddd] (depending on whether the angular methyl groups all lie near the same plane or whether two are near one plane and the third is further removed from it). The exact nature of the stereoisomeric forms of the two stable isomers are not known.

The only conclusive proof of isomerism due to the position of the methyl group of the propylenediamine molecule was made by Werner and Smirnoff[32] on the complex cis-[Co en pn (NO$_2$)$_2$]X (Fig. 8.15) (page 286).

A similar compound containing two active propylenediamine molecules has been investigated by Hurlimann[49] and by Watts[107]. The cis modification of this ion, [Co(d or l-pn)$_2$(NO$_2$)$_2$]$^+$, should exist in twelve forms as shown in Fig. 8.35. They were able to isolate only two active forms and concluded

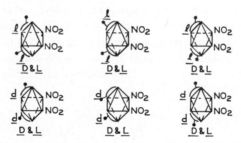

FIG. 8.35. Possible forms of cis-[Co pn$_2$ (NO$_2$)$_2$]$^+$

that the position of the methyl groups is immaterial, because except for these groups, the three position isomers for [Co(l-pn)$_2$(NO$_2$)$_2$]$^+$ or [Co(d-pn)$_2$(NO$_2$)$_2$]$^+$ are identical. The work of O'Brien, McReynolds, and Bailar[50] casts some doubt on this interpretation.

Complex Compounds Containing Polydentate Donor Molecules. Compounds containing polydentate coordinating groups have received only limited attention, but some of them have been shown to be optically active. A typical example of a tridentate molecule may be furnished by α,β,γ-triaminopropane which was investigated by Pope and Mann[41b, 139].

138. Tschugaeff and Sokoloff, *Ber.*, **42**, 55 (1909); Lifschitz and Rosenbohm, *Z. wiss. Phot.*, **19**, 209, 211 (1920).

The triamine is capable of displacing the ammonia molecules from hexammine complexes to yield the cation containing two moles of the organic amine, $[M(AA'A)_2]^{+++}$. Such a complex may possibly exist in three isomeric forms; (I) is symmetrical and inactive while (II) and (III) are asymmetric and, therefore, optically active (Fig. 8.36). Isomer(III) may appear to

I   II   III
FIG. 8.36. Possible forms of $[M(AA'A)_2]$

be symmetrical, but, on further consideration, it can be seen that the lateral displacement of the central atom in triaminopropane destroys the symmetry of the complex. Attempts to isolate these three isomers of the cobalt(III) ion were not successful and only the inactive form (I) was obtained. A consideration of the scale model of this complex tends somewhat to clarify these results. It is seen that it is sterically impossible for the triaminopropane molecule to occupy three positions along the edge of an octahedron since the five-membered chain which includes the 1 and 3 amine groups is by no means of sufficient length to span the trans positions. If this were not true, trimethylenediamine should be capable of spanning the trans positions. The shortest chain which has given any evidence indicative of such behavior contains seven members (pages 259 and 277). This factor eliminates the possibility of attaining structure (III). Models also indicate considerable strain when the base behaves in a tridentate manner with its functional groups distributed at the corners of an octahedral face. It might be suspected that the bonds in the molecule are subject to sufficient strain to allow rapid racemization of the structure (II), if it is formed, by an intramolecular rearrangement mechanism. Pope and Mann were able to obtain slight evidence for the existence of the active forms by repeated crystallization of the *dextro*-camphor-π-sulfonate, which gave a very faintly active chloride. The activity of this small quantity fell rapidly to zero and the final compound was always homogeneous and inactive.

The researches of Morgan and Main-Smith[140] with ethylenediamino-bis-(acetylacetone),

$$CH_3C(OH){=}CHC(CH_3){=}N{-}CH_2CH_2{-}N{=}C(CH_3)CH{=}C(OH)CH_3 ,$$

139. Pope and Mann, *Proc. Roy. Soc.*, London, **109A**, 444 (1925).
140. Morgan and Main-Smith, *J. Chem. Soc.*, **127**, 2030 (1925).

can be used to illustrate the isomerism resulting from a tetradenate chelating agent. The complex, $[Co(NH_3)_2C_{12}H_{18}O_2N_2]Cl$, may exist in five stereochemical arrangements (Fig. 8.37). The complex ion with two ammonia

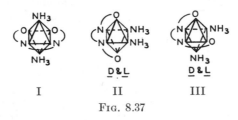

I   II   III

Fig. 8.37

groups in the trans positions (I) has a plane of symmetry and is, therefore, inactive. If the two ammonia groups are cis to one another, the tetradentate molecule can arrange itself so that the terminal oxygen groups are opposite (II), or adjacent to each other (III) and, in addition, each of these can exist in mirror image forms. Morgan and Main-Smith were able to obtain all five isomers by careful fractional crystallization of the *dextro*-camphor-π-sulfonate. The optically-active forms slowly changed into the trans isomer and all attempts to separate a resolvable material from it failed. It was believed that this may result from a seeding of the more stable trans form but, the authors were also unable to repeat this separation in a different laboratory with new equipment.* Basolo[141] has studied a tetradentate co-ordinating agent, triethylenetetramine,

$$NH_2CH_2CH_2NHCH_2CH_2NHCH_2CH_2NH_2 .$$

Several cobalt(III) salts containing this tetramine were isolated but none could be resolved due to poor solubility relationships. However, Das Sarma[141a] has obtained the dichloro complex, [Co trien Cl_2]Cl, in optically active forms.

Busch and Bailar[143] have resolved [Co enta Br]$^=$ and [Co enta]$^-$, in which the ethylenediaminetetraacetate ion is pentadentate and hexadentate, respectively. Dwyer and Lions[37, 39a, 39b, 141, 143] have conclusively shown that 3,6-dithia-1,8-bis(salicylideneamino)octane and its derivatives

---

* Although octahedral complexes involving linear tetradentate chelating agents theoretically can exist in the five stereochemical forms shown in Fig. 8.37, the Fisher-Hirschfelder models indicate that structures II and III involving ethylenediamine-bis(acetylacetone) would be badly strained as a result of the restricted rotation derived from the double bonds.

141. Basolo, *J. Am. Chem. Soc.*, **70**, 2346 (1948).
141a. Das Sarma, and Bailar, *ibid.*, **77**, 5480 (1955).
142. Dwyer and Gyarfas, *Nature*, **168**, 29 (1951).
143. Busch and Bailar, *J. Am. Chem. Soc.*, **75**, 4574 (1953).
143a. Das Sarma and Bailar, *ibid.*, **76**, 4051 (1954).

can function as hexadentate chelating compounds in one or another of two enantiomorphous, strainless configurations. The cobalt(III) cation,

$$[Co(C_{22}H_{22}N_2O_2S_2)]^+$$

was resolved by means of the *dextro*-bromocamphor-π-sulfonate and the molecular rotation (Hg green line) was $\pm 50,160°$. Solutions of these salts can be boiled for twenty minutes without racemization. Das Sarma and Bailar[143a] have reported the resolution of the cobalt(III), iron(III) and aluminum(III) complexes of

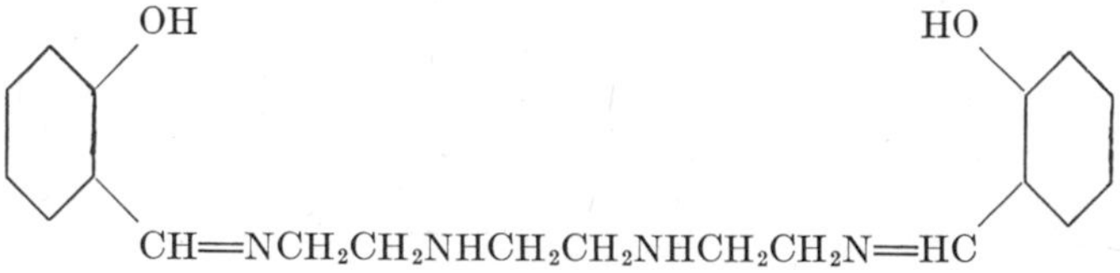

$$CH\!=\!NCH_2CH_2NHCH_2CH_2NHCH_2CH_2N\!=\!HC$$

Polynuclear Complex Compounds. Most of the work with polynuclear complexes was done by Werner who isolated the first optically-active dinuclear compound,

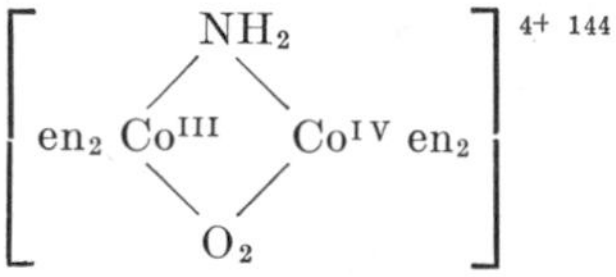

Since the two portions of the ion were different (Co(III) and Co(IV)), four different optically-active isomers should be possible; D-[Co(III)] and D-[Co(IV)]; L-[Co(III)] and L-[Co(IV)]; D-[Co(III)] and L-[Co(IV)]; L-[Co(III)] and D-[Co(IV)]. On the basis of the modern concept of resonance, the last two combinations are the same, which means that there are really only three possibilities. Werner succeeded in obtaining only two of these, one in which both the cobalt atoms were dextro and the other in which both the cobalt atoms were levo rotatory. The optically-active antipodes have large rotations, ($[\alpha]_D = \pm 815°$ and $[\alpha]_E = \pm 1200°$), and are rather stable although the active cation is completely racemized after some weeks. Werner suggests that the valence of the central atom has a marked influence on the magnitude of optical rotation, basing his suggestion on the fact that the specific rotation of similar dinuclear complexes containing two Co(III) atoms is considerably less. The data available are insufficient to support his postulate.

It can readily be seen that, had the asymmetric centers in the above com-

---

144. Werner, *Ann.*, **375**, 70 (1910); Werner, *Ber.*, **47**, 1961 (1914).

pound been structurally similar, there should exist an internally compensated or meso form as well as the dextro and levo rotary isomers. Such a binuclear complex would be analogous to tartaric acid amongst the active carbon compounds. The resolution of a complex of this type

$$\left[\begin{array}{c} NH_2 \\ \diagup \quad \diagdown \\ en_2\ Co \qquad Co\ en_2 \\ \diagdown \quad \diagup \\ NO_2 \end{array} \right] Br_4$$

was studied by Werner[145]. Fractional crystallization of the *dextro-α*-bromo-camphor-*π*-sulfonate yielded dextro and levo rotary compounds which gave a true racemate when equimolecular quantities of the enantiomorphs were combined. This racemate differed from a third optically-inactive isomeride, which must have been the meso complex (Fig. 8.38). The pres-

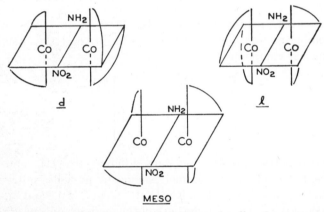

FIG. 8.38. Possible stereochemical forms of a dinuclear complex

ence of this meso form was used by Werner to show that the bridging bonds between the two cobalt(III) ions are the same.

Purely Inorganic Complex Compounds. Although Werner successfully resolved compounds of the types $[M(AA)_3]$ and $[M(AA)_2a_2]$ in which the optical activity could be ascribed to an octahedral spatial arrangement, some of his contemporaries objected to this interpretation on the basis that these compounds contained carbon atoms. It is now clear that the organic compounds in these complexes could not be responsible for the observed optical activity, but at that time it was necessary for Werner to resolve a purely inorganic complex in order to establish his theory. This was successfully accomplished in 1914 by the resolution of the tetranuclear

145. Werner, *Ber.*, **46**, 3674 (1913).

complex,

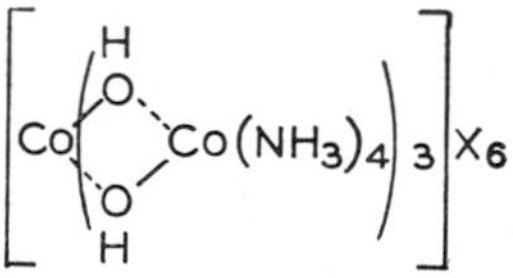

$$\left[Co \left(\begin{array}{c} H \\ O \\ \diagdown \\ O \\ H \end{array} Co(NH_3)_4 \right)_3 \right] X_6$$

The compound was prepared by the action of ammonia on chloroaquo-tetramminecobalt (III) chloride[5] and is analogous to the tris(ethylenedia-mine) salts with the bidentate group being

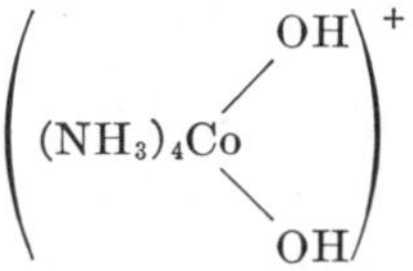

$$\left((NH_3)_4 \overset{..}{C}o \begin{array}{c} OH \\ \diagup \\ \diagdown \\ OH \end{array} \right)^+$$

(Fig. 8.39). The racemic mixture was resolved by means of *dextro-α*-bromo-

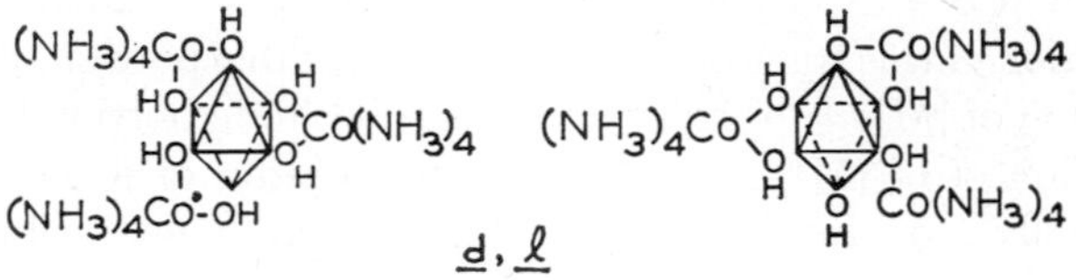

FIG. 8.39

camphor-π-sulfonate, which yielded the levo rotary ion in the less soluble fraction. The optically-active antipodes undergo rapid racemization and their rotation is best studied in mixtures of water and acetone. A very high molecular rotation ($[M]_{5600}$) of $-47, 610°$ was obtained.

Only one other purely inorganic complex compound has been resolved into its optically-active antipodes. Mann[122] has successfully resolved *cis*-$Na[Rh(SO_2N_2H_2)_2(H_2O)_2]$ into optical isomerides having $[M]_{5780} \pm 31–34°$, by means of *d*-phenylethylamine. It has been shown that sulphamide, $SO_2(NH_2)_2$, like dimethylglyoxime[146], will occupy only four positions in the complex of a hexacovalent element.

Optical Activity of Coordinated Atoms. It is sometimes possible for an atom of a donor molecule to be rendered optically active because the molecule is coordinated to a central ion.

Nitrogen. Meisenheimer, Angermann, Holsten, and Kiderlen[147] demon-strated the tetrahedral nature of the nitrogen atom by resolving (sarco-

146. Tschugaeff, *Z. anorg. Chem.*, **46**, 144 (1905); Tschugaeff, *Ber.*, **39**, 2692 (1906); Tschugaeff, *ibid.*, **40**, 3498 (1907); Tschugaeff, *ibid.*, **41**, 2226 (1908).
147. Meisenheimer, Angermann, Holsten, and Kiderlen, *Ann.*, **438**, 217 (1924).

sine)bis-(ethylenediamine)cobalt(III) chloride into more than two optically-active isomers.

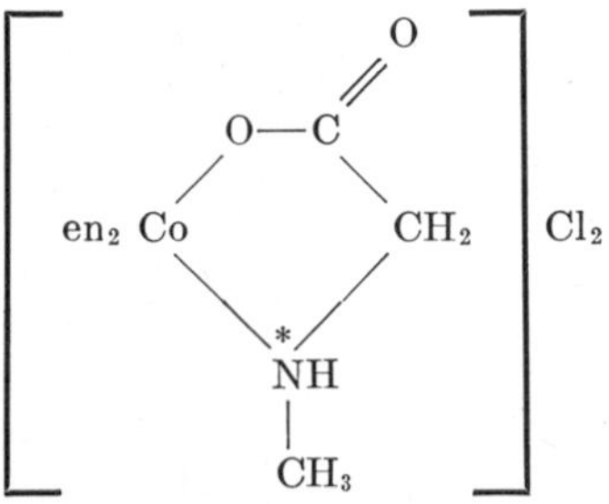

$$\left[\begin{array}{c} en_2\ Co \diagdown \begin{array}{c} O-C \diagup\diagdown^{O} \\ \diagdown CH_2 \\ \overset{*}{NH} \\ | \\ CH_3 \end{array} \end{array} \right] Cl_2$$

In this case, the complex is itself optically active, and the nitrogen atom acts as a secondary source of optical activity, so that there should be four active forms of this complex ([Co + N +], [Co + N −], [Co − N +], and [Co − N −]). Fractional crystallization of the *dextro*-α-bromocamphor-π-sulfonate gave indication that these forms exist. One fraction, believed to be [Co + N ±], had a rotation of $[M]_D = +2020°$ and further recrystallization of this fraction gave a slightly soluble portion, [Co + N +], with a rotation of $[M]_D = +2290°$ and a more soluble portion [Co + N −], with a rotation of of $[M]_D = +1775°$. The rotation of [Co + N +] decreased rapidly to approximately the orginal value while that of [Co + N −] increased only to $[M]_D = +1825°$.

An attempt to duplicate Meisenheimer's results was not successful[148]. Mann[40] attempted unsuccessfully to resolve the complex

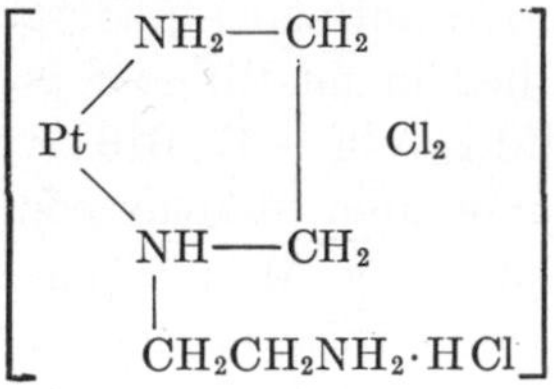

$$\left[\begin{array}{c} NH_2-CH_2 \\ \diagup \quad\quad | \\ Pt \quad\quad\quad Cl_2 \\ \diagdown \quad\quad | \\ NH-CH_2 \\ | \\ CH_2CH_2NH_2\cdot HCl \end{array} \right]$$

in which the only source of optical activity is the asymmetric nitrogen atom. Since the compound could not be resolved, it was suggested that other polyamines such as ββ'-diaminoethylmethylamine and β-aminodiethylmethylamine be used. In these compounds the asymmetric nitrogen is part of a tertiary amine group and should, therefore, possess much greater optical stability than the secondary amine compounds. At the same time the coordination of the tertiary amine group should be greatly strengthened by the chelate ring of which this group is a part. No report on the results of this work seems to have been published.

148. Basolo, thesis, University of Illinois, 1943.

Kuebler and Bailar[149] have prepared and investigated potassium dinitro-(N-methyl-N-ethylglycine)platinate(II), and have demonstrated the existence of an asymmetric optically-active nitrogen atom in this compound through its resolution by fractionation with l-quinine and also by adsorption on optically-active quartz powder. It should be noted that N-methyl-N-ethylglycine differs from sarcosine in having no hydrogen atom attached directly to the nitrogen. Part of the difficulty encountered with the sarcosine complex may result from the dissociation of the hydrogen atom from the nitrogen (Chapter 12), thus allowing racemization.

Sulfur. Tetrachloro(thiodiethylenediamine-N,S)platinum(IV) hydro-

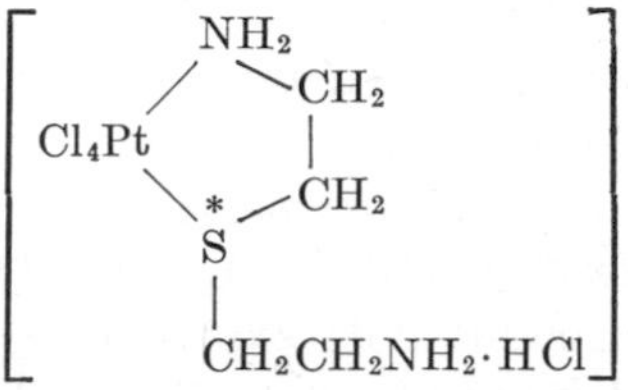

$$
\left[\begin{array}{c} \mathrm{NH_2} \\ Cl_4Pt \diagdown \diagup \overset{\displaystyle \diagdown CH_2}{\underset{\displaystyle \underset{|}{S} \diagup CH_2}{|}} \\ \overset{|}{\underset{\displaystyle CH_2 CH_2 NH_2 \cdot HCl}{}} \end{array} \right]
$$

chloride, is an example of a complex in which the optical activity is due to an element linked to the central atom[40b]. The sulfur atom in the original diaminodiethylsulfide molecule has become asymmetric by the process of coordination and is now stereochemically, and probably electronically, identical with the sulfur atom in the asymmetric sulfoxides, such as *p*-amino-*p*-methyl-diphenyl sulfoxide which has been resolved by Harrison, Kenyon and Phillips[150].

Racemic Modifications

Racemic modifications are obtained by mixing equal amounts of the enantiomorphs, by chemical syntheses, or by racemization of an optically-active material.

Optically-active inorganic complex compounds are generally optically unstable, and can easily be racemized. The process of racemization implies conversion of one form to the other until the dextro and levo isomers are present in equal amounts. Two theories have been proposed to explain the mechanism of such a conversion in coordination compounds: Dissociation and intramolecular rearrangement.

Dissociation Theory of Racemization. Most of the experiments related to racemization studies have involved the trisoxalato anions. The theory of racemization by dissociation[118] assumes that an oxalate ion dissociates from the complex; the residue, according to Thomas[157], undergoes reorientation to a planar distribution of the four coordinated groups; and,

149. Kuebler and Bailar, *J. Am. Chem. Soc.*, **74**, 3535 (1952).
150. Harrison, Kenyon, and Phillips, *J. Chem. Soc.*, **1926**, 2079.

upon recombination of the third oxalato group, the original configuration and its mirror image are formed with equal probability (Fig. 8.40). Thomas

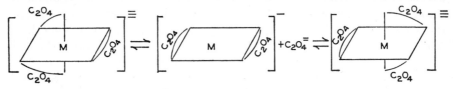

Fig. 8.40

based this theory on the fact that the addition of silver nitrate to a solution of $[Fe(C_2O_4)_3]^=$ gives an immediate precipitate of silver oxalate, but when silver nitrate is added to $[Cr(C_2O_4)_3]^=$ the precipitate forms only on long standing[151]. Other investigators have shown that the precipitate so obtained is not silver oxalate but is $Ag_3[M(C_2O_4)_3] \cdot 6H_2O$[152] or K_nAg_m-$[M(C_2O_4)_3] \cdot xH_2O$[153]. The conductivity experiments of Thomas and Fraser[154] could not be checked by Johnson[155].

Numerous investigations have been made to establish conclusively that the dissociation theory does not adequately account for the racemization of the tris(oxalato) complexes of cobalt(III) and chromium(III). For example, in no case could free oxalate ion be detected in solutions of tris-oxalatochromium(III) or cobalt(III) salts, nor was it possible to change the rate of racemization of these active substances by the addition of the common oxalate ion[156]. Johnson and Mead[157] were able to show that these salts racemize even in the crystalline state. Finally the fact that the dissociation theory is not correct was conclusively demonstrated by using oxalate containing radioactive carbon and determining the amount of oxalate exchange in solutions of these compounds. If this theory is correct, the rate of racemization should parallel the rate of interchange. However, Long[158] was able to detect no exchange although the active complex, $K_3[Cr(C_2O_4)_3]$, was slowly being racemized. A similar study using inactive $[Fe(C_2O_4)_3]^=$ and $[Al(C_2O_4)_3]^=$ resulted in a very rapid exchange, which implies that optical activity in these compounds is very unlikely[159]. Mathieu[71] has investi-

151. Thomas, *J. Chem. Soc.*, **121**, 196 (1922).
152. Kistiakowsky, *Z. physik. Chem.*, **6**, 96 (1890).
153. Kranig, *Ann. chim.*, **11**, 44 (1929).
154. Thomas and Frazer, *J. Chem. Soc.*, **123**, 2973 (1923).
155. Johnson, *Trans. Faraday Soc.*, **31**, 1615 (1935).
156. Beese and Johnson, *Trans. Faraday Soc.*, **31**, 1635 (1935); Bushra and Johnson,
     J. Chem. Soc., **1939**, 1941.
157. Johnson and Mead, *Trans. Faraday Soc.*, **31**, 1621 (1935).
158. Long, *J. Am. Chem. Soc.*, **61**, 570 (1939).
159. Long, *ibid.*, **63**, 1353 (1941).

gated the rate of change of optical rotation of a solution of *dextro*-[Co en$_2$ Cl$_2$]$^+$. He observed that the optical rotation changed to a fairly constant value at the same rate that chloride ion was formed. The resulting [Co en$_2$ H$_2$O Cl]$^{++}$ ion then racemized at a rate independent of the rate of formation of the diaquo complex. On the basis of these results it was suggested that the racemization of [Co en$_2$ H$_2$O Cl]$^{++}$ may occur as a consequence of the dissociation of the coordinated water molecule (Fig. 8.41).

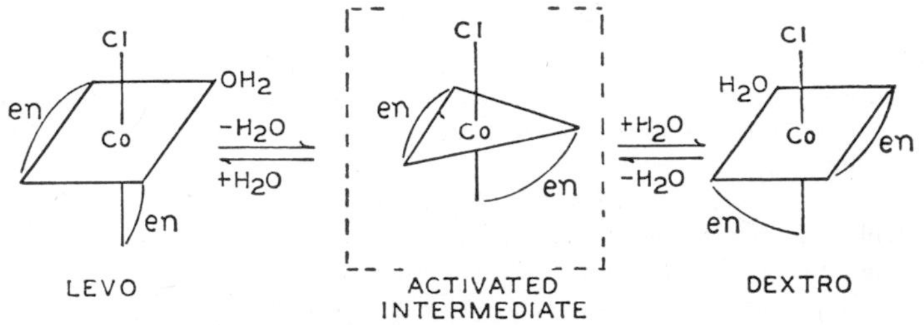

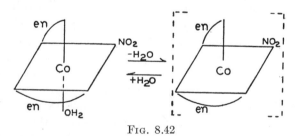

FIG. 8.41. Racemization of [Co en$_2$ (H$_2$O)Cl]$^{++}$

Mathieu observed that the analogous complex [Co en$_2$ H$_2$O NO$_2$]$^{++}$ does not racemize, even upon standing in solution for several months. If one assumes that the coordinated water dissociates at a measurable rate[82] then it would appear that the intermediate in this case has a tetragonal pyramid configuration (Fig. 8.42) instead of the trigonal by-pyramid structure.

FIG. 8.42

It has recently been shown[161] that the rate of racemization of dextro-[Co en$_2$ Cl$_2$]Cl in methanol is equal to the rate of radio-chlorine exchange. Therefore, racemization is thought to occur through a symmetrical penta-covalent intermediate.

Failure of the presence of excess 2,2′-dipyridyl to alter the rate of racemization of [Ni(dipy)$_3$]$^{++}$ [162] and of excess 1,10-phenanthroline to effect

160. Stone, thesis, Northwestern University, 1952.
161. Brown and Nyholm, *J. Chem. Soc.*, 2696 (1953).
162. Schweitzer and Lee, *J. Phys. Chem.*, **56**, 195 (1952).

TABLE 8.8*. RACEMIZATION AND DISSOCIATION RATES OF SOME NICKEL(II)
AND IRON(II) COMPLEXES

	Dissociation Constants −log K_3	Racemization			Dissociation		
		k (min⁻¹) 25°	Ea Kcal.	ΔS^I E.U.	k (min⁻¹) 25°	Ea Kcal.	ΔS^I E.U.
[Ni(o-phen)₃]⁺⁺	18ᵃ	6.3 × 10⁻⁴ ᵈ	25	+1.8	6.3 × 10⁻⁴ ᵈ	25	+1.8
[Ni(dipy)₃]⁺⁺	15ᵃ	1.4 × 10⁻¹ ᵉ	22	+2.7	1.4 × 10⁻¹ ᵈ	22	+2.7
[Fe(o-phen)₃]⁺⁺	21ᵇ	4.0 × 10⁻² ᵃ	31	30	4.5 × 10⁻³ ᶠ	—	—
[Fe(dipy)₃]⁺⁺	16ᶜ	3.6 × 10⁻² ᵃ	28	21	7.3 × 10⁻³ ᵍ	26	+10

* The values tabulated for the rates of racemization are in a form allowing direct
comparison with the rates of dissociation and hence are twice the values reported by
Davies and Dwyer.
   ᵃ Davies and Dwyer, *Trans. Faraday Soc.*, **49**, 180 (1953).
   ᵇ Lee, Kolthoff, and Leussing, *J. Am. Chem. Soc.*, **70**, 2348 (1948).
   ᶜ Boxendale and George, *Nature*, **162**, 777 (1948).
   ᵈ Basolo, Hayes and Neumann, *J. Am. Chem. Soc.*, **75**, 5102 (1953).
   ᵉ Schweitzer and Lee, *J. Phys. Chem.*, **56**, 195 (1952).
   ᶠ Brandt and Gullstrom, *J. Am. Chem. Soc.*, **74**, 3532 (1952).
   ᵍ Baxendale and George, *Trans. Faraday Soc.*, **46**, 55 (1950).

the racemization of [Ni(o-phen)₃]⁺⁺ [163] has recently been cited in support
of an intramolecular process. However, it does not necessarily follow that
an excess of the chelating agent should decrease the rate of racemization.
There would certainly be no change in the rate of racemization if the dissociated product were either symmetrical and thus optically inactive or
if it lost its optical activity very rapidly. In fact, Basolo, Hayes and Neumann[164] have recently observed that the rates of racemization of these
nickel(II) complexes are the same as the rates of dissociation. The energy
of activation is identical and, as is apparent from the data summarized in
Table 8.8, the two processes are the same. The data available for the
analogous iron(II) complexes are included in Table 8.8 so that all of these
may be conveniently compared. The racemization of these iron(II) compounds must involve an intramolecular process at least in part[164b]. It is interesting to speculate why the mechanism of racemization of the nickel(II)
complexes differs from that of the iron(II) compounds. The charges on the
cations are the same and their sizes must be practically identical. The
paramagnetism of [Ni(dipy)₃]⁺⁺ suggests sp^3d^2 type hybridization as compared to d^2sp^3 for diamagnetic [Fe(dipy)₃]⁺⁺. The more labile outer orbital
nickel(II) complex[165] may be expected to dissociate fairly readily and

163. Davies and Dwyer, *Trans. Faraday Soc.*, **48**, 244 (1952); *ibid*, **49**, 180 (1953).
164. Basolo, Hayes, and Neumann, *J. Am. Chem. Soc.*, **75**, 5102 (1953); **76**,
      3807 (1954).
165. Taube, *Chem. Rev.*, **50**, 69 (1952).

therefore possibly racemize by such a mechanism. However, this interpretation is not compatible with the fact that [Fe(o-phen)$_3$]$^{++}$ dissociates
faster than [Ni(o-phen)$_3$]$^{++}$.

Intramolecular Rearrangement Theory. If the complex does not
undergo dissociation, the racemization must result from an intramolecular
rearrangement. Werner[166] was the first to suggest such a mechanism, stating that trioxalatochromate(III) ions lose their rotatory power through the
momentary vacation of one coordination position by an oxalate radical,
thus permitting a rearrangement of positions as it becomes attached again
Fig. 8.43). Bushra and Johnson[167] have pointed out there is no apparent

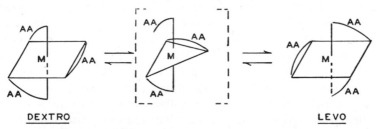

DEXTRO   LEVO

FIG. 8.43. Racemization of [M(C_2O_4)$_3$]$^{\equiv}$ (Werner)

racemization of [Co en$_3$]$^{+++}$ whereas [Co(C_2O_4)$_3$]$^{\equiv}$ racemizes at a measurable rate, thus indicating that the cobalt-ethylenediamine chelate ring is
not opened as readily as the cobalt-oxalate ring. They suggest that, if only
one chelate ring need open to allow racemization, one may expect the complex [Co en$_2$ C_2O_4]$^+$ to racemize. However, the loss of optical activity of this
compound was found to result from its decomposition rather than from
inversion. Although the complex [Co en (C_2O_4)$_2$]$^-$ was not obtained, the
analogous chromium(III) compound did racemize and with an activation
energy of 15.8 Kcal, the same as that for the racemization of [Cr(C_2O_4)$_3$]$^{\equiv}$.
On the basis of these observations Bushra and Johnson suggest that the
mechanism of racemization requires the opening of two rings which can
reattach at the same positions or at exchanged positions (Fig. 8.44).

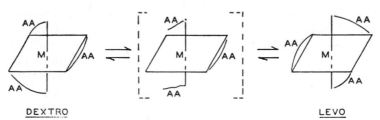

DEXTRO   LEVO

FIG. 8.44. Racemization of [M(C_2O_4)$_3$]$^{\equiv}$ (Bushra and Johnson)

166. Werner, *Ber.*, **45**, 3061 (1912).
167. Bushra and Johnson, *J. Chem. Soc.*, **1939**, 1937.

This mechanism of intramolecular change by opening two rings at two points of attachment in cis positions has been questioned by Ray and Dutt[168]. They suggest that the momentary rupture of the chemical bonds at these positions introduces the possibility of chemical decomposition during inversion and since all the six bonds in an octahedral complex are equivalent, (commonly the d^2sp^3 hybrid type) there is no obvious reason why two such bonds attached to one and the same chelate group will not be ruptured at the same time. But there is no experimental evidence that chemical decomposition is associated with inversion. Ray and Dutt have interpreted their kinetic data on the racemization of tris(biguanidinium)-cobalt(III) chloride in terms of a mechanism which does not necessitate the opening of any chelate rings. They point out that the existence of two enantiomers of the same energy content indicates a potential barrier between them and therefore some activation energy is necessary for interconversion. Addition of energy to a molecule leads to an increase in translational, rotational and vibrational motions, and the molecule is said to be activated. If sufficiently excited, the normal octahedral complex may lose its configuration and assume a metastable condition. On removal of the excess energy, the molecule returns to the octahedral form, and, since the two enantiomers have equal energy requirements they form with the same ease.

This mechanism proposed by Ray and Dutt is represented in Fig. 8.45. The dextro form (I) changes to the activated form (II) when the two pairs

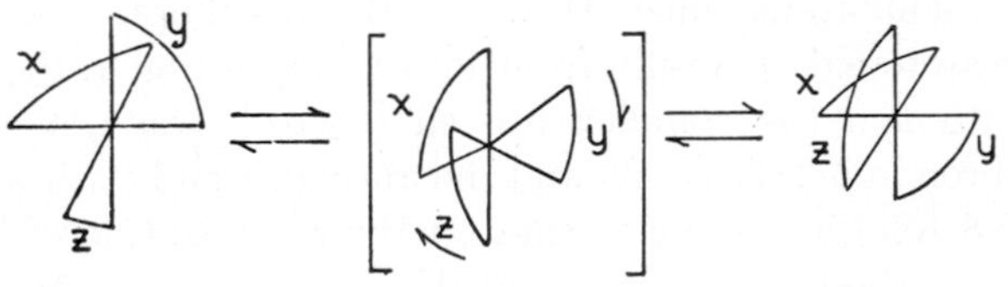

FIG. 8.45. Racemization of [M(AA)₃] (Ray and Dutt)

of bonds holding y and z rotate in opposite directions along their own plane through an angle of 45° to give a distorted octahedron with angles of 90° between the bonds. The distorted or activated molecule can then return to its normal state by retracing its previous steps to give the dextro form (I) or, by further rotation through 45° in the same direction, it may degenerate to produce the mirror image (III).

Since the structure of 1,10-phenanthroline does not allow an open ring structure, there is reason to feel that [Fe(o-phen)₃]++ must racemize by some process of this type[163, 164].

168. Ray and Dutt, J. Indian Chem. Soc., 20, 81 (1943).

Resolution of Racemic Modifications. The problems encountered and methods employed in the resolution of complex inorganic compounds are much the same as those used with organic compounds. No doubt the biggest difference is the fact that biochemical processes, commonly used for the resolution of organic compounds, have not been applied to coordination compounds.

Spontaneous Crystallization of the Antipodes. The mechanical separation of crystals, as used in 1848 by Pasteur[169] for the separation of *d* and *l* forms of sodium ammonium tartrate, has been used for a few complex compounds. Since most complex salts form well defined crystals, it is not surprising that resolution can be realized by this method. However, because of the skill and patience required to grow suitable crystals, as well as the tedious operation of picking out the different types, such a procedure is not practical. It might be mentioned that in such a process the racemic crystals must possess the requisite hemihedrism by which they may be distinguished, and crystallization must yield a *racemic mixture* rather than a *racemic compound* or *solid solution*.

This method of spontaneous crystallization of the antipodes from the racemoid was first demonstrated with $K_3[Co(C_2O_4)_3]$[170]. A comparison of the solubilities of the racemic compound and the racemic mixture at various temperatures (Fig. 8.46) demonstrates that the optically-active salts are the more stable phases with respect to the racemoid at all temperatures above 13.2°. This is, therefore, the maximum temperature for the formation of the racemate; the reaction taking place may be represented as

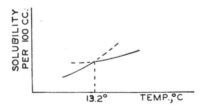

FIG. 8.46. Solubility of potassium tris-oxalato cobaltate(III)

$$2K_3[Co(C_2O_4)_3]\cdot 3\tfrac{1}{2}H_2O \overset{13.2°}{\rightleftharpoons} d\text{-}[K_3Co(C_2O_4)_3]\cdot H_2O +$$

$$l\text{-}[K_3Co(C_2O_4)_3]\cdot H_2O + 5H_2O$$

The antipodes may be allowed to crystallize at temperatures above 13.2° after which they may be separated mechanically. Jaeger[93] has also been able to obtain a racemic mixture of $[Rh\ cptn_3](ClO_4)_3\cdot 12H_2O$ at tempera-

169. Pasteur, *Ann. chim. phys.*, [37] **24**, 442 (1848).
170. Jaeger, *Rec. trav. chim.*, **38**, 250 (1919).

tures below 48° and to sort the octahedral crystals into the dextro and levo rotatory forms.

Preferential Crystallization. A much more practical way of accomplishing a direct separation of the enantiomorphs in a racemic mixture is to cause one, but not both, of the forms to crystallize. The principle involved is analogous to that of causing crystals to deposit from any supersaturated solution by the addition of a seed crystal of the desired material, or of any isomorphous crystal. This procedure was used successfully by Werner and Bosshart[171] in the resolution of $[Co\ en_2\ C_2O_4]^+$, $[Cr\ en_2\ C_2O_4]^+$ and $[Co\ en_2\ (NO_2)_2]^+$. They were able to show that if a crystal of d-$[Co\ en_2\ C_2O_4]^+$ is added to a concentrated solution of dl-$[Co\ en_2\ C_2O_4]^+$ followed by an immediate addition of a small amount of ethyl alcohol and ether, a precipitate of d-$[Co\ en_2\ C_2O_4]^+$ separates. The filtrate from this precipitate is predominantly l-$[Co\ en_2\ C_2O_4]^+$. A similar procedure was used to resolve dl-$[Co\ en_2\ (NO_2)_2]^+$, indicating that this method of resolution may be rather general. It was also demonstrated that dl-$[Co\ en_2\ (NO_2)_2]^+$ and dl-$[Cr\ en_2\ C_2O_4]^+$ can be resolved using d-$[Co\ en_2\ C_2O_4]^+$ as a seed crystal; this would indicate that it is not necessary to use an antipode of the same compound but instead any isomorphous crystal may be satisfactory.

Conversion to Diastereoisomers. The most convenient method available for the resolution of optically-active compounds is the conversion of a racemic modification into diastereoisomers, which may then be separated by fractional crystallization. The principle of this method and its limitations need not be discussed since they are analogous to those encountered with organic compounds. The resolution of complex cations is accomplished by the use of optically-active anions such as tartrate, antimonyl tartrate, α-bromocamphor-π-sulfonate, camphor-π-sulfonate, α-camphornitronate and malate; while for complex anions one employs such optically-active substances as strychnine, brucine, cinchonidine, α-phenylethylamine, morphine, quinidine and cinchonine. Removal of the resolving agent from the desired antipode can be accomplished in various ways depending upon the properties of the individual complex and also of the resolving agent. A convenient method is the separation by precipitation which is often instantaneous and can be carried out at low temperatures, therefore allowing a minimum amount of racemization to take place[172]. In other cases, where this is not possible, it has been found convenient to displace the resolving agent by means of an alcoholic acidic or basic solution and to extract the resulting acid or base by washing repeatedly with alcohol to leave the solid, insoluble antipode[173].

171. Werner and Bosshart, *Ber.*, **47**, 2171 (1914).
172. Jaeger, *Rec. trav. chim.*, **38**, 185 (1919).
173. Bailar, *Inorganic Synthesis*, **2**, 223 (1946).

Method of "Active Racemates". Molecules of inverse configuration may be associated in a crystal even though they may not have identical compositions[174]. This idea of the formation of active racemates (page 341) has been extended to provide a method of resolution of racemic substances[175] or to separate conglomerates, and to determine the relative configurations of homeomers such as the active trisoxalatocobaltate(III), chromate(III), and rhodate(III) in comparison with active ions such as trisoxalatoiridate(III). Thus, if the active racemate a^+ and b^- can exist, the addition of the active antipode a^+ to the racemic compound B (containing $b^+ + b^-$) will give a mixture of $[n(a^+ + b^-) + (1 - n)B]$ where n represents a fraction of the total amount of racemate. Analysis of the active racemate would then give data on the quantity and rotation of the fraction b^-. Since the mother liquor from these racemates contains an excess of b^+, it too will be optically active. The success of this method depends upon the racemate separating as a racemic compound rather than as a racemic mixture or solid solution.

Delépine[175] verified this supposition by studying the following systems:

d-$K_3[Rh(C_2O_4)_3]$ and dl-$K_3[Ir(C_2O_4)_3]$

d-$K_3[Ir(C_2O_4)_3]$ and dl-$K_3[Co(C_2O_4)_3]$

l-$K_3[Ir(C_2O_4)_3]$ and dl-$K_3[Co(C_2O_4)_3]$

d-$K_3[Ir(C_2O_4)_3]$ and dl-$K_3[Cr(C_2O_4)_3]$

d-$K_3[Ir(C_2O_4)_3]$ and dl-$K_3[Al(C_2O_4)_3]$

d-$K_3[Ir(C_2O_4)_3]$ and dl-$K_3[Fe(C_2O_4)_3]$

l-$[Co\ en_3]Br_3$ and dl-$[Rh\ en_3]Br_3$

From the results obtained it seems that the simultaneous crystallization of a compound B with an antipode (a^+ or a^-) of a homeomer A, should be considered as a sufficient reason for the existence of antipode B in the mixed crystal and, consequently, of the occurrence of B in the active forms b^+ and b^-, each enantiomorphic with a^- and a^+. The subsequent separation of b^+ from a^- or of b^- from a^+ results in the resolution of B. It may also be mentioned that these experiments did not lead to the resolution of $[Al(C_2O_4)_3]^{\equiv}$ or $[Fe(C_2O_4)_3]^{\equiv}$ [113, 118].

Preferential Adsorption on Optically-active Quartz. Asymmetric, nonionic coordination compounds cannot be converted into diastereoisomers, so this common method of resolution is not applicable to them. It has been demonstrated[28, 125] that enantiomorphs are preferentially adsorbed on optically-active quartz; this technique was applied to the resolution of

174. Delépine, *Bull. soc. chim.*, [4] **29**, 656 (1921).
175. Delépine, *Bull. soc. chim.*, [57] **1**, 1256 (1934).

the nonionic complex, [Co(DMG)$_2$NH$_3$ Cl]. The method has likewise been used[19b] for the resolution of the complex ion, cis-[Co en (NH$_3$)$_2$CO$_3$]$^+$ and in the resolution of K[Pt(NO$_2$)$_2$N(CH$_3$)(C$_2$H$_5$)CH$_2$COO][149]. The resolutions in these cases were not complete but the method is a useful tool for determining the resolvability of certain coordination compounds. It may also be useful in studying systems which racemize too rapidly to be studied by other methods.

Equilibrium Method of Resolution. Resolution by the equilibrium method has been used successfully for organic compounds[176], but examples of this type are not well known in the field of inorganic complex compounds. Since the reactions involved in the production of diastereoisomers of complex compounds are ionic, the reactions are instantaneous and shifts in equilibrium arise from the relative solubilities of the diastereoisomers. A typical example is the resolution of K$_3$[Cr(C$_2$O$_4$)$_3$] by means of strychnine[116b]. It was found that in an alcoholic solution the resolution yielded only the dextro rotatory complex ion, while in water only the levo rotatory antipode was obtained. The explanation must be that in solution, and especially at higher temperatures, there occurs a very rapid interconversion. Since the strychnine salt of the dextro ion is sparingly soluble in alcohol, it is precipitated and causes a shift in equilibrium which is in turn established by the interconversion of the levo component. Continued concentration results in additional deposition of the less soluble antipode which is replenished by interconversion to maintain equilibrium and accounts for the fact that only the less soluble antipode is obtained. In this particular case the strychnine salt of d-[Cr(C$_2$O$_4$)$_3$]$^≡$ is less soluble in alcohol while the l-[Cr(C$_2$O$_4$)$_3$]$^≡$ salt is less soluble in water. Dwyer and Gyarfas[177] have reported a similar observation with regard to the resolution of [Fe(o-phen)$_3$]$^{++}$. A solution of racemic-[Fe(o-phen)$_3$]$^{++}$ containing an excess of dextro antimonyl tartrate slowly precipitated the complex completely in the form of l-[Fe(o-phen)$_3$] d-(SbOC$_4$H$_4$O$_6$)$_2$·4H$_2$O. This was attributed to the lability of the complex which allowed the equilibrium between the dextro and levo cations to be shifted toward the less soluble diastereoisomer until finally none of the dextro complex remained. The partial resolution of inorganic complexes by the equilibrium method has been demonstrated by Jonassen, Bailar and Huffmann[131]. It was found that while both the D and L forms of dextro-tartratobis(ethylenediamine)cobalt(III) ion, [Co en$_2$ d-tart]$^+$, form when dextro-tartaric acid reacts with [Co en$_2$ CO$_3$]$^+$, they differ greatly in reactivity. When the mixture of the two is shaken with ethylenediamine, a 70 per cent yield of dextro-[Co en$_3$]$^{+++}$ is obtained and very little of the original material can be recovered. Evidently the less reactive form changes to the

176. King, *Ann. Repts. Chem. Soc., London*, **30**, 261 (1933).
177. Dwyer and Gyarfas, *J. Proc. Roy. Soc., N. S. Wales.*, **83**, 263 (1950).

more reactive as the latter is used up; this can be explained by assuming that the following reactions take place:

(I) *dextro*-[Co en$_2$ *d*-tart]$^+$ ⇌ *levo*-[Co en$_2$ *d*-tart]$^+$

(II) *dextro*-[Co en$_2$ *d*-tart]$^+$ + en → *dextro*-[Co en$_3$]$^{+++}$ + tart$^-$

(III) *levo*-[Co en$_2$ *d*-tart]$^+$ + en → *levo*-[Co en$_3$]$^{+++}$ + tart$^-$

Reaction (II) takes place more readily than reaction (III) and, therefore the equilibrium in reaction (I) is displaced to the left which would account for the fact that an excess of *dextro*-[Co en$_3$]$^{+++}$ is obtained. That this interpretation is not entirely justified has been recently demonstrated[132] by experiments which reveal that the reaction of *dextro*-tartaric acid with [Co en$_2$CO$_3$]$^+$ gives preferentially the *dextro-d*-tartrato complex.

"Configurational Activity" as a Method of Resolution. Dwyer and his coworkers[178] have concluded from their observations that, while the addition of electrolytes, such as sodium nitrate, to a pair of enantiomeric ions in solution alters the activity of each enantiomorph to the same extent, the addition of an electrolyte containing an optically-active anion or cation exerts slightly different effects on the two enantiomeric ions. Consequently, the possibility of effecting a resolution exists, and neither the separation of diastereoisomers nor the movement of the equilibrium position in an optically labile system is necessitated.

Dwyer has termed the effect "configurational activity," and has discovered that the solubilities of *d*- and *l*-tris(1,10-phenanthroline) ruthenium(II) perchlorate differ by as much 3.5 per cent in dilute solutions (1.0 to 1.5 per cent) of ammonium *d*-bromocamphor sulfonate or sodium potassium *d*-tartrate. At higher concentrations of the sulfonate or tartrate, the solubility curves of the *d*- and *l*-ruthenium(II) complexes begin to converge, probably, according to the authors, because "the normal nonspecific activity effect tends to outweigh the specific configurational effect at high ionic strengths."

The effect has also been exhibited for tris(2,2′-dipyridyl)nickel(II) iodide[178], and for the tris(acetylacetone)cobalt(III) complex[142], and Dwyer and his associates point out that, since the charges on a complex ion such as [Fe(CN)$_6$]$^{4-}$ are distributed over the peripheral atoms of the ligands[179], and since the enantiomers probably exhibit mirror image electric fields about the antipodes, the "configurational activity" effect may be due to the different interactions of the electric fields of the dextro and levo forms of the enantiomeric pair with the field of the added optically-active ion.

Other Probable Methods of Resolution. In addition to the methods of resolution which have been used successfully for separating enantiomers

178. Dwyer, Gyarfas, and O'Dwyer, *Nature,* **167,** 1036 (1951).
179. Pauling, *J. Chem. Soc.,* **1948,** 1461.

of coordination compounds, there is the probability that other techniques may also be applicable. In this connection some attention has been devoted to the influence of circularly-polarized light on various asymmetric complex compounds. Since it is known that circularly-polarized light is absorbed differently by enantiomers, the probability that the photochemically sensitive antipodes present in an optically-active solution will be decomposed at different speeds by light of that particular wave-length for which absorption is an optimum has been considered. In such a case the solution might be expected to become slightly active and the activity to be a function of time of exposure. Jaeger and Berger[180] attempted to show that this supposition is correct by subjecting both antipodes of $K_3[Co(C_2O_4)_3]$, in separate solutions, to such a radiation and in both cases measure directly the decomposition velocities. These experiments were performed under various conditions, but in no case could a difference in speed of decomposition of the dextro and levo components be detected.

It is also possible that resolution of optically-active complex compounds can be accomplished by a difference in rates of reaction of the enantiomers. Such a kinetic method, unlike the previously discussed equilibrium method, does not necessarily involve interconversion. In the kinetic method it is necessary to limit the amount of the active compound used or to stop the reaction at a given time before the reactions are complete. Although this type of resolution is applicable to relatively slow organic reactions[181], it has not been successful with the ionic reactions encountered in the production of diastereoisomers of inorganic complexes. However, reactions which involve the displacement of groups coordinated to the central ion are much slower, and there is a good probability that a resolving agent might displace a particular coordination group from enantiomers at different rates. If we recall, for example, the fact that D and L forms of [Co en$_2$ *d*-tart]$^+$ differ greatly in reactivity, it would be supposed that these cations are formed from the racemic carbonato salt at different rates.

Relative Configurations of Analogous Enantiomorphs

Absolute Configuration. The prefixes dextro and levo as used for optically-active compounds designate the direction of rotation only and do not supply any information about the absolute configuration of the compounds. Some progress has been made in determining absolute configuration by Kuhn and Bein[182] with the simpler complexes of the type [M(AA)$_3$]. The predictions of their theory agree with the experimental results so it is

180. Jaeger and Berger, *Rec. trav. chim.*, **40**, 153 (1921).
181. Marckwald and Paul, *Ber.*, **38**, 810 (1905); **39**, 3654 (1906).
182. Kuhn and Bein, *Z. anorg. Chem.*, **216**, 321 (1934); Kuhn and Bein, *Z. physik. Chem.*, **24B**, 335 (1934).

concluded that the model presented corresponds to the absolute configuration of the molecule. The determination of the absolute configuration of even the simplest antipode is extremely difficult and different theories[183] which may appear logical sometimes end up assigning opposite configurations to the same enantiomorph. An experimental approach which makes use of x-rays of appropriate wave-length was recently employed to determine the absolute configuration of sodium rubidium *dextro*-tartrate[184]. Although this is the only technique reported to be applicable to a determination of absolute configuration, several methods are available to determine relative configurations of homeomers with considerable certainty.

Werner's Solubility Method. Although the absolute configurations of a pair of optical isomers are generally not known, the relative space positions of analogous compounds may be found if the configuration of a given compound be designated. This has been realized with complexes of cobalt(III), chromium(III), rhodium(III), and iridium(III). Werner[185] suggested that the relative configurations of inorganic complex compounds could be determined by comparing the solubilities of analogous diastereoisomers. The resolution of tris(ethylenediamine) cations of cobalt(III), rhodium(III) and chromium(III) by means of camphornitronates and chlorotartrates was used as an example. Since the less soluble diastereoisomers were the dextro rotatory cobalt(III), chromium(III) ions and the levo rotatory rhodium(III) ion, it was concluded that these cations possess the same spatial arrangement. Jaeger criticized this theory, stating that, "This view is quite arbitrary because, in general, solubility is a so highly complicated and constituent property of matter that, even where we seem to have established rules for homologous series, sometimes most unexpected and surprising exceptions spring up. This makes these rules quite illusory"[100]. He suggested that the crystal form is a better criterion for relative configuration and attempted to demonstrate that the method suggested by Werner was incorrect[93]. Jaeger has since acknowledged that the method of solubilities is correct and has applied it in studies of relative configurations of analogous optically-active antipodes[94, 186].

Rotatory Dispersion Curves—Circular Dichroism. The fact that both the absorption spectra and the optical rotation are related to the resonance within a particular molecule suggests that some correlation exists between these two properties. It has also been shown that certain absorption bands are directly connected with the groups concerned with the optical rotatory power of the molecule. Hence, the specific rotation of a com-

183. Born, *Proc. Roy. Soc., London*, **150A**, 83 (1935).
184. Bijvolt, Peerdeman, and von Bommel, *Nature*, **168**, 271 (1951).
185. Werner, *Bull. soc. chim.*, [4] **11**, 1 (1912).
186. Jaeger, *Bull. soc. chim.*, [5] **4**, 1201 (1937); Jaeger, *Pro. Acad. Sci. Amsterdam*, **40**, 2, 108, 574 (1937).

pound is very different when the measurements are made with light of a wave length which corresponds to one of these absorption bands (Fig. 8.47).

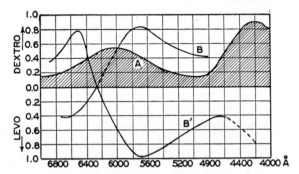

FIG. 8.47. Absorption spectrum and rotatory dispersion of potassium *tris*-oxalato cobaltate(III).

A. Racemic-absorption spectrum
B-Dextro-rotatory dispersion
B'-Levo-rotatory dispersion

The rotatory dispersion curves, B and B', undergo abrupt changes as the shaded region represented by the absorption curve, A, is approached and passed. At wave lengths of light remote from the absorption curve, very little change occurs in the optical rotation as the wave length is changed. This change of rotation with change of wave length of light is called *rotatory dispersion*.

The determination of the optical rotation of coordination compounds, which are usually colored and, therefore, have absorption bands in the visible range, is sometimes difficult. With such compounds it is advisable to determine the specific rotation at several different wave lengths or, at least, the wave length of the light used must always be specified.

Although numerous investigators[187] have studied the rotatory dispersion curves of complex compounds, none has applied this technique so extensively or so successfully as Mathieu. He has found this procedure extremely useful in comparing the configurations of analogous compounds[188] and in studying any changes in configuration during displacement reactions[189]. Mathieu showed[188c] (Fig. 8.48) that the tris(ethylenediamine) compounds

187. Bruhot, *Bull. soc. chim.*, [4] **17,** 223 (1915); Jaeger, *Rec. trav. chim.*, **38,** 309 (1919); Lifschitz, *Z. physik. Chem.*, **105,** 27 (1923); Longchambon, *Compt. rend.*, **178,** 1828 (1924).
188. Mathieu, *Compt. rend.*, **119,** 278 (1934); Mathieu, *ibid.*, **201,** 1183 (1935); Mathieu, *J. chim. phys.*, **33,** 78 (1936).
189. Mathieu, *Bull. soc. chim.*, [5] **3,** 463, 476 (1936); Mathieu, *ibid.*, [5] **5,** 105 (1938).

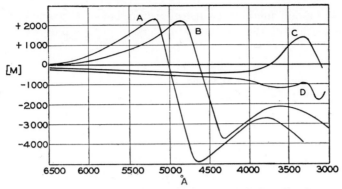

FIG. 8.48. Rotatory dispersion curves of some tris-ethylenediamine complexes. (A), d-[Co en$_3$]Br$_3$; (B), d-[Cr en$_3$]I$_3$; (C), l-[Rh en$_3$]I$_3$, (D), l-[Ir en$_3$]Br$_3$.

of d-[Co(III)], d-[Cr(III)], l-[Rh(III)] and l-[Ir(III)] have the same configuration. It is seen that these curves are similar, indicating analogous configurations, whereas if the curves are different (Fig. 8.47), the optically active ions have opposite configurations.

This same technique was employed by Mathieu[188a] to corroborate the conclusions which Werner[99] made by means of his solubility method. Werner investigated numerous reactions (page 344) involving the displacement of a donor ion or molecule from the coordination sphere of an optically-active complex compound and showed that in some of these reactions, although the sign of rotation may change when measured at the D line of sodium, the configuration of the product remains the same as that of the original material. A typical example of the application of rotatory dispersion curves in studies of this type might be illustrated by considering the reactions

$$levo\text{-}[Co\ en_2\ Cl_2]^+ \xrightarrow{\ KCNS\ } levo\text{-}[Co\ en_2\ Cl\ NCS]^+ \xrightarrow{\ Na\ NO_2\ } dextro\text{-}[Co\ en_2\ NCS\ NO_2]^+$$

These three complex cations have analogous rotatory dispersion curves (Fig. 8.49) and must, therefore, possess the same generic configuration.

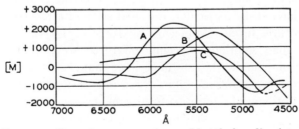

FIG. 8.49. Rotatory dispersion curves of some bis-ethylenediamine complexes. (A), l-[Co en$_2$ Cl$_2$]$^+$; (B), l-[Co en$_2$ Cl NCS]$^+$; (C), d-[Co en$_2$ NCS NO$_2$]$^+$.

Recently[50] a new method for distinguishing between geometrical isomers which makes use of their rotatory dispersion curves has been suggested (page 298).

The rotatory dispersion of an optical isomer is very closely related to another phenomena referred to as *circular dichroism* or "Cotton effect." Although plane-polarized light has been most widely used in the study of optical isomerism, some interesting and fundamental data have been secured by means of circularly-polarized light. It was found, for example, that the absorption of dextro or levo circularly-polarized light is dependent upon the wave length. If the circularly-polarized light is of a wave length in the neighborhood of the characteristic absorption bands of groups concerned with the optical activity of the molecule, then the beams of dextro and levo circularly-polarized light are absorbed to different extents, but at all other wave lengths the coefficients of absorption are equal. This phenomenon is designated as the "Cotton effect" because Cotton[190] first demonstrated it with alkaline solutions of copper tartrates.

The "Cotton effect" and rotatory dispersion of an optical isomer can be related qualitatively by the fact that a compound designated as having a positive "Cotton effect" has a rotatory dispersion curve which changes from a maximum rotation to a minimum rotation in the direction of shorter wave lengths. In the same manner, a compound whose rotatory dispersion curve changes from a minimum to a maximum rotation is said to have a negative "Cotton effect." Therefore, studies of rotatory dispersions are sometimes expressed in terms of positive or negative "Cotton effect." Analogous compounds with the same "Cotton effect" at corresponding absorption bands have the same generic configuration; whereas similar compounds of different "Cotton effect" have opposite configurations[188c]; thus, it is seen that studies of the "Cotton effect" may be used in determining structures, and, also, according to Mellor[191], in determining bond character.

Delépine's Active Racemate Method. The physical characteristics of a racemic modification often differ from those of the enantiomorphs from which it is derived. In particular, the solid state of a racemic modification may exist in three forms: (1) racemic mixtures (2) racemic compounds, or (3) racemic solid solutions. Racemic mixtures are produced by certain asymmetric compounds which form crystals that possess hemihedral facets and are themselves enantiomorphic. A racemic compound results whenever a pair of enantiomorphs unite to form a molecular compound, all of the crystals containing equal amounts of each isomer and being identical. These crystals have different physical properties from those of the indi-

190. Cotton, *Ann. chim. phys.*, **7**, 8 (1896).
191. Mellor, *J. Proc. Roy. Soc.*, *N. S. Wales*, **75**, 157 (1942).

vidual antipodes. Oftentimes a pair of enantiomorphs are also isomorphous. Whenever this situation exists they may crystallize together as a racemic solid solution without the formation of a compound.

As early as 1921, Delépine[174] suggested that similar optically-active salts which form isomorphous crystals have the same relative configuration regardless of their optical rotation. This led to the method referred to as Delépine's "active racemate" method[175] which can best be presented by a brief discussion. If two enantiomorphs, such as d-$K_3[Co(C_2O_4)_3]$ and l-$K_3[Co(C_2O_4)_3]$, the crystals of which possess hemihedral facets, are mixed in solution in equimolecular quantities and allowed to crystallize, crystals of the racemic mixture are formed. These crystals represent a mechanical mixture of the individual antipodes and, when put in solution, they are, of course, optically inactive. If d-$K_3[Cr(C_2O_4)_3]$ is substituted for d-K_3-$[Co(C_2O_4)_3]$, the crystals which form will give an optically-active solution ("active racemate"), because d-$K_3[Cr(C_2O_4)_3]$ and l-$K_3[Co(C_2O_4)_3]$ do not have equal rotatory power. Delépine points out that if the "active racemate" is a racemic mixture, then the generic configurations of the two antipodes are different; however, if it is either a racemic compound or racemic solid solution, then the generic configurations of the antipodes are the same.

Delépine was able to show by this method that l-$K_3[Ir(C_2O_4)_3]$ and d-$K_3[Rh(C_2O_4)_3]$, d-$K_3[Ir(C_2O_4)_3]$ and d-$K_3[Co(C_2O_4)_3]$, and d-$K_3[Ir(C_2O_4)_3]$ and l-$K_3[Cr(C_2O_4)_3]$ form racemic compounds or solid solutions of the optically-active type. It was, therefore, concluded that the generic configurations of the trioxalato complexes of these four metals are the same in d-$K_3[Co(C_2O_4)_3]$, l-$K_3[Cr(C_2O_4)_3]$, d-$K_3[Ir(C_2O_4)_3]$ and l-$K_3[Rh(C_2O_4)_3]$. This procedure has likewise been used to show that cobalt(III) and rhodium(III) complexes of the same sign of rotation have opposite generic configurations in the tris(ethylenediamine) series[192].

The method of active racemates is limited only by the fact that the salts in question must form crystals which have hemihedral facets and must be isomorphous. A careful choice of anions and cations can lead to isomorphism in quite different types of salts, and it may be possible to determine the generic configurations of hexacovalent metals having different valences. Thus, the configurations of analogous zinc(II), cobalt(III) and platinum(IV) complexes might be related through the possible isomorphism of such pairs as $[Zn\ en_3](NO_3)_2$-$[Pt\ en_3](CO_3)_2$ and $[Co\ en_3]PO_4$-$[Zn\ en_3]$-SO_4.

Preferential Adsorption on Optically-active Quartz. Tsuchida, Kobayashi and Nakamura[28] have suggested that the preferential adsorption of enantiomers on optically-active quartz might furnish a useful means of determining the relative configurations of analogous asymmetric compounds. This assumption has been checked experimentally[125] by determin-

192. Delépine and Charonnat, *Bull. soc. franc. mineral,* **53,** 73 (1930).

ing the adsorption of several complex compounds on finely ground *dextro-*
quartz powder. The results of this investigation confirm the opinion that
there is a close relationship between the adsorption and the spatial configuration of the complex.

Some Reactions of Optically-active Isomers

Polynuclear Complex Compounds. Werner observed that groups coordinated to an asymmetric central ion can be displaced and a product obtained which is still optically active, although in many cases the degree of
optical rotation or even the sign may change. The optical rotations of some
of the products obtained by the reaction of

$$l\text{-}\left[en_2\ Co^{(III)} \underset{O_2}{\overset{NH_2}{\diamondsuit}} Co^{(IV)}\ en_2 \right] X_4$$

with various reagents are shown in Table 8.9. It will be noted that, in every
case, the products obtained had rotations opposite in sign and smaller than
that of the starting material. Mathieu[189b] has investigated the rotatory
dispersions of some of these materials and has shown that although the sign
of rotation changed, the generic configuration of the products was the same
as that of the reactant. Thompson and Wilmarth[161a] have shown that the
reactions listed in Table 8.9 involve a one electron reduction and that the
oxidation-reduction reaction

$$\left[en_2\ Co^{(III)} \underset{O_2}{\overset{NH_2}{\diamondsuit}} Co^{(III)}\ en_2 \right]^{+++} \rightleftharpoons \left[en_2\ Co^{(III)} \underset{O_2}{\overset{NH_2}{\diamondsuit}} Co^{(IV)}\ en_2 \right]^{4+} + e$$

is reversible with an electrode potential of slightly more than -1.0 volt.
Therefore the structures designated by Werner and shown in Table 8.9 for
products 1 and 2 are in error; there is good evidence in support of the structure

$$\left[en_2\ Co^{(III)} \underset{O_2}{\overset{NH_2}{\diamondsuit}} Co^{(III)}\ en_2 \right] X_3 \cdot HX$$

for the product of reaction number 2[161a].

Substitution Reactions with No Change in Configuration. Werner[185] postulated that the replacement of groups a and b in complexes of

161a. Thompson and Wilmarth, *J. Phys. Chem.*, **56**, 5 (1952).

TABLE 8.9. REACTIONS OF l-[en$_2$ Co$^{(III)}$ $\overset{\displaystyle NH_2}{\underset{\displaystyle O_2}{\diamond}}$ Co$^{(IV)}$ en$_2$]X$_4$

$[\alpha]_D^{20} = -840°$; $[M]_D^{20} = -6854°$

(concentration 0.125%)

No.	Reagent	Product	$[\alpha]_D^{20}$	$[M]_D^{20}$
1	NH$_3$	[en$_2$ Co$^{(III)}$ $\overset{\displaystyle NH}{\underset{\displaystyle O_2}{\diamond}}$ Co$^{(IV)}$ en$_2$]X$_3$	+160	+1372
2	HX	[en$_2$ Co$^{(III)}$ $\overset{\displaystyle HX \atop NH}{\underset{\displaystyle O_2}{\diamond}}$ Co$^{(IV)}$ en$_2$]X$_3$	+192	+1625
3	NaI	[en$_2$ Co$^{(III)}$ $\overset{\displaystyle NH_2}{\underset{\displaystyle OH}{\diamond}}$ Co$^{(III)}$ en$_2$]X$_4$	+110	+990
4	HNO$_2$	[en$_2$ Co$^{(III)}$ $\overset{\displaystyle NH_2}{\underset{\displaystyle NO_2}{\diamond}}$ Co$^{(III)}$ en$_2$]X$_4$	+158	+1311
5	SO$_2$	[en$_2$ Co$^{(III)}$ $\overset{\displaystyle NH_2}{\underset{\displaystyle SO_4}{\diamond}}$ Co$^{(III)}$ en$_2$]X$_3$	+200	+1384

the type [M(AA)$_2$ab] takes place with no change in configuration. He suggested that during these reactions the labile groups, a and b, are easily displaced and the bidentate groups, AA, remain firmly bound, thus maintaining the same spatial arrangement of the atoms in the molecule. This was tested by numerous reactions involving optically-active compounds (Table 8.10).

Werner applied his method of solubilities to show that in every case the generic configuration of the product was the same as that of the reactant. This same conclusion was reached by Mathieu[189a] who investigated the rotatory dispersion of some of these materials.

TABLE 8.10. REACTIONS OF SOME OPTICALLY-ACTIVE [M(AA)₂ab] COMPOUNDS

No.	Sign of Rotation	Reactant	Reagent	Product	Sign of Rotation
1	−	[Co en₂ Cl₂]⁺	K₂CO₃	[Co en₂ CO₃]⁺	+
2	−	[Co en₂ Cl NCS]⁺	NH₃	[Co en₂ NH₃ NCS]⁺	+
3	−	[Co en₂ Cl NCS]⁺	NaNO₂	[Co en₂ NO₂ NCS]⁺	+
4	−	[Co en₂ Cl₂]⁺	(NH₄)₂C₂O₄	[Co en₂ C₂O₄]⁺	+
5	−	[Cr en₂ Cl₂]⁺	(NH₄)₂C₂O₄	[Cr en₂ C₂O₄]⁺	+
6	−	[Co en₂ NO₂ Cl]⁺	KCNS	[Co en₂ NO₂ NCS]⁺	−

The Walden Inversion* in Reactions of Complex Ions and Interconversion of Enantiomorphs. Contrary to Werner's assumption that labile groups are always displaced from the coordination sphere of a central atom without a change in configuration, Bailar and Auten[106] have demonstrated that certain reactions of this type can cause the interconversion of enantiomorphs. The experiments of Bailar and Auten (Fig. 8.50) brought

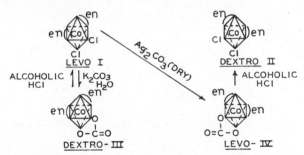

FIG. 8.50. Configuration change in the reaction of dichloro-bis-ethylenediamine cobalt(III) ion with carbonate.

to light the first example of a Walden inversion in the field of inorganic complex compounds. It was shown that the treatment of an aqueous solution of *levo*-dichloro-bis(ethylenediamine)cobalt(III) ion, (I), with a solution of potassium carbonate produces the *dextro*-carbonato ion, (III), but grinding with an excess of solid silver carbonate produced the levo isomer, (IV). This is converted to the *dextro*-dichloro ion, (II), by alcoholic hydrochloric acid. The relative configurations of the complex ions were assigned as the result of rotatory dispersion studies[71] and the inversion is represented as taking place in the silver carbonate reaction. Later develop-

* The use of the term "Walden Inversion,' in this connection has been challenged; however, the disagreement appears to be mainly in linguistics and not of a fundamental nature (⁷⁹ᵃ).

TABLE 8.11. EFFECT OF TEMPERATURE ON WALDEN INVERSION

$[Co\ en_2\ Cl_2]^+ + 2NH_3 \rightarrow [Co\ en_2\ (NH_3)_2]^{+++} + 2Cl^-$

Reagent	Temp.	Specific Rotation of Product
Liquid NH_3	$-77°$	$-32°$
Liquid NH_3	$-33°$	$-22°$
Liquid NH_3	$+25°$	$+29°$
Gaseous NH_3	$+80°$	$+43°$
NH_3 in CH_3OH	$+25°$	$+31°$
NH_3 in C_2H_5OH	$+25°$	$+29°$

TABLE 8.12. EFFECT OF TEMPERATURE ON WALDEN INVERSION

$[Co\ en_2\ Cl_2]^+ + Ag_2CO_3 \rightarrow [Co\ en_2\ CO_3]^+ + 2AgCl$

Temp.	Specific Rotation of Product
$0°$	$-10°$
$15°$	$-100°$
$25°$	$-106°$
$50°$	$-78°$
$75°$	$-28°$
$90°$	$0°$

ments[19b, 129, 195] show that the reagent is not the important factor; instead the conversions of l-[Co en_2 Cl_2]^+ to the *dextro*-carbonato complex proceeds through the formation of an aquated intermediate, while conversion to the *levo*-carbonato compound proceeds directly. The effect of various factors on the inversion are discussed below:

(1) *Effect of Temperature.* It should likewise be mentioned that experimental conditions play an important role in Walden inversions. For example, the effect of temperature on the inversion of complex inorganic compounds was first noticed with the reaction between l-[Co en_2 Cl_2]Cl and ammonia[108]. A levo rotatory salt, [Co en_2 (NH_3)_2]Cl_3 , was isolated if the reaction took place at $-77°$ or $-33°C$, but the dextro rotatory product was obtained from the reaction at $+25°C$ (Table 8.11). These results have been confirmed and extended by Keeley[196].

This effect of temperature was also studied for the reaction of l-[Co en_2 Cl_2]Cl with silver carbonate[195]. The data, which are summarized in Table 8.12, show that the chief effect of low temperatures is to decrease the rate of reaction, and the effect of high temperatures is to cause racemization.

(2) *Effect of Concentration.* It was found that[195], if an excess of silver carbonate were present, the levo salt was obtained, however, if an excess was not present, the dextro salt was obtained. On the other hand, potassium

195. Bailar, Jonelis, and Huffman, *J. Am. Chem. Soc.*, **58**, 2224 (1936).
196. Keeley, thesis, University of Illinois, 1952.

TABLE 8.13. EFFECT OF CONCENTRATION ON WALDEN INVERSION

$$[Co\ en_2\ Cl_2]^+ + CO_3^- \rightarrow [Co\ en_2\ CO_3]^+ + 2Cl^-$$

Molar Ratio of Ag_2CO_3 to Complex Present	Specific Rotation of Product
0.75	$+362°$
1.12	$+288°$
1.50	$-102°$
3.00	$-160°$
4.50	$-180°$
Molar Ratio of K_2CO_3 to Complex Present	Specific Rotation of Product
1.00	$+240°$
1.50	$+140°$
3.00	$+110°$
5.00	$+80°$

carbonate produced the dextro salt at all times although the specific rotation decreased with increasing concentration of potassium carbonate (Table 8.13). This marked racemization was probably due, however, to the formation of the optically-inactive trans-$[Co\ en_2\ H_2O\ OH]^{++}$ by the strongly basic solution.

(3) *Nature of Reagent.* The fact that the particular reagent chosen to effect a reaction exerts a predominating influence on the configuration of the product is clearly demonstrated by the different results obtained when Ag_2CO_3 and K_2CO_3 react with l-$[Co\ en_2\ Cl_2]Cl$. There is no adequate explanation for this. In an attempt to determine whether some correlation exists between the type of reagent and its influence on the configuration of a particular compound, the reaction of Hg_2CO_3 with l-$[Co\ en_2\ Cl_2]Cl$ was studied. Mercurous ion and silver ion both form insoluble chlorides and carbonates. They might, therefore, be expected to behave similarly. It was found however, that l-$[Co\ en_2\ Cl_2]Cl$ reacts with an excess of Hg_2CO_3 to give the dextro rotatory carbonato salt. This reaction, which is much slower than that with silver carbonate, gives results similar to those obtained with potassium carbonate.

(4) *Nature of Solvent.* It has been shown definitely for carbon compounds that the nature of the solvent plays an important role in the inversion of a molecule[197]. Although most of the reactions of complex inorganic salts are carried out in water, there is some indication that other solvents or no solvent may give different results. For example, it has been established that the conversion of l-$[Co\ en_2\ Cl_2]Cl$ to the *dextro*-carbonato complex proceeds through the formation of an aquated intermediate, while conversion to the

197. Senter, *J. Chem. Soc.*, **127**, 1847 (1925).

TABLE 8.14. EFFECT OF AGING A 4 PER CENT SOLUTION OF l-[Co en$_2$ Cl$_2$]Cl BEFORE TREATING WITH A TEN-FOLD EXCESS OF SILVER CARBONATE

t, represents the time of aging in minutes and $[\alpha]$ represents specific rotation of resultant carbonato salt in degrees

t	$[\alpha]$	t	$[\alpha]$
0	−212	75	+684
1	−183	120	+635
3	−96	170	+587
6	−19	186	+539
10	+87	235	+520
20	+250	260	+520
40	+501	296	+462
50	+530	360	+433
60	+578	1080	+147

levo-carbonato salt proceeds directly[198]. That aquation plays an important part in the reaction between l-[Co en$_2$ Cl$_2$]Cl and silver carbonate is shown by the fact that the rotation of the carbonato complex obtained depends upon how long the solution of the dichloro salt is allowed to stand before the silver carbonate is added (Table 8.14). This would suggest that other examples of inversion of optically-active complexes might be observed, if it were possible to employ noncoordinating solvents in order to enhance the possibility of a displacement (S$_N$2) reaction.

Theories of the Walden Inversion. The fact that Walden inversions have been demonstrated for complex compounds[106, 108, 195] is of interest in establishing whether the mechanisms proposed for inversions of the tetrahedral carbon are sufficiently general to be applicable to octahedral complex inorganic compounds. One of the mechanisms suggested for the Walden inversion postulates that every reaction which involves a single step in the displacement of one group by another on a tetrahedral atom should lead to inversion[199]. Accordingly, if the over-all reaction takes place in an odd number of steps the product will be the enantiomorph of the original material, but if it takes place in an even number of steps, the starting material and the product will have the same configuration. This theory was tested by Bailar, Haslam and Jones[108] who studied the reaction of l-[Co en$_2$ Cl$_2$]Cl with ammonia which yields the corresponding diammine complex. The two chloride atoms of the complex ion are attached to the cobalt in the same way and occupy like positions in the molecule. It seems logical to assume, therefore, that the same mechanism functions in their displacement from the complex. If this is correct, the conversion of the dichloro salt to the

198. Bailar and Peppard, *J. Am. Chem. Soc.*, **62**, 820 (1940).
199. Bergmann, Polanyi and Szabo, *Z. physik. Chem.*, **B20**, 161 (1933); Olson, *J. Chem. Phys.*, **1**, 418 (1933).

diammine salt must take place in an even number of steps, and the theory mentioned would allow no inversion. However, it was shown that the reaction does lead to inversion.

The authors[195] mention the possibility that the displacement of a negative chloride group by a neutral ammonia molecule may produce such a profound change in the complex ion that the second step of the reaction does not follow the same mechanism as the first. A more conclusive test of the theory of Bergmann, Polanyi and Szabo[199a] and of Olson[199b] can be had if the chloro groups were displaced by other univalent negative groups. There has been no report made to date of a Walden inversion of this type.

Meisenheimer's theory of the Walden inversion in reactions of organic compounds[200] postulates that the incoming group attaches itself to the face of the tetrahedron opposite the group expelled. An octahedron, however, has four faces "opposite" and equidistant from each corner. If it is assumed that the incoming group attaches to any one of these with equal ease, the theory of Meisenheimer will predict complete racemization, as a study of the model will show.

A consideration of the models of these complex cobalt compounds shows that the d isomer may be transformed into the l isomer merely by exchanging the point of attachment of a certain two groups. Hence, it is possible that the configuration of these optically-active cobalt complexes may be inverted by the properly oriented approach of the incoming group. Such a mechanism of inversion does not necessitate the formation of a new octahedron. Basolo, Stone and Pearson[74] (Figs. 8.29 and 8.30) and Brown Ingold, and Nyholm[79a] also give an interpretation of the Walden in octahedral structures.

Mutarotation. Experimental results show that in some instances the rotatory power of a freshly prepared solution of optically-active substances is not constant, but gradually changes, finally reaching a constant value (not zero) by reason of the establishment of an equilibrium. Such a change in rotatory power is termed *Mutarotation*. Numerous examples are known for organic compounds[201].

Burgess and Lowry[202] demonstrated that this phenomenon can occur in coordination compounds by discovering that benzoylcamphorberyllium(II) mutarotates. It had previously been reported[203] that 1-hydroxy-2-benzoyl-camphene exhibits mutarotation and it was suggested that this resulted

200. Meisenhiemer, *Ann.*, **456**, 126 (1927); Meisenhiemer and Link, *Ann.*, **479**, 211 (1930).
201. Schreiber and Shriner, *J. Am. Chem. Soc.*, **57**, 1306, 1445, 1896 (1935); Tanrent, *Compt. rend.*, **120**, 1060 (1895).
202. Burgess and Lowry, *J. Chem. Soc.*, **125**, 2081 (1924).

TABLE 8.15. MUTAROTATION OF BENZOYLCAMPHORALUMINUM(III)

2½ per cent solutions at 20°C.

Chloroform		Benzene		Ethylenebromide	
Time (min.)	$[\alpha]_{5461}$	Time (min.)	$[\alpha]_{5461}$	Time (min.)	$[\alpha]_{5461}$
0	(730)	0	(1175)	30	570°
15	748	25	1170.5	45	566
25	755	48	1167.7	75	565
40	760	90	1164.3	195	564
85	766	160	1161.8	360	562
235	769	265	1158.9	1320	558
final	772	365	1157.8	2820	550
		1890	1147.6	5640	545
		final	1143.8	9 days	538

from the reaction

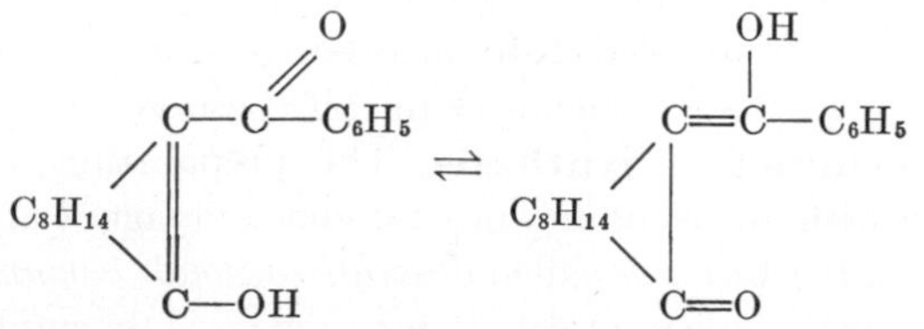

Since in benzoylcamphorberyllium(II) there is no longer a mobile hydrogen

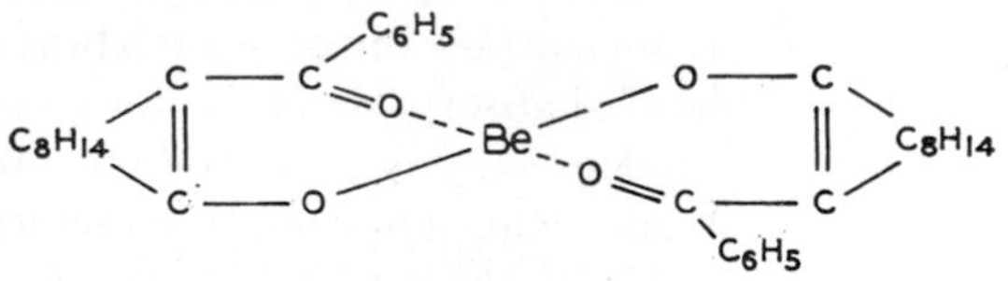

atom, any change in rotatory power to a final constant value must involve the racemization of the labile asymmetric beryllium(II) center. This interpretation was not, at first, universally accepted because the tetrahedral configuration of beryllium(II) had not yet been clearly demonstrated[204] and, therefore, a similar experiment was carried out making use of the octahedral aluminum(III) compound[205]. Some of the data obtained with solutions of benzoylcamphoraluminum(III) are given in Table 8.15 which shows the rate of mutarotation is dependent upon the solvent. This is in accord with the observations[162, 206, 207] that complex compounds racemize at different rates in various solvents.

203. Forster, *J. Chem. Soc.*, **79**, 987 (1901).
204. Mills and Gotts, *J. Chem. Soc.*, **1926**, 3121.
205. Faulkner and Lowry, *J. Chem. Soc.*, **127**, 1080 (1925).
206. Werner, *Ber.*, **45**, 3061 (1912).
207. Rideal and Thomas, *J. Chem. Soc.*, **121**, 196 (1922).

A slightly different type of mutarotation involving inorganic coordination compounds is found in the experiment reported by Meisenheimer, Angermann, Holsten and Kiderlen (page 324)[147].

Asymmetric Synthesis. The recent advances in synthetic organic chemistry have continually decreased the apparent gap between synthetic processes occuring in the living cell and similar reactions in the laboratory; thus, it would seem that even the most complicated processes of plant and animal metabolism are controlled by orthodox physical and chemical laws. Indeed, there is only one striking difference between vital syntheses and their laboratory counterparts. This is the fact that when a substance whose molecule displays only axial symmetry is produced by vital synthesis in a living cell, it is often found that one of the two possible antipodal forms predominates over the other in the resulting product; whereas, the synthesis of asymmetric molecules in the laboratory invariably produces the racemic modification. This pronounced difference between natural and laboratory products has intrigued stereochemists for all these years.

Absolute Asymmetric Synthesis. The preparation of an optically-active molecule without using an optically-active reagent and without any of the methods of resolution is called *absolute (or total) asymmetric synthesis*. Attempts have been made to effect such a synthesis by employing the phenomenon known as circular dichroism or "Cotton effect" (page 340). One theory[208] as to the origin of optically-active compounds depends upon the fact that sunlight reflected by the surface of the sea is always in part elliptically polarized[209]. The preferential absorption of one form of this polarized light by a pair of optical antipodes may account for the preferential formation or decomposition of one enantiomorph. Asymmetric decompositions, using dextro and levo circularly-polarized light of a wave length comparable to that of an absorption band of the compound in question, have been successfully carried out for several organic compounds[210]. Similarly, asymmetric formation of compounds under the influence of circularly-polarized light has given positive results for a few compounds of carbon[211].

Since coordination compounds are usually very highly colored and have a pronounced circular-dichroism in the visible region, it would appear that the decomposition or formation of an asymmetric compound of this type in the presence of dextro or levo circularly-polarized light should yield an

208. Eder, *Sitzk. Okad. Wiss, Wien, Abt.* [IIA] **90,** 1097 (1885); *ibid.,* **94,** 75 (1886).
209. Jamin, *Compt. rend.,* **31,** 696 (1850).
210. Kuhn and Braun, *Naturwissenschaften,* **17,** 227 (1928); Kuhn and Knopf, *ibia.,* **18,** 183 (1930); Mitchell, *J. Chem. Soc.,* **1930,** 1829.
211. Davis and Heggie, *J. Am. Chem. Soc.,* **57,** 377 (1935); Karagunis and Drikos, *Naturwissenschaften,* **21,** 607 (1933); Karagunis and Drikos, *Nature,* **132,** 354 (1933); Karagunis and Drikos, *Z. physik. Chem.,* **24B,** 428 (1934).

optically-active compound. Bredig and Mangold[212] have investigated the decomposition of diazocamphor, lactic acid, and various racemic cobalt-ammine salts by circularly-polarized ultraviolet light. In none of these experiments was there any evidence that optical activity was produced. A somewhat different approach was employed by Jaeger[180] (page 336). The absolute asymmetric synthesis of a complex inorganic compound has not yet been achieved.

Asymmetric Synthesis. "Asymmetric synthesis", as it is now interpreted, was first discussed by Fischer[213] and later defined by Marckwald[214] as that process which produces optically-active compounds from symmetrically constituted molecules by the intermediate use of optically-active reagents, but without the use of any of the methods of resolution. Numerous examples[215] of asymmetric syntheses are known for carbon compounds.

Coordination compounds containing optically-active donor molecules have been found[92-94, 126] to exist in only certain preferred stereoisomeric modifications, rather than in all the theoretically possible forms. Reactions leading to the formation of this type of compound cannot be regarded as examples of asymmetric synthesis, however, for, according to Marckwald's definition, the optically-active reagent is merely used as an intermediate in the subsequent preparation of an optically-active compound which no longer contains the reagent; this is not true of the numerous examples of coordination compounds containing optically-active donor molecules, in which the central ion is rendered optically-active as long as the donor molecules remain coordinated.

There is one example[131], however, in the field of inorganic complex compounds, which does fit the present definition of asymmetric synthesis (Fig. 8.51). It is believed that these results are achieved because of the

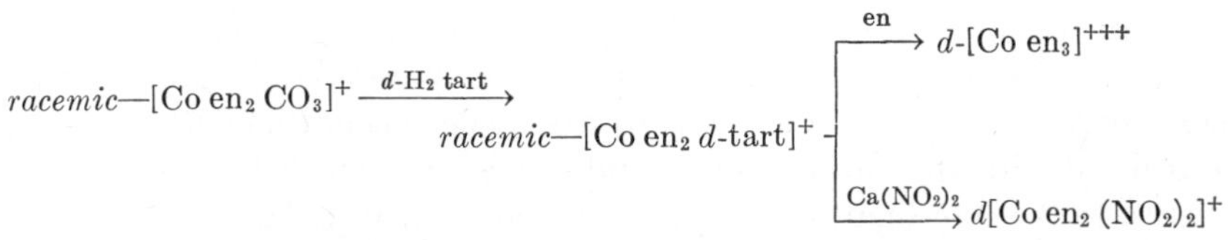

$$racemic\text{---}[\text{Co en}_2 \text{ CO}_3]^+ \xrightarrow{d\text{-H}_2 \text{ tart}} racemic\text{---}[\text{Co en}_2 \ d\text{-tart}]^+ \begin{cases} \xrightarrow{\text{en}} d\text{-}[\text{Co en}_3]^{+++} \\ \xrightarrow{\text{Ca(NO}_2)_2} d[\text{Co en}_2 \ (\text{NO}_2)_2]^+ \end{cases}$$

Fig. 8.51. Asymmetric synthesis

difference in stability of the D and L forms of *dextro*-tartratobis(ethylene-diamine)cobalt(III) ion, [Co en$_2$ d-tart]$^+$. The less stable D form reacts more readily with ethylenediamine or calcium nitrite to form the dextro

212. Bredig, Mangold, and Williams, *Z. Angew. Chem.*, **36**, 456 (1923).
213. Fischer, *Ber.*, **27**, 3231 (1894).
214. Marckwald, *Ber.*, **37**, 349 (1904).
215. Bredig and Fiske, *Biochem. Z.*, **46**, 7 (1912); McKenzie, *J. Chem. Soc.*, **85**, 1249 (1904).

rotatory tris(ethylenediamine) and dinitrobis(ethylenediamine)cobalt(III) ions respectively.

Asymmetric Induction. The phenomenon termed *asymmetric induction* has been defined by Kortüm[216] as the action of a force arising in an optically-active molecule, which influences adjacent molecules in such a way that they become asymmetric. This influence may be of two types, intramolecular and intermolecular, depending upon whether the systems involved are in the same or different molecules. The phenomenon, which is not entirely understood, has been well reviewed by Ritchie[217]. Examples of asymmetric induction in coordination compounds have been observed[218]. When a three molar portion of ortho-phenanthroline was added to a solution of zinc *dextro-α*-bromocamphor-π-sulfonate, the rotation of the solution was greatly enhanced, probably because of an asymmetric induction. With the addition of strychnine sulfate to [Zn(o-phen)₃]⁺⁺ an abnormal decrease in the rotation of the strychnine was noted. This anomaly was not so striking when α,α'-dipyridyl was substituted for the o-phenanthroline, and primary amines were without effect. The effect was attributed to an activation caused by the ortho-phenanthroline on coordination, forming an asymmetric configuration on the zinc complex.

This phenomenon has been investigated by Brasted[219] who concluded, on the basis of polarimetric, refractometric, conductimetric, and spectrographic measurements, that some type of compound is formed between the anion and cation (or complex and alkaloid). This would indicate that the forces, Van der Waals or ionic, have caused a distortion in the configuration which was responsible for the optical activity leading to a new observed rotation. Brasted also showed that cobalt(III) complexes behave in the same manner as the divalent metal complexes. Dwyer[178] attributes these observations to differences in the activities of the labile enantiomeric ions in the presence of optically active cations or anions.

Oxidation-Reduction. It has already been pointed out that with complex inorganic compounds it is possible to achieve conditions which cannot be realized with the carbon compounds. One case which has long been of interest to the coordination chemist is the possibility of changing the oxidation state of the central metal ion of an optically-active complex. The reactions of the binuclear complexes of cobalt(III) and cobalt(IV) which Werner studied evidently constitute the first examples of oxidation-reduc-

216. Kortüm, *Samml. Chem. Chem-Tech. Vortage*, 10 (1932).
217. Ritchie, "Asymmetric Synthesis and Asymmetric Induction," London, Oxford University Press, 1933.
218. Pfeiffer and Quehl, *Ber.*, **64**, 2667 (1931); Pfeiffer and Haimann, *Ber.*, **36**, 1064 (1903).
219. Brasted, thesis, University of Illinois, 1942.

tion reactions of optically-active complexes. It is interesting that these reactions proceed without racemization.

Dwyer[220] has recently resolved the tris(o-phenanthroline)ruthenium(II) cation and has obtained the optically pure, stable, orange-yellow dextro and levo perchlorates. Oxidation with ceric nitrate converts these enantiomers to the blue, optically-active [Ru(o-phen)₃](ClO₄)₃ , but there is a marked drop in the molecular rotation. However, on back reduction with ferrous sulfate the orange-yellow ruthenium(II) compound is recovered and the molecular rotation rises to the original value. The observed rotations are shown in Table 8.16. It is of interest to note that, contrary to the views of Werner, the complex of divalent ruthenium has the larger rotation.

TABLE 8.16. OPTICAL ROTATION OF TRIS(o-PHENANTHROLINE)RUTHENIUM(II) AND (III) CATIONS

Cations	$[M]_D^{20}$	$[M]_{5416}^{20}$
l-[Ru(o-phen)₃]⁺⁺	−1818°	−3482°
d-[Ru(o-phen)₃]⁺⁺	+1834°	+3494°
l-[Ru(o-phen)₃]⁺⁺⁺	−568°	−2354°
d-[Ru(o-phen)₃]⁺⁺⁺	+584°	+2330°

Dwyer and Gyarfas have performed similar experiments in which they utilized a different ligand[221] and a different central atom[222]. They also demonstrated[223] that a dynamic electronic equilibrium may exist between the oxidized and reduced forms of a complex ion. This was done by mixing a solution of d-[Os(dipy)₃]⁺⁺ with a solution containing an equivalent quantity of l-[Os(dipy)₃]⁺⁺⁺. The resulting mixture lost its optical activity very rapidly. This rapid loss of optical activity, plus the fact that the electron transfer is expected to occur without inversion, lends support to one of the current theories[224] of electron exchange reactions in aqueous solutions.

220. Dwyer and Gyarfas, *J. Proc. Roy. Soc. N. S. Wales*, **83**, 170 (1949).
221. Dwyer and Gyarfas, *J. Proc. Roy. Soc., N. S. Wales*, **83**, 174 (1949).
222. Dwyer and Gyarfas, *J. Proc. Roy. Soc., N. S. Wales*, **83**, 263 (1949).
223. Dwyer and Gyarfas, *Nature*, **166**, 481 (1950).
224. Libby, *J. Phys. Chem.*, **56**, 863 (1952).

9. Stereochemistry of Coordination Number Four

B. P. Block

The Pennsylvania State University, University Park, Pennsylvania

CONFIGURATIONS ENCOUNTERED

Complex compounds having the coordination number four are considered to be quite common, but there is good evidence for the existence of such complexes for only a small number of metallic elements. Mellor has summarized the more important spatial arrangements which have been suggested for these as regular tetrahedral, pyramidal, square or rectangular planar, and tetragonal or rhombic bisphenoidal[1]. The first arrangement to be established experimentally was the tetrahedral configuration for the carbon atom, and this three-dimensional concept of structure colored the thinking of chemists for many years. Although Werner explained several puzzling points in the chemistry of some platinum(II) complexes by assuming a planar arrangement of the four groups around the platinum[X50]†, the suggestion was not accepted by many, and even in rather recent times there have been attempts to explain the structures of these compounds on other bases[V27, V28, XI, X18, X40, X41, X42].† Two geometrical configurations for the coordination number four are now generally accepted, the regular tetrahedral and the square planar. These are the two configurations which Werner recognized. Table 9.1 shows those metallic elements for which a coordination number of four has been established. In some cases the element has the configuration in question only because the coordinating group or groups are such that a configuration which is unnatural to the element is forced upon it.

Tetrahedral Configuration

The evidence for a tetrahedral arrangement is found largely in complete structure determinations, either by x-ray or electron diffraction. Most of

---

The references in this chapter marked with an asterisk are of general interest.

*1. Mellor, *Chem. Revs.*, **33**, 137 (1943); *J. Proc. Roy. Soc., N. S. Wales*, **76**, 7 (1942).

† Reference numbers preceded by letters refer to annotated bibliography which appears at end of this chapter.

TABLE 9.1. CONFIGURATIONS OBSERVED AMONG FOUR-COORDINATE COMPLEXES

Meaning of symbols: t = tetrahedral, s = square planar, * = forced configuration only, ? = incomplete evidence, and (?) = interpretation of structure uncertain.

The superscript references refer to the section of the annotated bibliography concerning the element in question.

Be[D] 2+: t, s*											
									Al[H] 3+: t		
		Cr[P] 6+: t	Mn[R] 2+: s*, s?	Fe[S] 2−: t / 2+: s?, s*	Co[T] 1−: t / 2+: s?, t	Ni[U] 0: t / 2+: s, t	Cu[A] 1+: t / 2+: s, t	Zn[E] 2+: t	Ga[I] 3+: t		
	Nb[N] (?)	Mo[Q] 2+: (?)				Pd[V] 2+: s, t*	Ag[B] 1+: t / 2+: s	Cd[F] 2+: t, s?	In[J] 3+: t	Sn[L] 2+: s?	Sb[Y] 3+: t
	Ta[O] (?)			Os[W] 8+: t		Pt[X] 2+: s, t*	Au[C] 1+: s? / 3+: s	Hg[G] 2+: t	Tl[K] 1+: s? / 3+: t?, s?	Pb[M] 2+: s?	

these structures correspond to solid compounds and may have little relation to the configuration in solution. A few attempts have been made to apply Raman studies to solutions of species which have been studied as solids or gases, but the method does not lead to unambiguous results[2]. For some compounds of coordination number four, there have been reports of resolution into optical isomers, but in most cases the investigators have been unable to obtain optically-active fractions free of the optically-active resolving agent, so the validity of the evidence is doubtful. The Cotton effect has also been used to demonstrate the tetrahedral configuration; here, too, there is question as to the validity of the results[3].

In addition to the compounds in which directed covalent bonds are operative, there is a group in which the configuration is apparently determined by the principles of ionic interaction. Since there is no directed bonding in these compounds, the configuration is determined by the electrical interaction of the four ligands; in general, they have a like charge, so mutual repulsion leads to a tetrahedral arrangement. The possibility for this configuration is limited, geometrically, to cases in which the ratio of the radii of the ligand atoms to that of the central atom lies between 0.225 and 0.414[4]. Such compounds have been said to contain ionic bonding or to be nonpenetration coordination compounds.

Planar Configuration

Mellor[1] has discussed the subject of square planar coordination thoroughly. The earliest indication of planar configuration was Werner's suggestion that two of the compounds with the composition $Pt(NH_3)_2Cl_2$ were cis and trans isomers. He further postulated which was which, and correlated the structures of the isomers with their chemical behavior by means of a concept he called "trans elimination"[X50]. Several other examples of isomerism among platinum(II) compounds were known then, or were subsequently discovered, and a few palladium(II) compounds were known in two forms, but an analogous behavior was not found for other metals for some years. As a result, the concept was questioned more and more strongly, and the problem was not resolved to the satisfaction of most chemists until the advent of modern structural determinations.

The development of x-ray techniques for structure determinations furnished the additional evidence needed to satisfy most investigators. Dickinson demonstrated a square planar arrangement of the chloride ions about the platinum or palladium atoms in K_2PtCl_4, K_2PdCl_4 and $(NH_4)_2PdCl_4$[V10],

*2. Mathieu, *Compt. rend.*, **204**, 682 (1937).

3. Mellor, *J. Proc. Roy. Soc., N. S. Wales*, **75**, 157 (1942).

*4. Wells, "Structural Inorganic Chemistry," 2nd edition, Oxford, Oxford University Press, 1950.

see also[V29]. A few years later, Pauling explained[5, 6] the planar structure which had been observed for platinum(II) and palladium(II) compounds and predicted that diamagnetic compounds of nickel(II), gold(III), copper(III), and silver(III) are also planar. This theoretical pronouncement created a renewal of interest in the problem and a large number of papers on the subject soon appeared[A15, C5, U19, U34, V6, V19, V29, X10, X16, X34]. For the most part, these confirmed Pauling's ideas, but some investigators attacked the theory of planar configurations for platinum(II), palladium(II), and nickel(II)[U30, V26, V28, X18, X40, X41]. Others, particularly Jensen[7], answered these objections quite adequately. Jensen made extensive use of dipole moment determinations to show the existence of trans planar structures. While Pauling's prediction that diamagnetic nickel(II) and gold(III) compounds would be planar was verified, it was also found that some silver(II) and copper(II) compounds are planar. In addition, several other elements have been reported to exhibit the planar configuration. The reports are based mainly on incomplete x-ray studies, and more evidence is needed to establish the results conclusively. Other experimental methods which have been used to provide evidence for planar configuration are magnetic measurements, crystal optics, and resolution into optical isomers.

THEORETICAL CONSIDERATIONS

Isomer Patterns and Configuration

The classical chemical method for stereochemical investigation involves preparation, identification, and analysis of compounds, separation into isomers, and investigation of chemical behavior. After a compound has been prepared, the question of the number of isomers is most important in this method of attack. Pfeiffer elucidated the probable isomer patterns for compounds with the coordination number four, assuming the regular tetrahedral, square planar, and pyramidal configurations[8]. His results are summarized in Table 9.2. There is experimental evidence for the tetrahedral and planar configurations, but there is no case of isomerism which can be explained only by a pyramidal configuration, although the isomer pattern is quite distinct for this configuration. This approach is illustrated by the isolation of three geometrical isomers of $[Pt(NH_2OH)(NH_3)(py)(NO_2)]^+$ by Chernyaev[X9]. While this is not definitive proof that the ion is planar, it certainly eliminates the tetrahedral structure.

*5. Pauling, *J. Am. Chem. Soc.*, **53**, 1391 (1931).
*6. Pauling, *J. Am. Chem. Soc.*, **54**, 988 (1932).
 7. Jensen, *Z. anorg. allgem. Chem.*, **241**, 115 (1939).
*8. Pfeiffer, "Stereochemie," Freudenberg, pp. 1210–57, Leipzig and Vienna, Franz Deuticke, 1933.

TABLE 9.2. STEREOISOMERS OF TETRACOORDINATE STRUCTURES
(T = tetrahedral, S = square planar, and P = pyramidal)

	Ma_4			Ma_2b_2			Ma_2bc			$Mabcd$			$M(AB)_2$		
	T	S	P	T	S	P	T	S	P	T	S	P	T	S	P
Number of optically active isomers									2	2		6	2		2
Number of optically inactive isomers	1	1	1	1	2	2	1	2	1	—	3	—	—	2	1

Configuration and Chemical Reactions

The success of the chemical methods of determining configurations is dependent upon the retention of configuration during reaction. Although this point has not been investigated exhaustively, the coherence of the facts and theory and the compatibility with configurations assigned by physical methods indicate that the configurations are retained in reactions of platinum complexes.

Trans Effect. Some interesting principles have arisen from the study of the reactions of platinum(II) complexes. These originated in Werner's observations on the reactions of the isomers of [Pt(NH₃)₂Cl₂]. To assign the cis and trans configurations, he assumed that a phenomenon which he called "trans elimination" was operative in their reactions. This concept has been further developed by several Russian workers and is now one of the guiding principles in the assignment of cis and trans structures to planar complexes[9], as well as in the preparation of complexes of known configuration. The basic postulate is that in a substitution reaction the group trans to the most electronegative or most labilizing group will be replaced (page 146). Fundamentally, this is the basis for "Kurnakov's test"[X29], which is used frequently by the Russian investigators to assign a cis or trans configuration to a diacido platinum(II) complex. Treatment of the complex [PtabX₂] with thiourea gives [Pt(tu)₄]X₂ if the complex is cis, but [Pt(tu)₂ab]X₂ if the complex is trans. There are relatively few examples of this kind of isomerism among palladium(II) compounds; however, these react by trans elimination[10]. Quagliano and Schubert have recently discussed the trans effect[11]. The phenomenon has been well documented for only a few classes of platinum(II) compounds. The ultimate resolution of the problem awaits the extension of the observations to a broader area.

Reaction with a Bidentate Group. When a complex [Pta₂b₂] is treated with a bidentate reagent AA, the cis isomer reacts to give [Pt(AA)b₂],

9. Chernyaev, *Ann. inst. platine (U.R.S.S.)*, **5**, 102, 118 (1927); cf, *Chem. Centr.*, **1927**, II, 1557.
10. Jonassen and Cull, *J. Am. Chem. Soc.*, **73**, 274 (1951).
*11. Quagliano and Schubert, *Chem. Revs.*, **50**, 201 (1952).

whereas the trans isomer yields [Pt(AA)$_2$b$_2$], [Pt(AA)ab$_2$], or some other compound in which AA functions as a monodentate ligand. This method for assigning configurations is also widely used by the Russian workers[12, 13]. Grinberg showed that trans-[Pt(NO$_3$)$_2$(NH$_3$)$_2$] reacts with oxalic acid to form [Pt(HC$_2$O$_4$)$_2$(NH$_3$)$_2$] whereas the cis form yields [Pt(C$_2$O$_4$) (NH$_3$)$_2$]^{X20}.

Hybrid Type and Configuration

In general, it is not possible to predict whether a configuration will be planar or tetrahedral. However, the concepts introduced by Pauling[5, 6] and extended by Kimball[14], have met with great success in explaining the observed facts and in predicting the existence of diamagnetic planar nickel(II) and gold(III) compounds. Pauling approached the subject from the consideration that the formation of covalent bonds between the central atom and the ligands requires an overlapping of orbitals; this results in the bonds being so oriented in space that maximum overlapping occurs. From a consideration of the available orbitals in the atoms of any element it is possible to predicate what spatial arrangement the orbitals will take. In general, stronger bonds result from hybridization of the diverse orbitals (angular strengths are: dsp^2, 2.64; sp^3, 2.0). Kimball found that certain combinations should result in irregular tetrahedral or pyramidal configurations, in addition to the regular tetrahedral and square planar configurations proposed by Pauling, but these possibilities have not been observed for discrete coordination compounds. Kimball's results are summarized in Table 9.3.

TABLE 9.3. CONFIGURATIONS OF TETRACOORDINATE COMPLEXES

Configuration	Orbitals Involved
Regular tetrahedral	sp^3, d^3s
Irregular tetrahedral	d^2sp, dp^3, d^3p
Square planar	dsp^2, d^2p^2
Pyramidal	d^4

On the basis of Pauling's ideas, Mellor has suggested that the following species might also exhibit the planar configuration[15]: cobalt(I), cobalt(II), iron(II), manganese(II), manganese(III), rhodium(I), and iridium(I). Although he has searched for some of these, the planar configuration has not yet been proven for them.

The Magnetic Criterion. It is possible to relate the magnetic properties of some coordination compounds to the theory just discussed, and this is one of its striking successes. If we consider only the 3d, 4s, and 4p levels for

12. Gurin, *Doklady Akad. Nauk S.S.S.R.*, **50**, 201, 205, 209 (1945); cf. *Chem. Abs.*, **43**, 1674c, h, 1675c (1949).
13. Ryabchikov, *Compt. rend. acad. sci. U.R.S.S.*, **41**, 208 (1943).
14. Kimball, *J. Chem. Phys.*, **8**, 188 (1940).
15. Mellor, *J. Proc. Roy. Soc., N. S. Wales*, **74**, 129 (1940).

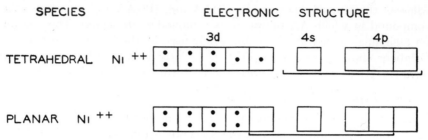

FIG. 9.1. Configuration and electronic structure of nickel complexes.

nickel (the same argument will apply to palladium and platinum with the substitution of the proper orbitals) from Hund's rule of maximum multiplicity in a given energy level[16], the nickel(II) ion should have two unpaired electrons. However, if nickel(II) is to form a square planar compound with dsp^2 bonding, these electrons will have to pair, as indicated in Fig. 9.1, so the determination of the magnetic moment of nickel(II) compounds shows whether dsp^2 bonding is present. All the elements which form complexes with planar configurations, except copper(II) and silver(II), should exhibit different magnetic behavior for dsp^2 bonding than for the bonding associated with the tetrahedral arrangement. The extension of the magnetic criterion to elements beyond the first transition series, with the exception of silver(II), has, however, not met with much success[17], so in some of these cases magnetic data will have to be supported by other facts.

EXPERIMENTAL PROOF OF CONFIGURATION

Werner's Use of the Concept of "Trans Elimination"

The classical arguments of Werner[X50] are of historical importance and are of interest in showing how elegantly a gifted mind can interpret chemical data. Two forms of $[Pt(NH_3)_2Cl_2]$ can be prepared, one by the reaction of $K_2[PtCl_4]$ with aqueous ammonia and the other by the reaction of $[Pt(NH_3)_4]Cl_2$ with aqueous hydrochloric acid. Two forms of $[Pt(py)_2Cl_2]$ are also known. Treating either form of $[Pt(NH_3)_2Cl_2]$ with pyridine yields $[Pt(NH_3)_2(py)_2]Cl_2$, but the two forms of reactant yield different isomers of the product. The same isomers of $[Pt(NH_3)_2(py)_2]Cl_2$ are formed by the treatment of the two forms of $[Pt(py)_2Cl_2]$ with ammonia. When these two isomers of $[Pt(NH_3)_2(py)_2]Cl_2$ are heated with hydrochloric acid, one yields $[Pt(NH_3)(py)Cl_2]$, whereas the second yields a mixture of $[Pt(NH_3)_2Cl_2]$ and $[Pt(py)_2Cl_2]$; the latter two compounds are identical

16. Hund, *Z. Physik*, **33**, 345 (1925).
17. Mellor, *J. Proc. Roy. Soc., N. S. Wales*, **77**, 145 (1944).

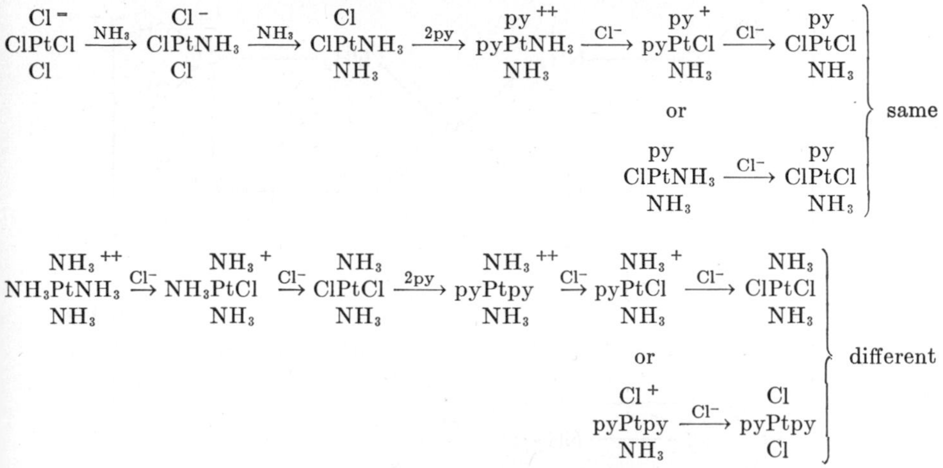

$$
\begin{array}{l}
\text{Cl}^- \\
\text{ClPtCl} \xrightarrow{\text{NH}_3} \\
\text{Cl}
\end{array}
\begin{array}{l}
\text{Cl}^- \\
\text{ClPtNH}_3 \xrightarrow{\text{NH}_3} \\
\text{Cl}
\end{array}
\begin{array}{l}
\text{Cl} \\
\text{ClPtNH}_3 \xrightarrow{2\text{py}} \\
\text{NH}_3
\end{array}
\begin{array}{l}
\text{py}^{++} \\
\text{pyPtNH}_3 \xrightarrow{\text{Cl}^-} \\
\text{NH}_3
\end{array}
\begin{array}{l}
\text{py}^+ \\
\text{pyPtCl} \xrightarrow{\text{Cl}^-} \\
\text{NH}_3
\end{array}
\left.\begin{array}{l}
\text{py} \\
\text{ClPtCl} \\
\text{NH}_3
\end{array}\right\}
$$

or · } same

$$
\begin{array}{l}
\text{py} \\
\text{ClPtNH}_3 \xrightarrow{\text{Cl}^-} \\
\text{NH}_3
\end{array}
\begin{array}{l}
\text{py} \\
\text{ClPtCl} \\
\text{NH}_3
\end{array}
$$

$$
\begin{array}{l}
\text{NH}_3^{++} \\
\text{NH}_3\text{PtNH}_3 \xrightarrow{\text{Cl}^-} \\
\text{NH}_3
\end{array}
\begin{array}{l}
\text{NH}_3^+ \\
\text{NH}_3\text{PtCl} \xrightarrow{\text{Cl}^-} \\
\text{NH}_3
\end{array}
\begin{array}{l}
\text{NH}_3 \\
\text{ClPtCl} \xrightarrow{2\text{py}} \\
\text{NH}_3
\end{array}
\begin{array}{l}
\text{NH}_3^{++} \\
\text{pyPtpy} \xrightarrow{\text{Cl}^-} \\
\text{NH}_3
\end{array}
\begin{array}{l}
\text{NH}_3^+ \\
\text{pyPtCl} \xrightarrow{\text{Cl}^-} \\
\text{NH}_3
\end{array}
\left.\begin{array}{l}
\text{NH}_3 \\
\text{ClPtCl} \\
\text{NH}_3
\end{array}\right\}
$$

or } different

$$
\begin{array}{l}
\text{Cl}^+ \\
\text{pyPtpy} \xrightarrow{\text{Cl}^-} \\
\text{NH}_3
\end{array}
\begin{array}{l}
\text{Cl} \\
\text{pyPtpy} \\
\text{Cl}
\end{array}
$$

Fɪɢ. 9.2. Trans elimination in platinum(II) complexes

with the isomers from which the second form of $[Pt(NH_3)_2(py)_2]Cl_2$ was prepared. An outline of Werner's explanation based on trans elimination is shown in Fig. 9.2. The original isomers of $[Pt(py)_2Cl_2]$ are similar in configuration to the isomers of $[Pt(NH_3)_2Cl_2]$ and are not shown.

Significance of Studies on Optical Isomers

Mills and his coworkers[V18, X34] have ingeniously used the resolution of an asymmetric substance into its optical isomers to gain evidence for the planar configuration of platinum(II) and palladium(II) compounds. Two chelating groups, isobutylenediamine and meso-stilbenediamine, were coordinated to the metal ion. The ion thus formed has a center of symmetry if the nitrogen to metal bonds are tetrahedral, but is asymmetric if the bonds are planar (Fig. 9.3). For both the platinum and palladium compounds, separation into optically-active isomers was successful, and the cations could be obtained in active form, free of the material used for resolution. After destruction of the complex, the amines were shown to be inactive. Both Mills and Jensen[7] have pointed out that this does not prove that the complexes have a planar configuration, but it certainly eliminates a regular tetrahedral configuration.

The Role of X-Ray Structure Determinations

Robertson and co-workers have carried out complete x-ray structure determinations on some metal phthalocyanines[A23, D3, U32, X44]. Because of the large number of atoms involved, this is a particularly interesting example of what can be done with structure determinations in favorable

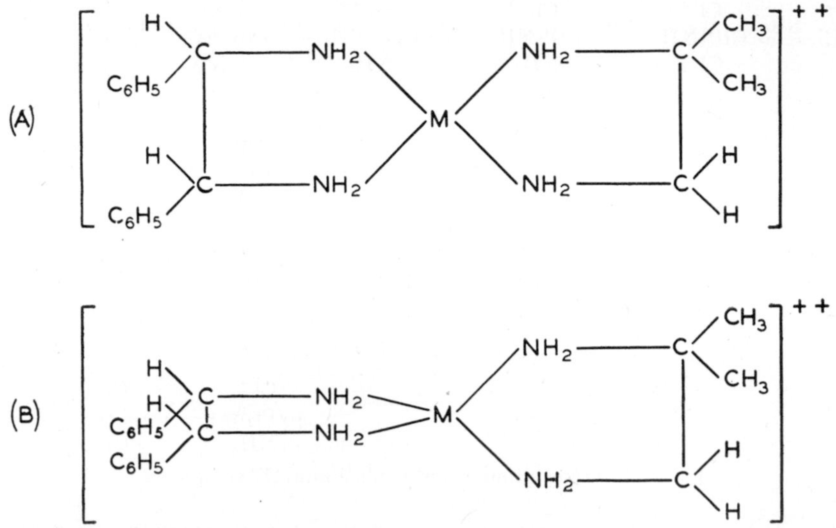

Fig. 9.3. Configurations of tetracoordinate complexes containing one molecule of isobutylenediamine and one molecule of *meso*-stilbenediamine bound to planar (a) and to tetrahedral (b) central atoms.

cases. The large organic molecule is tetradentate, with the four coordinating nitrogen atoms at the corners of a square. The planar structure (Fig. 9.4) does not vary greatly in dimension from metal to metal and is the same for all of the metallic ions, irrespective of whether they ordinarily form planar

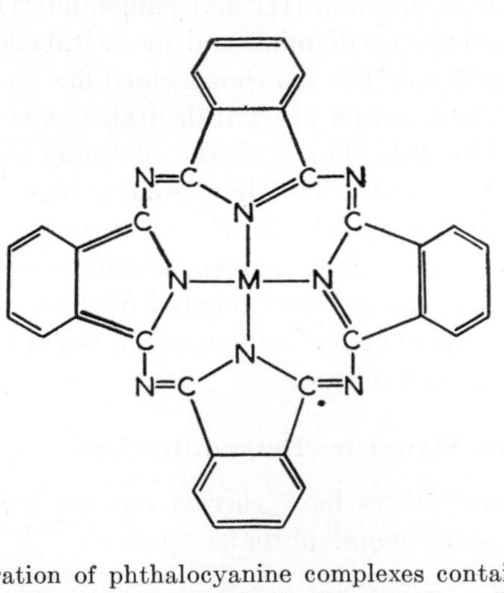

Fig. 9.4. Configuration of phthalocyanine complexes containing divalent metal ions. M = Cu(II), Be(II), Mn(II), Fe(II), Co(II), Ni(II), or Pt(II).

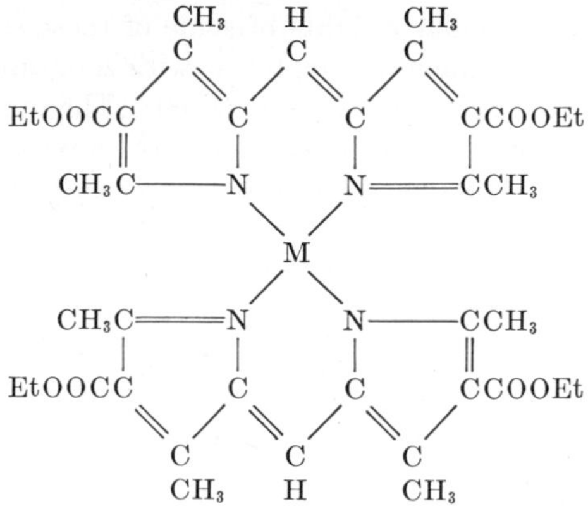

FIG. 9.5. Planar arrangement of nickel(II) and palladium(II) complexes with pyrromethene.

coordination compounds or tetrahedral ones. The stereochemistry of these compounds is determined by the ligand molecule.

Although actual structure investigations have not been carried out, a consideration of molecular models indicates that other forced configurations may also exist. The investigations and speculations of Porter on the pyrromethene derivatives[18] have been continued by Mellor and Lockwood, who measured the magnetic moments of the compounds indicated in Fig. 9.5[U25]. The nickel compound is paramagnetic as expected for a tetrahedral configuration, whereas the palladium compound is diamagnetic. The stereochemical significance of this is not known, but it is difficult to see how the palladium complex can be planar since the bond hybrid is most probably sp^3. Mann and Pope have prepared nickel, palladium, and platinum complexes with β,β',β''-triaminotriethylamine, $(NH_2CH_2CH_2)_3N$; these should be tetrahedral because of the geometry of the ligand[19], but, again, more work is required to complete the proof since octahedral coordination involving solvent molecules may occur.

Dipole Moments

A very complete study of the dipole moments of the compounds $[PtX_2(ER_3)_2]$ (X = Cl, Br, I, NO_2, or NO_3 ; E = P, As, or Sb; R = Et, Pr, Bu, or C_6H_5 ; but not all possible combinations) has been made by Jensen[V16]. The compounds fall into two groups, one, those compounds with zero dipole moment, and the other, those with an appreciable dipole

18. Porter, *J. Chem. Soc.*, **1938**, 368.
19. Mann and Pope, *J. Chem. Soc.*, **1926**, 482; *Proc. Roy. Soc. (London)*. **A109,** 444 (1925); Cox and Webster, *Z. Krist.*, **92,** 487 (1935).

moment. Since the molecular weights of some of these substances in solution show them to be monomeric, the forms with zero dipole moment must be trans planar, although not necessarily square. The other isomers do not have to be cis planar, of course, but might have any of a variety of configurations. If one form is planar, however, it is reasonable to assume the same geometry for the other form, expecially since x-ray studies have shown the planar form to occur in the solid state. With the possible exception of the purely chemical studies discussed earlier, this study probably affords the best demonstration that the planar configuration is not destroyed in solution although admittedly the use of a nonpolar solvent does not subject the hypothesis to the most rigorous test.

Other Properties

Mellor has attempted to relate various properties to structure so that complete x-ray study is not necessary to specify a configuration. He has used magnetic measurements extensively, particularly in assigning planar or tetrahedral structures to nickel(II) and cobalt(II) compounds. He has assumed that Pauling's criteria are correct, and, on the basis of structures assigned from them, he has studied the relationship of ligand atom to structure[U24], the relationship of Cotton effect to structure[3], and the relationship of absorption spectra to structure[20, 21]. In no case is there a clear pattern. He has also pointed out that large negative or positive birefringence in the crystal indicates a planar configuration[A15]. Wells has amplified the last point[4]. Lifschitz has related the color of nickel(II) complexes to their structures[U23], and Pauling has discussed the concept[22]. More recently Rây and Sen investigated the magnetic moments and colors of a large number of copper(II) complexes and concluded that the penetration complexes (i.e., dsp^2 bonding) have magnetic moments of 1.66 to 1.81 Bohr magnetons and are red, brown, or violet, whereas the nonpenetration complexes have moments of 1.90 to 2.20 Bohr magnetons and are blue to green[23]. It is interesting that both classes are said to have planar configurations although Pauling's considerations would not predict a planar configuration for a nonpenetration type of complex.

The Relationship of Oxidation State of Structure

The same metal in different oxidation states often shows different coordination numbers, but some instances are known in which an element has the coordination number four in two oxidation states. Copper(I) and

20. McKenzie, Mellor, Mills, and Short, *J. Proc. Roy. Soc., N. S. Wales*, **78**, 70 (1944).
21. Mills and Mellor, *J. Am. Chem. Soc.*, **64**, 181 (1942).
*22. Pauling, "The Nature of the Chemical Bond," 2nd edition, pp. 81–6, 98–106, 118–23, Ithaca, Cornell University Press, 1944.
23. Rây and Sen, *J. Indian Chem. Soc.*, **25**, 473 (1948).

silver(I) form tetrahedral compounds, whereas copper(II) and silver(II) form planar compounds[A8]. In [Ni(CO)$_4$], the nickel(0) is tetrahedral[U3]; in nickel(II) compounds, the configuration is usually planar but is possibly tetrahedral in some cases[24, U1, U18]. The oxidation states of iron and cobalt in the tetrahedral compounds [Fe(CO$_2$)(NO)$_2$] and [Co(CO)$_3$(NO)][S1] are somewhat of a problem but might be considered to be 2— and 1—, respectively. The only tetracovalent iron(II) compound of which the configuration has been determined completely is the planar phthalocyanine[D3]. Cobalt(II) is reported to have a tetrahedral configuration in some compounds such as bis(salicyladelyde)cobalt(II) and bis(1,2-naphthalenediamine)cobalt(II) acetate, and a planar configuration in others, as exemplified by bis(α-benzildioxime)cobalt(II) and bis(thiosemicarbazide)-cobalt(II)[T15].

Bridged Complexes

The aluminum, gallium, and indium halides, and, presumably, the corresponding iron(III) and gold(III) chlorides and bromides are bimolecular in the gaseous state. Palmer and Elliott have shown by electron diffraction that the aluminum halides have a bridged structure in which each aluminum is surrounded by a tetrahedron of halide ions, the tetrahedra sharing an edge[H5]:

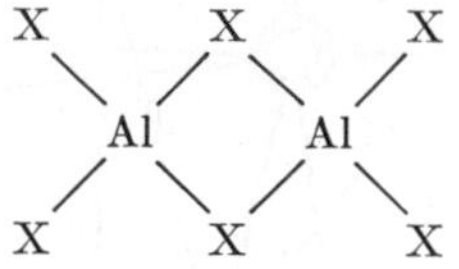

$$\begin{array}{ccccc}
X & & X & & X \\
\backslash & / & & \backslash & / \\
& Al & & Al & \\
/ & & \backslash & / & \backslash \\
X & & X & & X
\end{array}$$

(X = Cl, Br, or I)

For Au$_2$X$_6$ the molecule should be planar with the two square AuX$_4$ units sharing an edge[4]. This dimeric structure has been shown for [(Et$_2$AuBr)$_2$][C2], as well as [(Me$_3$AsPdCl$_2$)$_2$] and [(Me$_3$AsPdBr$_2$)$_2$][V21]. It is interesting that [(Pr$_2$AuCN)$_4$] has a different structure because of the rigidity of the triple bond between carbon and nitrogen. The M—C≡N—M group is linear, and double cyanide bridges are not possible. The cyanide group can serve as a bridging unit only by forming a large square molecule[C10]:

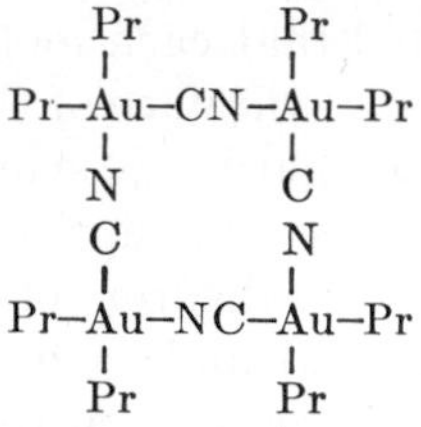

$$\begin{array}{ccc}
Pr & & Pr \\
| & & | \\
Pr-Au-CN-Au-Pr \\
| & & | \\
N & & C \\
C & & N \\
| & & | \\
Pr-Au-NC-Au-Pr \\
| & & | \\
Pr & & Pr
\end{array}$$

24. Nyholm, *Quart. Revs.*, **3**, 321 (1949).

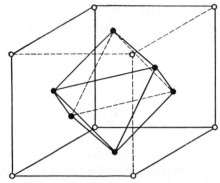

FIG. 9.6. Basic unit $[Mo_6Cl_8]^{4+}$ in the structures of $[Mo_6Cl_8](OH)_4 \cdot 14H_2O$, $Mo_6Cl_{12} \cdot 8H_2O$, and $HMo_3Cl_7 \cdot H_2O$. ●, Mo; ○, Cl.

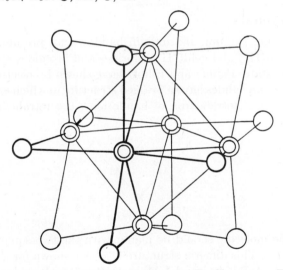

FIG. 9.7. Structures of the Nb_6Cl_{12}, Ta_6Br_{12} and Ta_6Cl_{12} groups. The double circles represent metal atoms and the single circles halogen atoms.

Extremely interesting structures have been found for $[Mo_6Cl_8](OH)_4 \cdot 14H_2O$, $Mo_6Cl_{12} \cdot 8H_2O$, and $HMo_3Cl_7 \cdot H_2O^{Q1, \, Q2, \, Q3}$. All of these compounds contain the polynuclear unit $[Mo_6Cl_8]^{4+}$, the structure of which is shown in Fig. 9.6. Pauling has suggested that each molybdenum atom forms bonds with the four chlorine atoms on the face of the cube nearest it in a nearly coplanar configuration[25]. Each chlorine is shared by three molybdenum atoms. A related structure has been found for $Nb_6Cl_{14} \cdot 7H_2O$ and $Ta_6Cl_{14} \cdot 7H_2O^{N1}$, in which the central octahedron of metal atoms is surrounded by twelve chloride ions (Fig. 9.7) and each metal ion has four chlorine atoms in a nearly square coplanar relation to it.

25. Pauling, *Chem. Eng. News*, **25**, 2970 (1947).

Ambiguities Arising from Some of the Techniques Employed to Establish Configurations

Incomplete X-ray Analysis

Unfortunately several of the conclusions concerning the configurations of four-coordinate complexes are based upon incomplete studies. This is particularly true of the x-ray studies, and in some cases this has led to results which were later shown to be incorrect. A structure based on x-ray analysis which is carried only to the unit cell dimensions may well be in error. It is safer to include also symmetry considerations from the space group, but even this has been insufficient to yield final answers in some

Fig. 9.8. Structure of $Cs_2Au_2Cl_6$. ● = Au; ○ = Cl.

cases. For example, on this basis, Cox, Shorter, and Wardlaw reported that $K_2SnCl_4 \cdot 2H_2O$ contains planar $[SnCl_4]^=$ groupings, but Brasseur and de Rassenfosse showed by a complete analysis that the structure consists of infinite chains of $[SnCl_6]^{-4}$ octahedra, sharing edges[L1]. It appears that the first investigators considered only discrete coordination units and were able to rule out the tetrahedral unit but neglected to consider the possibility of condensed structures. Because of this possibility of condensed structures, coordination numbers obtained from chemical analysis alone may not have much meaning. For example, the formula $Cd(NH_3)_2Cl_2$ appears to correspond to a compound of coordination number four, but actually, the structure consists of condensed octahedra similar to those of the $K_2SnCl_4 \cdot 2H_2O$ structure[26]. On the other hand, in $CsCuCl_3$, each copper atom is square planar, and the structure is said to consist of infinite chains of $CuCl_4^=$ units joined by opposite corners[A29].

26. MacGillavry and Bijvoet, *Z. Krist.*, **94**, 231 (1936).

Even though there is agreement on atomic coordinates there may still be disagreement on the structural interpretation. For example, Elliott and Pauling interpreted the structure of $Cs_2Au_2Cl_6$ (Fig. 9.8) as containing planar $[AuCl_4]^-$ and linear $[AuCl_2]^-$ units, whereas Ferrari concluded that the gold(III) occurs in octahedral $[AuCl_6]^=$ units[C5]. Similar disagreements exist about the structures of $K_2CuCl_4 \cdot 2H_2O$ and $CuCl_2 \cdot 2H_2O$[A10, 27, 28]. The point in dispute is the degree to which the different metal to ligand bonds can vary in length and still be considered part of the coordination sphere. In $Cs_2Au_2Cl_6$, for instance, there are four Au(III)-Cl_I distances of 2.42 A., and two Au(III) — Cl_{II} distances of 3.13 A. This problem does not arise with the tetrahedral structure, and with some of the platinum(II) compounds the structure is clearly planar since there are only four groups within a reasonable distance of the platinum. An example is found in the structure of $K_2[PtCl_4]$ shown in Fig. 9.9[V10]. Since most planar structures can be interpreted as octahedral in the condensed phase, it has been suggested that

FIG. 9.9. Structure of K_2PtCl_4 and K_2PdCl_4 . ● = Pt or Pd; ○ = Cl.

a planar structure should be established for some compound in the gaseous state[29]. So far, this has not been accomplished.

Uncertainties in the Resolution of Some Optical Isomers

There have been several reported resolutions in which the coordination compound has not been obtained in optically active form free of other optically active groups. In these investigations, some separation into diastereoisomers is accomplished, and the supposed diastereoisomers are shown to undergo mutarotation in solution. When the optically-active resolving component is removed, however, the solution of the coordination compound is not optically active. It is assumed that the coordination compound racemizes so rapidly that the active form cannot be detected. Undoubtedly some of the compounds reported to be tetrahedral on the basis of such evidence are tetrahedral, but, in view of the inconclusive nature of such studies, it is desirable to have additional proof before considering the structures to

27. Chrobak, *Z. Krist.*, **88**, 35 (1934).
28. Neuhaus, *Z. Krist.*, **97**, 28 (1937).
*29. Fernelius, "Chemical Architecture," Burk and Grummit, pp. 84–90, New York, Interscience Publishers, 1948.

be established. One of the more vigorous attacks on the theory of the planar structure of some platinum(II) compounds was based on incomplete resolutions of this sort[X40, X41, X42]. Reihlen and his collaborators reported optical activity resulting from the asymmetry of the complex in bis(isobutylenediamine)platinum(II) and bis(isobutylenediamine)palladium(II) ions, and also with a number of complex species containing active donor molecules and platinum(II). However, other investigators were not able to duplicate the reported partial resolutions[X17, X46], so this work is generally questioned.

Inconsistencies Among Observed Oxidation States and those Predicted by the Atomic Orbital Theory

The question of why copper(II) and silver(II) form planar complexes and yet show no great tendency to be oxidized to the tervalent state is an intriguing one. On the basis of Pauling's theory, the behavior of gold is readily explained, i.e., gold(I) and planar gold(III) compounds exist, but there is no satisfactory evidence for gold(II) compounds. The electrons in the outermost d, s, and p levels and the bonding possibilities are shown in Fig. 9.10 for the atom in oxidation states 0, I, II, and III. The tetrahedral configuration observed for silver(I) and copper(I), the linear configuration for all three univalent atoms, and the planar configuration for gold(III) are in agreement with Pauling's treatment. Pauling[22] explained the planar structure of the copper(II) compounds by assuming that the dsp^2 planar

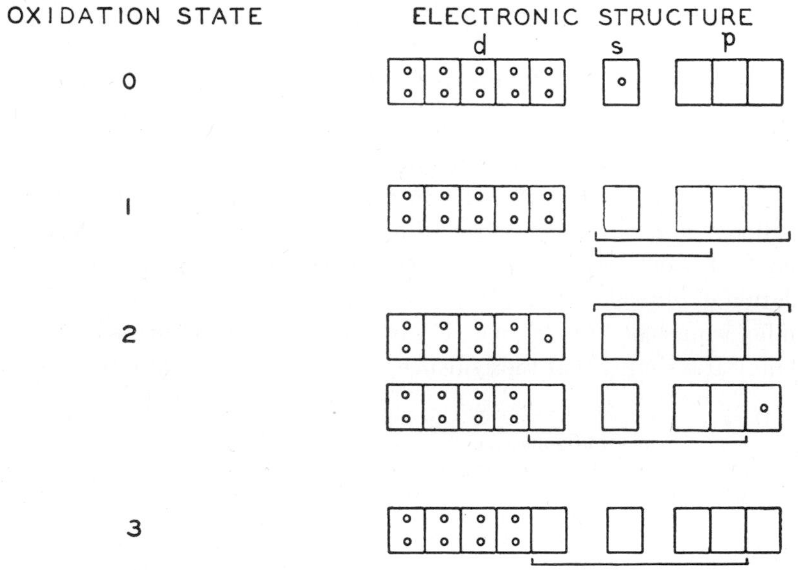

Fig. 9.10. Electronic structures of the atoms and ions of copper, silver, and gold.

bonds are enough stronger than the sp^3 bonds so that the slight difference in energy arising from the promotion of the unpaired electron from a $3d$ orbital to a $4p$ orbital is more than offset. If this argument is correct, it is difficult to see why copper(III) and silver(III) compounds are so hard to prepare. The chemistry of gold, on the other hand, is what one would expect.

Inferences Based on the Atomic Orbital Concept and on Analogy to Known Structures

In conclusion, some deductions with regard to probable structures will be mentioned. It has been proposed that $K_4[Ni(CN)_4]$ and $K_4[Pd(CN)_4]$ should be tetrahedral, since the central atoms resemble Ni(0) in $[Ni(CO)_4]$ in having an apparent oxidation state of zero[30]. Linstead and co-workers have prepared several phthalocyanine derivatives which have not been examined by x-ray methods, but which almost surely are planar[31]. Thallium(III) has been reported to form both tetrahedral and planar compounds[K1, K3], but a planar configuration is unlikely if dsp^2 or d^2p^2 bonding is required for its existence, since only sp^3 orbitals are available; and vacating of a d orbital would require promotion of a pair of electrons from the d level to the p level of the valence shell. The structure of the compounds containing central atoms with inert electron pairs is also of interest. From incomplete x-ray work, thallium(I)[K1, K2] and lead(II)[L1] are reported to form planar complexes. Complete structure determinations of some compounds in this group should be made to determine whether the coordination number is really four or if a condensed octahedral system is present.

Annotated Bibliography

The sources cited below on the stereochemistry of four-covalent compounds are listed by periodic family. The symbols used to indicate the kind of experimental work involved are: C, crystal optics; CE, Cotton effect; D, dipole moment; E, electron diffraction; G, isolation of geometrical isomers; I, isomorphism; IR, infrared spectrum; M, magnetic moment; O, isolation of optical isomers; R, Raman spectrum; X, x-ray diffraction. If a symbol is preceded by "i", e.g., iX, it indicates an incomplete study; while (?) indicates simply that the evidence reported supports the structure listed.

30. Deasy, *J. Am. Chem. Soc.*, **67**, 152 (1945).
31. Barrett, Dent, and Linstead, *J. Chem. Soc.*, **1936**, 1719.
*32. Cox and Wardlaw, *Science Progress* **32**, 463 (1938).
*33. Hückel, "Anorganische Strukturchemie," pp. 115–29, Stuttgart, Ferdinand Enke Verlag, 1948.
*34. Pfeiffer, *J. prakt. Chem.* **162**, 279 (1943).
*35. Sidgwick and Powell, *Proc. Roy. Soc. (London)*, **A176**, 153 (1940).

Family I:

Copper(I) and silver(I) form tetrahedral complexes and silver(II) and gold(III), square planar ones. Several copper(II) compounds are square planar, but at least one is tetrahedral. Incomplete x-ray studies indicate that gold(I) forms square planar bonds.

A1. Bezzi, Bua, and Schiavianto, *Gazz. chim. ital.*, **81,** 856 (1951). X. In copper dimethylglyoxime the 4 N atoms and the Cu atom are coplanar.

A2. Barclay and Nyholm, *Chemistry & Industry* **1953,** 378. M. CuI. $CH_3As(C_3H_6As-(C_3H_7)_2)_2$ contains tetrahedral Cu(I).

A3. Brink and van Arkel, *Acta Cryst.* **5,** 506 (1952). X. $(NH_4)_2CuCl_3$ and $(NH_4)_2CuBr_3$ contain infinite chains of $[CuX_4]^{3-}$ tetrahedra.

A4. Brink, Binnendijk, and van de Linde, *Acta Cryst.* **7,** 176 (1954). X. $CsCu_2Cl_3$ contains infinite double chains of $[CuCl_4]^{3-}$ tetrahedra.

A5. Brink and MacGillavry, *Acta Cryst.*, **2,** 158 (1949). X. K_2CuCl_3 contains infinite chains of $[CuCl_4]$ tetrahedra.

A6. Cambi and Coriselli, *Gazz. chim. ital.*, **66,** 779 (1936). IM. Some compounds of the type $[(R_2NCS_2)_2Cu]$ are tetrahedral. (?).

A7. Cox, Sharratt, Wardlaw, and Webster, *J. Chem. Soc.*, **1936,** 129. iX. $[Cu(py)_2Cl_2]$ and $[\{CH_3C:N(OH)C:N(OH)CH_3\}CuCl_2]$ have planar configurations.

A8. Cox, Wardlaw, and Webster, *J. Chem. Soc.*, **1936,** 775. iX, C. $[(C_6H_4NCOO)_2Cu]\cdot 2H_2O$ is planar; $K_3[Cu(CN)_4]$ is tetrahedral; X.$[Cu\{SC(NH_2)CH_3\}_4]Cl$ is tetrahedral; G. $[(C_5H_4NCOO)_2Cu]$ is planar.

A9. Cox and Webster, *J. Chem. Soc.*, **1935,** 731. iX, C. $[\{C_6H_4(O)(CH:NOH)\}_2Cu]$ and some substituted Cu β-diketonates are planar.

A10. Harker, *Z. Krist.*, **93,** 136 (1936). X. $[CuCl_2(H_2O)_2]$ contains planar Cu.

A11. Helmholz and Kruh, *J. Am. Chem. Soc.*, **74,** 1176 (1952). X. $Cs_2[CuCl_4]$ contains tetrahedral $[CuCl_4]^{=}$.

A12. Koyama, Saito, and Kuroya, *J. Inst. Polytech. Osaka City Univ. Ser. C.*, **4,** 43 (1953). X. Copper acetylacetonate is planar.

A13. Lifschitz, *Z. phys. Chem.*, **114,** 491 (1925). CE. $[Cu(d\text{-}oca)_4]^{++}$ contains tetrahedral copper (oca = oxymethylenecamphor).

A14. Mann, Purdie, and Wells, *J. Chem. Soc.*, **1936,** 1503. X, I. In $[(Et_3AsCuI)_4]$, $[(Et_3AsCuBr)_4]$, $[Et_3PCuI)_4]$, Cu(I) is tetrahedral.

A15. Mellor and Quodling, *J. Proc. Roy. Soc.*, *N.S. Wales*, **70,** 205 (1936). C. $Cs_2[CuCl_4]$ and $[CuCl_2(H_2O)_2]$ are planar.

A16. Mills and Gotts, *J. Chem. Soc.*, **1926,** 3121. iO. $[Cu\{C_6H_5C(O-):CHC(:O)-COONa\}_2]$ is tetrahedral.

A17. Müller, *Naturwissenschaften* **37,** 333 (1950). Copper phthalocyanine molecules appear planar in the field electron microscope.

A18. Peyronel, *Gazz. chim. ital.*, **73,** 89 (1943). X. $[(Pr_2NCS_2)Cu]$ is planar.

A19. Pfeiffer and Glaser, *J. prakt. Chem.*, **153,** 265 (1939). G. $[Cu\{C_{10}H_6(O-)(CH:NCH_3)\}_2]$ is planar.

A20. Rây and Chakravarty, *J. Indian Chem. Soc.*, **18,** 609 (1941). G. $[\{C_6H_5NHC(:NH)NHC(NH_3):N\}_2Cu]$ is planar.

A21. Rây and Dutt, *J. Indian Chem. Soc.*, **25,** 563 (1948). G. $[\{O_3SC_6H_4NH(:NH)-NHC(NH_2):NH\}_2Cu]$ is planar.

A22. Rây and Ghosh, *J. Indian Chem. Soc.*, **26,** 144 (1949). G. $[\{Et_2NC(:NH)NHC-(NH_2):N\}_2Cu]$ is planar.

A23. Robertson, *J. Chem. Soc.*, **1935**, 615. X. Copper(II) phthalocyanine is planar.

A24. Robertson, *J. Chem. Soc.*, **1951**, 1222. X. Copper(II) tropolone is planar.

A25. Schlesinger, *Ber.*, **58**, 1877 (1925). G. [{OOCCRR′NH(CH₂)ₓNHCRR″COO}Cu] is planar.

A26. Shugam, *Doklady Akad. Nauk S.S.S.R.*, **81**, 853 (1951); cf, *Chem. Abstracts*, **46**, 3894d (1952). X. Copper acetylacetonate is planar.

A27. Stackelberg, *Z. anorg. allgem. Chem.*, **253**, 136 (1947). iX, G. Some chelates formed from Cu(II) and aryl aldimines are planar.

A28. Watanabe and Atoji, *Science (Japan)*, **21**, 301 (1951); cf, *Chem. Abstracts*, **45**, 9982f (1951). X (?). [Cu(en)₂]⁺⁺ is planar.

A29. Wells, *J. Chem. Soc.*, **1947**, 1662. X. CsCuCl₃ contains infinite chains of square planar [CuCl₄]⁻ units.

B1. See A4. X. CsAg₂I₃ contains infinite double chains of [AgI₄]³⁻ tetrahedra.

B2. Brink and Stenfert Kroese, *Acta Cryst.* **5**, 433 (1952). X. K₂AgI₃ , Rb₂AgI₃ , and (NH₄)₂AgI₃ contain infinite chains of [AgI₄]³⁻ tetrahedra.

B3. See A5. X. Cs₂AgCl₃ and Cs₂AgI₃ contain infinite chains of [AgCl₄]⁼ tetrahedra.

B4. See A8. X. [Ag{SC(NH₂)CH₃}₄]Cl contains tetrahedral Ag(I). I, C. [(C₅H₄-NCOO)₂Ag] is planar.

B5. Hein and Regler, *Ber.*, **69B**, 1692 (1936). iO. [Ag(C₉H₆NO)(C₉H₆NOH)] and [Ag(C₉H₆NOH)₂]NO₃ contain tetrahedral Ag(I).

B6. Mann, Wells, and Purdie, *J. Chem. Soc.*, **1937**, 1828. I. [(Pr₃AsAgI)₄] (and [(Et₃AsAgI)₄] ?) contain tetrahedral Ag(I).

C1. Brain, Gibson, Jarvis, Phillips, Powell and Tyabji, *J. Chem. Soc.* **1952**, 3686. X. (C₇H₇)₂SAuCl₂ contains planar SAuCl₃ units.

C2. Burawoy, Gibson, Hampson, and Powell, *J. Chem. Soc.*, **1937**, 1690. X, C, D. [Et₂AuBr]₂ is planar.

C3. Cox and Webster, *J. Chem. Soc.*, **1936**, 1635. X. K[AuBr₄]·2H₂O contains planar [AuBr₄]⁻ ions.

C4. Dothie, Llewellyn, Wardlaw, and Welch, *J. Chem. Soc.*, **1939**, 426. iX. [Au(CN)₂-dipy]⁻ and [Au(CN)₂(o-phen)]⁻ are planar.

C5. Elliott and Pauling, *J. Am. Chem. Soc.*, **60**, 1846 (1938). X. Cs₂Au₂Cl₆ and Cs₂AgAuCl₆ contain planar [AuCl₄]⁻ units. Ferrari, *Gazz. chim. ital.*, **67**, 94 (1937), however, believes that the Au(III) is octahedrally coordinated.

C6. Goulden, Maccoll, and Millen, *J. Chem. Soc.*, **1950**, 1635. R. The Raman spectrum of [AuCl₄]⁻ is consistent with a planar configuration.

C7. Huggins, unpublished work referred to by Huggins in *J. Chem. Ed.*, **13**, 162 (1936). iX (?). [Me₄N][AuCl₄] contains planar [AuCl₄]⁻ ions.

C8. See A15. C. [Me₄N][AuCl₄], Na[AuCl₄]·2H₂O, and K[AuBr₄] contain planar Au(III).

C9. Perutz and Weisz, *J. Chem. Soc.*, **1946**, 438. iX. [Me₃PAuBr₃] is planar.

C10. Phillips and Powell, *Proc. Roy. Soc. (London)*, **A173**, 147 (1939). X. [(Pr₂AuCN)₄] is planar.

Family II:

Beryllium(II), zinc(II), cadmium(II), and mercury(II) are tetrahedral. Beryllium(II) is planar in the phthalocyanine. The report that cadmium(II) may be planar appears spurious.

D1. Bragg and Morgan, *Proc. Roy. Soc. (London)*, **A104**, 437 (1923). X. [Be₄O(AcO)₆] contains tetrahedrally coordinated Be(II).

D2. Burgess and Lowry, *J. Chem. Soc.*, **125**, 2081 (1924). iO. Beryllium benzoyl-camphor, $[C_{34}H_{38}O_2Be]$, is tetrahedral.

D3. Linstead and Robertson, *J. Chem. Soc.*, **1936**, 1736. X. Beryllium phthalocyanine is planar.

D4. O'Daniel and Tscheischwili, *Z. Krist.*, **103**, 178 (1941). iX. $Na_2[BeF_4]$ contains tetrahedral $[BeF_4]^=$.

D5. O'Daniel and Tscheischwili, *Z. Krist.*, **104**, 348 (1942). I. $K_2[BeF_4]$ contains tetrahedral $[BeF_4]^=$.

D6. Hultgren, *Z. Krist.*, **88**, 233 (1934). I, X. $(NH_4)_2[BeF_4]$ contains tetrahedral $[BeF_4]^=$.

D7. See A16. O. $[Be\{C_6H_5C(O-):CHC(:O)COONa\}_2]$ is tetrahedral.

D8. Busch and Bailar, *J. Am. Chem. Soc.*, **76**, 5352 (1954). O. Partial resolution of bis(benzoylacetone)beryllium indicates tetrahedral configuration. Compound did not racemize completely in five hours.

E1. Couture and Mathieu, *Ann. Phys.*, [12] **3**, 521 (1948). R. $[Zn(CN)_4]^=$ is tetrahedral in solution.

E2. Danilov, Finkelstein, and Levashevich, *Physik Z. Sowjetunion*, **10**, 223 (1936). X. $[ZnI_4]^=$ is tetrahedral in solution.

E3. Dickinson, *J. Am. Chem. Soc.*, **44**, 774 (1922). iX. $K_2[Zn(CN)_4]$ contains tetrahedral $[Zn(CN)_4]^=$.

E4. Klug and Alexander, *J. Am. Chem. Soc.*, **66**, 1056 (1944). X. $(NH_4)_3ZnCl_5$ contains tetrahedral $[ZnCl_4]^=$.

E5. Liu and Bailar, *J. Am. Chem. Soc.*, **73**, 5432 (1951). O. $[(HO_3SC_9H_5NO)_2Zn]$ contains tetrahedral $Zn(II)$.

E6. MacGillavry and Bijovet, *Z. Krist.*, **94**, 249 (1936). X. $[Zn(NH_3)_2Cl_2]$ and $[Zn(NH_3)_2Br_2]$ are tetrahedral.

E7. Mills and Clark, *J. Chem. Soc.*, **1936**, 175. iO. $K_2[Zn(CH_3C_6H_3S_2)_2]$ contains tetrahedral $Zn(II)$.

E8. See A16. iO. $[Zn\{C_6H_5C(O-):CHC(:O)COONa\}_2]$ is tetrahedral.

F1. Brasseur and Rassenfosse, *Z. Krist.*, **95**, 474 (1936). I. The Cd in $Ba[CdCl_4]\cdot$ $4H_2O$ is planar. Quodling and Mellor, *Z. Krist.*, **97**, 522 (1937), question the isomorphism on which this result is based.

F2. See E3. iX. $K_2[Cd(CN)_4]$ contains tetrahedral $Cd(II)$.

F3. Evans, Mann, Peiser, and Purdie, *J. Chem. Soc.*, **1940**, 1209. iX, I. $[(Et_3P)_2\text{-}$ $Cd_2Br_4]$ and similar compounds contain bridged tetrahedral Cd units. A tetrahedral structure is inferred for $[(R_3P)_2CdX_2]$.

F4. See E 7. iO. $K_2[Cd(CH_3C_6H_3S_2)_2]$ contains tetrahedral $Cd(II)$.

F5. Pitzer, *Z. Krist.*, **92**, 131 (1935). X. $[Cd(NH_3)_4](ReO_4)_2$ contains tetrahedral $[Cd(NH_3)_4]^{++}$.

G1. See E2. X. $[HgI_4]^=$ is tetrahedral in solution.

G2. Delwaulle, François, and Weimann, *Compt. rend.*, **206**, 1108 (1938). R. $[HgBr_4]^=$ is tetrahedral.

G3. See E3. iX. $K_2[Hg(CN)_4]$ contains tetrahedral $[Hg(CN)_4]^=$.

G4. See F3. iX, I. $[(Pr_3P)_2Hg_2Br_4]$ and similar arsine compounds contain bridged tetrahedral Hg units. A tetrahedral structure is inferred for $[(R_3P)_2HgX_2]$.

G5. Jeffery, *Nature*, **159**, 610 (1947). X. $Co[Hg(SCN)_4]$ contains tetrahedral HgS_4 units.

G6. Ketelaar, *Z. Krist.*, **80**, 190 (1931). X, I. $Ag_2[HgI_4]$ and $Cu_2[HgI_4]$ contain tetrahedral $[HgI_4]^=$.

G7. See E7. iO. $K_2[Hg(CH_3C_6H_3S_2)_2]$ contains tetrahedral $Hg(II)$.

G8. Scouloudi, *Acta Cryst.* **6**, 651 (1953). Same as G9.

G9. Scouloudi and Carlisle, *Nature*, **166**, 357 (1950). X. [Cu (en)₂][Hg(SCN)₄] contains tetrahedral HgS₄ units.

Family III:

Aluminum(III), gallium(III), and indium(III) are tetrahedral. The evidence for the structure of complexes containing thallium(I) and thallium(III) is incomplete and is conflicting in the latter case.

H1. Baenziger, *Acta Cryst.*, **4**, 216 (1951). X. Na[AlCl₄] contains tetrahedral [AlCl₄]⁻.

H2. Gerding and Smit, *Z. phys. Chem.*, **B50**, 171 (1941). R. Al₂X₆, with X = Cl⁻, Br⁻, or I⁻, contains bridged tetrahedral Al units. Kohlrausch and Wagner, *Z. Phys. Chem.*, **B52**, 185 (1942), say the Raman spectrum does not contradict such a structure, but does not prove it.

H3. Harris, Wood, and Ritter, *J. Am. Chem. Soc.*, **73**, 3151 (1951). X. Fused AlCl₃ contains pairs of bridged [AlCl₄]⁻ tetrahedra.

H4. Lippincott, *J. Chem. Phys.*, **17**, 1351 (1949). R, IR. Li[AlH₄] contains tetrahedral [AlH₄]⁻.

H5. Palmer and Elliott, *J. Am. Chem. Soc.*, **60**, 1852 (1938). E. Al₂X₆, with X = Cl⁻, Br⁻, or I⁻, contains bridged tetrahedral Al units.

I1. Brode, *Ann. Physik*, [5] **37**, 344 (1940). E. Ga₂Cl₆ and Ga₂Br₆ vapors contain bridged tetrahedral Ga units.

J1. See I1. E. In₂X₆, X = Cl⁻, Br⁻, or I⁻, contains bridged tetrahedral units in the vapor.

J2. Wood and Ritter, *J. Am. Chem. Soc.*, **74**, 1760 (1952). X. Fused InI₃ contains bridged tetrahedral units.

K1. Cox, Shorter, and Wardlaw, *J. Chem. Soc.*, **1938**, 1886. iX. [Tl(tu)₄]NO₃ or chloride contains planar [Tl(tu)₄]⁺, whereas [Me₂Tl{CH₃C(:O)CH:C(O—)CH₃}] is tetrahedral.

K2. Wardlaw, unpublished, 1940, cited by Sidgwick and Powell, *Proc. Roy. Soc. (London)*, **A176**, 153 (1940). X(i?). [Tl(o-phen)₂]NO₃ contains planar [Tl(o-phen)₂]⁺.

K3. Watanabe, Saito, Shiono, and Atoji, "Structure Reports for 1947–8," Vol. 11, pp. 393–4, edited by Wilson, N. V. A. Oosthock's Uitgevers mij Utrecht, 1951. iX. CsTlBr₄ contains planar [TlBr₄]⁻.

Family IV:

The evidence that lead(II) and tin(II) are planar is incomplete. The tin(II) compound has been shown to have a condensed, not discrete, structure involving coordination number six.

L1. Cox, Shorter, and Wardlaw, *Nature*, **139**, 71 (1937). iX. R₂[SnX₄]·2H₂O, with R⁺ = K⁺ or NH₄⁺ and X = Br⁻ or Cl⁻, contains planar [SnX₄]⁻. Brasseur and Rassenfosse, *Nature*, **143**, 332 (1939) report that K₂[SnCl₄]·H₂O contains condensed octahedral [SnCl₆]⁻ units.

M1. See L1. iX. K₂[Pb(C₂O₄)₂], [Pb{SC(CH₃)₂}₂Cl₂], [Pb(OOCC₆H₄OH)₂], and [Pb{C₆H₅C(O—):CHC(:O)CH₃}₂] contain planar lead groupings.

Family V:

Niobium and tantalum (in an indeterminate oxidation state) have four halogen neighbors in a displaced planar relationship and with four metal atom neighbors form a pyramid. Antimony(III) exhibits a distorted tetrahedral structure in one compound.

N1. Vaughan, Sturdivant, and Pauling, *J. Am. Chem. Soc.*, **72**, 5477 (1950). X. $Nb_6Cl_{14} \cdot 7H_2O$ contains $[Nb_6Cl_{12}]^{++}$ units. See Fig. 7.

O1. See N1. X. $Ta_6Br_{14} \cdot 7H_2O$ and $Ta_6Cl_{14} \cdot 7H_2O$ contain $[Ta_6X_{12}]^{++}$ units.

Y1. Byström and Wilhelmi, *Arkiv Kemi* **3**, 373 (1951). X. $CsSb_2F_7$ contains pairs of irregular tetrahedra of SbF_4^- sharing a corner.

Family VI:

Chromium(VI) is tetrahedral; molybdenum(II), in the halogen derivatives, has four halogen neighbors in an approximately planar relationship and, with four more molybdenum atoms, forms a pyramid.

P1. Helmholz and Foster, *J. Am. Chem. Soc.*, **72**, 4971 (1950). X. $K[CrO_3Cl]$ contains tetrahedral $[CrO_3Cl]^-$.

P2. Ketelaar and Wegeriff, *Rec. trav. chim.*, **57**, 1269 (1938). X. $K[CrO_3F]$ contains tetrahedral $[CrO_3F]^-$.

P3. Ketelaar and Wegeriff, *Rec. trav. chim.*, **58**, 948 (1939). I. $Cs[CrO_3F]$ contains tetrahedral $[CrO_3F]^-$.

Q1. Brosset, *Arkiv Kemi*, **1**, 353 (1949). X. $HMo_3Cl_7 \cdot H_2O$ contains $[Mo_6Cl_8]^{4+}$ units. See Fig. 9.6.

Q2. Brosset, *Arkiv Kemi, Mineral. Geol.*, **A20**, No. 7 (1945). X. $Mo_6Cl_8(OH)_4 \cdot 14H_2O$ contains $[Mo_6Cl_8]^{4+}$ units.

Q3. Brosset, *Arkiv Kemi, Mineral. Geol.*, **A22**, No. 11 (1946). X. $HMo_3Cl_7 \cdot H_2O$ contains $[Mo_6Cl_8]^{4+}$ units.

Family VII:

Manganese(II) may be planar, but the evidence is incomplete except for the phthalocyanine.

R1. Anspach, *Z. Krist.*, **101**, 39 (1939). X. $K_2Mn(SO_4)_2 \cdot 4H_2O$ contains planar $[Mn(H_2O)_4]^{++}$.

R2. Cox, Shorter, Wardlaw, and Way, *J. Chem. Soc.*, **1937**, 1556. I. $[Mn(py)_2Cl_2]$ is planar. Mellor and Coryell, *J. Am. Chem. Soc.*, **60**, 1786 (1938), have challenged this on the basis of the magnetic moment.

R3. See D3. X. Manganese(II) phthalocyanine is planar.

Family VIII:

Nickel(II), platinum(II), and palladium(II) are planar. Nickel(II), nickel(0), cobalt(II), osmium(VIII), cobalt in $[Co(CO)_3NO]$ and $[Co(CO_3)(COH)]$ and iron in $[Fe(CO)_2(NO)_2]$ and $[Fe(CO)_2(COH)_2]$ are tetrahedral. The evidence that cobalt(II) and iron(II) are planar in compounds other than the phthalocyanines is incomplete.

S1. Brockway and Anderson, *Trans. Faraday Soc.*, **33**, 1233 (1937). E. $[Fe(CO)_2(NO)_2]$ is tetrahedral.

S2. Cambi and Cagnasso, *Rend. ist. lombardo sci.*, **67**, 741 (1934). M. Some $Fe(SCN)_2$ complexes with o-phenanthroline and α,α'-dipyridyl are planar.

S3. Ewens and Lister, *Trans. Faraday Soc.*, **35**, 681 (1939). E. [Fe(CO)$_2$(COH)$_2$] is tetrahedral.

S4. See D3. X. Iron(II) phthalocyanine is planar.

T1. Biltz and Fetkenheuer, *Z. anorg. allgem. Chem.*, **89**, 97 (1914). G. [Co(NH$_3$)$_2$X$_2$], with X = Cl$^-$, Br$^-$, or I$^-$, is planar.

T2. See S1. E. [Co(CO)$_3$NO] is tetrahedral.

T3. Calvin, Bailes, and Wilmarth, *J. Am. Chem. Soc.*, **68**, 2254 (1946). X (?). Compounds of the type [Co(OC$_6$H$_4$CH:NCH$_2$-)$_2$] "appear to be coplanar."

T4. Calvin and Melchior, *J. Am. Chem. Soc.*, **70**, 3270 (1948). M. [Co(OHCC$_6$H$_4$O)$_2$] is planar although two to three unpaired electrons are present. Some cobalt salicylaldimines are planar. See T16.

T5. See S2. M. Some Co(CN)$_2$ complexes with o-phenanthroline and α,α'-dipyridyl are planar.

T6. Cambi and Malatesta, *Gazz. chim. ital.*, **69**, 547 (1939). M. [{C$_6$H$_5$O(:NO—)C-(:NOH)C$_6$H$_5$}$_2$Co] has one unpaired electron, *i.e.*, is planar.

T7. Cambi and Szegö, *Ber.*, **64B**, 2591 (1931). M. Cobalt acetylacetonate is highly paramagnetic, *i.e.*, is tetrahedral.

T8. See R2. iX, G. [Co(py)$_2$Cl$_2$] is planar. Mellor and Coryell (reference in R2) believe one form is tetrahedral, the other, condensed octahedral. See T10.

T9. See S3. E. [Co(CO)$_3$(COH)] is tetrahedral.

T10. Hantzsch, *Z. anorg. allgem. Chem.*, **159**, 273 (1927). G. [Co(py)$_2$Cl$_2$] is planar. Rhode and Vogt: *Z. phys. Chem.*, **B15**, 353 (1931), assign different coordination numbers to cobalt in the two forms. See T8.

T11. Jensen, *Z. anorg. allgem. Chem.*, **229**, 282 (1936). D. [Co(PR$_3$)$_2$Cl$_2$], with R = Et or Pr, is either cis planar or tetrahedral.

T12. Krishnan and Mookherji, *Phys. Rev.*, [2] **51**, 528 (1937). M. The magnetic moment for Cs$_2$[CoCl$_4$] corresponds to a spin only value for cobalt(II). A tetrahedral structure is inferred.

T13. M. Same as T12, p. 774, but for Cs$_3$CoCl$_5$.

T14. See D3. X. Cobalt(II) phthalocyanine is planar.

T15. Mellor and Craig, *J. Proc. Roy. Soc., N.S. Wales*, **74**, 495 (1941). M. The magnetic moments for a large number of cobalt compounds correspond to either one or else several unpaired electrons. This indicates members of the first group are probably planar, those of the second, tetrahedral. No geometrical isomers could be found.

T16. Mellor and Goldacre, *J. Proc. Roy. Soc., N. S. Wales*, **73**, 233 (1940). M. Some cobalt(II) compounds are tetrahedral.

T17. Powell and Wells, *J. Chem. Soc.*, **1935**, 359. X. Cs$_3$CoCl$_5$ contains tetrahedral [CoCl$_4$]$^-$.

T18. Rây and Ghosh, *J. Indian Chem. Soc.*, **20**, 323 (1943). M. Some cobalt (II) compounds are planar.

T19. Tyson and Adams, *J. Am. Chem. Soc.*, **62**, 1228 (1940). M. [Co(OC$_6$H$_4$CHO)$_2$] is tetrahedral. See T3.

T20. Váradi, *Acta Univ. Szeged, Chem. et Phys.*, **2**, 175 (1949); cf, *Chem. Abstracts*, **44**, 5661i (1950). M. [CoCl$_4$]$^-$ is tetrahedral in solution.

T21. Váradi, *Acta Univ. Szeged, Chem. et Phys.*, **3**, 62 (1950); cf, *Chem. Abstracts*, **46**, 372a (1952). Photometer data. [CoCl$_4$]$^-$ is tetrahedral.

T22. Zhdanov and Zvonkova, *Zhur. Fiz. Khim.*, **24**, 1339 (1950); cf, *Chem. Abstracts*, **45**, 6001e (1951). X. M$_2$[Co(NCS)$_4$]·nH$_2$O, in which M$^+$ = K$^+$ or NH$_4^+$, contains tetrahedral [Co(NCS)$_4$]$^-$ units.

U1. Basolo and Matoush, *J. Am. Chem. Soc.*, **75**, 5663 (1953). M. Bis(formylcamphor)-ethylenediimine-nickel(II) although planar in the solid is tetrahedral in benzene, toluene, *o*-, *p*-, and *m*-xylene, and mesitylene.

U2. Brasseur, Rassenfosse and Piérard, *Compt. rend.*, **198**, 1048 (1934); Brasseur and Rassenfosse, *Bull. soc. franc. mineral.*, **61**, 129 (1938). X. Ba[Ni(CN)$_4$]·4H$_2$O contains planar [Ni(CN)$_4$]⁻.

U3. Brockway and Cross, *J. Chem. Phys.*, **3**, 828 (1935). E. [Ni(CO)$_4$] is tetrahedral.

U4. Callis, Nielsen, and Bailar, *J. Am. Chem. Soc.*, **74**, 3461 (1952). M. One nickel (II)-containing dye is planar and three are tetrahedral.

U5. See T4. M. [Ni(OC$_6$H$_4$CHO)$_2$] is planar although paramagnetic. Some nickel salicylaldimines are planar.

U6. See A6. M. Some compounds of the type [(R$_2$NCS$_2$)$_2$Ni] are planar.

U7. See T7. M. Several nickel(II) complexes are diamagnetic (planar); nickel acetylacetonate is paramagnetic (tetrahedral?).

U8. Cavell and Sugden, *J. Chem. Soc.*, **1935**, 621. G, M. Several substituted nickel glyoximes are planar. M. [(R$_2$NCS$_2$)$_2$Ni], with R = Pr or Bu, is planar.

U9. Chugaev, *J. Russ. Phys. Chem. Soc.*, **42**, 1466 (1910); cf, *Chem. Abstracts*, **6**, 594 (1912). G. Nickel methylglyoxime is planar.

U10. Cox, Pinkard, Wardlaw, and Webster, *J. Chem. Soc.*, **1935**, 459. iX. [Ni(HON:CHC$_6$H$_4$O)$_2$] is planar.

U11. Cox, Wardlaw, and Webster, *J. Chem. Soc.*, **1935**, 1475. X.

$$K_2\left[\,Ni\!\left(\begin{matrix}S\!-\!C\!=\!O\\ |\\ S\!-\!C\!=\!O\end{matrix}\right)_{\!2}\right]$$

contains a planar NiS$_4$ unit.

U12. Crawford and Cross, *J. Chem. Phys.*, **6**, 525 (1938). IR. The infrared spectrum of [Ni(CO)$_4$] is compatible with either tetrahedral or square planar configuration.

U13. Crawford and Horwitz, *J. Chem. Phys.*, **16**, 147 (1948). R. The Raman spectrum of [Ni(CO)$_4$] is compatible with a tetrahedral structure.

U14. Curtiss, Lyle, and Lingafelter, *Acta Cryst.* **5**, 388, (1952). I, iX. [Ni(OC$_6$H$_4$CHO)$_2$] is tetrahedral because its powder pattern very closely resembles that of the corresponding Zn compound but not that of the Cu compound.

U15. Dwyer and Mellor, *J. Am. Chem. Soc.*, **63**, 81 (1941). M. [Ni$_2$(R$_2$N$_3$)$_4$], in which R = C$_6$H$_5$ or CH$_3$C$_6$H$_4$, contains a planar NiN$_4$ unit.

U16. French and Corbett, *J. Am. Chem. Soc.*, **62**, 3219 (1940). M, CE. Nickel formyl camphor, Ni(C$_{11}$H$_{15}$O$_2$)$_2$·2H$_2$O, contains a tetrahedral NiO$_4$ unit.

U17. French, Magee, and Sheffield, *J. Am. Chem. Soc.*, **64**, 1924 (1942). M, CE. Some substituted salicylaldehyde nickel(II) derivatives are tetrahedral, and some aldimine nickel(II) derivatives are planar. A camphor aldime nickel(II) derivative is planar in the solid state, distorted in an alcohol solution.

U18. Godycki and Rundle, *Acta Cryst.* **6**, 487 (1953). X. Nickel dimethylglyoxime is planar. iX. Nickel cyclohexanedionedioxime is planar.

U19. Jensen, *Z. anorg. allgem. Chem.*, **221**, 11 (1934). G. [(NH$_2$CSNHNH$_2$)$_2$Ni]SO$_4$ contains planar nickel(II).

U20. Jensen, *Z. anorg. allgem. Chem.*, **229**, 265 (1936). D. [NiX$_2$(R$_3$P)$_2$], with X = Cl⁻, Br⁻, or I⁻ and R = Et, Pr, or Bu, and [NiI$_2$(Et$_3$As)$_2$] are trans planar. [Ni(NO$_3$)$_2$(Et$_3$P)$_2$] is cis planar.

U21. Klemm and Raddatz, *Z. anorg. allgem. Chem.*, **250**, 207 (1942). M, G. [Ni(HN:CHC$_6$H$_4$O)$_2$] is planar. M. Some other nickel aldimines are planar.

U22. Ladell, Post, and Fankuchen, *Acta Cryst.* **5**, 795 (1952). X. At −55° Ni(CO)$_4$ is tetrahedral.

U23. Lifschitz, Bos, and Dijkema, *Z. anorg. allgem. Chem.*, **242**, 97 (1939). M. [Ni{C$_6$H$_5$CH(NH$_2$)CH(NH$_2$)C$_6$H$_5$}$_2$]X$_2$ and [Ni(C$_6$H$_5$CHNH$_2$CH$_2$NH$_2$)$_2$]X$_2$ contain planar nickel in some cases and possibly tetrahedral nickel in others (deductions by Pauling, ref. 8).

U24. Mellor and Craig, *J. Proc. Roy. Soc., N. S. Wales*, **74**, 475 (1941). M. Planar or tetrahedral configurations are assigned to many nickel compounds, all chelates. An attempt is made to relate configuration to kind of atoms directly bonded to nickel.

U25. Mellor and Lockwood, *J. Proc. Roy. Soc., N. S. Wales*, **74**, 141 (1940). M. A substituted nickel pyrromethene is tetrahedral.

U26. See A15. C. K$_2$[Ni(CN)$_4$]·H$_2$O contains planar [Ni(CN)$_4$]$^=$.

U27. Milone and Tappi, *Atti accad. sci. Torino, Classe sci. fis., mat. nat.*, **75**, 445 (1940). X. Nickel dimethylglyoxime and nickel methylethylglyoxime are planar.

U28. Peyronel, *Z. Krist.*, **103**, 157 (1941). X. [(Pr$_2$NCS$_2$)$_2$Ni] contains a planar NiS$_4$ grouping.

U29. Rayner and Powell, *J. Chem. Soc.* **1952**, 319. X. One half of the Ni atoms in Ni-(CN)$_2$(NH$_3$)·C$_6$H$_6$ are surrounded by 4C atoms in a plane.

U30. Reihlen and Hühn, *Ann.*, **499**, 144 (1932). iO. [(CH$_3$C$_9$H$_5$NCH$_2$NH$_2$)$_2$Ni] contains nonplanar nickel.

U31. See A 23. X. Nickel(II) phthalocyanine contains a planar NiN$_4$ group.

U32. Robertson and Woodward, *J. Chem. Soc.*, **1937**, 219. X. Nickel(II) phthalocyanine is planar.

U33. Speakman, *Acta Cryst.* **6**, 784 (1953). X. NiC$_{26}$H$_{14}$N$_8$ contains a planar NiN$_4$ unit.

U34. Sugden, *J. Chem. Soc.*, **1932**, 246. G, M. Nickel methylbenzylglyoxime is planar.

U35. See T19. M. [Ni(OC$_6$H$_4$CHO)$_2$] is tetrahedral and [Ni(OC$_6$H$_4$CH:NH)$_2$] is planar.

V1. Brasseur and Rassenfosse, *Mém. acad. roy. Belg., Classe sci.*, **16**, No. 7 (1937). I. Several complex cyanides contain planar [Pd(CN)$_4$]$^=$.

V2. Brasseur, Rassenfosse, and Piérard, *Z. Krist.*, **88**, 210 (1934). I. Ba[Pd(CN)$_4$]·4H$_2$O contains planar [Pd(CN)$_4$]$^=$.

V3. Cahours and Gal, *Compt. rend.*, **71**, 208 (1870). G. [(Et$_3$As)$_2$PdCl$_2$] exists in two forms.

V4. Chatt, Mann, and Wells, *J. Chem. Soc.*, **1938**, 2086. iX. [Bu$_3$PClPdC$_2$O$_4$-PdClPBu$_3$] contains bridged planar palladium units.

V5. See U 10. iX, I. [Pd(OC$_6$H$_4$CH:NOH)$_2$] is planar.

V6. Cox and Preston, *J. Chem. Soc.*, **1933**, 1089. iX. [Pd(en)$_2$]Cl$_2$, [Pd(NH$_3$)$_4$]Cl$_2$, and (NH$_4$)$_2$[PdCl$_4$] contain planar groupings.

V7. Cox, Saenger, and Wardlaw, *J. Chem. Soc.*, **1934**, 182. I. [(Me$_2$S)$_2$PdCl$_2$] contains a planar unit.

V8. See U 11. X. K$_2$[Pd(S—C=O | S—C=O)$_2$] contains a planar PdS$_4$ unit.

V9. Dickinson, *Z. Krist.*, **88**, 281 (1934). X. [Pd(NH$_3$)$_4$]Cl$_2$·H$_2$O contains planar [Pd(NH$_3$)$_4$]$^{++}$.

V10. Dickinson, *J. Am. Chem. Soc.*, **44**, 2404 (1922). X. K$_2$[PdCl$_4$] and (NH$_4$)$_2$[PdCl$_4$] contain planar [PdCl$_4$]$^=$.

V11. Dwyer and Mellor, *J. Am. Chem. Soc.*, **56**, 1551 (1934). G. Bis(antibenzylmethylglyoxime)palladium(II) is planar.

V12. See U 18. iX. Palladium dimethylglyoxime is planar.

V13. Grinberg and Shul'man, *Compt. rend. acad. sci. (U.R.S.S.) [N. S.]*, **1933**, 215. G. $[Pd(NH_3)_2X_2]$ and $[Pd(py)_2X_2]$, X = Cl^- or Br^-, are planar.

V14. Janes, *J. Am. Chem. Soc.*, **57**, 471 (1935). M. Several palladium complexes are diamagnetic.

V15. Jensen, *Z. anorg. allgem. Chem.*, **225**, 97 (1935). D. $[PdCl_2(SEt_2)_2]$ is trans planar.

V16. Jensen, *Z. anorg. allgem. Chem.*, **229**, 225 (1936). D. $[PdCl_2(Et_3Sb)_2]$ is trans planar.

V17. Krauss and Brodkorb, *Z. anorg. allgem. Chem.*, **165**, 73 (1927). G. $[Pd(py)_2Cl_2]$ and $[(EtNH_2)_2PdCl_2]$ are planar. Drew, Pinkard, Preston, and Wardlaw, *J. Chem. Soc.*, **1932**, 1895, believe the isomerism is not geometric but is polymerism, *i.e.*, $[Pd(py)_2Cl_2]$ and $[Pd(py)_4][PdCl_4]$.

V18. Lidstone and Mills, *J. Chem. Soc.*, **1939**, 1754. O. $[\{NH_2C(CH_3)_2CH_2NH_2\}\text{-}Pd(NH_2CHC_6H_5CHC_6H_5NH_2)]^{++}$ is planar.

V19. Mann, Crowfoot, Gattiker, and Wooster, *J. Chem. Soc.*, **1935**, 1642. iX. $[(NH_3)_2PdC_2O_4]$ is planar. iX, G. $[(NH_3)_2Pd(NO_2)_2]$ is planar.

V20. Mann and Purdie, *J. Chem. Soc.*, **1935**, 1549. C. $[PdX_2Cl_2]$, in which X = Et_2S, Et_3P, or Et_3As, is planar.

V21. Mann and Wells, *J. Chem. Soc.*, **1938**, 702. X. $[Me_3AsPdBr_2]_2$ contains bridged planar units.

V22. See U25. M. A substituted pyrromethene of palladium(II) is diamagnetic but cannot be planar.

V23. See A 15. C. $[Pd(NH_3)_4]Cl_2\cdot H_2O$ and $K_2[PdCl_4]$ contain planar palladium complexes.

V24. Pinkard, Sharratt, Wardlaw, and Cox, *J. Chem. Soc.*, **1934**, 1012. G. Palladium(II) glycinate is planar.

V25. Poraĭ-Koshits, *Doklady Akad. Nauk S.S.S.R.*, **58**, 603 (1947); cf, *Chem. Abstracts*, **46**, 4313d (1952). X. $K_2[Pd(NO_2)_4]$ structure determined. Abstract does not give full details.

V26. Reihlen and Hühn, *Ann.*, **489**, 42 (1931). iO. $[\{NH_2C(CH_3)_2CH_2NH_2\}_2Pd]^{++}$ is not planar.

V27. See U 30. iO. $[(CH_3C_9H_5NCH_2NH_2)_2Pd]^{++}$ is not planar.

V28. Rosenheim and Gerb, *Z. anorg. allgem. Chem.*, **210**, 289 (1933). iO. $[Pd(OC_6H_4COO)_2]$ is not planar.

V29. Theilacker, *Z. anorg. allgem. Chem.*, **234**, 161 (1937). X. $K_2[PdCl_4]$ contains planar $[PdCl_4]^-$.

V30. Wells, *Proc. Roy. Soc. (London)*, **A167**, 169 (1938). X. $[(CH_3)_3AsPdCl_2]_2$ contains bridged planar groupings.

W1. Jaeger and Zanstra, *Rec. trav. chim.*, **51**, 1013 (1932), also appeared in *Proc. Koninkl. Nederland. Akad. Wetenschap.*, **35**, 610, 779, 787, (1932). X. $M[OsO_3N]$, in which M^+ = K^+, NH_4^+, Rb^+, Tl^+, or Cs^+, contains tetrahedral $[OsO_3N]^-$.

X1. Angell, Drew, and Wardlaw, *J. Chem. Soc.*, **1930**, 349. G. The two forms of $[(Et_2S)_2PtCl_2]$ are structural, not cis-trans, isomers (the formulation proposed is much less likely than cis-trans isomerism when considered from the standpoint of modern concepts).

X2. Bokiĭ, Vaĭnshteĭn, and Babareko, *Izvest. Akad. Nauk S.S.S.R., Otdel. Khim. Nauk* **1951**, 667; cf, *Chem. Abstracts* **46**, 5927d (1952). Electronographic. $KPtCl_3NH_3$ and $KPtBr_3NH_3$ contain planar Pt.

X3. Bozorth and Pauling, *Phys. Rev.*, [2] **39**, 537 (1932). X. The data of Bozorth and

Haworth (*Phys. Rev.*, [2] **29,** 223 (1927)) show that $Mg[Pt(CN)_4]\cdot 7H_2O$ contains planar $[Pt(CN)_4]^=$.

X4. See V 1. I. Several complex platinum(II) cyanides contain planar $[Pt(CN)_4]^=$.

X5. See V 2. I. $Ba[Pt(CN)_4]\cdot 4H_2O$ contains planar $[Pt(CN)_4]^=$.

X6. Brosset, *Arkiv Kemi, Mineral. Geol.*, **A25,** No. 19 (1948). X. $[Pt(NH_3)_2Br_2][Pt(NH_3)_2Br_4]$ contains planar $[Pt(NH_3)_2Br_2]$.

X7. Cahours and Gal, *Compt. rend.*, **70,** 897 (1870). G. There are two forms of $[(Et_3P)_2PtCl_2]$.

X8. See V 3. G. $[(Me_3P)_2PtCl_2]$ and $[(Et_3As)_2PtCl_2]$ both exist in two forms.

X9. Chernyaev, *Ann. inst. platine (U.S.S.R.)* **4,** 243 (1926); cf, *Chem. Abstracts,* **21,** 2620 (1927). G. $[Pt(NH_2OH)(NH_3)(py)(NO_2)]_2[PtCl_4]$ contains a planar cation (three isomers found). Several other compounds contain planar platinum(II) because they exist as cis-trans isomers.

X10. Cox, *J. Chem. Soc.*, **1932,** 1912. X. $[Pt(NH_3)_4]Cl_2\cdot H_2O$ contains planar $[Pt(NH_3)_4]^{++}$.

X11. See U 10. G, iX. $[Pt(OC_6H_4CH:NOH)_2]$ is planar.

X12. See V 6. iX. $[Pt(en)_2]Cl_2$ is planar.

X13. See V 7. iX, G. $[\{(CH_3)_2S\}_2PtCl_2]$ is planar.

X14. See U 11. X. $K_2\left[Pt\begin{pmatrix} S-C=O \\ | \\ S-C=O \end{pmatrix}_2\right]$ contains a planar PtS_4 unit.

X15. See V 10. X. $K_2[PtCl_4]$ contains planar $[PtCl_4]^=$.

X16. Drew and Head, *J. Chem. Soc.*, **1934,** 221. G. $[Pt\{NH_2C(CH_3)_2CH_2NH_2\}_2]Cl$ and $[Pt(NH_3)(EtNH_2)\{NH_2C(CH_3)_2CH_2NH_2\}]Cl_2$ contain planar platinum(II).

X17. Drew, Head, and Tress, *J. Chem. Soc.*, **1937,** 1549. Attempted O. $[Pt\{NH_2C-(CH_3)_2CH_2NH_2\}_2]^{++}$ and $[Pt\{NH_2C(CH_3)_2CH_2NH_2\}\{NH_2CH_2CH(CH_3)-CH_2NH_2\}]^{++}$ could not be resolved.

X18. Drew, Pinkard, Wardlaw, and Cox, *J. Chem. Soc.*, **1932,** 988, 1004. G. A third isomer reported for $[Pt(NH_3)_2Cl_2]$. Structural isomerism proposed. The third isomer proved to be a mixture of the first two. See V 17.

X19. Drew and Wyatt, *J. Chem. Soc.*, **1934,** 56. G. $[PtCl_2(Et_2S)_2]$ is planar.

X20. Grinberg, *Helv, Chim. Acta,* **14,** 455 (1931). G. $[Pt(NH_3)_2Cl_2]$ reactions related to planar structure.

X21. Grinberg, *Z. anorg. allgem. Chem.,* **157,** 299 (1926); *Ann. inst. platine (U.R.S.S.),* **5,** 365 (1927). G. $[Pt(NH_3)_2(SCN)_2]$ is planar.

X22. Grinberg and Ptitzuin, *J. prakt. Chem.*, [2] **136,** 143 (1933); *Ann. inst. platine (U.R.S.S.),* **9,** 55 (1932). G. $[Pt(NH_2CH_2COO)_2]$ is planar.

X23. Grinberg and Razumova, *Zhur. Priklad. Khim.* **27,** 105 (1954); cf. *Chem. Abstracts* **48,** 6308a (1954). The reaction of $[Pt\{(C_6H_5)_3P\}_2Cl_2]$ with ethylenediamine shows it to be the cis isomer.

X24. Hantzsch, *Ber.*, **59,** 2761 (1926). G. $[Pt(py)_2Cl_2]$ is planar.

X25. Hel'man, Karandashova, and Essen, *Doklady Akad. Nauk S.S.S.R.*, **63,** 37 (1948); cf, *Chem. Abstracts,* **43,** 1678i (1949). G. $[Pt(py)(NH_3)ClBr]$ is planar (three isomers).

X26. See V15. D. $[PtX_2(R_2S)_2]$, in which $X = Cl^-$, Br^-, I^-, or NO_2^- and $R = Et$, Pr, i-Pr, Bu, s-Bu, i-Bu, or C_6H_5, is planar.

X27. See V 16. D. $[PtX_2(R_3E)_2]$, in which $X = Cl^-$, Br^-, I^-, NO_2^-, or NO_3^-, $R = Et$, Pr, Bu, or C_6H_5, and $E = P$, As, or Sb, is planar.

X28. Klason, *Ber.*, **28,** 1493 (1895). G. $[PtCl_2\{(CH_3)_2S\}_2]$ is planar.

X29. Kurnakov, *J. Russ. Phys. Chem. Soc.*, **25**, 565 (1893); cf, *Chem. Centr.*, **65**, I, 460 (1894). G. Thiourea reacts with cis-[Pt(NH₃)₂Cl₂] or -[Pt(py)₂Cl₂] to yield [Pt(tu)₄]Cl₂ and with the trans compounds to yield [Pt(tu)₂Cl₂].

X30. Lambot, *Bull. soc. roy. sci. Liége*, **12**, 541 (1943); cf, *Chem. Abstracts*, **40**, 5656⁸ (1946). X. K₂[Pt(NO₂)₄] contains a planar PtN₄ unit.

X31. Lifschitz and Froentjes, *Z. anorg. allgem. Chem.*, **233**, 1 (1937). G. [PtX₂(CH₃CHSEtCOOH)₂], in which X = Cl⁻, Br⁻, etc., is planar.

X32. Mathieu, *J. chim. phys.*, **36**, 308 (1939). R. [Pt(NH₃)₄]Cl₂·H₂O, [Pt(py)₄]Cl₂·3H₂O, [Pt(en)₂]Cl₂ , and [Pt(py)₂Cl₂] contain planar or octahedral platinum(II) in solution.

X33. See A15. C. [Pt(NH₃)₄]Cl₂·H₂O, K₂[PtCl₄], Ba[Pt(CN)₄]·4H₂O, Mg[Pt(CN)₄]· 7H₂O, and LiK[Pt(CN)₄]·3H₂O contain planar platinum(II).

X34. Mills and Quibell, *J. Chem. Soc.*, **1935**, 839. O. [Pt{NH₂CH₂C(CH₃)₂NH₂}- {NH₂CHC₆H₅CHC₆H₅NH₂}]⁺⁺ is planar.

X35. Monfort, *Bull. soc. roy. sci. Liége*, **11**, 567 (1942); cf, *Chem. Abstracts*, **38**, 4174³ (1944). X. KNa[Pt(CN)₄]·3H₂O contains planar [Pt(CN)₄]⁻.

X36. Petrén, *Z. anorg. allgem. Chem.*, **20**, 62 (1899). G. Two forms of [Pt(SEt₂)₂Cl₂] are reported.

X37. See V24. G. [Pt(NH₂CH₂COO)₂] is planar.

X38. Ramberg, *Ber.*, **43**, 580 (1910); **46**, 3886 (1913). G. [Pt(OOCCH₂SEt)₂] is planar.

X39. See V26. iO. [Pt{NH₂C(CH₃)₂CH₂NH₂}₂]⁺⁺ and [Pt{CH₃C₉H₅NCH₂NH₂}₂]⁺⁺ are not planar.

X40. Reihlen and Hühn, *Ann.*, **519**, 80 (1935). iO. [Pt(NH₂CH₂CHC₆H₅NH₂){CH₃- (C₂H₅)C₉H₄NCH₂NH₂}]⁺⁺ is not planar or tetrahedral.

X41. Reihlen and Nestle, *Ann.*, **447**, 211 (1926). G. "Trans" [Pt(NH₃)₂Cl₂] is a dimer in liquid ammonia and the planar nature of platinum(II) is therefore suspect.

X42. Reihlen, Seipel, and Weinbrenner, *Ann.*, **520**, 256 (1935). iO. [Pt(dipy){NH₂CH- (C₆H₅)CH₂NH₂}]⁺⁺ is not planar.

X43. See A23. Platinum(II) phthalocyanine contains a planar PtN₄ grouping.

X44. Robertson and Woodward, *J. Chem. Soc.*, **1940**, 36. X. Platinum(II) phthalo-cyanine is planar.

X45. See V28. iO. [Pt{(NH₂)₂C₆H₃CH₃}₂]⁺⁺ is not planar.

X46. Rosenheim and Händler, *Ber.*, **59**, 1387 (1926). Attempted O. [Pt{(NH₂)₂C₆H₃-CH₃}₂]⁺⁺ could not be resolved.

X47. Roy, *Indian J. Phys.*, **13**, 13 (1939). R. The Raman spectrum of [Pt(en)₂]Cl₂ is compatible with square planar [Pt(en)₂]⁺⁺.

X48. Ryabchikov, *Compt. rend. acad. sci. U.R.S.S.*, **27**, 349 (1940). G. K₂[Pt(S₂O₃)₂] contains a planar PtO₂S₂ grouping.

X49. See V29. X. K₂[PtCl₄] contains planar [PtCl₄]⁻.

X50. Werner, *Z. anorg. allgem. Chem.*, **3**, 267 (1893). G. [Pt(NH₃)₂Cl₂] and [Pt(py)₂Cl₂] are planar.

X51. Wunderlich and Mellor, *Acta Cryst.* **7**, 130 (1954). iX. In K[PtCl₃C₂H₂]H₂O the Pt and 3 Cl atoms are coplanar. The fourth planar position is occupied by the C₂H₂ double bond.

10. Stereochemistry and Occurrence of Compounds Involving the Less Common Coordination Numbers

Thomas D. O'Brien[*]

University of Minnesota, Minneapolis, Minnesota

The term "coordination number" in the chemical sense refers to the number of groups attached to a central atom and may depend upon the nature of the central atom, the valence of the central atom, the nature of the coordinating group and the nature of the anion. "Coordination number" in a crystallographic sense, however, is quite different. It refers to the number of nearest neighbors of an atom in the crystal, and is dependent only on the radius ratio. In many cases the two coordination numbers are identical, so there is no ambiguity, but this cannot always be assumed.

COORDINATION NUMBER TWO

Only those elements in Group I of the Periodic Table, including hydrogen, seem to have a consistent tendency to exhibit a coordination number of two. In a few cases, elements in other periodic groups, which can exist with a valence of one, may also be two-coordinate. There are only two possible geometrical configurations, linear, O—M—O, and angular, O—M

$$\diagdown$$

O,

and no cases of stereoisomerism are known.

It has been shown[1] that in the compounds KHF_2 and NH_4HF_2 the two fluorine atoms are linked linearly through the hydrogen, $(F—H—F)^-$, giving hydrogen a coordination number of two. There are many similar examples in compounds exhibiting hydrogen bonding, of which dimeric acetic acid,

---

* Now at Kansas State College, Manhattan, Kansas.
1. Helmholz and Rogers, *J. Am. Chem. Soc.*, **61**, 2590 (1939); *ibid.*, **62**, 1533 (1940).

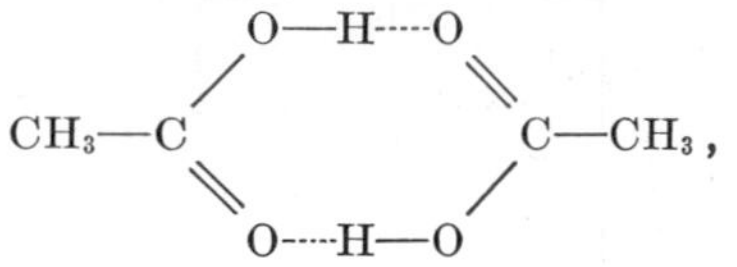

$$CH_3—C \underset{O\cdots H—O}{\overset{O—H\cdots O}{\diagup\diagdown}} C—CH_3 ,$$

is typical. The bonding in these cases is doubtless due to dipole attractions, and is not truely covalent.

The Group IB elements in their univalent state all exhibit the coordination number of two, although the copper(I) compounds are not so common and are often less stable than those of silver(I) and gold(I). Rosenheim and Loewenstamm[2] reported the preparation of bis(thiourea)copper(I) chloride, $[Cu\{SC(NH_2)_2\}_2Cl$, in which they believe the thiourea is coordinated to the copper atom through the sulfur[3]. Spacu and Murgulescu[4] report a number of compounds in which anionic copper(I) has a coordination number of two, assuming thiosulfate ion is a bidentate group, as in $Na[CuS_2O_3]$. This necessitates an improbably small angle for the covalences of the copper.

Silver(I) forms the well-known, linear diamminesilver(I)[5], $[Ag(NH_3)_2]^+$, and dicyanosilver(I)[6], $[Ag(CN)_2]^-$, ions. Fyfe[7] prepared silver(I) diammines with acridine, quinoline, isoquinoline, and pyridine and found that the order of stability of the complexes, acridine > quinoline > isoquinoline = pyridine, is the same as the order of the electron densities on the nitrogen atoms in the amines. It has also been shown that silver(I) forms only mono and bis benzoate complexes in solution[8]. With ethylenethiourea

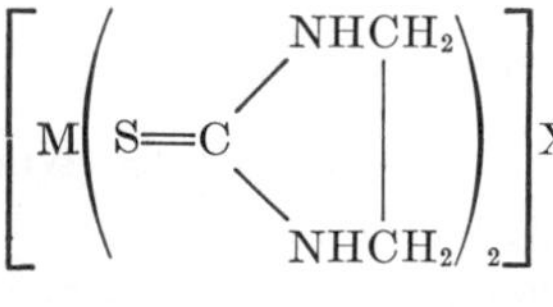

$$\left[M\left(S=C\underset{NHCH_2}{\overset{NHCH_2}{\diagup\diagdown}} \right)_2 \right] X$$

is formed, where M is silver(I) or gold(I). The silver salt in which X is a halide is unaffected by light.

A dimethyldithioethylene gold(I) complex salt,

2. Rosenheim and Lowenstamm, *Z. anorg. Chem.*, **34**, 62 (1903).
3. Rathke, *Ber.*, **17**, 297 (1884).
4. Spacu and Murgulescu, *Bull. Soc. stiinte cluj.*, **5**, 344 (1930).
5. Corey and Wyckoff, *Z. Krist.*, **87**, 264 (1934).
6. Hoard, *Z. Krist.*, **84**, 231 (1933).
7. Fyfe, *Nature*, **169**, 69 (1952).
8. Leder, *Acta Chem. Scand.*, **3**, 1318 (1949).

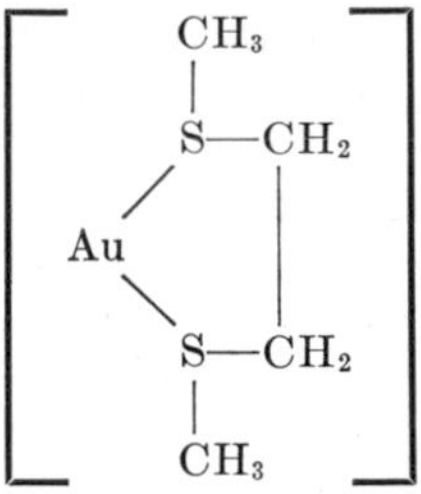

$$\left[\begin{array}{c} \text{CH}_3 \\ | \\ \text{S} - \text{CH}_2 \\ \diagup \qquad | \\ \text{Au} \qquad\qquad | \\ \diagdown \qquad | \\ \text{S} - \text{CH}_2 \\ | \\ \text{CH}_3 \end{array} \right] \text{Cl},$$

is also known. Two coordinate complexes of gold(I) have been prepared with tertiary arsines[9]. The compounds are characterized by their solubility in nonpolar solvents, insolubility in water and sharp melting points.

Many alkali metal salts of metal amides have been reported by Franklin[10]. Among them are compounds of the type $K[M(NH_2)_2]$, where M is silver(I) or thallium(I).

The rather curious halogen compounds $[Br(py)_2]ClO_4$, $[I(py)_2]NO_3$,

and $\left[\begin{array}{c} \text{py} \\ \diagup \\ \text{I} \\ \diagdown \\ \text{NO}_3 \end{array} \right]$ have been prepared[11]. On the basis of solubilities, Yatsi-

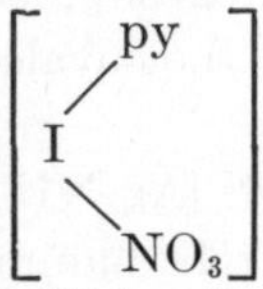

mirskii[12] has formulated a series of complexes which contain anionic central atoms and cationic ligands. These formulations are exemplified by the species, $[Ag_2Cl]NO_3$, $[Ag_2Br]NO_3$, and $[Ag_2I]NO_3$. The stability increases in the order, chloride < bromide < iodide. The conditions favorable to the formation of such complexes are low electron affinity of the anion, high electron affinity of the cation, and large radius of the cation.

COORDINATION NUMBER THREE

On the basis of theoretical considerations, Kimball[13] offers the trigonal plane (I), unsymmetrical plane (II), and trigonal pyramid (III) as possible structures for three coordinate complexes (Fig. 10.1). The unsymmetrical plane would give rise to geometric isomerism, and the trigonal pyramid would show optical isomerism in complexes of the type [MXYZ]. The other structure, being completely symmetrical, would give no stereoisomerism. Mann[14]

9. Dwyer and Stewart, *J. Proc. Roy. Soc., N. S. Wales*, **83**, 177 (1949).
10. Franklin, "Nitrogen System of Compounds," New York, Reinhold Publishing Corp., 1935.
11. Carlsohn, "Uber eine Neue Klasse von Verbindungendes positive einwertigen Jods," Leipzig, 1932; *Ber.*, **68B**, 2209 (1935).
12. Yatsimirskii, *Doklady Akad. Nauk S.S.S.R.*, **77**, 819 (1951).
13. Kimball, *J. Chem. Phys.*, **8**, 188 (1940).
14. Mann, *J. Chem. Soc.*, **1930**, 1745.

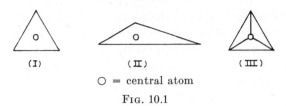

(I)   (II)   (III)

O = central atom

Fig. 10.1

proved that the sulfur atom in tetrachloro(β,β'-diaminodiethylsulfide)platinum (IV) has the trigonal pyramid configuration by resolving the complex into its optical antipodes. The complex has the structure

$$
\begin{array}{c}
\text{Cl} \\
\text{Cl} \diagup\diagdown \overset{\text{S}}{} \diagup \text{CH}_2\text{-CH}_2\text{-NH}_2 \\
\text{Cl} \diagdown\diagup \text{Pt} \diagdown \text{CH}_2 \\
\text{Cl} \diagdown\diagup \text{NH}_2 \\
\text{Cl}
\end{array}
$$

Silver(I) and copper(I), in addition to being two-coordinate, also form a number of compounds in which they are apparently three-coordinate. Compounds[15] containing ethylenethiourea, like $[Ag\{SC(NH)_2(CH_2)_2\}_3]Cl$ and $[Cu\{SC(NH)_2(CH_2)_2\}_3]_2SO_4$ are known, as are the corresponding thiourea salts[2]. The corresponding nitrates contain four molecules of the ethylene thiourea per metal atom, so that it might be suspected that the anions in the chloride and sulfate are coordinated.

The reddish chlorocuprates, the chlorocadmates, and the chloromercurates, $[CuCl_3]^-$, $[CdCl_3]^-$, and $[HgCl_3]^-$, are all well-known, but it has been shown that the metals in these do not have a coordination number of three in the solid state. The cadmium compound consists of chains of $CdCl_6$ octahedra joined laterally[16] as shown in Fig. 10.2. The mercury compound is of a different crystalline structure[17].

The red color obtained when potassium tetracyanonickelate(II) is re-

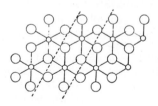

Fig. 10.2

15. Morgan and Burstall, *J. Chem. Soc.*, **1928**, 143.
16. Brasseur and Pauling, *J. Am. Chem. Soc.*, **60**, 2886 (1938).
17. Harmsen, *Z. Krist.*, **100**, 208 (1939).

duced[18] is believed to be due to the formation of potassium tricyanonickelate(I), $K_2[Ni(CN)_3]$. Dark red solutions of potassium tricyanonickelate(I), when exposed to the air, lose their color and precipitate part of their nickel as nickel(II) hydroxide and the remainder as potassium tetracyanonickelate(II). From polarographic studies, Caglioti, Sartori, and Silvestroni[19] estimate the potential of the couple $[Ni(CN)_4]^=-[Ni(CN)]_3^=$ to be -0.6844 volts. The validity of the measurement is disputed by Kolthoff and Hume[20], who found that the tetracyanonickelate(II) ion undergoes an irreversible two-electron reduction at the dropping mercury electrode. They have also shown that the tricyanonickelate(I) ion is subject to anodic oxidation but not to further polarographic reduction. Recent x-ray studies[20a] indicate that the tricyanonickelate(I) ion is dimeric, $[Ni_2(CN)_6]^{4-}$.

Other compounds in which copper is reported to have a coordination number of three are the blue-black $[CuNOCl_2]$, $[CuNOBr_2]$, and $[CuNOSO_4]^{21}$, the dark green triamminecopper(I) octacyanomolybdate (VI)[22], and triamminecopper(I) halides[23]. Although Biltz and Stollenwerk[23] write the formulas of the halides as $[Cu(NH_3)_3]X$, it is quite possible that the halogen is also coordinated, giving the copper a coordination number of four.

Franklin has reported amides of the general formula, $K[M(NH_2)_3]$, in which M is lead(II), beryllium, calcium, strontium, barium, or tin(II).

It is believed that the solubility of silver chloride in a concentrated solution of cesium chloride is due to the formation of the trichloroargentate(I) ion, $[AgCl_3]^=$, in which the silver is three-coordinate[24]. The simple ammino compound $[Ag(NH_3)_3]X$ has also been reported[25].

It is believed that the iodine is the central atom in a cationic complex

with three silver atoms attached as ligands, $\left[\begin{array}{c} Ag \\ / \\ Ag-I \\ \backslash \\ Ag \end{array}\right](NO_3)_2$[26]. This

complex ion was shown to migrate to the cathode during electrolysis.

Thallium alcoholates when dissolved in polar solvents are typically salt-like in their behavior. They are, however, also soluble in nonpolar sol-

18. Belluci and Corelli, *Atti. accad. Lincei*, **22**, II, 579 (1913).
19. Caglioti, Sartori, and Silverstroni, *Ricera Sci.*, **17**, 624 (1947).
20. Kolthoff and Hume, *J. Am. Chem. Soc.*, **72**, 4423 (1950).
20a. Mast and Pfab, *Naturwissenschaften*, **39**, 300 (1952).
21. Manchot, *Ann.*, **375**, 308 (1910); Gall and Mengdahl: *Ber.*, **60B**, 86 (1927).
22. Bucknall and Wardlaw, *J. Chem. Soc.*, **1927**, 2981.
23. Biltz and Stollenwerk, *Z. anorg. Chem.*, **119**, 97 (1921).
24. Wells and Wheeler, *Am. J. Sci.*, [3] **44**, 155 (1892).
25. Biltz and Stollenwerk, *Z. anorg. Chem.*, **114**, 1176 (1920); *ibid.*, **119**, 97 (1921).
26. Hellwig, *Z. anorg. Chem.*, **25**, 157 (1900).

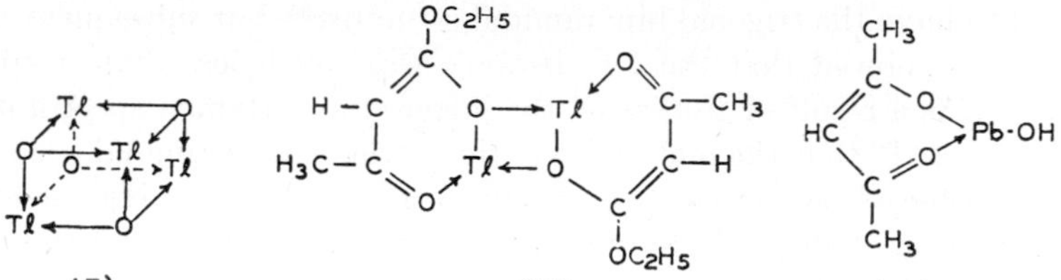

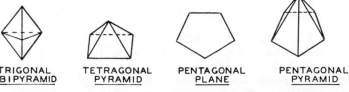

(I)   (II)   (III)

Fig. 10.3

vents such as benzene, and they have been shown[27] to be tetrameric in that solvent, possibly with a three-coordinate structure as in (I) (Fig. 10.3). In similar solvents, thallium(I) ethyl acetoacetate is dimeric and three-coordinate[27] (II).

Menzies[28] has reported a nonionic basic lead acetonylacetonate with the formula shown in (III) (Fig. 10.3). There is, however, no evidence to indicate that the substance is not dimeric, the lead atoms being linked together

$$\text{through the hydroxyl groups,} \quad \begin{array}{c} \text{OH} \\ \diagdown \diagup \diagdown \diagup \\ \text{Pb} \qquad \text{Pb} \\ \diagup \diagdown \diagup \diagdown \\ \text{OH} \end{array} \quad \text{, giving the metal a coor-}$$

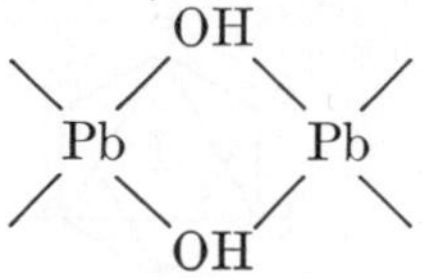

dination number of four.

COORDINATION NUMBER FIVE

From theoretical considerations, a coordination number of five should be the least likely to exist, although there are many examples in which atoms are apparently five-coordinate. Kimball[13] gives the following as geometrical possibilities:

TRIGONAL   TETRAGONAL   PENTAGONAL   PENTAGONAL
BIPYRAMID   PYRAMID   PLANE   PYRAMID

Fig. 10.4. Some possible configurations for coordination number five

Duffey has extended the study of the bipyramidal structure, calculating the extent to which d electrons are involved in the hybridization[29].

On the basis of electron diffraction studies, iodine(V) fluoride was first

27. Sidgwick and Sutton, *J. Chem. Soc.*, **1930**, 1461.
28. Menzies, *J. Chem. Soc.*, **1934**, 1755.
29. Duffey, *J. Chem. Phys.*, **17**, 196 (1949); *Proc. S. Dakota Acad. Sci.*, **28**, 97 (1949).

reported to have the trigonal bipyramidal structure[30], but subsequent x-ray examination showed that the I-F distance was much less than would be expected[31]. As a result of studies on the infrared and Raman spectra it has been postulated[32] that the molecule has the tetragonal pyramidal structure, with an unshared pair of electrons occupying a position equivalent to the unique position of the fifth fluorine atom, but below the base of the pyramid on the perpendicular to the plane, (Fig. 10.5). De Heer[33] states that the structure is still uncertain but that dipole moment studies could provide final proof of the structure. From the Raman spectrum[34], it is believed that bromine(V) fluoride also has the tetragonal pyramidal configuration.

For many years the structures of the pentahalides of phosphorus, arsenic, and antimony were debated, but it is now accepted that phosphorus(V) chloride in the vapor state is made up of trigonal bipyramidal molecules[35]. However, in the crystalline state it consists of PCl_4^+ and PCl_6^- ions[36, 37]. Measurements of the electrical moment[38], dielectric constant, and

Fig. 10.5. The structure of iodine pentafluoride

conductivity[39] in inert solvents indicate ionic character, so it is assumed that the same ions exist in solution as exist in the crystalline state. Phosphorus(V) bromide is composed of PBr_4^+ and Br^- ions[40].

Compounds of the type $R_2[MX_5]$ have been prepared, where R is an alkali metal ion, thallium(I), or an ammonium ion; X is a halide, and M is antimony or bismuth. In addition, bismuth forms a corresponding nitrate[40] and the trichlorodiamminebismuth(III) complex[41]. On the basis of color

30. Braune and Pinnow, Z. Physik, **B35**, 239 (1937).
31. Rogers, Wahrhaftig, and Schomaker, Abstracts, 111th Meeting of Am. Chem. Soc., April, 1947.
32. Lord, Lynch, Schumb, and Slowinski, J. Am. Chem. Soc., **72**, 522 (1950).
33. De Heer, Phys. Rev., **83**, 741 (1951).
34. Burke and Jones, J. Chem. Phys., **19**, 1611 (1951).
35. Brockway and Beach, J. Am. Chem. Soc., **60**, 1836 (1938).
36. Clark, Powell, and Wells, J. Chem. Soc., **1942**, 642.
37. Moureu, Magat, and Wetroff, Compt. rend., **205**, 545 (1937); Clark, Powell, and Wells: J. Chem. Soc., **1942**, 642.
38. Trunel, Compt. rend., **202**, 37 (1936).
39. Holroyd, Chadwick, and Mitchell, J. Chem. Soc., **127**, 2492 (1925).
40. Powell and Clark, Nature, **145**, 971 (1940).
41. Schwarz and Striebach, Z. anorg. Chem., **223**, 399 (1935).

and vapor pressure of ammonia, Schwarz and Strieback postulate that three chloride ions and two ammonia molecules are attached to each bismuth atom. However, an alternative structure could be

$$\left[(Cl)_2(NH_3)_2Bi \begin{array}{c} Cl \\ / \quad \backslash \\ \\ \backslash \quad / \\ Cl \end{array} Bi(Cl)_2(NH_3)_2 \right],$$

giving the bismuth a coordination number of six. A dark violet antimony salt of the formula $Tl[SbCl_5]$ is known, in which the antimony is apparently tetravalent[42]. A deep color of this kind is often attributed to the presence of two valence states of an element in one compound, so the compound may well be $Tl_2[Sb^{(III)}Sb^{(V)}Cl_{10}]$. The same applies to the dark violet $K_2[TiF_5]$. This may be a mixed titanium(II) and titanium(IV) dinuclear complex. However, discrete $[SbF_5]^=$ groups exist in K_2SbF_5 (page 8).

The metal-organic compound $(CH_3)_3SbCl_2$ in the crystalline form has been shown to have the three methyl groups in the plane of the metal atom with the two chlorine atoms at the two apices of a trigonal bipyramid[43]. The compound is not dissociated in inert solvents. It slowly undergoes stepwise hydrolysis in water, first to $(CH_3)_3SbClOH$ and finally to $(CH_3)_3Sb(OH)_2$. The first product is a very strong base while the latter is a very weak base, suggesting that the first may be a substituted stibonium hydroxide (coordination number, four), while the final dihydroxide is similar in structure to the original dihalide (coordination number, five).

Many compounds are known in which the central atoms appear to be five-coordinate in the solid state, but since dissociation takes place in solution, crystal structure studies are necessary to establish the true coordination number. Cs_3CoCl_5 has been shown[44] to be made up of tetrahedral tetrachlorocobaltate(II) ions and odd cesium and chloride ions, so the cobalt is actually four-coordinate. Klug and Alexander[45] showed that $(NH_4)_3ZnCl_5$ is composed of tetrachlorozincate(II) tetrahedra and ammonium and chloride ions as addenda. Perhaps diethylenetriamine pentachlorocuprate(II)[49], $[dien \cdot H_3]$ $[CuCl_5]$, is also composed of planar or tetrahedral tetrachlorocuprate(II) ions with odd chloride ions in the lattice.

It has been proved that the compound Tl_2AlF_5 is composed of infinite chains of hexafluoroaluminate(III) octahedra in which the two opposite corners are shared[46] (Fig. 10.6).

42. Wells: "Structural Inorganic Chemistry," p. 232, London, Oxford University Press, 1945.
43. Wells, Z. Krist., 99, 367 (1938).
44. Powell and Wells, J. Chem. Soc., 1935, 359.
45. Klug and Alexander, J. Am. Chem. Soc., 66, 1056 (1944).
46. Brosset, Z. anorg. Chem., 235, 139 (1937).

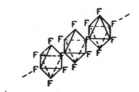

FIG. 10.6. The structure of Tl₂AlF₅

A number of fluoride and oxyfluoride compounds which apparently have the coordination number of five have been reported[47]. Of these, there is some evidence that tetrafluorooxychomate(V) and pentafluoromanganate(IV) ions are actually five-coordinate[48]. Potassium pentafluoromanganate(IV) is only slightly colored, and its x-ray powder patterns show that no impurities such as potassium fluoride, manganese(III) fluoride or potassium hexafluoromanganate(IV) are present. There is no proof of structure for these compounds.

Copper is also reported to be five-coordinate in the black crystalline compounds, K₃[Cu(NO₂)₅], Rb₃[Cu(NO₂)₅][50], and Tl₃[Cu(NO₂)₅][51]. Combes[52] prepared the ethylenediaminebisacetylacetone (enac) copper salt shown in

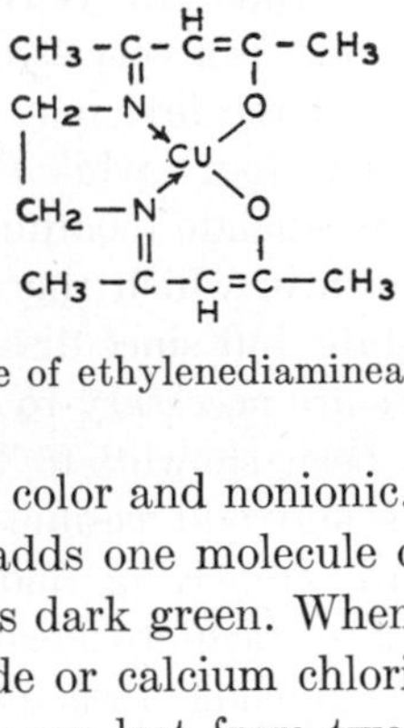

$$CH_3-C-\overset{H}{\underset{\parallel}{C}}=C-CH_3$$
$$CH_2-N \qquad O$$
$$| \qquad \underset{Cu}{\nwarrow} \diagdown$$
$$CH_2-N \qquad O$$
$$CH_3-C-\underset{\parallel}{C}=C-CH_3$$
$$\underset{H}{}$$

FIG. 10.7. The structure of ethylenediamineacetylacetone copper(II)

Fig. 10.7, which is violet in color and nonionic. Morgan and Main-Smith[53] showed that this complex adds one molecule of ethylenediamine and one molecule of water and turns dark green. When placed in a vacuum desiccator over sodium hydroxide or calcium chloride, two molecules of water and one of ethylenediamine are lost from two molecules of the salt, pro-

47. Huss and Klemm, *Z. anorg. Chem.*, **262**, 25 (1950); Zachariasen, *J. Am. Chem. Soc.*, **70**, 2147 (1948); Cefola and Smith, Natl. Nuclear Energy Ser., Div. IV, **14**, Transuranium Elements, Pt. I, 822 (1949).
48. Sharpe and Woolfe, *J. Chem. Soc.*, **1951**, 798.
49. Jonassen, Crumpler, and O'Brien, *J. Am. Chem. Soc.*, **67**, 1709 (1945).
50. Kurtenacker, *Z. anorg. Chem.*, **82**, 204 (1913).
51. Cuttica and Paciello, *Gazzetta*, **52**, 141 (1922).
52. Combes, *Compt. rend.*, **108**, 1252 (1889).
53. Morgan and Main-Smith, *J. Chem. Soc.*, **1925**, 2030; *ibid.*, **1926**, 913.

ducing the bridged dinuclear compound

$$[(enac)CuNH_2CH_2CH_2NH_2Cu(enac)],$$

in which the copper seems to have a coordination number of five.

Thorium forms the nonelectrolyte $[Th^{(IV)}Cl_4C_5H_5N]$ and the complex salt, $Na_6[Th^{(IV)}(CO_3)_5]\cdot12H_2O$, the latter being isomorphous with $Na_6[Ce^{(IV)}(CO_3)_5]\cdot12H_2O^{54}$. Lortie showed that ten of the twelve water molecules are removed very easily, while the other two are removed only with difficulty.

Ray and Dutt[55] carefully dehydrated the yellow diamagnetic silver penta-cyanoaquocobaltate(III) complex and obtained a compound with the formula $Ag_2[Co(CN)_5]$. This compound is deep blue in color and paramagnetic, both properties indicating unpaired electrons. Similarly, Adamson[56] has prepared potassium pentacyanocobaltate(II), $K_3[Co(CN)_5]$, and postulated that the cobalt has a coordination number of five in solution; however, the electronic configuration and molecular structure of the complex are still open to question. It is possible that the true ionic species in solution is pentacyanoaquocobalate(II) ion, $[H_2OCo(CN)_5]^{\equiv}$, as has been shown to be the case with pentachloroindate(III) ion, which is actually pentachloro-aquoindate(III)[57].

Cobalt is apparently five-coordinate in the bis-salicylaldehyde-γ,γ'-di-aminodipropylamine salt (I)[58]. The crystalline compound shown in (II)

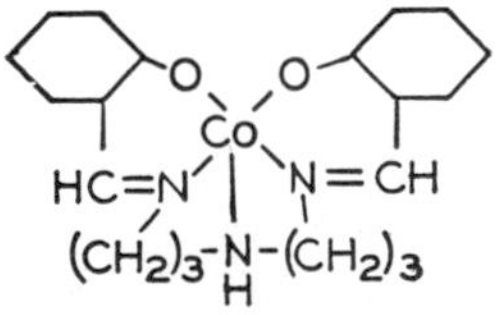

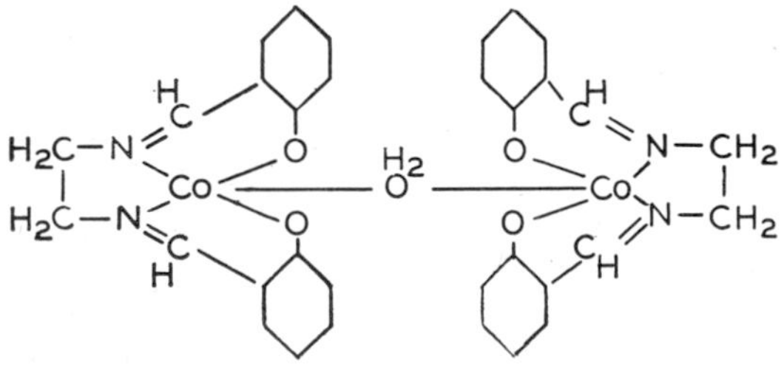

Fig. 10.8

(Fig. 10.8) was prepared by Diehl[59], who assumes a coordination number of five for the cobalt because of a water bridge in the dinuclear molecule. This seems to be the first case reported in which a water molecule acts as a

54. Lortie, *Compt. rend.*, **188**, 915 (1929).
55. Ray and Dutt, *Current Science*, **5**, 476 (1937).
56. Adamson, *J. Am. Chem. Soc.*, **73**, 5710 (1951).
57. Klub, Kummer, and Alexander, *J. Am. Chem. Soc.*, **70**, 3064 (1948).
58. Calvin, *et al.*, *J. Am. Chem. Soc.*, **68**, 2254, 2612 (1946).
59. Diehl, *et al.*, *Iowa State College J. of Sci.*, **21**, No. 3, 278 (1947).

bridging group. It is possible that this water is not actually coordinated but is lattice water.

Both iron and ruthenium form pentacarbonyls of the general formula $M(CO)_5$. It has been shown by electron diffraction studies that in iron pentacarbonyl the carbonyl groups are distributed around the iron at the apices of a trigonal bipyramid (Chapter 16).

Tribromobis(triethyl phosphine)nickel(III) is an unusual compound in two respects: it contains nickel(III) and it exhibits a coordination number of five. Molecular weight determinations in benzene solution indicate that it is monomeric and not dissociated. The magnetic moment is consistent with the presence of one unpaired electron. On the basis of dipole moment measurements, Jensen and Nygaard[60] have assumed that the molecule exists in the form of a tetragonal pyramid.

In postulating mechanisms for the reactions of complex compounds, especially aquation, some investigators propose the formation of intermediates, in which a normally 6-coordinate central atom has a coordination number of 5 or 7. The number 5 is indicated when the reaction seems to be a S_N1 type, and 7 when the reaction appears to be the S_N2 type. In view of the transient nature of such complexes they will not be discussed further here. (See pp. 327 and 329).

COORDINATION NUMBER SEVEN

The coordination number of seven is quite rare, and the fact that it appears generally in the heavier atoms, such as zirconium, niobium, tantalum, and iodine, leads one to suspect that f electrons are significant in bonding, although structures have been deduced which require only s, p, and d orbitals. The halogens in general (especially fluorine) seem to favor

(I)   (II)   (III)

FIG. 10.9. Coordination number seven

this coordination number. Three structures have been proposed for molecules and ions exhibiting the coordination number of seven (Fig. 10.9). They are (I) the trigonal prism[13] in which a seventh coordination position exists beyond one face, (II) the octahedron with a seventh bond beyond the center of one face[13], and (III) the pentagonal bipyramid[61]. The hybrid

60. Jensen and Nygaard, *Acta Chem. Scand.*, **3**, 474 (1949).
61. Duffey, *J. Chem. Phys.*, **18**, 943 (1950).

states proposed for these configurations are (I) d^4sp^2, d^4p^3, d^5p^2; (II) d^5sp, d^3sp^3; (III) sp^3d^3, and other hybrid configurations requiring f electrons[62].

Compounds of the general formula $R_3^{(I)}M^{(IV)}F_7$ are known, in which R is a sodium, potassium or ammonium ion, and M is silicon, titanium, zirconium, hafnium, or lead. The ammonium "heptafluorosilicate" has been reported to be made up of discrete hexafluorosilicate(IV), ammonium, and fluoride ions[63], so the authors propose to write the formula $(NH_4)_2[SiF_6] \cdot NH_4F$ to emphasize that the central atom is six- rather than seven-coordinate. On the other hand, the analogous compound, potassium heptafluorozirconate (IV), $K_3[ZrF_7]$, has been shown to consist of finite heptafluorozirconate(IV) ions in the crysalline state[64], the zirconium atom being at the center of an octahedron of fluorine atoms with the seventh or odd fluorine above the center of one face. The octahedron is somewhat distorted by a forced separation of the atoms at the corners of this face. Hassell and Mark[65] have shown that the hafnium and zirconium compounds are isomorphous, so hafnium probably has a coordination number of seven in its analogous compound. Another fourth group element, tin, is apparently seven-coordinate[66] in the compound $Na(C_5H_5NH)_2[Sn(NCS)_7]$.

Klemm and Huss prepared potassium heptafluorocobaltate(IV) by the action of gaseous fluorine on mixtures of potassium chloride and cobalt(II) chloride[67]. X-ray studies indicate that it probably has a structure similar to that associated with the salts of the heptafluorozirconate(IV) ion (Structure II, Fig. 10.9).

The elements of the fifth Periodic Group form compounds of the general formula $R_2^{(I)}[M^{(V)}F_7]$ where R is potassium, hydrogen or ammonium ion and M is antimony, niobium, or tantalum. Neither arsenic nor vanadium seems to form this type of compound. Both the niobium and tantalum compounds are truly seven-coordinate since their finite heptafluoro ions have been proved to exist. Hoard and coworkers[68] have shown that in the solid state the seventh fluorine atom is added beyond the center of one of the rectangular faces of a trigonal prism. A number of hydroxy organic derivatives of niobium and tantalum, such as those with catechol, $(NH_4)_3[NbO(C_6H_4O_2)_3]$, and with acetylacetone, $(NH_4)_4[NbO(C_5H_6O_2)_3]$, are reported to be seven-coordinate[69].

62. Shirmazan and Dyatkina, *Doklady Akad. Nauk S.S.S.R.*, **77**, 75 (1951).
63. Hoard and Williams, *J. Am. Chem. Soc.*, **64**, 633 (1942).
64. Hampson and Pauling, *J. Am. Chem. Soc.*, **60**, 2702 (1938).
65. Hassel and Mark, *Z. Phys.*, **27**, 89 (1924).
66. Weinland and Barnes, *Z. anorg. Chem.*, **62**, 250 (1909).
67. Klemm and Huss, *Z. anorg. Chem.*, **258**, 221 (1949).
68. Hoard, *J. Am. Chem. Soc.*, **61**, 1252 (1939); *ibid.*, **63**, 11 (1941).
69. Rosenheim and Roehrich, *Z. anorg. Chem.*, **204**, 342 (1932).

Other compounds reported to contain seven-coordinate atoms are the black $(CN_3NH_2 \cdot H)_3[Pt^{(IV)}I_7]^{70}$, dark red-brown $(CH_3NH_2H)_4[RuCl_7]^{71}$, and $K_3[UO_2F_5]$.

Iron enneacarbonyl, $Fe_2(CO)_9$, is postulated to contain seven-coordinate iron (Chapter 16).

On the basis of Raman and infrared spectra[32], iodine(VII) fluoride has been assigned the pentagonal bipyramidal structure ((III), Fig. 10.9).

COORDINATION NUMBER EIGHT

In general, substances containing eight-coordinate central atoms can give rise to so many stereoisomers that a chemical determination of their structures is almost impossible. The configurations of only a few eight-coordinate groups have been studied.

The cube (I) was the first structure proposed for eight-coordinate complexes[72]; this configuration was shown by Penny and Anderson[73] to be consistent with the theory of molecular orbitals. The Archimidean tetragonal antiprism[13, 74] (II), a trigonal prism with two extra bonds at the extremities of the unique axis[75] (III), the dodecahedron[13, 76] (IV), and a trigonal prism in which the two extra bonds extend beyond the centers of two of the rectangular faces[13] (V) have also been considered to be feasible configurations (Fig. 10.10).

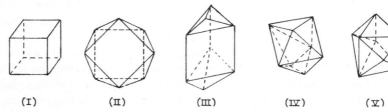

(I)   (II)   (III)   (IV)   (V)

FIG. 10.10. Coordination number eight

Calculations made by Duffey[77] indicate that either the dodecahedron or the tetragonal antiprism[77, 78] may be attained through a hybrid of the type d^4sp^3, while the trigonal prism[13] in which the extra bonds appear in rectangular faces may assume d^5sp^2 hybridization. However, the trigonal prismatic structure in which the last two ligands are added above the cen-

70. Anon., *Chem. Centr.*, II, 143 (1914).
71. Gutbier, *Ber.*, **56**, 1008 (1923).
72. Pfeiffer, *Z. anorg. Chem.*, **105**, 26 (1919).
73. Penny and Anderson, *Trans. Faraday Soc.*, **33**, 1363 (1937).
74. Huttig, *Z. anorg. allgem. Chem.*, **114**, 25 (1920).
75. Marchi and McReynolds, *J. Am. Chem. Soc.*, **65**, 333 (1943).
76. Hoard and Nordsieck, *J. Am. Chem. Soc.*, **61**, 2853 (1939).
77. Duffey, *J. Chem. Phys.*, **18**, 1444 (1950).
78. Duffey, *J. Chem. Phys.*, **18**, 746 (1950).

ters of the triangular faces cannot be realized in the absence of f orbitals[79]. It is also reported that f orbitals are required in the cubic structure[13, 80]. Definite evidence for the presence of f electrons in eight-coordinate molecules has been reported by Sacconi[81], who studied the magnetic properties of uranium(IV) complexes with a series of β-diketones. The results indicate that two $5f$ electrons are involved in the bonding.

Probably the most widely studied compounds are the octacyanides of molybdenum and tungsten, which have the formulas $M_4{}^{(I)}[M^{(IV)}(CN)_8]$ and $M_3{}^{(I)}[M^{(V)}(CN)_8]$. Potassium octacyanomolybdate(IV) is yellow and can be prepared by air oxidation of potassium hexachloromolybdate(III) in the presence of excess potassium cyanide, or by the reduction of molybdenum(V) compounds with potassium cyanide. Hoard and Nordsieck[76] have shown the existence of individual octacyanomolybdate(IV) ions, with the eight cyanide groups arranged at the apices of a dodecahedron. The carbonnitrogen bonds are colinear with the molybdenum-carbon bonds. It is presumed that the orbitals used are four $4d$, one $5s$ and three $5p$, although Van Vleck[82] has predicted, on theoretical grounds, that s, p, d, and f orbitals must all be available for bonding in order to attain symmetrical distribution of eight coordinated groups. It is interesting to note that f electrons do not appear in neutral atoms until element 58, cerium. One must assume, then, that in the octacyanomolybdate(IV) ion, where there are several more electrons than there would be if the system were electrically neutral, the $4f$ orbitals are comparable in stability to other orbitals in the 4 shell. On the basis of effective atomic number, one would expect a greater stability for octacyanomolybdate(IV) (E.A.N., 54) than for octacyanomolybdate(V) (E.A.N., 53), and the former is actually more stable.

Some of the substituted octacyanides which have been reported are $[W(OH)_3(CN)_5]^{4-}$ [83], $[Mo(CN)_7H_2O]^{4-}$ [84], $[Mo(OH)_4(CN)_4]^{4-}$ [85], and

$$[Mo(OH)_3(CN)_4H_2O]^{\equiv}\ {}^{86}.$$

Fluorine also seems to favor eight-coordination as exhibited in the compounds $(NH_4)_3H[PbF_8]$[87], $H_3[SbF_8]$[88], $Na_3[TaF_8]$[89], and the well-known,

79. Shirmazan and Dyatkina, *Doklady Akad. Nauk S.S.S.R.*, **82**, 755 (1952).
80. Racah, *J. Chem. Phys.*, **11**, 214 (1943).
81. Sacconi, *Atti accad. nazl. Lincei, Rend. Classe sci. fiz., mat. e nat.*, **6**, 639 (1949).
82. Van Vleck, *J. Chem. Phys.*, **3**, 803 (1935).
83. Collenberg, *Z. anorg. Chem.*, **136**, 249 (1924).
84. Young, *J. Am. Chem. Soc.*, **54**, 1402 (1932).
85. VonderHeide and Hofman, *Z. anorg. Chem.*, **12**, 285 (1896).
86. Bucknall and Wardlaw, *J. Chem. Soc.*, **1927**, 2989.
87. Ruff, *Z. anorg. Chem.*, **98**, 27 (1916).
88. Morgan and Burstall, "Inorganic Chemistry," p. 145, New York, Chemical Publishing Co., 1937.
89. de Marignac, *Compt. rend.*, **63**, 85 (1866).

highly volatile osmium(VIII) fluoride. Hoard[90] has shown by x-ray crystal analysis that the octafluorotantalate(V) ion forms a tetragonal antiprism. Kimball[13] predicts that osmium(VIII) fluoride will be found to have a face-centered prismatic structure.

An attempt by Marchi and McReynolds[91] to determine the structure of $K_4[U(C_2O_4)_4]$ by chemical means was only partially successful. They assumed four possible structures; the cube(I), the Archimidean antiprism(II), the trigonal prism with two extra bonds along the unique axis(III), and the dodecahedron with triangular faces(IV). The trigonal prism with two extra bonds along the normal to two of the rectangular faces(V) was also mentioned as an alternative structure. Of these, (I) and (III) would not show optical isomerism for an ion of the type of $[U(C_2O_4)_4]^{4-}$ while (II), (IV), and (V) would. Structure (II) would have six optical isomers, while (IV) and (V) would each have ten. The authors succeeded in isolating four optical isomers by fractional precipitation of the strychnine salt. One pair of optical isomers racemized rapidly, and the other pair was stable. These results eliminate structures (I) and (III) but do not distinguish between (II), (IV), and (V).

Other compounds reported in which the central atom apparently has a coordination number of eight are the octammines, $MX_2 \cdot 8NH_3$, where M is calcium, strontium, barium[92], or lead[93]; metal acetylacetonates, $M(C_5H_7O_2)_4$, where M is zirconium[94], hafnium[95], thorium[95], uranium[96], polonium[97], or cerium[98]; tetrakis(ethylenediamine)chromium(III) chloride[99], and tetrakis(ethylenediamine)cadmium(II) iodide[100]; other oxalate complexes similar to the uranium compound $[M(C_2O_4)_4]^{4-}$ discussed above, where M is zirconium[101], hafnium[101], thorium[102], or tin[103]; tin(IV) phthalocyanine[104]; and tetrakis(8-hydroxyquinoline)plutonium(IV)[105].

90. Hoard, Paper presented at the 6th annual symposium, Div. Phys., and Inorg. Chem., Columbus, Ohio, December, 1941.
91. Marchi and McReynolds, *J. Am. Chem. Soc.*, **65**, 333 (1943).
92. Huttig, *Z. anorg. Chem.*, **123**, 31 (1922); *ibid.*, **124**, 322 (1922); *ibid.*, **125**, 269 (1922).
93. Biltz and Fischer, *Z. anorg. Chem.*, **124**, 230 (1922).
94. Von Hevesy and Logstrup, *Ber.*, **59B**, 1890 (1926).
95. Young, Goodman, and Kovitz, *J. Am. Chem. Soc.*, **61**, 876 (1939).
96. Biltz, *Z. anorg. Chem.*, **40**, 220 (1904).
97. Servigni, *Compt. rend.*, **196**, 264 (1933).
98. Scagliarini, *Atti accad. Lincei*, [6] **4**, 204 (1926).
99. Lang and Carson, *J. Am. Chem. Soc.*, **26**, 759 (1904).
100. Barbier, *Compt. rend.*, **136**, 688 (1903).
101. Tchakirian, *Compt. rend.*, **204**, 356 (1937).
102. Brauner, *J. Chem. Soc.*, **73**, 956 (1898).
103. Rosenheim and Platsch, *Z. anorg. Chem.*, **20**, 309 (1899).
104. Barret, Dent, and Linstead, *J. Chem. Soc.*, **1936**, 1733.
105. Patton, Natl. Nuclear Energy Ser. Div. IV, **14B**, Transuranium Elements, Pt. I, 853 (1949).

Coordination Number Greater than Eight

Coordination numbers greater than eight have been postulated for such compounds as Na_5ZrF_9 and many hydrates and ammoniates. In some of these, such as $[Nd(H_2O)_9](BrO_3)_3$, the central atom has a coordination number of nine in the crystallographic sense, but it is doubtful whether these coordination numbers exist in the original Werner sense.

Duffey[106] has predicted that compounds of the type $M^{(1)}OsF_9$ should have a structure consisting of a trigonal prism with one atom added to each of the four-sided faces. He refers to this stucture as an irregular tripyramid. Shirmazan and Dyatkina[62] offer several hybrid configurations as consistent with this structure. Of these, only sp^3d^5 does not require f electrons.

106. Duffey, *J. Chem. Phys.*, **19**, 553 (1951).

11. Stabilization of Valence States Through Coordination

James V. Quagliano

Notre Dame University, Notre Dame, Indiana

and

R. L. Rebertus

Shell Development Co., Emeryville, California

One of the most familiar and useful chemical concepts is that of relative stability of chemical compounds, and the coordination theory accounts for the existence and relative stabilities of many complex compounds. Mulliken[1] has pointed out that by sharing or transferring electrons a nucleus in a molecule tends to be surrounded by a stable electronic configuration with a total charge approximately equal to that of the nucleus. However, the term "stability" is vague and is used in many different ways. Reference is made to stability toward aquation, thermal decomposition, oxidation, reduction, and other types of reactions. Hydrogen peroxide, for example, is unstable toward decomposition into water and oxygen but is very stable toward decomposition into hydrogen and oxygen[2].

In this chapter stability toward oxidation and reduction is emphasized, and of especial interest are those valence states which cannot exist unless stabilized through coordination.

QUANTITATIVE MEASUREMENT OF THE DEGREE OF STABILIZATION

Oxidation Potentials

The concept of electron loss or gain has long been associated with oxidation or reduction. As applied to the formation of an essentially ionic compound, as by the reaction of chlorine with sodium, this concept is nearly correct. Ambiguity arises, however, when an attempt is made to apply electron loss or gain to covalent compounds. Moeller[3] suggests that it is more

1. Mulliken, *Phys. Rev.*, **41**, 60 (1932).
2. Hildebrand, *Chem. Revs.*, **2**, 395 (1926).
3. Moeller, "Inorganic Chemistry," New York, John Wiley & Sons, Inc., 1952.

nearly correct to consider oxidation-reduction as an increase or decrease in oxidation state; this may be brought about with no change in the number of electrons associated with a particular nucleus. This tendency toward an increase or decrease in oxidation state can, in many instances, be measured quantitatively and expressed as the oxidation potential of a half-cell re-action.* Potential data have been published by Latimer[4].

In general, the oxidation potential of any half-reaction is altered when the activities of the reactants or products are changed. The potential of the half-cell reaction,

$$Fe^{++} \rightarrow Fe^{+++} + e^-,$$

can be described in terms of the Nernst equation,

$$E = E^0 - RT/nF \ln a_{Fe^{+++}}/a_{Fe^{++}},$$

where E is the potential at any activity of product or reactant, E^0 is the standard potential taken at unit activities, n is the number of electrons in-volved in the reaction, F is the Faraday constant, T is the absolute tempera-ture, R is the gas constant, and a is the activity of product or reactant.

One method of changing the activity of a product or a reactant is to co-ordinate the ion in question with a complexing agent. The resulting change in oxidation potential is a quantitative measure of the degree to which the particular valence is stablized relative to the couple consisting of aquated ions. (It is customary in writing equations for half-cell reactions in aqueous solutions not to describe aquated ions, though this would be more nearly correct.) A few examples of this phenomenon follow.

Iron(II)–Iron(III) Couple. It was shown in 1898 by Peters[5] that the oxidation potential of mixtures of iron(II) and iron(III) chlorides in hydro-chloric acid depends upon the concentration of the acid. The system was

---

* Confusion sometimes arises in the literature with regard to convention of sign of potentials for oxidation-reduction couples. See, for example, Latimer, *J. Am. Chem. Soc.*, **76**, 1200 (1954). If the number of electrons required to balance the equation is written on the right hand side, any half-cell reaction expressed as 'reduced state = oxidized state + n electrons' may be described with an oxidation potential. A positive value indicates that the reduced form of the couple is a better reducing agent than H_2. This is based on the selection of thermodynamic conventions by G. N. Lewis but is commonly referred to as Latimer's system. This convention will be adhered to in this chapter except in the discussion of polarography. Polarographers, in general, choose to write the requisite number of electrons on the left in the general form: oxidized state + n electrons = reduced state, and the sign of potential is the opposite of Latimer's sign for any half-cell reaction.

4. Latimer, "Oxidation Potentials," 2nd Edition, New York, Prentice-Hall, Inc., 1952.
5. Peters, *Z. physik.*, **26**, 193 (1898).

TABLE 11.1. EFFECT OF COORDINATION ON THE IRON(II)–IRON(III) COUPLE

Equation	Potential (E^0)
$Fe^{++} \leftrightharpoons Fe^{+++} + e^-$	-0.771
$[Fe(CN)_6]^{4-} \leftrightharpoons [Fe(CN)_6]^{=} + e^-$	-0.36
$Fe^{++} + 6F^- \leftrightharpoons [FeF_6]^{=} + e^-$	-0.40
$Fe^{++} + 2PO_4^{=} \leftrightharpoons [Fe(PO_4)_2]^{=} + e^-$	-0.61

TABLE 11.2. STABILIZATION OF IRON(II) BY COORDINATION

Equation	Potential (E^0)
$[Fe(dipy)_3]^{++} \rightleftarrows [Fe(dipy)_3]^{+++} + e^-$	-1.10
$[Fe(o\text{-phen})_3]^{++} \rightleftarrows [Fe(o\text{-phen})_3]^{+++} + e^-$	-1.14
$[Fe(nitro\text{-}o\text{-phen})_3]^{++} \rightleftarrows [Fe(nitro\text{-}o\text{-phen})_3]^{+++} + e^-$	-1.25

studied in more detail by Carter and Clews[6], who found that the oxidation potential decreases as the concentration of the acid is increased. The change in potential was explained by a change in the ratio of the iron(II) to iron-(III) ions as a result of the complexing of the iron(III) ion with chloride ions. Popoff and Kunz[7] confirmed the report of Carter and Clews. Similar investigations were made in sulfuric acid medium by Glover[8], and, again, evidence for complex formation was reported.

In Table 11.1 standard potentials are listed for the iron(II)–iron(III) couple in the presence of different complexing agents. The hexacyanoferrate(II) ion is thermodynamically less stable toward oxidation than is the aquated iron(II) ion, and the apparent chemical stability of the hexacyanoferrate(II) ion is attributed to the slowness of the rate of oxidation under usual experimental conditions. Rate of oxidation or reduction should not be confused with thermodynamic stability. The data in Table 11.1 indicate that cyanide, fluoride, and phosphate stabilize iron(III) against reduction to a greater degree than does water.

Many complexing agents stabilize the dipositive state of iron. Of these, the ones listed in Table 11.2 also possess properties desirable in indicators for oxidimetry.

Cerium(III)–Cerium(IV) Couple. A study of the influence of complex formation on the oxidation potentials of cerium(III)–cerium(IV) nitrates in nitric acid by Noyes and Garner[9] revealed the lack of dependence of the oxidation potential upon the acid concentration over a relatively short range. Kunz[10] found little change in the oxidation potential of cerium-(III) and cerium(IV) sulfates in solutions of sulfuric acid. G. F. Smith and

6. Carter and Clews, *J. Chem. Soc.*, **125**, 1880 (1924).
7. Popoff and Kunz, *J. Am. Chem. Soc.*, **51**, 382 (1929).
8. Glover, *J. Chem. Soc.*, **1933**, 10.
9. Noyes and Garner, *J. Am. Chem. Soc.*, **58**, 1265 (1936).
10. Kunz, *J. Am. Chem. Soc.*, **53**, 98 (1931).

his co-workers extended the potential measurements to acid concentrations as high as 8 normal[11]. They found that the potential of the system in mixtures of nitrate and sulfate at lower acid concentrations exhibited the constancy reported by the previous investigators but that at higher acid concentrations the oxidation potential decreased markedly. However, the results of experiments in perchloric acid solution showed an opposite effect. The formation and stability of complex ions are undoubtedly responsible for the potential changes in nitrate and sulfate media but not in perchloric acid solution. An extensive study of the system in perchloric acid solution was made by Sherrill, King and Spooner[12] to determine the effect of perchlorate ion concentration and hydrogen ion concentration. The potential was found to vary with hydrogen ion concentration and was dependent upon the hydrolysis of cerium(IV) perchlorate to form the ions $Ce(OH)^{+++}$ and $Ce(OH)_2^{++}$. Postulating that these complex ions exist in solution, Heidt and Smith[13] presented evidence for the formation of dimers resulting from the splitting out of water from the hydroxyl groups of these ions.

Thallium(I)-Thallium(III) Couple. Investigations of the thallium(I)-thallium(III) couple show that the oxidation potential depends to a large extent on the nature of various complex ions present[14]. Thallium(I) chloride in hydrochloric acid is more easily oxidized to thallium(III) than is thallium(I) sulfate or nitrate in solutions of sulfuric or nitric acid, resulting from the formation of stable chlorothallate(III) complexes. Since nitric acid and perchloric acid do not appreciably alter the oxidation potential of the thallium(I)-thallium(III) couple, it was assumed that no complex formation occurs with the anions of these acids.

Zinc(0)-Zinc(II) Couple. The complexes formed by zinc ion with hydroxyl ion are among the most stable and, from the standpoint of theoretical significance, the most interesting of the numerous zinc coordination compounds. The data of Table 11.3 indicate that amphoterism may lead to the stabilization of a valence state through coordination.

Cobalt(II)-Cobalt(III) Couple. The aquated cobalt(III) ion reacts with water to liberate oxygen. On the other hand, the hexacyanocobaltate-(II) ion is a powerful reducing agent and is oxidized by water with the

11. Smith, Sullivan, and Frank, *Ind. Eng. Chem., Anal. Ed.*, **8**, 449 (1936); Smith and Getz, *Ind. Eng. Chem., Anal. Ed.*, **10**, 191 (1938); *ibid.*, **10**, 304 (1938).
12. Sherrill, King, and Spooner, *J. Am. Chem. Soc.*, **65**, 170 (1943).
13. Heidt and Smith, *J. Am. Chem. Soc.*, **70**, 2476 (1948).
14. Spencer and Abegg, *Z. anorg. Chem.*, **44**, 379 (1905); Grube and Hermann, *Z. Elektrochem.*, **33**, 112 (1927); Partington and Stonehill, *Trans. Faraday Soc.*, **31**, 1357 (1935); Sherrill and Haas, *J. Am. Chem. Soc.*, **65**, 170 (1943); Noyes and Garner, *J. Am. Chem. Soc.*, **58**, 1268 (1936).

TABLE 11.3. STABILIZATION OF ZINC(II) THROUGH HYDROXYL ION COORDINATION

Equation	Potential (E^0)
$Zn \rightleftarrows Zn^{++} + 2 e^-$	0.762
$Zn + 2OH^- \rightleftarrows Zn(OH)_2 + 2e^-$	1.245
$Zn + 4OH^- \rightleftarrows ZnO_2^- + 2 H_2O + 2e^-$	1.216

TABLE 11.4. STABILIZATION OF COBALT(III) THROUGH COORDINATION

Equation	Potential (E^0)
$Co^{++} \rightleftarrows Co^{+++} + e^-$	−1.82
$[Co(NH_3)_6]^{++} \rightleftarrows [Co(NH_3)_6]^{+++} + e^-$	−0.1
$[Co(CN)_6]^{4-} \rightleftarrows [Co(CN)_6]^= + e^-$	+0.83

evolution of hydrogen[15]. Table 11.4 shows the wide variations in the oxidation potentials of the cobalt(II)–cobalt(III) couple in the presence of coordinating groups. The hexamminecobalt(III) ion, a slightly better oxidizing agent than the hydrogen ion, is a much weaker oxidizing agent than aquated cobalt(III) ion, but a more powerful oxidizing agent than the hexacyanocobaltate(III) ion. Stabilization of cobalt(III) against reduction to cobalt(II) is favored by coordination with cyanide ion as compared with ammonia and water.

Half-Wave Potentials—Polarography

Ease of reduction or oxidation of a complex ion at the dropping mercury electrode is different from that of the aquated metal ion, and half-wave potentials obtained under such conditions that the reactions are reversible have the great advantage of thermodynamic significance and may be related to ordinary standard potentials.* If the reduction of the complex proceeds reversibly, the values of dissociation constants of the complex and the number of coordinated groups can be calculated[16] from the change in half-wave potential. Irreversibility of a process can easily be determined by this method, and many processes reported in the literature as reversible by classic methods have been found to be irreversible at the dropping mercury electrode. Application of the polarographic technique has brought forth many examples of stabilization of oxidation states through coordination.

---

* The electropositive metals exhibit high energies of formation when they proceed from the pure metal to the amalgam, and, consequently, the half-wave potential is more positive than the standard potential. The less electropositive metals that readily form amalgams, zinc, lead, cadmium, bismuth, thallium, and silver, have reversible amalgam electrodes, and in certain instances the half-wave potentials of these metal ions may be nearly equal to the standard oxidation potentials.

15. Bigelow, *Inorganic Syntheses*, **2**, 225 (1946).
16. Kolthoff and Lingane, "Polarography," 1st ed., p. 164, New York, Interscience Publishers, Inc., 1941.

Polarography of Copper Complexes. Aquated copper(II) ions are reduced directly to the amalgam at the dropping mercury electrode, and only a single polarographic wave can be obtained in the absence of complexing agents. The potential of the $Cu^+ \rightleftarrows Cu(Hg)$ system is more positive than that of the $Cu^{++} \rightleftarrows Cu(Hg)$ system, and copper(I) ions cannot exist at the potential at which copper(II) ions are reduced.

The stability and composition of the complex ions formed by copper(II) ions (5×10^{-4} molar) with glycinate and alaninate ions were determined by Keefer[17]. The complexes formed are mainly $[Cu(gly)_2]$ or $[Cu(alan)_2]$ when the concentration of the complexing agent is from 0.08 to 0.1 molar, and the stable glycinate complex is $[Cu(gly)_3]^-$ at higher concentrations. Under the conditions of pH and concentration studied, two electrons are involved in the electrode reduction, indicating the instability of the copper(I) glycinate or alaninate complexes. Two-electron reductions were also observed by Onstott[18] for the bis(ethylenediamine), bis(propylenediamine), and bis(diethylenetriamine) complexes of copper(II).

TABLE 11.5. POTENTIALS FOR THE POLAROGRAPHIC REDUCTION OF COPPER AMMINES

Equation	E^0 vs. N.C.E.
$[Cu(NH_3)_2]^+ + Hg + e^- \leftrightarrows Cu(Hg) + 2NH_3$	-0.522
$[Cu(NH_3)_4]^{++} + Hg + 2e^- \rightleftarrows Cu(Hg) + 4NH_3$	-0.397
$[Cu(NH_3)_4]^{++} + e^- \rightleftarrows [Cu(NH_3)_2]^+ + 2NH_3$	-0.262

Certain complexing agents that form stable copper(I) complexes shift the half-wave potential of the $Cu^+ \rightleftarrows Cu(Hg)$ system in the negative direction more than that of the $Cu^{++} \rightleftarrows Cu^+$ system, so two distinct polarographic waves result. Table 11.5 lists potential values for the ammines of copper[19]. Two waves result when copper(II) ion is reduced in ammoniacal solution. Thiocyanate, chloride, and pyridine complexes behave similarly[19, 20].

Iron Oxalato Complexes. In the presence of oxalate ions, the half-wave potential of the aquated iron(III) ion shifts to a more negative value because of the formation of $[Fe(C_2O_4)_3]^{=}$ [19a]. Consideration of the half-wave potential of the tris(oxalato)ferrate(III) ion as a function of oxalate ion concentration revealed that the formula of the iron(II) complex produced in a

17. Keefer, *J. Am. Chem. Soc.*, **68**, 2329 (1946).
18. Onstott, thesis, University of Illinois, 1948; Laitinen, Onstott, Bailar, and Swann, *J. Am. Chem. Soc.*, **71**, 1550 (1949).
19. Stackelberg and Freyhold, *Z. Elektrochem.*, **46**, 120 (1940); Lingane, *Chem. Revs.*, **29**, 1 (1941); Schaap, Laitinen and Bailar, *J. Am. Chem. Soc.*, **16**, 5868 (1954).
20. Lingane and Kerlinger, *Ind. Eng. Chem., Anal. Ed.*, **13**, 77 (1941); Korshunov and Malyugina, *J. Gen. Chem., U.S.S.R.*, **20**, 425 (1950).

0.001 to 0.002 molar solution of iron(III) ion in the presence of 0.15 molar oxalate ion concentration is $[Fe(C_2O_4)_2]^-$, but when the concentration of oxalate ion is in greater excess, the species is the complex $[Fe(C_2O_4)_3]^{4-}$ [19b]. These results were essentially confirmed by Schaap[19c].

Tin Complexes. Although the standard potential of the tin(II)–tin(IV) couple is about 0.15 volts, the tin(IV) ion is not reduced at the dropping mercury electrode[21]. Solutions of tin(IV) ion in 1 to 2 molar perchloric acid solution give no indication of a reduction wave before the discharge of hydrogen. The predominant species in solution is believed to be the hexaquotin(IV) ion, and apparently the failure of this ion to be reduced can be attributed to its slow rate of reduction. Furthermore, no reduction of tin(IV) ion at the dropping mercury electrode takes place in sodium hydroxide, tartrate, or acidic oxalate media[22]. Either the complexes formed are too stable to be reduced, or they are reduced at such slow rates that no appreciable reduction can take place during the short life of each mercury drop.

The hexachlorostannate(IV) ion is reduced, however, when the chloride ion concentration is greater than 4 molar. The two well-defined waves which result are attributed to the reduction of the hexachlorostannate(IV) ion to the tetrachlorostannate(II) ion, followed by the reduction of the latter complex to the metal. A fairly well-defined doublet wave is also obtained in the reduction of the hexabromostannate(IV) ion in the presence of a large excess of bromide ion[21]. In these cases the activation energy has been greatly diminished by converting the hexaquotin(IV) complex to the chloro- or bromostannate(IV) complex.

Antimony Complexes. Pentapositive antimony is a fairly strong but slow oxidant. The failure of the reduction of antimony(V) in perchloric acid or dilute hydrochloric acid media indicates a situation analogous to that encountered with tin. In solutions containing large concentrations of chloride ion, antimony(V) shows reduction first to the tripositive state and then to the amalgam[23]. The failure of the reduction to take place in the presence of a small concentration of chloride is attributed to the presence of ions of the type $[SbO_2Cl_2]^-$ and $[SbOCl_4]^-$. Presumably, these species are converted to the hexachlorostibnate(V) ion as the chloride ion concentration is increased.

Uranium(V). Kolthoff and Harris have studied the polarographic behavior of uranium(VI) in acidic[24] and basic[25] solutions. In moderately con-

21. Lingane, *J. Am. Chem. Soc.*, **67**, 919 (1945).
22. Lingane, *Ind. Eng. Chem., Anal. Ed.*, **15**, 583 (1943).
23. Lingane and Nishida, *J. Am. Chem. Soc.*, **69**, 530 (1947).
24. Harris and Kolthoff, *J. Am. Chem. Soc.*, **67**, 1484 (1945); Kolthoff and Harris, *J. Am. Chem. Soc.*, **68**, 1175 (1946).
25. Harris and Kolthoff, *J. Am. Chem. Soc.*, **69**, 446 (1947).

centrated acid (0.01 to 0.2M HCl) uranium(VI) oxychloride gives two well-defined reduction waves, the first being one-half the height of the second. Consideration of current-voltage data revealed the first to correspond to a reversible reaction. Since the half-wave potential of this wave did not shift with changing hydrogen ion concentration, the following one-electron reduction was postulated.

$$[UO_2]^{++} + e^- \rightleftarrows [UO_2]^+$$

The second wave, a two-electron irreversible reduction, corresponds to the reduction of pentapositive uranium to the tripositive state.

Complexes of Cadmium—Successive Formation Constants. The chloro-, bromo-, and iodocadmium complexes were investigated polarographically by Strocchi[26]. It was reported that such species as CdX^+, CdX_2, CdX_3^-, and $CdX_4^=$ exist in solution, the species present depending upon the relative concentrations of the ions, and all are reduced to the amalgam reversibly. If only one complex species exists over a considerable range of concentration of complexing agent, and if this species is reduced reversibly, the formula and dissociation constant may be calculated according to the method described by Kolthoff and Lingane[16]. However, the method has not been applied to systems involving mixtures of consecutively formed complex ions. Bjerrum[27] and Leden[28] have developed methods for determining successive formation constants, and subsequently De Ford and Hume[29] have described a mathematical treatment of half-wave potential data which makes possible the identification of successively formed complex species and the calculation of their dissociation constants. These investigators successfully applied this mathematical analysis to the study of the complexes of cadmium, $CdSCN^+$, $Cd(SCN)_2$, $Cd(SCN)_3^-$, and $Cd(SCN)_4^=$; the calculated formation constants are 11, 56, 6, and 60, respectively[30].

Vanadium Complexes. The polarographic characteristics of vanadium in noncomplexing media have been studied by Lingane[31]. In both acid and ammoniacal solution, vanadium(V) undergoes stepwise reduction, first to the tetrapositive state, and then to the dipositive state. Evidence was presented for the existence of complexes in which vanadium displays valence states of 2^+, 3^+, 4^+, and 5^+ in the presence of some other complexing agents[32]. The formation of complexes is greatly influenced by the presence of hy-

26. Strocchi, *Gazz. chim. ital.*, **80**, 234 (1950).
27. Bjerrum, "Metal Ammine Formation in Aqueous Solution," Copenhagen, P. Maase and Son, 1941.
28. Leden, *Z. physik. Chem.*, **188A**, 160 (1941).
29. DeFord and Hume, *J. Am. Chem. Soc.*, **73**, 5321 (1951).
30. Hume, DeFord, and Cave, *J. Am. Chem. Soc.*, **73**, 5323 (1951).
31. Lingane, *J. Am. Chem. Soc.*, **67**, 182 (1945).
32. Lingane and Meites, *J. Am. Chem. Soc.*, **69**, 1021 (1947).

droxyl groups in the complexing agent, for vanadium tends to coordinate preferentially with oxygen. The tartrate ion with its two adjacent hydroxyl groups forms more stable complexes than does the citrate ion, which contains only one hydroxyl group. In alkaline solution the hydrogen of the hydroxyl group is replaced by an equivalent of the coordinating metal ion. Half-wave potentials show that the oxalate ion, which contains no hydroxyl group, forms the least stable complex of the series[33].

The Significance of Standard Potential Values for Irreversible Systems

It has been pointed out that oxidation potentials become altered when the activity quotient term of the Nernst equation is varied. This may arise when the equilibrium conditions of a system become changed through complex formation. Many oxidation potentials cannot be measured directly and must be calculated from thermal data, or estimated, for the Nernst equation applies without reservation only to reversible systems. Consequently, the significance of the standard potential, E^0, is limited in some cases.

On the basis of isotopic exchange studies, Taube[34] has observed that exchange between an oxidized form and a reduced form of the same complex, one of which contains a radioactive central atom, proceeds most easily when the electronic bonding orbitals of the two forms are identical. Such exchange could proceed by the electron transfer mechanism. For example, an exchange of electrons between $[Fe(CN)_6]^{4-}$ and $[Fe(CN)_6]^{3-}$ ions in neutral solution and in 0.05 molar sodium hydroxide was observed to take place within one minute[35]. Each of these ions has the d^2sp^3 octahedral configuration. Some investigators[36] have suggested that these conditions also favor electrode reversibility. Conversely, where a difference in electronic bonding orbitals exists between the oxidized form and the reduced form of a particular complex, slowness or lack of exchange is observed in most cases, and it is believed that electrode irreversibility should also exist. In many instances the interrelationship between the ligand and the central ion imposes a new electronic configuration upon either the oxidized or the reduced form of a complex, and oxidation states may be stabilized to a

33. Lingane and Meites, *J. Am. Chem. Soc.*, **69**, 1882 (1947).
34. Taube, *Chem. Revs.*, **50**, 69 (1952).
35. Thompson, *J. Am. Chem. Soc.*, **70**, 1045 (1948).
36. Lyons, *J. Electrochem. Soc.*, **101**, 363, 376 (1954); Lyons, Bailar and Laitinen, *ibid.*, **101**, 410 (1954). Libby, "Theory of Electron Exchange Reactions in Aqueous Solutions," p. 39, preprint, Symposium on Electron Transfer and Isotopic Reactions, Division of Physical and Inorganic Chemistry, American Chemical Society, and Division of Chemical Physics, American Physical Society, Notre Dame, June 11–13, 1952.

marked extent. When this happens, the bond between the central atom and the ligand of the stabilized form seems to lose all lability, and exchange studies indicate that an equilibrium no longer exists between the complex and its constituents.

STABILIZATION OF UNUSUAL OXIDATION STATES THROUGH COORDINATION

An interesting and important aspect of stabilization through coordination is the stabilization of unusual valence states. The methods for characterizing unusual oxidation states include the use of analytical data, chemical properties, magnetic susceptibility measurements, and x-ray studies[37].

Copper(I) and Copper(III)

The unipositive state of copper is stabilized by coordination with thiourea to such an extent that the copper(I) complex is formed even when copper(II) ion is used as a reactant[38]. Similarly, ethylenethiourea reacts with copper(II) ion to form the stable copper(I) complex,

$$[Cu(ethylenethiourea)_4]NO_3{}^{39}.$$

Copper(I) complexes with the cyanide ion are among the most stable cyanides, and hydrogen sulfide fails to precipitate any sulfide of copper when added to solutions of potassium tetracyanocuprate(I). In most of these complexes the copper achieves the coordination number of four. Some alkyl-substituted phosphines and arsines combine with equimolar quantities of copper(I)[40], but these complexes are polymeric.

The complex $K_3[CuF_6]$, prepared by allowing a mixture of potassium chloride and copper(II) chloride to react with fluorine at 250°[41], is decomposed by water. More stable copper(III) complexes have been prepared by the peroxysulfate oxidation of copper(II) with the periodate and tellurate complexing groups[42]. Some interesting analytical applications of copper(III) complexes are described by Kleinberg[43].

37. Kleinberg, "Unfamiliar Oxidation States," Lawrence, University of Kansas Press, 1950; Kleinberg, *J. Chem. Ed.*, **29**, 324 (1952); Mellor, "Some Recent Developments in the Chemistry of Metal Complexes." Report of the Brisbane Meeting of the Australian and New Zealand Association for the Advancement of Science, Vol. XXVIII, 131, (1951).
38. Rosenheim and Loewenstamm, *Z. anorg. Chem.*, **34**, 62 (1903).
39. Morgan and Burstall, *J. Chem. Soc.*, **1928**, 143.
40. Mann, Purdie, and Wells, *J. Chem. Soc.*, **1926**, 2018; Kabesh and Nyholm, *J. Chem. Soc.*, **1951**, 38.
41. Klemm and Huss, *Z. anorg. Chem.*, **258**, 221 (1949).
42. Malatesta, *Gazz. chim. ital.*, **71**, 467, 580 (1941).
43. Kleinberg, *J. Chem. Ed.*, **29**, 326 (1952).

Silver(II) and Silver(III)

The existence of higher oxidation states of silver is well established[44]. Silver has been found to be dipositive in the complex formed with quinolinic acid[45]. A. A. Noyes and co-workers established the presence of silver(II) and silver(III) in oxidizing solutions. When ozone was passed into a solution of silver(I) nitrate in nitric acid, it was shown that the metal oxidized to a nitrato silver(II) complex. This conclusion, drawn from a consideration of color, oxidizing potential of the solution, and increased solubility of the compound in solutions with higher nitrate concentration[45a], agrees with that given by Weber[46] on the basis of transference experiments.

A cooled aqueous solution of silver sulfate and ethylenedibiguanide reacts with potassium peroxysulfate to form a silky, red, crystalline precipitate of a silver(III) salt. It is stable at ordinary temperatures and can be recrystallized from warm, dilute nitric acid. The tripositive silver ion in this diamagnetic complex has the same electronic configuration as the nickel(II) ion[47]. A solution of the complex, acidified in the presence of potassium iodide, liberates two equivalents of iodine for every atom of silver, and the molar conductivity of the nitrate indicates the presence of a tripositive complex cation[48]. The constitution of this cation is represented by

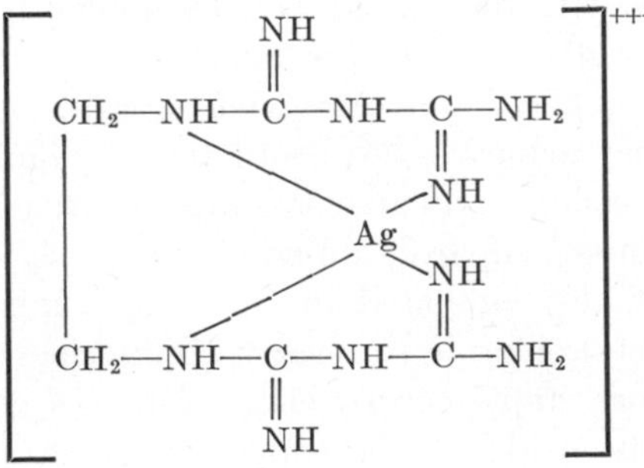

$$
\begin{bmatrix}
\text{CH}_2\text{—NH—C—NH—C—NH}_2 \\
\quad\quad\quad\; \overset{\displaystyle \|}{\text{NH}} \quad\quad \|\,\text{NH} \\
\text{Ag} \\
\text{CH}_2\text{—NH—C—NH—C—NH}_2 \\
\quad\quad\quad\; \|\,\text{NH}
\end{bmatrix}^{+++}
$$

and the quadridentate nature of the ligand explains the stability of the tripositive state of silver. The pK values for the dissociation of the complex and for the displacement of the silver(III) ion by hydrogen ion are 52 and 29, respectively[48b].

McClelland[49] has found that pyridine forms two complex ions with sil-

44. Bailar, *J. Chem. Ed.*, **21**, 523 (1944).
45. Berbieri, *Atti. Acad. Lincei*, **17**, 1078 (1933); Noyes, DeVault, Coryell, and Deahl, *J. Am. Chem. Soc.*, **59**, 1326 (1937).
46. Weber, *Trans. Am. Electrochem. Soc.*, **32**, 391 (1917).
47. Manchot and Gall, *Ber.*, **60**, 191 (1927).
48. Ray and Chakravarty, *J. Indian Chem. Soc.*, **21**, 47 (1944); Sen, Ray, and Ghose, *ibid.*, **27**, 619 (1950).
49. McClelland, thesis, University of Illinois, 1950.

ver(II), tris(pyridine)silver(II) ion and tetrakis(pyridine)silver(II) ion. Bis-(dipyridyl)silver(II) is formed by oxidizing silver(I) with ceric ammonium nitrate in nitric acid, and its dissociation constant is 2.5×10^{-19}. The standard potential of the dipyridyl complexes of silver(I) and silver(II) is 0.814 volts *vs.* the hydrogen electrode at 25°.

Manganese(I)

Manganese in the unipositive state was reported to have been prepared by the reduction of the cyano complex of divalent manganese with granulated aluminum[47] and by electrolytic reduction[50]. The crystalline product, $K_5[Mn(CN)_6]$, was said to be a powerful reducing agent. Klemm[51] questioned the identity of this compound because it was found to be paramagnetic, whereas the formula indicates it should be diamagnetic. However, Treadwell and Raths[52] have prepared the compound electrolytically and report it to be diamagnetic. Christensen, Kleinberg, and Davidson[53] have obtained excellent evidence for manganese in the zero and unipositive oxidation states by treatment of a liquid ammonia solution of potassium hexacyanomanganate(III) with potassium metal. The yellow product so obtained has the composition $K_5Mn(CN)_6 \cdot K_6Mn(CN)_6 \cdot 2NH_3$. Their conclusions are based on studies of reacting ratios, chemical analysis, reducing power, and magnetic measurements (the effective magnetic moment is 1.25 Bohr magnetons as compared to a calculated value of 1.73 for a single unpaired electron).

Nickel(0), Nickel(I), and Nickel(IV)

In a study of the reduction of nickel salts in anhydrous liquid ammonia, Eastes and Burgess[54] isolated a unipositive nickel compound $K_2[Ni(CN)_3]$. The reaction of this compound with an excess of the alkali metal produces $K_4[Ni(CN)_4]$, in which nickel has an apparent valence state of zero. The negative radical $[Ni(CN)_4]^{4-}$ is isoelectronic with nickel carbonyl, and based upon the electronic configuration of the latter molecule as postulated by Pauling[55], an explanation of the zero valence of nickel is offered by Deasy[56].

Many complexes of nickel(IV) have been reported. Klemm[57] reports the fluoro complex $K_2[NiF_6]$, and the tetrapositive state of nickel is confirmed

50. Grube and Brause, *Ber.*, **60**, 2273 (1927).
51. Klemm, *Angew. Chem.*, **63**, 396 (1951).
52. Treadwell and Raths, *Helv. chim. Acta*, **35**, 2259 (1952); *ibid*, **35**, 2275 (1952).
53. Christensen, Kleinberg, and Davidson, *J. Am. Chem. Soc.*, **75**, 2495 (1953).
54. Eastes and Burgess, *J. Am. Chem. Soc.*, **64**, 1187 (1942).
55. Pauling, "The Nature of the Chemical Bond," p. 252, Ithaca, Cornell University Press, 1944.
56. Deasy, *J. Am. Chem. Soc.*, **67**, 152 (1945).
57. Klemm and Huss, *Z. anorg. Chem.*, **25**, 221 (1949).

by magnetic evidence. Hieber and Bruck[58] describe nickel(IV) complexes of the types:

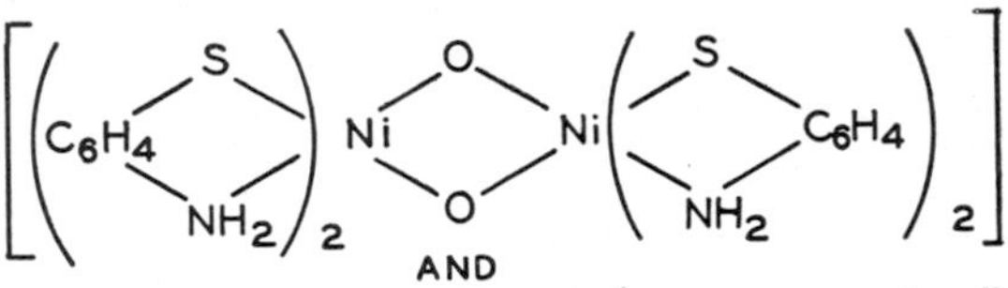

AND

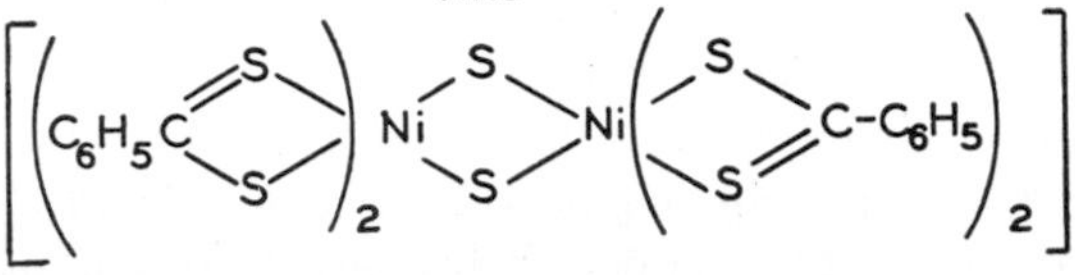

Cobalt(I), Cobalt(III), and Cobalt(IV)

A number of stable polynuclear compounds were prepared by Werner[59] in which the peroxide ion $O_2^=$ functions as a bridging group, and the analyses indicated the presence of both tripositive and tetrapositive cobalt. The compound

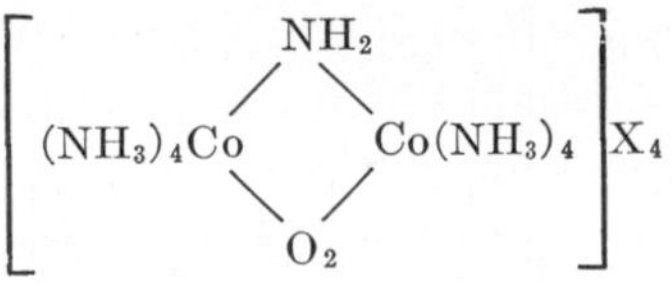

$$\left[(NH_3)_4 Co \underset{O_2}{\overset{NH_2}{\diamond}} Co(NH_3)_4 \right] X_4$$

was among those prepared, and the presence of both cobalt(III) and cobalt(IV) is supported by chemical and physical evidence. These μ-peroxo type compounds are decomposed by heating with sulfuric acid to produce mononuclear ammines with the liberation of oxygen. The presence of tetrapositive cobalt is supported by titration with arsenite[60] and by magnetic susceptibility measurements[60, 61].

When aqueous solutions of potassium hexacyanocobaltate(III) are reduced electrolytically, a deep brown solution of a unipositive cobalt complex results[62]. The existence of cobalt(I) was confirmed polarographically by Hume and Kolthoff[63]. According to Malatesta[64], most cobalt(II) salts react with aromatic isonitriles in alcoholic solution, undergoing reduction and forming complex salts of cobalt(I) with the formula $[Co(CNR)_5]X$. The salts in which X^- is perchlorate, chlorate, iodide, and nitrate were

58. Hieber and Bruck, *Naturwissenschaften*, **36**, 312 (1949).
59. Werner, *Ann.*, **375**, 1 (1910).
60. Gleu and Rehm, *Z. anorg. allgem. Chem.*, **237**, 79 (1938).
61. Malatesta, *Gazz. chim. ital.*, **72**, 287 (1942).
62. Grube, *Z. Elektrochem.*, **32**, 561 (1926).
63. Hume and Kolthoff, *J. Am. Chem. Soc.*, **71**, 867 (1949).
64. Malatesta, *Angew. Chem.*, **65**, 266 (1953).

isolated and found to be yellow or brown crystalline solids. They are soluble in polar solvents and are reported to be diamagnetic and of unlimited stability in air. The preparation of some of these salts requires the presence of mild reducing agents, while others form merely upon warming an alcoholic solution of the constituents.

Platinum(III), Platinum(V), Platinum(VI), and Platinum(VIII)

A number of compounds formed by the reaction of chloroplatinic acid with various thio compounds, such as sulfides, mercaptans, and disulfides, in which the platinum exhibits the unusual valence states of three, five, six, and eight have been described by Ray and his co-workers[65]. The evidence for the variations in the valency of platinum was obtained by the reaction of platinum(IV) chloride and the organic ligand given by the following equation[65a].

$$x \ (HSC_2H_4SK) + PtCl_4 \rightarrow [Pt(S \ C_2H_4 \ SH)_x] \qquad x = 3, 4, 5, 6, \text{ or } 8$$

Molecular weight determinations[65c] and chemical reactions[65d] were of much value in elucidating the constitution of the platinum complexes. Some of the compounds do not correspond to the empirical formulas but are polymers. The unusual valence states of platinum are explained by the great coordinating power of the sulfur atom in the organic ligand, and the particular valence state that platinum assumes is a function of the two variables, concentration and temperature. At low temperatures platinum exhibits its maximum valency, and at approximately 100° only trivalent platinum compounds are obtained. The relative ease with which the ligands are liberated might indicate that some of the organic groups are not truly bound to the platinum, and all of the valences mentioned above may not exist.

Chromium(II), Chromium(IV), and Chromium(V)

Chromium is stabilized in the dipositive, tetrapositive, and pentapositive oxidation states. Some chromium(II) complexes most stable toward oxidation contain hydrazine as a complexing agent[66]. The reducing properties of hydrazine account in part for this stability. The dihydrazine complexes of the chloride, bromide, and iodide of dipositive chromium have been prepared. Chromium(II) complexes of α,α'-dipyridyl, hexamethylenetetramine, *o*-phenanthroline, and 8-hydroxyquinoline have also been reported[67].

65. Ray and Ghose, *J. Indian Chem. Soc.*, **11**, 737 (1934); Ray, *J. Chem. Soc.*, **123**, 133 (1923); Ray and Ray, *J. Indian Chem. Soc.*, **2**, 178 (1925); Ray, Bose-Ray, and Ray-Chaudhury, *J. Indian Chem. Soc.*, **5**, 139 (1928).
66. Traube and Passarge, *Ber.*, **46**, 1505 (1913).
67. Beriberi and Tettamanzi, *Atti. Acad. Lincei*, **15**, 877 (1932); Hammett, Walden, and Edmonds, *J. Am. Chem. Soc.*, **56**, 1092 (1934); Hume and Stone, *J. Am. Chem. Soc.*, **63**, 1200 (1941).

A tetrapositive chromium compound was reported by Klemm and Huss[68]; the complex $K_2[CrF_6]$ is formed when a mixture of potassium chloride and chromium(III) chloride is fluorinated.

Chromium(V) was first reported by Weinland[69], who succeeded in isolating the complexes $K_2[CrOCl_5]$ and (pyH) $[CrOCl_4]$.

SOME FACTORS WHICH CONTRIBUTE TOWARD STABILIZATION OF OXIDATION STATES THROUGH COORDINATION

The factors contributing to the stabilization of valence are numerous and interdependent. Some conclusions, however, can be drawn from consideration of the nature of the coordinating group, the central metal ion, and the bond between them. Douglas[70] has reviewed several contributing factors, and his criteria are included in these considerations.

Nature of the Coordinating Group

Reducing Tendencies. Complex compounds formed by metallic ions with unsaturated compounds, such as the metal-olefin complexes, tend to stabilize the lower valence states of the central metal ion. Stable compounds have been prepared by the reaction of potassium tetrachloroplatinate(II) with unsaturated alcohols, acids, aldehydes, and ketones[71] (Chapter 15). The extremely stable dihydrazine complexes of chromium(II) are accounted for by the reducing character of the complexing agent.

Steric Factors. α,α'-Dipyridyl reacts with iron(II) to form the stable, intensely colored complex, $[Fe(C_{10}H_8N_2)_3]^{++}$, but the introduction of certain substituents into the ring produces a marked decrease in the coordinating ability of the base. This shielding effect is shown by the failure of α-(α'-pyridyl)-quinoline to complex with iron(II)[72]. Large groups often prevent an ion from exhibiting its maximum coordination number, and forced configurations may result. Mann and Pope[73] investigated complexes of nickel (II), palladium(II), and platinum(II) with tris(2-aminoethyl)amine and established the formula $[Mtren]^{++}$. Such an ion must be an irregular tetrahedron.

The steric effects associated with the replacement of hydrogen atoms of a coordinated amine by alkyl groups have been studied by Basolo and Murmann[74]. With the groups, methyl, ethyl, and *n*-propyl, the stabilities of the complexes formed by N-alkylethylenediamine with copper(II) and

68. Huss and Klemm, *Z. anorg. allgem. Chem.*, **262**, 25 (1950).
69. Weinland and Mitarb, *Ber.*, **38**, 3784 (1905).
70. Douglas, *J. Chem. Ed.*, **29**, 119 (1952).
71. Pfeiffer and Hoyer, *Z. anorg. allgem. Chem.*, **211**, 241 (1933).
72. Smirnoff, *Helv. chim. Acta*, **4**, 802 (1921).
73. Mann and Pope, *J. Chem. Soc.*, **1926**, 482.
74. Basolo and Murmann, *J. Am. Chem. Soc.*, **74**, 5243 (1952).

TABLE 11.6. THE EFFECT OF CHELATION ON THE STABILITY OF CADMIUM AMMINES

Complex	Dissociation Constant
$[Cd(NH_3)_4]^{++}$	3.3×10^{-7}
$[Cd(en)_3]^{++}$	6.7×10^{-13}
$[Cd(pn)_3]^{++}$	5.4×10^{-13}
$[Cd(dien)_2]^{++}$	7.6×10^{-15}

nickel(II) decrease as the size of the alkyl group increases. The *n-butyl* derivative is more stable than anticipated; this might arise from a shielding effect as a result of entwining of the butyl group about the metal ion. As might be expected, N-iso-propylethylenediamine forms complex ions of lesser stability than those formed by N-normal-propylethylenediamine. Steric effects are greater with hexacovalent than with tetracovalent nickel(II).

Chelation. Some complexing agents have a greater tendency to occupy two coordination positions than one. These so-called chelate groups form complexes of enhanced stability (Chapter 5), the most stable complexes resulting from the formation of five and six-membered rings. The effect of chelation is illustrated in Table 11.6 by the comparison of the dissociation constants of cadmium chelate complexes with that of the ammine complex.

The most probable explanation for the increased stability is the simple one that if one of the two coordinating linkages is broken, the other can keep the coordinating group near the central ion until the broken bond is reformed. This explanation is supported by experiments using radioactive "tracers." The study of the racemization of optically-active tris(oxalato)-chromate(III) ion revealed that the mechanism of the transformation does not involve an ionization of oxalate groups[75]. A suggested mechanism involves an intramolecular rearrangement (Chapter 8).

Nature of the Central Metal Ion

Electronegativity. Coordination, in general, is favored by a small ion of high charge. Preferential coordination of a metal ion with a given element is a function of the electronegativity of the metal ion. Thus, aluminum, beryllium, and zinc coordinate tightly with oxygen in a ligand; zinc, chromium, cadmium, cobalt, and nickel coordinate preferentially with nitrogen-containing ligands; and tin, lead, antimony, silver, mercury, and the platinum metals prefer either halogen or sulfur-containing ligands (Chapter 1).

Coordination Number. If a metal achieves its maximum coordination number in the formation of a complex compound, the resulting compound is generally more stable than compounds in which fewer groups are co-

75. Long, *J. Am. Chem. Soc.*, **61**, 570 (1939).

ordinated[76]. The exact reason why a metal fails to fill all available coordination positions is undoubtedly a combination of many factors, but certainly the size of the ligand relative to the metal is one such factor.

Availability of Bond Orbitals. Pauling[77, 78] points out that the d orbitals of the penultimate shell are of great significance in bond formation. The transition elements have inner d orbitals of about the same energy as the s and p orbitals of the valence shell, and it is with these elements that complex formation occurs most extensively if their d orbitals are not completely occupied by unshared electron pairs.

Nature of the Bond

Effective Atomic Number. The stability of coordination compounds is sometimes related to the attainment or near attainment of the number of electrons of the next rare gas in the period. Sidgwick[76] has described this number of electrons as the effective atomic number (E.A.N.) of the central metal ion. Thus the ammines, $[Pt(NH_3)_6]Cl_4$ and $[Co(NH_3)_6]Cl_3$, and the metal carbonyls, such as $Mo(CO)_6$ and $Ni(CO)_4$, appear to owe their stability to the rare gas configuration of the central atom. In the hexacyanoferrate(II) ion the coordinated metal has 36 electrons, but in the hexacyanoferrate(III) ion the metal has only 35 electrons. The proponents of the effective atomic number concept would explain the instability of the latter on the basis of its electron deficiency. In like manner, the great stability of tris(α,α'-dipyridyl)iron(II) bromide, which was resolved by Werner[79], and the instability of tris(ethylenediamine)iron(III) chloride may be related to the effective atomic number concept. Similarly, Gilchrist[80] has offered explanations of the stabilities of some of the platinum group complexes. The compounds, $K_3[RuCl_6]$ (E.A.N. = 53) and $K_3[OsCl_6]$ (E.A.N. = 85), are unstable, but if a nitrosyl group replaces a chloro group, the effective atomic number of each is increased to that of the next rare gas. The resulting compounds, $K_2[RuCl_5NO]$ and $K_2[OsCl_5NO]$, are extremely stable.

Although the above explanations on the basis of the effective atomic number concept seem plausible, it must be pointed out that not only is this highly formalistic, but direct application of the principle is possible only with a minority of complexes, and it is not possible to predict the stabil-

76. Sidgwick, "The Electronic Theory of Valency," p. 163. Oxford University Press, London, 1946.
77. Pauling, "The Nature of the Chemical Bond," p. 92, Ithaca, New York, Cornell University Press, 1944.
78. Pauling, *J. Am. Chem. Soc.*, **53**, 1367 (1931).
79. Werner, *Ber.*, **45**, 433 (1912).
80. Gilchrist, *Chem. Revs.*, **32**, 321 (1942).

ity of any complex on the basis of this concept alone. However, it holds for all volatile carbonyls and nitrosyls.

Hybridization of Orbitals. On the basis of quantum mechanics, Pauling[78] developed a theory which satisfactorily accounts for the relative strengths of bonds formed by the different atoms, the molecular configuration, and the magnetic behavior of complex compounds. Postulating that the stronger bond between two atoms will be formed by the two orbitals which can overlap more with each other and that the bond so formed will be in the direction in which the orbital has its greatest density, Pauling derived a number of results of chemical and stereochemical significance (Chapter 9).

12. Theories of Acids, Bases, Amphoteric Hydroxides and Basic Salts as Applied to The Chemistry of Complex Compounds

Fred Basolo[*]

Northwestern University, Evanston, Illinois

The fact that bases are electron pair donors and acids are electron pair acceptors was first pointed out by Lewis. It follows that the interaction of an acid and a base results in the formation of a coordination compound which subsequently may or may not yield ions. Excellent accounts of the early concepts of acids and bases have been written by Walden[1], by Luder and Zuffanti[2a], and by Audrieth[2b].

The oxonium theory of acids and bases, proposed by Werner[3] shortly after the advent of the water theory, was the first attempt to indicate the importance of the solvent in acid-base relationships (the Arrhenius theory disregarded the solvent). Although Werner's interpretations were only partially correct, he succeeded in showing that the solvent is a principal agent in electrolytic dissociation, instead of being merely a passive medium in which solutes are dispersed. In his studies of the hydroxoamminecobalt-(III) complexes, Werner discovered that they react with water in the following manner:

$$[Co(NH_3)_5OH]^{++} + HOH \rightleftharpoons [Co(NH_3)_5OH_2]^{+++} + OH^-$$

nonionized hydroxyl ⬩⬩⬩⬩⬩⬩⬩⬩⬩⬩⬩⬩⬩⬩⬩⬩⬩⬩⬩⬩⬩⬩⬩⬩⬩⬩⬩⬩ ionized hydroxyl

* Mr. Stephen J. Bodnar helped in the preparation of this chapter. His help is gratefully acknowledged.

1. Walden, "Salts, Acids and Bases," New York, McGraw-Hill Book Co., Inc., 1929.

2. Luder and Zuffanti, "The Electronic Theory of Acids and Bases," New York, John Wiley & Sons, Inc., 1946; Andreth, "Twenty third Annual Priestley Lectures: Acids, Bases, and Nonaqueous Systems" Ypsilanti, Michigan, University Lithoprinters, 1949.

3. Werner, *Z. anorg. Chem.*, **3**, 267 (1893); **15**, 1 (1897); Werner, *Ber.*, **40**, 4133 (1907); Werner, "New Ideas on Inorganic Chemistry," translated by Hedley, London, Longmans, Green and Company, 1911.

By analogy he postulated that no metal hydroxide dissociates until it is hydrated, indicating this by the reaction

$$\text{MOH} + \text{HOH} \rightleftharpoons [\text{MOH}_2]\text{OH} \rightleftharpoons [\text{MOH}_2]^+ + \text{OH}^-$$

He called the hydroxide, MOH, an anhydro base and the compound which actually dissociates, [MOH₂]OH, an aquo base. Similarly, Werner postulated that the ordinary "hydrogen" acids, in analogy to the complex platinic acids, form hydrates in aqueous solution, and that the acid hydrogen comes from the water and not the anhydro acid; viz:

$$[\text{PtCl}_2(\text{OH})_2] + 2\text{HOH} \rightleftharpoons \text{H}_2[\text{PtCl}_2(\text{OH})_4] \rightleftharpoons 2\text{H}^+ + [\text{PtCl}_2(\text{OH})_4]^-.$$

Thus, in effect, an anhydro acid is a compound which combines with the hydroxyl group of water, liberating an excess of hydrogen ions,

$$\underset{\text{anhydro acid}}{\text{A}} + \text{HOH} \rightleftharpoons \underset{\text{aquo acid}}{\text{H[AOH]}} \rightleftharpoons \text{H}^+ + [\text{AOH}]^-$$

while an anhydro base is a compound which combines with the hydrogen ion of water to produce an excess of hydroxyl ions,

$$\underset{\text{anhydro base}}{\text{B}} + \text{HOH} \rightleftharpoons \underset{\text{aquo base}}{[\text{BH}]\text{OH}} \rightleftharpoons [\text{BH}]^+ + \text{OH}^-$$

The reaction between an aquo base and an aquo acid results in the formation of an aquo salt,

$$\underset{\text{aquo acid}}{\text{H[AOH]}} + \underset{\text{aquo base}}{[\text{BH}]\text{OH}} \rightleftharpoons \underset{\text{aquo salt}}{[\text{BH}][\text{AOH}]} + \text{H}_2\text{O}$$

Therefore, the reaction between potassium hydroxide and hydrochloric acid was written:

$$\underset{\substack{\text{aquopotassium}\\\text{hydroxide}}}{[\text{KOH}_2]\text{OH}} + \underset{\substack{\text{aquohydrogen}\\\text{chloride}}}{\text{H}[\text{HCl}\cdot\text{OH}]} \rightarrow \underset{\substack{\text{aquopotassium}\\\text{chloride}}}{[\text{KOH}_2][\text{HCl}\cdot\text{OH}]} + \text{H}_2\text{O}$$

According to this theory, it is to be expected that basic metallic hydroxides and analogous compounds would always form aquo salts when neutralized with acids. Werner states that the instability of the free aquo salts in no way contradicts the assumption of the existence of aquo bases and aquo salts in solution, but shows rather that a relationship exists between the strength of the base and the stability of the aquo salts; the stability decreases as the strength of the base increases. Consequently, the phenomenon that the strongest metallic hydroxide bases (those of the alkali metals) preferably yield anhydrous salts is to be explained by the assumption that the aquo salts, which are originally formed, are too unstable to be isolated.

These ideas shocked the followers of Arrhenius and gave rise to severe criticism from numerous investigators in the field; others simply passed over Werner's oxonium theory as being of no importance[4]. A criticism raised by Walden[1] mentions the difficulty encountered if ethyl alcohol is used instead of water. He suggests that it would be necessary for the alcohol to dissociate in two different ways, allowing the formation of $[HClOC_2H_5]H$ and $[KC_2H_5]OH$. It would appear that this may not be a justifiable objection because of the analogy of OH^- and $OC_2H_5^-$ which allows a designation of $[KH]OC_2H_5$ for the alcoholobase. Although some of the ideas of the theory are wholly consistent with present views, it did not achieve wide acceptance.

Solvents other than water were seldom considered as media for acid-base reactions prior to 1905; in that year, Franklin[5] demonstrated the striking similarity between reactions carried out in liquid ammonia and those known to occur in aqueous solutions[6]. Liquid ammonia ionizes into ammonium and amide ions, just as water ionizes into hydronium and hydroxide ions.

$$2NH_3 \rightleftharpoons NH_4^+ + NH_2^-$$

$$2H_2O \rightleftharpoons H_3O^+ + OH^-$$

In liquid ammonia, substances like ammonium chloride are acids and substances like sodium amide are bases. Acids and bases in ammonia solution neutralize each other just as they do in aqueous solutions:

$$NH_4Cl + NaNH_2 \rightarrow NaCl + 2NH_3$$

$$H_3OCl + NaOH \rightarrow NaCl + 2H_2O$$

acid   base   salt   solvent

It was also observed that hydrogen was liberated by the reaction of an active metal and ammonium ions in liquid ammonia, a reaction which is exactly analogous to that which takes place in aqueous medium. Additional experimental evidence in support of the close similarity between water and liquid ammonia was furnished by the fact that zinc amide, insoluble in liquid ammonia, is dissolved upon the addition of either ammonium chloride or sodium amide, just as zinc hydroxide is soluble in either an excess of hydronium chloride or sodium hydroxide:

$$[Zn(H_2O)_4]^{++} \xrightleftharpoons[H_3O^+]{OH^-} [Zn(H_2O)_2(OH)_2] \xrightleftharpoons[H_3O^+]{OH^-} [Zn(OH)_4]^-$$

$$[Zn(NH_3)_4]^{++} \xrightleftharpoons[NH_4^+]{NH_2^-} [Zn(NH_3)_2(NH_2)_2] \xrightleftharpoons[NH_4^+]{NH_2^-} [Zn(NH_2)_4]^-$$

4. Lamb and Yngve, *J. Am. Chem. Soc.*, **43**, 2352 (1921).
5. Franklin, *J. Am. Chem. Soc.*, **27**, 820 (1905).
6. Franklin, "The Nitrogen System of Compounds," New York, Reinhold Publishing Corp., 1935.

This analogy between the hydronium ion and ammonium ion suggested that the acid properties result from the solvated proton in each instance. Some of the more extensively studied protonic solvents are acetic acid[7, 8], hydrogen sulfide[9, 10, 11], hydrogen fluoride[12], sulfuric acid [13, 14], and hydroxylamine[15]. Experiments carried out in nonprotonic solvents such as phosgene[16], sulfur dioxide[17], selenium oxychloride[18], and bromine trifluoride[19] revealed that certain generalizations can be made for any solvent system (Table 12.1). G. B. L. Smith[18], in an excellent review of the subject, defines an acid as an electron-pair acceptor toward the solvent, and a base as an electron-pair donor toward the solvent.

One of the more recent concepts of acid-base phenomena[20] (often referred to as the "Positive-negative" Theory) defines an acid as any substance capable of giving up a cation or combining with an anion or electron, and a base as any substance capable of giving up an anion or electron, or of combining with a cation. Usanovich suggests that neutralization reactions be considered as shown in Table 12.2. Sodium oxide is a base because it is capable of giving up the anion $O^=$ and silicon dioxide is an acid because it combines with this anion. In the reaction of sodium with chlorine, sodium is the base because it gives up an electron and chlorine is the acid since it combines with the electron. This implies that oxidation and reduction are nothing more than special cases of acid-base phenomena. Partly because of this[2a] and also because of the stress placed upon salt formation, and the reasoning involved in making ions so important, the theory has been widely criticized.

7. Davidson, *J. Am. Chem. Soc.*, **50**, 1890 (1928); Davidson, *Chem. Rev.*, **8**, 175 (1931).
8. Davidson and McAllister, *J. Am. Chem. Soc.*, **52**, 519 (1930).
9. Quam, *J. Am. Chem. Soc.*, **47**, 103 (1925).
10. Quam and Wilkinson, *J. Am. Chem. Soc.*, **47**, 989 (1925).
11. Wilkinson, *Chem. Rev.*, **8**, 237 (1931).
12. Weiser, "Inorganic Colloid Chemistry," Vol. II, New York, John Wiley & Sons, Inc., 1935; Simons, *J. Am. Chem. Soc.*, **54**, 129 (1932).
13. Kendall and Davidson, *J. Am. Chem. Soc.*, **43**, 979 (1921).
14. Kendall and Landon, *J. Am. Chem. Soc.*, **42**, 2131 (1920).
15. Audrieth, *J. Phys. Chem.*, **34**, 538 (1930); Audrieth, *Trans. Ill. State Acad. Sci.*, **22**, 385 (1930); Audrieth, *Z. physik. Chem.*, **A165**, 323 (1933).
16. Germann, *J. Am. Chem. Soc.*, **47**, 2461 (1925); Germann and Timparry, *ibid.*, **47**, 2275 (1925).
17. Jander and Wickert, *Z. physik. Chem.* **A178**, 57 (1936); Jander and Immig, *Z. anorg. allgem. Chem.*, **233**, 295 (1937); Jander and Ullmann, *ibid.*, **233**, 405 (1937); Jander and Schmidt, *Wien. Chem. Ztg.*, **46**, 49 (1943).
18. Smith, *Chem. Rev.*, **23**, 165 (1938).
19. Sharpe and Emeleus, *J. Chem. Soc.*, **1948**, 2135; Banks, Emeleus, and Woolf, *ibid.*, **1949**, 2861; Woolf and Emeleus, *ibid.*, **1949**, 2865; Sharpe, *Quart. Rev. Chem. Soc., London*, **IV**, No. 2 (1950).
20. Usanovich, *J. Gen. Chem., U.S.S.R.*, **9**, 182 (1939).

TABLE 12.1. DIFFERENT SOLVENT SYSTEMS

A. Ionization of Various Solvents:

   solvent → acid + base

   $2H_2O \rightleftarrows [H \cdot H_2O]^+ + OH^-$

   $2NH_3 \rightleftarrows [H \cdot NH_3]^+ + NH_2^-$

   $2HC_2H_3O_2 \rightleftarrows [H \cdot HC_2H_3O_2]^+ + C_2H_3O_2^-$

   $2H_2S \rightleftarrows [H \cdot H_2S]^+ + HS^-$

   $2H_2SO_4 \rightleftarrows [H \cdot H_2SO_4]^+ + HSO_4^-$

   $2COCl_2 \rightleftarrows [COCl \cdot COCl_2]^+ + Cl^-$

   $4SO_2 \rightleftarrows [SO \cdot 2SO_2]^{++} + SO_3^-$

   $2BrF_3 \rightleftarrows BrF_2^+ + BrF_4^-$

B. Neutralization reactions in Various Solvents:

   acid + base → salt + solvent

   $[H \cdot H_2O]^+, X^- + M^+, OH^- \rightarrow MX + 2H_2O$

   $[H \cdot HC_2H_3O_2]^+, X^- + M^+, C_2H_3O_2^- \rightarrow MX + 2HC_2H_3O_2$

   $[COCl \cdot COCl_2]^+, [AlCl_4]^- + M^+, Cl^- \rightarrow M[AlCl_4] + 2COCl_2$

   *$[SO \cdot 2SO_2]^{++}, X_2^- + M_2^+, SO_3^- \rightarrow 2MX + 4SO_2$

C. Reaction of a Metal with an Acid in Various Solvents:

   metal + acid → metal ion + reduction product + solvent

   $2M + 2[H \cdot H_2O]^+ \rightarrow 2M^+ + H_2 + 2H_2O$

   $2M + 2[H \cdot NH_3]^+ \rightarrow 2M^+ + H_2 + 2NH_3$

   $2M + 2[H \cdot NH_2OH] \rightarrow 2M^+ + H_2 + 2NH_2OH$

   $2M + 2[COCl \cdot COCl_2]^+ \rightarrow 2M^+ + CO + 3COCl_2$

D. Electrolysis of Various Solvents:

Cathode Reaction	Anode Reaction
	base → oxidation product +
acid + e⁻ → reduction product + solvent	*solvent + e⁻*
$2[H \cdot H_2O]^+ + 2e^- \rightarrow H_2 + 2H_2O$	$4OH^- \rightarrow O_2 + 2H_2O + 4e^-$
$2[H \cdot NH_3]^+ + 2e \rightarrow H_2 + 2NH_3$	$6NH_2^- \rightarrow N_2 + 4NH_3 + 6e^-$
$2[COCl \cdot COCl_2]^+ + 2e^- \rightarrow CO + 3COCl_2$	$2Cl^- \rightarrow Cl_2 + 2e^-$
*$[SO \cdot 2SO_2]^{++} + 2e^- \rightarrow SO + 2SO_2$	$SO_3^- \rightarrow SO_3 + 2e^-$

E. Amphoterism in Various Solvents:

$$cation \;\underset{acid}{\overset{base}{\rightleftarrows}}\; amphoteric\ precipitate \;\underset{acid}{\overset{base}{\rightleftarrows}}\; anion$$

$[M(H_2O)_x]^+ \;\underset{H_3O^+}{\overset{OH^-}{\rightleftarrows}}\; MOH \;\underset{H_3O^+}{\overset{OH^-}{\rightleftarrows}}\; [M(OH)_x]^{(x-1)-}$

$[M(NH_3)_x]^+ \;\underset{NH_4^+}{\overset{NH_2^-}{\rightleftarrows}}\; MNH_2 \;\underset{NH_3^+}{\overset{NH_2^-}{\rightleftarrows}}\; [M(NH_2)_x]^{(x-1)-}$

$[M(HC_2H_3O_2)_x]^+ \;\underset{[H \cdot HC_2H_3O_2]^+}{\overset{C_2H_3O_2^-}{\rightleftarrows}}\; MC_2H_3O_2 \;\underset{[H \cdot HC_2H_3O_2]^+}{\overset{C_2H_3O_2^-}{\rightleftarrows}}\; [M(C_2H_3O_2)_x]^{(x-1)-}$

$[M(H_2S)_x]^+ \;\underset{[H \cdot H_2S]^+}{\overset{HS^-}{\rightleftarrows}}\; M_2S \;\underset{[H \cdot H_2S]^+}{\overset{HS^-}{\rightleftarrows}}\; [MS_x]^{(2x-1)-}$

$[M(COCl_2)_x]^+ \;\underset{[COCl \cdot COCl_2]^+}{\overset{Cl^-}{\rightleftarrows}}\; MCl \;\underset{[COCl \cdot COCl_2]^+}{\overset{Cl^-}{\rightleftarrows}}\; [MCl_x]^{(x-1)-}$

* The rate of exchange of sulfur in solutions of thionyl halide in sulfur dioxide is extremely slow. These results indicate that there is a negligible amount of thionyl ion in these solutions so that the simple ionization picture represented here is in need of some modification. Johnson, Norris, and Huston, *J. Am. Chem. Soc.*, **73**, 3052 (1951).

Table 12.2. Some Neutralization Reactions According to the
Positive-Negative Theory

Acid	+	Base	→ Salt
SiO_2	+	Na_2O	→ $NaSiO_3$
SnS_2	+	$(NH_4)_2S$	→ $(NH_4)_2[SnS_3]$
$AgCN$	+	$NaCN$	→ $Na[Ag(CN)_2]$
$SnCl_4$	+	$2KCl$	→ $K_2[SnCl_6]$
Cl_2	+	$2Na$	→ $2NaCl$

The Proton Theory

The one-element theory of acids and bases has been very successfully modernized into what is known as the proton theory[21, 22], which defines an acid as a substance that gives up a hydrogen ion and a base as a substance that accepts a hydrogen ion:

$$A \rightleftharpoons B^- + H^+$$

acid   base

However, this equation is purely hypothetical, for an acid will not give up a proton unless a base is present to accept it, so that an exchange of a proton from an acid to a base produces an acid conjugate to the original base and a base conjugate to the original acid. The ionization of hydrogen chloride is written:

$$HCl + H_2O \rightleftharpoons H_3O^+ + Cl^-$$

acid   base   acid   base

The reaction toward the right takes place because of the tendency of hydrogen to form the coordinated $[H(OH_2)]^+$ ion.

The fact that this theory is both general and useful has been extensively discussed[21b, 23]. Its greatest shortcoming lies in the fact that it is not adaptable to nonprotonic systems and does not include as acids substances which contain no hydrogen.

The Electronic Theory

Lewis[24] suggested that the behavior of acidic and basic substances might be described entirely in terms of electrons. In his own words, "It seems to me that with complete generality we may say that a basic substance is one which has a lone pair of electrons which may be used to complete the stable

21. Brønsted, *Rec. trav. chim.*, **42**, 718 (1923); Brønsted, *Chem. Rev.*, **5**, 231 (1923).
22. Lowry, *Chemistry & Industry*, **42**, 1048 (1923).
23. Brønsted, *J. Phys. Chem.*, **30**, 777 (1926); Hall, Briscoe, Hammett, Johnson, Alyea, McReynolds, Hazlehurst, and Luder, "Acids and Bases," Journal of Chemical Education, Easton, Pennsylvania, 1941.
24. Lewis, *J. Franklin Inst.*, **226**, 293 (1938).

group of another atom, and that an acid substance is one which can employ a lone pair from another molecule in completing the stable group of one of its own atoms. In other words, the basic substance furnishes a pair of electrons for a chemical bond, the acid substance accepts such a pair."

The electronic theory of acids and bases has been reviewed by Luder[2a, 25]. Since the theory defines an acid as a substance capable of accepting a pair of electrons, and a base as a substance capable of donating a pair of electrons, it requires that the first step in a neutralization reaction be the formation of a coordinate covalent bond; this appears to be extremely general:

$$A \quad + \quad B \quad \rightarrow \quad A:B$$

acid   *base*   *coordination compound*

$$[H(OH_2)]^+ + \ :\overset{..}{\underset{..}{O}}:H^- \rightarrow 2H_2O$$

$$\begin{array}{ccc} \text{F} & \text{H} & \text{F H} \\ | & | & | \ | \\ \text{F---B} & + \ :\text{N---H} \rightarrow & \text{F---B:N---H} \\ | & | & | \ | \\ \text{F} & \text{H} & \text{F H} \end{array}$$

The theory makes no mention of the solvent (not even the necessity of a solvent), nor is anything said about protons.

THE ACID-BASE PROPERTIES OF SOME COORDINATION COMPOUNDS

The effect of coordination on acid-base properties may be considered, qualitatively, on the basis of ionic size and charge. The maximum amount of distortion is exerted by small cations of high ionic charge[26], acting on large, polarizable anions. This polarization effect explains why oxides of large metal ions with small positive charge react with water to form bases, e.g., $Na_2O + H_2O \rightarrow 2NaOH$, $CaO + H_2O \rightarrow Ca(OH)_2$, while oxides of nonmetals or of small metals in the higher oxidation states react with water to form acids, e.g., $Cl_2O + H_2O \rightarrow 2HClO$, $CrO_3 + H_2O \rightarrow H_2CrO_4$. In all of these compounds an atom of oxygen is interspersed between the hydrogen atom and the remainder of the molecule; the basic or acidic character seems to depend largely upon the relative attractive forces between the oxide ion and the hydrogen ion, on the one hand, and the remainder of the molecule on the other, modified by the energy of hydration of the resulting ions. This being the case, hydroxides of sodium and chlorine behave differently because of the difference in the sizes of the respective ions. Since the sodium atom is large, the bond between it and oxygen is weak and cleav-

25. Luder, *Chem. Rev.*, **27**, 547 (1940); Luder and Zuffanti, *ibid.*, **34**, 345 (1944).
26. Fajans and Joos, *Z. physik.*, **23**, (1924).

TABLE 12.3. IONIC POTENTIALS FOR CATIONS OF THE FIRST TWO SHORT PERIODS

Cations	Li^+	Be^{++}	B^{+++}	C^{4+}	N^{5+}	O^{6+}	F^{7+}
$\sqrt{\phi}$ Hydroxide	1.29 base	2.54 amphoteric	3.87 acid	5.16 acid	6.71 acid	(8.19) acid	(10) acid
Cations	Na^+	Mg^{++}	Al^{+++}	Si^{4+}	P^{5+}	S^{6+}	Cl^{6+}
$\sqrt{\phi}$ Hydroxide	1.02 base	1.76 base	2.45 amphoteric	3.13 amphoteric	3.83 acid	4.55 acid	5.20 acid

age occurs at (1), while the chlorine atom is small and forms a relatively strong bond with oxygen so that cleavage occurs at (4).

$$Na\ |\ \overset{\cdot\cdot}{\underset{\cdot\cdot}{O}}:\ |\ H \qquad Cl\ |\ \overset{\cdot\cdot}{\underset{\cdot\cdot}{O}}:\ |\ H$$
$$\ \ (1)\ \ (2) \qquad\qquad (3)\ \ (4)$$

The same conclusions were reached by Cartledge[27, 28] in his papers on *ionic
potential*. He defines the ionic potential, ϕ, as $\phi = \dfrac{Z}{r}$, in which Z is the oxidation state of the ion and r is the radius of the ion. Since, in any comparison
of the properties of two different ions, the increasing ionic charge and increasing ionic radius act in opposite directions, it is apparent that the ratio
of charge to radius (ϕ) must be considered in any predictions of relative
properties. Cartledge[28] has pointed out that ions in which $\sqrt{\phi} < 2.2$ are
basic, those with $3.2 > \sqrt{\phi} > 2.2$ are amphoteric, and those with $\sqrt{\phi} > 3.2$
are acidic (Table 12.3).

These observations on the relation between polarization and ionic potential can be used to explain the fact that although cobalt(III) hydroxide
is a very weak base, hexamminecobalt(III) hydroxide is as strong a base as
the alkali hydroxides[4]. This results from an increase in the effective radius
of the cation, and a consequent decrease in the ionic potential, since the
oxidation state is not changed. The unavailability of orbitals to form covalent bonds must also be considered. Boric acid[29] is an extremely weak
monobasic acid ($K = 6 \times 10^{-10}$); the phenolphthalein end point (Fig. 12.1)
is reached when only 10 to 20 % of the acid has been neutralized. Hildebrand[30] followed the change in pH when varying amounts of mannitol
were added to boric acid (Fig. 12.1). Curve E corresponds roughly to
$K = 10^{-5}$ and shows that the excess mannitol magnifies K by about 10^4,

27. Cartledge, *J. Am. Chem. Soc.*, **50**, 2855 (1928).
28. Cartledge, *ibid.*, **50**, 2863 (1928).
29. Jorgensen, *Z. angew. Chem.*, 549 (1896).
30. Hildebrand, *J. Am. Chem. Soc.*, **35**, 860 (1913).

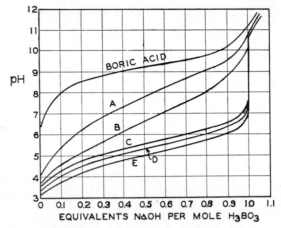

F IG. 12.1. Titration curves of mixtures of boric acid and mannitol.
Curve A   0.8 g mannitol per 100 ml. $0.1N$ H_3BO_3 .
Curve B   2.4 g mannitol per 100 ml. $0.1N$ H_3BO_3 .
Curve C   4.0 g mannitol per 100 ml. $0.1N$ H_3BO_3 .
Curve D   5.6 g mannitol per 100 ml. $0.1N$ H_3BO_3 .
Curve E   7.2 g mannitol per 100 ml. $0.1N$ H_3BO_3 .

making it possible to titrate boric acid conveniently using phenophthalien as the indicator. Although the exact structure of these complex acids has not been conclusively established, it is known that the hydroxy groups are attached to the boron in such a way as to displace a proton, and thus increase the acid strength. Lowry[31] proposes the quadricovalent structure for the mannito-boric acid complex:

$$H^+ \begin{bmatrix} HO & & O \\ & \diagdown \diagup & \\ & B & \quad C_6H_{12}O_4 \\ & \diagup \diagdown & \\ HO & & O \end{bmatrix}^-$$

Cationic Complexes

Bases. Werner has called attention to the variation in basicity of a series of hydroxo complexes[3b] (Table 12.4). His qualitative studies showed that: (1) will precipitate silver oxide from silver nitrate; (1) through (3) liberate ammonia from NH_4^+ in the cold; (1) through (5) absorb carbon dioxide; (1) through (8) react alkaline to litmus while (9) and (10) are neutral; (1) through (8) are more soluble in acetic acid than in water; from acetic acid solutions of (1) through (3) the salts precipitate as aquo salts, while (4) through (8) yield hydroxo salts; all of these cations appear to form

31. Lowry, *J. Chem. Soc.*, **1929**, 2853.

TABLE 12.4. WERNER'S SERIES OF BASIC CATIONS

No.	Cations	No.	Cations
1	$[Co(NH_3)_4(NO_2)OH]^+$	6	$[Cr(NH_3)_2(H_2O)_3OH]^{++}$
2	$[Co(NH_3)_5 OH]^{++}$	7	$[Cr(NH_3)_2(H_2O)_2(OH)_2]^+$
3	$[Co(NH_3)_4(H_2O)OH]^{++}$	8	$[Co(NH_3)_2py_2(H_2O)OH]^{++}$
4	$[Co en_2 (H_2O)OH]^{++}$ (1, 2)	9	$[Ru(NH_3)_4(NO)OH]^{++}$
5	$[Co en_2 (H_2O)OH]^{++}$ (1, 6)	10	$[Pt(NH_3)_4(OH)_2]^{++}$

TABLE 12.5. CONDUCTANCE RATIO OF SOME AMMINECOBALT(III) HYDROXIDES

No.	Cation	α (%) (1.33×10^{-3} M)	α' (%)
1	$[Co(NH_3)_4CO_3]^+$	97.6	
2	*trans*-$[Co(NH_3)_4(NO_2)_2]^+$	95.0	
3	$[Co(NH_3)_6]^{+++}$	89.5	
4	$[Co en_3]^{+++}$	88.6	
5	*cis* $[Co(NH_3)_4(NO_2)_2]^+$	81.2	
6	$[Co(NH_3)_5H_2O]^{+++}$	53.5	82.9
7	$[Co(NH_3)_3H_2O(NO_2)_2]^+$	36.0	
8	$[Co en_2 (H_2O)_2]^{+++}$	27.3	84.8
9	$[Co(NH_3)_4(H_2O)_2]^{+++}$	24.6	74.0

aquo salts with strong mineral acids but even from solutions of this type (9) and (10) are still isolated as the hydroxo complexes.

Werner ascribed this decrease in basic strength from the moderately strong base (1) to the nonbasic ion (10) to a difference in affinity for the hydrogen ion. Werner's observations have been reviewed by Brønsted[23a] and the results interpreted in terms of more modern concepts (page 421).

Coordination of the metal of a weak base, MOH, results in the formation of a stronger base, $[MA_x]OH$, due to the increase in cationic size. Lamb and Yngve[4] determined the conductance ratio $\left(\alpha = \dfrac{\lambda_v}{\lambda_o} \right)$ for a series of amminecobalt(III) hydroxides at 0°, and found that many of them are as highly ionized as the hydroxides of the alkalis (Table 12.5). Hall[34] points out that if the more probable assumption (rejected by Lamb and Yngve) is made, that the aquo cations are transformed to hydroxo compounds, in Werner's sense, the more useful figures (α') are obtained.

Acids. The acidity of aqueous solutions of salts can be accounted for by the loss of protons from the hydrated cations.

$$[M(H_2O)_x]^{++} + H_2O \rightleftharpoons [M(H_2O)_{x-1}OH]^+ + H_3O^+$$

For instance, as early as 1906 Bjerrum[35] reported a value of 0.89×10^{-4} as the dissociation constant at 25° for the reaction

34. Hall, *Chem. Rev.*, **19**, 89 (1936).
35. Bjerrum, *Kgl. Danske Videnskab. Selskabs Skeifter*, [7] **4**, 1 (1906).

$$[Cr(H_2O)_6]^{+++} + H_2O \rightleftharpoons [Cr(H_2O)_5OH]^{++} + H_3O^+$$

and a few years later Denham[36] assigned it a value about twice as great. Lamb and Fonda[37] arrived at an average value of 1.58×10^{-4} at 25° which is comparable to a more recent determination by Brønsted and Volqvartz[38].

The acidity of aquoammines is due to loss of protons from the coordinated water molecules, although with the ammines of heavier metals, the acidity of the coordinated ammonia is noticeable. Tschugaev[39] and Grünberg[40a, 41a, 41b] have demonstrated this by the conversion of platinum ammines to the corresponding amido or basic salts:

$$[Pt(NH_3)_5Cl]^{+++} + OH^- \rightleftharpoons [Pt(NH_3)_4NH_2Cl]^{++} + H_2O$$

Corresponding amido compounds of cobaltammines are not known, but evidence for this type of reaction has been obtained from exchange reactions with heavy water[42a, 42b].

$$[Co(NH_3)_6]^{+++} \rightleftharpoons [Co(NH_3)_5NH_2]^{++} + H^+$$

$$[Co(NH_3)_5NH_2]^{++} + HDO \rightleftharpoons [Co(NH_3)_5NH_2D]^{+++} + OH^-$$

$$H^+ + OH^- \rightleftharpoons H_2O$$

Ionization of a hydrogen ion from one of the coordinated ammine groups in the bis(ethylenediamine)gold(III) ion has been demonstrated by Bailar and Block[42c]. This phenomenon has also been reported by Dwyer and Hogarth, who studied the ethylenediamine complexes of osmium[42d]. The study of metal ammine complexes furnishes some insight into the properties of aquo ions. The dissociation constants for some of these ions are known fairly accurately (Table 12.6). The equilibrium constants are calculated

36. Denham, *J. Chem. Soc.*, **93**, 53 (1908).
37. Lamb and Fonda, *J. Am. Chem. Soc.*, **43**, 1154 (1921).
38. Brønsted and Volqvartz, *Z. physik Chem.*, **134**, 97 (1928).
39. Tschugajeff, *Z. anorg. allgem. Chem.*, **137**, 1, 401 (1924); Tschugajeff, *Compt. rend.*, **160**, 840 (1915); **161**, 699 (1915).
40. Grünberg and Faermann, *Z. anorg. allgem. Chem.*, **193**, 193 (1930); Grünberg and Gildengershel, *Izvest. Akad. Nauk S.S.S.R., Otel. Khim. Nauk*, 479 (1948).
41. Grünberg and Ryabchikov, *Acta. Physiocochim. U.S.S.R.*, **3**, 555 (1935); Grünberg, *ibid.*, **3**, 573 (1935); Grünberg and Ryabchikov, *Compt. rend. acad. sci. U.S.S.R.*, **4**, 259 (1936); Grünberg, *Bull. acad. sci. U.S.S.R., Classe sci. chim.*, 350 (1943).
42a. Anderson, Spoor, and Briscoe, *Nature*, **139**, 508 (1937).
42b. Anderson, Spoor, and Brisco, *Nature*, **139**, 508 (1937); Anderson, Briscoe, and Spoor, *J. Chem. Soc.*, **1943**, 361; Garrick, *Nature*, **139**, 507 (1937); James, Anderson, and Briscoe, *Nature*, **139**, 109 (1937).
42c. Block and Bailar, *J. Am. Chem. Soc.*, **73**, 4722 (1951).
42d. Dwyer and Hogarth, *J. Am. Chem. Soc.*, **75**, 1008 (1953).

Table 12.6*. Acid Strength of Some Complex Cations

Acid	pKa
[Co en$_2$ (OH)$_2$]$^+$	L, (13)
[Co(NH$_3$)$_4$(OH)$_2$]$^+$	L, (12)
[Co(NH$_3$)$_3$(NO$_2$)$_2$(H$_2$O)]$^+$	L, (11)
[Pt(NH$_3$)$_4$NH$_2$Cl]$^{++}$	G, 10.9
[Pt en$_2$ Cl$_2$]$^{++}$	G, 10.4
[Pt(NH$_3$)$_4$Cl$_2$]$^{++}$	G, 9.8
[Pt(NH$_3$)$_5$OH]$^{+++}$	G, pKa$_1$, 9.5; pKa$_2$, 10.7
[Pt(NH$_3$)$_5$Br]$^{+++}$	G, pKa$_1$, 8.2; pKa$_2$, 10.4
[Pt(NH$_3$)$_5$Cl]$^{+++}$	G, pKa$_1$, 8.1; pKa$_2$, 10.5
[Pt(NH$_3$)$_6$]$^{4+}$	G, pKa$_1$, 7.9; pKa$_2$, 10.1
[Ru(NH$_3$)$_4$(NO)OH]$^{++}$	W, 7
[Pt en (NH$_3$)$_4$]$^{4+}$	G, pKa$_1$, 6.2; pKa$_2$, 10.0
[Co(NH$_3$)$_4$NO$_2$H$_2$O]$^{++}$	W, 6
[Rh(NH$_3$)$_5$H$_2$O]$^{+++}$	B, 5.86
[Cr(H$_2$O)$_4$Cl$_2$]$^+$	L, 5.72; Bj, 5.42
[Co(NH$_3$)$_5$H$_2$O]$^{+++}$	B, 5.69; W, (5–6)
[Co(NH$_3$)$_4$(H$_2$O)$_2$]$^{+++}$	B, 5.22; W, (5–6)
[Pt en$_3$]$^{4+}$	G, pKa$_1$, 5.5; pKa$_2$, 9.8
**cis-[Co en$_2$ (H$_2$O)$_2$]$^{+++}$	W, (3–4)
**trans-[Co en$_2$ (H$_2$O)$_2$]$^{+++}$	W, (3–4)
[Al(H$_2$O)$_6$]$^{+++}$	B, 4.95
[Co(NH$_3$)$_3$(H$_2$O)$_3$]$^{+++}$	B, 4.73
[Cr(H$_2$O)$_6$]$^{+++}$	B, 3.90, L, 3.80, Bj, 4.05, D, 3.75
[Co(NH$_3$)$_2$(H$_2$O)$_4$]$^{+++}$	B, 3.40
[Co(NH$_3$)$_2$(H$_2$O)$_3$OH]$^{++}$	W, (2–3)
[Cr(NH$_3$)$_2$(H$_2$O)$_4$]$^{+++}$	W, (2–3)
[Co(NH$_3$)$_2$(H$_2$O)$_4$]$^{+++}$	W, (2–3)
[Ru(NH$_3$)$_4$NOH$_2$O]$^{+++}$	W, (2)
[Pt(NH$_3$)$_4$(H$_2$O)$_2$]$^{4+}$	W, (2)
[Fe(H$_2$O)$_6$]$^{+++}$	B, 2.20

* In this table, B refers to Brønsted, Bj to Bjerrum, D to Denham, G to Grünberg, L to Lamb, and W to Werner. This table is taken from a review article by Hall[34] to which the data of Grünberg[40] are added. Note that in a few cases Grünberg[40b] has demonstrated the polybasicity of the complex platinum(IV) ion acids. The third dissociation constant was evaluated with difficulty in only a few cases, and it was demonstrated that the ratio K_2/K_3 is much smaller than K_1/K_2 .

** Bjerrum and Rasmussen, *Acta Chem. Scand.* **6,** 1265 (1952) report the following pKa values: cis[Coen$_2$(H$_2$O)$_2$]$^{+++}$, pKa$_1$ = 6.06, pKa$_2$ = 8.19; trans [Co en$_2$ (H$_2$O)$_2$]$^{+++}$, pKa$_1$ = 4.45, pKa$_2$ = 7.94.

as shown below:

$$[Co(NH_3)_5H_2O]^{+++} \rightleftharpoons [Co(NH_3)_5OH]^{++} + H^+$$

$$K = \frac{[Co(NH_3)_5OH]^{++}[H^+]}{[Co(NH_3)_5H_2O]^{+++}} = 1 \times 10^{-6}\ [43]$$

In the case where the proton is liberated from a coordinated ammine group,

43. Brønsted and King, *Z. physik Chem.*, **130,** 699 (1927).

TABLE 12.7. RELATIVE STABILITIES OF AMMINECOBALT(III) IONS[44]

(1) *trans*-$[Co(NH_3)_4(NO_2)_2]^+$ (4) *cis*-$[Co(NH_3)_4(NO_2)_2]^+$
(2) $[Co(NH_3)_6]^{+++}$ (5) $[Co(NH_3)_4(H_2O)_2]^{+++}$
(3) $[Co(NH_3)_5NO_2]^{++}$ (6) $[Co(NH_3)_5H_2O]^{+++}$

TABLE 12.8. DISSOCIATION CONSTANTS OF SOME METAL AMMINES

Ammine	K_c
$[Ag(NH_3)_2]^+$	6.8×10^{-8}
$[Cu(NH_3)_2]^+$	1.5×10^{-9}
$[Cd(NH_3)_4]^{++}$	1.0×10^{-7}
$[Zn(NH_3)_4]^{++}$	2.6×10^{-10}
$[Co(NH_3)_6]^{++}$	1.75×10^{-5}

the expression for K is as illustrated below:

$$[Pt(NH_3)_5Cl]^{+++} \rightleftharpoons [Pt(NH_3)_4NH_2Cl]^{++} + H^+$$

$$K = \frac{[Pt(NH_3)_4NH_2Cl]^{++}[H^+]}{[Pt(NH_3)_5Cl]^{+++}} = 7.9 \times 10^{-9} \ [40]$$

In addition to dissociation constants, the relative stabilities of a series of amminecobalt(III) ions were determined[44] and it was found that the stabilities decrease in the order shown in Table 12.7. The concentration dissociation constants are very small ($K_c = 2.2 \times 10^{-34}$ for $[Co(NH_3)_6]^{+++}$) as is expected from the well known chemical stability of these cations. It can be supposed that the greater the dissociation constant (greater the tendency to liberate ammonia) of these ions, the weaker their acid strength; that this is usually true can be seen by a comparison of the relative stabilities of the complexes in Table 12.7 with their relative acid strengths given in Table 12.6. This is further illustrated by the very small acid strengths of the more highly dissociated metal ammines listed in Table 12.8.

Brønsted[43] deduced that in the homologous series of aquoamminecobalt(III) ions, the acid strength is a statistical factor based upon the number of coordinated aquo groups. This requires that a hexaaquo ion be six times as strong an acid as a monoaquo ion. Brønsted and Volqvartz[38] found that although the calculated influence of the statistical factor is in qualitative agreement with the values found for the dissociation constants of aquoamminecobalt(III) ions (Table 12.9), it is insufficient to account quantitatively for the differences found.

Brønsted[43] has called attention to the relation between acid strength and the charge on an aquo cation; Werner found $[Co(NH_3)_5OH]^{++}$ to be less basic than $[Co(NH_3)_4NO_2OH]^+$ which means that $[Co(NH_3)_5H_2O]^{+++}$ is more acidic than $[Co(NH_3)_4 NO_2 H_2O]^{++}$. Brønsted deduced from such examples that the higher the positive charge on the complex, the stronger

44. Lamb and Larson, *J. Am. Chem. Soc.*, **42**, 2024 (1920).

TABLE 12.9. DISSOCIATION CONSTANTS OF SOME TRIPOSITIVE ACIDS

No.	Cation	$K_a \times 10^6$	No.	Cation	$K_a \times 10^6$
1	$[Co(NH_3)_5H_2O]^{+++}$	2.04	5	$[Rh(NH_3)_5H_2O]^{+++}$	1.38
2	$[Co(NH_3)_4(H_2O)_2]^{+++}$	6.03	6	$[Al(H_2O)_6]^{+++}$	11.2
3	$[Co(NH_3)_3(H_2O)_3]^{+++}$	18.8	7	$[Cr(H_2O)_6]^{+++}$	126.
4	$[Co(NH_3)_2(H_2O)_4]^{+++}$	400.	8	$[Fe(H_2O)_6]^{+++}$	6300.

the acid. This is a logical consequence of the greater repulsion of a proton by the more positive cation. Lamb and Yngve[4] found that the substitution of an additional nitro group decreased the acid strength still further. Likewise, Tschugajeff[39] has prepared a series of hydroxoammineplatinum(IV) ions and noticed that $[Pt(NH_3)_5OH]^{+++}$ is a much weaker base than the corresponding cobalt(III) complex, $[Co(NH_3)_5OH]^{++}$, which has a smaller positive charge. There is also a considerable difference in the acidic strength of hexammineplatinum(IV) and hexamminecobalt(III) ions; the latter has little tendency to behave as an acid[42a] while the former is readily soluble in alkaline solution, from which the amido complex can be isolated[39a].

$$[Pt(NH_3)_6]^{4+} + H_2O \rightleftharpoons [Pt(NH_3)_5NH_2]^{+++} + H_3O^+$$

It should be mentioned, however, that this difference in acidity between $[Pt(NH_3)_6]^{4+}$ and $[Co(NH_3)_6]^{+++}$ is greater than anticipated merely on the difference in cationic charge.

The influence of the oxidation state of the central atom on the acid strength of complex ions has been demonstrated by comparing the properties of $[Co(NH_3)_6]^{+++}$ and $[Pt(NH_3)_5Cl]^{+++}$. The net charge on the cations is the same, but the cobalt(III) ion is almost neutral while the platinum(IV) is strongly acid.

A careful consideration of the relative acid strengths shown in Table 12.6 reveals the fact that no definite predictions can be made from the structure of the cation alone. However, it is apparent that the charge and size of the complex, the charge of the central atom and the statistical factor must all exert considerable influence. Likewise, the ammine cations are in general far less acidic than the corresponding aquo cations.

Grünberg has published a series of interesting papers[40a, 41] concerned with the effect of geometrical isomerism on acid strength. In investigating the acid-base properties of *cis*- and *trans*-diaquodiammineplatinum(II), he found that the first ionization of the trans isomer is greater than that of the cis form, and that the two ionization constants of the cis isomer are nearly alike, while those of the trans isomer are quite different from each other. The explanation of this observation is given in terms of the trans effect[45] (see Chapters 3 and 8).

45. Chernyaev, *ann. inst. platine*, **4**, 243 (1936).

This was illustrated by Grünberg[41] with the geometrical isomers of diaquodiammineplatinum(II):

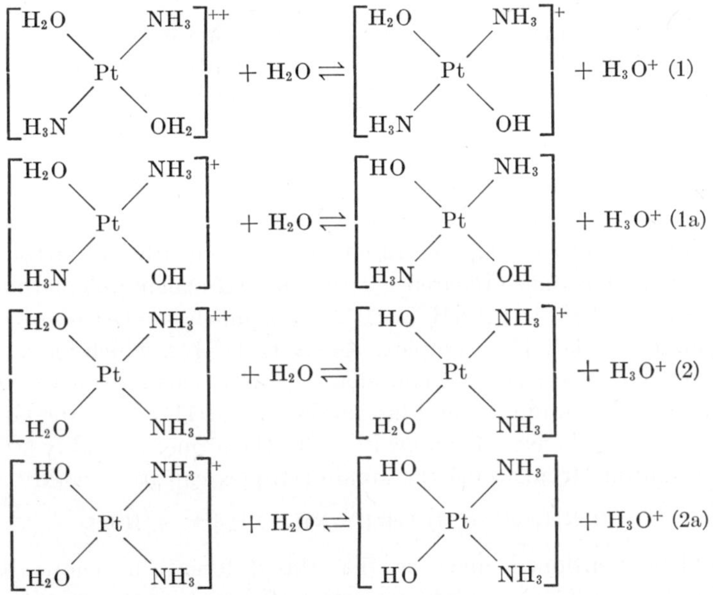

FIG. 12.2. The *trans-effect* principle as applied to the first and second acid dissociation constants of a Werner complex.

Since it is the group trans to the aquo group that affects its ionization, (Fig. 12.2), the first ionization (1) of the trans isomer is greater than that (2) of the corresponding cis form, because the polarizability of water is less than that of ammonia ($R_{H_2O} = 3.76$; $R_{NH_3} = 5.61$). The cis isomer should show very little difference in the two ionization constants, K_1 or (2) and K_2 or (2a), because the group opposite the ionizing group is NH_3 in both cases; while the two ionization constants of the trans isomer should differ markedly since K_1 or (1) is a measure of ionization with water opposite the ionizing group and K_2 or (1a) is the same measurement with a much more highly polarizing group ($R_{OH} = 5.1$) trans to the aquo group. In this case the stronger trans effect of the hydroxo group should result in a value of K_2 smaller than that of K_1. Although the same conclusions are reached on the basis of a smaller charge on the cation, this is not justified in that it also predicts different ionization constants for the cis isomer. Ryabchikov[46a] carried out potentiometric titrations with the cis and trans isomers of diaquodiammineplatinum(II) ion and found that the cis isomer behaves as a monobasic acid, while the trans isomer gives the type of curve characteristic of dibasic acids. The observation that the cis isomer is monobasic

46a. Ryabchikov, *Ann. secteri platine, Inst. chim., gen.* (U.S.S.R.) **15**, 35 (1938).

is indeed unexpected in view of the fact that the monovalent cation, $[Pt(NH_3)_2H_2O(OH)]^+$, should certainly be a weaker acid than $[Pt(NH_3)_2(H_2O)_2]^{+2}$. Therefore, the acid constants of these two isomers were carefully redetermined by Jensen[46c] and the pK_a values obtained were: *Cis* [Pt-$(NH_3)_2(H_2O)_2]^{+2}$ $pK_{a_1} = 5.56$, $pK_{a_2} = 7.32$; *trans* $[Pt(NH_3)_2(H_2O)_2]^{+2}$ $pK_{a_1} = 4.32$, $pK_{a_2} = 7.38$. These results are not inconsistent with Grünberg's interpretations of relative acid strength on the basis of the polarizability of the *trans* ligand. In the first place the *trans* isomer is the stronger acid as explained previously. Secondly the $\Delta pK_a = 1.76$ observed for the *cis* isomer may be attributed to the difference in charge on the cation. The greater difference, $\Delta pK_a = 3.06$, for the *trans* isomer can be said to result from the larger polarizing effect of the trans hydroxo group compared to the original aquo group in the first dissociation step. It is of interest that this same polarization treatment can account for the acid dissociation constants of *cis* and *trans* isomers of $[Co\ en_2(H_2O)_2]^{+3}$ [46d] and $[Co\ en_2NO_2H_2O]^{+2}$ [46b].

Anionic Complexes

Werner first called attention to the almost complete analogy between the union of anhydrides with water to give oxyacids, and the union of metal halides with hydrogen halides to form the halo acids.

$$H_2O + SO_3 \rightarrow H_2SO_4$$

$$HF + BF_3 \rightarrow HBF_4$$

$$2HCl + PtCl_4 \rightarrow H_2PtCl_4$$

The various factors known to effect the acid-base strengths of complex cations can be expected to have similar effects on complex anions. For example, it was pointed out (page 429) that the larger the charge on a cation, the greater its repulsion of a proton and consequently the stronger its acid properties; in much the same way it has been shown[47] that while $[Fe(CN)_6]^{\equiv}$ is a very weak base, $[Fe(CN)_6]^{4-}$ is about as strong a base as benzoate ion. This would indicate that the more negative a complex anion, the greater the proton attraction and therefore the stronger its basic properties.

Mention has also been made of the increased basic strength of $[Co\ a_6](OH)_3$ over $Co(OH)_3$ due to the coordination of six "a" groups to the cobalt-(III) ion. In much the same way, certain weak acids are greatly strengthened by coordination (page 423). This is illustrated by the weak acid HCN ($K_a = 7.2 \times 10^{-10}$) as compared to the relatively strong acid $H_4[Fe(CN)_6]$

46B. Stone, thesis, Northwestern University, 1952.
46C. Jensen, *Z. anorg. Chem.* **242**, 87 (1939).
46D. Bjerrum and Rasmussen, *Acta. Chem. Scand.*, **6**, 1265 (1952).
47. Kolthoff and Tomsicek, *J. Phys. Chem.*, **39**, 945 (1935).

$(K_4 = 6.8 \times 10^{-5})^{48}$. A similar explanation might be given for the fact that water is neutral while complexes in which oxygen is the donor atom ($H_2[SO_4]$, $H[ClO_4]$, etc.) are often strong acids.

Relative Acid-Base Strength

In the preceding discussion an attempt has been made to account for increasing or decreasing strengths of acids and bases. The generalizations made are concerned with the acid strength toward a reference base, OH^-, or the basic strength towards the acid, H_3O^+, in the solvent, water. The fact that it is impossible to arrange acids or bases in a single monotonic order of strength has been clearly stated by Lewis[24]. He points out that the relative acid-base strengths depend upon the solvent chosen as well as upon the particular base or acid used for reference.

It has, however, been suggested[25a] that on the basis of the electronic theory of acids and bases, the relative strengths of acids correspond to the tendency to accept pairs of electrons while the strengths of bases depend on their tendency to donate pairs of electrons. If this were all that need be considered it should certainly be possible to construct a monotonic series of acids and bases. Perhaps a more correct interpretation of acid-base strength is that suggested by Lingafelter[49]: (a) the strength of an acid corresponds to the strength of the bond it can form with a base, or (b) the strength of an acid corresponds to the decrease in free energy upon formation of a bond with a base. Certainly the interatomic forces of a coordination compound (neutralization product) involve not only the bonding forces of the covalent bond, but also electrostatic forces which depend upon the magnitude and separation of charges and the presence or absence of dipole moments in either acid or base and steric effects.

Pauling[50] has pointed out the variation in the strength of bonding orbitals of different types. Since the factors contributing to bond strength can vary more or less independently, the relative strengths of a series of bases may depend on the particular acid used in making the comparison. That this is the case has been shown[49] by a consideration of some equilibrium constants $\left(K = \dfrac{[\text{coordination}]}{[\text{acid}][\text{base}]}\right)$, as a measure of the strength of an acid or base. The equilibrium constants at 25° for the reactions

$$H^+ + B \rightleftharpoons HB^+, \qquad Ag^+ + 2B \rightleftharpoons [AgB_2]^+, \qquad Cu^+ + 2B \rightleftharpoons [CuB_2]^+,$$

$$\text{and} \qquad Hg^{++} + 4B \rightleftharpoons [HgB_4]^{++}$$

are given in Table 12.10.

48. Britton and Dodd, *J. Chem. Soc.*, **1933**, 1543; Lanford and Kiehl, *J. Phys. Chem.*, **45**, 300 (1941).

49. Lingafelter, *J. Am. Chem. Soc.*, **63**, 1999 (1941).

50. Pauling, "The Nature of the Chemical Bond," Ithaca, New York, Cornell University Press, 1945.

TABLE 12.10. EQUILIBRIUM CONSTANTS FOR SOME ACIDS WITH DIFFERENT REFERENCE BASES

Base		Acid		
	H^+	Ag^+	Cu^+	Hg^{++}
CN^-	2.5×10^9	2.6×10^{18}	1×10^{16}	2.5×10^{41}
NH_3	1.8×10^9	1.7×10^7		
$SO_3^=$	1×10^7	3.5×10^8		
Cl^-	Weak		3.4×10^5	9×10^{15}
Br^-	Weaker		8.3×10^5	4.3×10^{21}
I^-	Weakest		7.1×10^8	1.9×10^{30}

In each series there is a reversal of relative strengths of some of the bases upon changing the reference acid, showing that no single arrangement of basic strength can be made which will be applicable to all cases. These peculiarities in relative acid strengths seem to be connected with the fact that different metals have different coordinating power toward various ligands.

The difference in acid-base strengths depending on the reference base or acid can sometimes be explained on the basis of molecular structure; this possibility has been more carefully investigated with organic compounds than in the field of inorganic chemistry. A good example is the reversal of the relative strengths of triethylamine and ammonia; ammonia is the weaker base toward the proton, but much stronger toward *m*-dinitrobenzene. Lewis and Seaborg[51] explain this behavior as being a result of the double chelation which is possible through hydrogen bonding in the case of ammonia but not with triethylamine:

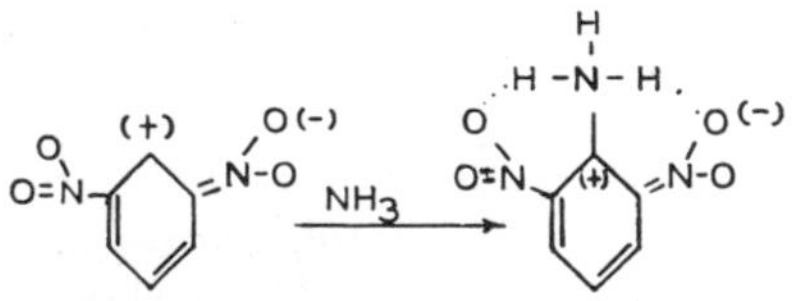

The researches of Brown and co-workers[52] demonstrated a complete reversal in the basic strength of ammonia and primary, secondary and tertiary amines. They collected data on the dissociation constants

$$R_3N:BR_3' \rightleftharpoons R_3N: + BR_3'$$

[R = CH_3 and/or H; C_2H_5 and/or H.   R' = CH_3 , C_2H_5 , $CH(CH_3)_2$ or $C(CH_3)_3$]

and equilibrium constants for the displacements

$$R_3N: + R''_3N:BR'_3 \rightleftharpoons R_3N:BR'_3 + R''_3N:$$

51. Lewis and Seaborg, *J. Am. Chem. Soc.*, **62**, 2122 (1940).
52. Brown, Moddie, and Gerstein, *J. Am. Chem. Soc.*, **66**, 431 (1944); Brown, Bartholomay, and Taylor, *ibid.*, **66**, 435 (1944); Brown, *ibid.*, **67**, 374 (1945); Brown, *ibid.*, **67**, 378 (1945); Brown, *ibid.*, **67**, 503 (1945); Brown, *ibid.*, **67**, 1452 (1945).

TABLE 12.11. RELATIVE BASE STRENGTH OF SOME AMINES COMPARED TO DIFFERENT REFERENCE ACIDS

Amine	H^+	$B(CH_3)_3$	$B(CH_2CH_3)_3$	$B(CH(CH_3)_2)_3$	$B(C(CH_3)_3)_3$
NH_3	4	4	1	1	2
CH_3NH_2	2	2			1
$(CH_3)_2NH$	1	1			3
$(CH_3)_3N$	3	3	2	2	4

(B)

NH_3	4	3			1
$C_2H_5NH_2$	2	1			2
$(C_2H_5)_2NH$	1	2			3
$(C_2H_5)_3N$	3	4			4

* Relative basic strengths, $1 > 2 > 3 > 4$.

Some of the results obtained are tabulated (Table 12.11) to show the relative base strength of different amines as compared to various reference acids. The steric effects arising from the substitution of organic groups on coordinated ethylenediamines have also been studied[53] (see Chapter 8).

AMPHOTERISM

An amphoteric substance is one which is capable of behaving either as an acid or a base. Kraus[57] considers all elements of the 4th, 5th, 6th and 7th groups, having a deficiency of electrons with respect to the rare gas configuration, to be amphoteric, and Cartledge[27] states that all substances of which the square roots of the ionic potentials lie between 2.2 and 3.2 are amphoteric. Contrary to such generalizations, even lithium[58] and barium[59] are amphoteric under some conditions. Again, the solvent is found to play an important role; iron(III) hydroxide is not amphoteric in water but iron(III) cyanide is definitely amphoteric in liquid hydrogen cyanide.

The mechanism of amphoterism is still obscure and there are several theories concerning the processes of dissolution of metallic hydroxides in an excess of alkali. The discussion which follows gives a brief account of three of these theories and some of the experimental evidence supporting each of them. A more general interpretation of amphoterism is also proposed and the mechanism of these reactions is related to the behavior of the more stable Werner complexes.

53. Basolo and Murmann, *J. Am. Chem. Soc.*, **74**, 5243 (1952); Irving, "A Discussion on Coordination Chemistry," Paper No. 4, Butterwick Research Lab., I.C.I., Sept. 21–22, 1950.
57. Krause, *J. Chem. Ed.*, **8**, 2126 (1931).
58. Krause and Krzyzanski, *Ber.*, **70**, 1975 (1937).
59. Scholder and Patsch, *Z. anorg. allgem. Chem.*, **222**, 135 (1935).

Theories on the Mechanism of Amphoterism

The Theory of Peptization. The fact that in most cases a large in-definite excess of hydroxide beyond that required for the formation of a compound such as Na_2ZnO_2 must be used to dissolve an amphoteric hydroxide has suggested the possibility that no true compound is formed, but that the insoluble hydroxide is merely peptized. Many experiments have failed to establish definitely the formation of a true compound. The studies of Britton[60] suggest that only in the case of aluminum is a true compound formed, while Mahin[61] considers that even aluminum forms mainly colloidal suspensions. Weiser[12a] believes it likely that the first step in the dissolution of some or all hydroxides is peptization, followed in most cases by compound formation.

The concentrations of the hydroxide ion in alkaline solutions of amphoteric hydroxides have been determined[62] (by measurements of electrical conductivity and of the velocity of esterification) to be larger than would be expected if neutralization of the metal hydroxide has taken place. According to this view, hydroxide ions are preferentially adsorbed by the particles of insoluble metal hydroxide, forming negatively charged colloids.[63] Evidence for this theory is given by the fact that in many cases (e.g., $Cu(OH)_2$ and $Cr(OH)_3$) precipitates of the metal hydroxide appear on standing, or precipitation may be brought about by the addition of an electrolyte.

Although colloidal suspensions are markedly different from most crystalloid solutions, it is well known that true solutions and colloidal dispersions of the same material are different in degree only. The gradual transition in properties from true solution to colloidal dispersion has been shown for hydrophilic colloids[64] in that the properties of true solutions of low molecular weight amino acids are similar to colloidal dispersions of high molecular weight amino acids and proteins. A similar observation has been made[65] for the transition in properties from a true solution of aluminum chloride, through the more basic salts, to the aluminum oxychloride hydrosol. In fact, some colloid chemists[66], concerned primarily with the structure of the micelle rather than the stability of the suspension, visualize the formation of certain colloids as a continual increase in the molecular weight of polynuclear complexes until colloidal dimensions are reached (see page 457).

60. Britton, "Hydrogen Ions," 3rd Ed., Vol. II, London, Chapman and Hall, 1942.
61. Mahin, Ingraham, and Stewart, *J. Am. Chem. Soc.*, **35**, 30 (1913).
62. Hantzsch, *Z. anorg. allgem. Chem.*, **30**, 289 (1902).
63. Davis and Farnham, *J. Phys. Chem.*, **36**, 1056 (1932).
64. Loeb, "Proteins and the Theory of Colloidal Behavior," 1st Ed., New York, McGraw-Hill Book Company, Inc., 1922.
65. Whitehead and Clay, *J. Am. Chem. Soc.*, **56**, 1844 (1934).
66. Whitehead, *Chem. Rev.*, **21**, 113 (1937).

The Oxy-acid Theory. The mechanism proposed in 1899 by Bredig[67] is often referred to as the *oxy-acid theory* and can be illustrated by the equilibria

$$M^+ + OH^- \rightleftharpoons MOH \rightleftharpoons MO^- + H^+$$

$$Al^{+++} + 3OH^- \rightleftharpoons Al(OH)_3 \rightleftharpoons AlO_3^\equiv + 3H^+.$$

Studies of the solubility of amphoteric hydroxides in excess of alkali have led to the conclusion that insoluble hydroxides react with excess alkali to form definite stoichiometric compounds instead of merely being peptized (page 435). For example, Hildebrand[68] followed the reaction between zinc hydroxide and sodium hydroxide by means of the hydrogen electrode. He came to the conclusion that the hydrogen zincate ion, $HZnO_2^-$, exists in the presence of excess sodium hydroxide. Mellor[69] mentions the formation of sodium meta- and ortho-chromite, $NaCrO_2$ and Na_3CrO_3, and Grube and Feucht[70] claim that dissolution of cobalt(II) hydroxide in potassium hydroxide is due to the formation of the compound K_2CoO_2. Copper(II) hydroxide dissolves appreciably in concentrated alkali solutions, giving a deep blue color, and the bulk of the evidence supports the view that the coloration is due to the cuprate ion, $CuO_2^\equiv$, and not to colloidal copper(II) oxide[71].

The most extensively studied hydroxide, by far, is that of aluminum; some of the observations made on this amphoteric hydroxide support the *oxy-acid theory*. Prescott[72] states that since one mole of sodium hydroxide is needed to dissolve one mole of aluminum hydroxide, the solution must contain the meta-aluminate ion, AlO_2^-; while Herz[73] points out that, if the aluminum hydroxide is dried before treatment with the excess of alkali, the ortho-aluminate, $AlO_3^\equiv$, is formed. Studies with the hydrogen electrode have indicated to Blum[74] and to Britton[60] that the meta-aluminate is formed.

The type of information which has been collected by these investigators, and by many others, can be illustrated by a brief review of some hydrogen electrode studies made by Britton and his co-workers (Fig. 12.3). The curve represents the titration of a solution of aluminum sulfate with a solution of sodium hydroxide. The solution becomes neutral when the sodium hydroxide is added in an amount slightly less than is required for the forma-

67. Bredig, *Z. Electrochem.*, **6**, 6 (1899).
68. Hildebrand and Bowers, *J. Am. Chem. Soc.*, **38**, 785 (1916).
69. Mellor, "A Comprehensive Treatise on Inorganic and Theoretical Chemistry," Vol. III, p. 191, New York, Longmans Green and Company, 1928.
70. Grube and Feucht, *Z. Electrochem.*, **28**, 568 (1922).
71. Jirsa, *Kolloid Z.*, **40**, 28 (1926).
72. Prescott, *J. Am. Chem. Soc.*, **2**, 27 (1880).
73. Herz, *Z. anorg. allgem. Chem.*, **23**, 222 (1900).
74. Blum, *J. Am. Chem. Soc.*, **35**, 1499 (1913).

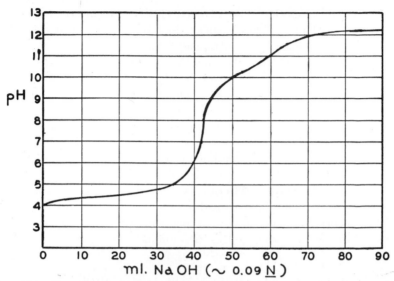

FIG. 12.3. Titration of aluminum ion with sodium hydroxide (100 ml of 0.00667 M $Al_2(SO_4)_3$.

tion of aluminum hydroxide, owing to the retention by the precipitate of some of the acid radical present in the original salt. This precipitate dissolves completely when approximately one more equivalent of sodium hydroxide is added, the dissolution being reflected by the characteristic aluminate inflexion of the titration curve, extending over a pH range from 8 to 10.5. The precipitate dissolved completely when 4.13 equivalents of sodium hydroxide had been added. Hence, it is concluded that the formula, $NaAlO_2$, probably represents the condition in which aluminum hydroxide exists in solutions of alkali. However, information of this type does not rule out the possibility that the formula is either $Na[Al(OH)_4]$ or $Na[Al(H_2O)_2(OH)_4]$.

Other so-called amphoteric ions, such as those of beryllium, zinc, chromium(III), tin(II), and zirconium, exhibit similar behavior, but according to Britton[60], none of them show such sharp inflexions as does aluminum. Britton also states that only in the case of aluminum hydroxide is the amount of alkali required for the solution of the hydroxide approximately equal to that suggested by the formula and also independent of the concentration of the sodium hydroxide used[75]. Britton suggests that this is possibly due to the fact that although other hydroxides may be acidic in their behavior toward alkali, they are such weak acids that the hydrogen ion concentration of the alkali solution is scarcely affected by their presence.

A consideration of the tremendous amount of information which has

75. Britton, *Analyst*, **46,** 363 (1921).

been collected reveals that there is no conclusive evidence for the existence
of ions such as AlO_2^-, PbO_4^{4-}, $ZnO_2^=$, in solution, as is proposed by the
oxy-acid theory. No doubt the strongest support for the existence of these
ions in solution comes from the fact that mixed oxides such as $NaAlO_2$,
K_2ZnO_2, and Ca_2PbO_4, are known to exist in the solid state. Most of these
compounds can be made only by fusion of a mixture of the constituent
oxides, and x-ray analyses[76] show that they are essentially ionic crystals,
often with structures closely related to those of the simple oxides. Although
it is customary to refer to substances in solution as having the same formulas as in the solid state, it is well known that this is not always necessarily
the case.

   The Hydroxo-Complex Theory. A somewhat different explanation of
the dissolving of metallic hydroxides (almost intermediate between the
oxy-acid theory and the theory of peptization) was first proposed by
Pfeiffer[77] in 1908. According to this view amphoterism is represented by the
equilibria

$$[M(H_2O)_n]^{x+} \xrightleftharpoons[H_3O^+]{OH^-} [M(H_2O)_{n-x}(OH)_x] \xrightleftharpoons[H_3O^+]{OH^-} [M(OH)_n]^{(n-x)-}$$

$$[Al(H_2O)_6]^{+++} \xrightleftharpoons[H_3O^+]{OH^-} [Al(H_2O)_3(OH)_3] \xrightleftharpoons[H_3O^+]{OH^-} [Al(OH)_6]^=$$

The maximum number of hydroxo groups which may combine with the
metal ion is determined by the coordination number of the metallic ion,
but the actual number varies with the concentration of hydroxide ion. This
concept, which is referred to as the *hydroxy-complex theory*, is mentioned in
only a few textbooks[78]; in fact, Wells[76] states, ". . . there is no evidence for
the existence of complex ions in these solutions." However, several pieces
of evidence can be marshalled to support the theory. The oxy-acids may be
divided roughly into three classes[78a]:

   (1) *Simple oxy-acids*, formed by the lighter, strongly electronegative
elements. The composition of these oxy-acids is governed primarily by
direct considerations of the valency of the central atom, and there is little
tendency to form true *ortho*-acids. (H_2SO_4 rather than $S(OH)_6$ and H_3PO_4
rather than $P(OH)_5$).

   (2) *Complex oxy-acids*, formed by the heavier, weakly electronegative
or amphoteric elements. The composition of these is determined by the
necessity of completing the coordination sphere of the central atom
($H[Sb(OH)_6]$ and $H_5[IO_6]$).

   76. Wells, "Structural Inorganic Chemistry," Oxford, Clarendon Press, 1945.
   77. Pfeiffer, *Ber.*, **40**, 4036 (1908).
   78. Emeleus and Anderson, "Modern Aspects of Inorganic Chemistry," New York,
        D. Van Nostrand Co., 1945; Pauling, "General Chemistry," San Francisco,
        W. H. Freeman and Company, (1947); Sneed and Maynard, "General Inor-
        ganic Chemistry," p. 396, New York, D. Van Nostrand Co., 1942.

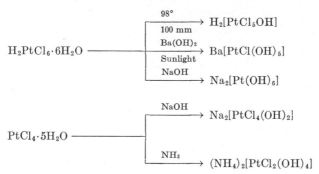

Fig. 12.4. Formation of the chloro-hydroxo complexes of platinum.

(3) *Poly-acids*, formed by the elements of groups VB and VIB. These are discussed in Chapter 14.

The second group, termed here complex oxy-acids, include the metal hydroxides capable of behaving as acids, that is, the amphoteric hydroxides. Reactions between these acids and varying amounts of alkali produce solutions which in some cases are known to yield crystalline compounds of definite composition not dependent on that of the original solution[79]. Thus, the alkali stannates and plumbates all contain three molecules of water $(Na_2O \cdot SnO_2 \cdot 3H_2O)$ which are lost only at temperatures considerably above 100°, when complete decomposition of the salt takes place[80]; the more highly hydrated salts $(BaO \cdot SnO_2 \cdot 7H_2O)$ lose water readily, down to the last three molecules. The salts may therefore be derived from an anion $[Sn(OH)_6]^=$, in which the coordination number of the central atom is satisfied; removal of the constitutional water breaks up the complex anion completely.

The fact that Pfeiffer, who worked with Werner, looked upon alkaline solutions of amphoteric hydroxides as coordination compounds with hydroxo groups attached to the central metal ion is not at all surprising. A considerable number of well defined complexes are known in which the hydroxyl ion is coordinated to the central atom, i.e., $[Co(NH_3)_5OH]^{++}$. In many instances the metal acceptor also forms an amphoteric hydroxide and it therefore seems reasonable to suppose that the metal could be completely surrounded by hydroxo groups instead of being attached to only one or two such groups. The analogy between Werner's complexes and hydroxo anions is particularly emphasized by the nearly complete series of compounds between $H_2[PtCl_6]$ and $H_2[Pt(OH)_6]$, worked out by Miolati[81] (Fig. 12.4). Numerous investigators have demonstrated that the amphoteric

79. Forster, *Z. Electrochem.*, **6**, 301 (1899); Scholder, *Angew Chem.*, **46**, 5090 (1933); Muller, *Z. Electrochem.*, **33**, 134 (1927).

80. Belucci and Parravano, *Z. anorg. Chem.*, **45**, 142 (1905).

81. Miolati, *Z. anorg. Chem.*, **22**, 445 (1900); **26**, 209 (1901); **33**, 251 (1903).

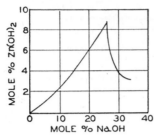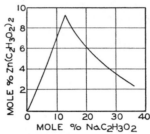

FIG. 12.5. Solubility of Zn^{++} in NaOH in water and $NaC_2H_3O_2$ in glacial acetic acid.

behavior observed in the water system is found in other solvent systems, and that reactions in different solvents support the hydroxy-complex theory of amphoterism.

The fact that certain amides which are insoluble in liquid ammonia, are dissolved either by acid, NH_4^+, or by base, NH_2^-, was reported independently by Franklin[82] and Fitzgerald[83] (see page 418). Franklin[6] has given an excellent summary of some other examples of salts of amphoteric amides and imides.

Similar observations have been made with glacial acetic acid as a solvent. Davidson[8] points out that when a small amount of sodium acetate solution is added to a solution of zinc chloride in acetic acid, a precipitate of zinc acetate is formed; this dissolves when additional sodium acetate is added. A detailed study of this phenomenon showed that the analogy between this reaction and that of zinc hydroxide and sodium hydroxide[84] in water is far from being a superficial one. The solubility curve of zinc acetate in acetic acid containing varying amounts of sodium acetate at constant temperature is strikingly similar to the curve for zinc hydroxide in aqueous sodium hydroxide solutions (Fig. 12.5). The solid phase which appears at high concentrations of the sodium compound may be formulated, in each case, as a ternary addition compound. The composition of these two ternary compounds is very similar, as is evident from the following comparison: $Zn(OH)_2 \cdot 2NaOH \cdot 2H_2O$ or $Na_2[Zn(OH)_4] \cdot 2H_2O$ in water and $Zn(C_2H_3O_2)_2 \cdot 2NaC_2H_3O_2 \cdot 4HC_2H_3O_2$ or $Na_2[Zn(C_2H_3O_2)_4] \cdot 4HC_2H_3O_2$ in acetic acid. The same sort of results have been obtained with copper(II)[7b, 85], lead (II)[86], and silver(I)[87].

Nonprotonic systems have likewise been investigated in connection with amphoterism[17a, 88]. It has been observed that the addition of a base

82. Franklin, *J. Am. Chem. Soc.*, **29**, 1274 (1907).

83. Fitzgerald, *ibid.*, **29**, 656 (1907).

84. Gourdioon, *Rec. trav. chim.*, **39**, 505 (1920).

85. Muller, *Z. physik. Chem.*, **105**, 73 (1924); **114**, 129 (1925).

86. Tehrman and Leifer, *J. Am. Chem. Soc.*, **60**, 142 (1938).

87. Peterson and Dienes, *J. Phys. and Colloid Chem.*, **55**, 1299 (1951).

88. Jander and Hecht, *Z. anorg. allgem. Chem.*, **240**, 287 (1943).

$[(CH_3)_4N]_2SO_3$, to a sulfur dioxide solution of aluminum chloride results in the precipitation of the amphoteric sulfite, $Al_2(SO_3)_3$, which can be dissolved by adding more of the base to yield the salt, $[(CH_3)_4N]_3[Al(SO_3)_3]$.

Acid-base reactions in different solvents were discussed on page 418 and the close analogy of amphoteric behavior in various systems was summarized in Table 12.1. It may be mentioned in addition that iron(III) cyanide[89] and silver cyanide[90] are amphoteric in liquid hydrogen cyanide and that several alcoholates, when dissolved in alcohol, increase the hydrogen ion concentration of the alcohol[91].

The existence of hydroxo complex compounds in solutions of amphoteric hydroxides in strong bases has found support in a determination of ionic weights by the dialysis method of Brintzinger[92]. Using chromate ion as a standard, it was found that the following ions exist in solution:

$$[Sb(OH)_6]^- \qquad [Ga_2(OH)_8]^-$$
$$[Sb(OH)_4]^- \qquad [Zn_2(OH)_8]^{4-}$$
$$[Ge(OH)_6]^- \qquad [Be_{10}(OH)_{40}]^{20-}$$
$$[Al_2(OH)_8]^-$$

Although these values, except for antimony and germanium, appear to differ markedly from what might be expected, they merely represent polynuclear forms of the mononuclear complex structures; aluminum, gallium, and zinc are present as binuclear complexes while beryllium is present in the decanuclear form of $[Be(OH)_4]^=$.

Much more convincing proof[79b] for the existence of these hydroxo complex compounds is furnished by the successful crystallization of well defined salts of definite composition from strongly alkaline solutions of amphoteric hydroxides (Table 12.12). Attempts to produce nickelates[100], bismuthates[101], mercurates[99], and borates[59] failed to yield well defined crystalline compounds, probably because the corresponding hydroxides are extremely weak acids. In general, the salts were made by adding a cold solution of a salt of the metal to a cold concentrated solution of sodium hydroxide.

89. Jander and Scholz, *Z. physik. Chem.*, **192,** 163 (1943).
90. Jander and Gruttner, *Ber.*, **81,** 114 (1948).
91. Meerwein, *Ann.*, **455,** 227 (1927).
92. Brintzinger and Osswold, *Z. angew. Chem.*, **47,** 61 (1934).
93. Scholder and Weber, *Z. anorg. allgem. Chem.*, **215,** 355 (1933); Scholder and Hendrich, *ibid.*, **241,** 76 (1939).
94. Scholder, Felsenstein, and Apel, *Z. anorg. allgem. Chem.*, **216,** 138 (1938).
95. Scholder and Weber, *Z. anorg. allgem Chem.*, **216,** 159 (1933).
96. Scholder and Patsch, *Z. anorg. allgem. Chem.*, **216,** 176 (1933).
97. Scholder and Patsch, *ibid.*, **220,** 411 (1934).
98. Scholder and Patsch, *ibid.*, **217,** 214 (1934).
99. Scholder and Staufenbiel, *Z. anorg. allgem Chem.*, **247,** 259 (1941).
100. Scholder, *Z. anorg allgem Chem.*, **220,** 209 (1934).
101. Scholder and Stobbe, *Z. anorg. allgem Chem.*, **247,** 392 (1941).

TABLE 12.12. SOME HYDROXO SALTS PREPARED BY SCHOLDER AND HIS CO-WORKERS

Zincates[93]

Na[Zn(OH)$_3$]·3H$_2$O   Ba[Zn(OH)$_4$]·H$_2$O

Na[Zn(OH)$_3$]   Sr[Zn(OH)$_4$]·H$_2$O

Na$_2$[Zn(OH)$_4$]·2H$_2$O   Ba$_2$[Zn(OH)$_6$]

Na$_2$[Zn(OH)$_4$]   Sr$_2$[Zn(OH)$_6$]

Cuprates (II)[94]

Na$_2$[Cu(OH)$_4$]   Ba$_2$[Cu(OH)$_6$]·H$_2$O

Sr[Cu(OH)$_4$]·H$_2$O   Sr$_2$[Cu(OH)$_6$]·H$_2$O

Cobaltates (II)[95]

Na$_2$[Co(OH)$_4$]   Sr$_2$[Co(OH)$_6$]

Ba$_2$[Co(OH)$_6$]

Stannates (II)[96]

Na[Sn(OH)$_3$]   Sr[Sn(OH)$_3$]$_2$·H$_2$O

Ba[Sn(OH)$_3$]$_2$·2H$_2$O   Ba[Sn(OH)$_3$]$_2$

Ba[(HO)$_2$Sn-O-Sn(OH)$_2$]   Sr[(HO)$_2$Sn-O-Sn(OH)$_2$]

Chromates (III)[97]

Na$_3$Cr(OH)$_6$ Ba$_3$[Cr(OH)$_6$]$_2$

Na$_4$Cr(OH)$_7$H$_2$O·2-3H$_2$O   Sr$_3$[Cr(OH)$_6$]$_2$

Na$_5$Cr(OH)$_8$·4H$_2$O

Plumbates (II)[98]

Na$_2$[Pb(OH)$_4$](?)   Ba[Pb(OH)$_4$]

Na[Pb(OH)$_3$]   Ba[Pb(OH)$_3$X]

Na$_2$[Pb(OH)$_3$X]   BaNa$_2$[Pb(OH)$_6$]

(X = Cl$^-$, CNS$^-$, Br$^-$, or I$^-$)

Cadmates[99]

Na$_2$[Cd(OH)$_4$]   Ba$_2$[Cd(OH)$_6$]

Na[Cd(OH)$_3$H$_2$O]H$_2$O(?)   Sr$_2$[Cd(OH)$_6$]

Na$_2$[Cd(OH)$_3$Br]

The compound, Na$_2$CuO$_2$·2H$_2$O or Na$_2$[Cu(OH)$_4$], loses one mole of water at approximately 200°C, at which temperature the color changes from blue to black. Additional heating to a temperature of 500°C results in a gradual loss of water amounting to less than 0.05 moles. However, if the black residue is intimately mixed with potassium dichromate, the second molecule of water is readily lost at approximately 500°C. If it is assumed that the structure of the compound is Na$_2$CuO$_2$·2H$_2$O (oxy-acid theory) it would be expected that the two moles of water would be liberated under approximately the same conditions, and probably below 200°. According to Scholder, removal of the first mole of water is not possible until the complex has been decomposed, which accounts for the high temperature required,

$$Na_2[Cu(OH)_4] \xrightarrow{200°} 2NaOH + Cu(OH)_2.$$

blue   blue

Following this decomposition the amphoteric hydroxide readily loses one mole of water,

$$Cu(OH)_2 \rightarrow CuO + H_2O$$

blue   black

The second mole of water is not easily liberated because of the extreme stability of sodium hydroxide; however, at much higher temperatures a small portion of this water is gradually lost due to the reaction

$$CuO + 2NaOH \xrightarrow{>200°} Na_2CuO_2 + H_2O$$

This is supported by the fact that, if potassium dichromate is mixed with the black residue, the second mole of water is readily lost at approximately 500°C,

$$K_2Cr_2O_7 + 2NaOH \xrightarrow{500°} Na_2CrO_4 + K_2CrO_4 + H_2O\uparrow$$

Similar dehydration experiments have been carried out with other hydroxo salts (Table 12.12) and analogous results obtained. Although most of the hydroxoplumbates are unstable, replacement of one or more of the hydroxo groups by halide or thiocyanate ions increases the stability of the complex, particularly if the halogen is iodine. The fact that partial replacement of the hydroxo groups by other anions is possible is further evidence that the amphoteric property depends upon the formation of complexes.

Experiments of this type have likewise been performed in the presence of pyrocatechol and crystalline compounds containing both hydroxo groups and pyrocatechol groups have been isolated[102].

It may be that the dissolution of some amphoteric metallic hydroxides is a result of peptization and that in other cases it involves the formation of true compounds. Seward[103] has pointed out that in many cases the hydroxy-complex theory is easily reconciled with the formation of colloidal solutions. In a slightly alkaline solution of a weak metallic hydroxide, the complexes formed may contain a large number of metal hydroxide molecules, a few of which may be coordinated to additional hydroxyl ions. A complex containing, for example, one hundred molecules of metal hydroxide and one extra hydroxyl ion which is coordinated to a metal ion would constitute a colloidal

102. Scholder and Schletz, *Z. anorg. allgem Chem.*, **211**, 161 (1933).
103. Seward, *J. Chem. Ed.*, **11**, 567 (1934).

particle. In such a case the amount of base used to dissolve the precipitate is small. When the concentration of base is increased, the relative number of molecules of metal hydroxide containing extra hydroxyl ions will increase until the coordination number of each of the metal ions is approximately satisfied. Thus, a true solution will form, and from it definite compounds may crystallize.

A consideration of the available data indicates that a much more generalized definition of amphoteric substances is required. On the basis of G. N. Lewis' extended acid-base concept, it can be said that an amphoteric substance is one which is capable of either donating or accepting a share in a pair of electrons. An application of this principle to inorganic amphoteric substances suggests that they are complexes which are capable of undergoing both of the following reactions to such an extent that the sign of the charge on the complex changes: (1) negative or neutral ligands may replace neutral or positive ligands of the complex, and (2) positive or neutral ligands may replace neutral or negative ligands of the complex. With this general interpretation of amphoterism the analogy between the reactions of certain metallic hydroxides and Werner complexes is immediately apparent (Fig. 12.6).

The chief difference between the reactions of the zinc complexes and those of the cobalt complexes is that the equilibria in the former are easily reversible, while those of the cobalt complexes can be made to go in either direction, but with some difficulty. The existence of easily reversible reactions in the case of the zinc complexes makes it difficult to isolate definite intermediate compounds, but the chemistry of the more stable Werner complexes is well defined and in many instances it has been possible to isolate all of the intermediates in a series of reactions similar to that given in Fig. 12.6. This general viewpoint allows a better understanding of amphoterism in any system than the older concepts, which are often limited to metallic hydroxides in aqueous medium.

$$[Zn(H_2O)_2(OH)_2] \begin{cases} \xrightarrow[(2)]{(1)} [Zn(H_2O)(OH)_3]^- \xrightarrow[(2)]{(1)} [Zn(OH)_4]^= \\ \\ \xrightarrow[(1)]{(2)} [Zn(H_2O)_3OH]^+ \xrightarrow[(1)]{(2)} [Zn(H_2O)_4]^{++} \end{cases}$$

$$[Co(NH_3)_3(NO_2)_3] \begin{cases} \xrightarrow[(2)]{(1)} [Co(NH_3)_2(NO_2)_4]^- \xrightarrow[(2)]{(1)} [Co(NH_3)(NO_2)_5]^= \xrightarrow[(2)]{(1)} \\ \qquad\qquad\qquad\qquad\qquad\qquad\qquad\qquad [Co(NO_2)_6]^= \\ \xrightarrow[(1)]{(2)} [Co(NH_3)_4(NO_2)_2]^+ \xrightarrow[(1)]{(2)} [Co(NH_3)_5(NO_2)]^{++} \xrightarrow[(1)]{(2)} \\ \qquad\qquad\qquad\qquad\qquad\qquad\qquad\qquad [Co(NH_3)_6]^{+++} \end{cases}$$

FIG. 12.6. Equilibria illustrating the general principle of amphoterism.

Basic Salts

Structures Based on the Coordination Theory

Any salt which contains an oxide or hydroxide group, either in the ionic or coordinated state, is referred to as a "basic salt." Many basic salts, such as white lead and antimonyl chloride, are of somewhat indefinite composition, and are often considered to be simple mixtures of the "normal" salt and the metallic hydroxide. Some of them, however, are polynuclear complexes, held together by oxide or hydroxide "bridges" in which an oxygen atom is coordinated to two metal atoms (see Chapter 13). These substances are insoluble in water, but tend to be hydrolyzed by it; acids convert them to normal salts; and bases, to hydroxides. These reactions account for the variable composition of precipitates obtained from their solutions. The hydroxoammines, however, are readily obtained as crystalline, water soluble basic salts of definite composition. They are formed by the action of bases on aquoammines, into which they can be readily reconverted.

$$[Co(NH_3)_5H_2O]X_3 \rightleftharpoons [Co(NH_3)_5OH]X_2 + HX^{3c,\ 43}$$

$$[Pt(NH_3)_4H_2O(OH)]Cl_3 \rightleftharpoons [Pt(NH_3)_4(OH)_2]Cl_2 + HCl^{39a}$$

There is little possibility of bridging in these cases as the coordination sphere of the metal ion is completely filled by groups which are tightly held.

Werner[3c] pointed out that many basic salts contain three moles of hydroxide for each mole of normal salt,

atacamite	$CuCl_2 \cdot 3Cu(OH)_2$
langite	$CuSO_4 \cdot 3Cu(OH)_2 \cdot H_2O$
basic zinc nitrate	$Zn(NO_3)_2 \cdot 3Zn(OH)_2$
basic cobalt carbonate	$CoCO_3 \cdot 3Co(OH)_2$
basic lead salts	$PbX_2 \cdot 2Pb(OH)_2$.

The amount of water present in any basic salt is almost without exception sufficient to permit the existence of the hydrated oxide or hydroxide groups. In cases where the water is in excess of that needed to form hydroxide groups Werner suggested that this is attached to the "outer" metal atoms.

The structures of solid basic salts proposed by Werner are in harmony with experimental studies of partially hydrolyzed salts in solution but not in complete accord with the results of x-ray studies of these salts[76]. However, the validity of Werner's views has been justified in certain cases by Weinland, Stroh, and Paul[104]. Their measurements of the electrical conductivity of solutions of basic lead salts, Pb(OH)X, showed the presence of a

104. Weinland, Stroh, and Paul, *Ber.*, **55**, 2706 (1922); *Z. anorg. allgem. Chem.*, **129**, 243 (1923).

bivalent cation. They therefore wrote the formula

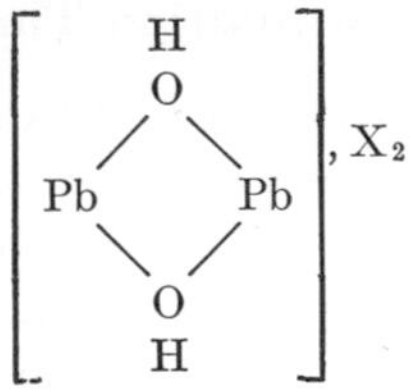

$$\left[\begin{array}{c} H \\ O \\ Pb \diagup \diagdown Pb \\ \diagdown \diagup \\ O \\ H \end{array} \right], X_2$$

just as Werner had written

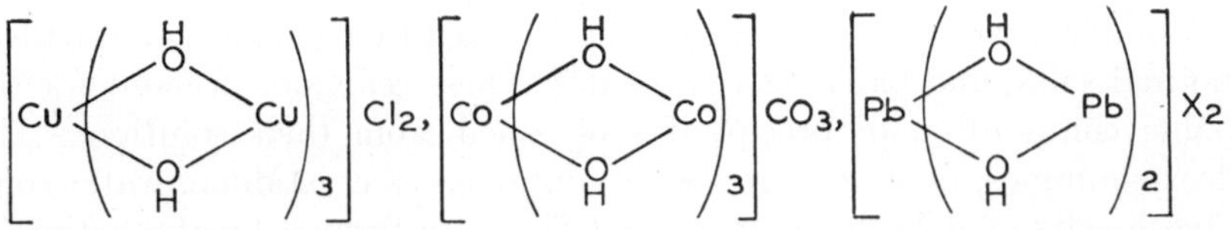

$$\left[Cu \left(\begin{array}{c} H \\ O \\ \diagup \diagdown \\ \diagdown \diagup \\ O \\ H \end{array} \right) Cu \right] Cl_2, \left[Co \left(\begin{array}{c} H \\ O \\ \diagup \diagdown \\ \diagdown \diagup \\ O \\ H \end{array} \right) Co \right]_3 CO_3, \left[Pb \left(\begin{array}{c} H \\ O \\ \diagup \diagdown \\ \diagdown \diagup \\ O \\ H \end{array} \right) Pb \right)_2 X_2$$

Potentiometric studies on the hydrolysis of uranium(VI)[105], bismuth(III)[106], copper(II)[107], and scandium(II)[108] indicate that the formation of bridged polymeric cations in basic solutions of metallic ions may be a general phenomenon (Chapter 13).

The hydrolysis of covalent halides probably proceeds through the addition of water to form aquo complexes which then lose protons to the solvent. This may be illustrated by the hydrolysis of stannic chloride. Step (1) involves the addition of water to satisfy the coordination number of tin, and step (2) is a hydrolysis reaction as already described; in step (3) the stronger acid, H_3O^+, displaces the weaker acid, $[Sn\ H_2O\ Cl_3\ OH]$. This displaced acid is in turn capable of accepting another pair of electrons which are donated by a molecule of water; the process is repeated until the final hydrolysis product, $H_2[Sn(OH)_6]$, is obtained.

(1) $[SnCl_4] + 2H_2O \xrightarrow{\text{hydration}} [Sn(H_2O)_2Cl_4]$

(2) $[Sn(H_2O)_2Cl_4] + H_2O \xrightarrow{\text{hydrolysis}} [Sn(H_2O)Cl_4\ OH]^- + H_3O^+$

(3) $[Sn(H_2O)Cl_4\ OH]^- \xrightarrow{\text{dissociation}} [Sn(H_2O)Cl_3\ OH] + Cl^-$

(4) $[Sn(H_2O)Cl_3\ OH] + H_2O \xrightarrow{\text{hydration}} [Sn(H_2O)_2Cl_3\ OH]$

In the particular case of tin(IV) chloride, the initial addition compound, $[Sn(H_2O)_2Cl_4] \cdot 3H_2O$ and the product of the second stage of hydration,

105. Ahrland, *Acta Chem. Scand.*, **3**, 374 (1949).
106. Graner and Sillén, *Nature*, **160**, 715 (1947); Graner and Sillén, *Acta Chem. Scand.*, **1**, 631 (1947).
107. Pedersen, *Kgl. Danske Videnskab. Selskab. math.-fys. medd.*, **20**, No. 7, 24 pp. (1943); cf. *Chem. Abs.*, **38**, 4854⁵ (1944).
108. Kilpatrick and Pokras, *J. Electrochem. Soc.*, **100**, 85 (1953).

$[Sn(H_2O)_2Cl_3OH] \cdot H_2O$, are both known. The acid nature of the latter compound, as required by the above mechanism, is shown by the formation of a salt with cineole[109]. The postulated mechanism for the hydrolysis of covalent halides is in accord with the fact that some compounds of this type in which the coordination number of the central atom is satisfied (CCl_4 and SF_6) are very difficultly hydrolyzed.

Structures Based on X-ray Studies

The x-ray studies of Feitknecht[110] show that the actual structure of basic salts is one in which the metals are equivalent in that they are surrounded by the same number of oxygen groups. In the structure proposed by Werner only the central metal atom is coordinated to six oxygens while the other metal atoms form a part of the chelate donor molecules and are attached to only two oxygens. The x-ray data, therefore, need not be regarded as a contradiction of Werner's views, but merely as a modification to the more logical structure in which the metal atoms are so arranged that they all tend to be coordinately saturated. This results in a type of polymerization similar to that found in silica, each macromolecular sheet of the crystal lattice representing a polynuclear complex of infinite size.

The structure suggested by Feitknecht is one in which there are layers of hydroxide interleaved with layers containing the metal ions and acid anions. For bivalent metals the layer lattice is of the cadmium iodide type. The spacing between the layers may be variable, and the intermediate layers may be almost unordered in structure. This gives rise to the possibility of nonstoichiometric compounds, which are formed by inserting different amounts of metal salt into the intermediate layers. It seems, however, that these double layer lattice structures are metastable, and tend to give compounds of the formula $MX_2 \cdot 3M(OH)_2$ as the limiting type. In such a structure the hydroxide layer is a giant molecule which permits varying amounts of water as well as normal salt and which is insoluble; these are all characteristic properties of basic salts.

109. Pfeiffer and Angern, *Z. anorg. Chem.*, **183**, 189 (1929).
110. Feitknecht, *Helv. Chim. Acta*, **16**, 427 (1933).

13. Olation and Related Chemical Processes

Carl L. Rollinson[*]

University of Maryland, College Park, Maryland

Olated compounds are complexes in which metal atoms are linked through bridging OH groups. Such a group is designated an *ol* group[1] to distinguish it from the hydroxo group; i.e., a coordinated OH linked to only one metal atom. The process of formation of *ol* compounds from hydroxo compounds is called *olation*. In a review of the theory of olated compounds, Basset[2] gives the following examples:

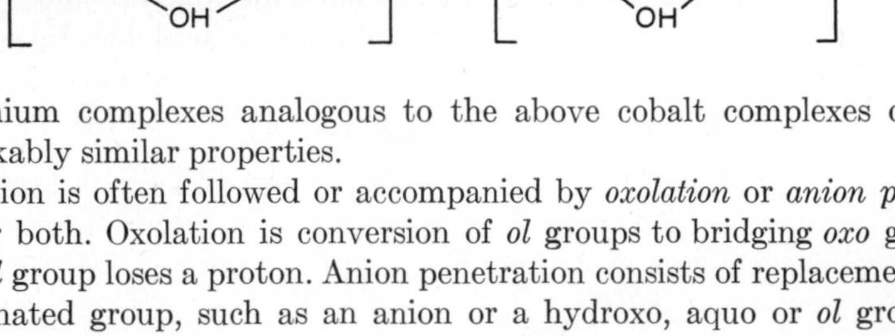

Chromium complexes analogous to the above cobalt complexes display remarkably similar properties.

Olation is often followed or accompanied by *oxolation* or *anion penetration* or both. Oxolation is conversion of *ol* groups to bridging *oxo* groups; each *ol* group loses a proton. Anion penetration consists of replacement of a coordinated group, such as an anion or a hydroxo, aquo or *ol* group by another anion.

---

* Mr. Harold J. Matsuguma helped in the preparation of this chapter. His assistance is gratefully acknowledged.

1. Werner, *Ber.*, **40**, 2113 (1907).
2. Basset, *Quart. Rev.*, **1**, 246 (1947).

The Nature and Significance of Olation

Pfeiffer[3] observed that a blue-violet compound is formed when the red hydroxo-aquo-bis(ethylenediamine)chromium(III) chloride is heated at 120°C. He had previously suggested[4] that one coordinate bond of each of two metal atoms might be shared by one OH group, and therefore formulated the reaction as follows:

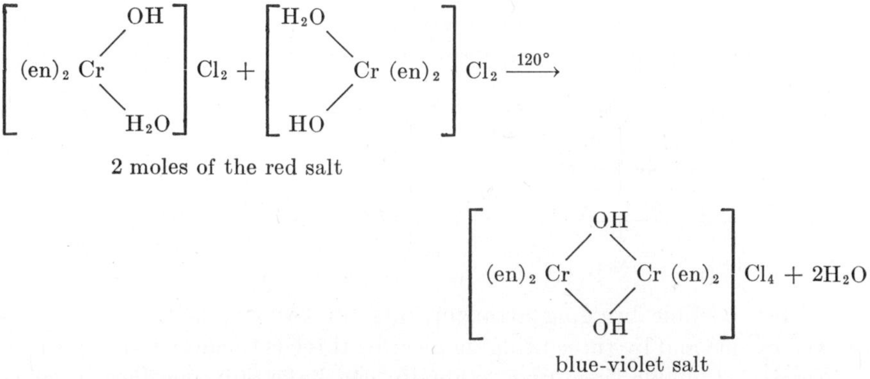

$$
\left[\begin{array}{c} \text{OH} \\ (en)_2\,Cr \\ H_2O \end{array} \right] Cl_2 + \left[\begin{array}{c} H_2O \\ Cr\,(en)_2 \\ HO \end{array} \right] Cl_2 \xrightarrow{\ 120°\ }
$$

2 moles of the red salt

$$
\left[\begin{array}{c} \text{OH} \\ (en)_2\,Cr \qquad Cr\,(en)_2 \\ \text{OH} \end{array} \right] Cl_4 + 2H_2O
$$

blue-violet salt

It is evident that a reaction of this type could occur readily only with a *cis* salt, since the trans salt would have to rearrange. The red salt is thus assigned the cis configuration[5]. Werner[6] prepared octammine-μ-diol-dicobalt(III) sulfate by a similar reaction:

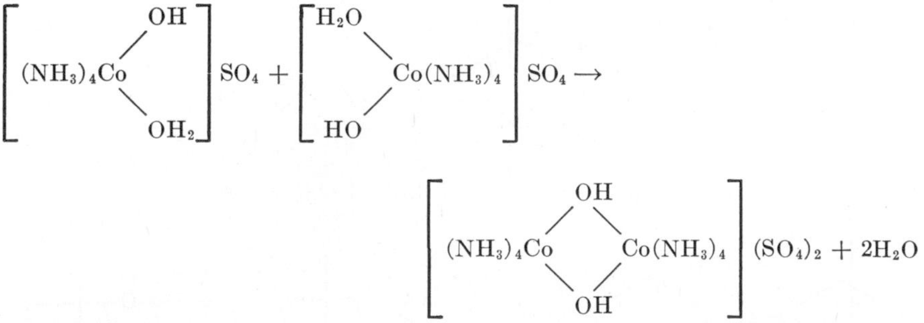

$$
\left[\begin{array}{c} \text{OH} \\ (NH_3)_4Co \\ OH_2 \end{array} \right] SO_4 + \left[\begin{array}{c} H_2O \\ Co(NH_3)_4 \\ HO \end{array} \right] SO_4 \rightarrow
$$

$$
\left[\begin{array}{c} \text{OH} \\ (NH_3)_4Co \qquad Co(NH_3)_4 \\ \text{OH} \end{array} \right] (SO_4)_2 + 2H_2O
$$

The following hexol[1,7] is of interest because it is a completely inorganic,

3. Pfeiffer, *Z. anorg. Chem.*, **56**, 261 (1907).
4. Pfeiffer, *Z. anorg. Chem.*, **29**, 107 (1901).
5. Eméleus and Anderson, "Modern Aspects of Inorganic Chemistry," p. 89, New York, D. Van Nostrand Company, Inc., 1938.
6. Werner, *Ber.*, **40**, 4437 (1907).
7. Jörgensen, *Z. anorg. Chem.*, **16**, 184 (1897).

optically-active compound; it was resolved by Werner[8]:

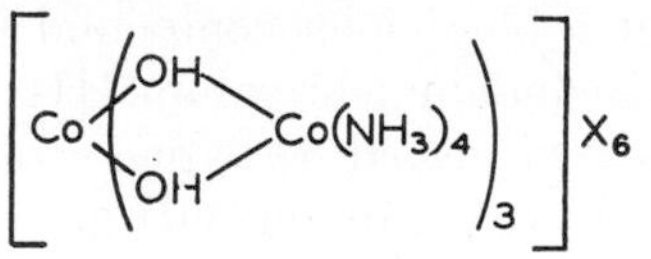

$$\left[Co\left(\begin{array}{c} OH \\ \diagdown \\ OH \end{array} Co(NH_3)_4 \right)_3 \right] X_6$$

In this compound each of three tetrammine-dihydroxo-cobalt(III) complexes acts as a bidentate chelating group.

The examples given may be represented conventionally as follows:

$$= \left[Co(NH_3)_4(OH)_2 \right]^+$$
or
$$NH_2 CH_2 CH_2 NH_2$$

The other possible bridging arrangements for two octahedral atoms are linkage by one and by three bridging groups; three is the maximum number of bridges attainable since two octahedra can have only one face in common:

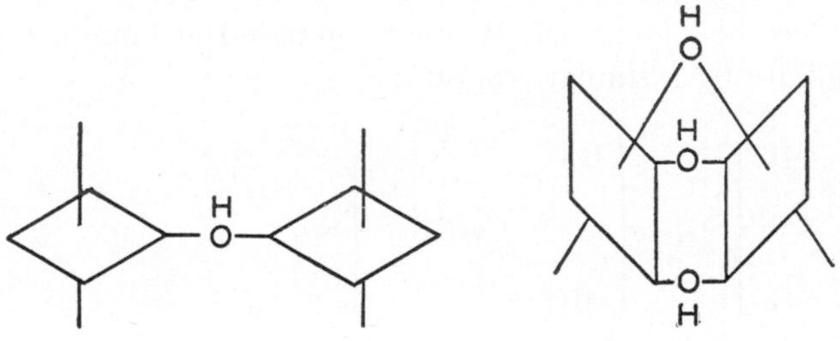

Moreover, more than two atoms can be linked chain-wise:

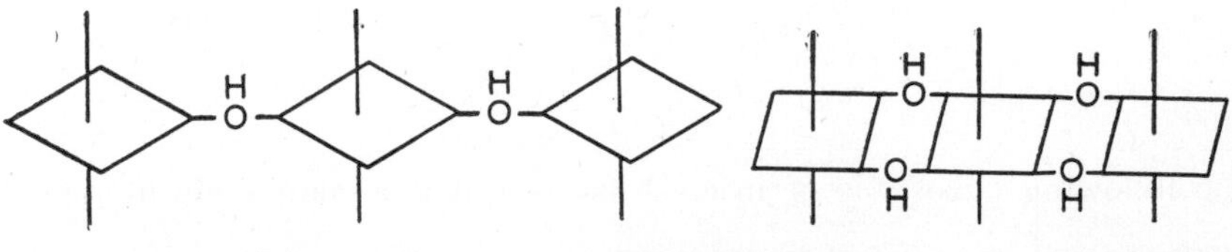

Gmelin's "Handbuch"[9] contains an excellent summary of bridged cobalt

8. Werner, Ber., **47**, 3087 (1914); *Compt. rend.*, **159**, 426 (1914).
9. Gmelin, "Handbuch der anorganischen Chemie," Teil B, S.N. 58, pp. 332–374, Berlin, Verlag Chemie, G.m.b.h., 1930.

compounds, including those in which the *ol* group is the only bridging group, and those in which the *ol* group and some other group, such as peroxo or nitro, act as bridges. The summary includes complexes containing as many as four cobalt atoms. Similarly, Mellor[10] lists polynuclear chromium compounds of from two to four chromium atoms.

The "Continued" Process of Olation

Instead of reaching a definite termination, as in the reactions just mentioned, the olation process may continue, with the formation of polymers. This may occur if the product of each successive step contains aquo or hydroxo groups. Although much of the evidence regarding such polymers is indirect, Werner's theory, as extended by Pfeiffer, Bjerrum, Stiasny, and others, has been consistently successful in accounting for the experimental observations and predicting the behavior of these compounds.

The continued process of olation starts with the hydrolysis of salts of such metals as aluminum and chromium. Pfeiffer[11] suggested that the acidity of solutions of such salts is due to conversion of aquo to hydroxo groups, e.g.:

$$[Cr(H_2O)_6]^{+++} \rightleftharpoons [Cr(H_2O)_5(OH)]^{++} + H^+$$

$$[Cr(H_2O)_5(OH)]^{++} \rightleftharpoons [Cr(H_2O)_4(OH)_2]^+ + H^+$$

The degree of hydrolysis increases as the temperature is raised[12]. It is also dependent on the nature of the anion[13], and especially on the pH of the solution.

If alkali is added to a warm solution of such a salt, but not enough for complete neutralization, polymerization occurs instead of the precipitation of the basic salt or hydroxide. For example, Bjerrum[14] showed that aggregates up to colloidal dimensions are formed when basic chromic chloride solutions are heated, and similar results have been obtained by other investigators[15].

These results may be explained on the basis of a series of hydrolytic and

10. Mellor, "A Comprehensive Treatise of Inorganic and Theoretical Chemistry," Vol. 11, pp. 407-9, London, Longmans Green and Co., Ltd., 1931.
11. Pfeiffer, *Ber.*, **40,** 4036 (1907).
12. Kullgren, *Z. phys. Chem.*, **85,** 466 (1913).
13. Cŭpr, *Collection Czechoslov. Chem. Communs.*, **1,** 467 (1929); cf., *Chem. Abs.*, **24,** 1013 (1930).
14. Bjerrum, *Z. phys. Chem.*, **59,** 336 (1907); **73,** 724 (1910); **110,** 656 (1924).
15. Riess and Barth, *Collegium*, **778,** 62 (1935).

olation reactions[16]. The first steps might be formulated as follows:

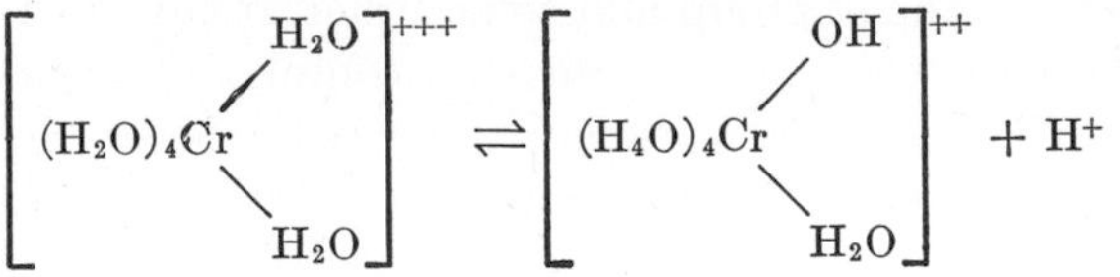

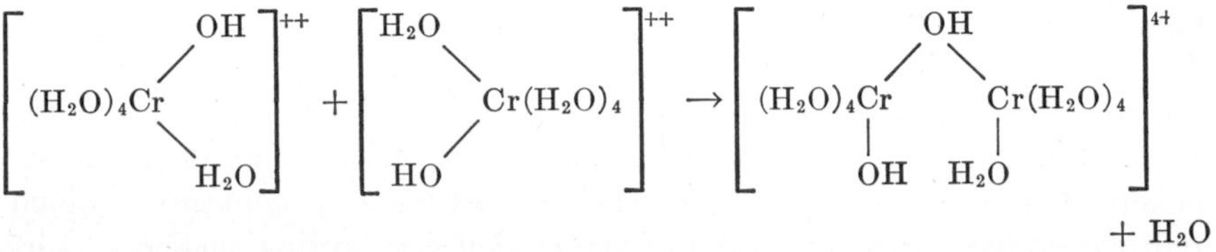

$$\left[(H_2O)_4Cr\overset{H_2O}{\underset{H_2O}{\diagup}}\right]^{+++} \rightleftharpoons \left[(H_4O)_4Cr\overset{OH}{\underset{H_2O}{\diagup}}\right]^{++} + H^+$$

$$\left[(H_2O)_4Cr\overset{OH}{\underset{H_2O}{\diagup}}\right]^{++} + \left[\overset{H_2O}{\underset{HO}{\diagup}}Cr(H_2O)_4\right]^{++} \rightarrow \left[(H_2O)_4Cr\overset{OH}{\underset{OH\ H_2O}{\diagup\diagdown}}Cr(H_2O)_4\right]^{4+}$$
$$+ H_2O$$

If the reacting groups in each ion are in the cis positions, a completely olated ion may be formed:

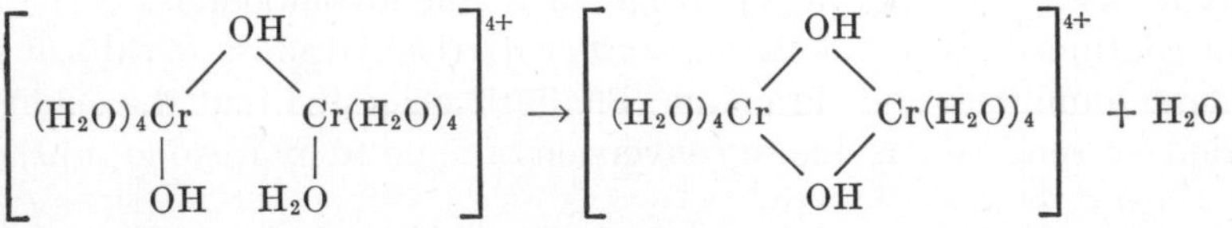

$$\left[(H_2O)_4Cr\overset{OH}{\underset{OH\ H_2O}{\diagup\diagdown}}Cr(H_2O)_4\right]^{4+} \rightarrow \left[(H_2O)_4Cr\overset{OH}{\underset{OH}{\diamondsuit}}Cr(H_2O)_4\right]^{4+} + H_2O$$

Further hydrolysis and olation might result in such polymers as the tetra-hydroxy-dodecaquo-μ-decaol-hexachromium(III) ion:

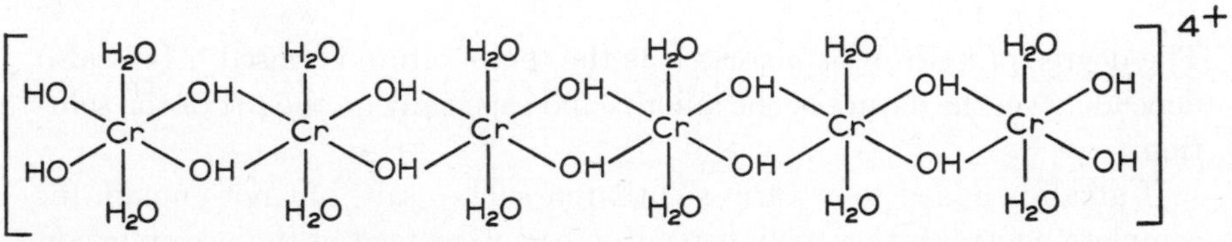

Stiasny[17] postulated the existence of such polymers in Bjerrum's solutions[14] and aggregates of ionic weight 400—1000 have been detected in such solutions[15]. The possibility of formation of the following types of olated compounds must also be admitted (A = a coordinated molecule or ion):

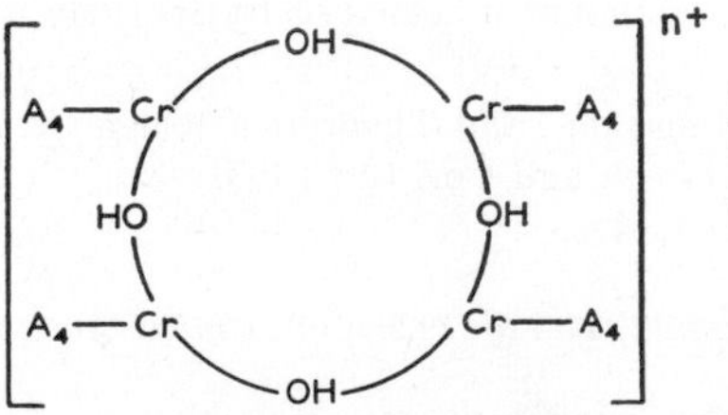

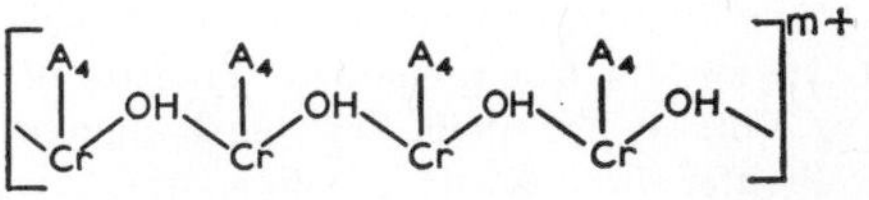

These processes involve the aquo groups attached to the metal atoms

16. Stiasny and Balanyi, *Collegium,* **682,** 86 (1927).
17. Stiasny, "Gerbereichemie", p. 348, Dresden und Leipzig, Theodor Steinkopff, 1931.

not at the ends of the chain, as well as those at the ends, so cross-linked polymers may be formed, as shown in the diagrammatic formula:

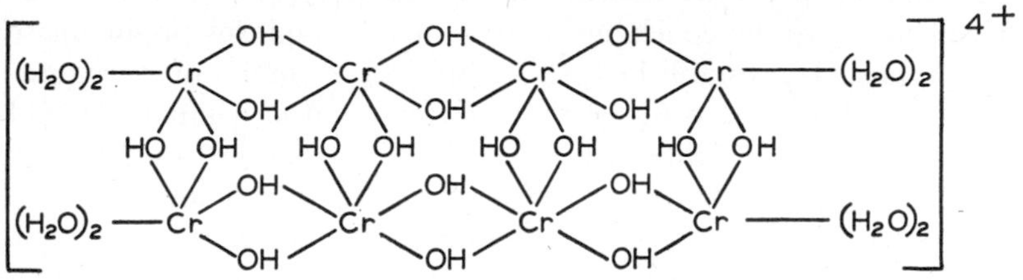

Because of the octahedral configuration of complexes of metals such as chromium, the bonds of a given metal atom occur in pairs, each of which lies in a plane perpendicular to the planes of the other two pairs. Thus such cross-linked polymers are three-dimensional.

These processes account for the results obtained when a warm solution of a chromium salt is titrated with a base. With the addition of an increment of base, the pH rises immediately, but falls slowly if the solution is allowed to stand before more base is added. This continues with successive increments of base until enough base has been added to precipitate the hydrated oxide. As base is added to the solution, the hydrogen ions are removed. The equilibrium then shifts in the direction of further hydrolysis and olation, with the formation of more hydrogen ions. In this way an amount of base can be added, without precipitation, which would cause precipitation if it were added all at once.

The changes in pH accompanying the titration of scandium perchlorate with base cannot be explained by the formation of hydroxo or dihydroxo monomers alone[18]. The data obtained are consistent with the assumptions that a monomeric monohydroxo compound is formed and is in equilibrium with dimeric, trimeric, and more highly aggregated species. Kilpatrick and Pokras[18] obtained the equilibrium constants for the reactions

$$[\mathrm{Sc(H_2O)_5OH_2}]^{+++} \rightleftharpoons [\mathrm{Sc(H_2O)_5OH}]^{++} + \mathrm{H}^+$$

$$2[\mathrm{Sc(H_2O)_5OH}]^{++} \rightleftharpoons [\mathrm{Sc(H_2O)_4OH}]_2^{4+}$$

They found that these two reactions predominate during the addition of the first 0.3 equivalent of base, but that the addition of more base leads to higher aggregation. Granér and Sillén[19] found similar behavior in the case of bismuth perchlorate.

Gustavson[20] conducted a series of studies on the chromium complexes

18. Kilpatrick and Pokras, *J. Electrochem. Soc.*, **100**, 85 (1953).
19. Granér and Sillén, *Acta Chem. Scand.*, **1**, 631 (1947); *Nature*, **160**, 715 (1947).
20. Gustavson, *J. Am. Leather Chem. Assoc.*, **47**, 151 (1952); **44**, 388 (1949); *J. Coll. Sci.*, **1**, 397 (1946).

involved in leather tanning. By ion exchange methods he found that, in strongly basic solutions, 30 per cent of the chromium complexes were cationic and 70 per cent noncationic. Since electrophoresis showed no negative complexes, he concluded that neutral complexes predominate in such solutions. He established the empirical formula of these to be $[Cr_2(OH)_5Cl]^0$. It was also found that hydroxo and *ol* compounds lead to cationic complexes in highly acid solutions. Electrophoresis of such chromium solutions showed the presence of complexes of very low or negligible ionic mobility. Extremely basic chromium(III) chlorides also contain components having little or no ionic mobility. Gustavson subjected these basic chromium solutions to dialysis for four weeks, and upon analysis of the dialysate he found that 91 per cent of the chromium had been removed. The remainder of the chromium was present in the form of compounds having the approximate formula $[Cr_4O_5(H_2O)_{12}Cl_2]$. The average molecular weight was found to be 600.

In another investigation of chromium complexes, Gustavson[20c] carried out the separation and quantitative determination of cationic, anionic, and neutral complexes in solutions of basic chromium chlorides and sulfates by filtering them through layers of cation and anion exchange organolites. He reports the existence of the following species:*

$$Cr_2(OH)_2Cl_4 \qquad Cr_2(OH)_2Cl_4 \cdot NaCl \qquad Cr_2(OH)_3Cl_3$$

$$Cr_4(OH)_7Cl_5 \qquad Cr_4(OH)_9Cl_3 \qquad Cr_4(OH)_2(SO_4)_5$$

$$Cr_2(OH)_2(SO_4)_2 \qquad Cr_4(OH)_6(SO_4)_3$$

In preparing his solutions, he boiled the appropriate chromium salts with sodium carbonate to effect a gradual change in the pH and the gradual olation of the various complexes. It was found that most of the complexes present in basic chromium sulfates or ordinary sulfates are of the form[20b]:

$$[Cr_2(OH)_2(SO_4)_3]^- \qquad or \qquad [Cr_2(OH)_2(SO_4)]^{++}$$

Castor and Basolo[21] have applied a kinetic technique to the study of heterogeneous dehydration of hydrated salts, and were able to identify hydrates intermediate between those found by thermodynamic methods. Thus, in addition to the 4-, 2-, and 1-hydrates of manganese(II) chloride, they identified a 3.5- and a 3-hydrate. Complete dehydration yields the anhydrous metal chloride. However, in the case of zirconyl choride 8-hydrate, dehydration was shown to proceed through 7.75-, 7.5-, 7-, and 6.5-

---

* In these formulas, and others in this chapter, the possible presence of coordinated water molecules is disregarded. It is probable that all of the complexes discussed contain at least enough water to fill the coordination spheres of the metal ions.

21. Castor and Basolo, *J. Am. Chem. Soc.*, **75**, 4804, 4807 (1953).

hydrates to the 6-hydrate; complete dehydration involves hydrolysis and produces zirconium dioxide. Fractional hydrate formation was explained on the basis of the reactions:

(a)
$$2[RM(OH)(H_2O)]^{n+} \rightleftharpoons \left[R(H_2O)M \overset{\overset{\textstyle H}{\underset{\textstyle O}{}}}{\diagup \diagdown} M(OH)R \right]^{2n+} + H_2O$$

(b)
$$\left[R(H_2O)M \overset{\overset{\textstyle H}{\underset{\textstyle O}{}}}{\diagup \diagdown} M(OH)R \right]^{2n+} \rightleftharpoons \left[R{-}M \overset{O}{\underset{O}{\diamond}} M{-}R \right]^{2n+} + H_2O$$

$$2\left[R(OH)M \overset{\overset{\textstyle H}{\underset{\textstyle O}{}}}{\diagup \diagdown} M(H_2O)R' \right]^{2n+} \rightleftharpoons$$

(c)
$$\left[R{-}M \cdots M{-}O{-}M \cdots M{-}R \right]^{4n+} + H_2O$$

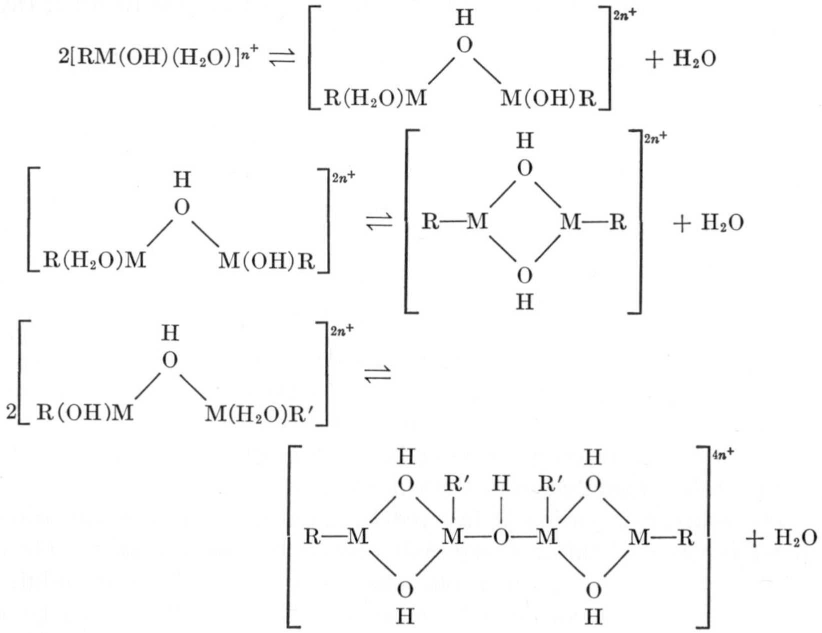

Denk and Bauer[22] found that when aluminum reacts with a deficiency of dilute hydrochloric acid, six times as much aluminum is dissolved as is required for the formation of simple aluminum chloride, $AlCl_3$, and, from the resulting solutions, they isolated the "$5/6$ basic" aluminum chloride in stable form. This compound is soluble in water and shows weak x-ray patterns. The $5/6$ basic sulfate, $[Al_2(OH)_5]_2SO_4$, was isolated by precipitation with sodium sulfate. Denk and Bauer also found that the basic chloride reacts slowly with more aluminum to give a colloidal product.

Factors Promoting Olation

Several methods have been suggested for the measurement of the degree of olation, but none is entirely accurate. Stiasny and Königfeld[23] assumed that olated hydroxo groups do not readily react with excess acid in the cold, but do react when boiled for an hour with excess acid. Back titration of the excess in the two cases measures the degree of olation. Theis and Serfass[24] found that conductometric titrations give more accurate and more

22. Denk and Bauer, *Z. anorg. allgem. Chem.*, **267,** 89 (1951).
23. Stiasny and Königfeld, *Collegium*, **752,** 897 (1932).
24. Theis and Serfass, *J. Am. Leather Chem. Assoc.*, **29,** 543 (1934).

reproducible results than potentiometric methods or those using indicators. Mitchell[25] determined the number of olated groups from the difference between the number of equivalents of alkali added to the solution when first prepared, and the number of equivalents of acid needed to bring the pH to 3.3.

In recent studies,[25b] Mitchell found that the degree of olation decreased from 100 to 50 per cent with the addition of increasing amounts of sodium hydroxide to freshly prepared solutions of chromium alum, but it decreased only to 75 per cent of its original value when aged solutions of the alum were used. She also found that solutions of chromium alum boiled with sodium hydroxide exhibited 100 per cent olation. Complexes of the composition $[Cr_4(OH)_3(SO_4)_3(H_2O)_{12}]^{+++}$ were formed by boiling, cooling, and aging solutions of chromium alum for fifteen minutes. In these solutions, there was a stoichiometric relationship between the formation of olated OH groups and the entry of sulfate groups into the complexes. If the hexaquo-chromium(III) ion was heated with alkali of the correct concentration, one *ol* bridge formed and one sulfate entered the complex. However, if the concentration of alkali was great enough, two *ol* bridges formed and the sulfate groups were eliminated from the complex.

The process of olation is favored by an increase in concentration, an increase in temperature, and especially, by an increase in basicity. The process reverses very slowly when solutions of olated complexes are diluted, or when such solutions are cooled; i.e., olation decreases the reactivity of coordinated OH groups[26].

THE OXOLATION PROCESS

Stiasny and co-workers[16, 27] observed that solutions of basic chromium salts become more acidic and the salts less soluble when the solutions are heated. When the solutions are cooled, the acidity drops to the original value, but only after a long time. To account for these facts, Stiasny suggested the process of *oxolation*; i.e., conversion of *ol* groups to *oxo* groups by the loss of protons:

$$\left[(H_2O)_4Cr \begin{array}{c} OH \\ \diagup \diagdown \\ \diagdown \diagup \\ OH \end{array} Cr(H_2O)_4 \right]^{4+} \rightleftharpoons \left[(H_2O)_4Cr \begin{array}{c} O \\ \diagup \diagdown \\ \diagdown \diagup \\ O \end{array} Cr(H_2O)_4 \right]^{++} + 2H^+$$

This appears to be a resonable explanation, especially in view of the acid

25. Mitchell, *J. Soc. Leather Trades' Chem.*, **35,** 154, 397 (1951).
26. Werner, *Ber.*, **40,** 4436 (1907).
27. Stiasny and Grimm, *Collegium*, **691,** 505 (1927); **694,** 49 (1928).

reaction of the "erythro" chromium salts[10]; the equilibrium

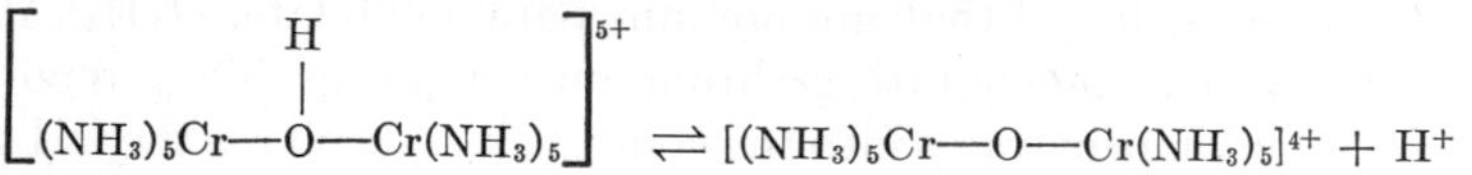

$$\left[\begin{array}{c} H \\ | \\ (NH_3)_5Cr—O—Cr(NH_3)_5 \end{array}\right]^{5+} \rightleftharpoons [(NH_3)_5Cr—O—Cr(NH_3)_5]^{4+} + H^+$$

may be involved.

While olation and oxolation are both reversible, the long time required for the acidity of solutions, which have been heated and then cooled, to return to the original value leads to the conclusion that de-oxolation is extremely slow. In general, *ol* compounds are more readily depolymerized than *oxo* compounds, since protons react more rapidly with *ol* groups than with *oxo* groups.

Jander and Jahr[28] found that the addition of base to solutions of iron(III) perchlorate causes the formation of hydroxo and finally oxolated bimolecular hydrolysis products, which they formulated as follows:

$$2[Fe(OH)(ClO_4)(H_2O)]^+ \rightleftharpoons [(ClO_4)Fe—O—Fe(ClO_4)(H_2O)]^{++} + 2H_2O$$

The addition of more base leads to such products as:

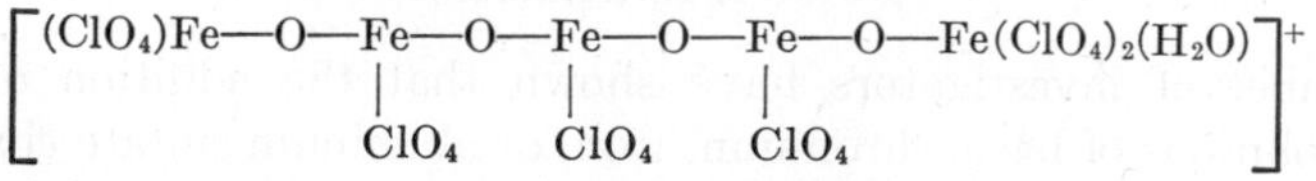

$$\left[\begin{array}{c} (ClO_4)Fe—O—Fe—O—Fe—O—Fe—O—Fe(ClO_4)_2(H_2O) \\ \quad\quad\quad | \quad\quad | \quad\quad | \\ \quad\quad\quad ClO_4 \quad ClO_4 \quad ClO_4 \end{array}\right]^+$$

Jander and Jahr[28] also found that the addition of one mole of ammonia to one mole of aluminum nitrate causes the formation of

$$[Al(OH)(NO_3)_2(H_2O)]_m .$$

A second mole of base causes the formation of the oxolated aggregate, $[Al \cdot O \cdot (NO_3)]_n$. These reactions were represented in a manner analogous to that used by Thomas and Whitehead[29]. Jander and Jahr report that the addition of more base does not cause the precipitation of aluminum hydroxide, but increases the degree of aggregation:

$$[(NO_3)_2Al(H_2O)—O—Al(NO_3)(OH)(H_2O)] + [(OH)Al(NO_3)_2(H_2O)] \rightleftharpoons$$

$$[H_2O(NO_3)_2Al—O—Al(NO_3)(H_2O)—O—Al(NO_3)_2(H_2O)]$$

Continued aggregation would lead to the formation of such condensation products as

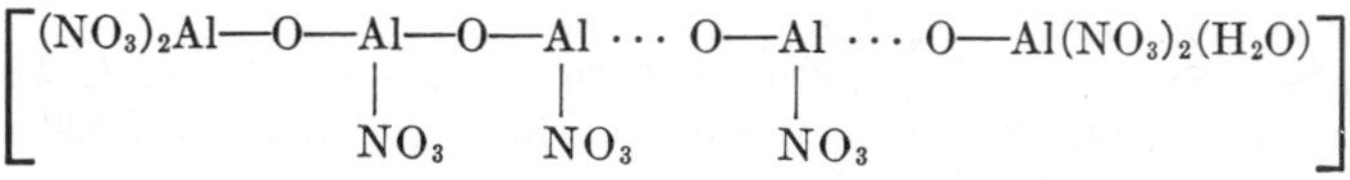

$$\left[\begin{array}{c} (NO_3)_2Al—O—Al—O—Al \cdots O—Al \cdots O—Al(NO_3)_2(H_2O) \\ \quad\quad\quad\quad | \quad\quad | \quad\quad\quad | \\ \quad\quad\quad\quad NO_3 \quad NO_3 \quad\quad NO_3 \end{array}\right]$$

Similar reactions take place in solutions of zirconium perchlorate[30].

28. Jander and Jahr, *Kolloid Beihefte*, **43**, 323, 305 (1936).
29. Thomas and Whitehead, *J. Phys. Chem.*, **35**, 27 (1931).
30. Reference 28, p. 315.

Hall and Eyring[31], in a study of the constitution of chromium salts in aqueous solutions, found that ammonium paramolybdate, $(NH_4)_6Mo_7O_{24} \cdot 4H_2O$, is effective in precipitating chromium complexes. They report that the $HMoO_4^-$ anion penetrates into the complex and displaces the OH groups and aquo groups, but it does not affect the *ol* groups. They also found that the process of oxolation is facilitated by the addition of 90 per cent ethanol. They suggest that the competition between the alcohol and the chromium for the aquo and hydroxo groups leads to the loss of protons from the *ol* bridges with the formation of *oxo* bridges. Their work also seems to show that there is a greater amount of oxolation than Stiasny postulated.

Küntzel[32] is also in partial disagreement with Stiasny. He found that a ⅓ basic chromium chloride solution contains only single *ol* bridges which give rise to long chain colloidal aggregates. Upon aging, these aggregates break up into smaller groups which contain two or three *ol* bridges joining each pair of chromium atoms. Stiasny proposed, on the other hand, that the aging process causes oxolation of the long, large aggregates.

Anion Penetration

A number of investigators have shown that the addition of neutral salts to solutions of basic chromium, iron, or aluminum sulfate changes the hydrogen ion concentration[33]. Different anions were found to differ in their effectiveness in this respect. Early explanations were based on hydration and the formation of addition compounds[34]. Stiasny, however, explained the phenomenon by postulating "anion penetration," i.e., replacement of a coordinated group, such as aquo, hydroxo, or an anion, by an anion. Reactions of this type are common among complexes of low ionic weight. When a solution of the violet form of chromium(III) chloride 6-hydrate is heated, the bright green form (tetraquo) is produced[35]:

$$[Cr(H_2O)_6]Cl_3 \underset{\text{cool}}{\overset{\text{heat}}{\rightleftharpoons}} [Cr(H_2O)_4Cl_2]Cl + 2H_2O$$
$$\text{violet} \qquad\qquad\qquad \text{green}$$

In pure water the reaction reverses slowly when the solution is cooled, but

31. Hall and Eyring, *J. Am. Chem. Soc.*, **72**, 782 (1950).
32. Küntzel, *Colloquimsber. Insts. Gerbereichem. tech. Hochschule Darmstadt*, No. 2, 31 (1948); cf., *Chem. Abs.*, **43**, 1591a (1949).
33. Stiasny and Szegö, *Collegium*, **670**, 41 (1926); Wilson and Kern, *J. Am. Leather Chem. Assoc.*, **12**, 450 (1917); Wilson and Kuan, *ibid.*, **25**, 15 (1930); Thomas, *Paper Trade J.*, **100**, 36 (1935).
34. Wilson and Gallun, *J. Am. Leather Chem. Assoc.*, **15**, 273 (1920); Thomas and Foster, *Ind. Eng. Chem.*, **14**, 132 (1922).
35. Ephraim, "Inorganic Chemistry," p. 291, New York, Nordeman Publishing Co., Inc., 1939; Mellor, "Modern Inorganic Chemistry", p. 776, New York, Longmans Green and Co., 1939.

the extent of reversal is decreased by sodium chloride. Lamb[36] states that all of the chloride can be precipitated from chromium(III) chloride solutions by silver acetate, but not by silver nitrate. The acetate ion can displace chloro groups from the complex chromium(III) ion, but the nitrate ion cannot. This is in accordance with the well-known difference in the coordinating power of these groups.

Stiasny postulated that an equilibrium exists between the complex cation of a basic chromium salt and the anion. This equilibrium is shifted by changing the relative concentrations of anion and chromium complex. The following examples indicate why the pH is changed by such reactions:

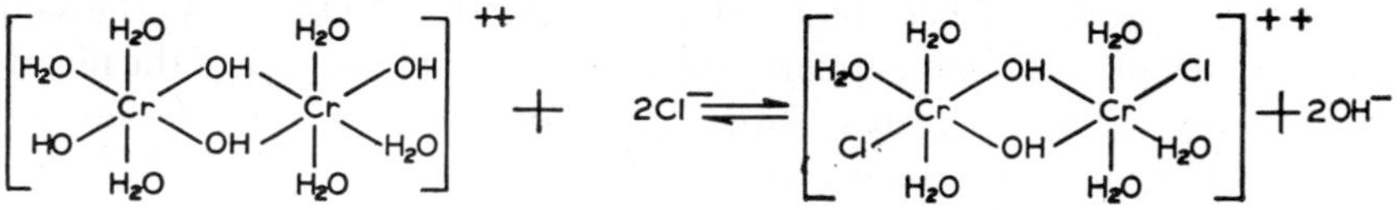

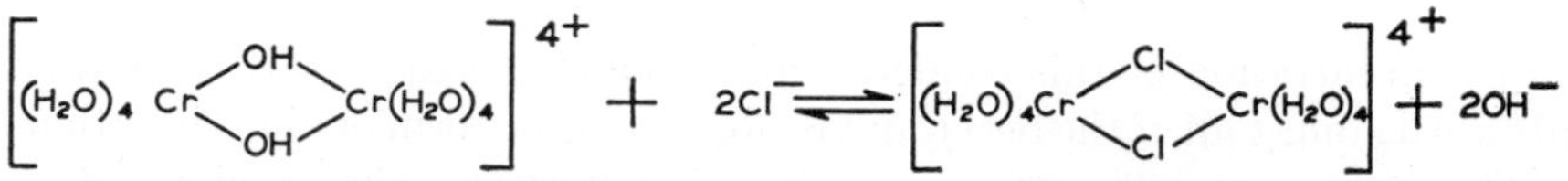

The extent to which anion penetration occurs with *ol* complexes is determined by the relative concentrations of the reactants, the relative coordinating tendencies of the entering anion and the group which it displaces, and the length of time which the solutions are allowed to stand[37]. Anions that can enter the coordination sphere easily and displace OH groups effectively prevent olation. Penetration by anions decreases in the order: oxalate > citrate > tartrate > glycolate > acetate > formate > sulfate. In stock solutions of basic chromium(III) sulfate, however, Serfass, *et al.*[37] found ionic species having weights of 68,000.

Shuttleworth[38], in studying the bond forces involved in chrome tanning, examined a series of complex chromium ions by means of ion exchange resins, potentiometric titrations, and spectrophotometric curves. He obtained most of the compounds that he used from $[Cr_2(H_2O)_6(OH)_2(SO_4)]^{++}$, which will be called (a) in the following discussion.

By boiling a solution of (a) (96 g. of chromium ion per liter) with stoichiometric proportions of sodium oxalate and then aging for one week he obtained

$$[Cr_2(H_2O)_6(OH)_2(C_2O_4)]^{++}, \quad [Cr_2(H_2O)_4(OH)_2(C_2O_4)_2]^0,$$

and

$$[Cr_2(H_2O)_2(OH)_2(C_2O_4)_3]^=.$$

36. Lamb, *J. Am. Chem. Soc.*, **28**, 1710 (1906); Weinland and Koch, *Z. anorg. Chem.*, **39**, 256 (1904).
37. Serfass, Theis, Thorstensen, and Agarwall, *J. Am. Leather Chem. Assoc.*, **43**, 132 (1948).
38. Shuttleworth, *J. Am. Leather Chem. Assoc.*, **47**, 387 (1952).

When (a) (at the same concentration) was warmed at 37° for 24 hours with proportional amounts of sodium sulfite, and aged for one week,

$$[Cr_2(H_2O)_6(OH)_2(SO_3)]^{++} \qquad \text{and} \qquad [Cr_2(H_2O)_4(OH)_2(SO_3)_2]^0$$

were obtained. When sodium formate instead of the sulfite was used,

$$[Cr_2(H_2O)_5(OH)_2(HCO_2)_3]^+ \qquad \text{and} \qquad [Cr_2(H_2O)_4(OH)_2(HCO_2)_4]^0.$$

were produced.

Making use of conductimetric, potentiometric, and diffusion measurements, Jander and Jahr have found that the most abundant ionic species present in solutions of beryllium nitrate is $[Be(H_2O)NO_3]^+$ [39]. As the solutions age, the pH decreases, apparently due to the replacement of the nitrate in the complex by hydroxo groups. The resulting hydroxo complex was thought to be capable of dimerizing:

$$2[Be(H_2O)(OH)]^+ \rightleftharpoons [(H_2O)Be-O-Be(H_2O)]^{++} + H_2O$$

The concentration of this condensation product increases with decreasing pH until almost all of the beryllium is present in the form of dimeric cations.

Thorstensen and Theis[40] have studied the effect of adding sodium citrate to solutions of basic iron(III) salts used in iron tannage. They found compounds having the following empirical formulas:

$$[Fe_2(SO_4)(OH)_2]\cdot Na\text{-citrate}$$

$$[Fe_2(OH)_4]\cdot Na\text{-citrate}$$

$$[Fe_2(SO_4)_2(OH)_2(OCH_2CO_2Na)_2]^-$$

$$[Fe_2(SO_4)(OH)_4(OCH_2CO_2Na)_2]^-$$

$$[Fe_2(OH)_6(OCH_2CO_2Na)_2]^-$$

Chelation as a Factor in Anion Penetration

Since displacement of OH groups from the complex ion involves coordination of the displacing group with the central metal ion, the reactivity of various anions should be determined, in part, by the number of donor groups in the anion and their relative positions. Thomas and Kremer[41] compared the effects of potassium salts of aliphatic monocarboxylic acids, from formate to valerate inclusive, and of aliphatic dicarboxylic acids, from oxalate to pimelate inclusive. The differences in effectiveness of the homologous monocarboxylic anions is very slight. This might be expected, since coordination of these anions with the metal of the complex cation is presumably controlled by the single carboxyl group.

39. Reference 28, p. 301.
40. Thorstensen and Theis, *J. Am. Leather Chem. Assoc.*, **44**, 841 (1949).
41. Thomas and Kremer, *J. Am. Chem. Soc.*, **57**, 1821, 2538 (1935).

With the dicarboxylic anions the order of reactivity was pimelate $\leq$ adipate $\leq$ glutarate $<$ succinate $<$ malonate $<$ oxalate. Evidently the carboxyl groups in glutarate and higher homologues are so far apart that these anions behave like the monocarboxylates. Conversely, the closer together the carboxyl groups are, the more reactive the anion is, as would be expected from the fact that chelate rings of five or six members are more stable than larger ones. As might be expected, no measurable difference was found in the effects of structural isomers, such as butyrate and isobutyrate, valerate and isovalerate. With cis-trans isomers, however, the effects are quite different. Malate is more effective than fumarate, presumably because of chelation.

Spectrophotometric studies on penetration of anions into basic chromium complexes by Serfass and his co-workers[42] indicated that the order of decreasing penetrating ability is oxalate $>$ glycinate $>$ tartrate $>$ citrate $>$ glycolate $>$ acetate $>$ monochloracetate $>$ formate. This order is the same as the coordinating ability observed for the anions mentioned. Kubelka[43] found that pyrogallol can expel sulfate, but that resorcinol and hydroquinone cannot.

An investigation of the effect of dicarboxylic acids, especially phthalic acid, on chromium complexes has been carried out by Plant[44]. He believes that only one of the carboxyl groups can readily displace another anion and coordinate with the metal ion. He found a drop in the pH of the solution after the addition of the acid, and he concluded that with only one carboxyl group coordinated the other acid group becomes stronger and approaches the strength of benzoic acid. However, Shuttleworth[45] disputes these findings. He asserts that the dicarboxylic acids can chelate without displacing anions. Such coordination would cause the formation of anionic complexes.

Shuttleworth[46] has conducted conductimetric studies on chromium complex compounds which are used in tanning. He found that high dilution of chromium sulfate causes the formation of *ol* bridges and the expulsion of sulfate groups. He pointed out that the formation of sulfato and olated complexes involves the formation of 4-membered rings, while oxalato complexes involve the more stable 5-membered rings. He also suggested the presence of hydrogen bonds between the oxygens of a hydroxo group and an adjacent aquo group. The following structures were suggested for such

42. Serfass, Wilson, and Theis, *J. Am. Leather Chem. Assoc.*, **44**, 647 (1949).
43. Kubelka, *Technicka Hlidka Kozeluzska*, **24**, 97 (1949); *J. Am. Leather Chem. Assoc.*, **44**, 824 (1949).
44. Plant, *J. Soc. Leather Trades' Chem.*, **32**, 88 (1948).
45. Shuttleworth, *J. Soc. Leather Trades' Chem.*, **33**, 112 (1949).
46. Shuttleworth, *J. Soc. Leather Trades' Chem.*, **33**, 92 (1949); **34**, 3, 186 (1950)· *J. Am. Leather Chem. Assoc.*, **44**, 889 (1949); **45**, 41 (1950); **46**, 56 (1951).

compounds:

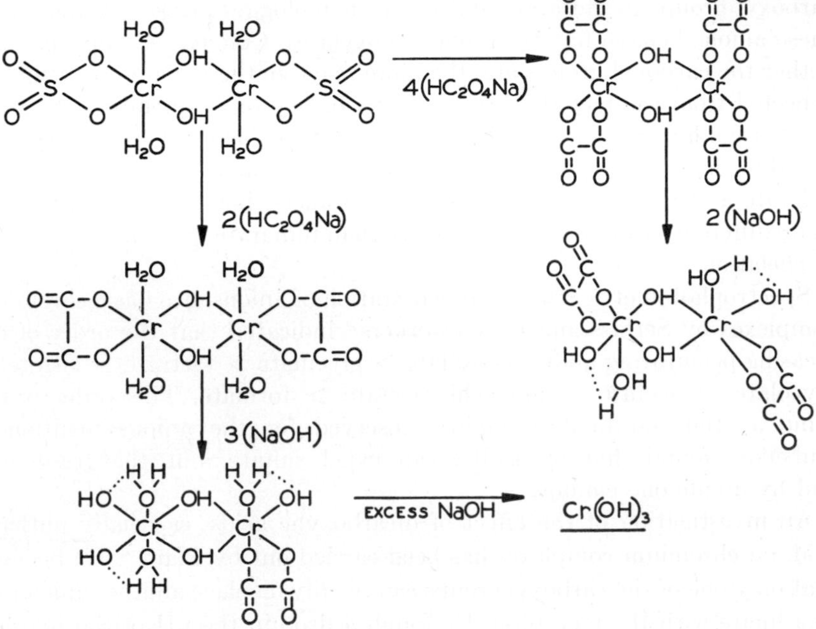

Mixed Bridge Formation

Various anions can function as bridging groups in polynucleate ions, and dinucleate compounds containing chloride[47], acetate, sulfate, and selenate[48] as bridging groups have been identified, e.g.:

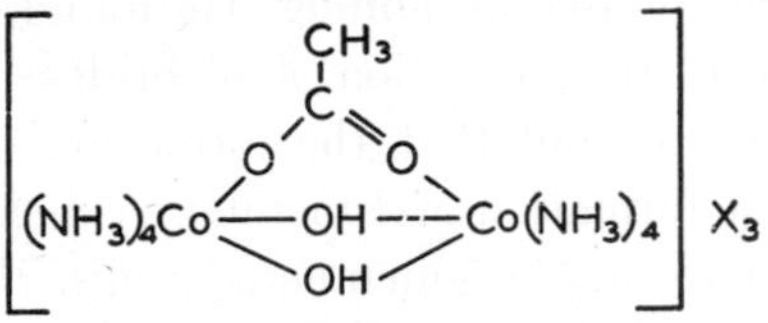

Moreover, the formation of the μ-acetato-μ-diol compound by the action of acetic acid on the *triol* might be regarded as an example of "anion penetration," since, whatever the mechanism, an acetate radical has replaced an *ol* group.

47. Reference 5, p. 131.
48. Reference 9, pp. 341, 343, 362, 366, 368.

Küntzel[49] found that bidentate anions can bridge between two chromium atoms, and that carbonates, sulfates, sulfites and organic anions displace *ol* groups readily. Küntzel has proposed the following structure for the fatty acid-chromium complexes:

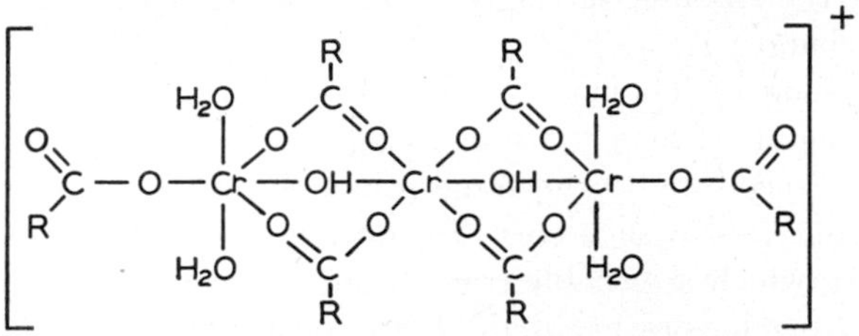

The basic acetato complexes may be formed as follows:[50]

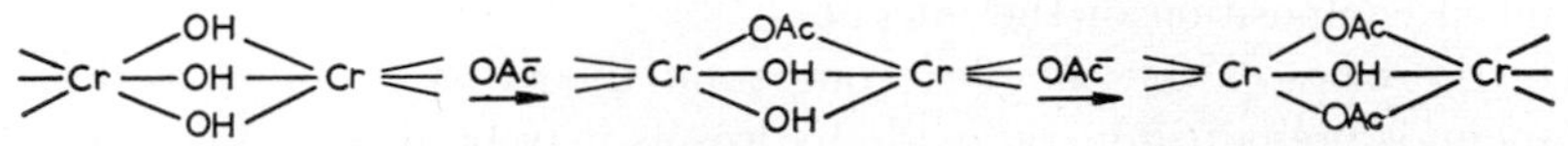

Compounds containing three bridging acetate anions were formed by heating the reactants in sealed tubes.[50b]

HYDROUS METAL OXIDES

On the basis of the results of extensive investigations, Thomas and co-workers have concluded that the formation and composition of colloidally dispersed metal oxides, and of precipitated hydrous oxides, may be explained in terms of olation, oxolation and anion penetration. Whitehead[51] has compared this "complex compound theory of hydrous oxides" with other theories of colloidal behavior.

Any adequate theory of the stability of colloidal oxides must account for the fact that the presence of some ion, other than the metal ion, hydrogen ion, and hydroxide ion, seems to be necessary for the stability of a metal oxide hydrosol. For example, Graham peptized iron(III) oxide with iron(III) chloride, and concluded that pure iron(III) oxide sols cannot be prepared since they flocculate, when dialyzed, before all the chloride is removed. Apparently all investigators except Sorum[52], who has reported the preparation of pure iron(III) oxide sols, are in agreement on this point.

49. Küntzel, *Colloquimsber. Insts. Gerbereichem. tech. Hochschule Darmstadt*, No. 4, 19 (1949); cf., *Chem. Abs.*, **43**, 6851 f (1949).
50. Küntzel, Erdmann and Spahrkäs, *Das Leder* **4**, 73 (1953); **3**, 30 (1952); cf., *Chem. Abs.*, **47**, 12087 f (1953); **46**, 5479 g (1952).
51. Whitehead, *Chem. Revs.*, **21**, 113 (1937).
52. Sorum, *J. Am. Chem. Soc.*, **50**, 1263 (1928).

According to the adsorption theory, which has been developed in great detail and has found wide acceptance, the "foreign" ions are adsorbed on the surfaces of the dispersed particles. Thus the dispersed particles are electrically charged, and mutual repulsion of the similarly charged particles accounts for the stability of the sol. Flocculation is caused by neutralization of the charges.

In the opinion of Thomas and his co-workers, however, the colloidal particles in metal oxide sols are aggregates of definite chemical structure which behave according to the same principles as do the so-called crystalloids[53]. The micelles in such sols are considered to be polymeric ol or oxo compounds in which a variable fraction of the coordination positions may be occupied by anions rather than ol, oxo, or hydroxo groups. Each micelle is thus regarded as a very large ion, whose charge is inherent in its structure. What has been regarded as an "adsorbed" ion is actually a part of the chemical composition of the micelle.

On the basis of the complex compound theory of colloidal oxides, the compounds present in metal oxide hydrosols may be regarded as oxy salts, and it is convenient to name them as such. For example, Thomas designates the compounds in aluminum oxide sols which contain chloride ion as "aluminum oxychlorides." This terminology will be used in the following outline of Thomas' work.

Thomas and Whitehead[29] prepared aluminum oxychloride sols by peptizing (with HCl) aluminum hydroxide, which had been precipitated from aluminum chloride solution with NH_4OH or $NaOH$. According to the coordination theory, this caused formation of larger and larger olated ions until aggregates of zero charge precipitated. Peptization reversed these processes to an extent sufficient to cause dispersion of the precipitates. These sols exhibited the usual properties of colloids, i.e., Tyndall effect, migration of the particles in an electric field (in this case to the cathode), and failure of the particles to diffuse through membranes. Sedimentation was not effected by centrifuging. Tests for aluminum ions were negative, indicating that all the aluminum was bound in the complex micelle. Nearly all of the chloride was present as chloride ion.

The changes in hydrogen ion concentration in aluminum oxychloride sols due to various treatments were investigated by Thomas and Whitehead[29]. The fact that sols prepared and aged at room temperature became more acidic was attributed to hydrolysis of the highly polymeric ions. Sols which were prepared at room temperature became more acidic when heated. The reaction reversed very slowly after the sols were cooled, and the original pH was attained after several weeks. Heating the sols evidently caused increased hydrolysis followed by olation and oxolation, while the reversal

53. Thomas, J. Chem. Ed., 2, 323 (1925).

was due to slow conversion of *oxo* groups to *ol* groups, according to the scheme

$$\left[\overset{\_}{\underset{\_}{\equiv}}Al\overset{H_2O}{\underset{H_2O}{\diagdown}}\right]^n \rightleftharpoons \left[\overset{\_}{\underset{\_}{\equiv}}Al\overset{OH}{\underset{H_2O}{\diagdown}}\right]^{n-1} + \ H^+$$

$$\left[\overset{\_}{\underset{\_}{\equiv}}Al\overset{OH}{\underset{H_2O}{\diagdown}}\right]^{n-1} + \left[\overset{H_2O}{\underset{HO}{\diagdown}}Al\overset{\_}{\underset{\_}{\equiv}}\right]^{n-1} \longrightarrow \left[\overset{\_}{\underset{\_}{\equiv}}Al\overset{OH}{\underset{OH}{\diagdown}}Al\overset{\_}{\underset{\_}{\equiv}}\right]^{2n-2} + \ 2H_2O$$

$$\left[\overset{\_}{\underset{\_}{\equiv}}Al\overset{OH}{\underset{OH}{\diagdown}}Al\overset{\_}{\underset{\_}{\equiv}}\right]^{2n-2} \underset{\text{SLOW}}{\rightleftharpoons} \left[\overset{\_}{\underset{\_}{\equiv}}Al\overset{O}{\underset{O}{\diagdown}}Al\overset{\_}{\underset{\_}{\equiv}}\right]^{2n-4} + \ 2H^+$$

Sols which were prepared at elevated temperature slowly became more basic when aged at room temperature. Evidently, the complexes in such sols initially contained *oxo* groups which slowly reacted with hydrogen ions.

The pH of zirconium oxide sols[54] was found to decrease less rapidly upon aging than did the pH of chromium oxide sols[55]. The pH decreased irreversibly when the sols were boiled, perhaps because of the strong tendency of zirconium oxy salt complexes to oxolate.

Anion Penetration in Hydrosols

The addition of solutions of neutral salts to aluminum oxide sols increased the pH of the sols in all cases[29]. This was evidently not due to dilution, since there was practically no effect on the pH when water was added in quantities equal to the volume of the salt solutions used. The magnitude of the effect depended on the salt added. This phenomenon may be explained by anion penetration, since displacement of a hydroxo or an *ol* group by an anion would increase the pH of the hydrosol.

The increase in pH accompanying the addition of a given amount of a particular salt was much less if the sol was heated before the salt was added. Heating may have converted many of the *ol* groups to *oxo* groups which are much less reactive and more difficult to replace. Since *ol* groups are less reactive than hydroxo groups, the effect may be partially due to increased olation caused by heating the sols.

The order of decreasing tendency of anions to penetrate into the complex

54. Thomas and Owens, *J. Am. Chem. Soc.*, **57**, 1825, 2131 (1935).
55. Thomas and von Wicklen, *J. Am. Chem. Soc.*, **56**, 794 (1934).

was found to be approximately the same for aluminum oxide, chromium oxide and thorium oxide sols[29, 55, 41], the order indicating the order of ability of the anions to coordinate.

The decrease in hydrogen ion concentration on addition of neutral salts to aluminum oxychloride, oxybromide, oxyiodide and oxyacetate sols is so great in some cases that the sols become quite alkaline[56]. The order of effectiveness of anions is nitrate < chloride < acetate < sulfate < oxalate. The magnitude of the effect of a particular salt was different for the different sols, the order being oxyiodide > oxybromide > oxychloride > oxyacetate. This result is consistent with the order of penetrating ability of the ions. Heating such sols makes them less sensitive to the action of added salts.

Whitehead and Clay[57] applied the idea of anion penetration in a comparison of the properties of true solutions and colloidal dispersions. The addition of various anions decreases the hydrogen ion concentration with both types of substances but the effect is greater with sols than with true solutions. This is to be expected since the number of OH groups replaceable by anions depends on the total number present, which will increase with the degree of olation, i.e., with the size of the ion. The order of the effect as determined by these investigators is $AlCl_3$ < $Al(OH)Cl_2$ < $Al(OH)_2Cl$ < sol, which indicates a gradual transition from crystalloidal to colloidal dispersion.

Thomas and Miller[58] investigated the effect of anions on the conductivity of beryllium oxychloride sols by titrating the sols with solutions of silver nitrate, silver acetate, and silver tartrate in concentrations so small that the anions could not displace hydroxo groups to any great extent, but could displace chloro and aquo groups. In each case there was an initial decrease in the conductivity of the sol (greatest with tartrate and least with nitrate) followed by an abrupt increase. The initial decrease was due to the displacement of aquo groups from the complex cationic micelles with a resultant decrease in net charge on the complex cations. The magnitude of this charge would be greatest with the most strongly penetrating anion (tartrate) and least with the most weakly penetrating anion (nitrate).

Extremely interesting results were obtained by Thomas and Kremer[41] with anions of hydroxy acids. The addition of potassium salts of such acids to thorium oxychloride sols reverses the charge on the particles. Moreover, peptization of hydrous thorium oxide by salts of hydroxy acids produces hydrosols in which the micelles are anionic. It was also observed that concentrated nitric acid reverses the charge of thorium oxychloride micelles, producing short-lived nitrato thoreate micelles.

56. Thomas and Tai, *J. Am. Chem. Soc.*, **54**, 841 (1932).
57. Whitehead and Clay, *J. Am. Chem. Soc.*, **56**, 1844 (1934).
58. Thomas and Miller, *J. Am. Chem. Soc.*, **58**, 2526 (1936).

These results are explained by the change in charge on a complex ion when an anion penetrates the complex:

$$\left[\begin{array}{c} \equiv Th \underset{OH}{\overset{H_2O}{\diagdown}} \end{array}\right]^n + an^- \longrightarrow \left[\begin{array}{c} \equiv Th \underset{OH}{\overset{an}{\diagdown}} \end{array}\right]^{n-1} + H_2O$$

$$\left[\begin{array}{c} \equiv Th \overset{OH}{\underset{OH}{\diagdown}} Th \equiv \end{array}\right]^n + an^- \longrightarrow \left[\begin{array}{c} \equiv Th \overset{an\ HO}{\underset{OH}{\diagdown}} Th \equiv \end{array}\right]^{n-1}$$

If enough anions enter, the complex acquires a negative charge. This reversal of charge was also noted with zirconium oxide hydrosols[54].

Since hydrolysis (conversion of aquo to hydroxo groups) and oxolation (conversion of *ol* to *oxo* groups) decrease the positive charge on the complex ions, boiling the sols, which favors both processes, should decrease the amount of added anion necessary to precipitate the micelles or reverse their charge. In general, this was found to be the case. Zirconeate sols formed by such processes are very stable.

Acid zirconeate sols were also prepared by the action of acids of great coordinating tendency on hydrated zirconium oxide. Peptization of the oxide by tartaric acid produces sols containing both positive and negative micelles. All of the salts effective in causing the reversal of charge are those containing alpha hydroxy anions. Two types of combination are possible; (a) the OH group coordinates as such, (b) it acts like an acidic group:

$$\left[\begin{array}{c} HO \overset{R}{\overset{|}{\underset{}{}}} C-H \\ \equiv Zr \underset{O}{\diagdown} C=O \end{array}\right]^n \qquad \left[\begin{array}{c} O \overset{R}{\overset{|}{\underset{}{}}} C-H \\ \equiv Zr \underset{O}{\diagdown} C=O \end{array}\right]^m$$

$$\qquad\qquad (a) \qquad\qquad\qquad\qquad (b)$$

Chelation of type (b) is twice as effective in reducing the ionic charge as that of type (a). Because of the effectiveness of alpha hydroxy anions in reversing the charge of zirconium oxide micelles, Thomas and Owens[54] concluded that type (b) is more probable. If this is true, dissociation of the OH groups of the hydroxy anion will produce hydrogen ions. Evidence for such a phenomenon was obtained by adding salt mixtures to the zirconium oxide sols. Mixtures of anions which do not reverse the charge produce nearly the same pH values, while oxalate-lactate and oxalate-tartrate mixtures produce lower pH values. It was found that oxalate precipitates basic zirconium oxide sols without reversing the charge, but subsequent addition of a salt of an alpha hydroxy acid peptizes the precipitate with the formation of a complex zirconeate sol. Moreover, if sufficient alpha hydroxy salt is first added to a zirconium oxychloride sol, the addition of oxalate does not cause precipitation. These phenomena are entirely consistent with the behavior of crystalloidal zirconium salts which usually form stable complexes with alpha hydroxy acids.

Precipitation, Peptization, and Dissolution of Hydrous Metal Oxides

It is well known that metal oxide sols can be flocculated by prolonged boiling or by the addition of alkali. According to the coordination theory, flocculation occurs because of hydrolysis, olation, and oxolation of the complex cations. Hydrolysis, followed by olation, leads to the formation of larger aggregates. The loss of hydrogen ions by aquo groups (hydrolysis) and by *ol* groups (oxolation) reduces the charge on the cation, the stability of the sol decreasing as the ratio of charge of the micelle to its mass decreases. Beryllium oxide hydrosols precipitate immediately when boiled, and in about two hours at 60°. This is attributed to oxolation and the consequent formation of complexes of zero charge. This type of neutralization occurs more readily with beryllium sols than with *ol* complexes of the trivalent metals whose coordination number is six, simply because the loss of fewer protons is required, the valence and coordination number of beryllium being only two and four, respectively.

A precipitated hydrous oxide may contain such complexes as

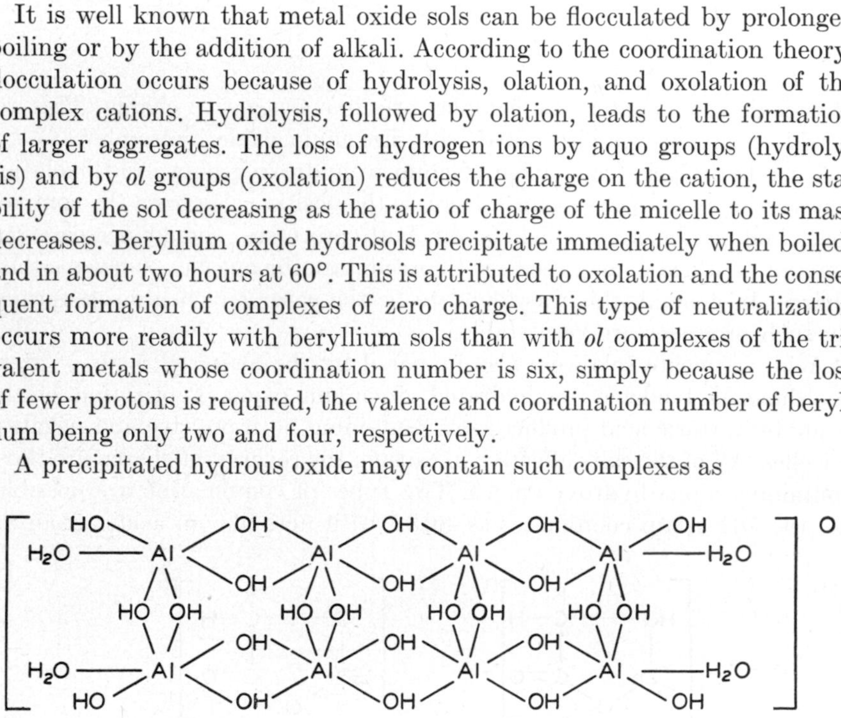

which are not appreciably soluble in water. In the presence of acid, however, a number of reactions occur, i.e., conversion of hydroxo to aquo groups, penetration of anions into the complex nucleus, and deolation. The final result depends to a large extent on the penetrating ability of the anion. In any event, the complex acquires one positive charge for each hydroxo group converted by a hydrogen ion to an aquo group, and one or more negative charges (depending on the anion) for each anion entering the complex. Deolation also occurs to some extent. Whether the oxide is dissolved or peptized depends on the nature of the anion, since this determines the extent of anion penetration and therefore, of deolation. If an acid whose anion is a weak penetrator is added, anion penetration only partly neutralizes any positive charge which the complex acquires by the conversion of hydroxo groups to aquo groups by the action of the hydrogen ions. When the ratio of charge to mass becomes large enough, peptization occurs, provided the number of equivalents of acid present is much less than the number of equivalents of aluminum.

On the other hand, with an acid whose anion is a powerful penetrator, a considerable number of aquo or hydroxo groups, or both, are displaced by anions. This offsets the increase in positive charge due to conversion of hydroxo to aquo groups. With a small ratio of acid to aluminum, acid disappears from solution, i.e., hydrogen ions and anions are said to be "adsorbed" by the alumina. With a sufficiently large ratio of acid to alumina, complete deolation results in crystalloidal dispersion of the oxide, provided it were not oxolated.

Experimental results are in accord with these ideas[59]. The following order of effectiveness of acid in peptizing hydrous alumina was found: trichloroacetic > dichloroacetic > nitric > hydrobromic > hydrochloric > monochloroacetic > formic > glycolic > acetic > oxalic > tartaric > sulfuric. With the exceptions of dichloroacetic, sulfuric and tartaric (discrepancies which are not accounted for), the peptizing ability of the acids approximates the reverse of the order of the effectiveness of their anions in raising the pH of hydrosols. Both orders reflect the tendency of the anions to become coordinately bound in the complex cations. The acids having strongly penetrating anions were removed from solution as indicated by an increase in pH. To the extent that they dispersed hydrous alumina, they produced a large proportion of crystalloidal compounds because of their deolating effect.

Thomas and Miller[58] produced stable anionic beryllium oxide hydrosols by the use of powerfully coordinating anions. In contrast to the behavior of cationic hydrosols, which become more acid on aging at room temperature (due to oxolation and possibly to dissociation of aquo groups), these complex beryllate hydrosols become less acid. This is due to aquotization or anation and may be exemplified by a reaction of a hypothetical basic citrato beryllate ($R = C_6H_5O_7^=$):

$$\left[\begin{array}{cccc} & OH & OH & OH \\ & | & | & | \\ R\equiv Be{-}OH{-}Be{-}OH{-}Be{-}OH{-}Be{-}H_2O \\ & | & | & | \\ & OH & OH & OH_2 \end{array}\right]^= + H_2O \rightarrow$$

$$\left[\begin{array}{cccc} & OH & OH & H_2O \\ & | & | & | \\ R\equiv Be{-}OH{-}Be{-}OH{-}Be{-}OH{-}Be{-}H_2O \\ & | & | & | \\ & OH & OH & H_2O \end{array}\right]^- + OH^-$$

59. Thomas and Vartanian, *J. Am. Chem. Soc.*, **57**, 4 (1935).

The conclusion is that, in general, acids with anions of great coordinating ability are poor peptizers of hydrous oxides while acids of weakly coordinating anions are good peptizers.

Other Properties of Hydrous Metal Oxides

According to the coordination theory, precipitated hydrous oxides are considered polymeric compounds not different in kind from those existing in crystalloidal solutions and colloidal dispersions[33d, 60]. They are regarded as complexes of zero charge produced by a continued process of olation, accompanied or followed by oxolation and perhaps by anion penetration. This point of view furnishes an explanation of two well-known characteristics of hydrous oxides, such as those of aluminum and chromium—their decreased chemical reactivity after aging or heating and their ability to retain certain impurities even after exhaustive washing.

As to the first of these, a freshly precipitated hydroxide may consist of complexes of relatively low aggregate weight containing a high ratio of *ol* to *oxo* groups. For a given weight of hydroxide, the smaller the aggregates, the more "end groups" there will be, i.e., hydroxo and aquo groups. The hydroxo groups are easily convertible to aquo groups by the action of hydrogen ions and may easily be displaced by anions. *Ol* groups are not so readily attacked by hydrogen ions or displaced by anions but do react slowly. Thus, low molecular weight aggregates, which are not too highly oxolated, may be dissolved readily in acid[60].

However, the process of olation, by which the hydrous oxide was presumably formed, may continue slowly after precipitation, even at low temperature. There is a decrease in the relative number of hydroxo groups, and a corresponding increase in the number of *ol* and *oxo* groups[60]. The completely oxolated oxide is quite inert.

It is common knowledge that precipitated hydrous oxides almost invariably contain the anion of the salt from which the oxide was formed, and that such impurities are extremely difficult to remove[61]. The explanation often given is that the impurity is adsorbed, or occluded. However, this phenomenon can also be accounted for by the coordination theory.

If anion penetration occurs during precipitation, the complexes contain anions as an integral part of their structure. Washing the precipitate may ultimately cause replacement of the anions by aquo groups. On this basis, anions of greatest coordinating tendency are hardest to remove. This has been found to be the case[51]. The facts that such anions are displaced by other anions of greater penetrating ability[61b], and that freshly precipitated

60. Graham and Thomas, *J. Am. Chem. Soc.*, **69**, 816 (1947).
61. Thomas and Frieden, *J. Am. Chem. Soc.*, **45**, 2522 (1923); Charriou, *Compt. rend.*, **176**, 679, 1890 (1923).

hydrous aluminum oxide liberates hydroxide ions on treatment with neutral salts[62] are explainable by anion penetration.

In addition to results specifically mentioned in the foregoing discussion, evidence consistent with the interpretation given has been obtained, in investigations of titanium oxide sols[63], of the effect of anions on the pH of maximum precipitation of aluminum hydroxide[64], and of the catalytic activity of aluminum oxyiodide sols in the decomposition of hydrogen peroxide[65]. Summaries of the coordination theory of hydrous oxides have been compiled by Whitehead[51], Thomas[66], and Perkins and Thomas[67]. Other investigators, notably Pauli and co-workers[68], have applied the coordination theory to colloidal systems.

Olation and oxolation are of great importance in leather chemistry as shown by Stiasny and other investigators.[69] In tanning, only olated compounds are effective. Briggs[70] is studying the separation of basic chromium salts by means of aqueous ethyl alcohol. His work shows that it may be possible to separate such compounds fairly simply and easily. Basic iron, aluminum and zirconium compounds are also of interest as tanning agents.[71]

It must be admitted that the theory is controversial, at least in certain aspects. Weiser and co-workers, in particular, have criticized it mainly on the basis of results of x-ray studies and isobaric and isothermal dehydration studies[72].

62. Sen, *J. Phys. Chem.*, **31,** 691 (1927).
63. Thomas and Stewart, *Koll. Z.*, **86,** 279 (1939).
64. Marion and Thomas, *J. Coll. Sci.*, **1,** 221 (1946).
65. Thomas and Cohen, *J. Am. Chem. Soc.*, **61,** 401 (1939).
66. Thomas, "Colloid Chemistry," Chapt. 7, New York, McGraw-Hill Book Company, 1934.
67. Perkins and Thomas, *Stiasny Festschr.*, 307, Darmstadt, Ed. Roether Verlag, 1937.
68. Pauli and Valko, "Elektrochemie der Kolloide," Vienna, Julius Springer, 1929.
69. Reference 17, chapters 14–18; McLaughlin and Theis, "The Chemistry of Leather Manufacture," chapters 14–16, New York, Reinhold Publishing Corporation, 1945, Shuttleworth, *J. Soc. Leather Trades' Chem.*, **34,** 410 (1950); *J. Am. Leather Chem. Assoc.*, **46,** 582 (1951).
70. Briggs, *J. Soc. Leather Trades' Chem.*, **35,** 235 (1951).
71. References 69b, chapters 19, 20, 22.
72. Weiser, Milligan, and Coppoc, *J. Phys. Chem.*, **43,** 1109 (1939); Weiser and Milligan, *ibid.*, **44,** 1081 (1940); Weiser, Milligan, and Purcell, *Ind. Eng. Chem.*, **33,** 669 (1941); Weiser, Milligan and Simpson, *J. Phys. Chem.*, **46,** 1051 (1942); Weiser and Milligan, *Chem. Revs.*, **25,** 1 (1939).

14. The Poly-Acids

Hans B. Jonassen

Tulane University, New Orleans, Louisiana

and

Stanley Kirschner

Wayne University, Detroit, Michigan

The poly-acids are characterized by the fact that they contain more than one acid anhydride molecule per acid anion[1]. If they have only one kind of acid anhydride, they are called *isopoly-acids* (e.g., $H_2Mo_4O_{13}$ or $H_2O \cdot 4MoO_3$); if they contain more than one kind of acid anhydride, they are called *heteropoly-acids* (e.g., $H_4SiW_{12}O_{40}$ or $SiO_2 \cdot (WO_3)_{12} \cdot 2H_2O$).

The elements whose oxides are capable of undergoing condensation to form isopoly- and heteropoly-acids are those in groups V-B (V, Nb, Ta) and VI-B (Cr, Mo, W, and U[2]) of the periodic table.

EARLY STRUCTURAL STUDIES

As long ago as 1826 Berzelius[3] described ammonium phosphomolybdate; and, although silicotungstates were known as early as 1847[4, 5], the first careful determination of the composition of a silicotungstate was not carried out until 1862[6]. The compositions of many isopoly- and heteropoly-acids and salts were subsequently established, but very few structural studies were undertaken. Klein[7] attempted to explain the structure of the paratungstic acid prepared by Laurent[8], but his ideas met with little success after the discovery of many other more complex acids.

1. Rosenheim, "Handbuch der Anorganischen Chemie," Abegg and Auerbach, Vol. 4, Part 1, ii, pp. 977–1065, Leipzig, Hirzel, 1921.
2. Wamser, *J. Am. Chem. Soc.*, **74**, 1020 (1952).
3. Berzelius, *Pogg. Ann.*, **6**, 369 (1826).
4. Laurent, *Ann. chim. phys.*, [3] **21**, 54 (1847).
5. Riche, *Ann. chim. phys.*, [3] **50**, 5 (1857).
6. Marignac, *Compt. rend.*, **55**, 88 (1862).
7. Klein, *Bull. soc. chim.*, [2] **36**, 546 (1881).
8. Laurent, *Compt. rend.*, **31**, 692 (1850).

Blomstrand[9, 10] attempted to explain the structure of the poly-acids by assuming a chain or ring configuration. For phosphomolybdic acid, for example, he proposed a straight chain containing twelve MoO_3 groups with an OH group at one end and an H_2PO_3 group at the other:

$$\text{HO—Mo}\underset{\displaystyle O}{\overset{\displaystyle O}{\vphantom{|}}}\text{—O—Mo}\underset{\displaystyle O}{\overset{\displaystyle O}{\vphantom{|}}}\text{—O—Mo}\underset{\displaystyle O}{\overset{\displaystyle O}{\vphantom{|}}}\text{—O—} \cdots\cdots\cdots \text{Mo}\underset{\displaystyle O}{\overset{\displaystyle O}{\vphantom{|}}}\text{—O—P}\underset{\displaystyle \text{OH}}{\overset{\displaystyle \text{OH}}{\vphantom{|}}}\!\!=\!\!O$$

However, the hypotheses set forth by these and other early investigators[11] proved to be unsatisfactory.

LATER STRUCTURAL STUDIES

The Work of Copaux, Werner, Miolati, and Rosenheim

In 1906, Copaux[12] attempted a classification of these complex acids based upon their isomorphism, and he concluded that the isopoly-acids were quite similar in structure to the heteropoly-acids. For the isopoly-acids he assumed that two water molecules condensed to form an H_4O_2 unit which then behaved as an anhydride group; thus he considered these acids as heteropoly-acids, in which the H_4O_2 group is assumed to be the second anhydride. Although it is now regarded as incorrect, Copaux's hypothesis is of historical importance, since it started later workers along the path which ultimately led to the currently accepted structures for these acids.

Even though it is possible to form condensed aggregates of a single metalloid anhydride molecule with various numbers of molecules of a group V-B or VI-B metal anhydride, two types of aggregates are much more common than any of the others. They are the heteropoly-acids (and salts) which contain six or twelve molecules of the metal anhydride for each molecule of the metalloid anhydride. These acids are called *limiting acids* or "Grenzsäuren." Table 14.1 depicts those elements which have been reported as central atoms of the "metalloid" anhydride.

Table 14.2 lists a few examples of the limiting acids and their salts.

Werner[13] applied his ideas on coordination compounds to the structure of silicotungstic acid and its salts. He assumed that the central group is an SiO_4^{4-} ion surrounded by four $(RW_2O_6)^+$ groups (R = a unipositive ion) which are linked to the central group by primary valences. In addition, he

9. Blomstrand, *Z. anorg. Chem.*, **1**, 10 (1892).
10. Rosenheim, *Z. anorg. Chem.*, **75**, 141 (1912).
11. Gibbs, *J. Am. Chem. Soc.*, **5**, 391 (1883); Friedheim and Castendyck, *Rev.*, **33**, 1611 (1900).
12. Copaux, *Ann. chim. phys.*, [8] **7**, 118 (1906); *Bull. soc. chim* , **13**, 820 (1913).
13. Werner, *Ber.*, **40**, 40 (1907).

TABLE 14.1. ELEMENTS REPORTED AS CENTRAL ATOMS IN HETEROPOLY-ACIDS

Group Number	Elements
I-A	H
II-A	Be
III-A	B, Al, Ce
IV-B	Ti, Zr, Th
V-B	V, Nb, Ta
VI-B	Cr, Mo, W, U
VII-B	Mn
VIII	Fe, Co, Ni, Rh, Os, Ir, Pt
I-B	Cu
IV-A	C, Si, Ge, Sn
V-A	N, P, As, Sb
VI-A	S, Se, Te
VII-A	I

TABLE 14.2. EXAMPLES OF LIMITING POLY-ACIDS AND SALTS

Type	Formula	Name
6-poly-acids	$2Na_2O \cdot P_2O_5 \cdot 12WO_3 \cdot aq.$	Sodium phospho-6-tungstate
	$2H_2O \cdot TeO_3 \cdot 6MoO_3 \cdot aq.$	Tellurium-6-molybdic acid
	$3H_2O \cdot P_2O_5 \cdot 12WO_3 \cdot aq.$	Phospho-6-tungstic acid
12-poly-acids	$3K_2O \cdot P_2O_5 \cdot 24WO_3 \cdot aq.$	Potassium phospho-12-tungstate
	$3H_2O \cdot B_2O_3 \cdot 24WO_3 \cdot aq.$	Boro-12-tungstic acid
	$5(NH_4)_2O \cdot 2P_2O_5 \cdot 24V_2O_5$	Ammonium ph ospho-12-vanadate

postulated that two $R_2W_2O_7$ groups are linked by secondary valences to this same central group, and he felt that this would result in an octahedral configuration for the poly-acids. Although this structure accounted for the behavior of some of the limiting poly-acids containing a tetravalent central ion, difficulties were encountered with those acids having a central ion with a valence other than four, and with those containing metal anhydride aggregations which are not multiples of six.

Miolati[14] and Rosenheim and co-workers[1, 10, 15] extended Werner's ideas to include those poly-acids which do not belong to a limiting acid series and attempted to explain the large number of replaceable hydrogens in many of these acids. They considered the poly-acids as being formed in a manner analogous to the stepwise displacement of hydroxyl groups by chloride ions from platinic acid, $H_2[Pt(OH)_6]$, ultimately yielding hexa-chloroplatinic acid, $H_2[PtCl_6]$. Telluric acid, $H_6[TeO_6]$, and para-periodic acid, $H_5[IO_6]$, for example, were regarded as parent acids which show six-coordination and which possess octahedral structures. They were thought to form heteropoly-acids by the stepwise displacement of the oxygens by $WO_4^=$ groups to give $H_6[Te(WO_4)_6]$ and $H_5[I(WO_4)_6]$, respectively. It was

14. Miolati, *J. prakt. Chem.*, **77**, 417 (1908).
15. Rosenheim, *Z. anorg. Chem.*, **69**, 247 (1910); Rosenheim and Jaenicke, *ibid.*, **100**, 304 (1912).

TABLE 14.3. ROSENHEIM-MIOLATI CLASSIFICATION OF THE 6-POLY-ACIDS

Valence of Central Atom	Central Atom (= X)	Parent Acid	Typical Heteropoly-salt
2	Mn, Ni, Cu	$H_{10}[XO_6]$	$(NH_4)_3H_7[Mn(MoO_4)_6] \cdot 3H_2O$
3	Al, Cr, Co	$H_9[XO_6]$	$K_9[Co(MoO_4)_6] \cdot xH_2O$
6	Te	$H_6[TeO_6]$	$(C(NH_2)_3)_6[Te(WO_4)_6] \cdot 3H_2O$
7	I	$H_5[IO_6]$	$Na_5[I(WO_4)_6] \cdot 8H_2O$

TABLE 14.4. ROSENHEIM-MIOLATI CLASSIFICATION OF THE 12-POLY-ACIDS

Valence of Central Atom	Central Atom (= X)	Parent Acid	Typical Heteropoly-salt
3	B	$H_9[BO_6]$	$Hg_9[B(W_2O_7)_6] \cdot 12.5H_2O$
4	Si, Ge, Sn, Ti	$H_8[XO_6]$	$K_4H_4[Si(W_2O_7)_6] \cdot 7H_2O$
5	P, As, Sb	$H_7[XO_6]$	$Ag_7[Sb(Mo_2O_7)_6] \cdot 15H_2O$

believed that a WO_3 group was bonded to an oxygen at each corner of the octahedron containing the central atom.

Rosenheim and Miolati expanded this concept by postulating an entire series of hypothetical parent oxy-acids showing six-coordination and having oxygen atoms at the corners of the octahedra containing the central metal atoms. Each oxygen was then considered to be coordinated to a metal anhydride molecule. Table 14.3 lists some of the parent acids postulated by these workers for the 6-poly-acid series, along with compounds which were thought to be derived from them.

In a similar manner, parent acids were postulated for the 12-poly-acid series, and Table 14.4 lists some of these along with examples of salts of the 12-heteropoly-acids.

The structures of the unsaturated heteropoly-acids (i.e., those which do not belong to the six or twelve limiting acid series) can be explained, according to Rosenheim[10], by assuming that not all of the six oxygens are displaced by acid anion groups. For example, if only five of the oxygens of the parent acid $H_7[AsO_6]$ are replaced by $Mo_2O_7^=$ groups, then the arsenic-10-molybdic acid $(H_7[AsO(Mo_2O_7)_5] \cdot aq.)$ is formed[16]. Similarly, the unsaturated 11-, 10½-, and 9-poly-acids of the phosphotungstic series can be explained by Rosenheim's postulates, provided that polyoctahedral aggregates are assumed, as is shown in Table 14.5.

The unsaturated poly-acids below the 12-series and above the 6-series are formed by the loss of M_2O_7 groups from one or more corners of the octahedron with the resultant formation of bridge structures of different types. For the unsaturated acids below the 6-series, Rosenheim and Pieck[17] postulated that MO_4 groups do not replace all of the oxygen atoms surrounding

16. Rosenheim, *Z. anorg. Chem.*, **91**, 75 (1915).
17. Rosenheim and Pieck, *Z. anorg. Chem.*, **96**, 139 (1916).

Table 14.5. Rosenheim-Miolati Classification of Unsaturated Poly-Acids

Class of Acid	Heteropoly-Acid	Typical Salt	Remarks
11-acid	$H_7[P(OH)(W_2O_7)_5]W_2O_7[(W_2O_7)_5(OH)P]H_7$	$K_{14}[(OH)_2(W_2O_7)_{11}P_2]$	All salts show highest possible basicity
10½-acid	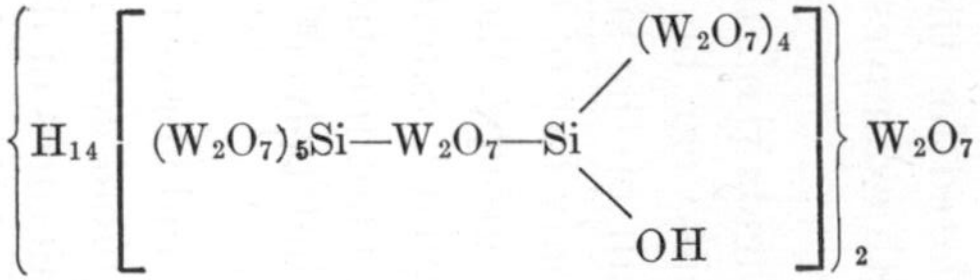 $H_{14}\left\{(W_2O_7)_5Si-W_2O_7-Si{\begin{smallmatrix}(W_2O_7)_4\\ W_2O_7\\ OH\end{smallmatrix}}\right\}_2$	$3(NH_4)_2O \cdot P_2O_5 \cdot 21WO_3$	Only a few show highest basicity
10-acid	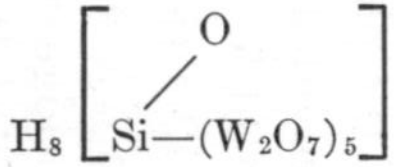 $H_8\left[O{=}Si-(W_2O_7)_5\right]$	$K_8[SiO(W_2O_7)_5] \cdot 17H_2O$	Only a few show highest basicity
9-acid	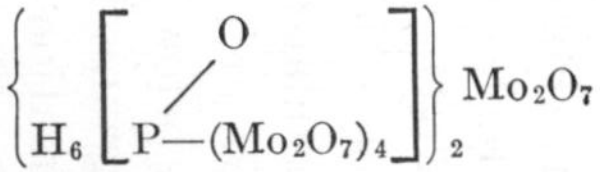 $H_6\left[O{=}P-(W_2O_7)_4{\begin{smallmatrix}Mo_2O_7\\ Mo_2O_7\end{smallmatrix}}\right]_2$	$[CN_3H_6]_{12}[P_2O_2(Mo_2O_7)_9] \cdot 30H_2O$	Only a few show highest basicity
8½-acid	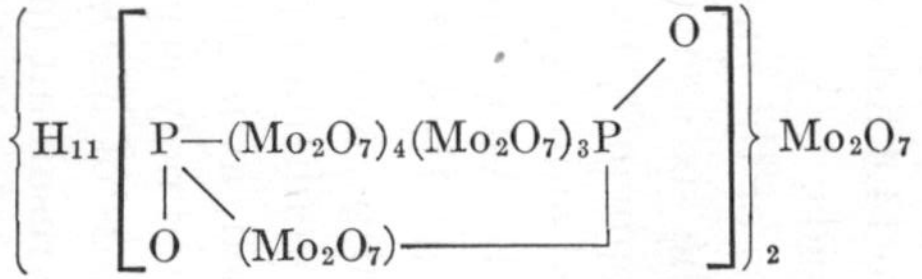 $H_{11}\left[O{=}P-(Mo_2O_7)_4(Mo_2O_7)_3P{\begin{smallmatrix}O\\ (Mo_2O_7)\\ O\end{smallmatrix}}Mo_2O_7\right]_2$	$Ag_{22}[P_4O_4(Mo_2O_7)_{17}] \cdot 40H_2O$	Only a few show highest basicity
8-acid	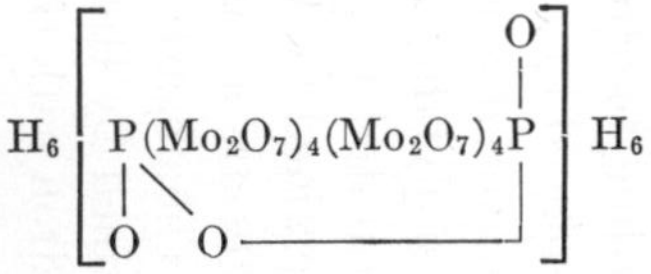 $H_6\left[{\begin{smallmatrix}O\\ O\end{smallmatrix}}{=}P(Mo_2O_7)_4(Mo_2O_7)_4P{\begin{smallmatrix}O\\ O\end{smallmatrix}}\right]H_6$	$Ag_{12}[P_2O_3(Mo_2O_7)_8] \cdot 20H_2O$	Other parent acids have also been formulated

TABLE 14.6. SOME POLY-ACIDS AND SALTS IN WHICH TETRACOORDINATION IS EXHIBITED

Class of Acid	Acid	Salt
3-acid	$H_3[AsO(MoO_4)_3]$	$Na_3[AsO(MoO_4)_3] \cdot 7H_2O$
$2\frac{1}{2}$-acid	$(H_3[P(O)(OH)(MO_4)_2])_2MO_4$	$Li_6[P_2(MO_4)_5O_2(OH)_2] \cdot 16H_2O$

the central atom. They proposed that in the case of mangano(IV)-5-tungstic acid, for example, the parent acid has the formula $H_8[Mn^{IV}O(WO_4)_5]$ and they describe the salt $Na_6H_2[MnO(WO_4)_5]$.

Difficulties are encountered with the acids and salts lower than the 5-series. Only by assuming tetracoordination of the central atom of these acids was Rosenheim[16] able to include them in his system of classification. Some typical examples of such compounds are given in Table 14.6.

Isopoly-Acids

Since the isopoly 12-tungstates are isomorphous with the 22-hydrates of the boro-, silico-, and phospho-12-tungstates, and since 12-tungstic acid does not lose all of its water on ignition, Rosenheim and Felix[18] proposed that these isopoly-acids be considered as a type of heteropoly-acid. They postulated the hypothetical parent acid $(H_2O)_6$ or $H_{10}[H_2O_6]$, with the H_2^{++} group acting as the central ion of the heteropoly-acid. The six oxygen atoms, supposedly octahedrally located about the H_2^{++} central group, are then replaced by $W_2O_7^=$ groups producing the hydrated 12-tungstic acid, $H_{10}[H_2(W_2O_7)_6]$. The 6-acids were similarly included in Rosenheim's scheme[17] by proposing a replacement of the six oxygens by $WO_4^=$ groups to give the hydrated 6-tungstic acid, $H_{10}[H_2(WO_4)_6]$. Rosenheim treated the isopoly molybdic acids in a like manner by postulating the replacement of the six oxygens of the "aquo acid" core, $H_{10}[H_2O_6]$, by $Mo_2O_7^=$ or $MoO_4^=$ groups.

The vanadium poly-acids were also brought into this classification by Rosenheim and Pieck[17] who proposed the existence of another hypothetical aquo acid, $H_4[H_2O_3]$. By replacing each oxygen with two VO_3^- groups, the aquo-6-vanadic acid, $H_4[H_2(VO_3)_6]$, is formed. In order to explain the penta-vanadates, it was postulated that aquo-6-vanadic acid undergoes partial hydrolysis with the replacement of a VO_3^- group by an OH^- group to give aquopentavanadic acid, $H_4[H_2(VO_3)_5OH]$.

It was proposed that the aggregation processes occurred in solution through the following reaction mechanisms:

Polymolybdates:

$$(MoO_4)^- \underset{OH^-}{\overset{H^+}{\rightleftharpoons}} (Mo_2O_7)^- \underset{OH^-}{\overset{H^+}{\rightleftharpoons}} (H_2(MoO_4)_6)^{10-} \rightleftharpoons (H_2(Mo_2O_7)_6)^{10-} \rightleftharpoons (MoO_3)_x$$

18. Rosenheim and Felix, *Z. anorg. Chem.*, **79**, 292 (1913).

Polytungstates:

$$(WO_4)^- \xrightleftharpoons[OH^-]{H^+} (W_2O_7)^= \rightleftharpoons (H_2(WO_4)_6)^{10-} \rightleftharpoons (H_2(W_2O_7)_6)^{10-} \rightleftharpoons (WO_3)_x$$

Polyvanadates:

$$(VO_4)^= \xrightleftharpoons[OH^-]{H^+} (V_2O_7)^{4-} \rightleftharpoons (V_3O_9)^= \rightleftharpoons (H_2(VO_3)_6)^{4-} \rightleftharpoons (V_2O_5)_x$$

Critical Discussion of Rosenheim's Postulates

Rosenheim's work was based upon several different types of chemical and physical evidence, but he did not have access to methods, such as x-ray analysis[19], which were developed and refined several years after his ideas were published. As a result, his structural theories suffered accordingly. A very important part of his work, however, involved the careful preparation and analysis of salts with the accurate determination of the amount of constitutional water which cannot be removed except by ignition at high temperatures. His work in this field was extensive and carefully carried out.

Determinations of the maximum basicities of the different salts were also made, but Rosenheim was able to isolate only a few salts in which the maximum basicity of his hypothetical acids was attained (see Tables 14.3 to 14.6). In most cases, the compounds formed could be explained only by postulating a partial replacement of the hydrogen ions by basic groups to give the acid salts. Conductivity measurements and conductometric titrations were also utilized by Rosenheim, but the results obtained by these methods can easily be interpreted to fit other theories. Furthermore, later workers, using modern experimental techniques, have shown that several of his proposed structures (e.g., those for the polyvanadates) are incorrect.

One of the most important objections to Rosenheim's theory, however, is the postulate concerning the existence of M_2O_7 groups in solution. Although such "pyro" radicals have definitely been shown to exist in acid solution in the chromic acid series, it has not been conclusively demonstrated that such radicals exist in other acid series. (However, Ripan and Poppei[20] have concluded that the $W_2O_7^=$ group may exist as such in silico-12-tungstic acid.)

Another objection to Rosenheim's postulates arises when one considers that almost all of the poly-acids and salts reported contain a great deal of water of hydration. Rosenheim proposed that the 12-acids could contain up to only thirty molecules of water of hydration for each central metalloid atom, but hydrates containing more than thirty tightly bound waters per central atom have since been reported[21]. It becomes impossible, therefore, to reconcile the large numbers of water molecules with the structural ideas proposed by Rosenheim for the poly-acids.

19. Sturdivant, *J. Am. Chem. Soc.*, **59**, 530 (1937).
20. Ripan and Poppei, *Bul. Soc. Stunte Cluj*, **10**, 85 (1948).
21. Kraus, *Z. Krist*, **91**, 402 (1935); **93**, 379 (1936).

The Work of Pfeiffer

The many objections to Rosenheim's postulates brought forth by different investigators initiated extensive studies in this field. Various experimental approaches were used, among them x-ray diffraction techniques[22]. After Laue, Bragg, Delize, and others had shown that crystals follow the crystallographic coordination laws, Pfeiffer[23] attempted to explain the structures of the heteropoly tungstates by utilizing these laws. He accepted Rosenheim's view that the poly-acids are derived from hypothetical parent acids (i.e., $H_{12-n}X^{n+}O_6$), and he postulated that WO_3 groups, for example, coordinate in a second coordination sphere about the central $[XO_6]^{n-12}$ group, which can have a coordination number as high as twelve. Hence, phospho-12-tungstic acid should really be formulated as $H_7[(PO_6)(WO_3)_{12}]$, according to Pfeiffer.

He proposed an imaginary cube containing the $[XO_6]^{12-n}$ group at the center as the basis for the structure of the poly-acids, since this would allow coordination numbers of various magnitudes. For tetracoordination, the four WO_3 groups would occupy alternate corners of the cube, giving a tetrahedral type of structure about the central $[XO_6]^{n-12}$ group. For a coordination number of six, the WO_3 groups would be at the face-centers of the cube, giving an octahedral structure, and for twelve-coordination, the WO_3 groups would be located at the centers of the edges of the cube, giving a cubo-octahedral arrangement.

Although the structures postulated by Pfeiffer are no longer believed correct, his ideas foreshadowed the developments made by Pauling, Keggin, and others which led to the structures accepted today for many of the poly-acids.

LATER VIEWS ON THE STRUCTURE OF THE POLY-ACIDS

The Work of Pauling

In 1928, Pauling[24] and later Riesenfeld and Tobiank[25] proposed some ideas concerning the structure of the 12-heteropoly-acids which are quite different from those of Rosenheim, but which bear some resemblance to those of Pfeiffer. Pauling postulated a tetrahedral $[XO_4]^{n-8}$ central ion, where X is Sn^{IV}, P^V, etc. (see Table 14.1), which is surrounded by twelve WO_6 octahedra, each octahedron sharing three of its oxygens with three neighboring octahedra—thus forming a shell of these octahedra about the central tetrahedral group. Consequently, a total of eighteen oxygen atoms would act as bridging oxygens. In addition, each of the three free oxygens

22. Groth, "Chemische Kristallography," Vol. II, Leipzig, Englemann, 1908.
23. Pfeiffer, *Z. anorg. allgem. Chem.*, **105**, 26 (1919).
24. Pauling, *J. Am. Chem. Soc.*, **51**, 2868 (1929).
25. Riesenfeld and Tobiank, *Z. anorg. allgem. Chem.*, **221**, 287 (1935).

TABLE 14.7. PAULING'S FORMULATION OF SOME 12-POLYTUNGSTIC ACIDS

Formula	Name
$H_4[(SiO_4)W_{12}O_{18}(OH)_{36}]$	Silico-12-tungstic acid
$H_3[(PO_4)W_{12}O_{18}(OH)_{36}]$	Phospho-12-tungstic acid
$H_6[(H_2O_4)W_{12}O_{18}(OH)_{36}]$	12-Tungstic acid

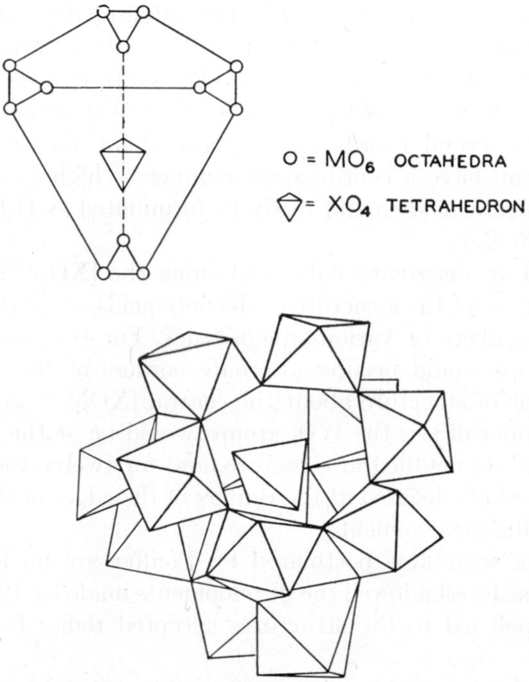

O = MO$_6$ OCTAHEDRA

▽= XO$_4$ TETRAHEDRON

FIG. 14.1. Structure of the 12-heteropoly-acids as proposed by Pauling[24]

on every octahedron is believed to take up a proton (making a total of thirty-six OH groups) which results in compounds such as shown in Table 14.7. The isomorphous isopoly-acids were postulated as having a similar structure with an $[H_2O_4]^{6-}$ ion acting as the central group.

It was felt that the stability of these ions is due to the presence of the negative central group surrounded by highly charged metal cations in the octahedra, and to the completion of a close-packed structure, which is due to oxygen-oxygen contact between the tetrahedrally and octahedrally located oxygens. Figure 14.1 shows the location of the octahedra (each octahedron having an oxygen in common with each of its three nearest neighbors) about the central tetrahedron, as proposed by Pauling[24].

Pauling's structures account for the high basicities observed in the alkali metal salts of these acids quite well. In addition, those salts containing eighteen or more molecules of water per acid anion can readily be explained using these structures. However, Scroggie and Clark[26] and Kahane and Kahane[27] report dehydrated acids, such as the silico-12-tungstic acid, $H_4[SiW_{12}O_{40}]$, and an 8-hydrate, $H_4[SiW_{12}O_{40}] \cdot 8H_2O$, the structures of which are quite difficult to explain on the basis of Pauling's ideas, since these acids contain considerably less than eighteen molecules of water per acid anion.

Keggin's Contributions

Subsequently, additional investigations were undertaken by Horan[28] and Keggin[29] using x-ray techniques. Keggin[29c] studied the phospho-12-tungstic acid having the formula $H_3[PW_{12}O_{40}] \cdot 5H_2O$ and found that the $[PW_{12}O_{40}]^{\equiv}$ anion has the following structure (see Fig. 14.2): a central PO_4 tetrahedron is surrounded by a total of twelve WO_6 octahedra, each oxygen of the PO_4 tetrahedron being common to three of the WO_6 octahedra. In addition, each WO_6 octahedron has four of its remaining five oxygens in common with its four nearest neighbors, while one oxygen on each octahedron remains free (bonded only to the central metal atom of the octahedron), thus making a $[PW_{12}O_{40}]^{\equiv}$ group.

The twelve tungsten atoms lie just about on the centers of the edges of a large cube ($a_0 = 12.14$ A) which has the phosphorus atom at the center. It can be seen that there are large spaces between the atoms in such an arrangement, which accounts for the existence of hydrates containing a large number of water molecules, such as $H_3[PW_{12}O_{40}] \cdot 29H_2O$ [30]. Such hydrates should be readily dehydrated by heat without undergoing any important structural changes with respect to the framework of interconnected octahedra. This has been found to be the case by Signer and Gross[31], Santos[32], and Jander and his co-workers[33].

A large number of heteropoly 12-tungstates have been prepared by Kraus and his co-workers[22, 34] and others[35, 36, 37], and the x-ray data for these salts

26. Scroggie and Clark, *Proc. Nat. Acad. Sci., Wash.*, **15**, 1 (1929).
27. Kahane and Kahane, *Bull. soc. chim.*, [4] **49**, 557 (1931).
28. Horan, *Z. Krist.*, **84**, 217 (1933).
29. Keggin, *Nature*, **131**, 908 (1933); **132**, 351 (1933); *Proc. Roy. Soc., A*, **144**, 75 (1934); Illingsworth and Keggin, *J. Chem. Soc.*, **1935**, 575.
30. Bradley and Illingsworth, *Proc. Roy. Soc., A*, **157**, 113 (1936).
31. Signer and Gross, *Helv. Chim. Acta*, **17**, 1076 (1936).
32. Santos, *Proc. Roy. Soc., A*, **150**, 309 (1935).
33. Jander and Heukeshoven, *Z. anorg. allgem. Chem.*, **187**, 60 (1930); Jander and Banthieu, *ibid.*, **225**, 162 (1935); Jander and Exner, *Z. phys. Chem.*, **190**, 195 (1942).
34. Kraus, *Z. Krist., A*, **94**, 256 (1936); **96**, 330 (1937); **100**, 394 (1939); Kraus, *Naturwissenschaften*, **27**, 740 (1939); **28**, 304 (1940); Kraus and Musgnug, *ibid.*, **28**, 238 (1940).
35. Ferrari and Nanni, *Gaz. chim. ital.*, **69**, 301 (1939).
36. Brintzinger, *Naturwissenschaften*, **18**, 354 (1930); Brintzinger and Ratanarat, *Z. anorg. allgem. Chem.*, **224**, 97 (1935).

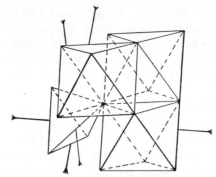

FIG. 14.2A. An oxygen of the central tetrahedron shown in common with three MO_6 octahedra[29c]

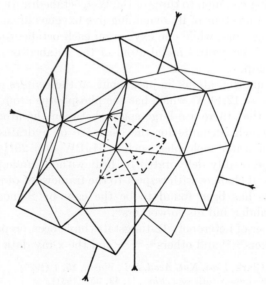

FIG. 14.2B. The structure of the $PW_{12}O_{40}^=$ anion[29c]

indicate that they possess the basic $[X^{n+}W_{12}O_{40}]^{n-8}$ structure proposed for the 12-acids by Keggin, so it can now be considered essentially correct.

Furthermore, the cage structure proposed by Keggin is complete in itself, even if the four innermost oxygens are not bonded to a central X^{n+} atom. Therefore, the artificial postulate of a central ion formed from condensed water molecules, such as $[H_2O_4]^{6-}$, which was proposed for the metatungstates, may now be abandoned, and metatungstic acid can be formulated as $H_8[W_{12}O_{40}]$.

37. Schulz and Jander, *Z. anorg. allgem. Chem.*, **162**, 141 (1927); Horan, *J. Am. Chem. Soc.*, **61**, 2022 (1939); Jander and Schulz, *Kolloid. Z.*, **36**, 113 (1925).

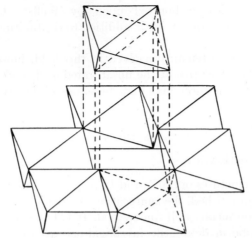

FIG. 14.3. The structure of the $[TeMo_6O_{24}]^{6-}$ anion[38]

Structural Studies on the 6-Poly-Acids

The 6-heteropoly-acids, such as $H_{12-n}[X^{n+}Mo_6O_{24}]$, and the para-isopoly-acids, such as $H_6[Mo_7O_{24}]$, have been shown to possess structures which are quite different from those of the 12-poly-acids, although they still contain the basic octahedral unit in their structures.

Anderson[38] has suggested that in the case of the 6-heteropoly molybdates, for example, six MoO_6 octahedra are located at the corners of an imaginary hexagon, and that each octahedron shares two corners (i.e., an edge) with each of its two nearest neighbors, giving the (Mo_6O_{24}) unit. Such a configuration results in an opening at the center of the hexagon which will just accommodate another octahedron, so the central cation X^{n+} can then be centrally placed in the hexagon where it will share the six nearest oxygens of the (Mo_6O_{24}) unit, resulting in the $[X^{n+}Mo_6O_{24}]^{n-12}$ anion (see Fig. 14.3).

Evans[39] was able to verify this type of structure for $(NH_4)_6[TeMo_6O_{24}] \cdot 7H_2O$, and it is interesting to note that only those elements which can exhibit a coordination number of six (with valences directed octahedrally) have been reported as central ions in the 6-poly-acids (e.g., I, Te, Fe, etc.) lending additional support to the above structure.

According to Lindqvist[40], the para-molybdates, $R_6[Mo_7O_{24}]$, have a structure similar to that of the heteropoly molybdates. In this case, a molybdenum atom is centrally located, to give $R_6[MoMo_6O_{24}]$.

38. Anderson, *Nature*, **140**, 850 (1937).
39. Evans, *J. Am. Chem. Soc.*, **70**, 1291 (1948).
40. Lindqvist, *Arkiv. F. Kemi*, **2**, 325, 349 (1950).

These proposals are elaborated upon by Wells[41], O'Daniel[42], and others[43, 44] who include other acids in addition to the limiting 6- and 12-acid series.

Additional problems remain unsolved in this field, however, especially with regard to the structures of the unsaturated acids and to the relationship between the structures and high basicities observed for these compounds.

AGGREGATION STUDIES OF THE POLY-ACIDS IN SOLUTION

Methods of Investigation

Although the structures of the 6- and 12-poly-acids in the solid state have been fairly well established, the aggregation and degradation phenomena in solution are by no means well understood. It is beyond the scope of this volume to describe in detail the investigations carried out in this field, although brief mention may be made of the different types of physical and chemical methods employed in these researches.

In attempting to determine the degree of aggregation of poly-anions in solution, Bjerrum[45] and others[46, 47] utilized pH measurements, but met with difficulties due to the simultaneous occurrence of hydrolysis, olation, and other poly-nuclear aggregation processes (see Chapter 13).

Potentiometric, conductometric, and thermometric titration methods have also been employed[33a, 33c, 48], as well as spectral absorption measurements, in efforts to determine the extent of aggregation of these acid anions.

Diffusion measurements were used in an attempt to obtain the molecular

41. Wells, *Phil. Mag.*, **30**, 103 (1940).
42. O'Daniel, *Z. Krist. A*, **104**, 225 (1942).
43. Jahr, *Naturwissenschaften*, **29**, 505 (1941).
44. Santos, *Rev. faculdade ciênc., Univ. Coimbra*, **16**, 5 (1947).
45. Bjerrum, *Z. phys. Chem.*, **59**, 350 (1907); **110**, 657 (1924).
46. Souchay, *Ann. chim.*, [11] **18**, 61, 169 (1943); Carpeni and Souchay, *J. chim. phys.*, **42**, 149 (1945); Souchay and Carpeni, *Bull. soc. chim.*, **13**, 160 (1946); Souchay and Faucherre, *ibid.*, **1951**, 355; Souchay, *ibid.*, **1953**, 395.
47. Britton, *J. Chem. Soc.*, **1930**, 1249; Vallance and Pritchett, *ibid.*, **1935**, 1586; Buchholz, *Z. anorg. allgem. Chem.*, **244**, 168 (1940); Bye, *Bull. soc. chim.*, **9**, 360 (1942); Britton and Wellford, *J. Chem. Soc.*, **1940**, 764; Ripan and Liteanu, *Compt. rend.*, **224**, 196 (1947).
48. Mayer and Fisch, *Z. anal. Chem.*, **76**, 418 (1929); Bye, *Ann. chim.*, [11] **20**, 463 (1945); Britton, *Endeavor*, **2**, 148 (1943); Ghosh and Biswas, *J. Indian Chem. Soc.*, **22**, 287, 295 (1945); Dullberg, *Z. phys. Chem.*, **45**, 119 (1903); Murgulescu and Alexa, *Z. anal. Chem.*, **123**, 341 (1942); Carrier and Guiter, *Bull. soc. chim.*, **12**, 329 (1945); Pierce and Yntema, *J. Phys. Chem.*, **34**, 1822 (1930); Britton and Robinson, *J. Chem. Soc.*, **1932**, 2265; Bye, *Bull. soc. chim.*, **1953**, 390; Hormann, *Z. anorg. Chem.*, **177**, 145 (1928).

weights of the poly-acids in solution. Prytz[49] and Jander and Jahr and co-workers[33b, 37a, 50] utilized Riecke's Law[51] that the square root of the molecular weight of a substance is inversely proportional to its diffusion coefficient, and they felt that they were able to estimate molecular weights with an accuracy of about 5 per cent.

Brintzinger and his co-workers[36, 52] were fairly successful in utilizing electrodialysis methods for the determination of molecular weights, and this method was later used by Jander[33c, 53] for the same purpose.

Gupta[54] and Theodoresco[55] have investigated poly-acids and their salts in solution and in the crystalline state by means of Raman spectra, but it appears difficult to draw definite conclusions concerning the degree of aggregation of these materials in solution from their spectra.

Doucet[56] and other workers[48b, 57] attempted cryoscopic determinations of molecular weights, and obtained results which were in agreement with those obtained polarographically by Souchay.

Magneto-chemical studies were carried out by Das and Râit[58], who noted changes in magnetic susceptibility with changes in pH, and phase studies were performed by Kiehl and Manfredo[59] and Makarow and Repa[60] which gave evidence for the existence of poly-anionic aggregates.

Preparations of the Poly-Acids

Many other investigations have been conducted, employing variations of one or more of the above methods. Furthermore, a large number of studies

49. Prytz, *Z. anorg. allgem. Chem.*, **174**, 360 (1928).
50. Jander and Jahr, *Koll. Beihefte*, **41**, 1 (1934); Jander, Mojert, and Aden, *Z. anorg. allgem. Chem.*, **162**, 141 (1927); Jahr and Witzmann, *ibid.*, **208**, 145 (1932); Jander and Jahr, *Koll. Beihefte*, **41**, 297 (1935); Jander and Drew, *Z. phys. Chem.*, **190**, 217 (1942); Jander and Jahr, *Z. anorg. allgem. Chem.*, **220**, 201 (1934); **212**, 1 (1933); Jahr and Witzmann, *Z. phys. Chem.*, **168**, 283 (1934); Jander and Aden, *ibid.*, **144**, 197 (1929); Jander and Schulz, *Z. anorg. allgem. Chem.*, **144**, 225 (1925).
51. Riecke, *Z. phys. Chem.*, **6**, 564 (1890).
52. Brintzinger, *Z. anorg. allgem. Chem.*, **196**, 55 (1931); Brintzinger and Wallok, *ibid.*, **224**, 103 (1935).
53. Jander, *Z. phys. Chem.*, **187**, 149 (1940).
54. Gupta, *J. Indian Chem. Soc.*, **12**, 223 (1938).
55. Theodoresco, *Compt. rend.*, **208**, 1308 (1939); **210**, 175 (1940); **210**, 297 (1940); **211**, 28 (1940); **214**, 169 (1942); **215**, 530 (1942); **216**, 56 (1943).
56. Doucet, *Compt. rend.*, **208**, 577 (1939); *J. phys. radium*, [8] **4**, 41 (1943).
57. Souchay, *Ann. chim.*, [11] **20**, 74, 96 (1945); [12] **1**, 232, 249 (1946); [12] **2**, 203, 229 (1947).
58. Das and Râit, *J. Indian Chem. Soc.*, **21**, 159 (1944).
59. Kiehl and Manfredo, *J. Am. Chem. Soc.*, **59**, 2118 (1933).
60. Makarow and Repa, *Bull. ac. sci. U.R.S.S.*, **1940**, 349.

concerned with the preparation and properties of heteropoly- and isopoly-
acids, in addition to those already mentioned, have been carried out in
recent years[61]. Among these are reports[61o, 61p, 61y] of some interesting compounds composed of heteropoly anions and chelate-containing cations, such
as [Cu(en)$_2$]$_2$[SiW$_{12}$O$_{40}$]·2H$_2$O.

These studies have greatly increased our knowledge of the poly-acids and
their salts. However, much remains to be clarified, especially with regard to
the solution chemistry of these acids and salts, and it is hoped that research
workers will continue to investigate the many unsolved problems in this
field.

61. Bye, *Bull. soc. chim.*, **10**, 239 (1943); Klason, *Ber.*, **34**, 153 (1901); Junius, *Z. anorg. allgem. Chem.*, **46**, 428 (1905); Wempe, *ibid.*, **78**, 298 (1912); Sand and Eisen-lohr, *ibid.*, **52**, 68 (1907); Jander, Jahr, and Heukeshoven, *ibid.*, **194**, 383 (1930); Ullik, *Ann.*, **153**, 373 (1870); Travers and Malaprade, *Compt. rend.*, **183**, 292, 533 (1926); Garelli and Tettamanzi, *Chem. Abstr.*, **29**, 7864 (1935); Ray and Siddhanta, *J. Indian Chem. Soc.*, **18**, 397 (1941); Ray, *ibid.*, **21**, 139 (1944); Guiter, *Ann. chim.*, [11] **15**, 5 (1941); Rosenheim, *Z. anorg. allgem. Chem.*, **96**, 139 (1916); **220**, 73 (1934); **96**, 139 (1916); Lachartre, *Bull. soc. chim.*, **35**, 321 (1924); Parks and Prebluda, *J. Am. Chem. Soc.*, **57**, 1676 (1935); Huffman, *ibid.*, **60**, 2227 (1938); Guiter, *Compt rend.*, **209**, 561 (1939); Marignac, *Ann. chim.*, [4] **8**, 5 (1866); Windmaisser, *Oster. Chem. Ztg.*, **45**, 201 (1942); Balke and Smith, *J. Am. Chem. Soc.*, **30**, 1651 (1908); Russ, *Z. anorg. Chem.*, **31**, 60 (1902); Sue, *Ann. chim.*, **7**, 493 (1937); Sue, *Compt. rend.*, **208**, 440 (1939); Ferrari, Cavelca, and Nardelli, *Gazz. chim. ital.*, **78**, 551 (1948); **79**, 61 (1949); **80**, 352 (1950); Jean, *Ann. chim.*, [12] **3**, 470 (1948).

15. Coordination Compounds of Metal Ions with Olefins and Olefin-Like Substances

Bodie E. Douglas

The University of Pittsburgh, Pittsburgh, Pennsylvania

Coordination compounds of olefins with compounds of the heavy metals were discovered before the advent of Werner's theory, but the problem of explaining how they are formed and why they are stable is still perplexing. Ethylene has no unshared pair of electrons which it can share with the metal as do ammonia and other common ligands. Olefinic complexes take on added importance since some workers believe that they supply a crucial test of the generally accepted view that the coordinate covalent bond results from the sharing of a "lone pair" of electrons furnished by the ligand. Excellent reviews on these compounds have been written by Keller[1] and by Chatt[2].

The complexes of platinum with unsaturated molecules are generally more stable than those of other metals, and the olefins generally form more stable complexes than do unsaturated alcohols, aldehydes, acids, esters, halogenated hydrocarbons, and aromatic substances. Because of their stability, the platinum-olefin complexes have been studied most extensively.

Compounds That Have Been Reported

Platinum-olefin Compounds

The first report of a platinum-olefin compound was published by Zeise[3] in 1827. The work was further described in later publications[4]. In 1830 Berzelius[5] announced that by refluxing a mixture of alcohol and sodium hexachloroplatinate(IV), a very acid solution was formed; this yielded

1. Keller, *Chem. Rev.*, **28,** 229 (1941).
2. Chatt, *J. Chem. Soc.*, **1949,** 3340.
3. Zeise, *Pogg. Ann.*, **9,** 632 (1827).
4. Zeise, *Magaz. f. Pharm.*, **35,** 105 (1830); *Pogg. Ann.*, **21,** 497 (1931); *Schweiggers Journal der Chemic v. Physik*, **62,** 393 (1831); **63,** 121 (1831).
5. Berzelius, *Jahresber*, **9,** 162 (1830).

yellow crystals when concentrated and treated with potassium chloride. The analysis of this compound conformed to the composition reported by Zeise. Zeise had prepared the compound (reported on an anhydrous basis as $KCl \cdot PtCl_2 \cdot C_2H_4$) by boiling platinum(IV) chloride with alcohol and adding potassium chloride. The analyses were challenged by Liebig[6], but Zeise[7] repeated them and confirmed the presence of ethylene. The potassium and ammonium salts usually obtained by such a procedure are the 1-hydrates, which probably accounts for Liebig's insistence that the radical $C_4H_{10}O$ was present and that the correct formula was $2KCl \cdot 2PtCl_2 \cdot C_4H_{10}O$.

Zeise also prepared a compound reported as $PtCl_2 \cdot C_2H_4$, but it is more likely that this was impure $H[PtC_2H_4Cl_3]$, now known as "Zeise's acid." The nonionic compound $[Pt(NH_3)(C_2H_4)Cl_2]$ was also reported by Zeise.

Zeise's formula was confirmed by Griess and Martius[8], who also demonstrated that ethylene was liberated during the thermal decomposition of Zeise's salt. Some doubt concerning the presence of ethylene in the original compound still existed, however, since appreciable amounts of platinum and carbonaceous substances were among the decomposition products. Birnbaum[9] proved the presence of ethylene when he synthesized Zeise's salt by treating platinum(II) chloride in hydrochloric acid solution with ethylene, followed by the addition of potassium chloride. Birnbaum also prepared the propylene and amylene analogs of Zeise's salt. He described Zeise's preparation by the equation

$$PtCl_4 + 2C_2H_5OH \rightarrow PtCl_2 \cdot C_2H_4 + CH_3CHO + H_2O + 2HCl$$

Allyl alcohol[10] and unsaturated acids[11] with the double bond in the β-position, or farther from the carboxyl group, form compounds similar to those of ethylene. Additional analogs of Zeise's salt, containing unsaturated acids, esters, alcohols, and aldehydes, have been prepared[12].

The compound containing only platinum(II) chloride and ethylene, $PtCl_2 \cdot C_2H_4$ (actually shown later to be a dimer), was prepared by Anderson[13] by reducing sodium hexachloroplatinate(IV) with alcohol. The resulting solution was evaporated in a high vacuum and the ethylene-platinum(II) chloride was extracted with chloroform from the tarry, strongly acid mass. Anderson[14] was also able to isolate $PtCl_2 \cdot C_6H_5CH{=}CH_2$

6. Liebig, *Ann.*, **9**, 1 (1834); **23**, 12 (1837).
7. Zeise, *Ann.*, **23**, 1 (1837); *Pogg. Ann.*, **40**, 234 (1837).
8. Griess and Martius, *Ann.*, **120**, 324 (1861); *Compt. rend.*, **53**, 122 (1861).
9. Birnbaum, *Ann.*, **145**, 67 (1869).
10. Biilmann, *Ber.*, **33**, 2196 (1900).
11. Biilmann and Hoff, *Rec. trav. chim.*, **36**, 306 (1916).
12. Pfeiffer and Hoyer, *Z. anorg. allgem. chem.*, **211**, 241 (1933).
13. Anderson, *J. Chem. Soc.*, **1934**, 971.
14. Anderson, *J. Chem. Soc.*, **1936**, 1042.

by the essentially quantitative displacement of ethylene by styrene from $PtCl_2 \cdot C_2H_4$. By the same method, Anderson prepared $K[Pt(C_6H_5CH{=}CH_2)Cl_3]$ from Zeise's salt and styrene. He established an order of stability for the complexes based on the displacement reactions and considerations of the relative volatility of the hydrocarbons. The stability decreased from ethylene in the order $CH_2{=}CH_2 > C_6H_5CH{=}CH_2 >$ indene > cyclohexene > $(C_6H_5)_2C{=}CH_2$, $(C_6H_5)(CH_3)C{=}CH_2$.

A fairly general method of preparation of the olefin complexes was devised by Kharasch and Ashford[15], who treated anhydrous platinum(IV) chloride or bromide with the unsaturated substance in an anhydrous solvent. Chloro-substituted olefins react satisfactorily, but unsaturated acids and esters do not yield complexes by this method.

A variety of compounds of platinum with unsaturated substances has been prepared by Russian workers. Chernyaev and Hel'man[16] prepared Zeise's salt by passing ethylene, for 15 days, through a concentrated aqueous solution of potassium tetrachloroplatinate(II) containing 3 to 5 per cent of hydrochloric acid, followed by precipitation of $[Pt(NH_3)_4]$ $[PtC_2H_4Cl_3]_2$. Compounds of the type $[Pt\ R\ C_2H_4\ X_2]$ were also prepared. The stability[16a] of these compounds was reported to decrease in the order: R = quinoline > pyridine > ammonia > thiourea and X = Cl^- > Br^- > I^- > NO_2^- > NCS^- > CN^-. From the study of a series of complexes containing several unsaturated substances, Hel'man[17] arrived at a stability series differing from Anderson's in that styrene was placed above ethylene. The order given by her is NO > CO > styrene > butadiene, ethylene > propene > butene. The difference is probably due to the qualitative nature of the work, since relative volatilities and solubilities were not considered. Butadiene was found to occupy only one coordination position per metal ion instead of forming a chelate ring, although a compound was isolated in which one butadiene was coordinated to two platinum atoms, forming the bridged $(NH_4)_2[(PtCl_3)_2C_4H_6]$[18]. The bridged butadiene complex was found to react with ethylenediamine to give a long-chain polymer, $[-CH_2NH_2PtCl_2-CH_2{=}CHCH{=}CH_2-PtCl_2NH_2CH_2-]_n$[19]. Similarly Zeise's salt was found to react with ethylenediamine to give a bridged compound, $[C_2H_4Cl_2Pt-NH_2C_2H_4NH_2-PtCl_2C_2H_4]$, rather than the expected chelate compound.

15. Kharasch and Ashford, *J. Am. Chem. Soc.*, **58**, 1733 (1936).
16. Chernyaev and Hel'man, *Ann. secteur platine, Inst. chim. gen.* (U.S.S.R.), No. 14, 77 (1937); Hel'man, *Sci. Repts. Leningrad State Univ.*, **2**, No. 2, 5 (1936); Chernyaev and Hel'man, *Compt. rend. Acad. Sci.*, *U.R.S.S.(N.S.)*, **4**, 181 (1936).
17. Hel'man, *Compt. rend. acad. sci.*, *U.R.S.S.*, **20**, 307 (1938); **32**, 347 (1941).
18. Hel'man, *Compt. rend. acad. sci.*, *U.R.S.S.*, **23**, 532 (1939).
19. Hel'man, *Doklady Akad. Nauk S.S.S.R.*, **38**, 272 (1943).

Cationic complexes[20] have been prepared by the following reactions:

cis-[PtNH$_3$C$_2$H$_4$Cl$_2$] $\xrightarrow{\text{AgNO}_3}$ [PtNH$_3$C$_2$H$_4$ClNO$_3$] $\xrightarrow{\text{H}_2\text{O}}$

$$[PtH_2ONH_3C_2H_4Cl]\ NO_3 \xrightarrow{\text{pyridine}} [Pt\ py\ NH_3C_2H_4Cl]NO_3\ .$$

Hel'man reported that the final compound was a white crystalline substance which was very soluble in water and which decomposed on standing in air. It reacted with chloride ion to give the original starting material. All three possible isomers of the compound [PtNH$_3$C$_2$H$_4$ClBr] were isolated by Hel'man and co-workers[21]. The compound with the halides in trans positions was obtained by treating Zeise's salt with potassium bromide and then with ammonia. The other isomers were prepared as follows:

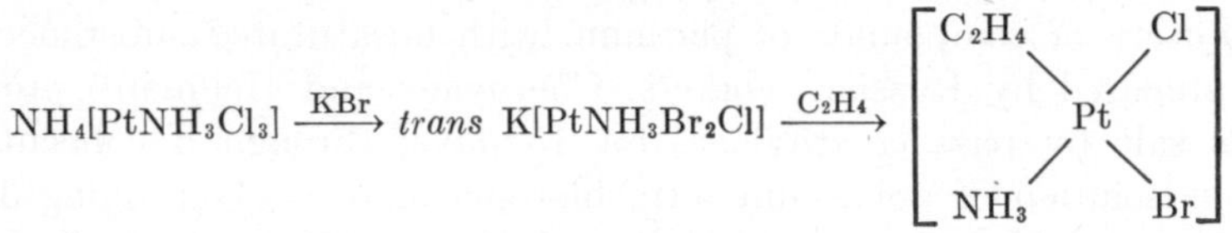

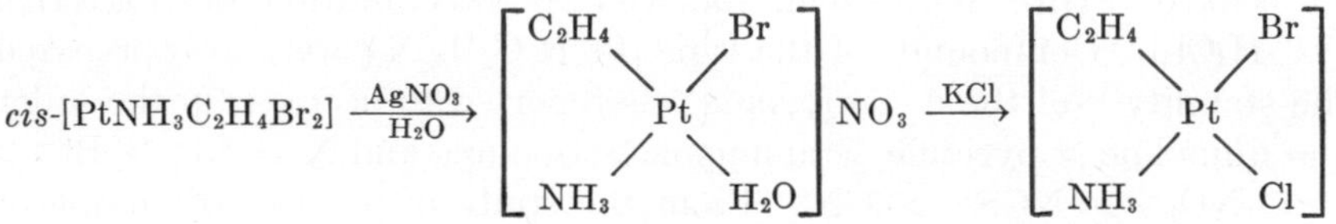

$$NH_4[PtNH_3Cl_3] \xrightarrow{\text{KBr}} trans\ K[PtNH_3Br_2Cl] \xrightarrow{\text{C}_2\text{H}_4}
\begin{bmatrix} C_2H_4 & & Cl \\ & Pt & \\ NH_3 & & Br \end{bmatrix}$$

$$cis\text{-}[PtNH_3C_2H_4Br_2] \xrightarrow[\text{H}_2\text{O}]{\text{AgNO}_3}
\begin{bmatrix} C_2H_4 & & Br \\ & Pt & \\ NH_3 & & H_2O \end{bmatrix} NO_3 \xrightarrow{\text{KCl}}
\begin{bmatrix} C_2H_4 & & Br \\ & Pt & \\ NH_3 & & Cl \end{bmatrix}$$

Cis and trans isomers of the compounds [Pt R C$_2$H$_4$ Cl$_2$], where R is ammonia or pyridine, have also been obtained by Chernyaev and Hel'man[22]. In the preparation of the isomers of the platinum ethylene compounds, the Russian workers have taken advantage of the high *trans effect* of ethylene, resulting in easy substitution in the position trans to ethylene. The trans compounds result from the addition of an amine to Zeise's salt, while the cis isomers are formed by the addition of ethylene to compounds of the type K[PtNH$_3$Cl$_3$]. (Chapter 4)

Hel'man and Essen[23] studied the complexes of allylamine with platinum. Addition of allylamine to K$_2$PtCl$_6$ gave [Pt(C$_3$H$_7$N)$_2$Cl$_2$] in which the allylamine was said to coordinate only through the nitrogen. A similar reaction carried out in strongly acidic solution produced [Pt(C$_3$H$_7$N·HCl)Cl$_2$]$_2$ in which the coordination presumably involved only the double bond. This product was converted to H[Pt(C$_3$H$_7$N·HCl)Cl$_3$](I) by heating with 10 per cent hydrochloric acid. Careful neutralization of (I) with 5 per cent alkali

20. Hel'man and Meilakh, *Compt. rend. acad. sci. U.S.S.R.*, **51**, 207 (1946).
21. Hel'man, *Doklady Akad. Nauk S.S.S.R.*, **38**, 327 (1943); Hel'man and Gorushkina, *Compt. rend. acad. sci. U.S.S.R.*, **55**, 33 (1947).
22. Chernyaev and Hel'man, *Ann. secteur platine, Inst. chim. gen. U.S.S.R.*, No. 15, 5 (1938).
23. Hel'man and Essen, *Doklady Akad. Nauk S.S.S.R.*, **77**, 273 (1951).

produced $[Pt(C_3H_7N)Cl_2]$(II) in which the allylamine was presumed to function as a bidentate group, coordinating through the nitrogen and the double bond. Hel'man stated that this was proved by the fact that allylamine hydrochloride displaced ethylene from $NH_4[PtC_2H_4Cl_3]$ to produce the ammonium salt of (I), which produced (II) on neutralization. Actually these reactions do not eliminate a dimeric structure for (II) similar to that of $[PtC_2H_4Cl_2]_2$, in which the ethylene is monodentate. The platinum complexes of diallylamine (abbreviated dlm) have been studied by other investigators[24] who report that the action of two moles of diallylamine on one mole of ammonium tetrachloroplatinate(II) gave a dark precipitate and more slowly a light-yellow precipitate of the same empirical composition, $PtCl_2 \cdot dlm$. The light-yellow material was shown to be a dimer by the fact that it could be prepared by the addition of $(NH_4)_2[PtCl_4]$ to a solution of $[Pt(dlm)_2]Cl_2$ (prepared from [Pt dlm Cl$_2$] and an excess of dlm) to give $[Pt(dlm)_2][PtCl_4]$. The dark precipitate could be converted to $[Pt(NH_3)_2 \, dlm]Cl_2$ by treatment with ammonium hydroxide. Thus, in each compound the diallylamine apparently occupies two coordination positions, at least one of which must be filled by an olefinic linkage. It is unlikely that both double bonds function as donor groups since large chelate rings are not frequently encountered and the ability of the nitrogen to coordinate is doubtless greater than that of the olefinic linkage. The data reported for the diallylamine complexes lend support to the structure proposed by Hel'man for the allylamine complexes.

Chatt and Wilkins[25] prepared the first compound containing two double bonds linked to the same platinum atom, although Anderson[14] had found some evidence for the existence of the compound $PtCl_2 \cdot 2C_6H_5CH{=}CH_2$, which he could not isolate. Hel'man[26] disputed the existence of such a compound on theoretical grounds. The compound described by Chatt and Wilkins, $[Pt(C_2H_4)_2Cl_2]$, was prepared by passing ethylene through a solution of $[PtC_2H_4Cl_2]_2$ in acetone at $-70°$. It dissociates at $-6°$ in an ethylene atmosphere and probably has a trans configuration. Chatt and Wilkins considered the low stability of the compound to be due to the high *trans effect* of ethylene and the relatively weak bond between platinum and ethylene. They were able to prepare two complexes of platinum with dipentene, both of which had the same empirical composition, $Pt(C_{10}H_{16})Cl_2$. One of these was monomeric and must have been a complex in which the dipentene functioned as a chelate group unless it was simply an addition compound. Kharasch and Ashford[15] had prepared a dipentene compound of the same composition, but assumed it to be a dimer.

24. Rubinshtein and Derbisher, *ibid.*, **74**, 283 (1950).
25. Chatt and Wilkins, *Nature*, **165**, 859 (1950); *J. Chem. Soc.*, **1952**, 2622.
26. Hel'man, *Compt. rend. acad. sci. U.R.S.S.*, **24**, 549 (1939).

Hel'man and her co-workers[27] prepared a compound analogous to Zeise's salt containing an acetylene derivative, 2,5-dimethyl-3-hexyne-2,5-diol. The product was treated with pyridine to form [Pt $C_8H_{14}O_2$ py Cl_2]. The molecular weight of the pyridine compound, determined cryoscopically in benzene solution, indicated it to be a monomer. Its properties led the authors to assume that it had a trans configuration.

The properties of the olefinic complexes of platinum are extremely interesting. The simplest stable compounds, [$PtUnCl_2$]$_2$ (Un represents an unsaturated group), are decomposed by water, but are soluble in the common organic solvents except glacial acetic acid, and only moderately soluble in cold benzene. Most of the compounds are thermally unstable and decompose before melting. Some decompose on standing for several days, but the dipentene complex remains unchanged after standing in air for ten months[15].

The olefins in most olefinic complexes can be substituted readily by other olefins[14] or by coordinating agents such as pyridine[15] or chloride ion (when treated with concentrated hydrochloric acid). These reactions liberate the coordinated olefin unchanged. Bromine decomposes the complexes with the formation of the brominated olefin. The ethylene complex is rapidly and quantitatively reduced by hydrogen at room temperature to platinum, hydrogen chloride, and ethane[13].

Zeise's salt reacts with potassium cyanide to liberate ethylene quantitatively, and other complexing agents, such as pyridine, tend to react similarly[13]. Hot water decomposes the salt according to the equation

$$K[PtC_2H_4Cl_3] + H_2O \rightarrow KCl + 2HCl + Pt + CH_3CHO.$$

Anderson's stability series[14], as well as the results of Kharasch and Ashford[15], indicate that in general the stability of the platinum-olefin compounds decreases with increasing substitution adjacent to the double bond. The effect seems to be largely steric. However, the behavior of cis-trans isomers does not appear to be completely consistent. Kharasch and Ashford were able to isolate complexes with cyclohexene, dipentene, pinene, ethylene, isobutylene, styrene, and *trans*-dichloroethylene. The first three compounds have a cis configuration, but *cis*-dichloroethylene and *cis*-diphenylethylene have not yet yielded complexes, although those of the trans compounds are known. Anderson isolated the indene (a cis compound) complex and reported that a crystalline complex formed with a compound which he stated to be presumably *trans*-2-pentene. Oppegard[28] prepared a crystalline complex with *cis*-2-pentene, but obtained only a red oil with *trans*-2-pentene.

27. Hel'man, Bukhovets and Meilakh, *ibid.*, **46**, 105 (1945).
28. Oppegard, thesis, University of Illinois (1946).

Palladium-olefin Compounds

The first palladium-olefin compound reported was $PdCl_2 \cdot C_5H_{10}$ which was said to be formed when palladium(II) chloride, trimethylethylene and a trace of some basic substance were allowed to react[29]. However, Kharasch, Seyler, and Mayo[30] were not able to repeat this work. Although they were not able to cause palladium(II) chloride to react directly with unsaturated compounds, they found that bis-benzonitrile palladium(II) chloride reacted readily with olefins. Palladium(II) complexes of the type $[PdCl_2 \cdot Un]_2$ were prepared with cyclohexene, ethylene, styrene, butylene, pinene and camphorene. The stability of the complexes decreased in the order given and when a less stable compound was treated with the olefin substituent of a more stable one, the latter compound was formed by replacement. The complexes were colored, unstable, and rather insoluble in the common organic solvents. They were less stable than the corresponding platinum compounds.

Iron-olefin Compounds

The compound $FeCl_2 \cdot C_2H_4 \cdot 2H_2O$ was reported by Kachler[31] to be formed by the reaction of iron(III) chloride with ether in the presence of a small amount of phosphorus in a sealed tube. The equation was given as

$$2C_2H_5OC_2H_5 + 2FeCl_3 \rightarrow 2FeCl_2 \cdot C_2H_4 + 2C_2H_5OH + Cl_2 \,.$$

Alcohol did not give the same product under similar conditions. Chojnacki[32] was unable to prepare Kachler's compound from iron(II) chloride and ethylene, but did prepare the bromide, $FeBr_2 \cdot C_2H_4 \cdot 2H_2O$. He reported that, when treated with potassium bromide, a solution of this compound gave almost colorless crystals containing iron, bromine, potassium, and ethylene. Manchot and Haas[33] were unable to duplicate the work of Kachler and Chojnacki and felt that Kachler's compound was a partially decomposed ether addition compound.

The compound $Fe(CO)_3 \cdot C_4H_6$ has been reported[34] to be formed by long heating of iron pentacarbonyl with butadiene. Less well-defined compounds were obtained with other olefins.

The most interesting olefinic compound of iron was reported only recently. Kealy and Pauson[35] added a solution of iron(III) chloride in anhydrous ether to a benzene solution of cyclopentadienyl magnesium bro-

29. Kondakov, Bolas, and Vit, *Chem. Listy*, **23**, 579 (1929); **24**, 1, 26 (1930).
30. Kharasch, Seyler, and Mayo, *J. Am. Chem. Soc.*, **60**, 882 (1938).
31. Kachler, *Ber.*, **2**, 510 (1869); *J. prakt. chem.*, **107**, 315 (1869).
32. Chojnacki, *Jahresber.*, **23**, 510 (1870); *Z. Chem.*, **2**, 6, 419 (1870).
33. Manchot and Haas, *Ber.*, **45**, 3052 (1912).
34. Reihlen, Gruhl, Hessling, and Pfrengle, *Ann.*, **482**, 161 (1930).
35. Kealy and Pauson, *Nature*, **168**, 1039 (1951).

mide. The solution was allowed to stand overnight, was refluxed for an hour, and was then treated with an ice-cold solution of ammonium chloride, after which evaporation gave an orange solid which melted at 173-174°C with sublimation. The composition of the solid was $FeC_{10}H_{10}$. Miller, Tebboth, and Tremain[36] found that reduced iron, in the presence of potassium oxide, reacted with cyclopentadiene in nitrogen at 300°C to give a yellow solid, $FeC_{10}H_{10}$, which melted at 172.5-173°C with sublimation. Bis(cyclopentadienyl)iron(II) is soluble in alcohol, ether, and benzene. It is insoluble in, and unattacked by water, 10 per cent sodium hydroxide, or concentrated hydrochloric acid. It dissolves in dilute nitric acid or concentrated sulfuric acid to give a deep red solution with strong blue fluorescence. It decolorizes permanganate. Wilkinson and co-workers[37] found the compound to be diamagnetic. It is easily oxidized to a blue cation $Fe(C_5H_5)_2{}^+$ (polarographic half-wave potential, -0.59 volt), which is paramagnetic with a magnetic moment suggesting the presence of one unpaired electron. The structure of the compound will be considered later (page 507).

Iridium-olefin Compounds

Several iridium-olefin compounds have been reported[38]. Treatment of iridium(III) chloride with absolute alcohol produced $IrCl_2 \cdot C_2H_4$ which, when treated with ammonium or potassium chloride, gave mixtures of other products. Formulas, for the products isolated, indicated the presence of iridium chloride, ammonium or potassium chloride, ethylene, and sometimes water. No compounds of iridium could be obtained from ethylene and iridium(III) chloride or a solution of iridium(III) chloride.

Copper-olefin Compounds

The absorption of ethylene and propylene by a hydrochloric acid solution of copper(I) chloride was observed by Berthelot[39]. The mole ratio of ethylene to copper(I) chloride was 0.17 and of propylene to copper(I) chloride, 0.25. An unstable compound, $CuCl \cdot C_2H_4$, was reported by Manchot and Brandt[40], although they could not isolate it. It has, however, been isolated from the reaction of ethylene under pressure with solid copper(I) chloride[41]. It is not known whether this substance is a coordination compound or only an addition compound. The absorption of propylene and

36. Miller, Tebboth, and Tremaine, *J. Chem. Soc.*, **1952**, 632.
37. Wilkinson, Rosenblum, Whiting, and Woodward, *J. Am. Chem. Soc.*, **74**, 2125 (1952).
38. Sadtler, *Chem. News*, **24**, 280 (1871); *Bull. soc. chim.*, **17**, 54 (1872).
39. Berthelot, *Ann. chim. phys.*, **23**, 32 (1901).
40. Manchot and Brandt, *Ann.*, **370**, 286 (1909).
41. Tropsch and Mattox, *J. Am. Chem. Soc.*, **57**, 1102 (1935).

isobutylene[42] and butadiene[43] by solid copper(I) chloride has also been demonstrated. Gilliland and co-workers[44] prepared a complex containing two moles of copper(I) chloride and one mole of butadiene. From the studies of vapor pressures of olefins over copper(I) chloride, they found that one mole of copper(I) chloride absorbed 0.336 mole of isoprene, 0.62 mole of isobutylene, and formed 1:1 complexes with ethylene and propylene. Neither cyclopentadiene nor amylene reacted. Ward and Makin[45] characterized complexes containing one mole of 1,3-pentadiene or isoprene to two moles of copper(I) chloride.

Osterlöf[46] identified two compounds, $3CuCl \cdot C_2H_2$ and $2CuCl \cdot C_2H_2$, formed from copper(I) chloride in acid solution with acetylene at pressures up to 2 atmospheres. However, from the x-ray powder photograms, he concluded that they were interstitial compounds.

On the basis of studies involving the distribution of copper(I) chloride between water and an organic solvent in the presence of an unsaturated substance, Andrews and co-workers have obtained formation constants for a variety of copper(I) complexes. Only 1:1 complexes were indicated with all the unsaturated alcohols[47] and acids[48] investigated. The compounds formed by the unsaturated alcohols were generally more stable than those with the acids, as one might expect, since the carboxyl group should decrease the electron density in the vicinity of the double bond. Substitution of H by —CH_3 or —CO_2H decreased stability, probably due also to steric effects. Of the two complexes generally formed, $Cu \cdot Un^+$ and $CuCl \cdot Un$, the cationic complexes were the more stable.

Silver-olefin Compounds

Most of the silver-olefin complexes are too unstable to be isolated and much of the available information has been obtained from distribution studies. Lucas and co-workers used this method for the study of silver complexes containing isobutylene[49], a series of mono- and diolefins[50] and a few

42. Gilliland, Seebold, Fitzhugh, and Morgan, *ibid.*, **61**, 1960 (1939).
43. Lur'e, Marushkin, Afanas'ev, and Pimenov, *Sintet. Kauchuk*, **3**, No. 6, 19 (1934).
44. Gilliland, Bliss, and Kip, *J. Am. Chem. Soc.*, **63**, 2088 (1941).
45. Ward and Makin, *ibid.*, **69**, 657 (1947).
46. Österlöf, *Acta Chem. Scand.*, **4**, 374 (1950).
47. Kepner and Andrews, *J. Org. Chem.*, **13**, 208 (1948); *J. Am. Chem. Soc.*, **71**, 1723 (1949); Keefer, Andrews, and Kepner, *ibid.*, **71**, 3906 (1949).
48. Andrews and Keefer, *ibid.*, **70**, 3261 (1948); **71**, 2379 (1949); Keefer, Andrews, and Kepner, *ibid.*, **71**, 2381 (1949).
49. Eberz, Wilge, Yost, and Lucas, *ibid.*, **59**, 45 (1937).
50. Winstein and Lucas, *ibid.*, **60**, 836 (1938); Lucas, Moore, and Pressman, *ibid.*, **65**, 227 (1943); Hepner, Trueblood, and Lucas, *ibid.*, **74**, 1333 (1952); Trueblood and Lucas, *ibid.*, **74**, 1338 (1952).

unsaturated oxygenated compounds[50a]. Compounds with a 1:1 mole ratio were observed in all cases and several unsaturated molecules gave ratios of two unsaturated groups to one silver ion. Most of the systems showed evidence for compounds containing two silver ions and one unsaturated group at high silver ion concentrations.

cis-2-Pentene gave a more stable complex than the trans isomer and the stability of the compounds of the isomeric butenes indicated that steric effects were very important and that substitution around the double bond decreased the stability of the complexes. Similarly, Nichols[51] found that the silver complex of the methyl ester of oleic acid (cis form) was more stable than that of the methyl ester of elaidic acid (trans form). Lucas *et al.* observed no isomerization or polymerization when any of the organic molecules combined with silver ion.

Keefer, Andrews, and Kepner[47c] studied the silver complexes formed by a series of unsaturated alcohols and found them to be much less stable than the corresponding copper(I) complexes. The stability trends within the series were similar.

Andrews and Keefer[52] obtained formation constants for a series of silver complexes with aromatic substances by the distribution method. They observed that most simple aromatic systems formed complexes containing one silver ion and one aromatic molecule as well as a less stable complex containing two silver ions and one aromatic molecule. The relative stabilities of the complexes were associated primarily with the inductive effects of ring substituents and steric factors. Thus, the substitution of a methyl group on benzene increases its basicity and also the stability of the silver complex. However, further substitution of methyl groups on toluene increases the basicity, but the stability of the silver complexes decreases or increases only slightly while the increase in basicity is great. Allowing for the very important steric effects, the stability of the aromatic complexes generally increases with the basicity of the aromatic nucleus[53].

Andrews and Keefer[54] found that aromatic and olefinic iodides gave far more stable silver complexes than related substances, presumably because the coordination occurs through the iodine atom.

Mercury-olefin Compounds

The mercury-olefin compounds have been studied extensively and excellent reviews are available[1, 55]. Lucas, Hepner, and Winstein[56] used the

51. Nichols, *ibid.*, **74**, 1091 (1952).
52. Andrews and Keefer, *ibid.*, **71**, 3644 (1949); **72**, 3113 (1950); **74**, 640 (1952).
53. Brown and Brady, *ibid.*, **71**, 3573 (1949); McCaulay and Lien, *ibid.*, **73**, 2013 (1951).
54. Andrews and Keefer, *ibid.*, **73**, 5733 (1951).
55. Chatt, *Chem. Rev.*, **48**, 7 (1951).
56. Lucas, Hepner, and Winstein, *J. Am. Chem. Soc.*, **61**, 3102 (1939).

distribution method to study the complexes of mercury(II) ion with cyclohexene. They obtained equilibrium constants for two reactions:

$$C_6H_{10} + Hg^{++} \rightarrow C_6H_{10}Hg^{++}$$

$$C_6H_{10} + Hg^{++} + H_2O \rightarrow C_6H_{10}HgOH^+ + H^+$$

The equilibrium constant for the second reaction is slightly greater than that for the first, and other slower reactions were said to proceed concurrently with these two. The first reaction is probably analogous to the complex formation by silver(I) ion, but the second reaction seems to be more characteristic of mercury(II).

Some of the mercury-olefin compounds probably exist as coordination compounds, at least as intermediates. However, the structure in which there is addition across the double bond

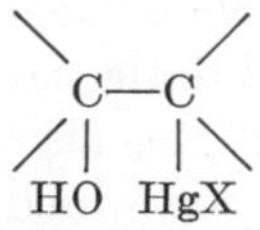

$$\begin{array}{c} \diagdown \qquad \diagup \\ C\!-\!C \\ \diagup \; | \qquad | \diagdown \\ HO \quad HgX \end{array}$$

is generally accepted for these compounds[57]. The existence of optically-active mercury compounds with olefins of the type RR′C=CRR′ [58] rather conclusively supports this structure.

Miscellaneous Compounds

Some evidence[29, 59] is available for the existence of addition compounds of zinc chloride and amylene, but the exact nature of the compounds is not clear.

Unstable aluminum compounds with ethylene, other unsaturated hydrocarbons, acids, aldehydes, and alcohols have been isolated[60], but the composition of such materials is difficult to determine because of their instability and hygroscopic character. Aluminum compounds with acetylene[60b], benzene[61], and substituted benzenes[62] have also been prepared.

Winstein and Lucas[50a] found that olefins failed to form complexes in aqueous solution with Cd^{++}, Co^{++}, Cr^{+++}, Cu^{++}, Fe^{+++}, Ni^{++}, Pb^{++}, Tl^+ and Zn^{++}. However, Jura and his co-workers[63] found that the reaction of

57. Adams, Roman, and Sperry, *ibid.*, **44**, 1781 (1922).
58. Sandborn and Marvel, *ibid.*, **48**, 1409 (1926).
59. Kondakoff, *J. Russ. Phys.-Chem. Soc.*, **24**, 309 (1892); **25**, 345, 456 (1893); *Bull. soc. chim* [3] **7**, 576 (1892).
60. Gangloff and Henderson, *J. Am. Chem. Soc.*, **39**, 1420 (1917); Henderson and Gangloff, *ibid.*, **38**, 1382 (1916).
61. Weinland, "Einführung in die Chemie der Komplex-Verbindungen," p. 340, Stuttgart, Verlag von Ferdinand Enke, 1924.
62. Norris and Ingraham, *J. Am. Chem. Soc.*, **62**, 1298 (1940).
63. Jura, Grotz, and Hildebrand, Abstracts of Papers presented at the 118th Mtg. of A.C.S., Chicago, Sept. 1950.

metal ions with aromatic hydrocarbons is quite general. On a silica gel surface, mesitylene was found to react with the ions of most heavy metals. Naphthalene reacted to about the same extent as mesitylene, cyclohexanone to a lesser extent, xylene and toluene only very weakly, and benzene showed no effect. This order is essentially the same as that found by Andrews and Keefer[52] for silver and by Brown and Brady[53a] for the basicity of aromatic hydrocarbons.

The compound $Ni(CN)_2 \cdot NH_3 \cdot C_6H_6$[64] which has been considered as a coordination compound, has been shown to be a clathrate compound[65] in which the nickel is coordinated only to ammonia and cyanide ion with the benzene trapped in the lattice (page 378).

The interesting and unusual character of bis(cyclopentadienyl)iron(II) led to the investigation of other metal derivatives of the cyclopentadienyl radical. Wilkinson[66] prepared the analogous bis(cyclopentadienyl)ruthenium(II) which could be oxidized to the cationic ruthenium(III) compound and isolated as a salt. Wilkinson[67] was also able to prepare the monovalent bis(cyclopentadienyl)cobalt(III) ion which could be reduced to the easily oxidizable, neutral cobalt(II) compound[68], which could also be prepared from $Co_2(CO)_8$ and cyclopentadiene in the vapor phase at 300°C. The corresponding rhodium(III) and iridium(III) compounds were also prepared[69]. The rhodium(III) compound could be reduced polarographically although at a higher potential than that required for the reduction of the cobalt(III) compound. The iridium compound showed no clear cut polarographic wave.

The neutral bis(cyclopentadienyl)nickel(II) compound was prepared, but it slowly decomposed[70]. It could be oxidized to the cationic nickel(III) compound, but the latter decomposed in water. The neutral palladium(II) compound[68] was obtained in solution, but it was less stable than the nickel(II) compound. No copper(II) derivative was obtained.

Moving in the other direction in the periodic table, Wilkinson and co-workers[68] obtained evidence for a neutral cyclopentadienyl derivative of manganese, but the material was oxidized rapidly in air. Bis(cyclopentadienyl)chromium(II) was prepared from chromium hexacarbonyl and cyclopentadiene in a hot tube[68b]. The corresponding molybdenum compound was prepared in small yield. The compounds $C_{10}H_{10}TiBr_2$, $C_{10}H_{10}ZrBr_2$, $C_{10}H_{10}VCl_2$, and $C_{10}H_{10}NbBr_3$ were also obtained[68, 70]. The titanium(IV)

64. Hoffmann and Küspert, Z. anorg. Chem., **15**, 203 (1897).
65. Powell and Rayner, Nature, **163**, 567 (1949).
66. Wilkinson, J. Am. Chem. Soc., **74**, 6146 (1952).
67. Wilkinson, ibid., 6148.
68. Wilkinson, Private communication, July, 1953; J. Am. Chem. Soc., **76**, 209 (1954); Pauson and Wilkinson, J. Am. Chem. Soc., **76**, 2024 (1954).
69. Cotton, Whipple, and Wilkinson, J. Am. Chem. Soc., **75**, 3586 (1953).
70. Wilkinson, Pauson, Birmingham, and Cotton, ibid., 1011.

compound could be reduced in solution to the $C_{10}H_{10}Ti^+$ ion and there was some polarographic evidence for the neutral compound.

Wilkinson and co-workers have shown that the formation of compounds with the cyclopentadienyl radical is quite general for the transition metals, but not for the metals with filled d orbitals. The maximum stability is achieved for those metals such as iron(II) which can complete the d ortibals through bonding to two cyclopentadienyl radicals. It is possible to prepare compounds with only one cyclopentadienyl ring attached to a metal ion if the metal can be satisfied with groups on the side opposite to the ring. Wilkinson[68b] prepared the compounds $C_5H_5Mo(CO)_5MoC_5H_5$ and $C_5H_5W(CO)_6WC_5H_5$ in which the metals are bridged by the carbonyl groups. Pauson and Wilkinson[68c] prepared bis(indenyl)iron(II) and salts of bis(indenyl)cobalt(III) from indenyllithium and indenylmagnesium bromide, respectively.

The well-known metal complexes of the azo and azomethine dyes certainly involve bond formation between some part of the —N=N— or —CH=N— system, but it is not known whether coordination is through the double bond or through the nitrogen (Chapter 22).

PRACTICAL IMPORTANCE OF METAL-OLEFIN COMPOUNDS

The exact role of many metal salts in reactions involving olefins is not known, but it is significant that the most important metal salts used to polymerize or otherwise change olefins are those known to form metal-olefin compounds.

In the presence of aluminum chloride, olefins are reported to polymerize, isomerize, cyclize, and form paraffins and more highly unsaturated compounds[71]. Aluminum chloride has been used for converting gaseous and high-boiling olefins into low-boiling liquids[72], viscous oils[73], synthetic lubricating oils[74], and synthetic resins[75]. The preparation of a compound of aluminum chloride with ethylene, used for condensing hydrocarbons, has been patented. It is likely that the Friedel-Crafts reactions involve alumi-

71. Egloff, Wilson, Hulla, and Van Arsdell, *Chem. Rev.*, **20**, 345 (1937); National Research Council, "Twelfth Report of the Committee on Catalysis," pp. 182–3, New York, John Wiley & Sons, Inc., 1940.
72. Ricard (to Soc. Ricard, Allenet et Cie), U. S. Patent 1,745,028 (Jan. 28, 1930); cf. *Chem. Abst.*, **24**, 1390 (1930).
73. N. V. de Bataafsche Petroleum Maatschappij, British Patent 479,632 (Feb. 9, 1938); cf. *Chem. Abs.*, **32**, 5197 (1938); Sixt (to Consortium für elektrochemische Industrie G. m. b. H.), U. S. Patent 2,183,154 (Dec. 12, 1939); cf. *Chem. Abs.*, **34**, 2392 (1940).
74. Perquin (to Shell Development Co.), Canadian Patent 380,056 (Mar. 14, 1939); cf. *Chem. Abs.*, **33**, 4016 (1939).
75. Dayton Synthetic Chemicals, Inc., German Patent 651,668 (Oct. 18, 1937); cf. *Chem. Abs.*, **32**, 680 (1938).

num chloride complexes; indeed, some of the supposed intermediate aluminum halide complexes have been isolated[76].

Heavy metal carbonyls have served to convert high-boiling hydrocarbons into lower boiling forms by high-pressure hydrogenation[77].

The polymerization of butadiene is effected by boron fluoride[78], aluminum chloride[79], heavy metal carbonyls[80], and the iron phthalocyanine sulfonic acid complex[81]. Vinylacetylene is prepared by the dimerization of acetylene by copper(I) chloride solutions[82].

Many complex-forming metal salts have been found to be effective in the hydration of olefins in acid solutions[83].

Gaseous olefins may be extracted from mixtures with saturated hydrocarbons by aqueous solutions of copper(I), silver, mercury(II), and platinum(II) salts[84]. The olefins can be subsequently recovered by heating the solutions or by reducing the pressure. Diolefins can be separated from monoolefins as a result of the formation of insoluble complexes by the diolefins and certain heavy-metal salts[85].

76. Norris and Wood, *J. Am. Chem. Soc.*, **62**, 1428 (1940).
77. I. G. Farbenindustrie A.-G. (Zorn and Vogel, inventors), German Patent 579,565 (June 29, 1933); cf. *Chem. Abs.*, **28**, 1045 (1934).
78. Harmon (to E. I. du Pont de Nemours and Co.), U. S. Patent 2,151,382 (Mar. 21, 1939); cf. *Chem. Abs.*, **33**, 5096 (1939).
79. Zelinskiĭ, Densienko, Eventova, and Khromov, *Sintet Kauchuk*, **1933**, No. 4, 11.
80. Ambros, Reindel, Eisele, and Stoehrel (to I. G. Farbenindustrie A.-G.), U. S. Patent 1,891,203 (Dec. 13, 1932); cf. *Chem. Abs.*, **27**, 1893 (1933); I. G. Farbenindustrie A.-G., British Patent 340,004 (Aug. 12, 1929); cf. *Chem. Abs.*, **25**, 2878 (1931).
81. I. G. Farbenindustrie A.-G. (Gumlich and Dennstedt, inventors), German Patent 679,587 (Aug. 9, 1939); cf. *Chem. Abs.*, **33**, 9328 (1939).
82. Burk, Thompson, Weith, and Williams, "Polymerization and its Applications in the Fields of Rubber, Synthetic Resins and Petroleum," p. 76, New York, Reinhold Publishing Corp., 1937; Klebanskiĭ, Tzyurikh, and Dolgopol'shiĭ, *Bull. acad. sci. U.R.S.S.*, **1935**, No. 2, 189; *J. Research Assoc. Brit. Rubber Mfrs.*, **4**, 505 (1935).
83. Dreyfus, British Patent 397,187 (Aug. 21, 1933); cf. *Chem. Abs.*, **28**, 777 (1934); Standard Alcohol Co., British Patent 493,884 (Oct. 17, 1938); cf. *Chem. Abs.*, **33**, 2533 (1939).
84. Ellis, "The Chemistry of Petroleum Derivatives," p. 142, New York, The Chemical Catalog Co., Inc., (Reinhold Publishing Corp.), 1934; N. V. de Bataafsche Petroleum Maatschappij, German Patent 622,965 (Dec. 10, 1935); cf. *Chem. Abs.*, **30**, 3442 (1936); Gilliland (to Standard Oil Development Co.), U. S. Patent 2,209,452 (July 30, 1940) and 2,289,773 (July 14, 1942); cf. *Chem. Abs.*, **35**, 134 (1941) and **37**, 386 (1943) resp.; Gilliland and Seebold, *Ind. Eng. Chem.*, **33**, 1143 (1941); Imperial Chemical Industries, Ltd., French Patent 662,099 (Mar. 12, 1928); cf. *Chem. Abs.*, **24**, 376 (1930); Stern, Reichsant Wirtschaftsaubau, Pruf-Nr., 43, (PB52003) 15–56 (1940); cf. *Chem. Abs.*, **41**, 6490 (1947).
85. Hebbard and Lloyd (to Dow Chemical Co.), U. S. Patents 2,188,899 and 2,189,173 (Feb. 6, 1940); cf. *Chem. Abs.*, **34**, 3760 (1940).

The Structure of Metal-Olefin Compounds

Although many structures have been proposed for the metal-olefin compounds, satisfactory structures have been proposed only recently. Various suggested structures have been reviewed by Keller[1] and more recently by Chatt[2]. Although most of the proposed structures and some structural data can be elminated on the basis of the evidence, much remains to be learned about the structure of metal-olefin compounds.

The compound $[PtCl_2 \cdot C_4H_8]_2$ is known to be dimeric on the basis of an accurate molecular weight determination in benzene[15]. An approximate molecular weight determination for ethylene-platinum(II) chloride indicated it to be a dimer[13]. Styrene-palladium(II) chloride is probably dimeric, although an exact molecular weight could not be obtained by the freezing-point method[28].

Pfieffer[86] proposed formula (I) for the ethylene-platinum(II) chloride complex, although he did not indicate the nature of the Pt-Un bond. Kharasch and Ashford[15] objected to (I) because of the formation of two coordinate bonds by the same chloride ion. They proposed structure (II),

(I)   (II)

in which the double bond is broken to permit the olefin to act as the bridge. Halide ions act as bridges in many stable polymeric complexes[87] so the objection of Kharasch and Ashford is without foundation. The representation of the platinum-olefin complexes as metal-alkyls seems objectionable on the basis of the ready displacement of one olefin by another[14] or by other coordinating groups such as pyridine and cyanide ion[13].

Although most complexes of the type [Pt a $C_2H_4Cl_2$] (a = ammonia or pyridine) are too insoluble for molecular weight determinations, Chatt[2] was able to establish that the corresponding p-toluidine complex is monomeric. Oppegard[28] found the complexes [PtC_2H_4 quinoline Cl_2] and [Pt styrene quinoline Cl_2] to be monomeric in benzene. Thus, an olefin bridge cannot be used to explain the structure of these complexes and there is no reason to suppose that such a bridge exists in other platinum-olefin compounds.

86. Pfeiffer, "Organische Molekülverbindungen," p. 161, Stuttgart, Verlag von Ferdinand Enke, 1922.
87. Gibson and Simonsen, *J. Chem. Soc.*, **1930**, 2531; Mann and Purdie, *Ibid.*, **1936**, 873; Palmer and Elliott, *J. Am. Chem. Soc.*, **60**, 1852 (1938); Wells, *Z. Krist.*, **100**, 189 (1938).

From an x-ray structure analysis, Bokii and co-workers[88] reported the compound *cis*-[PtC$_2$H$_4$NH$_3$Cl$_2$] to be dimeric with a platinum-platinum bond length of 1.4 Å.; however, the results mentioned above indicate that a dimeric structure is unlikely and there seems to be no other evidence for a platinum-platinum bond. Apparently the interpretation of the x-ray data was erroneous.

Bennett and Willis[89] proposed structure (III), in which one pair of electrons from the double bond migrates to one carbon to be shared with the platinum atom. This leaves the other carbon as a carbonium ion, which should be very reactive. Similarly, Stiegman[90] proposed structure (IV) in

$$\left[\begin{array}{c} \text{H} \ \ \text{H} \\ \overset{\cdot\cdot}{\text{H}:\underset{+}{\text{C}}:\overset{\cdot\cdot}{\text{C}}:\text{PtCl}_3} \\ \overset{\cdot\cdot}{\text{H}} \end{array} \right]^{-} \qquad \left[\begin{array}{c} \text{H} \ \ \text{H} \\ \overset{\cdot\cdot}{\text{H}:\underset{-}{\overset{\cdot\cdot}{\text{C}}}:\overset{\cdot\cdot}{\text{C}}:\text{PtCl}_3} \\ \overset{\cdot\cdot}{\text{H}} \end{array} \right]^{-}$$

(III)   (IV)

which the double bond is broken, but the carbonium ion shares a pair of electrons furnished by the platinum. Here the remaining carbon would be a carbanion which should also be very reactive. In addition, if the platinum, and not the ethylene, is the donor, one would not expect the ethylene to behave as a typical ligand and be readily replaced by ligands such as chloride ion and ammonia. These structures seem unlikely.

Drew, Pinkard, Wardlaw, and Cox[91] proposed structure (V) (written as (VI) by Chatt) for the ion [PtC$_2$H$_4$Cl$_3$]$^-$. It is objectionable on the same

$$\left[\begin{array}{c} \text{ClCH}_2\text{CH}_2 \\ \diagdown \\ \qquad \text{Pt—Cl} \\ \diagup \\ \text{Cl} \end{array} \right]^{-} \qquad \left[\begin{array}{c} \text{H}_2\text{C—MCl}_2 \\ | \qquad | \\ \text{H}_2\text{C—Cl} \end{array} \right]^{-}$$

(V)   (VI)

grounds as a platinum-alkyl structure. Chatt[2] mentioned that an attempt to prepare 2-benzoylethyl chloride by heating ethylene-platinum(II) chloride with an excess of benzoyl chloride was unsuccessful. He believed that this reaction should proceed if the olefin complexes had structure (V).

Chatt[92] emphasized the similarity between the platinum complexes with olefins and those with carbon monoxide. Both groups, unlike most neutral

88. Bokiǐ, Usikov, and Trusevich, *Bull. acad. sci., U.R.S.S., Classe sci. Chem.*, **1942**, 413; Bokiǐ and Baishteǐl, *Doklady Akad. Nauk S.S.S.R.*, **38**, 323 (1943); Bokiǐ and Vainshtein, *Compt. rend. acad. sci. U.R.S.S.*, **38**, 307 (1943).
89. Bennett and Willis, *J. Chem. Soc.*, **1929**, 259.
90. Stiegman, thesis, University of Illinois, 1937.
91. Drew, Pinkard, Wardlaw, and Cox, *J. Chem. Soc.*, **1932**, 897.
92. Chatt, *Nature*, **165**, 637 (1950).

ligands, show a very marked *trans effect*, which Chatt stated is probably associated with double bond character between the metal and donor group as suggested by Pauling[93] for the metal carbonyls.

Hel'man[94] found that Zeise's salt resists oxidation by permanganate, giving an initial potential in an electrometric titration of 650 to 700 m.v., comparable to that observed for typical platinum(IV) complexes. Platinum(II) salts are readily oxidized by permanganate at a lower potential. She considered this to be evidence that the platinum is present as platinum(IV) as a result of the sharing of a pair of d electrons from the platinum with the ethylene which in turn shares a pair of its electrons with the platinum to form a four electron bond[26]. Hel'man did not specify the nature of the four electron bond, show how the ethylene accommodates the two electrons from the platinum, or what happens to the carbon-carbon double bond. She believed that only one ethylene molecule could be coordinated to a platinum atom, since the platinum would be required to furnish a pair of electrons for each ethylene coordinated. Chatt[25] discredited Hel'man's structure by preparing the compound [Pt(C₂H₄)₂Cl₂]. However, this would require only a slight modification by Hel'man, since the consideration of the oxidation state of the platinum is purely formal.

The bulk of the evidence is in favor of the view that the platinum-olefin compounds are derivatives of platinum(II). This is indicated by the fact that the olefins readily replace other ligands in platinum(II) compounds or are readily replaced by other ligands to give platinum(II) compounds. However, such an argument tells only what is put into and what is obtained from olefin complexes and ignores the fact that the assignment of the oxidation state of the platinum is purely formal if the bond order differs in any case.

Chatt[95] proposed the structure

$$\left[\begin{array}{ccc} CH_3CH & & Cl \\ & \diagdown\!\!\!\diagup & \\ & Pt & \\ & \diagup\!\!\!\diagdown & \\ Cl & & Cl \end{array} \right] ,$$

representing the ethylene compound as a substituted ethylidene complex formed as a result of migration of a hydrogen atom on coordination. However, Chatt[96] no longer believes this structure to be correct. Objections to it were cited by Douglas[97] and by Chatt[96].

93. Pauling, "Nature of the Chemical Bond," 2nd. ed., pp. 251 et seq., Ithaca, Cornell University Press, 1940.
94. Hel'man and Ryabchikov, *Compt. rend. acad. sci. U.R.S.S.*, **33**, 462 (1941).
95. Chatt, *Research*, **4**, 180 (1951).
96. Chatt, *J. Chem. Soc.*, **1953**, 2939.
97. Douglas, *J. Am. Chem. Soc.*, **75**, 4839 (1953).

Oppegard[28] found that *cis*-2-pentene gave a crystalline complex with platinum, while *trans*-2-pentene gave a red oil. The infrared spectra for the two compounds were also found to differ. This is in agreement with the observations of Winstein and Lucas[50] that the silver-olefin complexes give no rearrangements and that cis and trans isomers possess different coordinating properties with respect to silver. On the basis of the ethylidene structure, one would predict the isomerization of *cis-trans* isomers during coordination to and subsequent liberation from platinum(II) salts.

Oppegard also found that the ultraviolet spectra of *trans*-stilbene and the complex, [Pt stilbene Cl₂]₂ , were almost identical, indicating that the

resonance of stilbene, involving $\diagdown C = C \diagup$, was not greatly disturbed.

The results were not conclusive because the spectra for the styrene and 2-pentene complexes could not be interpreted so simply. The infrared data indicated that the carbon-carbon distance in the olefinic complexes was lengthened considerably, although the different spectra obtained with the isomeric 2-pentenes indicated that free rotation was not permitted.

Chatt[96] has found from infrared data that the olefin retains its double bond in platinum complexes and that the double bond is symmetrically coordinated to the platinum. The greater lowering of the double bond stretching band for the platinum complexes as compared with those of silver was attributed to the stronger bonding in the platinum complexes. Wunderlich and Mellor[98] obtained x-ray structural data for Zeise's salt and determined that the C-C axis is approximately perpendicular to the plane of the $PtCl_3$ group and probably symmetrically arranged with respect to the platinum atom. The distance between platinum and the chloride trans to the ethylene molecule is abnormally great.

Dempsey and Baenziger[98a] determined the crystal structure of $(PdCl_2C_2H_4)_2$ by x-ray diffraction methods. The dimer has the trans bridged structure similar to structure *I* (p. 501) for the corresponding platinum compound. The axis of the ethylene molecule is perpendicular to the plane of the dimer and the center of the ethylene bond lies in the plane of the dimer. Holden and Baenziger[98a] obtained the structure of the corresponding styrene complex since the carbons of the ethylene molecule could not be resolved. The general features of the structure are the same as those of the ethylene complex except that the palladium is slightly off center with respect to the carbon-carbon double bond in the styrene complex. The Pd-Cl bonds opposite the Pd-olefin bonds are somewhat longer than the other Pd-Cl bonds.

98. Wunderlich and Mellor, *Acta Cryst.*, **7**, 130 (1954); **8**, 57 (1955).

98a. Dempsey and Baenziger, *J. Am. Chem. Soc.*, **77**, 4984 (1955); Holden and Baenziger, *ibid.*, **77**, 4987 (1955).

Winstein and Lucas[50] proposed a structure for the silver-olefin complexes based on resonance involving three forms.

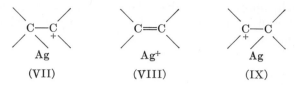

$$(VII) \qquad (VIII) \qquad (IX)$$

The resonance hybrid would not have the properties of a molecule containing a carbonium ion, nor would the double bond need to be activated sufficiently to lead to polymerization or rearrangement of *cis-trans* isomers. They stated that the C—C—Ag bond angle would be greater than the 60° angle for cyclopropane and that the resonance energy could compensate for the strain.

Pitzer[99] indicated that the protonated double bond type of structure which he proposed for the boron hydrides can be applied to the silver-olefin complexes. He pointed out that silver has an s orbital which it can use for bond formation with the olefin.

Dewar[100] and Walsh[101] stated that bonding electrons can, under certain conditions, be utilized in the formation of a coordinate covalent bond. Walsh pointed out that the π electrons of ethylene lie in an orbital of ionization potential 10.45 volts, almost equal to that (10.8 volts) of the ammonia lone pair. Werner[102] and Bateman[103] related these views to the olefin complexes and Bateman mentioned that they were essentially those expressed by Winstein and Lucas and restated more precisely by Pitzer.

Dewar[104] described the structure of the silver-olefin complexes in terms of molecular orbitals. The structure involved the combination of the vacant s orbital of silver with the π-orbital of the olefin and the combination of a filled $4d$ orbital of silver with the p orbital of the olefin.

Chatt[95] discarded the Pitzer structure for the platinum complexes since platinum does not have a vacant s orbital (see footnote p. 506). However, in view of more recent data, Chatt[96] considers a similar structure to be correct.

Chatt[2] found no evidence for association between ethylene and trimethylborine and interpreted this to mean that "the donation of electrons in any manner from the ethylene molecule to the metal cannot, of itself, be responsible for the coordination of ethylene." He felt that the distin-

99. Pitzer, *J. Am. Chem. Soc.*, **67**, 1127 (1945).
100. Dewar, *J. Chem. Soc.*, **1946**, 408.
101. Walsh, *ibid.*, **1947**, 89.
102. Werner, *Nature*, **160**, 644 (1947).
103. Bateman, *ibid.*, 56.
104. Dewar, *Bull. soc. chim.*, **18**, C79 (1951).

guishing feature of platinum as compared to boron is the ability to donate *d* electrons to form a double bond. However, he did allow that Pitzer's structure might apply to the silver-olefin complexes. He considered the structure of the silver complexes to differ from that of the platinum-olefin complexes, since it is known that olefins existing as *cis-trans* isomers do not rearrange in the silver complexes and because of the presence of a vacant *s* orbital in the case of silver. Since new evidence indicates that *cis-trans* isomers should not rearrange in the platinum complexes, this distinction between the silver and the platinum complexes cannot be made.

Professor Pitzer[105] has been kind enough to make a statement* which removes the misconception that he has excluded the possibility that a metal ion without a vacant *s* orbital could form a complex with the protonated double bond type of structure.

Douglas[97] has proposed a modification of the Winstein-Lucas structure, (VII), (VIII), and (IX), by adding two resonance forms, (X) and (XI), nvolving the sharing of a pair of *d* electrons from the platinum.

This is similar to the molecular orbital structure proposed by Dewar for the silver-olefin complexes. Chatt[96] has made the similarity even greater by extending Dewar's structure to include the platinum-olefin compounds. He considers the sharing of electrons from the olefin to occur through the overlap of a $5d6s6p^2$ hybrid orbital of the platinum atom with the π-orbital of the olefin and the sharing of electrons from the platinum to occur by the overlap of a hybridized $5d6p$ orbital with the antibonding orbitals of the olefin. This is essentially the same as the resonance structure proposed, but is more detailed in terms of the orbitals involved. The structures of the palladium and platinum complexes determined by x-ray methods[98, 98a] seem to be consistent with the orbital assignment given by Chatt.

105. Pitzer, private communication, Sept. 17, 1952.

* "Because of their non-directional property, *s* orbitals can be combined into the protonated double bond type of orbitals better than *p* or *d* orbitals. This is not to imply that it is impossible to use *p* or *d* or hybrid orbitals for this purpose—indeed I now feel that there is adequate evidence in favor of bridge bonds of this type.

"I believe we should use some caution in assuming larger and more complex groups to be bounded to a pair of electrons in a double bond. However, I do not pretend to prescribe any particular limit and I feel it probable that a limitation to single atoms with *s* orbitals available would be incorrect."

Andrews and Keefer[52] suggested that a likely structure for the silver-benzene complexes is one with the silver ion above the ring on the six-fold axis of symmetry; in the disilver complexes, there would be one silver ion on each side of the ring. X-ray analysis of the solid silver perchlorate-benzene complex shows that each silver is bonded equally to two carbon atoms of each of two rings lying above and below the rings, suggesting π bonding[106]. However, the structure in solution might differ from this. No conclusions could be reached concerning the bonding between silver and toluene[107].

Interesting developments in the structure determination of bis(cyclopentadienyl)iron(II) have been presented. The compound almost certainly contains iron(II) since it is diamagnetic and is readily oxidized to a blue cation $Fe(C_5H_5)_2^+$ which has a magnetic moment corresponding to one unpaired electron[37]. The structure was originally assumed to be one represented by two resonance forms (XII)[36], but the diamagnetic character suggests structure (XIII),

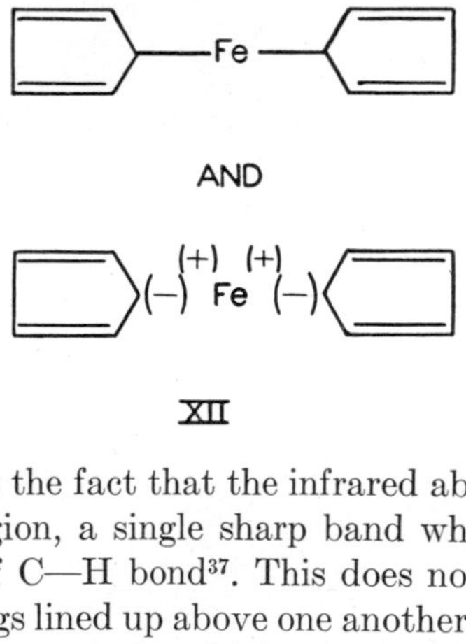

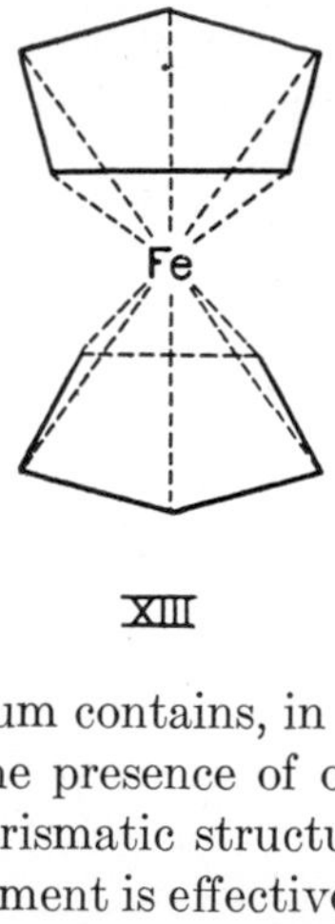

as does the fact that the infrared absorption spectrum contains, in the 3 to 4 μ region, a single sharp band which indicates the presence of only one type of C—H bond[37]. This does not exclude the prismatic structure with the rings lined up above one another. The dipole moment is effectively zero.

A structure in which the iron atom is symmetrically placed between two cyclopentadienyl rings (XIII) was confirmed by x-ray analysis[108]. The x-ray data support the antiprismatic structure (XIII) in the solid state. However, the isomers of derivatives of ferrocene are those to be expected if free rotation of the rings occurs in solution[109].

The structure of bis(cyclopentadienyl) compounds has been presented in

106. Rundle and Goring, *J. Am. Chem. Soc.*, **72**, 5337 (1950).
107. Murray and Cleveland, *ibid.*, **65**, 2110 (1943).
108. Eiland and Pepinsky, *J. Am. Chem. Soc.*, **74**, 4971 (1952); Fisher and Pfab, *Z. Naturforschung*, **7B**, 377 (1952); Dunitz and Orgel, *Nature*, **171**, 121 (1953).
109. Woodward and Rosenblum, private communication, August, 1953.

terms of molecular orbitals by Moffitt[110]. The bonding is described as a delocalized two electron covalent bond between the metal ion and each cyclopentadienyl ring. Such bonding is consistent with free rotation of the rings and with the magnetic data. It also explains the absence of a copper compound and the fact that $Ti(C_5H_5)_2^+$ can exist although there are only two metal electrons which can bond with the unpaired π electrons of each ring. Since only one π electron of each cyclopentadienyl ring is used in bonding, the rings have aromatic character.

110. Moffitt, *J. Am. Chem. Soc.*, **76**, 3386 (1954).

16. Metal Carbonyls and Nitrosyls

J. A. Mattern

University of Buffalo, Buffalo, New York

and

Stanley J. Gill

University of Illinois, Urbana, Illinois

EARLY HISTORY

Upon observing that nickel valves were corroded by hot gases containing carbon monoxide, Mond and his co-workers[1] studied the action of carbon monoxide upon nickel under various conditions. They found that a stream of carbon monoxide, after passing over finely divided nickel, burned with a luminous flame which deposited metallic spots upon a cold surface. From such a stream of gas they isolated a colorless liquid with a musty odor and remarkably high refractive index and coefficient of expansion. This compound has the formula $Ni(CO)_4$. In 1834 von Liebig[2] prepared a compound having the empirical formula KCO by passing carbon monoxide over molten potassium; this however, is the potassium salt of hexahydroxybenzene[3] and is quite different from the covalent carbonyls discussed in this chapter.

A volatile iron carbonyl was discovered in 1891[4] and was shown to have the formula $Fe(CO)_5$[5]. Dewar and Jones[6] showed the photodecomposition product of the pentacarbonyl to be the enneacarbonyl, $Fe_2(CO)_9$, and demonstrated the existence of a third carbonyl, $Fe_3(CO)_{12}$.

The known mononuclear and polynuclear metal carbonyls and their hydrides are listed in Table 16.1.

1. Mond, Langer, and Quincke, *J. Chem. Soc.*, **57**, 749 (1890); Mond, *J. Soc. Chem. Ind.*, **14**, 945 (1895).
2. Liebig, *Pogg. Ann.*, **30**, 90 (1834).
3. Nietski and Benckiser, *Ber.*, **18**, 499, 1833 (1885).
4. Berthelot, *Compt. rend.*, **112**, 1343 (1891); Mond and Quincke, *Ber.*, **24**, 2248 (1891); *J. Chem. Soc.*, **59**, 604 (1891); *Chem. News*, **63**, 301 (1891).
5. Mond and Langer, *J. Chem. Soc.*, **59**, 1090 (1891).
6. Dewar and Jones, *Proc. Roy. Soc.*, *(London)*, **A76**, 558 (1905); **A79**, 66 (1906).

TABLE 16.1. METAL CARBONYLS AND CARBONYL HYDRIDES[7]

Met-als	Monomeric Carbonyls with Rare Gas Config., Volatile, Soluble in Organic Liquid		Polynuclear Carbonyls, Less Volatile or Non-volatile, Less or Not Soluble	
	Carbonyls	Carbonyl Hydrides	Dinuclear Carbonyls	Higher Carbonyl Polymers
Cr	$Cr(CO)_6$ color-less, rhomb., sublimes			
Mn			$Mn_2(CO)_{10}$	
Fe	$Fe(CO)_5$ yel., volatile, M.P. $-20°C$. B.P. $103°C$	$Fe(CO)_4H_2$ col-orless, volatile M.P. $-70°C$	$Fe_2(CO)_9$ gold-yel-low, pseudo-hex-agonal, dec. $100°C$	$Fe_3(CO)_{12}$ green monocl. pris-matic, dec. $140°C$
Co		$Co(CO)_4H$ light yel., volatile M.P. $-26°C$	$Co_2(CO)_8$ orange, cryst. M. P. $51°C$	$Co_4(CO)_{12}$ black, cryst. dec. $60°C$
Ni	$Ni(CO)_4$ color-less, volatile M.P. $-25°C$. B.P. $43°C$			
Mo	$Mo(CO)_6$ color-less, sublimes	rhomb.,		
Tc				
Ru	$Ru(CO)_5$ color-less, M.P. $-22°C$	volatile	$Ru_2(CO)_9$ orange monoclinic pris-matic, sublimes	$Ru_3(CO)_{12}$ green, insoluble
Rh		$Rh(CO)_4H$ dark yel., volatile M.P. $-12°C$	$Rh_2(CO)_8$ yel.-red, dec. $76°C$	$Rh_n(CO)_{3n}$† dark red crystl., sub-limes $150°$ $Rh_4(CO)_{11}$ black, dec. $200°C$
Pd				
W	$W(CO)_6$ colorless rhomb., sub-limes			
Re		$Re(CO)_5H$*	$Re_2(CO)_{10}$ color-less, monocl. prismatic, sub-limes M.P. $177°C$	
Os	$Os(CO)_5$ color-less, volatile M.P. $ca. -18°C$	$Os(CO)_4H_2(?)$	$Os_2(CO)_9$ light yel-low, pseudo-hex-agonal M.P. $224°C$	
Ir		$Ir(CO)_4H^+$	$Ir_2(CO)_8$ green-yel. cryst., sub-limes	$Ir_n(CO)_{3n}$† ca-nary yel. tri-gonal, dec. $210°C$
Pt				

* Formula qualitatively established.
† Degree of polymerization greater than 4 not definitely established.

7. Hieber, FIAT Rev. German Sci., 1939–46, Inorg. Chem., Pt. II, 108 (1948).

Methods of Preparation

Direct Combination; $xM + yCO \rightarrow M_x(CO)_y$

Passage of carbon monoxide over the finely divided metal at suitable temperatures and pressures has been used for the preparation of $Ni(CO)_4$, $Fe(CO)_5$, $[Co(CO)_4]_2$[8], $Mo(CO)_6$[8, 11], $W(CO)_6$[11], $Ru(CO)_5$[8, 9] and $[Rh(CO)_4]_2$[10]. Pressure greater than atmospheric is required in the preparation of all except nickel carbonyl, and the yields are small except for the carbonyls of iron and nickel. In general, the metal must be in a finely-divided, active state. In the case of nickel, the metal has been prepared by reduction of the oxide by hydrogen at 400°C or of the oxalate at 300°C. The lower the temperature of reduction, the more active is the resulting metal. The presence of copper or iron in the nickel increases the rate of formation of nickel carbonyl. A very active metal has been prepared by electrolysis of a solution of nickel sulfate with a mercury cathode and subsequent low temperature distillation of the mercury[12].

Nickel carbonyl may be formed at atmospheric pressure and a temperature of 30 to 100°[13]. Processes have been developed for the preparation by passing carbon monoxide through suspensions of nickel in inert liquids, such as paraffin oils.

The preparation of iron pentacarbonyl employs a pressure of 20 to 200 atmospheres and a temperature of 200°C. The presence of oxygen or an oxide coating on the iron hinders the reaction, but the presence of finely divided alumina, bismuth, nickel, or copper accelerates it, as do ammonia, hydrogen, and small quantities of sulfur compounds.

Preparation from Grignard Reagents

The hexacarbonyls of chromium, molybdenum, and tungsten, as well as the carbonyl of nickel, have been prepared by the reaction between carbon monoxide and Grignard reagents in the presence of the anhydrous chloride of the metal[14]. Hieber and Romberg[14b], studying the mechanism of the

8. Mond, Hirtz, and Cowap, *J. Chem. Soc.*, **97**, 798 (1910).
9. Manchot and Manchot, *Z. anorg. Chem.*, **226**, 385 (1936).
10. Hieber and Lagally, *Z. anorg. Chem.*, **251**, 96 (1943).
11. I. G. Farbenindustrie, A.-G., German Patents 531402 (Jan. 21, 1930)- cf. *Chem. Abs.*, **25**, 5523 (1931)- and 531479 (Feb. 13, 1930)- cf. *Chem. Abs.*, **25**, 5521 (1931); French Patents 708269 (Dec. 23, 1930)- cf. *Chem. Abs.*, **26**, 1399 (1932)- and 708379 (Dec. 26, 1930)- cf. *Chem. Abs.*, **26**, 1401 (1932).
12. Bennett (to Catalyst Research Corporation), U. S. Patent 1975076 (October 2, 1934).- cf. *Chem. Abs.*, **28**, 7439 (1934).
13. Gilliland and Blanchard, *Inorganic Syntheses*, **2**, 234 (1946).
14. Job, *et al.*, *Compt. rend.*, **177**, 1439 (1923); **183**, 58, 392 (1926); **187**, 564 (1928); *Bull. Soc. chim.*, **41**, 1041 (1927); Hieber and Romberg, *Z. anorg. Chem.*, **221**, 321 (1935).

process, showed that no chromium carbonyl is formed before the hydrolysis of the Grignard reagent. Presumably an organic carbonyl derivative, such as $Cr(CO)_2R_4$, is an intermediate product.

The hexacarbonyls are colorless, crystalline solids, much more stable than the carbonyls of iron or nickel. They are not oxidized in air, and they may be sublimed without decomposition. (Chromium hexacarbonyl deposits some chromium above 140°C.)

High-pressure Synthesis

Almost all of the known carbonyls have been prepared by reactions between metallic halides, sulfides, or oxides and carbon monoxide under pressure. Such reactions are especially useful in cases in which the metallic compounds are largely covalent. For example, CoS (NiAs structure) is quantitatively converted into $[Co(CO)_4]_2$ at 200° and 200 atmospheres pressure, but cobalt oxide does not react[15]. Generally, some free metal must be present to act as an acceptor for the nonmetal. If no such acceptor is present, the lining metal of the autoclave (for example, copper) may enter into the reaction:

$$2CoS + 8CO + 4Cu \rightarrow [Co(CO)_4]_2 + 2Cu_2S$$

For the reaction

$$2CoX_2 + 4Cu + 8CO \rightarrow [Co(CO)_4]_2 + 4CuX,$$

at 250° and 200 atmospheres in a copper lined autoclave, the percentages of conversion into the carbonyl are[16]:

X =	F	Cl	Br	I
% conversion	0	3.5	9	100

A volatile carbonyl halide, such as $Co(CO)I_2$, is assumed to be an intermediate:

$$CoI_2 + CO \rightarrow Co(CO)I_2$$

$$2Co(CO)I_2 + 4Cu + 6CO \rightarrow 4CuI + [Co(CO)_4]_2$$

The increase in reactivity with increasing covalency of the cobalt halide is explained by an increase in the ease of formation of the carbonyl halide in the order chloride-bromide-iodide.

In some cases (e.g., iridium halides at 110° and atmospheric pressure) the order of reactivity is reversed[17]; this suggests a different mechanism, such as

15. Hieber, Schulten, and Marin, *Z. anorg. Chem.*, **240,** 261 (1939).
16. Hieber and Schulten, *Z. anorg. Chem.*, **243,** 145 (1939).
17. Hieber, *et al.*, *Z. anorg. Chem.*, **245,** 321 (1940); **246,** 138 (1940).

$$2IrX_3 + 5CO \rightarrow 2Ir(CO)_2X_2 + COX_2$$

$$2Ir(CO)_2X_2 + 3CO \rightarrow 2Ir(CO)_3X + COX_2$$

$$2Ir(CO)_3X + CO \rightarrow 2[Ir(CO)_3]_x + COX_2$$

It is assumed that the formation of a stable compound COX_2 is necessary for the completion of these reactions. Carbonyl iodide is not known and the reaction $2IrI_3 + 4CO \rightarrow 2Ir(CO)_2I_2 + I_2$ takes place, but there is no further reaction. The chloride is the only halide of iridium that gives appreciable yields of the carbonyl by this method; even here the chief product is $Ir(CO)_3Cl$. However, with iridium halides at high pressure in the presence of a halogen acceptor, the order of reactivity is as originally given.

The use of such nonmetals as iodine[7, 18] and sulfur[19] (or their compounds) as catalysts in the synthesis of carbonyls can be understood in terms of these reactions. Sulfur, for example, may form metal carbonyl sulfides which upon further reaction with carbon monoxide produce the metal carbonyl:

$$3Fe + 2S + 8CO \rightarrow Fe_3S_2(CO)_8$$

$$Fe_3S_2(CO)_8 + 7CO \rightarrow 3Fe(CO)_5 + 2S$$

This mechanism is given support by Hieber's isolation[7] of both $Fe_3S_2(CO)_8$ and $Fe_3Se_2(CO)_8$.

It is not often that oxides can be used for the preparation of carbonyls. However, the best synthesis of osmium carbonyl is the reaction of carbon monoxide and the covalent oxide OsO_4 :

$$OsO_4 + 9CO \rightarrow Os(CO)_5 + 4CO_2 \text{[20]}.$$

In some cases the extreme stability of the intermediates makes the preparation of the simple carbonyls difficult. For example, rhenium carbonyl halides are the only products of the reaction of rhenium halides or complex halides with carbon monoxide. Their stability is demonstrated by such reactions as

$$2Re + NiX_2 + 14CO \rightarrow 2Re(CO)_5X + Ni(CO)_4$$

in which rhenium acts as the halogen acceptor for the formation of nickel carbonyl, and[21]

$$KReO_4 + CCl_4 + 8CO \rightarrow KCl + Re(CO)_5Cl + COCl_2 + 3CO_2 .$$

In order to obtain a simple rhenium carbonyl by this method it is necessary

18. Geisenberger, unpublished experiments.
19. Mittasch, *Z. angew. Chem.*, **41**, 587, 827 (1928).
20. Hieber, *et al.*, *Z. Elektrochem.*, **49**, 288 (1943); *Ber.*, **75**, 1472 (1942).
21. Hieber, *et al.*, *Z. anorg. Chem.*, **243**, 164 (1939); **248**, 243 (1941); **248**, 256 (1941).

to use Re_2S_7, Re_2O_7 or $KReO_4$ as the starting material, the reaction being carried out in the absence of halogens.

The nature of the metal used as the acceptor influences the extent to which these reactions go. If cobalt bromide is heated with silver, copper, cadmium or zinc in an inert atmosphere, the extent to which free cobalt is liberated increases in the order Ag, Cu, Cd, Zn. When the inert atmosphere is replaced by carbon monoxide, the extent to which carbonyls are formed increases in the same order. The product in the case of zinc or cadmium is not $[Co(CO)_4]_2$ but a mixed carbonyl, $[Co(CO)_4]_2M$. This tendency of the more active metals to form mixed compounds must be considered in selecting the acceptor.

In the experiment just described, the extent of carbonyl formation is much greater than the extent of the corresponding displacement reaction in the absence of carbon monoxide, and the high pressure synthesis may not actually involve reduction to the free metal followed by combination to form the carbonyl. This is supported by the fact that iridium and osmium, which are inert toward carbon monoxide, form carbonyls by the high pressure synthesis.

Formation by Disproportionation Reactions

When nickel(I) cyanide is treated with carbon monoxide, nickel carbonyl and nickel(II) cyanide are formed[22]:

$$2NiCN + 4CO \rightarrow Ni(CN)_2 + Ni(CO)_4$$

A similar reaction takes place when a complex of univalent nickel is employed, an intermediate probably being formed:

$$K_2Ni(CN)_3 + CO \rightarrow K_2[Ni(CN)_3CO]$$

$$2K_2[Ni(CN)_3CO] + 2CO \rightarrow Ni(CO)_4 + K_2Ni(CN)_4 + 2KCN$$

Nickel carbonyl is also produced when carbon monoxide is passed into an alkaline mixture of a nickel(II) salt and ethyl mercaptan or potassium hydrogen sulfide in water; the formation of a univalent carbonyl compound, followed by disproportionation, is postulated[22]

$$2Ni(SH)_2 + 2nCO \rightarrow 2NiSH(CO)_n + H_2S_2 \text{ (absorbed by alkali)}$$

$$2NiSH(CO)_n + (4 - 2n)CO \rightarrow Ni(CO)_4 + Ni(SH)_2$$

Disproportionations are also responsible for the preparation of certain carbonyls from carbonyl derivatives[23]:

22. Manchot and Gall, *Ber.*, **59**, 1060 (1926); *Ber.*, **62**, 678 (1929); Beducci, *Z. anorg. Chem.*, **86**, 88 (1914); Blanchard, Rafter, and Adams, *J. Am. Chem. Soc.*, **56**, 16 (1934).
23. Hieber *et al.*, *Ber.*, 63, 1405 (1930); *Z. anorg. Chem.*, **221**, 337 (1935).

$$3Fe(CO)_3 \cdot CH_3OH + 4H^+ \rightarrow Fe(CO)_5 + 2Fe^{++} + 3CH_3OH + 2H_2 + 4CO$$

$$2[Fe(CO)_4]_3 + 3py \rightarrow 3Fe(CO)_3py + 3Fe(CO)_5$$

$$Cr(CO)_4py_2 + py \rightarrow Cr(CO)_3py_3 + CO$$

$$3Cr(CO)_3py_3 + 15HCl + 2H_2O \rightarrow Cr(CO)_6$$

$$+ 2[CrCl_5H_2O] (pyH)_2 + 5pyHCl + 3CO + 3H_2$$

Similar reactions are shown by some of the carbonyls themselves. For example, iron enneacarbonyl is formed from the pentacarbonyl by the action of light of wave length shorter than 4100Å.

$$2Fe(CO)_5 \rightarrow Fe_2(CO)_9 + CO$$

The product undergoes disproportionation when heated in benzene or ether solution.

$$3Fe_2(CO)_9 \rightarrow Fe_3(CO)_{12} + 3Fe(CO)_5$$

THE FORMATION OF CARBONYL HYDRIDES

The High-pressure Synthesis

Carbonyl hydrides sometimes form as byproducts of the high pressure synthesis of carbonyls. If moist cobalt sulfide or iodide is treated with carbon monoxide under high pressure and in the presence of an acceptor, cobalt carbonyl hydride forms[15]. The reaction is probably $2CoS + H_2O + 9CO + 4Cu \rightarrow 2Co(CO)_4H + CO_2 + 2Cu_2S$. This method has also been used to prepare $Rh(CO)_4H$, $Ir(CO)_4H$, and $Os(CO)_4H_2$. Cobalt carbonyl hydride also results when cobalt carbonyl is heated with hydrogen and carbon monoxide (to prevent decomposition) by the reversible reaction $[Co(CO)_4]_2 + H_2 = 2Co(CO)_4H$. Some cobalt carbonyl hydride forms when cobalt or cobalt sulfide is heated with hydrogen and carbon monoxide.

$$2Co + 8CO + H_2 \rightarrow 2Co(CO)_4H$$

$$2CoS + 8CO + H_2 + 4Cu \rightarrow 2Co(CO)_4H + 2Cu_2S$$

The same methods have been used for the preparation of rhodium carbonyl hydride, but attempts to produce iron carbonyl hydride always result in the formation of the pentacarbonyl.

Hydrolysis of Carbonyls

Hieber and his co-workers[24] reported the formation of an unstable iron carbonyl hydride by the action of bases upon iron pentacarbonyl:

$$Fe(CO)_5 + Ba(OH)_2 \rightarrow Fe(CO)_4H_2 + BaCO_3$$

---

24. Hieber and Leutert, *Z. anorg. Chem.*, **204**, 145 (1932); Hieber and *Z.* Vetter, *anorg. Chem.*, **212**, 145 (1933); Hieber, Muhlbauer, and Ehmann, *Ber.*, **65**, 1090 (1932).

Treatment of certain derivatives of iron carbonyl with acid also produces the carbonyl hydride

$$Fe_2(CO)_4en_3 + 8H^+ \rightarrow Fe(CO)_4H_2 + Fe^{++} + 3(enH_2)^{++}$$

Disproportionation Reactions

Reactions similar to those used to prepare carbonyls may be used to prepare carbonyl hydrides. An alkaline solution of a cysteine cobalt(II) complex absorbs carbon monoxide[25], presumably forming a carbonyl intermediate which disproportionates to form cobalt carbonyl hydride and a cobalt(III) complex:

$$9[Cocy_2]^- + 8CO + 2H_2O \rightarrow 6[Cocy_3]^= + Co(OH)_2 + 2Co(CO)_4H$$

Further treatment with carbon monoxide produces more carbonyl hydride and regenerates the cysteine

$$[Cocy_3]^= + 6CO + 7OH^- \rightarrow 2CO_3^= + 3Cy^- + 3H_2O + Co(CO)_4H$$

The carbonyl hydrides behave as very weak acids. Hieber and co-workers[26] give the following data:

$$2[Co(CO)_4]^- \rightleftharpoons [Co(CO)_4]_2 + 2e^- \quad E^{\circ}_{293} = -0.40$$

$$3[Fe(CO)_4]^- \rightleftharpoons [Fe(CO)_4]_3 + 6e^- \quad E^{\circ}_{293} = -0.74$$

$$3[Fe(CO)_4H]^- \rightleftharpoons [Fe(CO)_4]_3 + 3H^+ + 6e^- \quad E^{\circ}_{293} = -0.35$$

$$Fe(CO)_4H_2 - \text{dibasic acid at } 0°$$

$$K_1 = 3.6 \times 10^{-5}$$

$$K_2 = 1.10 \times 10^{-14}$$

True salts of the carbonyl hydrides are formed only with alkali and alkaline earth metals and large ammine cations. Compounds with other metals do not have the properties of salts and are discussed under mixed carbonyls.

Behrens[27] prepared carbonyl salts directly in liquid ammonia:

$$[M(CO)_n]_x + xyNa \rightleftharpoons x\ Na_y[M(CO)_n]$$

Attempts to prepare a chromium carbonyl hydride by means of this reaction have been unsuccessful[26b].

METAL CARBONYL HALIDES AND RELATED COMPOUNDS

Some metal carbonyl halides have been isolated as intermediates in the preparation of metal carbonyls by high pressure synthesis; in other cases

25. Schubert, *J. Am. Chem. Soc.*, **55**, 4563 (1933).
26. Hieber and Hübel, *Z. Naturforschung*, **7b**, 322 (1952); Hieber and Abeck, *Z. Naturforschung*, **7b**, 320 (1952).
27. Behrens, *Z. Naturforschung*, **7b**, 321–22 (1952).

their existence is only postulated. The list of elements which form carbonyl halides is not the same as the list of those which form simple carbonyls. For palladium, platinum, copper, and gold, which form no simple carbonyls, the stability of the carbonyl halides appears to be iodide < bromide < chloride[28]. The stability, ease of formation, and volatility of the compounds of the carbonyl-forming metals, however, all show trends in the opposite direction.

Carbonyl halides are obtained by the action of halogen upon carbonyl hydrides, mixed carbonyls, simple carbonyls, or other carbonyl halides: For example[29],

$$FeI_2 + 4CO \rightarrow Fe(CO)_4I_2$$

$$Fe(CO)_5 + I_2 \rightarrow Fe(CO)_4I_2 + CO$$

$$Fe(CO)_4H_2 + 2I_2 \rightarrow Fe(CO)_4I_2 + 2HI$$

$$Fe(CO)_4Hg + 2I_2 \rightarrow Fe(CO)_4I_2 + HgI_2$$

Mixed Carbonyls

Mixed carbonyls, such as $[Co(CO)_4]_2Zn$, are covalent compounds and are soluble in organic solvents; they are therefore not to be classed with the salts of the carbonyl hydrides. Typical reactions which produce these compounds are illustrated by the equations:

$$2CoBr_2 + 3Zn + 8CO \rightarrow 2ZnBr_2 + [Co(CO)_4]_2Zn$$

$$2Co + Zn + 8CO \rightarrow [Co(CO)_4]_2Zn$$

$$[Co(CO)_4]_2 + Zn \rightarrow [Co(CO)_4]_2Zn$$

$$Fe(CO)_4H_2 + HgCl_2 \rightarrow 2HCl + [Fe(CO)_4]Hg$$

Mercury forms mixed carbonyls most readily; among the other metals which form them are zinc, cadmium, indium, thallium, and tin.

Structure of the Carbonyls and Their Derivatives

Bond Type

The carbonyl group, at least in the mononuclear carbonyl, may be considered to be a carbon monoxide molecule (not greatly modified) coordinated to a central metal atom in much the same way that other neutral molecules or ions are coordinated to central cations. This postulate is the most consistent with the energetics involved and with the properties of the compounds, thus excluding the possibility of important contributions from

28. Wagner, *Z. anorg. Chem.*, **196,** 364 (1931).
29. Hieber *et al.*, *Ber.*, **61,** 1717 (1928); *Z. anorg. Chem.*, **245,** 295 (1940); **245,** 305 (1940).

van der Waals bonding[30]. The evidence supporting this view may be summarized as follows:

(1) spectroscopic data, showing that the pairing of d electrons requires energy of the order of 50 kcal;

(2) the nonpolar character of simple carbonyls as shown by their volatility;

(3) the liberation of carbon monoxide, either by decomposition or by stepwise replacement with neutral molecules;

(4) the diamagnetic character of the simple carbonyls;

(5) the C—O bond distance (from electron diffraction data) of between 1.13 and 1.15 Å., which is very close to that in carbon monoxide itself (1.13 Å);

(6) the strongest Raman frequency of nickel carbonyl (2039 cm^{-1}) compares favorably with that in carbon monoxide itself (2155 cm^{-1});

(7) the analogy between the simplest carbonyl compound-borine carbonyl BH_3CO- and BF_3NH_3, and that between $[PtCl_2 \cdot PR_3]$ and $[PtCl_2 \cdot CO]$; and

(8) the relation between the position of a metal in the periodic table and the composition of the carbonyls it forms.

Such evidence leads to the conclusion that the bonding between the metallic element and the carbonyl group in the mononuclear compounds is essentially an electron pair bond. The supposition of a higher electron density than that supplied by a two-electron bond finds support from both resonance considerations and a shortening of bond distance observed in diffraction studies. Spectroscopic analyses of all of the mononuclear compounds show that the bond between the carbon and oxygen in the carbonyl group retains the characteristics of carbon monoxide. However, with the polynuclear carbonyls there is evidence suggesting a similarity in structure between the carbonyls and aldehydes or ketones. This evidence has been studied in particular with the iron carbonyls.

It should be noted that elements of odd atomic number form no mononuclear carbonyls, whereas elements of even atomic number, in forming mononuclear carbonyls, acquire enough carbonyl groups to give the effective atomic number of the next inert gas.

Structure of the Mononuclear Carbonyls

There was an early tendency to regard the carbonyls as ring compounds. Werner first suggested that all the carbonyl groups are attached directly to the metal atoms, leading to the supposition by Langmuir that in these compounds the central atom attains the number of electrons of the next

30. Syrkin and Dyatkina, "Structure of Molecules and the Chemical Bond," p. 358, New York, Interscience Publishers, Inc., 1950.

TABLE 16.2. COMPOUNDS WITH THE Cr(CO)$_6$ CONFIGURATION

Cr $1s^2 2s^2 2p^6 3s^2 3p^6 3d^6$ forms 6 covalent bonds $(3d^4 4s^2 4p^6)$

M(—CN)$^-$	M(—CO)	M(—NO)$^+$
Mn(CN)$_6^{5-}$	—	Mn(CN)$_5$NO$^=$
Fe(CN)$_6^{4-}$	Fe(CN)$_5$CO$^=$	Fe(CN)$_5$NO$^-$
Co(CN)$_6^=$	—	

inert gas[31]. Sidgwick termed this total number of electrons the "Effective Atomic Number" (E.A.N.)[32]. Langmuir's suggestion has been found to hold without exception for the simple carbonyls[33]. It is assumed that each carbon monoxide molecule donates two electrons to the central metal atom; thus, chromium, iron, and nickel, having 12, 10, and 8 fewer electrons than krypton, add 6, 5, and 4 molecules of carbon monoxide, respectively. It is interesting that similar electronic configurations result with several different complexing groups to give the same E.A.N., as shown in Table 16.2[34].

Numerous methods have been employed in the determination of the structures of these compounds. Perhaps the most conclusive are x-ray and electron diffraction methods, which are in turn supported by applications of Raman spectra, infrared spectra, dipole moments, and magnetochemical techniques. The metal atom is surrounded by the carbonyl groups; bonding to the metal occurs through the carbon atom, and the metal, carbon, and oxygen atoms are collinear.

The structural determination of nickel tetracarbonyl illustrates the conclusions and adds insight into the possible electronic configuration. Early evidence from Raman spectra was interpreted to indicate a planar configuration[35], but electron diffraction studies by Brockway and Cross[36] led to the conclusion that the molecule is tetrahedral. Further study by means of infrared absorption[37], Raman spectra[38] and the observation that the compounds show no dipole moment[39] add support to the tetrahedral configuration. According to Pauling's theory of directed valence, Ni^{++} has the configuration $(3s^2 3p^6 3d^8)$. The eight added electrons go into the states $3d^2 4s^2 4p^4$, giving rise to dsp^2 hybrid bonds, which are planar. The atom Ni^0 has the configuration $(3s^2 3p^6 3d^8 4s^2)$. Degeneration of the $4s$ electrons to the $3d$ level permits the formation of sp^3 hybrid bonds, which are tetrahedral

31. Langmuir, *Science*, **54,** 65 (1921).
32. Sidgwick, "Electronic Theory of Valency," p. 163, Oxford Press, 1927.
33. Blanchard, *Chem. Revs.*, **26,** 409 (1940).
34. Hieber, *Z. angew. Chem.*, **55,** 7 (1942).
35. Duncan and Murray, *J. Chem. Phys.*, **2,** 636 (1934).
36. Brockway and Cross, *J. Chem. Phys.*, **3,** 828 (1935).
37. Crawford and Cross, *J. Chem. Phys.*, **6,** 525 (1938).
38. Crawford and Horiwitz, *J. Chem. Phys.*, **16,** 147 (1948).
39. Sutton, New, and Bentley, *J. Chem. Soc.*, **1933, 652.**

TABLE 16.3. INTERATOMIC DISTANCES FROM ELECTRON DIFFRACTION
DATA (Å)

	C—O	M—C	N—O	M—N	M—C(calc.)	Bond Shortening
Ni(CO)$_4$	1.15	1.82			1.98	0.16
Fe(CO)$_5$	1.15	1.84			2.00	0.16
Cr(CO)$_6$	1.15	1.92			2.02	0.10
Mo(CO)$_6$	1.15	2.08				
W(CO)$_6$	1.13	2.06				
Co(CO)$_3$NO	1.14	1.83	1.10	1.76	1.99	0.16
Fe(CO)$_2$(NO)$_2$	1.15	1.84	1.12	1.77	2.00	0.16
Co(CO)$_4$H	1.16	1.83*			1.99	0.16
Fe(CO)$_4$H$_2$	1.15	1.82*			2.00	0.18

* Average bond lengths.

and commensurate with the known configuration for the nickel carbonyl[40]. This situation is comparable to that found in [Cu(CN)$_4$]$^=$ and [Zn(CN)$_4$]$^=$, which are tetrahedral.

For the hexacarbonyls of chromium, molybdenum, and tungsten the octahedral configuration of the carbonyl groups has been established by x-ray[41], electron diffraction[42], and infrared spectra studies[43].

Because it shows the unusual coordination number of five, iron penta carbonyl has inspired a great deal of experimental work and many theoretical speculations. Most of the evidence supports the trigonal bipyramid structure (as in PF$_5$) proposed by Ewens and Lister (based on their electron diffraction study)[44]. The small dipole moment has been interpreted to indicate a nonequivalence of bonds[45] but experimental conditions or a polarization in the molecule may account for the observed dipole moment[46]. Infrared spectra add evidence for the trigonal bipyramid (dsp^3) structure[46].

Table 16.3 summarizes electron diffraction determinations of interatomic distances in some carbonyls, carbonyl hydrides, and nitrosyls[47].

The M—C bond distance is, in each case, shorter by approximately 0.16Å than the sum of the corresponding covalent radii. Brockway and his co-workers attributed this bond shortening to the contribution of a double

40. Pauling, "Nature of the Chemical Bond," 2nd ed., p. 251, Ithaca, N. Y., Cornell University Press, 1940.
41. Rudorff and Hofmann, Z. phys. Chem., **B28,** 351 (1935).
42. Brockway, Ewens, and Lister, Trans. Faraday Soc., **34,** 1350 (1938).
43. Sheline, J. Am. Chem. Soc., **72,** 5761 (1950).
44. Ewens and Lister, Trans. Faraday Soc., **35,** 681 (1939); Ann. Reports, **36,** 166 (1939).
45. Bergmann and Engel, Z. phys. Chem., **B13,** 232 (1931); Graffunder and Heymann, Z. phys. Chem., **B15,** 377 (1932).
46. Sheline and Pitzer, J. Am. Chem. Soc., **72,** 1107 (1950).
47. Anderson, Quart. Revs., **1,** 331 (1947).

bond structure, assuming the resonance forms[36, 42]

$$M \leftarrow C\!\!\equiv\!\!O \quad \text{and} \quad M\!\!=\!\!C\!\!=\!\!O$$

Similar and extended considerations are to be found in other sources[40, 48]. Hieber has suggested that the decrease in bond distance may be due to secondary interactions between the π electrons of the $C\!\!\equiv\!\!O$ bond and the $3d$ electrons of the metal atom[49]. Whichever explanation is invoked, the C—O distance corresponding to the carbon monoxide triple bond character must be preserved to conform with experimental evidence. Thus the two-electron bond structure is dominant. This conclusion is borne out by the calculated force constants of the Fe—C bond in iron pentacarbonyl, given by Sheline[46] as nearly the same as those found in the metal alkyls[50].

Structure of the Polynuclear Carbonyls

Since elements of odd atomic numbers cannot attain the rare gas configuration by simple coordination of electron pairs, polymerization occurs in carbonyl formation. This polynuclearity is also evidenced in the lower carbonyls of the even numbered elements. The postulation of the structures of the polynuclear compounds presents greater problems than in the case of the mononuclear carbonyls, and these problems have not as yet been completely solved.

Sidgwick and Bailey[51] proposed to account for the formulas of polynuclear carbonyls on the assumptions that (1) the metal atoms acquire the configuration of the next inert gas, and (2) the carbon monoxide molecule is able to join two metal atoms by linking through carbon to one and through oxygen to the other. Iron enneacarbonyl was represented as $(CO)_4Fe \leftarrow C\!\!\equiv\!\!O \rightarrow Fe(CO)_4$, each iron achieving the krypton configuration by accepting five pairs of electrons. Cobalt carbonyl was pictured as $(CO)_4Co\!\!-\!\!CO\!\!-\!\!Co(CO)_3$, in which one cobalt has an effective atomic number of 37 and the other 35; the excess electron on the former is passed to the latter to give a krypton structure. A similar formulation was suggested for $[Co(CO)_3]_4$ in which the cobalt atoms are assumed to be linked to each other by carbonyl groups in the form of a tetrahedron; an electron transfer between two cobalt atoms effects an inert gas structure. Such an unsymmetrical structure appears somewhat tenuous. Brill[52] inferred a trigonal symmetry of iron enneacarbonyl from x-ray studies. Powell and Ewens[53]

48. Syrkin and Dyatkina, *Acta Physicochim. U.R.S.S.*, **20,** 137 (1945); Long and Walsh, *Trans. Faraday Soc.*, **43,** 342 (1947).
49. Hieber, *Die Chemie,* **55,** 25 (1942).
50. Gutowsky, *J. Chem. Phys.*, **17,** 128 (1949).
51. Sidgwick and Bailey, *Proc. Roy. Soc.*, A, **144,** 521 (1934).
52. Brill, *Z. Krist,* **65,** 85 (1927).
53. Powell and Ewens, *J. Chem. Soc.*, **1939,** 286.

confirmed this by means of Patterson and Fourier analysis, ascribing structure (I).

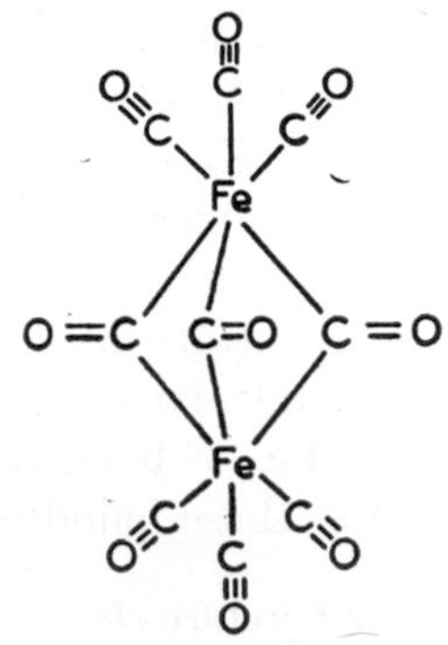

(I)

Thus the Sidgwick-Bailey rule does not apply here. In order to account for the observed diamagnetism, Klemm[54] suggested spin coupling between the unpaired electrons of each iron atom. Powell and Ewens support this view, noting that the iron-iron distance is only 2.46 Å. Three of the CO groups are predicted to be ketonic in character, while the terminal CO groups are linear and are true carbon monoxide types. These assignments are supported by the spectral data of Sheline[46]. An alternative viewpoint is that of Jensen[55], who thinks of $Fe_2(CO)_9$ as a hybrid of the resonance forms (II) and (III).

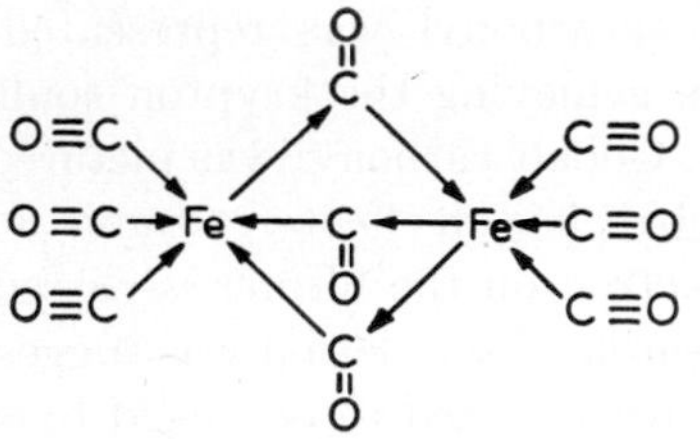

(II) 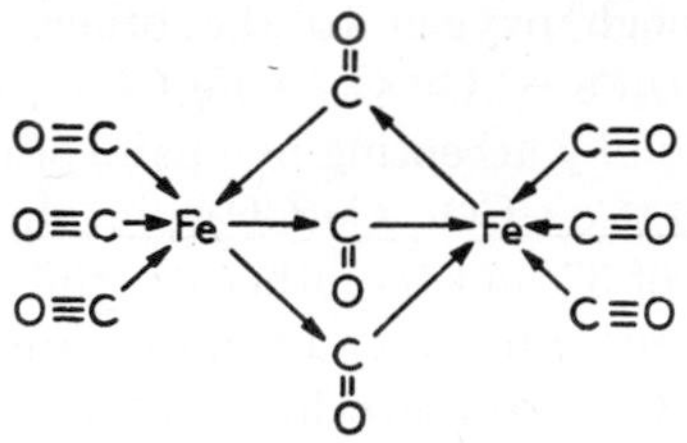   (III)

Ewens has criticized these resonance structures, stating that they contain the equivalent of a covalent iron-iron bond but the compounds do not have the color expected from an iron-iron bond[56]. The assumption of a metal-metal bond appears logical in view of these findings and other recent studies on intermetallic bonding. The postulation of structures for the

54. Klemm, Jacobi, and Tilk, *Z. anorg. Chem.*, **201**, 1 (1931).
55. Jensen and Asmussen, *Z. anorg. Chem.*, **252**, 234 (1944).
56. Ewens, *Nature*, **161**, 530 (1948).

polynuclear compounds of elements such as cobalt presents the same difficulties, if the two cobalt atoms have the same effective atomic number. If they do, however, this number is 35, and other hypotheses are necessary to account for the absence of paramagnetism. Spectral studies have not yet confirmed the presence of a ketonic group in $Co_2(CO)_8$. There is the possibility of direct metal-metal bonding without the ketonic bridge structure $(CO)_4Co:Co(CO)_4$, but in view of the presence of ketonic bonds in iron enneacarbonyl, the bridge-like structure appears more plausible, perhaps coupled with the intermetallic bond.

Similar bridge-like structures have been suggested for $[Cu(CO)_3]_2$[57] $[Re(CO)_5]_2$[58] and other dinuclear compounds[56].

Osmium enneacarbonyl, which is soluble in benzene and which sublimes, differs markedly from the corresponding iron compound, which is insoluble in benzene and does not sublime. Such properties might indicate a difference in structure, though the enhanced covalent character of the osmium compound may arise simply from the larger size of the metal atoms, permitting a more strictly covalent intermetallic bond.

Few of the more complex polynuclear carbonyls have been examined, only the structure of the iron tetracarbonyl having been studied in detail. In 1930, Hieber and Becker[59] proposed the following structures, which are based on the properties and reactions of the material:

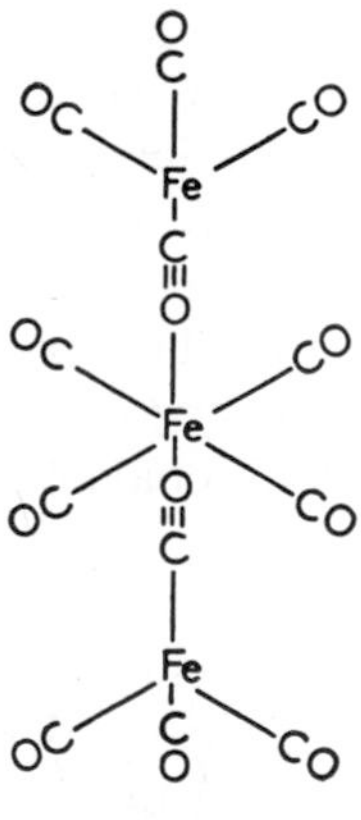

(IV)

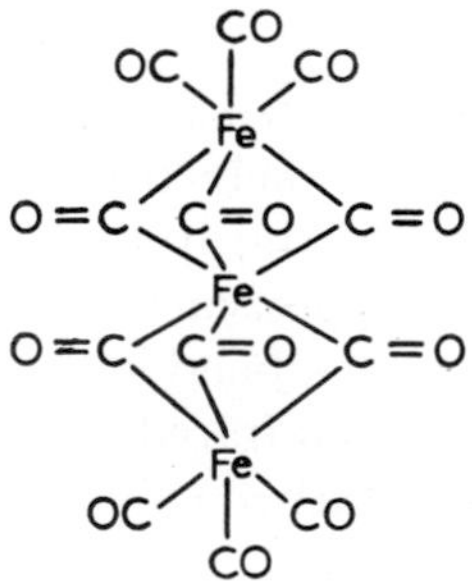

(V)

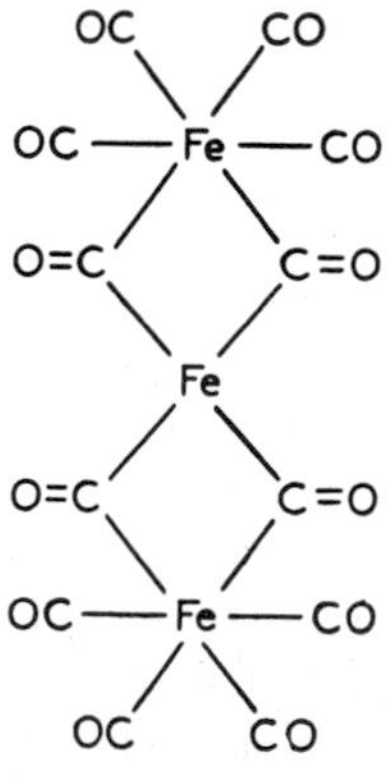

VI

Brill[60] performed the only x-ray diffraction studies yet made on this com-

57. Robinson and Stainthorpe, *Nature*, **153**, 24 (1944).
58. Hieber and Fuchs, *Z. anorg. Chem.*, **248**, 256 (1941).
59. Hieber and Becker, *Ber.*, **63B**, 1406 (1930).
60. Brill, *Z. Krist.*, **77**, 36 (1931).

pound and found that although all of Hieber's structures find correspondence with the crystal structure determination, structure (VI) is the most logical. He depicted it in (VII).

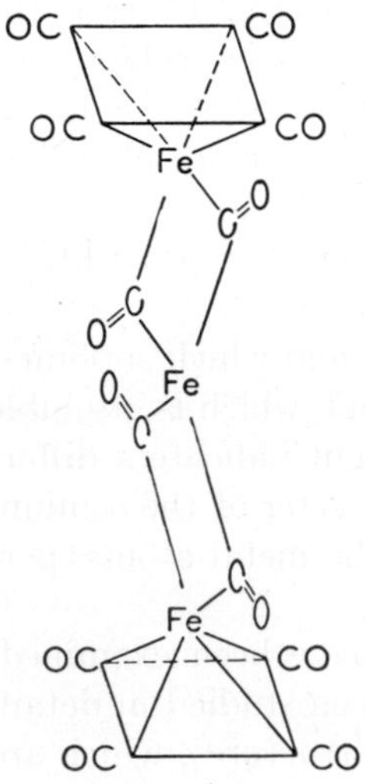

(VII) 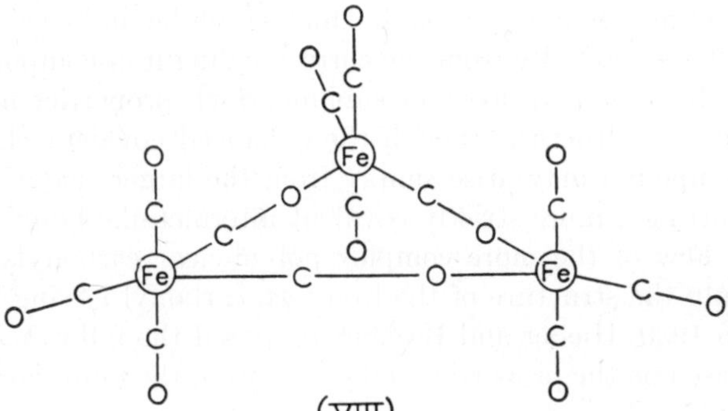   (VIII)

Sidgwick and Bailey[51] represented the structure as shown in (VIII). Such a structure does not appear likely from the preceding discussions of the dinuclear compound. The central iron atom of Brill's structure would be expected to exhibit paramagnetism unless a form of metallic bond exists between the iron atoms; such a bond appears quite reasonable. The spectra of this compound[61] show both infrared and ultra violet bands corresponding to the known frequencies of carbon monoxide and of the ketonic or aldehydic group.

The high solubility of the tetracarbonyl in organic solvents has been interpreted to mean that the three empty $4p$ orbitals of the central atom furnish convenient sets of empty orbitals through which the $Fe_3(CO)_{12}$ molecule can solvate[61]. The solubility might also be explained by the increase of metallic covalent bonding. In any case, the assignments of electrons to specific locations is tenuous. Electron densities may be depicted by the possible resonance structures. Syrkin[62] has suggested that perhaps one of the main resonance forms for the tetracarbonyl is (IX).

61. Sheline, *J. Am. Chem. Soc.*, **73**, 1615 (1951).

62. Syrkin and Dyatkina, "Structure of Molecules and the Chemical Bond," p. 364, New York, Interscience Publishers Inc., 1950.

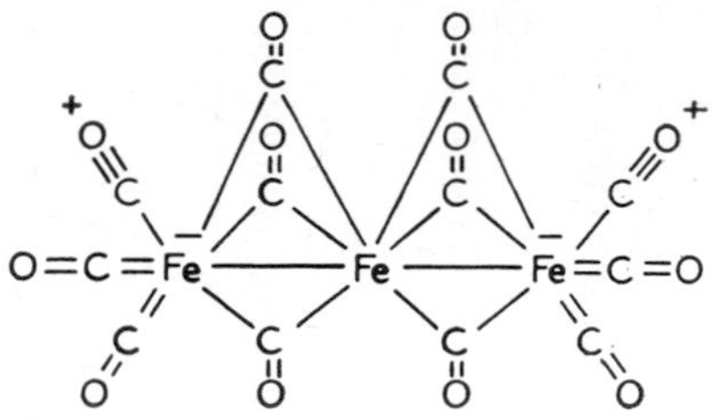

IX

Such a representation, though differing from the above structures, satisfies the general properties and observations previously made.

By analogy with the iron carbonyls, similar rules and theories should apply to other polymeric carbonyls. Higher degrees of polymerization lead to structures which give the molecules low solubility and nonvolatility. An example is $Rh_4(CO)_{11}$[10]. Ormont[63] has studied the conditions of formation and the stability of the carbonyls. His conclusions are summarized in several rules which relate stability to effective atomic number and steric configuration. From heat of formation data, Ormont advances the idea that metals of the zinc group should form tricarbonyls.

Pospekhov[64] has outlined a principle of formation for the polynuclear carbonyls which stems largely from Ormont's considerations and is markedly similar to the Sidgwick analysis. It is general enough that it does not necessitate the hypothesis of bonding through both oxygen and carbon. An intermetallic bond accounts for the observed diamagnetism. Assuming that each CO molecule supplies two electrons to the metal atom, a quantity Δ is defined as the effective atomic number of the central atom, minus the atomic number of the next inert gas. A metal carbonyl will be polymeric if $\Delta < 0$. The degree of polymerization is equal to $1 - \Delta$. The resulting polymers are assumed to be bonded through the metal atoms. This rule, though not in strict accord with the ketonic bridge structures, accounts for all the known formulas for metal carbonyl polymers. The rule predicts formulas for materials the molecular weights of which have not yet been determined, such as $[Ru(CO)_4]_3$, $[Ir(CO)_3]_4$, $[Ag(CO)_3]_2$, and $[Cu(CO)_3]_2$. Mechanisms for formation have been suggested[65]. The recently prepared manganese carbonyl[66] has the predicted composition, $[Mn(CO)_5]_2$.

63. Ormont, *Acta Physicochim., U.R.S.S.*, **11**, 585 (1939); *J. Phys. Chem. (USSR)*, **12**, 259 (1938); *Acta Physicochim., U.R.S.S.*, **19**, 571 (1944); *Acta Physicochim, U.R.S.S.*, **21**, 413 (1946).
64. Pospekhov, *J. Phys. Chem. (U.S.S.R.)*, **21**, 11 (1947); *Zhur. Obshekei Khim*, **18**, 2045 (1948).
65. Pospekhov, *Zhur. Obshekei Khim.*, **18**, 610 (1948).
66. Brimm, private communication; see also Hund, Sentell, and Norton, *J. Am. Chem. Soc.*, **71**, 1899 (1949).

TABLE 16.4. METAL CARBONYL HALIDES[7]

Molecules CO per Metal Atom	Mn	Fe	Co	Ni	Cu
5	—	$[Fe(CO)_5X_2]$	—	—	—
4	—	$[Fe(CO)_4X_2]$	—	—	—
3	—	$[Fe(CO)_3(IHg)_2]_n$	—	—	—
2	—	$[Fe(CO)_2(Cl, I)_2]$	—	—	—
		$[Fe(CO)_2I]_2$			
1	—	$[Fe(CO)Py_2I_2]_n$	$[CoI_2 \cdot CO]_n$	—	$[Cu(Cl, Br) \cdot CO]_4$[2]
Cyano-complex	—	$[Fe(CN)_5CO]M_3$	$[Co(CN)_5CO]K_3$	$[Ni(CN)_3CO]K_3$	—

Molecules CO per Metal Atom	Tc	Ru	Rh	Pd	Ag
2	—	$[Ru(CO)_2X_2]$	$[Rh(CO)_2X]_2$	—	—
1	—	$[Ru(CO)Br]_n$	—	$[Pd(CO)Cl_2]_2$	$1/2CO/Ag : Ag_2(CO)SO_4$
				$[Pd(CO)Cl_3]H$	

Molecules CO per Metal Atom	Re	Os	Ir	Pt	Au
5	$[Re(CO)_5X]$	—	—	—	—
4	—	$[Os(CO)_4X_2]$	—	—	—
		$[Os(CO)_4X]_2$			
3	$[Re(CO)_3py_2X]$	—	$[Ir(CO)_3X]$	—	—
2	—	$[Os(CO)_2X_2]_2$	$[Ir(CO)_2X_2]$	$[Pt(CO)_2X_2]$	—
		$[Os(CO)_2X_2]_n$		$[Pt_2(CO)_3Cl_4]$	
				$[Pt(CO)X_2]_2$	
1	—	—	—	$[Pt(CO)X_3]MH$	$[AuCl \cdot CO]_4$

X = Cl, Br, I; M = K, Na;

The Metal Carbonyl Halides; Their Derivatives and Properties Related to Structure

The most common metallic carbonyl halides are listed in Table 16.4. Iron pentacarbonyl adds free halogens at low temperatures to form $Fe(CO)_5X_2$, which in turn decomposes below 0° to give $Fe(CO)_4X_2$[67]. This suggests that there is a tendency for the iron to acquire a coordination number of six, though the tendency is lessened by the size of the carbonyl groups. Mixed halides such as $Fe(CO)_4ICl$ form, but decompose to mixtures of the symmetrical compounds, e.g., $Fe(CO)_4I_2$ and $Fe(CO)_4Cl_2$. The diamagnetic compounds $Fe(CO)_4SbCl_5$ and $Fe(CO)_4SnCl_4$ have been shown, both by molecular weight determination in benzene and nitrophenol, and by conductivity measurements, to be nonelectrolytes, represented by the structures[68]

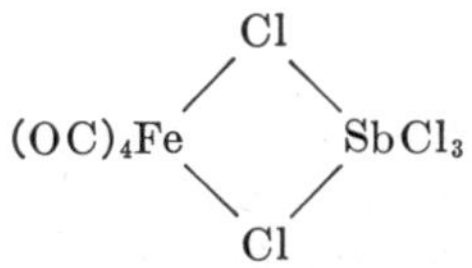

$$(OC)_4Fe \underset{Cl}{\overset{Cl}{\diamond}} SbCl_3 \quad \text{and} \quad (OC)_4Fe \underset{Cl}{\overset{Cl}{\diamond}} SnCl_2.$$

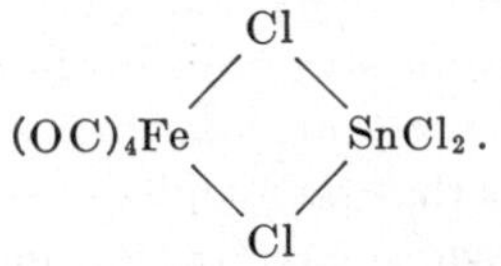

The lower carbonyl halides are probably dimeric, containing halogen bridges, as in $[Fe(CO)_2I]_2$[7, 68].

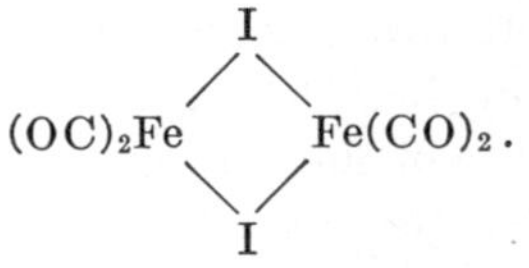

$$(OC)_2Fe \underset{I}{\overset{I}{\diamond}} Fe(CO)_2.$$

This compound reduces silver nitrate in nitric acid and reacts with water to give iron (II) hydroxide and hydrogen. The only other carbonyl halides of the first transition series are the unstable cobalt iodide monocarbonyl and the tetrameric copper carbonyls; the latter are thought to be structural analogs of $[(C_2H_5)_3As \cdot CuI]_4$[69].

The osmium halides show an increasing tendency towards the formation of the dimeric $[Os(CO)_4X_2]_2$[7] (Table 16.5). Again a halogen bridge appears

67. Hieber and Lagally, *Z. anorg. Chem.*, **245**, 305 (1940); Hieber and Bader, *Z. anorg. Chem.*, **190**, 193, 215 (1930); *Z. anorg. Chem.*, **201**, 329 (1931).
68. Hieber and Lagally, *Z. anorg. Chem.*, **245**, 295 (1940).
69. Mann, Purdie, and Wells, *J. Chem. Soc.*, **1936**, 1503; Eméleus and Anderson, "Modern Aspects of Inorganic Chemistry," p. 117, New York, D. Van Nostrand Company, Inc., 1938.

TABLE 16.5. STABILITY AND COMPOSITION OF OSMIUM CARBONYL HALIDES

Type	$Os(CO)_4X_2$	$Os(CO)_3X_2$	$Os(CO)_2X_2$	$[Os(CO)_4X]_2$
Cl ↑	colorless	colorless	—	—
Br	colorless and light-yellow	yellow	light yellow	canary yellow
I	yellow and dark-yellow	dark yellow	light yellow	orange yellow

maximum stability

in the most logical structures, as in

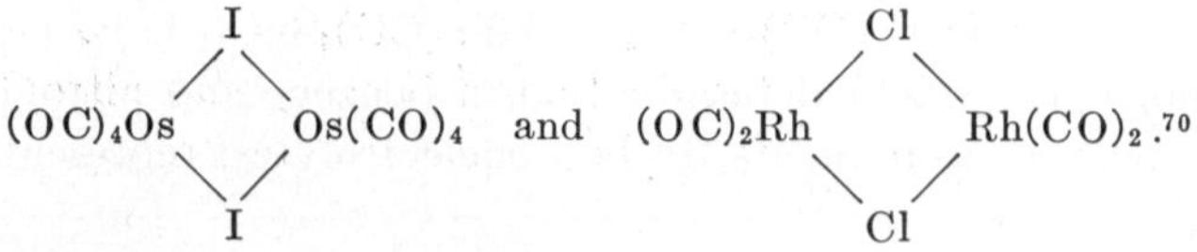

$$(OC)_4Os \diagdown_I^I \diagup Os(CO)_4 \quad \text{and} \quad (OC)_2Rh \diagdown_{Cl}^{Cl} \diagup Rh(CO)_2 .^{70}$$

The rhenium compound $Re(CO)_5X$ illustrates the significance of the inert gas type of structure in determining the formulas for carbonyl halides[71]. An increase in volatility and color from the chloride through the iodide implies that the iodide is essentially nonpolar; the chloride, however, has been shown to have partial ionic character in dioxane[72].

The carbonyl halides show typical carbonyl character in volatility, solubility in organic solvents, and other properties. The ease of formation increases down the groups of the periodic table, maximum CO contents being found in $Re(CO)_5X$, $Os(CO)_4X$, $Ir(CO)_3X$, and $Pt(CO)_2X_2$. The last two have an incomplete rare gas configuration, involving sixteen electrons, which is also found in $[Ni(CN)_4]^=$.

In relation to the structure of the carbonyls, it is interesting that the CO groups may be replaced by molecules of ammonia, pyridine, or alcohol, and two CO groups may be replaced by one bidentate chelating group like ethylenediamine or o-phenanthroline, yielding $Fe(CO)_3(NH_3)_2$, $Cr(CO)_3py_3$, $Fe_2(CO)_5en_2$, or $Ni(CO)_2(o\text{-phen})$[73b]. The compound

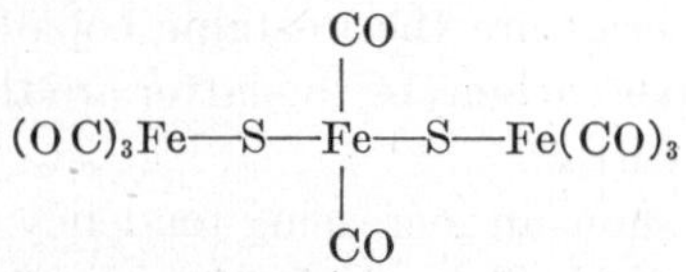

$$(OC)_3Fe \underset{\underset{CO}{|}}{\overset{\overset{CO}{|}}{-}} S-Fe-S-Fe(CO)_3$$

is similar in some respects to iron tetracarbonyl[74]. Analogs are known in which sulfur atoms are replaced by selenium, and the CO groups by pyridine

70. Hieber and Stallman, *A. Electrochem. angew.*, **49**, 288 (1942).
71. Hieber and Schulten, *Z. anorg. Chem.*, **243**, 164 (1939).
72. Schuh, *Z. anorg. Chem.*, **248**, 276 (1941).
73. Hieber, *Z. Elektrochem.*, **43**, 390 (1937); Hein, *Z. angew. Chem.*, **62A**, 205 (1950).
74. Hieber and Geisenberger, *Z. anorg. Chem.*, **262**, 15 (1950).

molecules. Examples of mercapto forms[75] are the monomeric $(OC)_3Fe—S—C_6H_5$ and the dimeric $[(OC)_3Fe—S—C_2H_5]_2$[76]. These compounds indicate the influence of steric hindrance in the formation of carbonyl derivatives. A number of other carbonyl derivatives with organic bases, phosphonium and arsonium compounds[77] and organometallic bases[78] have been prepared. The structure of such nonsalt-like heavy metal derivatives as $[Co(CO)_4]_{1-3}M$, where M = Tl^+, Zn^{++}, Cd^{++}, Hg^{++}, Ga^{+++}, In^{+++} or Tl^{+++}, is best represented[34] by a bridge-like form:

$$
\begin{array}{c}
CO \\
OC—Co—CO \\
CO \qquad \diagdown \\
\qquad Hg \\
\qquad \diagdown \qquad CO \\
\qquad OC—Co—CO \\
\qquad CO
\end{array}
$$

Theoretical considerations have been applied by Ormont[79] to the formation of the metal carbonyl halides and their derivatives. With the halide forms such as $Fe(CO)_5X_2$ the conclusion was reached that an energetically unstable compound forms, independent of the value of Δ. (see p. 525). This accounts for the fact that the compounds $Fe(CO)_4X_2$ are thermally unstable at 298°K, whereas $CuCl_2·2CO$ and $CuBr_2·2CO$ are stable at this temperature. The argument is further advanced that elements with valence electrons in different quantum levels must form halides with a small number of carbonyl groups although Δ is often quite different from zero. This tendency has been noted above with platinum and iridium compounds. This explanation is useful in interpreting the properties of these compounds when the rules of effective atomic number are inapplicable.

Pospekhov[80] has concluded that the volatility and the color of the carbonyls and nitrosylcarbonyls are determined by Δ, calculated on the basis that the carbonyl group supplies two electrons and the nitrosyl group, three electrons. For Δ = 0 the properties of high volatility and the absence of color are observed. A more negative value of Δ is accompanied by deeper color unless the formation of polymers counteracts the effect. When the carbonyl molecules are replaced by amines and other groups, the intensification of color is attributable to dissymmetry in the electron cloud. In

75. Hieber and Spacu, Z. anorg. Chem., 233, 353 (1937).
76. Reihlen, et al., Ann., 465, 95 (1928).
77. Reppe, et al., Ann., 560, 104, 108 (1948).
78. Hein and Heuser, Z. anorg. Chem., 249, 293 (1942).
79. Ormont, Acta Physicochim. U.R.S.S., 21, 741 (1946); Acta Physicochim. U.R.S.S., 12, 757 (1940).
80. Pospekhov, Zhur. Obshekei Khim., 20, 1737 (1950); J. Gen. Chem. U.S.S.R., 20, 1797 (1950).

nonvolatile molecules of $Fe_2(CO)_9$ and $Ru_2(CO)_9$ it is postulated that dissymmetry leads to crowding the carbonyl and the formation of closed cycles, wherein the number of electrons supplied to the metal atom per carbonyl group is less than two ($\Delta < 0$).

The Structures of Carbonyl Hydrides

The comparison of the formulas of the carbonyl hydrides with the formulas of mononuclear carbonyls for the series iron, cobalt, nickel

| $Fe(CO)_5$ | — | $Ni(CO)_4$ |
| $Fe(CO)_4H_2$ | $Co(CO)_4H$ | — |

shows that the effective atomic number of 36 is achieved in each case if each carbonyl group contributes two electrons and each hydrogen atom, one. However, the hydrogen atom does not appear to contribute to the spatial arrangement, since both of the above hydrides, like nickel carbonyl, are tetrahedral. Two proposals have been made to account for the structure. Hieber's postulation[24a, 49] of a structure into which the hydrogen atoms are incorporated as protons is similar to the diborane structure proposed by Pitzer[81]. Ewens and Lister proposed[82] that an electron from hydrogen is transferred to the metal atom and that the resulting proton is coordinated to the oxygen atom of a carbonyl group. The resulting group $(:C:::O:H^+)$ would be isoelectronic with the nitrosyl group $(:N:::O:^+)$, and the formula for cobalt carbonyl hydride, for example, should be written $Co(CO)_3(COH)$. Similarities between carbonyl hydrides and nitrosylcarbonyls will be pointed out later. Hieber[49] has pointed out that this proposal is equivalent to the proposal of a quaternary oxonium ion (with a formal charge of 2+ on the oxygen atom), which is unlikely. Although such a group ought to be stablized by alkylation, no alkyl derivatives have yet been formed. Moreover, evidence for the existence of two different M—C and C—O bond distances within the molecule is lacking.

However, by reviewing some of the properties of the carbonyl halides, a logical structure can be proposed. The existence of mixed carbonyls such as $[Co(CO)_4]_2Zn$ suggests the possibility of such anions as $[Co(CO)_4]^-$ and $[Fe(CO)_4]^=$. The existence of these anionic forms has been shown in the determination of acid equilibrium constants and electrode potential values. The conductivity of $M(CO)_4H_n$ in pyridine is similar to that of a strong electrolyte. The hydrides are soluble in liquid ammonia, forming low-melting ammonia derivatives like $[Fe(CO)_4]$ $(NH_4)_2$ and $[Co(CO)_4]NH_4$. These compounds behave as acids in liquid ammonia[7, 83]. Typical acid re-

81. Pitzer, *J. Am. Chem. Soc.*, **67**, 1126 (1945).

82. Ewens and Lister, *Trans. Faraday Soc.*, **35**, 681 (1939).

83. Hieber and Schulten, *Z. anorg. Chem.*, **232**, 17 (1937); Hieber and Fack, *Z. anorg. Chem.*, **236**, 83 (1938).

actions are to be found in titrations, salt formation, and liberation of hydrogen by alkali metals. Ionic properties are found in all of the derivatives containing alkali and alkaline earth metals.

Thus the most likely resonance forms[7] may be depicted as

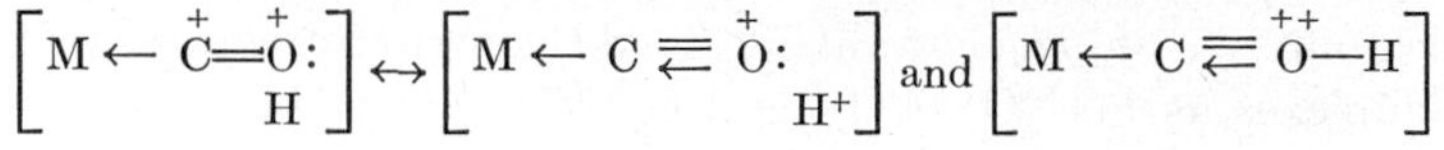

$$\left[M \leftarrow \overset{+}{C}\!\!=\!\!\overset{+}{O}\!: \atop H \right] \leftrightarrow \left[M \leftarrow C \rightleftharpoons \overset{+}{O}\!: \atop H^+ \right] \text{ and } \left[M \leftarrow C \rightleftharpoons \overset{++}{O}\!-\!H \right]$$

As noted above, there is disagreement as to the last of these.

Hieber has offered a reaction mechanism to explain the formation of these hydrides:

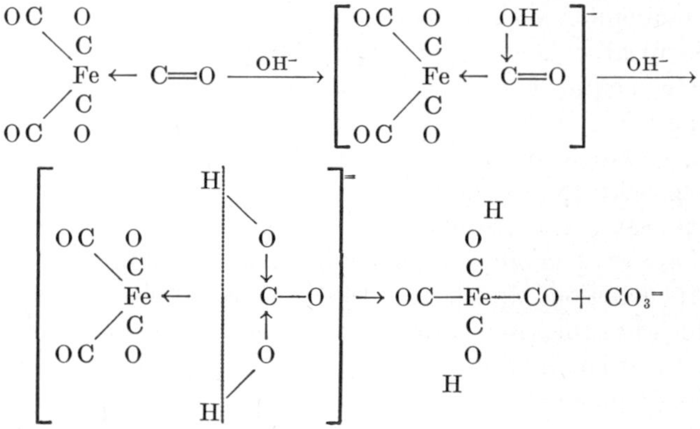

The structures of the low-melting ammonia derivatives are postulated to contain hydrogen bonds.

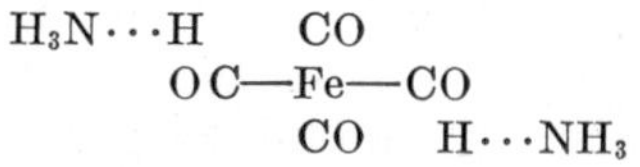

$$\begin{array}{ccc} H_3N\cdots H & CO \\ OC\!-\!Fe\!-\!CO \\ CO & H\cdots NH_3 \end{array}$$

Coordination Compounds Containing the Nitrosyl Group

Nitric oxide is able to form coordination compounds in much the same way that carbon monoxide does. However, nitric oxide differs from carbon monoxide in one important respect—it is an *odd molecule*. It may therefore be expected to form coordination compounds in three different ways: (1) loss of the odd electron followed by coordination of the resultant NO^+ group, (2) the gain of an electron followed by the coordination of the resultant NO^- group, (3) coordination of the neutral NO group[84]. To these must be added the possibility that the nitrosyl group forms a double bond with the metal atom; this will be considered later.

The fact that reduction of $[Fe(CN)_5NO]^=$ yields an ammine

84. Moeller, *J. Chem. Ed.*, **23**, 441 (1946); **23**, 542 (1946); **24**, 149 (1947); Seel, *Z. anorg. Chem.*, **249**, 321 (1942).

$$[Fe(CN)_5NH_3]^{=}$$

and that treatment with alkali yields a nitro compound $[Fe(CN)_5NO_2]^{4-}$, indicates that nitrogen is the donor atom[51, 85].

There is little experimental evidence that nitric oxide coordinates as a neutral group. As an *odd molecule* it should contribute paramagnetism to such complexes as $Fe(NO)_2(CO)_2$ and $Co(NO)(CO)_3$, but these are diamagnetic[86]. Hückel[87] states that the black paramagnetic form of

$$[Co(NH_3)_5NO]^{++}$$

exemplifies the coordination of nitric oxide as a neutral group. Loose addition compounds such as $Fe(NO)SO_4$ may be of the same type but magnetochemical evidence is lacking. The formation of the unstable, paramagnetic pentacyanonitrosyl compounds, $M_3[Fe(CN)_5(NO)]$, by the reaction $[Fe(CN)_5NH_3]^{=} + NO \rightarrow [Fe(CN)_5(NO)]^{=} + NH_3$ may be an example of coordination of the nitrosyl group as a neutral molecule, although Sidgwick[88] thinks these substances are true nitroso compounds.

In very few cases is there any indication that nitric oxide may coordinate as the ion NO^{-}[89]. The only simple compound containing the NO^{-} group is $NaNO$[90]. Its reactions are entirely distinct from those of sodium hyponitrite, which has the same empirical formula. It is diamagnetic[91], as would be expected if it contains the NO^{-} ion.

The pink diamagnetic form of $[Co(NH_3)_5NO]^{++}$ is believed to be an example of a case in which NO^{-} is present and plays the same role as Cl^{-} in $[Co(NH_3)_5Cl]^{++}$[92]. The neutral molecule $[Co(CO)_3NO]$ allows a thorough analysis of the NO coordination. This compound is monomeric, diamagnetic, and pyridine does not replace the NO[93]. Since the compound is diamagnetic, the NO group does not function as a neutral molecule. If NO were functioning as a negative group, corresponding halides, $Co(CO)_3X$, would be expected, but these are not known. Finally, these compounds cannot be derivatives of hyponitrous acid, because the mononitrosyls are

85. Emeléus and Anderson, "Modern Aspects of Inorganic Chemistry," p. 414, New York, D. Van Nostrand Company, Inc., 1938.

86. Reiff, *Z. anorg. allgem. Chem.*, **202**, 375 (1931).

87. Hückel, "Structural Chemistry of Inorganic Compounds," translated by L. H. Long, Vol. II, p. 516., Amsterdam, Elsevier Publishing Company, 1951; Ray and Bhar, *J. Indian Chem. Soc.*, **5**, 499 (1928).

88. Sidgwick, "Chemical Elements and Their Compounds," Vol. II, p. 1360, London, Oxford University Press, 1950.

89. Cambi, *Z. anorg. Chem.*, **247**, 22 (1941); Hieber and Nast, *Z. anorg. Chem.*, **247**, 31 (1941).

90. Zintl and Harder, *Ber.*, **66B**, 760 (1933).

91. Frazer and Long, *J. Chem. Phys.*, **6**, 462 (1938).

92. Mellor and Craig, *J. Proc. Roy. Soc., N. S. Wales*, **78**, 25 (1944).

93. Hieber and Anderson, *Z. anorg. Chem.*, **208**, 238 (1932); **211**, 132 (1932).

not dimers, and the dinitrosyls do not correspond to the halides. The suggestion has also been made that nitric oxide functions as NO^- in a complex cation but functions as NO^+ in a complex anion.

It is well established that nitric oxide can coordinate as the NO^+ ion. This ion is isosteric with carbon monoxide and with cyanide ion:

$$:N{\equiv}O:^+ \qquad :C{\equiv}O: \qquad :C{\equiv}N:^-$$

Isonitrile complexes, in which $C{\equiv}N$—R groups replace CO groups in carbonyl structures, have been prepared (p. 92); $[Ni(CNCH_3)_3CO]$ and $[Co_2(CNC_6H_5)_5(CO)_3]$ are examples[94]. In such series as $K_4[Fe(CN)_6]$, $K_3[Fe(CN)_5CO]$, $K_2[Fe(CN)_5NO]$ the differences in the charge of the anion are as expected if a cyanide group in the first is replaced by a neutral carbonyl group in the second or by a positive nitrosyl group in the third. That the last compound, potassium nitroprusside, represents an oxidation state of 2^+ for iron is shown by its diamagnetism and its conversion by alkali to $K_4[Fe(CN)_5NO_2]$.

In calculating the effective atomic number of the central atom in these nitrosyl or nitrosyl-carbonyl complexes one must assume that the nitrosyl group contributes three electrons to the central atom. With this stipulation, the effective atomic number for most of the nitrosyls is that of an inert gas.

However, the case of a positive group (instead of a neutral or negative group) donating an electron pair to a metal atom or ion presents a difficulty in that a certain amount of negative charge is imparted to the metal $:M^-:N^+:::O:$. Pauling points out that the accumulation of such negative charge is unlikely. An alternative suggestion is that the metal also contributes two electrons for the combination, producing a double bond $M::N^+::\overset{..}{O}$. Hel'man[95] has suggested that nitric oxide, as well as carbon monoxide and ethylene, forms bonds of this type with platinum. An analogy is noted between $[PtNOCl_3]^-$ and $[PtC_2H_4Cl_3]^-$.

Evidence for considerable double bond character also comes from estimation of bond distances by electron diffraction methods[96]. In $Co(NO)(CO)_3$ and $Fe(NO)_2(CO)_2$ the metal-nitrogen bond is shorter than that calculated for a single bond, and the nitrogen-oxygen bond distance is intermediate between those for $N{=}O$ and $N{\equiv}O$. (Table 16.6). Both of the above compounds, like nickel carbonyl, are tetrahedral. Neither the contribution of three electrons by the nitric oxide nor the possibility of double-bond character changes the structure. Furthermore, the possibility of

94. Hieber and Böckly, *Z. anorg. Chem.*, **262,** 344 (1950); Hieber, *Z. Naturforsch.*, **56,** 129 (1950).
95. Hel'man, *Compt. rend. acad. sci. U.R.S.S.*, **24,** 549 (1939).
96. Brockway and Anderson, *Trans. Faraday Soc.*, **33,** 1233 (1937).

TABLE 16.6. BOND DISTANCES IN NITROSYL-CARBONYL COMPOUNDS

	M—N (Å.)		N—O (Å.)	
	Obs.	Calc.	Obs.	
$Co(CO)_3NO$	1.76	1.95	1.10	Calculated for N=O, 1.15 Å
$Fe(CO)_2(NO)_2$	1.77	1.93	1.12	Calculated for N≡O, 1.05 Å

double-bond character does not disturb the effective atomic number relationship.

Assuming that the nitrosyl group contributes three electrons to the metal atom, and the hydrogen atom in carbonyl hydrides contributes one electron, one notes the existence of isoelectronic series:

$Fe(CO)_2(NO)_2$	$Co(CO)_3NO$	$Ni(CO)_4$
$Fe(CO)_4H_2$	$Co(CO)_4H$	$Ni(CO)_4$

The replacement of the nucleus $_{28}Ni$ by $_{27}Co$ corresponds electronically to the formation of the ion $[Co(CO)_4]^-$. Replacement of one CO group in this with one NO^+ group forms a neutral molecule. The process may also be represented by $NO \rightarrow NO^+ + e^-$, the metal atom gaining the additional electron. The acquisition of a negative charge by the central atom makes it understandable that only a limited number of NO molecules can be bound, and the stability of such compounds decreases in the order $Ni(NO)Cl$, $Co(NO)_2Cl$, $Fe(NO)_3Cl$[7]. Ewens[56] believes the structure of $[Fe(NO)_2X]_2$ and other dimeric forms to be:

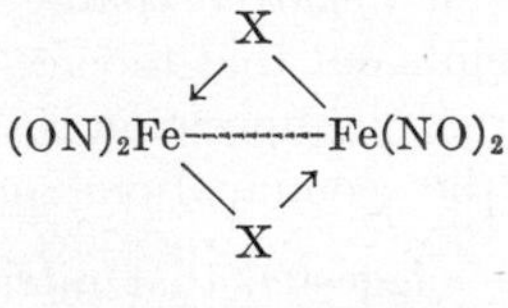

$$(ON)_2Fe \overset{\displaystyle X}{\underset{\displaystyle X}{\diagdown\!\!\!\!\diagup}} Fe(NO)_2$$

Similar postulations have been made by Seel[84d] concerning the Roussin salts $[(NO)_2FeS]K$, $[(NO)_7Fe_4S_3]K \cdot H_2O$, and $[(NO)_2Fe \cdot S \cdot C_2H_5]_2$. It is noteworthy that the sum of the atomic number and the maximum number of bonded NO molecules has the constant value 29 with the metals of the first transition series.

PREPARATION AND PROPERTIES OF NITROSYLS

Preparation by the Action of Nitric Oxide Upon Metallic Salts

The familiar brown ring test for nitrites and nitrates is based on the absorption of nitric oxide by solutions of iron(II) salts[97]. The reaction is

97. Kohlschutter and Kutscheroff, *Ber.*, **40**, 873 (1907); Kohlschutter and Sazanoff, *Ber.*, **44**, 1423 (1911); Manchot, *Ber.*, **47**, 1601 (1914); Manchot and Zechentmayer, *Ann.*, **350**, 368 (1906).

readily reversed by heating, nitric oxide being evolved and the iron(II) salt recovered[97a, 98]. It is difficult to isolate solid compounds, especially since most solid salts do not absorb nitric oxide extensively. However, such compounds as $Fe(NO)HPO_4$[97c] and $Fe(NO)SeO_4 \cdot 4H_2O$[99] have been isolated from solution. Such solutions may be red, green or brown[100]. More than one species is present, as shown by absorption spectra data[101] and transference studies[97a], (which indicate that the complexes may be cationic, anionic, or neutral). An iron(III) derivative, $Fe_2(NO)_2(SO_4)_3$, has also been reported[97c].

Copper(II) salt solutions in the presence of free acid absorb a molar quantity of nitric oxide to form deep blue-violet solutions[97b, 97c, 102]. Comparable reactions result in the formation of palladium(II) nitrosyl derivatives, $Pd(NO)_2Cl_2$ and $Pd(NO)_2SO_4$[103]. A chromium(II) nitrosyl dithiocarbamate can be prepared by treating chromium(II) acetate with alcoholic R_2NCS_2Na (R = ethyl or propyl) and nitric oxide at $0°$[104].

In these nitrosyl compounds (except the iron(III) salt) the oxidation state of the metal is presumably 2^+, but there is no confirmatory experimental evidence. Many examples are known of the formation of nitrosyl derivatives of normally divalent metals in the univalent state. Iron(II) chloride forms the derivative $Fe(NO)_3Cl$ when treated with nitric oxide in the presence of zinc[105]. In a similar manner anhydrous cobalt halides form $Co(NO)_2X$[106], and nickel halides form $Ni(NO)X$[105], the ease of formation decreasing in the orders Fe > Co > Ni and I > Br > Cl. These compounds are characterized by thermal instability, coordinate unsaturation, and extreme reducing ability. Most of them react readily with such donors as pyridine and o-phenanthroline.

The number of combined nitric oxide molecules decreases in the order Fe > Co > Ni. Seel[107] has suggested a nitrosyl displacement series comparable with Grimm's hydride displacement series, in which the addition of n molecules of nitric oxide is supposed to convert a metal atom into a pseudo atom n groups to the right in the Periodic Table. This series would

98. Manchot and Haunschild, *Z. anorg. allgem. Chem.*, **140**, 22 (1924).
99. Manchot and Linckh, *Z. anorg. allgem. Chem.*, **140**, 37 (1924).
100. Manchot and Huttner, *Ann.*, **372**, 153 (1910).
101. Manchot and Linckh, *Ber.*, **59B**, 406 (1926); Schlesinger and Salathe, *J. Am. Chem. Soc.*, **45**, 1863 (1923).
102. Manchot, *Ann.*, **375**, 308 (1910).
103. Manchot and Waldmüller, *Ber.*, **59B**, 2363 (1926).
104. Malatesta, *Gazz. chim. ital.*, **70**, 729, 734 (1940).
105. Hieber and Nast, *Z. anorg. allgem. Chem.*, **244**, 23 (1940).
106. Hieber and Marin, *Z. anorg. allgem. Chem.*, **240**, 241 (1939).
107. Seel, *Z. anorg. allgem. Chem.*, **249**, 308 (1942).

contain such pseudo atoms as

Fe	Co	Ni	Cu
	Fe(NO)	Co(NO)	Ni(NO)
		Co(NO)$_2$	Ni(NO)
		Fe(NO)$_2$	Co(NO)$_2$
			Fe(NO)$_3$

These monovalent halides correspond to copper(I) halides. In order to achieve a coordination number of four, the compound Fe(NO)$_3$Cl is represented as monomeric (analogous to Cu(NH$_3$)$_3$I), the compounds Co(NO)$_2$X (analogous to [Cu(PEt$_3$)$_2$I]$_2$) as dimeric, and the compounds Ni(NO)X (analogous to[CuAsEt$_3$I]$_4$) as tetrameric. Other known compounds fitting into the series are Fe(NO)I, Fe(NO)$_2$I (see p. 538) and Co(NO)I, which is known only in addition compounds such as Co(NO)I·6py[106].

A number of nitrosyl thio compounds are known, but further work is necessary to establish their structures. The best known of these compounds are the so-called red and black salts of Roussin, who first prepared them in 1857. Upon treatment with Fe(NO)SO$_4$, the red salts, M^I[Fe(NO)$_2$S], are converted to the more stable black salts, M^I[Fe$_4$(NO)$_7$S$_3$], which may be reconverted to the red salts by the action of alkali[108]

$$3Na[Fe(NO)_2S] + Fe(NO)SO_4 \rightarrow Na[Fe_4(NO)_7S_3] + Na_2SO_4$$

$$2Na[Fe_4(NO)_7S_3] + 4NaOH \rightarrow 6Na[Fe(NO)_2S] + Fe_2O_3 + N_2O + 2H_2O$$

According to Seel's scheme the red compounds must be dimeric and Ewens[56] reported that they have the same structure as Fe$_2$(CO)$_9$ with a direct link between iron atoms.

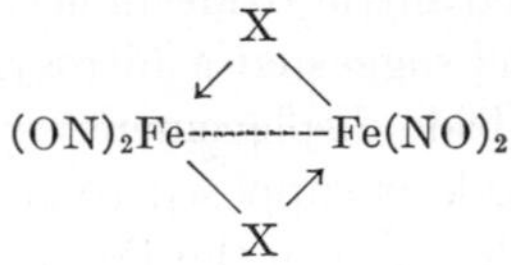

$$(ON)_2Fe \overset{\displaystyle X}{\underset{\displaystyle X}{-\!-\!-\!-\!-\!-}} Fe(NO)_2$$

Whereas iron forms the series Fe(NO)$_2$SA, cobalt and nickel form the series Co(NO)$_2$(SA)$_2$ and Ni(NO)(SA)$_2$. Thiosulfate derivatives,

$$K_3[Co(NO)_2(S_2O_3)_2]$$

and K$_3$[Ni(NO)(S$_2$O$_3$)$_2$], have been prepared by the action of nitric oxide and potassium thiosulfate upon solutions of cobalt(II) acetate and nickel (II) acetate[109]. Ethyl mercaptan derivatives have also been prepared[99, 110]

108. Marchlewski and Sachs, *Z. anorg. Chem.*, **2**, 175 (1892); Hofman and Wiede, *Z. anorg. Chem.*, **9**, 295 (1895).
109. Manchot, *Ber.*, **59B**, 2445 (1926).
110. Manchot and Kaess, *Ber.*, **60B**, 2175 (1927).

$$Co(SR)_2 + 3NO \rightarrow Co(NO)_2SR + NOSR$$

$$Ni(SR)_2 + 2NO \rightarrow Ni(NO)SR + NOSR$$

The exact structure of the $[Fe_4(NO)_7S_3]^-$ ion has not been determined. It is believed that each iron is tetracoordinate, with sulfur atoms acting as bridging groups; nitrosyl groups occupy the remaining positions[84d].

Solutions of cobalt(II) salts containing ammonia absorb nitric oxide to form the complex ion $[Co(NH_3)_5(NO)]^{++}$ [111]. Such compounds exist in isomeric forms. The black compounds (of which only the chloride and iodate have been reported) are unstable and paramagnetic. The pink compounds are diamagnetic and do not evolve nitric oxide upon treatment with acids. The pink compounds probably contain the NO^- group whereas the black compounds may contain cobalt in the divalent state with nitric oxide coordinating as a neutral group.

Treatment of saturated ammonium or potassium tetrachloroplatinate-(II) solution with nitric oxide yields a green solution from which $[Pt(NH_3)_4]$ $[Pt(NO)Cl_3]$ is precipitated by a solution of tetrammineplatinum(II) chloride[112]. The addition of pyridine to the green solution precipitates *trans*-$[Pt(NO)pyCl_2]$. The nitric oxide group therefore appears to be trans directing. Such compounds show a marked resemblance to the corresponding ethylene and carbonyl compounds.

Pentacyanoiron(II) complexes such as $Na_3[Fe(CN)_5NH_3]$ react with nitric oxide to form $Na_3[Fe(CN)_5(NO)]$ [113]. This is one of the few cases in which nitric oxide replaces a neutral group without change of charge. Such compounds are entirely distinct from the nitroprussides. They are dark yellow in neutral solution but violet in acid solution. Baudisch[114] reports that such complexes also result from the action of light upon a nitroprusside, the nitrosyl group being activated. Thus, sodium nitroprusside, in the presence of light and hydrogen peroxide, is able to convert benzene into *o*-nitrosophenol. Light also catalyzes the reaction of sodium nitroprusside with cupferron, with thiourea, and with a mixture of hydrogen peroxide and sodium azide.

Preparation by the Action of Nitric Oxide upon Carbonyls or Related Compounds

The nitrosyl carbonyls of cobalt and iron are generally prepared by the action of nitric oxide upon the carbonyls. The cobalt compound, Co(NO)-

111. Sand and Genssler, *Ber.*, **36**, 2083 (1903); Werner and Karrer, *Helv. Chim. Acta*, **1**, 54 (1918).
112. Hel'man and Maximova, *Compt. rend. acad. sci. U.R.S.S.*, **24**, 549 (1939).
113. Manchot, Merry, and Woringer, *Ber.*, **45**, 2869 (1912).
114. Baudisch, *Science*, **108**, 443 (1948).

$(CO)_3$, was first obtained by Mond and Wallis[115] by reaction of dry nitric oxide with cobalt tetracarbonyl. It has also been prepared by treating alkaline suspensions of cobalt(II) cyanide with carbon monoxide, followed by saturation with nitric oxide[22c, 96, 116]. This probably involves the intermediate formation of cobalt carbonyl hydride or its salt. The nitrosyl-carbonyl is a yellow gas which condenses to a red liquid. The iron compound, $Fe(NO)_2(CO)_2$, has been obtained in similar manner by the action of nitric oxide upon iron tetracarbonyl[93a].

Reactions of the nitrosyl-carbonyls indicate that the nitrosyl group is more tightly bound than the carbonyl group. Treatment of iron nitrosyl-carbonyl with pyridine (py) and with o-phenanthroline (o-phen) produces $[Fe_2(NO)_4(py)_3]$ and $[Fe(NO)_2(o\text{-phen})]$, respectively, and treatment of cobalt nitrosyl-carbonyl in the same way yields $[Co_2(NO)_2(CO)(py)_2]$ and $[Co(NO)(CO)(o\text{-phen})]$. Further evidence is given by the formation of $Fe(NO)_2I$ from iron nitrosyl-carbonyl and iodine[93b].

Other nitrosyls have been prepared from carbonyls. Nitric oxide reacts with iron pentacarbonyl under pressure to form the interesting compound, iron tetranitrosyl, $Fe(NO)_4$[117]. This black crystalline substance is converted into $Fe(NO)_3NH_3$ by liquid ammonia, into $Fe(NO)SO_4$ by dilute sulfuric acid, into $K[Fe(NO)_2S_2O_3]$ by potassium thiosulfate, and into

$$K[Fe_4(NO)_7S_3]$$

by potassium bisulfide. Manchot and Manchot[9] have reported that a similar reaction with ruthenium enneacarbonyl produces a pentanitrosyl, $Ru(NO)_5$, as well as a tetranitrosyl, $Ru(NO)_4$. These results have been questioned by Eméleus and Anderson[69].

Nickel carbonyl reacts with nitric oxide in the presence of a trace of moisture to form a water-soluble nitrosyl-hydroxide, $Ni(NO)OH$. This blue basic compound shows the reducing power expected for univalent nickel[118].

Carbonyl derivatives also react with nitric oxide in some cases. An unusual nitrosyl iodide, $Fe_2(NO)_4I_3$, results from the treatment of the tetracarbonyl iodide, $Fe(CO)_4I_2$, with nitric oxide. This compound is presumed to contain both univalent and divalent iron[67b].

Miscellaneous Methods of Preparation

Nitrosyls may be prepared by reactions involving the oxidation or reduction of some nitrogen compound other than nitric oxide. The nitro

115. Mond and Wallis, *J. Chem. Soc.*, **121**, 32 (1922).
116. Blanchard and Gilmont, *J. Am. Chem. Soc.*, **62**, 1192 (1940).
117. Manchot and Enk, *Ann.*, **470**, 275 (1929).
118. Anderson, *Z. anorg. allgem. Chem.*, **229**, 357 (1936).

prussides, $M_2[Fe(CN)_5NO]$, were first prepared[119] by the action of 30% nitric acid upon a ferrocyanide or ferricyanide, a complicated and violent reaction which is still used for their preparation. Another method involves the action of nitrite ion upon ferrocyanide ion[120].

$$[Fe(CN)_6]^{4-} + NO_2^- \rightleftarrows [Fe(CN)_5NO_2]^{4-} + CN^-$$

$$[Fe(CN)_5NO_2]^{4-} + H_2O \rightleftarrows [Fe(CN)_5NO]^- + 2OH^-$$

These reactions are reversible, but may be brought to completion by adding acid to combine with the cyanide ion or hydroxide ion. The corresponding ruthenium compound, $K_2[Ru(CN)_5(NO)]\cdot 2H_2O$, has been prepared by the action of nitric acid upon the ruthenocyanide, $K_4[Ru(CN)_6]$[121], and the manganese compound, $K_3[Mn(CN)_5(NO)]$, by the action of nitric oxide upon manganous salts in the presence of cyanide ion[122].

The nitroprussides develop intense violet colorations when treated with alkali sulfides (Gmelin reaction) but not with hydrogen sulfide[123]. Intense red colorations with alkali sulfites (Bödecker reaction) are due perhaps to the formation of $[Fe(CN)_5(NOSO_3)]^{4-}$ [124]. The insolubility of mercury(II) nitroprusside has been suggested as a basis for the quantitative determination of the radical[125]. Recent work[126] has confirmed the dipositive state of iron in the nitroprussides and has indicated that one cyanide group is attached to iron through nitrogen and the other four through carbon.

Osmium nitrosyl compounds $K_2[OsCl_5(NO)]$ and $K_2[OsBr_5(NO)]$, result when the hexanitro compound, $K_2[Os(NO_2)_6]$, is heated with hydrochloric or hydrobromic acid[127]. The ruthenium compound, $K_2[RuCl_5NO]$, is obtained when metallic ruthenium is dissolved in a molten mixture of potassium hydroxide and potassium nitrate or nitrite and the resulting mass treated with hydrochloric acid[128].

Hydroxylamine can be used to introduce a nitrosyl group into a complex[129]. The nickel compound $K_2[Ni(CN)_3(NO)]$ has also been prepared by

119. Playfair, *Phil. Mag.*, [3] **36**, 197 (1850); *Ann.*, (*Liebig's*), **74**, 317 (1850).
120. Shwarzkopf, *Abhandl. deut. Naturw. Med. Ver. Bohmen*, **3**, 1 (1911).
121. Manchot and Dusing, *Ber.*, **63B**, 1226 (1930).
122. Blanchard and Magnusson, *J. Am. Chem. Soc.*, **63**, 2236 (1941); Manchot and Schmid, *Ber.*, **59B**, 2360 (1926).
123. Sas, *Anales soc. espan. fis. quim.*, **34**, 419 (1936); Scagliarini, *Atti congr. naz. chim. pura applicata 4th Cong.*, **1933**, 597 (1932).
124. Scagliarini, *Atti accad. Lincei*, **22**, 155 (1935); Morgan and Burstall, "Inorganic Chemistry: A survey of Modern Developments," p. 364, Cambridge, W. Heffer and Sons, Ltd., 1936.
125. Tomicek and Kubik, *Collection Czechoslov. Chem. Commun.*, **9**, 377 (1937).
126. Sas, *Anales fis. quim. (Spain)*, **39**, 55 (1943).
127. Wintrebert, *Ann. chim. phys.*, [7] **28**, 15 (1903).
128. Joly, *Compt. rend.*, **107**, 994 (1888).
129. Hieber, Nast and Gehring, *Z. anorg. allgem. Chem.*, **256**, 159, 169 (1948); Hieber and Nast, *Z. Naturforsch.*, **2b**, 321 (1947).

the action of nitric oxide upon the complex cyanide $K_2Ni(CN)_3$ in liquid ammonia or absolute alcohol[130].

INDUSTRIAL SIGNIFICANCE OF METAL CARBONYLS

The Metallurgy of Nickel

The discovery that nickel readily forms a volatile carbonyl was utilized by Ludwig Mond[131] for the separation of nickel from ores containing cobalt and other metals. He built an experimental plant for separating nickel from Canadian matte. The plant was torn down and rebuilt several times, but within five years from the discovery of nickel carbonyl it was successfully producing 1.5 tons of nickel per week.

For the Mond process, the ore is heated with coke and limestone with the result that some of the iron sulfide is converted to oxide. The matte is further concentrated in a Bessemer converter until it contains about 80 per cent nickel and copper. The finely ground matte is subject to calcination at 700 to 800°C and extracted with dilute sulfuric acid, which dissolves most of the copper oxide but attacks the nickel oxide only slightly. The nickel oxide is then led through a series of reducers and volatilizers. The reducing agent is water gas at 330 to 350°C; 97 per cent of the reduction results from the hydrogen, while the carbon monoxide acts upon the metallic nickel in the volatilizer at a temperature of 50°C to form the carbonyl.

The gases from the volatilizers are passed into decomposers, where they come into contact with nickel pellets at 180°C, whereupon the carbonyl is decomposed and the nickel deposits on the pellets. From time to time the pellets are sorted, the smaller ones being returned to the decomposers.

Carbonyls as Antiknock Agents

Antidetonants, or antiknocks, are now added to most gasolines. The most widely used antiknock agent is lead tetraethyl; however, the carbonyls of iron, cobalt, and nickel have been found to be almost as effective. The substitution of a carbonyl for lead tetraethyl may result in a considerable increase in maximum power output. In one process the carbonyl is heated with an unsaturated hydrocarbon, such as butadiene, and the resulting complex is added to the gasoline[132].

Iron pentacarbonyl has been most often suggested as a replacement for

130. Hieber, Nast and Proeschel, Z. anorg. allgem. Chem., **256**, 145 (1948).
131. Trout, J. Chem. Ed., **15**, 113 (1938); Mond, J. Soc. Chem. Ind., **T49**, 271, 283, 287 (1930).
132. Johnson (to Texaco Development Corp.), U. S. Patent 2406544 (Aug. 27, 1946) cf. Chem. Abs., **41**, 266 (1947); Veltman (to Texaco Development Corp.), U. S. Patent 2409167 (Oct. 8, 1946) cf. Chem. Abs., **41**, 595 (1947).

lead tetraethyl. Although iron carbonyl is poisonous, it probably does not have the cumulative effect that is associated with lead compounds and the products of its combustion are less toxic. It is soluble in all proportions in gasoline and vaporizes readily in the carburetor. There are, however, two serious disadvantages in the use of iron pentacarbonyl. Iron(III) oxide produced by combustion tends to foul the combustion chamber and its decomposition to $Fe_2(CO)_9$ is light catalyzed. Lead tetraethyl alone also fouls the combustion chamber, but the addition of small amounts of ethylene dibromide prevents lead oxide from accumulating. The decomposition of iron pentacarbonyl is not a serious problem, since a number of stabilizers are known[133]. In alcohol fuels, iron pentacarbonyl is a good antiknock agent, while lead tetraethyl is said to have a negative effect and actually depresses the octane rating[134].

King[135] describes experiments to show that the oxidation of hydrocarbons in the presence of iron carbonyl is a heterogeneous reaction on the surface of iron which results from decomposition of the carbonyl. The fuel is therefore partly oxidized to carbon dioxide and steam *prior to ignition*. The consequent dilution of the fuel causes a reduction of inflammability which is sufficient to prevent the completion of combustion by detonation.

The Preparation of "Carbonyl Metals"

Nickel produced by the decomposition of the carbonyl is remarkably pure, and Mond[131d] suggested that nickel carbonyl may be used for the deposition of metallic mirrors (as in the preparation of Dewar flasks) or to build up nickel articles by decomposing the carbonyl in contact with a suitably shaped mold. Carbonyl nickel has been used as a hydrogenation catalyst[136].

In similar manner, iron pentacarbonyl has been used to prepare metallic iron. By varying the conditions, it is possible to prepare iron as scales, grains, sponge, or powder. "Carbonyl iron" is remarkably free of impurities except for small amounts of carbon and oxygen. Its grains are nearly spherical and quite uniform in size. When the powder is subjected to mechanical pressure in hydrogen or in vacuum at a temperature below its melting point, it may be compressed into a solid without pores. Most of the carbon and oxygen are driven off as carbon monoxide and carbon dioxide, leaving a pure, fresh iron surface which sinters readily. The iron thus prepared is soft, ductile, and resistant to corrosion. The chief use of carbonyl iron is in the making of magnetic cores for electronic equipment. It is ex-

133. Leahy, *Refiner Natural Gasoline Mfr.*, **14**, 82 (1935).
134. Pitesky and Wiebe, *Ind. Eng. Chem.*, **37**, 577 (1945).
135. King, *Canadian J. Research*, **26F**, 125 (1946).
136. Shukoff, German Patent 241823 (Jan. 18, 1910), cf. *Chem. Abs.*, **6**, 2145 (1912).

cellent for that purpose because of its uniform particle size and shape as well as its purity.

Nickel-iron alloys and cobalt-molybdenum alloys have been prepared by the sintering of powders obtained from the decomposition of the respective carbonyls. These alloys have electromagnetic properties which compare favorably with alloys prepared by other methods.

Carbonyl iron has been entered in The National Formulary as a substitute for iron reduced by hydrogen[137].

Preparation of Oxides

Very finely divided iron oxide may be obtained by heating iron carbonyl below 100°C under carefully controlled conditions. Catalysts may be used to accelerate the formation of the oxide. This oxide is suitable for use as a coloring agent, polishing powder, or decarbonizing agent for cast iron or steel[138].

Carbonyls in Synthesis

Much work has been done on the use of carbonyls of iron, cobalt, and nickel as catalysts, particularly when carbon monoxide is a reactant. In some of these reactions the carbonyl functions as a homogeneous catalyst. In others the carbonyls are added in stoichiometric amounts and may or may not be regenerated in the course of subsequent reactions.

Reppe[139] has carried out carboxylation reactions with acetylene or ethylene at high pressure for the preparation of various types of organic compounds. Some typical reactions are

1. (a) Preparation of acrylic acid from acetylene:
$$Ni(CO)_4 + 4C_2H_2 + 2HCl + 4H_2O \rightarrow 4CH_2{=}CHCOOH + NiCl_2 + H_2$$
   (b) Regeneration of the carbonyl:
$$NiCl_2 + 2NH_3 + H_2O + 5CO \rightarrow Ni(CO)_4 + 2NH_4Cl + CO_2$$
   (Cobalt carbonyl can also be used in this reaction, but iron carbonyl cannot.)
2. (a) Preparation of *n*-propyl alcohol from iron carbonyl hydride:
$$Fe(CO)_4H_2 + 2C_2H_4 + 4H_2O \rightarrow 2CH_3CH_2CH_2OH + Fe(HCO_3)_2$$
   (b) Preparation of the carbonyl hydride:
$$Fe(CO)_5 + H_2O \rightarrow Fe(CO)_4H_2 + CO_2$$
3. Preparation of hydroquinone from acetylene (in the presence of iron carbonyl hydride or cobalt carbonyl hydride):
$$2C_2H_2 + 3CO + H_2O \rightarrow C_6H_4(OH)_2 + CO_2$$

Reppe[77] has also used carbonyls for the polymerization of acetylene to

137. *Bull. Nat. Formulary Comm.*, **18**, 87 (1950).
138. Ehrmann, *Rev. chim. ind.*, **44**, 10 (1935).
139. Reppe, *Modern Plastics*, **23**, 162 (1945); U. S. Dept. of Commerce OTS *PB1112* (Jan. 25, 1946); Bigelow, *Chem. Eng. News*, **25**, 1038 (1947); Hanford and Fuller, *Ind. Eng. Chem.*, **40**, 1171 (1948).

benzene and the polymerization of vinyl compounds to the corresponding trimers. Possible catalysts are of the types (1) $(R_3P)_2MX_2$, (2) $(R_3P)Ni-(CO)_3$, and (3) $(R_3P)_2Ni(CO)_2$ (R is an alkyl or aryl radical; iron or cobalt may be substituted for nickel). Types (2) and (3) are made by the action of the carbonyl upon one or two moles of R_3P, or the action of the carbonyl upon compounds of type (1). The catalysts are first treated with acetylene under pressure at 100–120°C, and the polymerization of acetylene is carried out at a temperature of 60–70°C. The polymerization of acetylene to cycloctatetraene (which was accomplished by Reppe, using a catalyst of nickel cyanide) has been carried out by Cech[140] using nickel carbonyl in tetrahydrofuran at 60–70°C.

According to Lopez-Rubio and Pacheco[141], the activity of iron, cobalt, and nickel in the Fischer-Tropsch hydrocarbon synthesis is due to the formation of carbonyls as intermediates. They postulate such reactions as

$$20\ CO + 4Fe \rightarrow [Fe(CO)_5]_4$$

$$[Fe(CO)_5]_4 + 33H_2 \rightarrow 2C_8H_{18} + 15H_2O + CO_2 + 3CO + 4Fe$$

The so-called Oxo Process[142] involves the addition of carbon monoxide and hydrogen to olefins in the presence of solid catalysts (e.g., metallic cobalt) to produce aldehydes. Adkins and Krsek[143] came to the conclusion that the real catalyst is cobalt carbonyl. They found, in fact, that the reaction proceeded more rapidly and at a lower temperature with dicobalt octacarbonyl as a catalyst than with a solid catalyst. The reactions they propose (with ethylene) are

$$2Co + 8CO \rightarrow [Co(CO)_4]_2$$

$$[Co(CO)_4]_2 + H_2 \rightarrow 2Co(CO)_4H$$

$$4Co(CO)_4H + 4C_2H_4 + 2H_2 \rightarrow 4CH_3CH_2CHO + [Co(CO)_3]_4$$

$$[Co(CO)_3]_4 + 4CO \rightarrow 2[Co(CO)_4]_2$$

The reaction has been extended to produce compounds other than aldehydes by the use of water or alcohols instead of hydrogen. Du Pont, Piganion, and Vialle[144] consider that the carbonyl first reacts with an active compound AH (H_2, H_2O, ROH, etc.) to form a complex, which reacts with the olefin in the presence of carbon monoxide to regenerate the metal carbonyl and give the corresponding organic carbonyl derivative. For

140. Cech, *Chemie, (Prague)*, **4**, 4 (1948).
141. Lopez-Rubio and Pacheco, *Ion*, **8**, 86 (1948).
142. Roelen, U. S. Patent 2327066 (Aug. 17, 1943); cf. *Chem. Abs.*, **38**, 550 (1944).
143. Adkins and Krsek, *J. Am. Chem. Soc.*, **70**, 383 (1948); **71**, 3051 (1949).
144. Du Pont, Piganion, and Vialle, *Bull. soc. chim., France*, **1948**, 529.

example, with nickel carbonyl:

$$Ni(CO)_4 + AH \rightarrow (CO)_3Ni\!\!-\!\!\underset{\underset{H}{|}\,\underset{A}{|}}{C}\!\!=\!\!O$$

$$(CO)_3Ni\!\!-\!\!\underset{\underset{H}{|}\,\underset{A}{|}}{C}\!\!=\!\!O + RCH\!\!=\!\!CHR + CO \rightarrow Ni(CO)_4 + RCHCH_2R$$
$$\underset{A\,C=O}{|}$$

Sternberg and his co-workers[145] have used cobalt carbonyl as a catalyst for the conversion of dimethylamine to dimethylformamide:

(1) $3[Co(CO)_4]_2 + 20(CH_3)_2NH \rightarrow 2[Co\{(CH_3)_2NH\}_6]^{++}$

$$+ 4[Co(CO)_4]^- + 8HCON(CH_3)_2$$

(2) $2[Co\{(CH_3)_2NH\}_6]^{++} + 4[Co(CO)_4]^- + 8CO \rightarrow 3[Co(CO)_4]_2 + 12(CH_3)_2NH$

The Presence of Carbonyls in Industrial Gases

Since carbonyls, particularly those of nickel and iron, may be formed when gases containing carbon monoxide are brought into contact with the metal, they may be present as adulterants in industrial gases. The formation of iron carbonyl in this way is of some significance in dealing with artificial gases. The carbonyl is not formed during the manufacture of the gases but only at temperatures below 250°C in purifying boxes, distributing pipes and gas meters. Mittasch[146] found almost 500 ml. of liquid iron pentacarbonyl in an iron tank containing illuminating gas. The carbonyl has also been found in tanks of hydrogen which contains carbon monoxide as an impurity[147].

Blueprints

The instability of iron pentacarbonyl toward light has been used for the preparation of blueprints[148]. Paper is soaked in iron pentacarbonyl in the dark. After exposure to light and washing with water, the exposed part has a brown deposit of $Fe_2(CO)_9$. This is converted to Prussian blue by an acid solution of potassium ferrocyanide.

THE PHYSIOLOGICAL ACTION OF METAL CARBONYLS

The increasing use of metallic carbonyls makes it imperative that investigators realize their poisonous nature[149]. The highly volatile nickel carbonyl is particularly hazardous, but any volatile carbonyl is dangerous. The

145. Sternberg, Wender, Friedel, and Orchin, *J. Am. Chem. Soc.*, **75**, 3148 (1953).
146. Mittasch, *Z. angew. Chem.*, **41**, 831 (1928).
147. King and Sutcliffe, *J. Soc. Chem. Ind.*, **T47**, 356 (1928).
148. Frankenburger, German Patent 416995 (1924).
149. Trout, *J. Chem. Educ.*, **15**, 77 (1938).

danger with nickel carbonyl may be emphasized by the example of the chemist, who, in the process of pouring nickel carbonyl from one container to another, inhaled enough to cause his death[150].

Although a study of the toxicology of nickel carbonyl was made as early as 1890 by McKendrick and Snodgrass[151] and precautions were taken by the Mond Nickel Company to avoid poisoning of its employees, an accident took place in which ten men were poisoned, two of them fatally. Immediately, Armit[152] was employed to study the problem anew, and his suggestions have enabled the company to reduce the danger.

The assumption that metallic carbonyls are poisonous because of the carbon monoxide they produce upon decomposition is not valid. Nickel carbonyl is at least five times as deadly as carbon monoxide. Armit found that a rabbit is killed by an exposure of one hour to air containing 0.018 per cent by volume of the carbonyl. On the other hand, he has shown that a rabbit would not absorb harmful amounts of cobalt carbonyl in the course of two hours' exposure even if the atmosphere were saturated with this carbonyl[153]. This is not to say, however, that continued exposure to cobalt carbonyl would not be injurious.

Immediately after being exposed to the fumes of nickel carbonyl, a person has a sensation of giddiness, a throbbing headache, and nausea, sometimes with vomiting[154]. If the carbonyl is mixed with carbon monoxide, unconsciousness may result. If the amount of carbonyl in the air is very small, exposure of the person for some time may result only in a throbbing headache. These symptoms may disappear rather quickly. This period, however, is frequently followed by such symptoms as difficult breathing, pain in the chest, and cyanosis. The skin may be pale, the forehead cold and clammy, and the general expression one of anxiety. A trace of nickel may be found in the urine, and the blood may show the presence of carboxyhemoglobin. Post mortem examinations of fatal cases show that tissues of the lungs and brain are severely damaged.

The treatment depends upon the severity and the presence or absence of poisoning by carbon monoxide. The patient must be kept warm and should, if necessary, be given stimulants to aid respiration and heart action. Absolute rest is necessary to relieve the heart and lungs of undue strain. The effects of the poisoning are not chronic; persons who have received nonfatal doses have shown complete recovery.

Persons working with carbonyls must use the same precautions which

150. Brandes, *J. Am. Med. Assoc.*, **102**, 1204 (1934).
151. McKendrick and Snodgrass, *Proc. Phil. Soc., Glasgow*, **22**, 204 (1890–91).
152. Armit, *J. Hyg.*, **7**, 525 (1907); **8**, 565 (1908).
153. Armit, *J. Hyg.*, **9**, 249 (1909).
154. Amor, *J. Ind. Hyg.*, **14**, 216 (1932).

are used for any deadly gas or vapor. A well-ventilated hood must be used for all experiments. The compounds must be kept in strong glass or steel containers, preferably under carbon dioxide or nitrogen. Continual tests for leaks should be made. One part of nickel carbonyl in 80,000 parts of air may be detected by the luminosity which it adds to a flame.

General Bibliography on Carbonyls and Nitrosyls

1. Welch, *Ann. Repts. Progr. Chem.*, **38,** 71 (1941).
2. Blanchard, *Chem. Revs.*, **26,** 409 (1940).
3. Anderson, *Quart. Revs.*, **1,** 331 (1947).
4. Hieber, FIAT Rev. German Sci., 1939–1946, Inorg. Chem., Pt. II, p. 108 (1948).
5. Hieber, *Z. Elektrochem.*, **43,** 390 (1937).
6. Hieber, *Z. angew. Chem.*, **55,** 11 (1942).
7. Smith, *Science Progr.* **35,** 283 (1947).
8. Trout, *J. Chem. Education*, **14,** 573, 575 (1937); **15,** 77, 113, 145 (1938).
9. Emeléus and Anderson, "Modern Aspects of Inorganic Chemistry," Second Edition, Chapter XIV, New York, D. Van Nostrand Co., Inc., 1952.

Nitrosyls

1. Hieber and Nast, FIAT Rev. German Sci., Pt II, p. 148 (1948).
2. Moeller, *J. Chem. Ed.*, **23,** 441, 542 (1946).

17. Organic Molecular Compounds

Leallyn B. Clapp

Brown University, Providence, Rhode Island

"A molecular compound is a substance formed from two different components each of which may have an independent crystal structure and which, in solution (or the vapor state), decomposes into its components according to the law of mass action. The force which holds them together in the molecular compound has been called secondary valence or residual affinity."

This translation of a paragraph from Hertel[1] is a working definition of the term "molecular compound." Modifications necessary to fit more recent concepts will pervade the text to follow.

One early idea associated with the words "molecular compound" indicated that there was a center of addition in each component. The work of Werner and Pfeiffer led them to suggest that the center of addition in a molecule could be precisely located on a particular atom. The hypothesis of a directed valence in molecular compounds has been attenuated considerably by modern talk of "electron smears" and by the ideas associated with the word "resonance."

The concept of a center of addition may be put into symbols[1] in the following way: if A is an addition center in molecule M which contains a reactive group R, then a true molecular compound is formed, if the product in Equation (1) results from the reaction. On the other hand, if

$$A_1-M_1-R_1 + A_2-M_2-R_2 \rightarrow R_1-M_1-A_1 \ldots A_2-M_2-R_2 \qquad (1)$$

the reaction takes place according to Equation (2), the primary valences are involved. The products in the two reactions are, of course, isomers. As an example, the reaction of $2,4,6$-trinitroanisole and dimethylaniline[2]

$$A_1-M_1-R_1 + A_2-M_2-R_2 \rightarrow A_1-M_1-R_1-R_2-M_2-A_2 \qquad (2)$$

gives two isomeric products, one a molecular compound (Equation 3) and the other a salt, a substituted ammonium picrate (Equation 4)[3]. The

1. Hertel and Römer, *Ber.*, **63B**, 2446 (1930).
2. Hertel and van Cleef, *Ber.*, **61,** 1545 (1928); Hertel, *Ber.*, **57,** 1559 (1924).
3. Hertel and Schneider, *Z. phys. Chem.*, **151A**, 413 (1930); **13B**, 387 (1931).

product from the reaction shown in Equation (3) occurs as unstable red
needles and is made by cooling a solution of trinitroanisole in dimethylaniline. If the solution is heated, it turns yellow and deposits yellow needles
on cooling. This is the substituted ammonium salt (Equation 4); it is soluble in water and exhibits other salt-like properties.

In the product from (3) the centers of addition cannot be precisely located
on particular atoms but rather exist throughout the aromatic ring in each
moiety. The linkage (designated by a dotted line in Equation 1) may,
perhaps, best be described as a weak coordinate covalent bond arising from
resonance conditions in the two rings.

This discussion of organic molecular compounds will be limited to the
first three of the following classes:

1. Products formed from benzoquinone, substituted quinone, or closely
related compounds with aromatic hydrocarbons, amines, phenols, and
aromatic ethers. Quinhydrone is an example known to all chemists.

2. Products of nitro compounds (generally polynitro) with aromatic
hydrocarbons, halides, amines, and phenols. Picrates of aromatic hydrocarbons are well known in this group.

3. Compounds of the bile acids (desoxycholic and apocholic, for example)
with fatty acids, esters, paraffins, and a few other compounds, of importance
in biochemistry. The clathrates and other occlusion compounds are included in this group.

4. Compounds containing a hydrogen bond.

General Properties of Organic Molecular Compounds

Many properties of organic molecular compounds are held in common
by the first two of these classes. Students of organic chemistry are familiar
with these compounds since they are useful in identifying a number of substances, particularly aromatic hydrocarbons, ethers, and tertiary amines.

The picrates[4], especially, and some other molecular compounds[5] have found wide usage for this purpose. Many of them are readily prepared merely by mixing alcohol solutions of the two components. The stability of organic molecular compounds varies but most of them decompose rather than melt. Many of them cannot be recrystallized from any solvent after they have been precipitated because they dissociate into their components in solution.

The influence of the solvent[6] is quite important. If either component is insoluble in a given solvent, the compound will always decompose. This indicates that the bonding in such compounds is quite weak. In general, the strength of the bond is somewhat less than that of a hydrogen bond; it is, perhaps, 5 kcal per mole and certainly never more than 10 kcal per mole[7].

In a series of fifty papers, the last of which appeared in 1925, Kremann[8] and his coworkers reported studies of the formation of a large group of organic compounds from binary mixtures. They concluded that the ease of formation (some measure of stability) depends on an interaction of a number of factors. By far the most important of these is what might now be called the difference in electronegativity (electron affinity) of the two components. If the threshold value of this primary affinity is exceeded, then the ease of formation of the molecular compound depends on the positions of the groups in the aromatic ring (asymmetry of the molecule) and steric hindrance. In this way Kremann accounted for the fact that frequently not all members of a given homologous series nor all ortho, meta, and para isomers of the same compound will form a given molecular compound.

Quinhydrones and Related Compounds

If an alcohol solution of hydroquinone is mixed with an alcohol solution of quinone, the solution turns brown-red, and dark green crystals with a metallic luster form. The original hydroquinone solution is colorless and the quinone solution is yellow. This profound change is due to the formation

4. Dermer and Dermer, *J. Org. Chem.*, **3**, 289 (1938); Baril and Megrdichian, *J. Am. Chem. Soc.*, **58**, 1415 (1936); Wang, *J. Chinese Chem. Soc.*, **1**, 59 (1933); Brown and Campbell, *J. Chem. Soc.*, **1937**, 1699; Mason and Manning, *J. Am. Chem. Soc.*, **62**, 1639 (1940).
5. Stephens, Hargis, and Entrikin, *Proc. Louisiana Acad. Sci.*, **10**, 210 (1947); cf., *Chem. Abs.*, **42**, 1921 (1948); Reichstein, *Helv. chim. Acta*, **9**, 799 (1926); Sutter, *Helv. chim. Acta* **21**, 1266 (1938); Buehler, Wood, Hull, and Irwin, *J. Am. Chem. Soc.*, **54**, 2398 (1932).
6. Dimroth, *Ann.*, **438**, 58 (1924); Dimroth and Bamberger, *Ann.*, **438**, 67 (1924).
7. Wheland, "The Theory of Resonance," p. 46, New York, John Wiley & Sons, Inc., 1944.
8. Pfeiffer, "Organische Verbindungen," 2nd Ed., p. 272, Stuttgart, Ferdinand Enke, 1927. (See author index in Pfeiffer for original references to Kremann's work.)

of quinhydrone, a molecular compound, from equivalent amounts of hydro-quinone and quinone.

In solution, quinhydrone dissociates into its two components to an equilibrium point. The oxidation and reduction of quinhydrone to quinone and hydroquinone, respectively, is quantitative, reversible, and rapid enough to be used as an organic half-cell with a reproducible electrode potential of 0.699 volts[9] (for system from quinone). It is a useful half-cell for determining pH values below 8.

Both components of the quinhydrone molecule may be considerably modified and still yield a molecular compound. Pfeiffer found that aromatic ethers and even aromatic hydrocarbons, such as durene or hexamethyl-benzene, could be used with certain quinones, (chloranil, etc.) to give deeply colored molecular compounds. Although the phenolic group is unnecessary, the presence of the unsaturated carbons of the benzenoid nucleus is essential. Hexahydrodurene, for example, does not give a colored product with any quinone.

Only one olefinic double bond is necessary for the quinone moiety. As a general formula, $RCOCH\!\!=\!\!CHCOR$ may be substituted for the quinone and, even here, the R groups may be substituted by a bridging oxygen atom, for example, in 3,4,5,6-tetrachlorophthalic anhydride. Quinhydrone itself, then, is a special case of a more general type of molecular compound.

In the solid state the ratio of phenolic component to quinone component may be 1:1, 1:2, or 2:1, but in solution the ratio is always 1:1, regardless of substitutions on hydroxyl groups in the phenolic part. Michaelis and Granick[10] have pointed out that crystalline quinhydrones have been isolated only when there was at least one free hydrogen on a hydroxyl group in the phenolic component. Yet, in solution, the affinity of the phenolic component for the quinone is not changed by alkylation of the phenol to an ether, so a hydrogen bond cannot play an essential role in forming the compounds. However, even as recently as 1944, Pfeiffer[11] clung to the opinion that there is probably a hydrogen bond (carbonyl oxygen to hydrogen) in quinhydrone itself, although workers in the field of x-ray analysis have since rejected the notion that it plays any important rôle in holding the compound together.

Gradation in the color of organic molecular compounds has been found to be a qualitative measure of the stabilities of these compounds. The more deeply colored compounds are usually more stable. In the benzenoid part of the quinhydrone, the groups —CH_3, —OH, —OCH_3, —NH_2, and —$N(CH_3)_2$ deepen the colors of the molecular compounds while halogens

9. Lammert and Morgan, *J. Am. Chem. Soc.*, **54**, 910 (1932).

10. Michaelis and Granick, *J. Am. Chem. Soc.*, **66**, 1023 (1944).

11. Pfeiffer, *Ber.*, **77A**, 59 (1944).

TABLE 17.1. COLOR GRADATION IN COMPOUNDS RELATED TO QUINHYDRONE

Hydroquinone Component	quinone	Quinone Component chloranil	duroquinone
Benzene	green-yellow	green-yellow	
Hexamethylbenzene	orange-yellow	red-violet	pure yellow
Phenol	orange	blood red	deep yellow
Aniline	blood red	violet	bright orange
Dimethylaniline	violet red	deep blue	orange red
Anisole	yellow	orange red	

have a hypsochromic effect. Substitution of halogens in the quinoid part, on the other hand, deepens the color of the molecular compound and substitution of —CH₃ , —OH, and —OCH₃ attenuates the colors. These effects are shown qualitatively in Table 17.1.

Some properties of a number of compounds related to quinhydrone are shown in Table 17.2.

Picrates and Related Compounds

Picric acid is an organic acid of strength comparable to that of the short chain carboxylic acids. With strong organic bases it forms picrates having some of the properties of substituted ammonium salts. In many cases these salts may be recrystallized from water without decomposition and differ only slightly in color from the bright yellow of picric acid, itself. But with very weak bases, picric acid forms molecular compounds which show pronounced color deepening and none of the properties commonly associated with salts (Table 17.3). One of the satisfying evidences that these two kinds of picrates are of different character is that, in a few cases, a single amine can be made to form two picrates, one having salt-like character and the other exhibiting molecular character. (Table 17.3) It was once suggested[12] that the existence and colors of these isomeric amine picrates could be accounted for on a purely ionic basis, the formulas of the two picrate ions being:

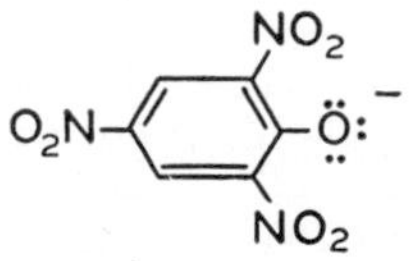

PICRATE ION   PICRATE ION FOR
FOR SALT   MOLECULAR COMPOUND

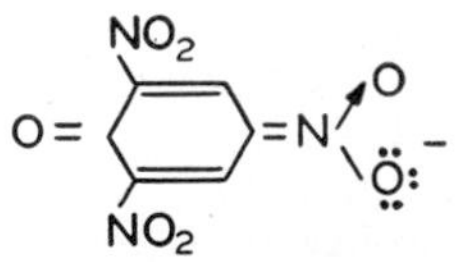

While this may be a reasonable picture, and might account for the colors of the two kinds of picrates, it cannot account for the picrates of aromatic hydrocarbons, ethers, phenols, and amine oxides, or the closely related derivatives of polynitro compounds.

12. Bennett and Willis, *J. Chem. Soc.*, **1929**, 256.

TABLE 17.2. PROPERTIES OF SOME COMPOUNDS RELATED TO QUINHYDRONE

Components		Properties	Ref.
Quinone	thiophenol	ratio 1:2; dark bronze plates sol. benzene, ligroin.	a
Quinone	phenol	ratio 1:2; red needles.	b
Chloranil	p-phenyl-enediam-ine	blue-black needles.	c
Chloranil	p C_6H_4-$(NMe_2)_2$	red needles, m.p. 80°, sol. hot alcohol.	c
Fluorenone	benzidine	yellow prisms, m.p. 126 to 127°, sol. hot alcohol.	c
Quinone	2-nitrohy-droqui-none	dark red cryst., m.p. 89 to 90°.	d
Quinone	p-phenyl-enediam-ine	dark brown ppt. from acetic acid, insol. H_2O.	e
Naphthoqui-none	hydroqui-none	dark green cryst. refl. light, ruby red transmitted light, m.p. 123°.	f
Fluorenone	α-naphthol	short red cryst. from benzene, m.p. 89°	g
Chloranil	acenaph-thene	violet mass by melting components together, sol. benzene.	h
Bromanil	durene	red needles from acetic acid, decomp. in air on standing, decomp. rapidly 80 to 90°.	i
Chloranil	diethoxydi-naphtho-stilbene	ratio 1:2, heavy black cryst. from benzene.	i
Dibenzalace-tone	resorcinol	yellow needles from benzene, m.p. 95°.	j
2,5-Dichloro-quinone	hexamethyl-benzene	bright red needles from acetic acid, m.p. 132 to 136°, stable a few days in a desiccator.	k
Chloranil	hexamethyl-benzene	fine, long, brown-violet needles from acetic acid, stable for a long time.	k
Tetrachloro-quinone	benzene	ratio 1:3, benzene sol. slowly evaporated in a vacuum desiccator gives dark red cryst., m.p. 37 to 42°, decomp. in air in a few minutes.	k
Tetrachloro-quinone	p-xylene	dark red prisms from xylene sol. in vacuum, m.p. near 83°, stable in air few minutes.	k

a Troeger and Eggert, *J. prakt. Chem.*, [2] **53,** 478 (1896).

b Nietzki, *Ann.*, **215,** 125 (1882).

c Schlenk and Knorr, *Ann.*, **368,** 277 (1909).

d Richter, *Ber.*, **46,** 3434 (1913).

e Erdmann, *Z. angew. Chem.*, **8,** 424 (1895).

f Urban, *Monatsh.*, **28,** 299 (1907).

g Meyer, *Ber.*, **43,** 157 (1910).

h Haakh, *Ber.*, **42,** 4594 (1909).

i Pfeiffer, *Ann.*, **404,** 1 (1914).

j Pfeiffer, Goebel, and Angern, *Ann.*, **440,** 241 (1925).

k Pfeiffer, Jowleff, Fischer, Monti, and Mully, *Ann.*, **412,** 253 (1917).

TABLE 17.3. THE TYPES OF PICRATES FORMED WITH VARIOUS AMINES

| Amine | Compound with Picric Acid | | Ref. |
	Salt-like	Molecular	
α-Naphthyl amine	green yellow 161°		a, p. 343
Methylamine	yellow 207°		b
β-Naphthyl amine	yellow 198 to 199°		c
Carbazole		red	d
Indene		red	a, p. 344
p,p'-dimethylaminodi-phenylmethane	straw yellow 185°		a, p. 343
C_6H_5—CH=N—NHC_6H_5		dark violet 117°	a, p. 344
m-$O_2NC_6H_4$—CH=N—NHC_6H_5		dark red 118°	a, p. 344
o-Bromoaniline	yellow trans. pt. 85°	orange-red 128°	a, p. 347
o-Iodoaniline	yellow trans. pt. 90°	deep orange 112°	a, p. 347
1-Chloro-2-aminonaph-thalene	yellow trans. pt. 130°	dark red 174°	a, p. 347
1-Bromo-2-aminonaph-thalene	yellow trans. pt. 114°	violet-red 178°	a, p. 347

[a] Pfeiffer, "Organische Verbindungen," 2nd Ed., Stuttgart, Ferdinand Enke, 1927.
[b] Jerusalem, *J. Chem. Soc.*, **95**, 1275 (1909).
[c] Liebermann and Scheiding, *Ann.*, **183**, 258 (1876).
[d] Graebe and Glaser, *Ann.*, **163**, 343 (1872).

The introduction of radicals into the polynitro unit of the molecule or into the hydrocarbon part has color effects comparable to those shown by the quinhydrone compounds. In the nitro part of the molecular compound, an alkyl group in the ring has a hypsochromic effect, as it does in the quinoid kernel of quinhydrones. Halogens, methoxyl, and amino groups in

TABLE 17.4. INFLUENCE ON COLOR OF SUBSTITUENTS IN THE NITRO COMPONENTS OF MOLECULAR COMPOUNDS

Benzenoid Component	With Nitro Component	With Substituted Nitro Component
Hydroquinone	p-dinitrobenzene, red-orange	dinitrodurene, bright yellow
Dimethylaniline	p-dinitrobenzene, deep orange-red	dinitrodurene, greenish yellow
Durene	p-dinitrobenzene, greenish yellow	dinitrodurene, almost colorless
Naphthalene	sym-trinitrobenzene, yellow	picryl chloride, canary yellow
α-Naphthyl amine	sym-trinitrobenzene, red	picryl chloride, brown
α-Naphthyl amine		picramide, red
α-Naphthyl amine		2,4,6-trinitroanisole, red

the nitro derivative (already strongly electronegative due to the presence of the nitro group) have very little influence on the color. This will be evident from the data in Table 17.4.

In the benzenoid component of the picrates and related compounds, alkyl groups, fused rings, double and triple bonds, hydroxyl, methoxyl, and amino groups all act as bathochromes. Alkyl- and aryl-amino groups have an even more marked effect in deepening the colors while an acyl group lessens the effect slightly. Halogens in the benzenoid component have a hypsochromic effect.

Structures of Molecular Compounds

Three theories have been advanced to account for the structures of organic molecular compounds. None of the three has attained complete acceptance, and none of the three has been completely discarded.

1. Formation of a coordinate covalent bond between the two components.
2. Formation of polarization aggregates which mutually saturate the residual valences in the two parts.
3. Formation of an essentially ionic bond by transfer of an electron from one component to the other.

Coordination Theory

The first proponents of the theory of formation of a coordinate covalent bond between the two components of an organic molecular compound were Bennett and Willis[12, 13], closely followed by Moore, Shepherd, and

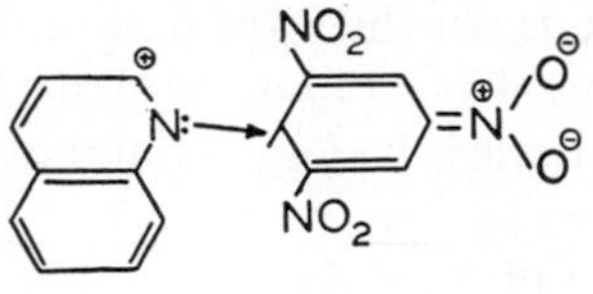

FIG. 17.1. Molecular addition compound of quinoline with sym-trinitrobenzene.

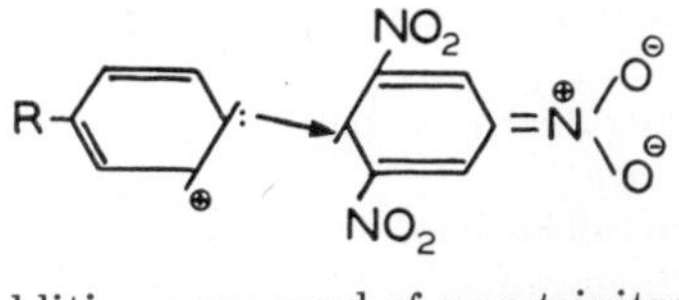

FIG. 17.2. Molecular addition compound of sym-trinitrobenzene with an aromatic hydrocarbon.

Goodall[14]. In the molecular compound formed from quinoline and sym-trinitrobenzene, the bonding was represented as shown in Fig. 17.1. If the

13. Bennett and Wain, *J. Chem. Soc.*, **1936**, 1108.
14. Moore, Shepherd, and Goodall, *J. Chem. Soc.*, **1931**, 1447.

amine is replaced by an aromatic hydrocarbon, it becomes more difficult to locate the donor (Fig. 17.2) and acceptor atoms. Further difficulty must be faced in some of the quinhydrone type molecular compounds in having to draw unfavorable electronic distributions in some canonical forms. However, if one pair of the π electrons of a double bond in an aromatic hydrocarbon may be considered as the donor pair, then the theory is still tenable and such pictures as Fig. 17.2 will account for the color of such molecular compounds. The bathochromic and hypsochromic effects, described previously for the quinhydrone type (see page 550) and the picrates and related compounds (see page 553), when functional groups are substituted in the aromatic nucleus, are all plausible in terms of modern electronic concepts of electron withdrawal from (and electron supply to) the ring.

Polarization Theory

The second theory, the saturation of residual valences, was proposed by Pfeiffer[15] as a means of accounting for the colors and other properties of organic molecular compounds. Briegleb[16] expressed the view that the residual valences arise from an inductive effect. In a compound of sym-trinitrobenzene and an aromatic hydrocarbon, for example, the polar groups (nitro) induce an electric dipole in the polarizable aromatic hydrocarbon. The resulting electrostatic attraction between the two aromatic nuclei maintains the compound.

In compounds containing completely conjugated rings, there are two types of polarization—that induced in the localized σ bonds of the hydrocarbon and that due to distortion of charge distribution of the π electrons (double bonds). Briegleb determined these polarizations spectroscopically. The heats of formation of a number of molecular compounds calculated from the polarization values agreed with those found experimentally. Since the heats of formation of organic molecular compounds are of the order of 1 to 5 kcals per mole and the force between components of the system (if electrostatic) varies as the inverse sixth power, Briegleb infers that the components cannot approach each other closely enough (1 to 2 Å) to form a chemical bond.

The chief objection to the concept of polarization aggregates due to electrostatic interactions is that it does not account for the simple ratios of the components which form molecular compounds. Even though one would be inclined to consider residual valences as integral since they arise from electrons, the field about the components could not be uniform.

15. Ref. 8, Chapt. I
16. Briegleb, "Zwischenmolekulare Krafte und Molekulstruktur," Stuttgart, Ferdinand Enke, 1937 (Ahrens Vorträge, Vol. 37, 1937); Briegleb, *Z. Elektrochem.*, **50,** 35 (1944).

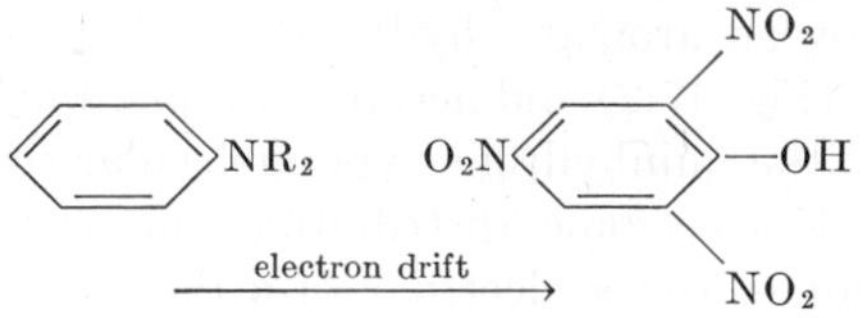

FIG. 17.3. Molecular addition compound of picric acid with a tertiary amine, according to the polarization theory.

Hence one would not expect molecules of greatly different sizes (such as benzene and anthracene) to form molecular compounds with a second component in which the ratios were the same; but the contrary is the case. Rheinboldt[17] has compiled statistics which show that of 598 organic molecular compounds recorded in the literature, 85.3 per cent have the 1:1 ratio of components and 98.2 per cent bear the ratios 1:1, 1:2, or 2:1. Compounds in which the ratios do not appear to be whole numbers[18] are not numerous enough to remove the objection to the theory of Pfeiffer and Briegleb.

As an example of a colored molecular compound we may take a tertiary amine picrate. From the standpoint of the theory of residual valences, the color in the picrate of a weak base may be thought of as due to the recession of electrons into the picric acid end of the pair, that is, in the direction indicated by the arrow in Fig. 17.3.

Ionization Theory

The polarization mechanism for the production of color[19] is the primary step in the incipient oxidation-reduction mechanism (the basis for the third theory) proposed by Gibson and Loeffler[20]. They suggested that primary inductomeric or electromeric polarized associations (and not simply Briegleb's dipole aggregates) do occur and that they account for the color change. They suggested that there is an electron drift in the direction indicated in Fig. 17.3 and that the components are brought into close contact in solution by thermal agitation. The fact that polynitro compounds give more deeply colored molecular compounds than mononitro compounds is accounted for, since the former would promote a greater electron drift.

The point of distinction between the second theory and the third theory is just the difference (an important one) between an electrostatic bond and a chemical bond.

Weiss[21] has modified this theory of the bonding in molecular compounds

17. Rheinboldt, Z.angew. Chem., **39**, 765 (1926).
18. Emmert, Schneider, and Koberne, Ber., **64**, 950 (1931).
19. Hammick and Sixsmith, J. Chem. Soc., **1935**, 580.
20. Gibson and Loeffler, J. Am. Chem. Soc., **62**, 1324 (1940).
21. Weiss, J. Chem. Soc., **1942**, 245.

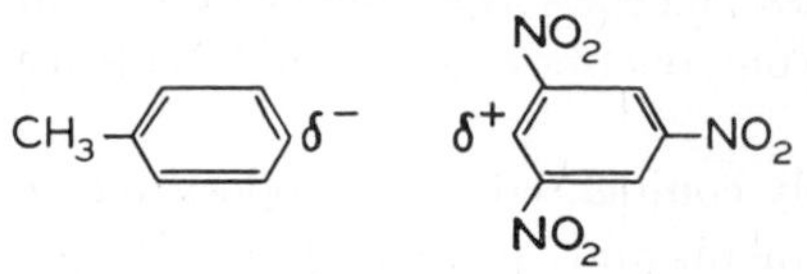

Fig. 17.4. Transition state in the formation of a molecular addition compound.

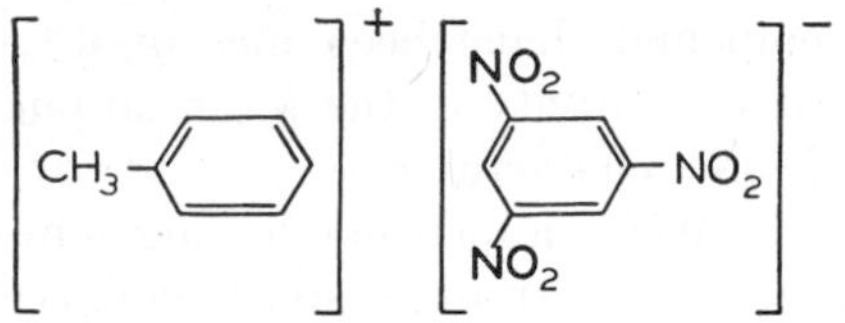

Fig. 17.5. Ionic bonding in a molecular addition compound.

to the point where it amounts to assuming an ionic bond, though this, of course, is the limiting case. His suggestion is that the bonding electron pair is transferred to some extent. This really amounts to a difference in degree rather than kind since Weiss' theory does not suppose 100 per cent ionic character for the bond. Molecular compound formation is represented in Equation (5),

$$A + B \rightleftharpoons (AB)_t \to A^{\delta+}B^{\delta-} \tag{5}$$

where $(AB)_t$ is a transition complex probably resulting from dipole and dispersion interactions. The formation of the transition complex is followed by the actual electron transfer, A being the donor and B the acceptor.

The quantum mechanical picture derived from the potential energy curves for the ionic state of these organic molecular compounds is consistent with the observation that the formation of such compounds is rapid and often reversible and that only a low heat of activation is necessary.

The transition state in equation 5 might be represented in an early stage by Fig. 17.4, the partial negative charge representing a position of high electron density and the partial positive charge, a position of electron deficiency as a result of the positions of the methyl and nitro groups. After the electron transfer is consummated, it is probably best to consider the extra electron in the negative ion (Fig. 17.5) as "smeared out" over the whole radical. The electron deficiency in the cation likewise cannot be precisely located. The conductivities of solutions of polynitro compounds in liquid ammonia[22] and of aromatic hydrocarbons in sulfur dioxide[23] indicate that the polynitro compounds may act as electron acceptors and the aromatic hydrocarbons may act as electron donors.

It was found that m-dinitrobenzene is a much better conductor than the ortho and para derivatives, which fits in with the present electronic concepts. In addition to the conductometric evidence for the existence of ionic entities in solution, the dielectric properties of some solid molecular

22. Franklin and Kraus, *Am. Chem. J.*, **23**, 277 (1900); *J. Am. Chem. Soc.*, **27**, 197 (1905); Franklin, *Z. phys. Chem.*, **69**, 272 (1909); Kraus and Bray, *J. Am. Chem. Soc.*, **35**, 1315 (1913); Field, Garner, and Smith, *J. Chem. Soc.*, **127**, 1227 (1925); Garner and Gillbe, *J. Chem. Soc.*, **1928**, 2889.
23. Walden, *Z. phys. Chem.*, **43**, 385 (1903).

compounds have been measured[24]. Weiss suggests that deviations from strict additivity of the polarizations of components is additional evidence of ionic character.

To Weiss, a molecule having completely conjugated double bonds represents an electronic system similar to a metal and so interaction between two such molecules could correspond to "alloy formation." If the two compounds are similar in electronic character, one would expect only solid solutions of the two "metals," whereas if there are loosely bound electrons in one and relatively large electron affinity in the other, molecular compound formation will result. This corresponds to intermetallic compound formation. One group of organic molecular compounds which show some analogies to the intermetallic compounds consists of the colored compounds of sym-trinitrobenzene with unsaturated ketones[25].

However, there is evidence against the assumption of ionic structures for these compounds. Work in x-ray analysis[26] of organic molecular compounds points to the nonexistence of ions in the lattice. Powell and coworkers point out that ionic bonds should mean stronger crystal lattice structures, which would result in increased hardness and higher melting points for the complex. They list a number of molecular compounds in which the melting points are lower than that of one or both components. This has been noted previously[27]. The occurrence of diffuse x-ray reflections in some compounds, e.g., that of picryl chloride with hexamethylbenzene[28], shows that the bonds in the crystal are not stronger than the bonds between molecules of picryl chloride itself, where electron transfer is not postulated.

Cook[29] voiced the opinion that further experimental verification is needed before the ionic theory of binding in organic molecular compounds can be accepted. Anderson[30] has stated that the constitutions of organic molecular compounds is the major unsolved problem confronting the theory of valency.

OCCLUSION COMPOUNDS

The third class of organic molecular compounds is a group in which the chemical properties of the components play a secondary role to the sizes and geometries of the molecules.

24. Kronberger and Weiss, *J. Chem. Soc.*, **1944**, 464.
25. Weiss, *J. Chem. Soc.*, **1943**, 462; Reddelien, *J. prakt. Chem.*, **91**, 213 (1915).
26. Powell, Huse, and Cooke, *J. Chem. Soc.*, **1943**, 153; Powell and Huse, *J. Chem. Soc.*, **1943**, 435; *Ann. Repts. Chem. Soc.*, **40**, 93 (1943).
27. Buehler, Hisey, and Wood, *J. Am. Chem. Soc.*, **52**, 1939 (1930).
28. Powell and Huse, *Nature*, **144**, 77 (1939); *Ann. Repts. Chem. Soc.*, **36**, 184 (1939).
29. Cook, *Ann. Repts. Chem. Soc.*, **39**, 167 (1942).
30. Anderson, *Aust. Chem. Inst. J., Proc.*, **6**, 232 (1939).

Choleic Acids

The choleic acids are a group of water soluble molecular compounds of the bile acids (the most prominent being desoxycholic acid) with a variety or organic compounds such as fatty acids[31], esters[32], ketones which enolize[33], camphor[34], long chain paraffins[35], polycyclic aromatic compounds[36], and unsaturated acids[36a]. They may also coordinate solvent molecules[37], such as ether, ethanol, benzene, or dioxane, to form less stable lattices containing solvent of crystallization.

It is remarkable that the numbers of molecules of desoxycholic acid which coordinate with one molecule of a fatty acid are also the coordination numbers commonly found in inorganic complexes, namely, 4, 6, and 8; in a few cases, other numbers are found. The coordination number exhibited toward desoxycholic acid (and apocholic acid) by formic acid is zero; by acetic acid, one; by propionic acid, three; by acids containing carbon chains C_4 to C_8, four; C_9 to C_{14}, six; and C_{15} to C_{29}, eight. In branch-chain acids, such as isobutyric, trimethylacetic, and isovaleric, the coordination number drops to two, while in the unsaturated long chain acids (both cis and trans) such as oleic, erucic, brassidic, and elaidic, the coordination number is eight. In dicarboxylic acids, the coordination numbers are as follows: C_4, two; C_6, three; C_7 to C_{11}, four; and C_{12} to C_{20}, six. In esters of the fatty acids, the length of the acid part of the ester still determines the coordination number unless the alcohol part is long in comparison with the alkyl group of the acid.

Sobotka[38] was led to suggest that, since desoxycholic and apocholic acid both have hydroxyl groups at C_3 and C_{12}, in contrast to the bile acids, which do not form choleic acids, their coordinating abilities must be due to these two groups and the shapes of these molecules. Soon after, Kratky, Go, and Giacomello[39], from a series of x-ray studies, concluded that the

31. Rheinboldt, Pieper, and Zervas, *Ann.*, **451**, 256 (1927).
32. Rheinboldt, König, and Otten, *Ann.*, **473**, 249 (1929).
33. Sobotka and Kahn, *Biochem. J.*, **26**, 898 (1932); *Ber.*, **65B**, 227 (1932).
34. Rheinboldt, König, and Flume, *Z. physiol. Chem.*, **184**, 219 (1929).
35. Rheinboldt, Braun, Flume, König, and Lauber, *J. prakt. Chem.*, [2] **153**, 313 (1939).
36. Marx and Sobotka, *J. Org. Chem.*, **1**, 275 (1936); Fieser and Newman, *J. Am. Chem. Soc.*, **57**, 1602 (1935).
37. Wieland and Sorge, *Z. physiol. Chem.*, **97**, 1 (1916); Boedecker, *Ber.*, **53**, 1852 (1920).
38. Sobotka, *Chem. Revs.*, **15**, 311 (1934).
39. Herzog, Kratky, and Kurijama, *Naturwissenschaften*, **19**, 524 (1931); Go and Kratky, *Z. phys. Chem.*, **26B**, 439 (1934); Go, *IX Congr. intern. quim. pura aplicada*, **4**, 193 (1934); cf, *Chem. Abs.*, **30**, 5091 (1936); Kratky and Giacomello, *Monatsh.*, **69**, 427 (1936); Go and Kratky, *Z. Krist.*, **92A**, 310 (1935); Giacomello and Kratky, *Z. Krist.*, **95A**, 459 (1935); Caglioti and Giacomello, *Gazz. chim. ital.*, **69**, 245 (1939); Giacomello, *Gazz. chim. ital.*, **69**, 790 (1939); Giacomello and Romeo, *Gazz. chim. ital.*, **73**, 285 (1943).

crystal structure of desoxycholic acid acts as an enveloping shell leaving a "channel" parallel to the longitudinal carbon axis in which the coordinating molecules can lie. The unit cell, then, is cylindrical.

The fact that space relations play an important part in the formation of this kind of organic molecular compound suggests the possibility of resolving optical antipodes by the use of molecular compounds. Although only partial resolutions have been accomplished by this method, as yet, it is important because it allows the resolution of compounds containing no functional groups. Windaus, et al.[40], were able to resolve dl-α-terpineol with digitonin. Weiss and Abeles[41] resolved dl-sec-butylpicramide by forming a molecular compound with d-β-naphthylcamphylamine, and dl-resorcylmethyl carbinol has been resolved with brucine[42]. Partial resolutions of methylethylacetic acid[43], α-phenylbutanol, dipentene, and camphor[44] have been accomplished by the use of desoxycholic acid.

Other Molecular Compounds Involving a Channel Type Lattice

Closely related to the choleic acids from the standpoint of structure are the colored molecular compounds of 4,4'-dinitrobiphenyl with various adducts, such as benzidene, 4-bromobiphenyl, 4-hydroxybiphenyl, and 4-aminobiphenyl. The ratios of the components in these compounds are respectively, 4:1, 7:2, 3:1, and 3:1, depending in large measure on the length of the rod-like molecules which fill in the cylindrical channels in the 4,4'-dinitrobiphenyl lattice[45].

Other known molecular compounds which may be described as having a channel type lattice are the urea[46] adducts with paraffins and other compounds, and the thiourea[47] adducts with the same wide variety of components. Both urea and thiourea furnish a loose hexagonal lattice for the second component. The ratios[48] of adduct to urea vary from 1:4.0 with butyric acid to 1:21.4 with octaeicosane, the ratios not necessarily being integral. The calculated length of the holes in the lattice approximate very closely the calculated lengths of fully extended adduct molecules.

40. Windaus, Klänhardt, and Weinhold, Z. physiol. Chem., **126,** 308 (1923).
41. Weiss and Abeles, Monatsh., **59,** 238 (1932).
42. Eisenlohr and Meier, Ber., **71B,** 1005 (1938).
43. Sobotka, Naturwissenschaften, **19,** 595 (1931).
44. Sobotka and Goldberg, Biochem. J., **26,** 905 (1932).
45. Rapson, Saunder, Stewart, J. Chem. Soc., **1946,** 1110; Saunder, Proc. Roy. Soc., **188A,** 31 (1946); **190A,** 508 (1947); James and Saunder, Proc. Roy. Soc., **190A,** 518 (1947).
46. Schlenk, Ann., **565,** 204 (1949); Zimmerschied, Dinerstein, Weitkamp, and Marschner, Ind. Eng. Chem., **42,** 1300 (1950); J. Am. Chem. Soc., **71,** 2947 (1949).
47. Schlenk, Experientia, **6,** 292 (1950); Ann., **573,** 142 (1951); Angla, Ann. chim., [12] **4,** 639 (1949); Bengen and Schlenk, Experientia, **5,** 200 (1949).
48. Smith, Science Progress, **36,** 656 (1948); **38,** 698 (1950).

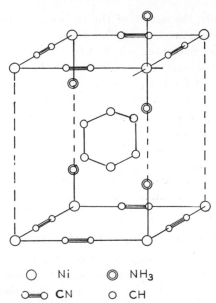

| O | Ni | ◎ | NH₃ |
| O≡O | CN | O | CH |

Fig. 17.6. "Cage" lattice structure of a clathrate of benzene, ammonia, and nickel cyanide of formula [Ni(C₆H₆)(NH₃)(CN)₂].

For example, in urea-*n*-nonane, the molecular ratio 7.7:1 allows a hole of 14.1Å in the lattice and in urea-*n*-tetraeicosane, the ratio 18.0:1 allows a hole of 33Å. The fully extended *n*-nonane and *n*-tetraeicosane molecules should measure 11.7Å and 30.6Å respectively.

Schlenk[49] has reviewed the chemistry of the organic occlusion compounds, including in the channel type the zeolite adsorption compounds which have remarkable powers of adsorbing straight chain hydrocarbons and rejecting branch chains of the same number of carbons. Chabasite, for example, can be used to separate *n*-butane from isobutane rather effectively.

Clathrates

Another group of molecular compounds in which the geometry of the crystal lattice is of prime importance is the clathrates[50]. These are compounds in which one component is trapped in a "cage" lattice structure of the second component. It is evident that the ratio of the two components might be integral only in the limiting case, that is, in the event of a perfect lattice where every cage is filled with the requisite number of molecules of the other component.

49. Schlenk, *Fortschr. Chem. Forsch.*, **2**, 92 (1951).
50. Powell, *Endeavor*, **9**, 154 (1950).

In these compounds, the nature of the trapped component depends not at all on chemical properties but only on molecular size. This is illustrated very sharply by the clathrates which hydroquinone[51] forms with such chemically unrelated substances as H_2S, SO_2, CH_3OH, CH_3CN, $HCOOH$, CO_2, HCl, HBr, $HC\equiv CH$, A, Kr, and Xe. The three inert gases emphasize the point that chemical bonds cannot be involved in the formation of these compounds. The x-ray work of Powell has been instrumental in elucidating the structures of clathrate compounds. The framework of the clathrate formed by benzene and ammonia with nickel cyanide, $[Ni(C_6H_6)(NH_3) \cdot (CN)_2]$[52] is shown in Fig. 17.6.

Water and the aliphatic hydrocarbons found in natural gas form crystalline clathrates which sometimes cause considerable trouble in pipeline transportation systems.

Occlusion Compounds Involving a Layer Type of Lattice

A third group of occlusion compounds[49] is formed from substances which are trapped in the lattice of a second component by being caught between layers of molecules forming the lattice. As examples, the following may be cited: mineral clay adsorbates, such as montmorillonite with alcohols, glycols, and aromatic hydrocarbons; basic zinc salts of organic acids, such as naphthol yellow, with water, alcohols, and nitriles; and the liquid of crystallization adsorbed in certain protein molecules, such as haemoglobin and horse methaemoglobin.

51. Palin and Powell, *J. Chem. Soc.*, **1947**, 208; **1948**, 571, 817; Powell, *J. Chem. Soc.*, **1948**, 61; **1950**, 298, 300, 468; *Proc. Intern. Congr. Pure and Applied Chem.*, **11**, 585 (1947); Powell and Guter, *Nature*, **164**, 240 (1949).
52. Powell and Rayner, *Nature*, **163**, 566 (1949); Rayner and Powell, *J. Chem. Soc.*, **1952**, 319.

18. Physical Methods in Coordination Chemistry

Robert C. Brasted

University of Minnesota, Minneapolis, Minnesota

and

William E. Cooley*

University of Illinois, Urbana, Illinois

The study of coordination compounds has benefited greatly from data accumulated through the use of physical methods. These methods are quite numerous, and they vary widely in degree of usefulness and breadth of application. This chapter describes briefly the nature of the more important methods, and cites examples of their application.

Spectrophotometric Methods

The spectra of metal complexes may be broadly classified as absorptions due to electron vibrations, absorptions due to molecular vibrations, and spectra characterized by emitted frequencies different from a given single irradiating frequency. The first type of absorption is found in the ultraviolet and visible ranges; the second, in the infrared. The third is due to the Raman effect and is a shifting of frequencies. The Raman effect is also produced by molecular vibrations.

Correct interpretation of the absorption and Raman spectra of complexes may lead to conclusions regarding their formulas, relative stabilities, mechanisms and rates of their formations, their configurations, and in certain cases, their coordination numbers. Raman spectra serve also as a tool for the measurement of the homopolarity of the coordination link and of valence bond angles, and as a basis for certain deductions concerning spatial arrangements.

Exact and complete interpretation of visible and ultraviolet spectra is usually not attempted. Instead, comparisons are made between spectra to be analyzed and standard spectra of known compounds. Variations in

---

* Now at Procter and Gamble Co., Cincinnati, Ohio.

positions of absorption maxima may often be given semi-quantitative interpretations with respect to stability or displacement of one ligand by another.

Color and Absorption Spectra

Before the announcement of Werner's theory, attempts were made to relate the color of complex compounds to the presence of certain groups. Color was seen to be related to composition, but the presence of a given group in a complex was found not to be uniquely correspondent to a specific color. Kastle[1] and Houston[2] were among the first to note a relationship between color and the positions of constituent elements in the periodic table, as well as the effect of temperature on colored compounds. In general, heating a compound having a color in the list below was found to produce successively the colors to the right, while cooling was found to reverse the process.

White $\rightleftarrows$ Violet $\rightleftarrows$ Blue $\rightleftarrows$ Green $\rightleftarrows$ Yellow $\rightleftarrows$ Orange $\rightleftarrows$ Red $\rightleftarrows$ Brown $\rightleftarrows$ Black.

Violet, blue, and green may often be omitted because of greater absorption of the more refrangible visible rays, and the presence of white in the list refers only to cooling of normally colored salts.

According to Connelly[3], if the mass of a molecule is small, its period of vibration in the presence of light energy will be small, leading to absorption in the ultraviolet. An increase in mass causes a slower vibrational period and shifts absorption to the visible. Connelly's interpretation of the effect of temperature was based on the concept of vibration of molecules about a mean position. He suggested that a rising temperature increases the amplitude of vibration and thus results in a weakened restoring force, hence a longer period of vibration and a lower frequency.

The first systematic study of the color of complex compounds was made by Werner[4], who concluded that color is more a function of arrangement of groups about the central metal atom than of composition.

Shibata[5], while studying the spectra of complexes of cobalt, nickel, and chromium, concluded that color is a function of bonding and structural arrangement. He noted that a complex may show color even though its constituents are transparent to visible and ultraviolet light. He related the positions of metals in the periodic table to their color-forming ability in complexes. The metals of Groups I, II, and III tend to form simple

1. Kastle, *Am. Chem. J.*, **23**, 500 (1900).
2. Houston, *J. Franklin Inst.*, **62**, 115 (1871).
3. Connelly, *Phil. Mag.*, (5) **18**, 130 (1884); Nichols and Snow, *Phil. Mag.*, (5) **32**, 401 (1891).
4. Werner, *Z. anorg. Chem.*, **22**, 91 (1900).
5. Shibata, *J. Tokyo Chem. Soc.*, **40**, 463 (1919).

ions, but in the higher groups, in which complexing tendencies are more pronounced, most salts are colored. There are such apparent exceptions as titanium tetrachloride and tetrammine platinum(II) chloride; however, the former shows color upon aquation, and the latter absorbs strongly in the near ultraviolet. Shibata attributed all color in inorganic compounds to complexing, the color resulting from molecular vibrations or vibrations of small localizations of electrons.

Theories of Absorption

The origin of the absorption bands characteristic of coordinated structures is thought to be in the electronic vibrations occurring within the metal ion, within the coordinated groups, and between the metal and ligands. There is no general agreement as to the number of absorption bands which should be considered significant in structural studies. Since a large number of authors have interpreted structures in terms of three bands in the visible and ultraviolet, these bands will be considered standard in this discussion. The first band is usually found in the range 450 to 550 mμ, the second in the range 320 to 400 mμ, and the third in the range 195 to 250 mμ.

In 1913 Luther and Nikolopulos[6] postulated that the first band arises from the metal-ligand bond. Pauling[7] and Mead[8] have modified this by attributing the band to a combination of the translational energy of the bonding electrons and the vibrational energies of the central ion and coordinated groups. It is now frequently assumed that the greatest single factor leading to absorption in the first range is vibration of the nonbonding electrons of the metal ion.

The coordinate-bond electrons are generally thought to be responsible for the second absorption band. Although there is evidence that both the first and second bands result from energy differences in excited states of the bonding electrons[8, 9], there are dissimilarities in the behaviors of the two bands[10]. In the nitroammine cobalt(III) series, the substitution of a nitro group for an ammine group has a hypsochromic effect (shift toward the violet) on the first band and a bathochromic effect (shift toward the red) on the second. For this reason Tsuchida supports the idea that these bands have different sources.

The work of Kiss and Czegledy[11] with cobalt(III) complexes leads them to conclude that any assignment of absorption bands to particular elec-

6. Luther and Nikolopulos, *Z. physik. Chem.*, **82**, 361 (1913).
7. Pauling, *J. Am. Chem. Soc.*, **53**, 1367 (1931).
8. Mead, *Trans. Faraday Soc.*, **30**, 1052 (1934).
9. Mathieu, *Bull. soc. chim.*, (5) **3**, 463 (1936).
10. Tsuchida, *Bull. Chem. Soc. Japan*, (5) **13**, 388 (1938).
11. Kiss and Czegledy, *Z. anorg. allgem. Chem.*, **235**, 407 (1938).

tronic influences is only approximate. Accordingly, they attribute the first band to the general nature of the complex, rather than any specific group of electrons. Their data show that complexes of similar type, such as $[Co(NH_3)_6]^{+++}$ and $[Co \ en_3]^{+++}$, have absorption curves of similar shapes. Successive replacement of ammine groups by nitro groups in the hexammine changes the magnitude of the extinction at the maxima. This effect is additive with respect to the number of nitro groups present, and is typical of changes in the spectra of complexes having varying numbers of like groups.

Some coordinating groups have characteristic absorption bands:

Group	λ_{max} of free ligand, $m\mu$
NO_2^-	366
NO_3^-	302
$S_2O_3^-$	216
SO_3^-	300
SCN^-	215
CN^-	220
C_5H_5N	250

These bands may or may not be shifted upon coordination. The absorption of the nitrite group, for example, is shifted on coordination to give values ranging from 330 to 350 $m\mu$, which fall within the limits of the second band.

Two absorption maxima corresponding to the second and third bands are shown by $K_2[HgI_4]$[12]. No "first band" maximum is present. Since coordination electrons are certainly involved in the structure of this complex, Tsuchida concludes that the first band does not necessarily appear because of the formation of coordinate bonds. Similar observations made with other complexes[13] suggest that the first band cannot result from vibrations of bonding electrons. Tsuchida suggests that it arises from vibrations in an incomplete electron subshell. The second band, however, seems to be a function of bonding, and this band is considered by Tsuchida to be the most general absorption characteristic of complexes. This conclusion is supported by the fact that incident light of the same frequency as the second band maximum may weaken or break coordinate bonds.

Among the cobalt ammine complexes containing ligands in addition to ammonia, Tsuchida has assigned the following order of stability, based on hypsochromic effects in the second band: Most hypsochromic, most stable—NO_2^-, ONO^-, H_2O, SCN^-, OH^-, NO_3^-, Cl^-, $CO_3^=$, Br^-—least hypsochromic, least stable.

A number of studies of complexes have shown more than three absorp-

12. Tsuchida, *Bull. Chem. Soc. Japan*, (5) **13**, 392 (1938).
13. Kashimoto and Tsuchida, *J. Chem. Soc. Japan*, **60**, 347 (1939).

tion bands. Thus Csokan and Nyiri[14], working with inner complexes containing the Schiff's base of salicylaldehyde and ethylenediamine, observed more than three bands and concluded that hydrogen bonding, aromatic character, and polarization of molecules, as well as electronic shifts, are sources of absorption. Czegledy[15] noted four distinct bands between 200 and 700 mμ in studying a number of cobalt complexes.

Babaeva[16, 17] has noted the effects on band maxima of successive substitution of ammine groups in platinum complexes. Nearly all the complexes studied show a maximum in the range 280 to 290 mμ. This range is also common to cyanide complexes of cobalt, chromium, ruthenium, rhodium, and palladium. Platinum complexes containing anionic ligands with nitrogen donors show another maximum in the range 256 to 267 mμ. Substitution of nitro and chloro groups for ammonia produces a maximum in the range 330 to 340 mμ. Replacement of two or more ammonia groups results in complete absorption above about 450 mμ. Extensive substitution by several different groups, such as chloro, nitro, and amido, increases the number of bands to six or more.

In studying chloro complexes of the platinum group, Babaeva[18] concluded that when two complexes are identical except for the metal, the complex of the metal of lower atomic number shows absorption bands at greater wave lengths. This relation applies only to metals of the same periodic group. Babaeva attributes the effect to differences in excitation energies of d electrons.

It has been generally assumed that groups outside the coordination sphere do not contribute to the spectrum of the complex, but this assumption seems unjustified. Linhard[19] observed cobalt(III) and chromium(III) ammines and ethylenediamine complexes in the presence of halide, perchlorate, and nitrate ions, and found that weak associations yielding ions of the type $[Co(NH_3)_6]I^{++}$ produce absorption bands.

The Third Band

The complex absorption maximum of shortest wave length was first given systematic consideration by Shibata and Tsuchida and their co-workers[20, 21, 22]. Data accumulated by these authors for the cobalt nitro-

14. Csokan and Nyiri, *Magyar Chem. Folyoirat*, **47**, 149 (1941).
15. Czegledy, *Acta Lit. Sci. Regiae Univ. Hung. Frencsico-Josephinae, Sect. Chem., Mineral. Phys.*, **6**, 121 (1937).
16. Babaeva, *Compt. rend. acad. sci., U.R.S.S.*, **20**, 365 (1938).
17. Babaeva, *Compt. rend. acad. sci., U.R.S.S.*, **40**, 61 (1943).
18. Babaeva, *Bull. acad. sci. U.R.S.S., Classe sci. chim.*, 171 (1943).
19. Linhard, *Z. Elektrochem.*, **50**, 224 (1944).
20. Shibata, *J. Coll. Sci. Imp. Univ. Tokyo*, **37**, Art. 2, 1–28 (1915); **37**, Art. 8, 1–12 (1916).
    Shibata and Urbain, *Compt. rend.*, **157**, 593–5 (1914).

ammine complexes showed that a third band was consistently found when two nitro groups occupied *trans* positions in the complex. Tsuchida[23] also found a third band for *trans*-[Co(NH₃)₄Cl₂]Cl. Extension of these studies showed that the presence of a third band could be quite generally related to a *trans*-diacido structure. Tsuchida noted that the presence of a third band seemed independent of the configuration of the complex, the identity of the ligands, and the ionic charge of the complex, so long as two negative groups occupied *trans* positions. Tsuchida's explanation of the presence of the third band describes it as a polarization phenomenon possible only when two negative groups occupy antipodal positions in the coordination sphere.

More recent spectral studies by Basolo[24] have shown that *cis*-diacido complexes also show absorption in the third band region. Older investigations generally extended only to a lower limit of 250 mμ. Basolo has found that the *cis* complexes absorb at wave lengths which are usually less than 250 mμ, and these absorptions were undetected by Shibata, Tsuchida, and others. The hypotheses attributing the third band to phenomena peculiar to *trans* structures are therefore disproved. Nevertheless, Basolo's data point out that the *cis* and *trans* forms of a given complex do exhibit consistent differences in the positions of absorption maxima in the second and third bands, as shown below:

Complex	λ_{max}, mμ		
cis-[Co(NH₃)₄(NO₂)₂]⁺	238	327	
trans-[Co(NH₃)₄(NO₂)₂]⁺		255	356
cis-[Co en₂ (NO₂)₂]⁺	240	325	
trans-[Co en₂ (NO₂)₂]⁺		250	345

The positions of the second and third maxima are therefore useful in determining geometric configurations when the maxima are known for analogous complexes.

Special Bands

Complexes containing certain ligands, among them chromate, isothiocyanate, and dimethylglyoxime, sometimes show absorption maxima which are not attributable to the causes previously discussed. Tsuchida[25, 26] has classified these special bands into two types: those which are characteristic of the ligands, whether coordinated or free, and those appearing only on coordination. The ion [Co(NH₃)₅CrO₄]⁺ shows special band ab-

21. Shibata and Matsuno, *J. Tokyo Chem. Soc.*, **39**, 661 (1918).
22. Tsuchida and Kashimoto, *Bull. Chem. Soc. Japan*, **11**, 785 (1936).
23. Tsuchida, *Bull. Chem. Soc. Japan*, **11**, 721 (1936).
24. Basolo, *J. Am. Chem. Soc.*, **72**, 4393 (1950).
25. Tsuchida and Kibayashi, *Bull. Chem. Soc. Japan*, (7) **13**, 474 (1938).
26. Tsuchida, *Bull. Chem. Soc. Japan*, (6) **13**, 437 (1938).

sorption of the first type. A complex having special band absorption of the second type is $[Cr(NH_3)_5NCS]^{++}$. This absorption is present also when more than one isothiocyanato group is present, and the extinction is additive with respect to the number of these groups.

Determinations of the Nature and Stability of Complexes

Complexes In Solution. The spectrophotometric method is especially well suited to the study of complexes not sufficiently stable to permit their isolation from solution. Work of this type has been done by Job[27], who developed the *Method of Continuous Variations*. This method makes use of any measurable additive property of two species in solution, so long as the property has different values for the two species. Any complex formed by the two species must give a value for the same property which is different from the weighted mean of the values for the separate species. The simplest application of the method involves an equilibrium of the type $A + nB \rightleftharpoons AB_n$, where A represents a metal, B a coordinating group, and AB_n a complex. Solutions are prepared in which the mole fractions of the components are varied and the total number of moles of both together is kept constant. Volume changes are usually ignored, unless they are so great that the volume may be used as the additive property. The extinction coefficients of the solutions are measured, using a monochromatic light source. If there is no complexing, the plot of extinction coefficient against mole fraction of one component is a straight line. But if a complex is formed, the plot deviates from linearity, the deviation being a maximum at the mole fraction corresponding to the composition of the complex. When the deviation is plotted against mole fractions, the maximum point gives the desired composition. The conclusion may be verified by repeating the process at other wave lengths, since the position of the maximum is independent of wave length.

A good example of the use of the method is given by a study of complexes of iron(III) with various anions[28]. The data showing formation of a citrate complex are given in Figure 18.1. The dotted lines represent solutions ten times as concentrated as those plotted with solid lines. The single maxima support the conclusion that only one complex is formed.

The Job method has been extended by Vosburgh and his associates[29, 30], particularly to deal with the formation of more than one complex. In working with *o*-phenanthroline complexes of nickel(II), Vosburgh and Cooper[29]

27. Job, *Ann. chim.*, **9**, 113 (1928).
28. Lanford and Quinan, *J. Am. Chem. Soc.*, **70**, 2900 (1948).
29. Vosburgh and Cooper, *J. Am. Chem. Soc.*, **63**, 437 (1941).
30. Gould and Vosburgh, *J. Am. Chem. Soc.*, **64**, 1630 (1942).

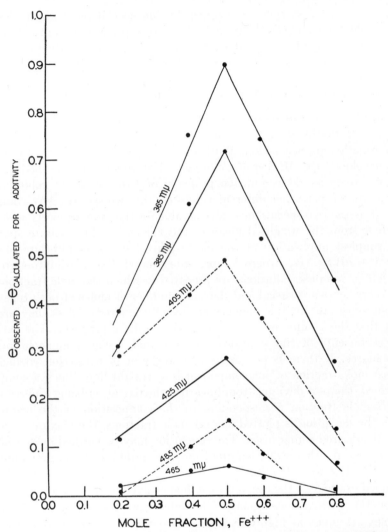

F ɪ ɢ. 18.1. Deviations of extinction coefficients from additivity, iron(III)-citrate solutions.

first determined the optical densities of solutions of the components having mole fractions of nickel ion equal to 0.50, 0.33, and 0.25. A range of wave lengths between 500 and 650 mμ was used. Mathematical analysis shows that if complexes are formed with molar ratios of 1:1, 1:2, and 1:3, determination of the first complex is most conveniently made at a wave length corresponding to nearly equal extinction coefficients of the first two complexes. Similarly, the second is determined by use of a wave length giving nearly equal extinction coefficients for the second and third. For determination of the third complex, its extinction coefficient should be much greater than that of the second, provided no fourth complex is formed. The appropriate wave lengths in each case were found from the optical density curves for the 1:1, 1:2, and 1:3 solutions. It is assumed that formation of the first complex, having a 1:1 ratio, consumes all the free metal ion. Then the linear plot (assuming no reaction) of extinction coefficient against mole fraction is made between pure 1:1 complex and pure complexing agent. Accordingly, Vosburgh and Cooper used light at 620 mμ to establish the existence of [Ni(o-phen)]$^{++}$. This complex was then assumed to be mixed with o-phenanthroline in the solutions of greater concentration of the latter; no uncomplexed nickel was considered to be present. A new linear plot, of a different slope, was next required, and the existence of [Ni(o-phen)$_2$]$^{++}$ was demonstrated with light at 580 mμ. Finally, a wave length of 528 mμ served to determine the [Ni(o-phen)$_3$]$^{++}$ complex with a third linear plot. In each case the deviations from linearity reach a maximum at the composition sought, as in the original method.

The extended method of continuous variations enabled Haendler[31] to show that diethylenetriamine forms copper(II) and nickel(II) complexes containing either one or two amine molecules. This implication of a coordination number of six is supported, in the case of nickel, by Vosburgh[29, 30], who reports the existence of [Ni en]$^{++}$, [Ni en$_2$]$^{++}$, and [Ni en$_3$]$^{++}$. As with the other applications of this method, the presence of water molecules in the coordination sphere is usually not detected. Thus the apparent coordination numbers in [Ni en]$^{++}$ and [Ni(o-phen)]$^{++}$, for example, are not necessarily the true coordination numbers.

Job[27] has shown that when the formula is known for a complex in solution, the equilibrium constant of its formation (or its reciprocal, the dissociation constant) may be found mathematically through a relation between concentration and extinction coefficient. As part of his continuous variations studies, Job found constants for a number of complexes.

Babko[32] has investigated the formation of copper(II) salicylate complexes at various pH values. A plot of extinction coefficient against pH shows sharp breaks at pH 3–5 and pH 7–9, indicating the presence of [Cu(salicylate)] and [Cu(salicylate)$_2$]$^=$, respectively. The same author has studied iron(III) thiocyanate complexes in aqueous solution[33, 34]. Variations in extinction coefficient with thiocyanate concentration give evidence for formation of the complexes [Fe(SCN)$_x$]$^{3-x}$, where x ranges from 1 to 6.

31. Haendler, *J. Am. Chem. Soc.*, **64**, 686–8 (1942).
32. Babko, *J. Gen. Chem.*, *U.S.S.R.*, **17**, 443 (1947).
33. Babko, *J. Gen. Chem.*, *U.S.S.R.*, **16**, 33, 1549 (1946); **15**, 758, 874 (1945).
34. Babko, *Compt. rend. acad. sci.*, *U.R.S.S.*, **52**, 37 (1946).

Studies on decolorization of the thiocyanate complexes by addition of fluoride ion have shown the existence of such equilibria as

$$[Fe(SCN)]^{++} + nF^- \rightleftharpoons [FeF_n]^{3-n} + SCN^-.$$

If the magnitude of the extinction at an absorption peak is proportional to the concentration of the complex giving rise to the absorption, the method of Moore and Anderson[35] is useful in determining the stability of the complex. From the equilibrium

$$m A + n B \rightleftharpoons A_m B_n; \quad K = \frac{[A]^m [B]^n}{[A_m B_n]},$$

whence $\qquad \log [A_m B_n] = m \log [A] + n \log [B] - \log K.$

If [A] is kept constant and [B] is varied, $\log [A_m B_n]$ is a linear function of $\log [B]$. If the logarithm of the optical density, which is proportional to $\log [A_m B_n]$, is plotted against $\log [B]$, the slope of the resulting straight line is the value of n. The value of m may be similarly determined, and the constant K may then be found. In studying the system involving cerium(IV), sulfate, and perchlorate, these authors have concluded from concordant results of the logarithmic and continuous variations methods that no colored complex is formed between cerium and perchlorate ions. In solutions having total ionic concentrations up to $0.01M$ the complex $[CeSO_4]^{++}$ exists. At higher concentrations the complexes $[Ce(SO_4)_2]$ and $[Ce(SO_4)_3]^=$ appear.

Thoms and Gantz[36] noted the effect of various anions on the absorption of iron(III) chloride solutions between 350 and 750 mμ. From the data, the authors ranked the various anions with respect to relative ease of replacement of any one in the series by any other: most stable—CN^-, citrate, $C_2O_4^=$, $C_4H_4O_6^=$, $C_2H_3O_2^-$, $PO_4^{\equiv}$, F^-, SCN^-, $B_4O_7^=$, $SO_4^=$, Cl^-, Br^-, I^-, NO_3^-—least stable. Studies of this type have also been made by Kossiakoff and Sickman[37] on copper(II) nitrite complexes; they concluded that one, two, or three nitrite ions may be attached to copper, but each successive nitrite group is more difficultly added. Bjerrum[38] has studied the chloro complexes of copper(II) and reports that only the complex $[CuCl_4]^=$ is sufficiently stable to produce absorption measurably different from that of the components.

Numerous investigations have been made of the substitution of chloro groups for water molecules in the hexaquocobalt(II) ion. Howell and Jackson[39] observed maxima in the plot of extinction coefficient against

35. Moore and Anderson, *J. Am. Chem. Soc.*, **67**, 168 (1945).
36. Thoms and Gantz, *Proc. Indiana Acad. Sci.*, **56**, 130 (1946).
37. Kossiakoff and Sickman, *J. Am. Chem. Soc.*, **68**, 442 (1946).
38. Bjerrum, *Kgl. Danske Videnskab Selskhb, Math.-fys. Medd.*, **22**, (18), 43 (1946).
39. Howell and Jackson, *J. Chem. Soc.*, 1268 (1936).

mole fraction of added chloride. They propose the equilibria:

$$[Co(H_2O)_6]^{++} + 2Cl^- \rightleftharpoons [Co(H_2O)_4Cl_2] + 2H_2O$$

$$[Co(H_2O)_4Cl_2] + Cl^- \rightleftharpoons [Co(H_2O)_3Cl_3]^- + H_2O$$

Gerendes[40], however, found it possible to identify six separate maxima with increasing chloride concentration, hydrochloric acid acting as the source of chloride. From this evidence Gerendes concluded that complete and stepwise replacement of water by chloride takes place, resulting ultimately in the formation of $[CoCl_6]^{4-}$. Kiss and his co-workers[41, 42] have extended this study to nonaqueous solvents, noting tendencies toward solvent coordination, particularly with pyridine. Kiss has also found that in nonaqueous solvents there are frequent exceptions to the commonly assumed rule that all red cobalt(II) complexes are six-coordinate, and all blue cobalt(II) complexes are four-coordinate.

Spectral methods have been useful in examining possibilities of the formation of unusual oxidation states. Strong spectrometric evidence for the formation of the pentavalent molybdenum complex $[Mo(SCN)_5]$ was found by Babko[43]. A sharp extinction maximum corresponds to the formation of the complex with thiocyanate concentrations in the vicinity of $0.1M$. Greater concentrations lead to the formation of $[Mo(SCN)_6]^-$, whereas dilution produces $[Mo(SCN)_2]^{+++}$ and $[Mo(SCN)]^{4+}$. The possible existence in solution of tin(III) and antimony(IV) species was investigated spectrally by Whitney and Davidson[44], who concluded that no evidence suggests the existence of these states.

Much information concerning the mechanisms of reactions of complexes may be obtained spectrophotometrically. If the absorption spectra of two complexes are known, for example, and one of them may undergo stepwise reaction to form the other, the nature of the intermediate products may frequently be determined. For this purpose it is possible to compare the spectra taken during the reaction with the spectra of known species thought to be logical intermediate products. A second approach involves measuring the total effect of the reaction on the position and intensity of the absorption bands, then using the intermediate spectra as a basis for calculated identification of any transient species formed. Serfass and Theis[45] have shown that sulfato complexes of chromium(III) may undergo successive replacement of sulfato groups by hydroxy groups. This

40. Gerendes, *Magyar Chem. Folyoirat*, **43,** 31 (1937).
41. Kiss, Csokan and Richter, *Acta Univ. Szeged. Sect. Sci. Nat., Acta Chem., Mineral Phys.*, **7,** 119 (1939).
42. Loss and Csokan, *Z. physik. Chem.*, **A186,** 239 (1940).
43. Babko, *J. Gen. Chem., U.S.S.R.*, **17,** 642 (1947).
44. Whitney and Davidson, *J. Am. Chem. Soc.*, **69,** 2076 (1947).
45. Serfass and Theis, *J. Am. Leather Chemists' Assoc.*, **43,** 206 (1948).

replacement may be followed spectrophotometrically by observing the pronounced increase in extinction at 420 mμ, as well as a lesser increase at 580 mμ, caused by the entry of each hydroxy group into the complex. Addition of sulfuric acid reverses the reaction and reduces these maxima.

Uemura and Hirasawa[46] have studied the effect of pH upon ethylenediamine complexes of cobalt. The spectrum of tris(ethylenediamine)cobalt(III) ion shows little variation between pH 1 and pH 10. By comparison with standard curves, however, these authors noted the following changes with bis(ethylenediamine) complexes:

$$cis\text{-}[Co\ en_2\ (H_2O)_2]^{+++} \underset{H^+}{\overset{OH^-}{\rightleftharpoons}} cis\text{-}[Co\ en_2\ (H_2O)\ OH]^{++} \xrightarrow{Cl^-}$$

$$cis\text{-}[Co\ en_2\ (H_2O)\ Cl]^{++} \xrightarrow{H_2O}$$

$$trans\text{-}[Co\ en_2\ (H_2O)_2]^{+++} \xrightarrow{OH^-} trans\text{-}[Co\ en_2\ H_2O\ OH]^{++}.$$

The complexes [Co en$_2$ (H$_2$O)$_2$]$^{+++}$, [Co en$_2$ (H$_2$O) Cl]$^{++}$, and [Co en$_2$ Cl$_2$]$^+$ all were observed to be stable in acid solution; in basic solution they are transformed to [Co en$_2$ (H$_2$O) OH]$^{++}$. It was also noted that the differences in the absorption spectra of the *cis* and *trans* forms of [Co en$_2$ (H$_2$O) NO$_2$]$^{++}$, useful for distinguishing these isomers in acid solution, are lost upon the addition of base.

The three isomeric species [Cr(H$_2$O)$_6$]Cl$_3$, [Cr(H$_2$O)$_5$Cl]Cl$_2$·H$_2$O, and [Cr(H$_2$O)$_4$Cl$_2$]Cl·2H$_2$O were studied by Datar and Quereski[47]. It was found that a transition from the third complex to the first takes place on standing in aqueous solution. Irradiation by ultraviolet light weakens the metal-chlorine bond and increases the rate of aquotization. This is significant in that the frequency range chosen for a spectral investigation may include frequencies which affect the system under study.

Hagenmuller[48] has developed a graphical method for determination of complex dissociation constants from continuous variations data. As in Job's original method, a curve is drawn to show the deviations of a property from the values it would assume if no complex formation took place. Whereas Job's calculations of dissociation constants involve application of the law of mass action, Hagenmuller's method permits direct calculation of the constants from the shape of the deviation curve. The reader is referred to Hagenmuller's discussion for mathematical details. For the equilibrium,

$$Hg(NO_2)_2 + Zn(NO_2)_2 \rightleftharpoons Zn[Hg(NO_2)_4],$$

46. Uemura and Hirasawa, *Bull. Chem. Soc. Japan*, **13**, 379 (1938).
47. Datar and Quereski, *J. Osmania Univ.*, **8**, 6 (1940).
48. Hagenmuller, *Compt. rend.*, **230**, 2190 (1950).

Job's method of calculation of K_d for $Zn[Hg(NO_2)_4]$ yields the value 0.50. The graphical method yields $K_d = 0.56$.

Brigando[49] has carried out a spectrophotometric continuous variations study on solutions of cobalt(II) chloride and histidine. Her data indicate formation of cobalt(III) complexes containing four and six molecules of histidine per cobalt(III) ion. These complexes form slowly, the four-coordinate one forming from 30 to 180 minutes after mixing the cobalt(II) solution with histidine. The six-coordinate complex is present at equilibrium, attained in five hours. Although the complexes form slowly, they are sufficiently stable so that the trivalent cobalt cannot be precipitated by the addition of thiocyanate or hydroxide ions.

A large number of spectral studies of reactions of complexes have been carried on by Basolo and his associates[50, 51]. These studies give special emphasis to the kinetics and mechanisms of reactions. Basolo, Hayes, and Neumann[50] investigated the mechanism of racemization of the optically active ions tris(*o*-phenanthroline)nickel(II) and tris(2,2'-dipyridyl)-nickel(II). The rates of racemization for the two complexes in water solution were compared with the rates of dissociation in acid solution, according to the equations:

$$[Ni\ (o\text{-phen})_3]^{++} \rightarrow [Ni(o\text{-phen})_2]^{++} + o\text{-phen}$$

$$H^+ + o\text{-phen} \rightarrow H\ o\text{-phen}^+.$$

The products of the dissociation show different absorption characteristics from those of the reactants. Measurement of the changes in absorption at 400, 420, 440, and 520 mμ was sufficient to provide quantitative rate data. Mathematical analysis shows that under the same conditions the rates of racemization and dissociation are equal, within experimental error, and that the activation energies for the two processes are equal. It is evident, therefore, that racemization of these complexes takes place by a mechanism of dissociation. This mechanism is to be contrasted with the intramolecular rearrangement process which probably characterizes the racemization of the tris(oxalato)cobalt(III) ion.

Infrared Spectra

Absorption of radiations in the infrared range is attributed to molecular vibrations of the absorbing material. These vibrations comprise motions of the atomic masses in the material about centers of vibration. For pur-

49. Brigando, *Compt. rend.*, **237**, 163 (1953).
50. Basolo, Hayes, and Neumann, *J. Am. Chem. Soc.*, **75**, 5102 (1953).
51. Basolo, Stone and Pearson, *J. Am. Chem. Soc.*, **75**, 819 (1953); Pearson, Boston, and Basolo, *J. Am. Chem. Soc.*, **75**, 3089 (1953); Basolo, Stone, Bergmann, and Pearson, *J. Am. Chem. Soc.*, **76**, 3079 (1954); Basolo, Chen, and Murmann, *J. Am. Chem. Soc.*, **76**, 956 (1954).

poses of description, two atoms which are covalently bound to each other may be thought of as the simplest vibrational system. The two atomic masses represent the bodies which are displaced during vibration, and the strength of the bond corresponds to the restoring force. Thus each such system has a characteristic vibrational frequency depending upon these factors, and it absorbs infrared radiations of the same frequency. In general, only vibrations of an unsymmetrical nature are detected by infrared absorption. Only completely homopolar bonds are thereby excluded, however, and even these must be isolated from any other vibrating systems in order to be free of coupling effects. In actual practice, the molecular vibrations in complex compounds are of such abundance and variety that complete and precise interpretations of spectra are usually impossible. Conclusions of a general nature are feasible with respect to ligand chain length, presence or absence of certain functional groups, multiple bonding, isomerism, free or bound state of a ligand, and degree of molecular symmetry.

Duval and his co-workers[52, 53] have made many valuable contributions to the study of complexes by the use of infrared absorption measurements. In examining a large number of hexacovalent cobalt and chromium ammines, Duval found that nearly all of them absorbed in three principal regions. The first region, quite intense, extends between 800 and 850 cm^{-1} for the cobalt complexes, and appears at about 770 cm^{-1} for the chromium complexes. Duval attributes this absorption to triply degenerate vibration of the complex as a whole, in the case of hexammines, and to doubly degenerate vibration in the case of pentammines. A second prominent region of absorption, near 1300 cm^{-1}, is considered to be due to deformation vibration of the ammine groups. A third region, extending from 1500 to 1600 cm^{-1}, shows variable and generally less intensity. This absorption region results from various molecular effects, depending upon the nature of the complex.

The work of Freymann[54] illustrates the phenomenon of dissimulation. The absorption band characteristic of a trivalent nitrogen atom, bound to at least one hydrogen atom, is found in the spectra of ammonia and amines. If the nitrogen atom forms a coordinate bond, thus becoming quaternary, the band for the trivalent atom weakens or disappears. Thus ammine complexes, as well as ammonium salts, do not show the trivalent absorption. Freymann's measurements of a number of ammines of copper, cobalt, platinum, silver, and rhodium show the consistent dissimulation of the trivalent band in the spectra of these complexes.

52. Duval, Duval and Lecomte, *Bull. soc. chim. France*, 1048 (1947).
53. Duval, Duval and Lecomte, *Compt. rend.*, **224**, 1632 (1947).
54. Freymann, Freymann and Rumpf, *J. phys. radium*, **7**, 30 (1936); Freymann, *Ann. chim.*, **11**, 40 (1939); Freymann and Mathieu, *Bull. soc. chim.*, (5) **4**, 1297 (1937); Freymann and Freymann, *Proc. Indian Acad. Sci.*, **8A**, 301 (1938).

Duval, Freymann, and Lecomte[55] have measured the infrared absorption of powdered acetylacetone derivatives of beryllium, magnesium, aluminum, scandium, samarium, chromium, iron(III), cobalt(II), cobalt(III), copper(II), and zinc. Whereas in acetylacetone itself both the keto and enol structures are evident from infrared absorption, with the metal salts only the enol form of the ligand could be detected. The C=O group, which normally absorbs in the range 1710 to 1730 cm^{-1}, is evidently modified through chelation so that a large degree of single-bond character results, and a shift of electron density toward the metal strengthens the coordinate structure.

Infrared evidence was used by Busch and Bailar[56] to confirm the existence of a cobalt(III) complex containing ethylenediaminetetraacetic acid (EDTA) as a hexadentate ligand. The free acid shows a maximum of absorption at 1697 cm^{-1}, attributable to the carbonyl structure in the four carboxyl groups, which are normally associated through hydrogen bonding. The complexes Na[Co(EDTA)Br] and Na[Co(EDTA)NO$_2$], in which EDTA is pentadentate, were found to exhibit two carboxyl absorptions each, at 1635 and 1740 cm^{-1} for the nitro complex, and 1628 and 1723 cm^{-1} for the bromo complex. The lower-frequency absorptions may be ascribed to the three complexed carboxyl groups, while the single free group is responsible for the somewhat weaker higher-frequency bands. The barium salt of the bromo complex was ground with silver oxide to remove the bromine and induce the free carboxyl group to coordinate. The resulting hexadentate complex shows only one carbonyl absorption band, at 1638 cm^{-1}, which may be assigned to the four equivalent coordinated carboxyl groups.

A frequent problem in infrared absorption studies is the choice of a suitable solvent. Since solvent molecular vibrations, particularly those arising from hydrogen bonding, may interfere with the absorption of the substance studied, samples are frequently suspended or emulsified in a medium such as Nujol. A significant development in the technique of sample preparation is the solid disk method of Stimson and O'Donnell[57]. If a solid complex compound is finely ground, mixed intimately with potassium bromide in the same state, and subjected to a high mechanical pressure, a transparent solid mass results. This solid may be quite conveniently handled and examined spectrophotometrically.

The solid disk technique has been used to advantage by Quagliano and his co-workers. Faust and Quagliano[58] report that the *cis* and *trans* forms of dinitrotetramminecobalt(III) chloride, examined as solid disks, show different infrared absorptions. The *cis* isomer shows a greater multiplicity

55. Duval, Freymann, and Lecomte, *Bull. soc. chim. France*, **1952**, 106.
56. Busch and Bailar, *J. Am. Chem. Soc.*, **75**, 4574 (1953).
57. Stimson and O'Donnell, *J. Am. Chem. Soc.*, **74**, 1805 (1952).
58. Faust and Quagliano, *J. Am. Chem. Soc.*, **76**, 5346 (1954).

of absorption peaks than does the *trans* isomer. This result is concordant with the antisymmetric nature of infrared absorption, inasmuch as the *cis* isomer has a lesser degree of symmetry.

Mizushima, Sen, Curran, and Quagliano[59] have measured the infrared absorption characteristics of the glycine complexes of copper, nickel, and cobalt. The free carboxyl group in glycine hydrochloride absorbs strongly at 5.85μ, whereas the carboxylate group in potassium glycinate absorbs strongly at 6.35μ. The copper, nickel, and cobalt glycinates absorb strongly in the 6.3–6.5μ region, but not at all at 5.9μ. The resonance of the negative carboxylate is evidently preserved in the complexes, with the metal-oxygen bond being virtually completely electrostatic. On the other hand, the nitrogen band in potassium glycinate found at $3.1\ \mu$, is shifted in the copper, nickel, and cobalt complexes; copper glycinate absorbs at $3.22\ \mu$, and cobalt and nickel glycinates at $3.30\ \mu$. Evidently the metal-nitrogen bonds in these complexes are primarily covalent.

Infrared evidence for symmetrical platinum-olefin coordinate bonds has been presented by Chatt (p. 504).

Raman Spectra

The emission spectra resulting from the Raman effect are attributable to molecular vibrations which are symmetrical in nature. Raman spectra thus complement infrared spectra as means of studying molecular structures. Because of the complexity of most molecules studied by the Raman technique, many symmetric effects arise from coupling of simpler individual vibrating systems. Usually, therefore, both the Raman and infrared methods yield significant data concerning molecular structures, and these data in some cases overlap. Frequently it is necessary to use crystallographic methods in order to choose among several structures, each of which is compatible with Raman measurements.

The Raman effect is produced when a molecule is irradiated with a beam of monochromatic light of wave length greater than the size of the molecule. The radiation undergoes interaction with the molecule, loses some of its energy, and then scatters. The wave length of the scattered light is greater than that of the incident light unless the molecule is in an excited state. The scattered light may be passed through a spectrometer and received on a photographic plate. The spectrum on the plate contains a strong central line corresponding to the incident beam, and removed at various distances are the less intense Raman lines. The differences in energy result from a distribution of frequencies among the various degrees of freedom of the molecule.

59. Mizushima, Sen, Curran, and Quagliano, *Abstracts of Papers*, Am. Chem. Soc., 124th Meeting. Sept. 6–11, 1953, 43R; *J. Am. Chem. Soc.*, **77,** 211 (1955).

Frequency shifts of Raman lines from the frequency of the principal line are the quantities of significance in use of the method. The numerical values of these shifts are in the same range as the frequencies of infrared absorption. If a molecular vibrational system is characterized by symmetric and antisymmetric vibrations of equal energies, its Raman spectrum shows a shift equal in magnitude to the corresponding absorption frequency in the infrared spectrum. The mathematical theory of the Raman effect shows that any Raman emission may be completely described by measurement of its frequency shift, its intensity, and a third coordinate, called degree of depolarization.

Krishnamurti[60] used the Raman method to study the formation of chloro complexes of mercury. A strong Raman line (frequency shift $= \Delta \tilde{\nu} = 269$ cm^{-1}) is observable with solutions of mercury(II) chloride and ammonium chloride in a 1:2 molar ratio. This line compares with the strong line ($\Delta \tilde{\nu} = 273$ cm^{-1}) for solid ammonium tetrachloromercurate(II) and indicates the formation of the ion $[HgCl_4]^=$ in solution. Solutions containing varying ratios of mercury(II) bromide and alkali bromide show Raman shifts ascribed to the formation of $[HgBr_3]^-$ and $[HgBr_4]^=$. Both complexes have been depicted as tetrahedral structures by Delwaulle[61]. The mercury ion occupies a central position in $[HgBr_4]^=$ and a vertex in $[HgBr_3]^-$.

An extensive investigation of the structures of complexes has been carried out by Mathieu and Cornevin[62]. These authors measured the Raman spectra for many complexes. It was found that complexes of different metals which have similar structures and bond types yield similar Raman lines. The authors classified the observed frequency shifts into two general groups— those arising from metal-ligand bonds, and those arising from the vibrations of the coordinated groups themselves. The second class of shifts contains those characteristic of uncoordinated ligands, as well as those appearing only on coordination.

A number of applications of the Raman method have been made in the study of metal complexes of unsaturated hydrocarbons. Nesmeyanov[63] has reported data for the compound ClCHCH·HgCl, proposing both the structures [Hg(ClCH=CH)Cl] and [Hg(CH≡CH)Cl]Cl. Taufen and his co-workers[64] have suggested that complex formation between unsaturated hydrocarbons and silver(I), copper(I), mercury(II), and platinum(II) ions accounts for the marked alterations in the Raman spectra of the hydrocarbons when these metal ions are present. The hydrocarbons used by

60. Krishnamurti, *Indian J. Physics*, **6,** 7 (1931).
61. Delwaulle, Francois, and Wiemann, *Compt. rend.*, **206,** 1108 (1938); **207,** 340 (1938).
62. Mathieu and Cornevin, *J. chim. phys.*, **36,** 271 (1939).
63. Nesmeyanov, *Bull. acad. sci.*, *U.R.S.S.*, *Classe Sci. chim.*, 239 (1945).
64. Taufen, Murray, and Cleveland, *J. Am. Chem. Soc.*, **63,** 3500 (1941).

Taufen with silver(I) ion were cis-2-butene, trans-2-butene, cyclopentene, cyclohexene, ethylacetylene, propylacetylene, and phenylacetylene. The presence of the metal ion lowers the strong olefinic frequency shift by 65 cm^{-1} and the acetylenic shift by 100 cm^{-1}.

It has been found by Mathieu[65] that Raman spectra provide no positive differentiation between square and octahedral configurations of the platinum and rhodium ammines. Spacu[66] has reported different Raman spectra for the cis and trans isomers of [Pt(NH$_3$)$_2$ py$_2$]Cl$_2$, but identical spectra for the isomers of [Pt py$_2$ Cl$_2$] and [Co en$_2$ (NO$_2$)$_2$]NO$_3$. It seems reasonable, in view of the differences of degree of symmetry of these cis-trans isomers, that differences in the spectra actually exist, although the distinguishing lines may be so weak that they have escaped detection.

Venkateswaran[67] used Raman data to study the symmetry of a number of complexes of the type [MO$_n$], as well as the azide ion. Telluric acid was found to be octahedrally symmetrical in agreement with the formula H$_6$[TeO$_6$]. Tetrahedral structures were confirmed for CrO$_4^=$, MoO$_4^=$, WO$_4^=$, and IO$_4^-$, pyramidal structures for ClO$_3^-$ and BrO$_3^-$, and a linear structure for N$_3^-$. Raman spectra of solid NaReO$_4$ and KReO$_4$, studied by Fonteyne[68], show a distorted tetrahedral arrangement, changing in water solution to the octahedral [ReO$_6$]$^{5-}$ complex.

The infrared spectral studies of Crawford and Cross, and the Raman spectral studies of Crawford and Horiwitz, each of which supports the postulated tetrahedral structure of nickel tetracarbonyl, have been cited in Chapter 16 (p. 519).

OPTICAL METHODS

Polarimetry

The ability of a substance to rotate a beam of plane polarized light is a function of molecular or crystalline asymmetry. Optical activity of coordination compounds is almost exclusively due to molecular asymmetry which persists in solution.

Rotation of polarized light is detected and measured with the polarimeter. Solutions of varying concentrations may constitute the sample. Greater concentrations produce a larger observed rotation, but in many cases the intense colors of the solutions prevent sufficient transmission of the polarized beam unless very strong light sources or solutions of low concentration are used. A substance whose solution rotates polarized light in a clockwise direction is said to be dextrorotatory, and one giving counterclockwise

65. Mathieu, Compt. rend., 204, 682 (1937).
66. Spacu, Bull. soc. chim. (5) 4, 364 (1937).
67. Venkateswaran, Proc. Indian Acad. Sci., 7A, 144 (1938).
68. Fonteyne, Natuurw. Tijdschr., 20, 20 (1938); 20, 112 (1938).

rotation is called levorotatory. The two optical isomers of the complex are referred to as the d and l forms according to the sign of rotation. Dextrorotation is assigned a plus value.

It should be emphasized that the sign of rotation cannot be used to find absolute configurations of complex substances. Different species with the same sign of rotation may have the same or opposite configurations; indeed, the sign and degree of rotation of any given complex usually vary with the wave length of the light source. This variation is often of much greater use in elucidating structures than are isolated rotational measurements at single wave lengths.

An important polarization phenomenon in structural studies of complexes is the Cotton effect[69, 70]. A normal rotatory dispersion curve, or plot of magnitude of rotation against wave length of incident light, is hyperbolic in form. The Cotton effect is evidenced by an abnormality in rotation in the vicinity of maximum light absorption of the complex. This abnormality is generally characterized by a maximum of rotation, a sharp decrease to zero rotation, and an increase in rotation of the opposite sign. All these variations take place with a small change in wave length[71]. Mellor[72] has reported a relationship between the Cotton effect and the magnetic moments of several nickel, copper, and cobalt chelates. The effect evidently is found only among complexes of the covalent type. Pfeiffer[73] attributes the Cotton effect in certain heavy metal tetracovalent complexes to the chromophoric nature of the central metal atom. Mathieu[74] states that the presence of asymmetric carbon atoms in ligands produces a Cotton effect by vicinal influence, but Pfeiffer's work shows no evidence of such influence, so long as the dispersion curves of the ligands are normal. A variation in vicinal influence with bond lengths may well account for this difference.

The effect of asymmetric molecules, not necessarily coordinated, in producing anomalous rotations in solutions of complexes is termed asymmetric induction. Pfeiffer and Quehl[75] noted that the optical rotation of zinc d-α-camphor-β-sulfonate is reduced nearly to zero upon addition of three moles of *ortho*-phenanthroline per mole of zinc. Likewise, the specific rotation of zinc d-α-bromocamphor-π-sulfonate is 4.55°, but that of tris (*o*-phenanthroline)zinc d-α-bromocamphor-π-sulfonate is 8.44°. Active cat-

69. Jaeger, "Optical Activity and High Temperature Measurements," New York, McGraw-Hill Book Co., 1930.
70. Cotton, *Ann. chim. phys.*, **8**, 347 (1896).
71. Bruhat, *Bull. soc. chim.*, **17**, 223 (1915).
72. Mellor, *J. Proc. Roy. Soc. N. S. Wales*, **75**, 157 (1942).
73. Pfeiffer, Christeleit, Hesse, Pfitzner, and Thielert, *J. Prakt. Chem.*, **150**, 261 (1938).
74. Mathieu, *Ann. phys.*, **19**, 335 (1944).
75. Pfeiffer and Quehl, *Ber.*, **64B**, 2667 (1931); **65B**, 560 (1932).

ions do not exercise the inductive effect in these instances. The findings of Pfeiffer and Quehl have been confirmed by Brasted[76]. Biswas[77] has observed a similar effect of *d*-tartaric acid in molybdic acid solutions. Dwyer[78] has done extensive work with this effect, using racemic complexes whose active forms are optically stable, as well as those having optically labile active forms. Addition of an asymmetric substance such as bromocamphorsul-fonate to a racemic complex appears to affect the rotatory powers of the *d* and *l* forms of the complex by different amounts, thus producing a net rotation different from zero. Another change consists of a shift in the equilibrium of the isomers away from the normal 1:1 ratio. This second change may be immediate or slow, and it further affects the observed rotation. These effects Dwyer attributes to alterations of the thermodynamic activities of the isomers in the presence of the asymmetric substance.

Determinations of structure from polarimetric data usually involve analysis of rotatory dispersion curves. Mathieu[79] has shown that if two complexes of analogous composition yield curves characterized by the Cotton effect, those portions of the curve displaying the effect will have slopes of the same sign if the complexes have the same configuration. If the configurations are opposite, the slopes of the dispersion curves will have opposite signs in the area of the Cotton effect.

An empirical rule of Werner[80] states that optically active ions of the same configuration, when crystallized with the same optically active substance (e.g., *d*-tartrate), will have analogous solubilities, either both less or both greater than the compounds of their respective antipodes. This rule has been applied by Jaeger[81] in his investigation of diamine complexes of cobalt, rhodium, and chromium. Delepine[82] has noted that the active isomers of certain complexes may crystallize in forms which are different from those of the racemic crystal of the same complex. The crystals of complexes of the same chemical type, containing different metals, sometimes show the same differences in crystal form between active crystals and racemic crystals. In such cases the active forms of the complex of the one metal are generally isomorphous with the active forms containing the other metal. Similarly, the racemic crystals are isomorphous with each other. But a crystal may also be formed by the *d* isomer containing the first metal,

76. Brasted, Thesis, University of Illinois, 1942.
77. Biswas, *J. Indian Chemical Soc.*, **22**, 351 (1945).
78. Dwyer and Gyarfas, *J. Proc. Roy. Soc. N. S. Wales*, **83**, 170 (1949); Dwyer, Gyarfas, and O'Dwyer, *Nature*, **167**, 1036 (1951).
79. Mathieu, *J. chim. phys.*, **33**, 78 (1936); *Bull. soc. chim.*, [5], **4**, 687 (1937).
80. Werner, *Ber.*, **45**, 121, 1228 (1912).
81. Jaeger, *Proc. Acad. Sci. Amsterdam*, **40**, 2 (1937); Jaeger and Bijkerk, *Proc. Acad. Sci. Amsterdam*, **40**, 116 (1937).
82. Delepine, *Bull. soc. chim.*, [4], **29**, 656 (1921); [5], **1**, 1256 (1934).

and the l isomer containing the second metal. This crystal has the habit of the racemates, but it is optically active, since the two metals do not in general form analogous complexes with exactly the same rotational values. Such crystals are termed "active racemates" by Delepine. If one of the constituents of the active racemate has a known configuration, the other may be considered to have the opposite configuration. This method of determining relative configurations is clearly limited, since only complexes of similar size and chemical type are isomorphous.

Polarimetric observations enabled Dwyer[83] to verify his asymmetric synthesis of an iron(III) cationic complex, the first such preparation to be reported. By oxidizing one of the isomers of tris(dipyridyl)iron(II) perchlorate with cerium(IV) ammonium nitrate solution, then adding sodium perchlorate in excess, Dwyer was able to precipitate blue crystals of optically active $[Fe(dipy)_3](ClO_4)_3 \cdot 3H_2O$.

Refractometry

Refractometric measurements of solutions may be used in applying the continuous variations method of Job. The work of Spacu and Popper[84] is outstanding in this field. These authors have reported refractometric evidence for existence of acetato, tartrato, and citrato complexes of aluminum, as well as such complexes as $[HgCl_3]^-$, $[HgCl_5]^\equiv$, $[CdBr_5]^\equiv$, $[BaCl_4]^\equiv$, and numerous others. Refraction data have also led Spacu and Popper to assign the nitrile structure to potassium cyanide, potassium thiocyanate, and potassium selenocyanate. Criticism of the broad conclusions of Spacu and Popper has been advanced by Haldar[85], Tahvonen[86], and Grinberg[87], who dispute the original authors' use of additive refraction values for certain functional groups. While the contributions of constituent groups in a molecule to the molecular refraction are roughly additive, care must be exercised in drawing highly specific conclusions from refraction data.

The nature of complex ions in highly concentrated solutions of the metal ion and ligand (as cadmium ion and cyanide ion) have been examined by Brasted. A plot of direct dipping refractometer readings $vs.$ mole fraction of metal ion shows a maximum at the point of stable complex ion formation. The sharpness of this peak is indicative of the stability of the complex. Addition of cyanide ion solution to cadmium ion solution (both at $2M$ concentration) indicates by the sharp maximum the species $[Cd(CN)_4]^\equiv$.

83. Dwyer and Gyarfas, *J. Am. Chem. Soc.*, **74**, 4699 (1952).
84. Spacu and Popper, *Bull. soc. stiinte Cluj*, **8**, 5 (1934); **7**, 400 (1934); *Kolloid Z.*, **103**, 19 (1943); *Z. physik. Chem.*, **A180**, 154 (1937); **A182**, 389 (1938).
85. Haldar, *J. Indian Chem. Soc.*, **23**, 205 (1946).
86. Tahvonen, *Ann. Acad. Sci. Tennicae*, **A49**, No. 6, No. 7 (1938).
87. Grinberg, *Zhur. Priklad. Khim.*, **21**, 425 (1948).

At such high concentrations optical or spectrographic methods would not in general be applicable.

ELECTROMETRIC METHODS

Polarography*

The polarograph received wide use in analytical chemistry immediately following its invention by Heyrovsky and Shikata[88] in 1925, but not until ten years later did its usefulness in coordination chemistry become significant. Among the important quantitative data obtainable by polarographic means are dissociation constants of complexes, coordination numbers of metal ions, and the degree of stabilization of various oxidation states.

Polarographic studies are carried out with an apparatus which combines an electrolytic cell with a recording device. The usual cell is composed of a dropping mercury cathode, a mercury pool anode, and a solution containing a known concentration of the substance to be studied and an indifferent, or supporting, electrolyte. The recording device plots current as ordinate against a continuously increasing potential as abscissa. Direct current sources are usual, although alternating current has been used to advantage. A typical analysis may involve the reduction of a complex cation in solution. As the electrolysis begins, the potential is chosen less than the reduction potential of the species in solution. The current flowing through the cell is small. So long as the cell potential is less than the reduction potential of the complex ion, this current remains practically constant. The recording device traces a nearly horizontal line. Since the growth and fall of each mercury drop causes a slight oscillation in the current value, the actual plot is a composite of many waves of small amplitude, tracing the over-all horizontal line. When the reduction potential (decomposition potential) is reached, a sharp rise in the current occurs with reduction, usually to the metallic state, with amalgamation of the previously complexed metal with the cathode. Mercury ionizes correspondingly at the anode. The current continues to increase with increasing potential, but a limiting value is reached in unagitated systems. As electrolysis proceeds, the concentration of reducible material falls in the immediate vicinity of the cathode. Then more reducible material diffuses from the body of the solution to the cathode. The rate of diffusion depends upon the concentration gradient between the solution proper and the reducing area near the surface of the cathode. The potential eventually reaches a value corresponding to a negligible concentration next to the cathode, the substance being reduced virtually instantly upon diffusion. Then the rate of diffusion becomes constant and essentially

---

* The presentation of much of the material in this section was suggested by Dr. H. F. Holtzclaw of the University of Nebraska.

88. Heyrovsky and Shikata, *Rec. trav. chim.*, **44**, 496 (1925).

independent of further potential increase, but dependent on the concentration of reducible substance in the solution proper. The current assumes the limiting value under these conditions, and the current and rate of diffusion may be seen to be proportional to the concentration of reducible substance. Strictly considered, the migration of ions also contributes to the limiting current, but in the presence of a comparatively large amount of indifferent electrolyte, the limiting current is due nearly entirely to diffusion; it is therefore known as the diffusion current (i_d).

When the current has reached a value one-half that of the limiting current, the corresponding potential is the half-wave potential ($E_{\frac{1}{2}}$). This potential is the characteristic value sought for the substance under study, and it is independent of concentration and type of electrode. If several substances are present and electroactive, each may be determined, provided no two half-wave potentials are closer than 0.2 volts. The total range of the dropping mercury electrode is taken as +0.6 volts to −2.6 volts against the standard calomel electrode. In most solutions the full range is not realizable. The substance to be studied must be in true solution and must be resistant to oxidation, reduction, and decomposition from outside sources. Cations and anions, oxidizable and reducible materials, and simple and complex ions may be studied by appropriate applications of the polarographic method.

A number of factors may affect the electrolysis and alter the recorded curve. In this discussion the most important factor is the presence of complexes. Normally a complexed ion resists the electrolytic reduction more than the corresponding uncomplexed ion, and the half-wave potential is more negative for the complex. The pH of the solution may affect the half-wave potential either by altering the nature of complexes or by varying the products of the electrolysis. In the presence of agar, gelatin, or other capillary-active substances, undesirable maxima in curves may often be avoided; however, these materials may alter the diffusive properties of the ions present, thus affecting the diffusion current. Supporting electrolytes which supply coordinating groups may deter the decomposition of complex ions and thus bring about a more negative half-wave potential.

The polarographic method is unique among electrometric methods in that only a small fraction of the solution is electrolyzed. A further advantage is that quite small concentrations of the material to be studied are sufficient. Among the favorable features of the dropping mercury electrode are its smooth, reproducible, and renewable surface; ready ascertainment of the surface area of the drops; the ability of nearly all metals to amalgamate with mercury; and the high overvoltage for hydrogen liberation on mercury, so that electrolysis of hydrogen ions is minimized.

A thorough treatment of the methods of polarography is given by Kolthoff and Lingane[89]. Pertinent discussions of the theory and application of polarography are noted in references 89 and 90. In the following treatment of applications, no effort has been made to derive mathematical relations.

For convenience Heyrovsky and Ilkovic[91] separate the reduction of a metal complex into two reactions,

$$MXp^{(n-pb)} \rightleftharpoons M^{n+} + pX^{b-}, \tag{I}$$

$$M^{n+} + ne^- + Hg \rightleftharpoons M(Hg), \tag{II}$$

where X is the complexing agent and M(Hg) symbolizes the amalgam formed on the surface of the electrode. These reactions may or may not actually occur as written, but they serve as convenient references. The dissociation constant of the complex is given by

$$K_c = \frac{[M^{n+}][X^{b-}]^p}{[MXp^{(n-pb)}]}. \tag{III}$$

This constant may be calculated from the negative shift of the half-wave potential upon complexing, as indicated by

$$(E_{\frac{1}{2}})_c - (E_{\frac{1}{2}})_s \cong \frac{RT}{nF} \ln K_c - p \frac{RT}{nF} \ln [X^{b-}] \tag{IV}$$

In this formula the subscripts c and s refer to the complex and simple (hydrated) ion, respectively. Thus the difference between the half-wave potentials leads to the determination of K_c, provided that p, the coordination number of the metal, is known. The following formula is useful in determining p from half-wave measurements at different concentrations of complexing agent.

$$\frac{\Delta E_{\frac{1}{2}}}{\Delta \ln [X^{b-}]\gamma_x} = - p \frac{RT}{nF} \tag{V}$$

Usually assumption of the value of unity for the activity coefficient γ_x yields sufficient accuracy.

Kolthoff and Lingane[90d] point out that Equation (IV) is not a good approximation when the rates of diffusion of the simple and complex ions are appreciably different. In such cases the ratio of the diffusion coefficients enters the calculation. Sometimes a state of equilibrium is not rapidly reached, and the calculations suffer further losses in accuracy. Pines[92],

89. Kolthoff and Lingane, "Polarography," New York, Interscience Publishers, Inc., (1946).
90. Muller, *J. Chem. Ed.*, **18**, 65, 320 (1941); Page, *Nature*, **154**, 199 (1944); Quagliano, thesis, University of Illinois, 1946; Kolthoff and Lingane, *Chem. Rev.*, **24**, 1 (1939).
91. Heyrovsky and Ilkovic, *Collection Czechoslov. Chem. Commun.*, **7**, 198 (1935).
92. Pines, *Collection Czechoslov. Chem. Commun.*, **1**, 387 (1929).
    Pines, *Chem. News*, **139**, 196 (1929).

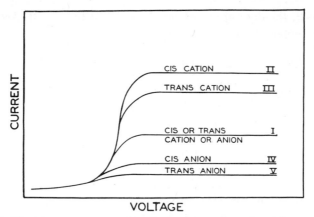

FIG. 18.2. Limiting currents and cis-trans isomerism. I: with supporting electrolyte-diffusion current only. II, III, IV, V: Without supporting electrolyte-diffusion and migration currents.

Brocket and Petit[93], Foerster[94] and Herman[95] report delayed equilibria caused by slow dissociation of cyano complexes of zinc and gold. Another nonideality factor is found with stable complexes which reduce directly without the dissociation suggested by Equation (I). If the metal is well shielded by the complexing groups, its capture of electrons from the cathode may be hindered. The extra potential required for reduction leads to error in the calculated value of the constant K_c .

Normally an excess of indifferent electrolyte suppresses any migration current of reducible ions. In the absence of an indifferent electrolyte, however, the limiting current is made up of both diffusion and migration currents. This fact is useful in differentiating between cis and trans forms of complexes of the type $[MA_4B_2]^{n\pm}$. Both forms of the complex migrate in the same direction, but the greater rate of migration is shown by the cis form, which has a dipole moment different from zero. An orientation attraction to the electrode causes the cis form to produce a higher limiting current than the trans form of both cationic and anionic complexes. The limiting current for either form of an anionic complex is less than the diffusion current because of cathodic repulsion (see Fig. 18.2[95]).

Lingane's investigation of the biplumbite ion[96] furnishes a good example of polarographic analysis. The object of the study was to determine the number of hydroxyl groups coordinated to lead in the biplumbite complex. Various concentrations of hydroxide ion were used, and the half-wave potential corresponding to each was taken. With the value of n in Equation

93. Brochet and Petit, *Z. Elektrochem.*, **10**, 909 (1904).
94. Foerster, *Z. Elektrochem.*, **13**, 561 (1907).
95. Herman, *Collection Czechoslov. Chem. Commun.*, **6**, 37 (1934).
96. Lingane, *Chem. Rev.*, **29, 1** (1941).

(V) taken as 2, the data are most nearly satisfied by $p = 3$. Accordingly, Lingane has proposed the following equilibria:

$$Pb^{++} + 3OH^- \rightleftharpoons [H_3PbO_3]^- \underset{+H_2O}{\overset{-H_2O}{\rightleftharpoons}} [HPbO_2]^-$$

The soluble form of lead(II) in basic solution is then evidently $[HPbO_2]^-$ rather than $[PbO_2]^=$, which would be in equilibrium with the four-coordinate ion $[H_4PbO_4]^=$. Malyugina and his co-workers[97] have found a coordination number of four for lead(II) and mercury(II) in the presence of iodide ion. The dissociation constants for $[PbI_4]^=$ and $[HgI_4]^=$ are given as 10^{-7} and 10^{-27}, respectively.

A reduction to a lower oxidation state but not to the metal takes place with the tris(oxalato)iron(III) ion. Stackelberg and Freyhold[98] conclude that the iron(II) complex $[Fe(C_2O_4)_2]^=$ forms with concentrations of oxalate less than $0.15M$ in $0.001M$ iron(II) ion solution. With greater concentrations of oxalate, the complex formed is $[Fe(C_2O_4)_3]^{4-}$. Toropova[99] confirms the existence of $[Fe(C_2O_4)_2]^=$ and gives dissociation constants for it and for $[Fe(C_2O_4)_3]^=$. This reduction of complexed iron(III) to one of two complex iron(II) species has also been studied by Lingane[100] and by Schaap, Laitinen, and Bailar[101]. Their findings agree substantially with those of Toropova, and of Stackelberg and Freyhold, the most notable differences being in the values found for the dissociation constants, summarized below.

Reaction	K_d, found by		
	Lingane	Schaap	Toropova
$[Fe^{II} (C_2O_4)_2]^- \rightleftharpoons Fe^{++} + 2C_2O_4^=$	8×10^{-6}	2.7×10^{-5}	2.7×10^{-10}
$[Fe^{II} (C_2O_4)_3]^{4-} \rightleftharpoons Fe^{++} + 3C_2O_4^=$	6.1×10^{-7}	6.1×10^{-6}	—
$[Fe^{III} (C_2O_4)_3]^= \rightleftharpoons Fe^{+++} + 3C_2O_4^=$	6×10^{-20}	1.0×10^{-18}	1.2×10^{-24}

The tendency of polymetaphosphates to form complexes has been studied polarographically by Caglioti and his co-workers[102]. Copper(II) and cadmium(II) ions do not form such complexes under the conditions which they used, while zinc(II), manganese(II), and lead(II) form unstable complexes, and iron(II) forms a stable complex.

Harris and Kolthoff[103] have presented data which support the following

97. Malyugina, Shchemukova, and Korshunov, *J. Gen. Chem.*, *U.S.S.R.*, **16**, 1573 (1946).
98. Stackelberg and Freyhold, *Z. Elektrochem.*, **46**, 120 (1940).
99. Toropova, *J. Gen. Chem.*, *U.S.S.R.*, **11**, 1211 (1941).
100. Lingane, *J. Am. Chem. Soc.*, **68**, 2448 (1946).
101. Schaap, Laitinen, and Bailar, *J. Am. Chem. Soc.*, **76**, 5868 (1954).
102. Caglioti, Sartori, and Bianchi, *Gazz. chim. ital.*, **72**, 63 (1942).
103. Harris and Kolthoff, *J. Am. Chem. Soc.*, **67**, 1484 (1945).

reaction of the uranyl ion in 0.01 to $0.2M$ hydrochloric acid

$$UO_2^{++} + e^- \rightleftharpoons UO_2^+.$$

This reaction suggests that uranium(V) compounds may be preparable in acid solution. The compound UCl_5 is known, but its water solution contains only uranium(VI) and uranium(II).

From studies of cyano and thiocyanato complexes of rhodium, Willis[104] concludes that complexes of rhodium(III) reduce first to those of rhodium(II) and then to the metal. There is some experimental evidence for the intermediate formation of rhodium(I), but Willis considers its existence questionable. A stability series for the cyano complexes of the Group VIII metals has been drawn up by Willis. Relative shifts in half-wave potentials indicate that if the metals are arranged in the usual periodic order, stability of the cyano complexes increases downward in each column.

More stable ↓	Fe(II), Fe(III) Ru(II) Os(II)	Co(III) Rh(III) Ir(III)	Ni(II) Pd(II) Pt(II)	↑ Less stable

Wheelwright, Spedding, and Schwarzenbach[105] have found the polarographic method useful in determining formation constants of the heavier rare earth complexes of ethylenediaminetetraacetic acid (EDTA). Measurements were made of solutions containing the complexing agent and both copper(II) and a rare earth metal ion, in order to determine the amount of free copper(II) ion present. These data, the original composition of the solutions, and the known dissociation constants of the ligand and its copper complex are sufficient for the calculation of the formation constant K_f in the expression

$$RE^{+++} + EDTA^{4-} \rightleftharpoons [RE\ EDTA]^-; \qquad K_f = \frac{[RE\ EDTA^-]}{[RE^{+++}][EDTA^{4-}]}.$$

All experimental work was done at constant temperature and ionic strength. A potentiometric method was employed as a check and found to be somewhat more precise for the lighter rare earths. Comparative values for the formation constants are listed below.

Metal complex	K_f (polarographic)	K_f (potentiometric)
[Ce EDTA]⁻	15.6 ± 0.4	15.39 ± 0.06
[Gd EDTA]⁻	16.6 ± 0.15	16.70 ± 0.08
[Lu EDTA]⁻	19.65 ± 0.12	19.06 ± 0.4

Frank and Hume[106] have studied the formation of thiocyanate complexes

104. Willis, *J. Am. Chem. Soc.*, **66**, 1067 (1944).
105. Wheelwright, Spedding, and Schwarzenbach, *J. Am. Chem. Soc.*, **75**, 4196 (1953).
106. Frank and Hume, *J. Am. Chem. Soc.*, **75**, 1736 (1953).

of zinc in solutions containing zinc salts, potassium thiocyanate, and potassium nitrate. Half-wave potentials of the zinc ion indicate the formation of complexes containing up to four thiocyanate groups per zinc ion. The zinc complexes have been shown to be much less stable than their cadmium analogs, but the gradations of stability within each series are quite similar.

A polarographic distinction between *cis* and *trans* forms of complexes containing two negative groups has been reported by Holtzclaw and Sheetz[107]. In the presence of potassium chloride as a supporting electrolyte, the *cis* form reduces at a more positive potential than the *trans* form for the complexes $[Co(NH_3)_4(NO_2)_2]^+$, $[Co\ en_2\ (NO_2)_2]^+$, and $[Co\ en_2\ (NCS)\ NO_2]^+$. The ions $[Co\ en_2\ (NH_3)NO_2]^{++}$, $[Co\ en_2\ (NH_3)NCS]^{++}$, and $[Co\ en_2\ (NH_3)_2]^{+++}$, which contain one or no negative groups, do not exhibit this difference.

Electrometric Titrations; Electromotive Force Measurements

Electrometric titrations are generally classified into three groups: potentiometric, conductometric, and amperometric. Potentiometric titrations are characterized by changes in the potential of an electrode in the solution which is being examined. Potentials are referred to some standard electrode system. As a titration proceeds, a change in concentration of the species studied will be reflected in a change in electrode potential, with the equivalence point corresponding usually to an abrupt potential shift. The measurement of pH by electrode methods is a special application of potentiometric theory. A hydrogen electrode serves as the classical electrode for pH measurements, since its potential variations are directly related to changes in hydrogen-ion activity. Other electrodes, such as the quinhydrone electrode and the glass electrode, are often more convenient.

The electrode in a potentiometric titration is chosen appropriately for a given titration reaction. Since it may be regarded as a specific indicator for the reaction, it is often called an indicator electrode. Indicator electrodes for pH measurement have been mentioned above. Oxidation-reduction titrations usually involve noble-metal electrodes such as platinum wire or platinum gauze. Silver and mercury electrodes are often used in determinations of metal-ion concentrations.

Conductometric titrations involve measurement of the conductivity of the tested solution as the desired reaction proceeds. In potentiometric titrations, foreign ions are permissible so long as they do not affect the potential of the indicator electrode. In conductometric titrations, however, all ions present contribute to the conductivity and require consideration. The equivalence point of a conductometric titration is not characterized by an abrupt change in conductivity, but by a change in the slope of the plot

107. Holtzclaw and Sheetz, *J. Am. Chem. Soc.*, **75**, 3053 (1953).

of conductivity against volume of titrant added. It is quite possible to find the equivalence point of a conductometric titration by extrapolating to intersection the lines obtained at the beginning and at the end of the titration. Such a procedure is valuable when the reaction product of the titration shows appreciable dissociation, solubility, or tendency toward hydrolysis. The experimental values near the equivalence point in such cases will be in error, but the intersection of the two straight-line portions of the plot shows the theoretical values. Conductometric techniques are thus applicable when potentiometric techniques may fail. Generally, however, conductometric titrations are not widely used because of the interference of foreign ions.

Amperometric titrations are concerned with measurement of diffusion currents at constant potential. Since the diffusion current of a solution at the dropping mercury electrode is in general proportional to the concentration of the reducible or oxidizable species, changes in the diffusion current may be related to changes in concentration. Either the material in solution or the titrant, or both, may produce a diffusion current at the potential chosen. The plot of an amperometric titration usually consists of two intersecting straight lines, the coordinates of the intersection point being the equivalence diffusion current and the equivalence volume of titrant. Interference of the reaction product frequently requires extrapolation to the equivalence point, as with conductometric titrations[108].

Jaques[109] has given a thorough mathematical treatment of the determination of the formula of a complex by potentiometric titration. If a metal ion, M^+, reacts with an anion, A^-, to form a complex, the general equilibrium is given by

$$qM^+ + rA^- \rightleftharpoons [M_qA_r]^{q-r}; \qquad K = \frac{[M^+]^q[A^-]^r}{[M_qA_r]}.$$

Potentiometric measurements are made for various concentrations of metal ion and anion. The values for q and r may be found from the following equations.

$$\Delta E_\mathrm{I} = \frac{RT}{nF} \ln \left(\frac{[M_qA_r]_1}{[M_qA_r]_2} \right)^{1/q} ; \tag{I}$$

$$\Delta E_\mathrm{II} = \frac{RT}{nF} \ln \left(\frac{[A^-]_3}{[A^-]_4} \right)^{r/q} . \tag{II}$$

ΔE_I is the difference in potential between concentrations 1 and 2 at constant anion concentration, while ΔE_II is the difference between concentrations 3 and 4 at constant complex concentration.

108. Kolthoff and Laitinen, "pH and Electro Titrations," 2nd ed., New York, John Wiley & Sons, Inc., 1941.
109. Jaques, "Complex Ions in Aqueous Solution," Longmans Green and Co., 1914.

Leden[110] has used the potentiometric titration method to demonstrate complex formation between cadmium ions and various anions. Cadmium perchlorate–sodium perchlorate solutions were titrated with other sodium salt solutions, and the data were interpreted by Leden to indicate the formation of $[CdCl]^+$, $[CdCl_2]$, $[CdCl_3]^-$, $[CdBr_2]$, $[CdBr_3]^-$, $[CdBr_4]^=$, $[CdI]^+$, $[CdI_2]$, $[CdI_4]^=$, $[Cd(SCN)_2]$, $[Cd(SCN)_3]^-$, $[CdNO_3]^+$, and $[CdSO_4]$. Some of these complexes are seen to be undissociated forms of normal cadmium salts. The dinuclear complex $[Cd_2Br_3]^+$ also appears to form in bromide solutions.

An important method for determining complex formation constants has been described by Bjerrum[111]. This method is essentially one of pH titrations. The general equilibrium between a metal ion M and ligands A is written in steps:

$$M + A \rightleftharpoons MA$$

$$MA + A \rightleftharpoons MA_2$$

$$MA_{N-1} + A \rightleftharpoons MA_N$$

The individual formation constants are given by

$$k_1 = \frac{[MA]}{[M][A]}$$

$$k_2 = \frac{[MA_2]}{[MA][A]}$$

$$k_N = \frac{[MA_N]}{[MA_{N-1}][A]}$$

Bjerrum defines the quantity $\bar{n}$ as the average number of coordinated groups per metal ion present; all metal ions are counted whether coordinated or not.

$$\bar{n} = \frac{[MA] + 2[MA_2] + \cdots + N[MA_N]}{[M] + [MA] + [MA_2] + \cdots + [MA_N]}$$

The value of $\bar{n}$ is determined experimentally by measurement of pH, since removal of free donor groups by coordination alters the pH by amounts which may be used to calculate the number of groups coordinated. The quantity of ligand added must be known, as well as the value the pH would have if no ligand were present. The difference between concentration of ligand added and concentration of ligand coordinated is the concentration of free ligand, [A]. Bjerrum has shown mathematically that when the

110. Leden, Z. physik. Chem., **A188,** 160 (1941).
111. Bjerrum, "Metal Ammine Formation in Aqueous Solution," Copenhagen, P. Haase and Son, 1941.

experimental concentrations are adjusted to specific values for $\bar{n}$, the following relations hold for the case $N = 2$.

$$\text{If } \bar{n} = \tfrac{1}{2}, \quad k_1 = \frac{1}{[\text{A}]}.$$

$$\text{If } \bar{n} = \tfrac{3}{2}, \quad k_2 = \frac{1}{[\text{A}]}.$$

$$\text{If } \bar{n} = 1, \quad \sqrt{k_1 k_2} = k = \frac{1}{[\text{A}]}.$$

The "average constant," k, is also the square root of the constant K of the over-all reaction

$$\text{M} + 2\text{A} \xrightleftharpoons{\quad K \quad} \text{MA}_2 \ (N = 2).$$

Application of Bjerrum's method is exemplified by the work of Calvin and Melchior[112] with the 5-sulfosalicylaldehyde complex of copper(II). These authors titrated 5-sulfosalicylaldehyde with sodium hydroxide and then repeated the titration in the presence of copper(II) ions. Plots of the two titrations were made on the same set of axes, with the separation of the two curves at a given pH value corresponding to the amount of hydroxide needed to neutralize the protons freed by the coordinating organic groups. This amount of hydroxide gives the quantity of coordinated ligand, and, when divided by the known metal concentration, the value of $\bar{n}$. The value of [A], the concentration of aldehyde anion, was found from the known concentration of uncoordinated aldehyde and its known dissociation constant. The values of [A] at $\bar{n} = \tfrac{1}{2}$, $\bar{n} = 1$, and $\bar{n} = \tfrac{3}{2}$ were used to calculate log k_1, log k, and log k_2 as approximately 5.2, 4.5, and 3.7, respectively.

A similar application of Bjerrum's method has been made by De, Ghosh, and Ray[113], who studied tris(biguanide)cobalt(III) and tris(phenylbiguanide)cobalt(III) complexes. These complexes were found to be quite stable, more so than the cobalt ammines.

A number of workers have obtained values for dissociation and formation constants of complexes by potentiometric means other than pH measurements. Quite often it is possible to calculate standard oxidation potentials by correcting experimental oxidation potentials with activity or concentration data. Constants may then be calculated with the formula $E^0 = \dfrac{RT}{nF} \ln K$. E^0 is here the difference in standard potential between the oxidation of metal to simple ion and metal to complex ion. Leden[110] has used this method to find an increasing stability of cyano complexes of

112. Calvin and Melchior, *J. Am. Chem. Soc.*, **70**, 3270 (1948).
113. De, Ghosh, and RâY, *J. Indian Chem. Soc.*, **27**, 493 (1950).

cadmium as the number of cyano groups increases from one to four. Sillén and Liljeqvist[114] have reported that halo complexes of zinc increase in stability in the series iodo < bromo < chloro. Grinberg and his co-workers[115], by determining the oxidation potential for the system

$$[PtX_4]^- + 2X^- \rightleftharpoons [PtX_6]^- + 2e^-, \ (X = Cl^-, Br^-, SCN^-),$$

have found the stability of the platinum(II) complexes to increase in the series thiocyanato < bromo < chloro. Further studies by Grinberg[116] have established that the oxidation of the platinum in such complexes as $[Pt(NH_3)_4][Pt(CN)_4]$ and $[Pt(NH_3)_4][PtBr_4]$ actually takes place in two steps, with the ammine platinum being more easily oxidized. Higher temperatures accentuate the difference in potential between the two steps, and low temperatures frequently eliminate it. The complex $[Pt(NH_3)_2(CN)_2]$ shows only one oxidation step.

Potentiometric titrations by Treadwell and Huber[117] have confirmed the conclusion of Manchot[118] that iron(I) is present in the nitroso Roussin salts, red $K[Fe(NO)_2S]$ and black $K[Fe_4(NO)_7S_3] \cdot H_2O$. Unipositive cobalt and nickel also appear to be present in the black salts $K_3[Co(NO)_2(S_2O_3)_2]$ and $K_3[Ni(NO)(S_2O_3)_2] \cdot 2H_2O$.

The cis and trans isomers of dichlorobis(ethylenediamine)cobalt(III) and dichlorotetramminecobalt(III) have been the subjects of a number of potentiometric studies. Mathieu[119] has made pH measurements during aquation of these complexes and has postulated the following steps.

$$[Co \ en_2 \ Cl_2]^+ \rightarrow [Co \ en_2 \ Cl(H_2O)]^{++} + Cl^-$$

$$[Co \ en_2 \ ClH_2O]^{++} \rightleftharpoons [Co \ en_2(H_2O)_2]^{+++} + Cl^-.$$

The first reaction is considered to be complete in solution, and the equilibrium of the second is found to vary with temperature, pH, and concentration of the chloride and complex ions. At elevated pH values a hydroxo complex tends to form.

$$[Co \ en_2 \ Cl \ (H_2O)]^{++} \rightleftharpoons [Co \ en_2 \ Cl(OH)]^+ + H^+$$

The rates of reaction are markedly different for the cis and trans isomers. Similarly, differences in rate between cis and trans forms have been noted by Jensen[120] and Grinberg[121] for the following platinum(II) system.

$$[Pt(NH_3)_2(H_2O)_2]^{++} \overset{k_1}{\rightleftharpoons} [Pt(NH_3)_2(H_2O)OH]^+ + H^+ \overset{k_2}{\rightleftharpoons} [Pt(NH_3)_2(OH)_2] + 2H^+.$$

114. Sillen and Liljeqvist, *Svensk Kem. Tid.*, **56**, 89 (1944).
115. Grinberg, Ptitsyn and Lavrent'ev, *J. Phys. Chem.*, *U.S.S.R.*, **10**, 661 (1937).
116. Grinberg and Ryabchikov, *J. Phys. Chem.*, *U.S.S.R.*, **14**, 119 (1937).
117. Treadwell and Huber, *Helv. chim. Acta*, **26**, 18 (1943).
118. Manchot, *Ber.*, **59B**, 2445 (1926).
119. Mathieu, *Bull. soc. chim.*, [5] **3**, 2121 (1936).
120. Jensen, *Z. anorg. allgem. Chem.*, **242**, 87 (1939).
121. Grinberg and Ryabchikov, *Acta Physicochem.*, *U.R.S.S.*, **3**, 555, 569 (1933).

These authors also point out an inequality in equilibrium constant values:

	cis	*trans*
K_1	1.6×10^{-8}	6.3×10^{-8}
K_2	1.6×10^{-8}	1×10^{-10}

Grinberg and Gil'dengershel[122] have used pH titrations to demonstrate acidic properties of ammine complexes of platinum(IV). In one experiment, a solution of tris(ethylenediamine)platinum(IV) chloride was titrated with sodium hydroxide, using a glass electrode. It was found that each of the ethylenediamine molecules in turn releases a proton from an amine group to render the complex in effect a tribasic acid. Equilibria and dissociation constants as found by this study are given below:

$$[Pt\ en_3]^{4+} \rightleftharpoons [Pt\ en_2(en - H)]^{+++} + H^+; \qquad K_1 = 3.5 \times 10^{-6}$$

$$[Pt\ en_2(en - H)]^{+++} \rightleftharpoons [Pt\ en(en - H)_2]^{++} + H^+; \qquad K_2 = 1.76 \times 10^{-10}$$

$$[Pt\ en(en - H)_2]^{++} \rightleftharpoons [Pt\ (en - H)_3]^+; \qquad \frac{K_3}{K_2} \sim \frac{1}{5}$$

Biswas[123] has combined potentiometric and conductometric titration techniques to study the molybdic acid–tartaric acid system. A highly ionized complex $H_2[MoO_3(tart)(H_2O)]$ is evidenced by peaks in acidity and conductivity at a 1:1 mole ratio.

$$H_2\ tart \qquad H_2MoO_4 \qquad H_2[MoO_3(tart)(H_2O)]$$

$$\Updownarrow \qquad\qquad \Updownarrow \qquad\qquad\qquad \Updownarrow$$

$$2H^+ + tart^- + 2H^+ + MoO_4 \rightleftharpoons 2H^+ + [MoO_3(tart)(H_2O)]^-$$

Dey[124] has used conductivity data to confirm the existence of a number of copper(II) ammine complexes. Mixtures of copper(II) nitrate or copper(II) sulfate and ammonium hydroxide show conductivities different from the sum of those of the constituents. By plotting the deviations from additivity against composition, Dey has found maxima corresponding to three, four, five, and six moles of coordinated ammonia per mole of copper nitrate. The hexammine complex forms in the presence of sulfate as well.

If a complex ion dissociates negligibly at all concentrations, the conductivity of its salts will be practically a linear function of the square root of the concentration. Swift[125] has found the relationship to be linear for $K_4[Fe(CN)_6]$, indicating stability of the iron complex. On the other hand, Brasted[76] has reported an incomplete ionization for tris(o-phenanthroline)

122. Grinberg and Gil'dengershel, *Izvest. Akad. Nauk. S.S.S.R., Otdel. Khim. Nauk,* **1948**, 479.
123. Biswas, *J. Indian Chem. Soc.,* **24,** 345, 103 (1947).
124. Dey, *Nature,* **158,** 95 (1946).
125. Swift, *J. Am. Chem. Soc.,* **60,** 728 (1938).

zinc d-α-bromocamphor-π-sulfonate from conductivity, refractometric and cryoscopic measurements.

$$[Zn(o\text{-phen})_3](C_{10}H_{14}OBrSO_3)_2 \rightleftharpoons [Zn(o\text{-phen})_3]^{++} + 2C_{10}H_{14}OBrSO_3^-.$$

Shuttleworth[126] has made some interesting qualitative tests of the stability of oxalato, tartrato, and citrato chromium(III) complexes. Conductometric titration of each of the complexes with hydrochloric acid yields a straight-line conductivity plot, indicating that there is virtually no replacement of organic anions by chloride ions. Similar titrations with sodium hydroxide show only slight replacement by hydroxy groups.

A conductometric study[127] of the carbonatopentamminecobalt(III) ion indicates that solutions of the ion undergo successive reactions to form an equilibrium mixture containing $[Co(NH_3)_5HCO_3]^{++}$, $[Co(NH_3)_5H_2O]^{+++}$, and $[Co(NH_3)_5OH]^{++}$. This example serves to point out the importance of determining the true compositions of solutions, in order to avoid attributing to pure substances the measurable properties of mixtures.

A conductometric study of chromium lactate complexes has been reported by Shuttleworth[128]. Conductometric titration in very dilute solution shows that when chromium alum is boiled in the presence of lactate ion, protons are liberated from the lactate, and coordination takes place, evidently forming $H_3[Cr(lactate)_3]$. This complex acid may be titrated completely with base without precipitation of any of the chromium. Its characteristics are those of a fairly strong acid ($K_a \sim 10^{-2}$). The formation of the anionic complex is not complete unless the protons liberated from the lactate are neutralized.

Conductance measurements by Nayar and Pande[129] on solutions containing lead nitrate and the heavier alkali nitrates give evidence of complex formation. The existence of $4RbNO_3 \cdot Pb(NO_3)_2$, $2RbNO_3 \cdot Pb(NO_3)_2$, and $RbNO_3 \cdot Pb(NO_3)_2$, for example, has been demonstrated by the conductance method and confirmed by viscosity and transference measurements.

Dipole Moments

For the purpose of this discussion, molecules of compounds may be considered as being composed of positively and negatively charged particles. The number of positive charges will numerically equal the negative charges, resulting in electronegativity of the compound. Each molecule has what may be thought of as centers of positive and negative charges, much as masses have centers of gravity. If the centers of positive and negative charge coincide, the molecule is nonpolar. Otherwise it is polar, and the measure of the degree of polarity is the dipole moment, μ. Dipole mo-

126. Shuttleworth, *J. Intern. Soc. Leather Trades Chem.*, **30**, 342 (1946).
127. Lamb and Stevens, *J. Am. Chem. Soc.*, **61**, 3229 (1939).
128. Shuttleworth, *J. Am. Leather Chemists' Assoc.*, **45**, 447 (1950).
129. Nayar and Pande, *J. Indian Chem. Soc.*, **28**, 107 (1951).

ment is defined as the product of the net charge of either sign and the distance between the centers of charge. Neither quantity may be measured directly, but the product may be obtained in a number of ways.

All molecules, whether polar or nonpolar, exhibit induced polarity when placed in an electric field. This induced polarity, symbolized by P_D, results in a degree of orientation in the field. Furthermore, all polar molecules show a permanent, or orientation, polarization, symbolized by P_μ, which also produces orientation in an applied field. The total molar polarization P is the sum of the induced and orientation polarizations; it may be found experimentally because of its relationship with the measurable dielectric constant ϵ.

$$P = \frac{\epsilon - 1}{\epsilon + 2} \cdot \frac{M}{d} \tag{I}$$

M is the molecular weight of the substance measured, and d is its density.

The dielectric constant is measured as the ratio of capacitances of a condenser when filled with the substance studied and with air, respectively. Actually the constant measures the force required to orient the molecules in the field. Debye[130] has shown that the orientation polarization P_μ is related to the dielectric constant by the formula

$$P_\mu = \left(\frac{4}{3}\pi N\right)\frac{\mu^2}{3kT} \tag{II}$$

where N is Avogadro's number, k is the Boltzmann constant per molecule, and T is the Kelvin temperature. If a substance is measured in the gaseous state, the average distance between molecules is sufficient to render the induced polarization P_D practically constant. Then

$$P = \frac{\epsilon - 1}{\epsilon + 2} \cdot \frac{M}{d} = P_D + P_\mu = P_D + \left(\frac{4}{3}\pi N\right)\frac{\mu^2}{3kT} \tag{III}$$

and the value of P, obtainable from values of ϵ, is a linear function of $\frac{1}{T}$.

Experimentally, a plot is made of corresponding values of P and $\frac{1}{T}$, and the slope of the resulting line is set equal to the coefficient of $\frac{1}{T}$ on the right side of Equation (II). This expression then leads to the dipole moment.

Most complex compounds cannot be volatilized without decomposition. A method for determining dipole moments of such substances involves the following relation, which holds true at infinite dilution in solution.

$$P_D = \frac{n^2 - 1}{n^2 + 2} \cdot \frac{M}{d} \tag{IV}$$

130. Debye, "Polar Molecules," New York, Chemical Catalog Co., (Reinhold Publishing Corp.) 1929.

The refractive index n should be known for the far infrared region, but an index for visible light is a good approximation for substances with fairly high dipole moments. Experimental values for total molar polarization, found as before, are extrapolated to infinite dilution. The values of P_D from Equation (IV) are subtracted, and the result is equal to the right side of Equation (II).

A third method for determining dipole moments makes use of the Stern-Gerlach molecular beam technique. The material to be studied must be volatilized and passed through collimating slits. The molecules of the material are then subjected to the deflecting force of an electrical field and condensed onto a plate so designed that the molecular trace may be observed or photographed. The permanent moments of polar molecules cause them to be deflected more than nonpolar molecules and to yield a broader trace. A calibration technique is used to evaluate the traces by comparison with standard dipoles.

Dipole moments have the dimensions esu-cm. Their values are always of the order of 10^{-18} esu-cm, and for convenience the quantity 10^{-18} esu-cm has been chosen as the dipole moment unit and named the Debye unit (D.U.).

The measurement of dipole moments has been only recently applied to structural studies of complexes. When two or more structures for a molecule each agree substantially with data from other physical methods, dipole studies frequently permit choice of a most likely structure. Dipole moment data have been used also in estimating degrees of partial ionic character and in distinguishing between cis and trans isomers. Several examples of dipole moment studies are given below.

Martin[131] reports the values for dipole moments of several halides and correlates the values with the tendency toward bonding between the halides and boron trichloride. The data are given in part in Table 18.1. Martin qoints out the value 2.00 D.U. as an apparent demarcation between bonding and nonbonding halides. Evidently the polar character of the halides determines the degree of availability of bonding electrons. Chlorine itself, with a dipole moment of zero, forms no compound.

Jensen[132] investigated the dipole moments of platinum(II) complexes with tertiary phosphines, arsines, and stibines. The dipole moments fall into two distinct groups. The group called α by Jensen is characterized by very small dipole moments, suggesting trans configuration. The dipole moment of dinitratobis(triethyl phosphine)platinum(II) is considerably larger than the others, presumably because of unsymmetrical coordination of the nitrate group. The dipoles of the β group are quite marked, suggesting

131. Martin, *J. Phys. and Colloid Chem.*, **51**, 1400 (1947).
132. Jensen, *Z. anorg. allgem. Chem.*, **229**, 225 (1936).

TABLE 18.1. DIPOLE MOMENTS OF CERTAIN HALIDES AND COMPOUND FORMATION
WITH BCl_3

Halide	μ(D.U.)	Compound Formed
HCl	1.03	None
CH_3Cl	1.84	None
C_2H_5Cl	2.01	$C_2H_5Cl(BCl_3)_2$
n-C_3H_7Cl	1.97	None
iso-C_3H_7Cl	2.02	$(C_3H_7Cl)_3BCl_3$

cis forms. Similar results for analogous trans palladium complexes are reported by Mann and Purdie[133].

Lamb and Mysels[134] report a thorough study of carbonatotetramminecobalt(III) and carbonatopentamminecobalt(III) complexes, using the method of dielectric increments. This method involves measurement of electrical capacitance of a substance in a pulsating electrical field generated by an electronic oscillator. The frequency of the oscillator is varied, and the corresponding capacitances are measured. In order to calculate the dipole moment of the substance, one must first determine the electrical conductance in solution. The calculation formula involves the conductance, the frequency used, the capacitance observed, and several correction factors. Resulting values of the dielectric constant at several low frequencies are compared with the theoretically obtained value for infinite frequency. The average difference, or dielectric increment for low frequencies, may be used to find the dipole moment. Lamb and Mysels show by this method that the dipole moment of $[Co(NH_3)_5(CO_3)]^+$ is sufficiently greater than that of $[Co(NH_3)_4(CO_3)]^+$ to warrant postulation of the structures

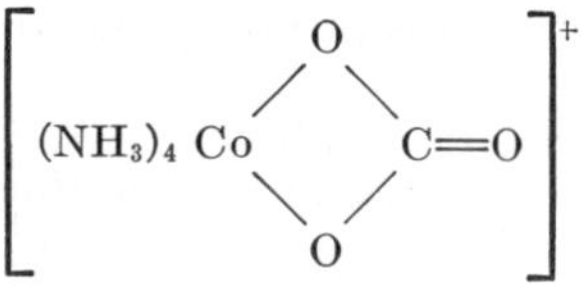

$$\left[(NH_3)_4\, Co \underset{O}{\overset{O}{\diamond}} C{=}O \right]^+$$

and

$$\left[(NH_3)_5Co{-}O \underset{\underset{O}{\diagdown}}{\overset{O}{\diagup}} C \right]^+$$

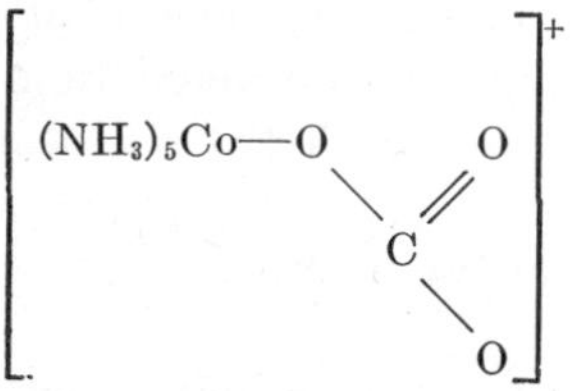

In the second structure the dipole is more pronounced. The complex behaves as if it were formed by loss of a proton from the bicarbonatopentammine complex, with subsequent localization of negative charge.

133. Mann and Purdie, *J. Chem. Soc.*, 1549 (1935); 873 (1936).
134. Lamb and Mysels, *J. Am. Chem. Soc.*, **67**, 468 (1945).

Magnetic Measurements

While electrical dipoles result from unbalanced distribution of positive and negative charges within molecules of a compound, magnetic dipoles result from unbalanced electronic spin and orbital contributions to molecular magnetism. All substances display some sort of magnetic dissymmetry, however, in contrast to the existence of electrical nonpolarity.

The intensity of a magnetic field is always changed within a material through which the field passes. All materials have in common a tendency to lessen the intensity of the field and thus to be repelled by it. This property, called diamagnetism, is attributable to the effect of the field on electron pairs within molecules. Some materials also contain unpaired electrons or unbalanced orbitals, which increase the intensity of the field within the material. This property is called paramagnetism, and its magnitude is so much greater than that of diamagnetism that the latter may usually be neglected in paramagnetic materials. A special case of paramagnetism, in which the field increase within the material is of the order of a million times, is termed ferromagnetism. This phenomenon is exhibited by only a few materials, those which are capable of "permanent magnetism."

Changes in field intensity are expressed mathematically by the relation

$$B = H + 4\pi I, \tag{I}$$

where B is the intensity in oersteds within the substance, H the outside field intensity, and I the intensity of magnetization. I has negative values for diamagnetism and larger positive values for paramagnetism. The quantity $K = \dfrac{I}{H}$ is termed magnetic susceptibility per unit volume. Susceptibility per unit mass, χ, is obtained as the quotient of K and the density of the substance. Molar susceptibility, χ_M, is the product of χ and the molecular weight.

Experimental measurements generally determine the susceptibility of a substance, but a quantity of great theoretical interest is the magnetic moment, μ. The relationship between magnetic moment and susceptibility is expressed by

$$\chi_M = N\alpha + \frac{N\mu^2}{3kT} \tag{II}$$

where N is Avogadro's number, α is diamagnetic susceptibility per molecule, and k is the Boltzmann constant. Magnetic moments are expressed in Bohr magnetons. If the orbital contributions to magnetic moment are neglected, the moment may be related to the number of unpaired electrons per molecule by the "spin only" formula.

$$\mu = \sqrt{n(n + 2)} \tag{III}$$

This theoretical value for the magnetic moment agrees well with experimental values for substances whose orbital contributions are not shielded and may be neutralized by interaction with surrounding particles. Unpaired electrons of the rare earth elements lie in the $4f$ level and are not subject to interaction. For these elements the "spin only" formula fails to agree with experiment, and refinements must be introduced into theoretical calculations.

Comprehensive treatments of magnetic theory are given by Selwood[135], Klemm[136], Van Vleck[137], and Pauling[138].

Numerous methods have been developed for measurement of magnetic susceptibilities. The most widely used method was developed by Gouy[139]. This method measures the force exerted upon a sample by a magnetic field of high intensity at one end of the sample and nearly negligible intensity at the other end. The force is measured on a balance in terms of the apparent added weight upon application of the magnetic field. It is necessary to calculate susceptibility values from the experimental data.

Other useful methods have been worked out by Quincke[140], Faraday[141, 142], Curie and Chéneveau[143], Rankine[144], and Iskenderian[145].

Measurements of magnetic susceptibility have been of great value in determining bond types and structures of complexes. The various types of bonding possible in a given complex may often be distinguished on the basis of the number of unpaired electrons present with each type. If experiment establishes the magnetic susceptibility and thus the number of unpaired electrons, questions may frequently be settled concerning orbital hybridization, degree of covalent character, and probable structure. Theories of bonding, orbitals, and structure in coordination chemistry have not been thoroughly evolved, but magnetic data constitute a powerful tool for the improvement of current ideas.

Tyson and Adams[146] have used magnetic data to postulate structures for

135. Selwood, "Magnetochemistry," New York, Interscience Publishers, Inc., 1943.
136. Klemm, "Magnetochemie," Leipzig, Akademische Verlagsgesellschaft m.b.H., 1936.
137. Van Vleck, "Theory of Electric and Magnetic Susceptibilities," pp. 283–301, Oxford, The Clarendon Press, 1932.
138. Pauling, "The Nature of the Chemical Bond," Ithaca, N. Y., Cornell University Press, 1940.
139. Gouy, *Compt. rend.*, **109**, 935 (1889).
140. Quincke, *Ann. Physik.*, **24**, 347 (1885); **34**, 401 (1888).
141. Stoner, "Magnetism and Matter," London, Methuen and Co., Ltd., 1934.
142. Curie, *Ann. chim. phys.*, (7) **5**, 289 (1895).
143. Cheneveau, *Phil. Mag.*, **20**, 357 (1910).
144. Rankine, *Proc. Phys. Soc. London*, **46**, 1, 391 (1934).
145. Iskenderian, *Phys. Rev.*, **51**, 1092 (1937).
146. Tyson and Adams, *J. Am. Chem. Soc.*, **62**, 1228 (1940).

TABLE 18.2. MAGNETIC MOMENTS OF SOME INNER COMPLEXES OF COPPER, NICKEL, AND COBALT

COMPLEX	MEASURED MOMENT	NEAREST THEORETICAL VALUE AND CORRESPONDING NUMBER OF UNPAIRED ELECTRONS	POSSIBLE ORBITAL AND STRUCTURAL CONFIGURATIONS
(a)	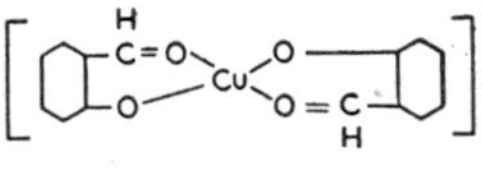 1.9	1.73:1	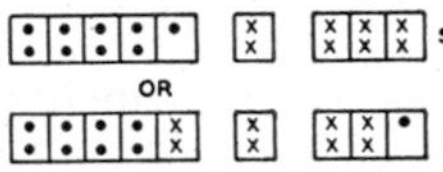 sp^3, TETRAHEDRAL OR dsp^2, PLANAR
(b)	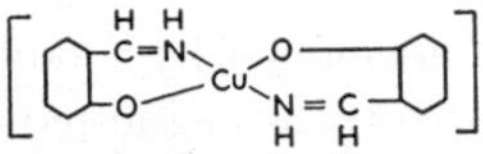 1.9	1.73:1	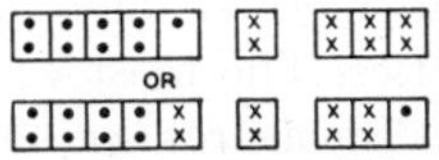 sp^3, TETRAHEDRAL OR dsp^2, PLANAR
(c)	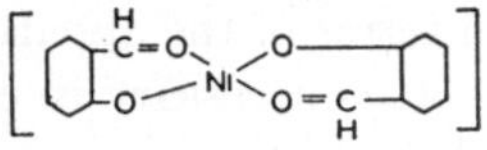 3.1	2.83:2	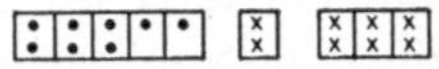 sp^3, TETRAHEDRAL
(d)	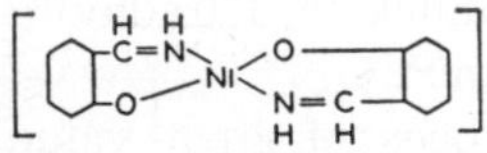 ~0	~0:0	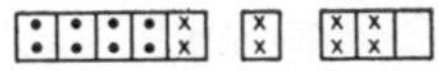 dsp^2, PLANAR
(e)	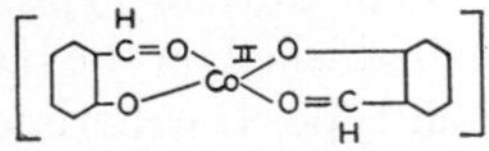 4.5	3.88:3	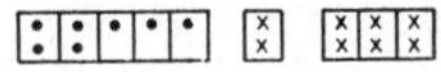 sp^3, TETRAHEDRAL

salicylaldehyde and salicylaldimine complexes of divalent copper, nickel, and cobalt (Table 18.2). It is apparent that magnetic data alone are not sufficient to choose between the two reasonable structures for complexes (a) and (b). Cox and Webster[147] have established by x-ray methods that both complexes are planar. The two inner complexes of nickel are of special interest. Their difference in structure is further confirmed by a pronounced difference in absorption maxima.

The work of Mellor and Goldacre[148] has shown that a number of cobalt(II) nitrogen- and oxygen-bonded complexes display the high magnetic moments characteristic of ionic complexes of divalent cobalt. Most values are considerably above the theoretical three-electron moment of 3.88, and such values are to be expected. The magnetic moments of $[Co(NH_3)_6]Cl_2$, $[Co(en)_3]Cl_2$, and $Na_2[Co(C_6H_4\{COO\}_2)_2]$ are given as 4.96, 3.82, and 5.35 Bohr magnetons, respectively. Orbital magnetism is evidently a contributing factor in these instances.

A relationship between complex stability and magnetic moments has been reported by Russel and his co-workers[149] for certain nickel(II) and

147. Cox and Webster, *J. Chem. Soc.*, 731 (1935).
148. Mellor and Goldacre, *J. Proc. Roy. Soc. N. S. Wales*, **73**, 233–9 (1940).
149. Russel, Cooper, and Vosburgh, *J. Am. Chem. Soc.*, **65**, 1301 (1943).

copper(II) complexes. Aqueous solutions of the metal sulfates were treated with excesses of various nitrogen- and oxygen-donating groups, two types of donor molecules at a time. Measurement of maximum light absorption and comparison with known values permitted a conclusion in several cases as to the relative coordinating abilities of the two ligands used. Each complex was also isolated and tested magnetically. A nearly linear relationship was discovered between stability as shown spectrally and by magnetic moment. The coordinating groups for which stability conclusions could be drawn are shown below.

Nickel(II) complexes: Least stable-aquo < pyridine < ammine < ethylenediamine
$\mu \cong 3.24$

< o-phenanthroline-Most stable
$\mu \cong 3.08$

Copper(II) complexes: Least stable-aquo < pyridine < ammine < aminoacetate
$\mu \cong 1.95$

< ethylenediamine-Most stable
$\mu \cong 1.85$

Srivastava, Pande, and Nayar[150] have described an interesting application of magnetic measurements to the method of continuous variations. Lead nitrate was added to aqueous solutions of potassium nitrate and ammonium nitrate, respectively. The magnetic susceptibility was measured at intervals and plotted against composition of the solution. The results correspond to compound formation involving one, two, and four molecules of lead nitrate per molecule of potassium or ammonium nitrate. The results have been confirmed by a conductometric method.

Apparently anomalous magnetic moments may sometimes be found among complexes containing optically active ligands. French and his associates[151] have noted that certain complexes of nickel(II), which would be expected by analogy to be diamagnetic and planar, are actually paramagnetic and therefore probably tetrahedral. An example is bis(formyl-camphor)nickel(II), [Ni(C$_{10}$H$_{14}${CHO}O)$_2$]. Both magnetic data and rotatory dispersion measurements point to the nickel in this complex as a source of asymmetry and optical activity resulting from tetrahedral coordination. Presumably the optically active ligand exercises a kind of inductive influence.

Mellor and Lockwood[152] have furnished additional evidence for the distorting influence of certain ligands. These investigators found that coordination of substituted pyrromethenes with nickel(II) produces a tetra-

150. Srivastava, Pande, and Nayar, *Current Sci.*, **16**, 225–6 (1947).
151. French, Magee, and Sheffield, *J. Am. Chem. Soc.*, **64**, 1924–8 (1942).
152. Mellor and Lockwood, *J. Proc. Roy. Soc. N. S. Wales*, **74**, 141–8 (1940); *Nature*, **145**, 862 (1940).

TABLE 18.3. ORBITAL ARRANGEMENTS FOR SILVER(II) AND SILVER(III) COMPLEXES

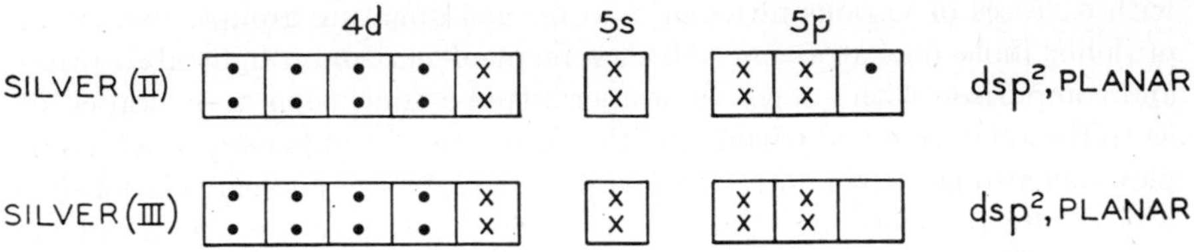

hedral configuration. Bis(3,3′,5,5′-tetramethyl-4,4′-dicarbethoxydipyr-romethene)nickel(II), [Ni($C_{19}H_{23}O_4N_2)_2$], has a magnetic moment of 3.2 Bohr magnetons, corresponding to two unpaired electrons. The analogous complex of palladium(II), however, is diamagnetic.

Rây[153] has used magnetic measurements to demonstrate the existence of silver(III) complexes with ethylene biguanide ($C_4N_5H_9$ = big H). He prepared the salts [Ag(big H)$_2$]X_3, where X may be nitrate, perchlorate, or hydroxide, as well as [Ag(big H)$_2$]$_2$(SO$_4$)$_3$. All these salts are diamagnetic, as would be expected for silver(III); a corresponding silver(II) salt with the same ligand is paramagnetic. See Table 18.3.

A comparison technique has enabled Mellor and Craig[154] to support the idea that the diphenylmethylarsine copper complex, [$Cu_2Cl_3(Ph_2MeAs)_3$], has a dinuclear structure containing both monovalent and divalent copper. Two forms of this complex may be isolated, one blue and the other brown. Mellor and Craig determined that the magnetic moment of each form has a value in the neighborhood of 1.73 Bohr magnetons. The cyanoammine copper complex [$Cu_3(CN)_4(NH_3)_3$], known to contain one copper(II) atom per molecule, and thus one unpaired electron, has a moment of 1.78 Bohr magnetons. The following structures for the two forms of the arsine complex are proposed:

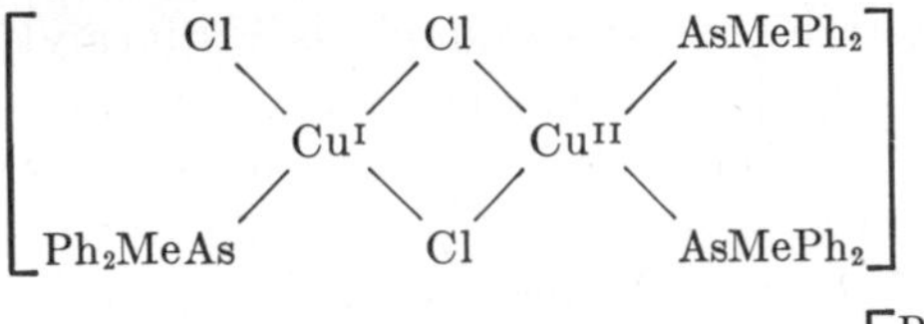

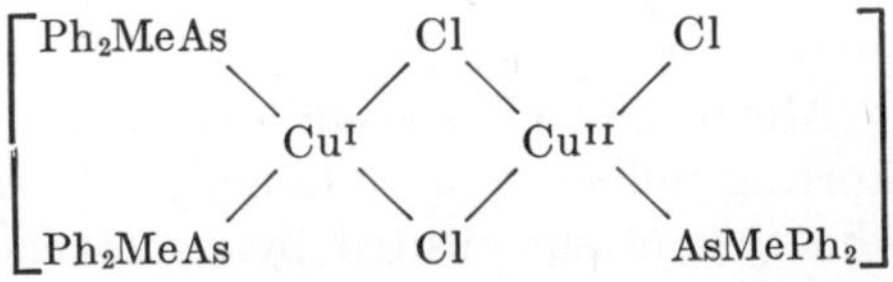

This work has been seriously questioned on other grounds (see p. 609).

153. Rây, *Nature*, **151**, 643 (1943).
154. Mellor and Craig, *J. Proc. Roy. Soc. N. S. Wales*, **74**, 475–94 (1941).

A systematic study of the relations among magnetic moment, color, and configuration of complexes has been made by Willis and Mellor[155]. An interesting transition pointed out by this study is that of bis(ethylenediamine-formylcamphor)nickel(II) in pyridine solution. When the solution is freshly prepared, the complex exhibits diamagnetism and a green color, corresponding to a tetracovalent planar structure. Upon standing for two weeks the solution turns brown, and paramagnetism appears, reaching a value of 3.15 Bohr magnetons. Evidently the complex combines with two pyridine molecules per nickel atom and rearranges to an octahedral structure, with unpairing and promotion of two $3d$ electrons to the $4d$ shell.

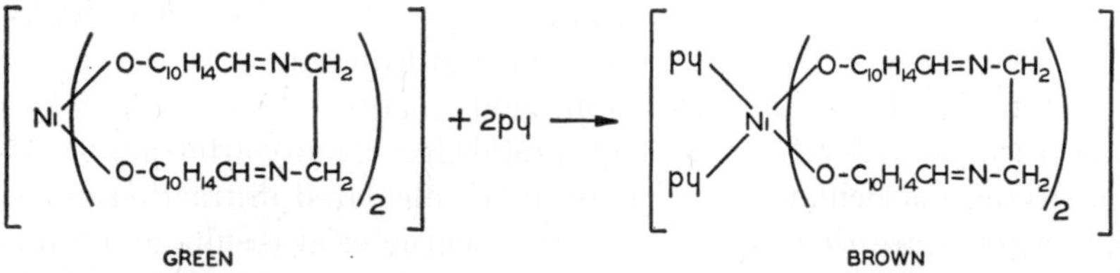

Consideration of the completely paired electron structure of cobalt(III) complexes showing d^2sp^3 hybridization suggests that all such complexes should be diamagnetic. That this is not the case has been demonstrated by Cambi, Ferrari, and Nardelli[156], who report magnetic measurements on a series of hexanitrocobaltate(III) complexes. The appreciable paramagnetism of these compounds suggests contributions from incompletely quenched orbital magnetism.

Complex	μ_B
$Na_3[Co(NO_2)_6]$	0.57
$K_3[Co(NO_2)_6] \cdot H_2O$	0.79
$(NH_4)_3[Co(NO_2)_6] \cdot 2H_2O$	0.63
$Tl_3[Co(NO_2)_6]$	0.52
$Ba_3[Co(NO_2)_6]_2 \cdot 12H_2O$	0.59
$Pb_3[Co(NO_2)_6]_2 \cdot 11H_2O$	0.84
$(Me_4N)_2Na[Co(NO_2)_6] \cdot 2\frac{1}{2}H_2O$	0.52

Jonassen and Frey[157] have shown that cobalt(II) ion forms a complex with tetraethylenepentamine in which the bonding is principally ionic. A solution of cobalt(II) perchlorate containing tetraethylenepentamine is green, but after standing for 72 hours, it is red. The cobalt(II) complex which may be isolated from the solution shows a magnetic susceptibility of 4.52

155. Willis and Mellor, *J. Am. Chem. Soc.*, **69**, 1237–40 (1947).
156. Cambi, Ferrari, and Nardelli, *Gazz. chim. ital.*, **82**, 816 (1952).
157. Jonassen and Frey, *J. Am. Chem. Soc.*, **75**, 1524 (1953).

Bohr magnetons. This value is in the usual range for cobalt(II) complexes containing three unpaired electrons.

X-Ray and Electron Diffraction

X-Rays[158, 159, 160]

The radiations known as x-rays have wave lengths of the same order as interatomic distances in molecules and crystals. For this reason Laue in 1912 suggested that the regular arrangement of crystal lattices should act as a three-dimensional diffraction grating for x-rays. It remained for Friedrich and Knipping to substantiate Laue's idea by passing x-rays through various crystals and onto a photographic plate. The developed plate showed a prominent central area exposed by undiffracted rays, and a symmetrical concentric pattern of rings in diffraction zones outward from the center. This Laue transmission method has proved to be of great value in structural analyses. Hypothetical crystals having any arbitrary structure are analyzed mathematically to determine calculated diffraction patterns; these patterns are then compared with experimental results and adjusted until they are identical. The crystal under study is assigned the calculated structure.

A more direct and convenient approach to x-ray analysis is given by the Bragg method. This method treats the crystal as a series of reflecting planes arranged in space so that they permit reflection and interference of x-rays entering at appropriate angles. The fundamental equation for the Bragg method is

$$n\lambda = 2d \sin \theta, \tag{1}$$

where n is the order of reflection, d is the distance between crystal reflecting planes, and θ is the angle at which the rays strike the crystal face. Successive orders of reflection are spread outward from the center of the reflection pattern, as well as weakened in intensity. Knowledge of the wave length and incident angle of the x-rays permits calculation of the distance between crystal planes.

For practical application of the Bragg analysis a crystal is mounted on a rotating table. An x-ray generator is so arranged that the rays are produced and collimated directly toward the center of rotation. After striking the crystal, the rays travel to a photographic plate or an ionization chamber, where their intensities are measured. A plot is made of the intensity as a

158. Zachariasen, "Theory of X-Ray Diffraction in Crystals," New York, John Wiley & Sons, Inc., 1945.
159. Reinmuth, *J. Chem. Ed.*, **7**, 138, 860, 1313 (1930).
160. Pirenne, "The Diffraction of X-Rays and Electrons by Free Molecules," Cambridge, Cambridge University Press, 1946.

function of angle of incidence; the most pronounced maximum corresponds to first-order reflection, and so on. The Bragg equation serves to determine the interplanar distance for all axes of crystal rotation, and after all feasible orientations of the crystal on the table have been individually tested, the data are taken to be complete.

The simplest applications of x-ray analysis have been made in determining the lattice structure of such ionic crystals as the alkali halides. More complicated structures are also amenable to treatment by the methods just described. Data from Laue or Bragg tests are sometimes subjected to complete mathematical analyses of the Fourier type. The ultimate aim is construction of an accurate three-dimensional model which represents completely the distribution of electron density in a crystal and thus shows the arrangement and separations of all atoms present. This objective is not realizable for structures containing hydrogen, since the hydrogen atom is two small for detection by x-rays. Models which are otherwise complete have been arrived at for some systems, but only with great difficulty and tedious calculation. Fortunately, such complete analyses are not usually necessary to establish structures.

A quick and relatively simple method of x-ray analysis employs crystalline powders rather than a large crystal. The reflection patterns obtained by this method are not usually so sharp as those obtained with larger particles. Powders are often readily available, however, when preparation of single crystals is difficult. Powder patterns sometimes serve to identify unknown substances by comparison with known patterns. In such cases mathematical analyses are unnecessary.

Electron Diffraction[161, 162, 163]

The useful diffractive and reflective properties of x-rays are found also in rapidly moving beams of electrons. Electron beams are usually generated electronically as cathode rays. A uniform voltage of the order of 40,000 to 60,000 volts per centimeter is maintained. The beam is directed toward a photographic plate, and vapor of the substance to be examined is interposed between the source and the plate. After development, the plate shows a prominent central spot and concentric rings, which may be analyzed in a manner analogous to x-ray analysis. Since the penetrating power of electrons is much lower than that of x-rays, the electron diffraction method is suited particularly to studies of gases, while x-ray methods are best for solid and liquid measurements. Photographic plates may be made more sensitive to electrons than to x-rays, at the intensities normally generated

161. Brockway, *Rev. Modern Phys.*, **8**, 231 (1976).
162. Clark and Wolthius, *J. Chem. Ed.*, **15**, 64 (1938).
163. Pauling and Brockway, *J. Am. Chem. Soc.*, **57**, 2684 (1935).

in the laboratory. Thus electron diffraction patterns may be taken in a few seconds, while exposure of plates to x-rays usually extends over several hours. More rings are usually produced by the electron diffraction method; this fact is important, inasmuch as inner rings are often obscured by the central beam.

Applications

X-ray and electron diffraction studies on complex compounds have yielded valuable information concerning properties of symmetry; spatial configuration; orientation of complex ions and molecules in crystal lattices; differentiation between racemates and optically inactive forms; determination of bond angles and distances; estimation of molecular weights of complexes; differentiation between mixtures and single-phase crystals; and identification of bridging groups.

Electron diffraction studies have enabled Palmer and Elliott[164] to propose a structure for dimeric aluminum chloride consisting of two tetrahedra sharing an edge. Chloride ions are thought to occupy the corners of the tetrahedra, with aluminum ions at the centers. Partial covalent character reduces to some extent the separation and magnitude of charges which purely ionic bonding would produce.

Electron diffraction data lead to the conclusion that nickel carbonyl has a tetrahedral structure[165]. Measured bond distances for nickel-carbon and carbon-oxygen bonds are 1.82 A and 1.15 A, respectively. These distances are in agreement with Pauling's suggestion that the nickel-carbon bonds should be considered as hybrids, partaking of both single-bond and double-bond character. The CO groups in $Ni(CO)_4$ are evidently tetrahedrally distributed about the nickel, with the character of the carbon-oxygen bonds quite similar to that found in carbon monoxide. The carbonyl hydrides $Fe(CO)_4H_2$ and $Co(CO)_4H$ were studied by Ewens and Lister[166], who attributed tetrahedral structures to both on the basis of electron diffraction patterns. The hydrogen atoms are thought to be bonded to oxygen, so that formulas for these hydrides may also be written $Fe(CO)_2(COH)_2$ and $Co(CO)_3(COH)$. The iron-carbon distance for the CO groups is 1.84 A, while for the COH groups it is 1.79 A. Respective distances for the cobalt compound are 1.83 A and 1.75 A. Volatility of the carbonyls and carbonyl hydrides facilitates their study by this method.

Beach and Bauer[167] have obtained electron diffraction patterns for the vapor of the compound AlB_3H_{12}. The data indicate that an aluminum atom

164. Palmer and Elliott, *J. Am. Chem. Soc.*, **60**, 1852 (1938).
165. Pauling, *J. Am. Chem. Soc.*, **53**, 1367 (1931); **54**, 988 (1932).
166. Ewens and Lister, *Trans. Faraday Soc.*, **35**, 681 (1939).
167. Beach and Bauer, *J. Am. Chem. Soc.*, **62**, 3440 (1940).

is bonded to three BH_4 groups in a planar configuration with the bonds at angles of 120°. Each boron atom is near the center of a trigonal bipyramid formed by four hydrogen atoms and the aluminum atom. The compound is electron-deficient, and the authors interpret the normal aluminum-boron bond lengths to indicate that the deficiency resides in the boron-hydrogen bonding.

Dipole moment studies of tetrachlorobis (trimethylarsine) palladium(II) suggest three possible forms for this complex.

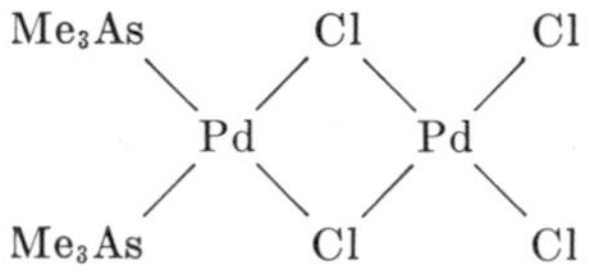

(I)

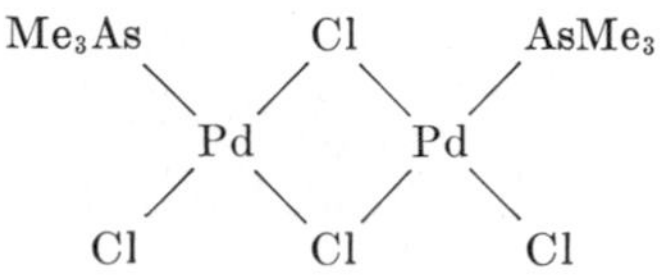

(II)

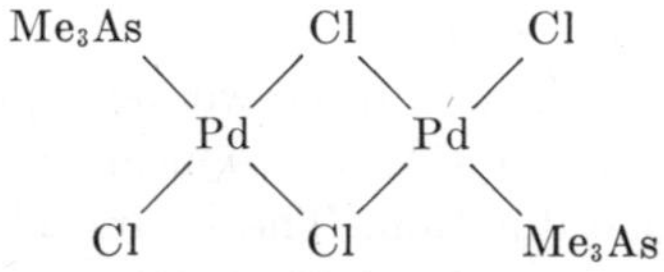

(III)

X-ray examination in the solid state led Mann and his co-workers[168] to the conclusion that only form (III) exists as a solid, although the other forms probably exist in organic solvents (p. 604). Replacement of two chloro groups by an oxalato group in the analogous tributylphosphine complex raises the question of identifying the bridging groups. Chatt and his associates[169] showed by x-ray investigation that the separation of 5.3 A between the palladium atoms corresponds to oxalato bridging. Chloro bridges would give the metal-metal distance a value of 3.4 A.

Complex metal cyanides have been the objects of considerable study by x-ray techniques. Dothie[170] has shown that both dicyanodipyridylaurate(I) and dicyano-*o*-phenanthrolineaurate(I) have planar structures, four ions comprising a unit cell.

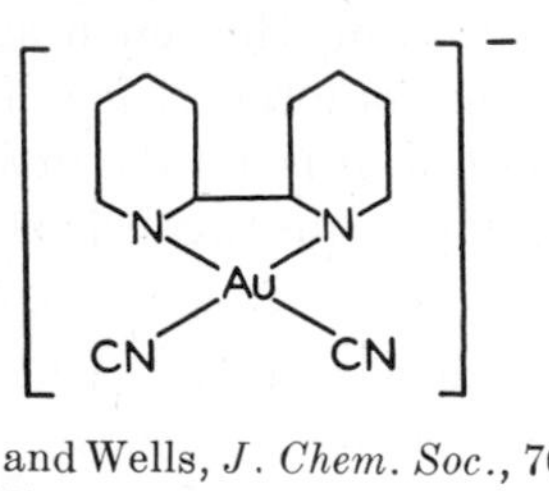

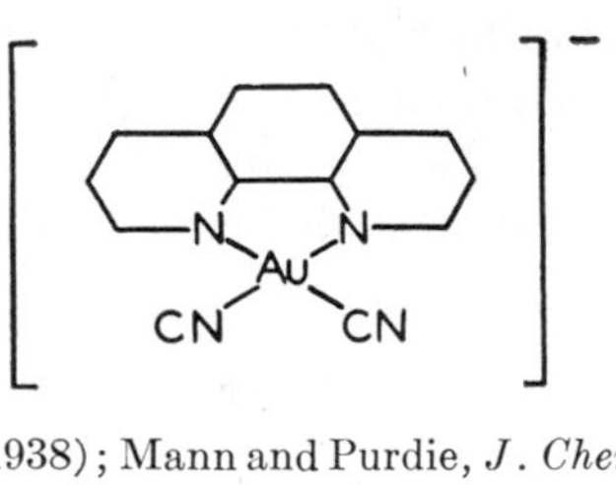

168. Mann and Wells, *J. Chem. Soc.*, 702 (1938); Mann and Purdie, *J. Chem. Soc.*, 873 (1936).
169. Chatt, Mann, and Wells, *J. Chem. Soc.*, 1949, 2086 (1938).
170. Dothie, Llewellyn, Wardlaw, and Welch, *J. Chem. Soc.*, 426 (1939).

Keggin and Miles[171] have studied a number of cyano complexes. The compound $Fe^{II}M_2[Fe^{II}(CN)_6]$, where M signifies an alkali metal or ammonium ion, has a cubic lattice structure. The iron atoms occupy corner positions, and the cyano groups bridge the iron atoms along all edges of the cubes. The alkali metal ions are located at the centers of the cubes. Oxidation of this compound first produces alkali-containing Prussian blue and then Berlin green, $Fe[Fe(CN)_6]$.

$$7FeM_2[Fe(CN)_6] \rightarrow 2Fe_4[Fe(CN)_6]_3 + 6MCN + 8M^+ + 8e^-$$

$$2Fe_4[Fe(CN)_6]_3 + 6MCN \rightarrow 7Fe[Fe(CN)_6] + 6M^+ + 6e^-.$$

It is interesting that Weiser[172] has found identical x-ray patterns for Prussian blue and Turnbull's blue, which are formally written as

$$Fe_4^{III}[Fe^{II}(CN)_6]_3 \quad \text{and} \quad Fe_3^{II}[Fe^{III}(CN)_6]_2 ,$$

respectively.

Cox and his co-workers[173] have interpreted x-ray data for the tetrachlorostannate(II) ion to mean that four-coordination is present rather than six-coordination. The hydrated potassium salt is therefore $K_2[SnCl_4] \cdot 2H_2O$, and not $K_2[SnCl_4(H_2O)_2]$. Cox has also established the planar structures of potassium bis(oxalato)plumbate(II), bis(thiourea)lead(II) chloride, bis-(salicylato)lead(II), and bis(benzoylacetone)lead(II).

Beintema[174] has made a detailed study of hexaquo complexes of divalent metals in which the hexahydroxoantimonate(V) anion is present. Two crystalline modifications of $[Mg(H_2O)_6][Sb(OH)_6]_2$ are reported. One is a trigonal form, isomorphous with $[Ni(H_2O)_6][Sb(OH)_6]_2$, and the other is triclinic pseudo-monoclinic, isomorphous with $[Co(H_2O)_6][Sb(OH)_6]_2$.

Lambot[175] has used x-rays to confirm a planar structure for $K_2[Pt(NO_2)_4]$. The platinum-nitrogen distance is calculated as 2.02 A, and the nitrogen-oxygen distance as 1.22 A. The O—N—O angle in the nitro groups is 127°.

Heneghan and Bailar[176] have shown that the *cis* and *trans* isomers of dichlorobis(ethylenediamine)platinum(IV) nitrate yield quite different x-ray patterns. Formerly all the preparative methods used to synthesize this compound had produced only the *trans* form. Heneghan and Bailar have developed a method of synthesis for the *cis* form. It is optically resolvable, and its x-ray pattern shows clearly that it is not the *trans* isomer.

Moeller and Ramaniah[177] have used x-ray data to distinguish between two

171. Keggin and Miles, *Nature*, **137,** 577 (1936).
172. Weiser, Milligan and Bates, *J. Phys. Chem.*, **46,** 99 (1942).
173. Cox, Shorter, and Wardlaw, *Nature*, **139,** 71 (1937).
174. Beintema, *Rec. trav. chim.*, **56,** 931 (1937).
175. Lambot, *Roy. soc. Liege*, **12,** 463 (1943).
176. Heneghan and Bailar, *J. Am. Chem. Soc.*, **75,** 1840 (1953).
177. Moeller and Ramaniah, *J. Am. Chem. Soc.*, **75,** 3946 (1953).

complexes of thorium with oxine (8-hydroxyquinoline). If a solution of thorium(IV) nitrate is treated with oxine under appropriate conditions, a product may be isolated which contains four oxinate anions and one molecule of oxine per thorium(IV) ion. Heating this product to 120 to 125°C for five hours and then to 130 to 135° for one hour produces the normal inner complex, [Th(oxinate)$_4$]. X-ray diffraction studies show that the two complexes are different, and that the 1:5 complex is different from a mixture of the 1:4 complex and one mole of oxine. The fifth molecule of oxine is lost in solution, and it seems therefore to be bound by weak lattice forces. An analogous situation occurs with scandium[178].

TRACER TECHNIQUES; EXCHANGE REACTIONS

Any molecules, atoms or ions of any given species are indistinguishable from all the other members of the same single species when subjected to most physical measurements. This failure is a limiting factor in chemical studies, since apparently inert chemical combinations may be in equilibrium with their constituents without this equilibrium being detected. Tracer techniques take advantage of the fact that isotopic species may be distinguished, yet their presence in any ratio seldom affects the course or rate of a reaction by any measurable amount. It is theoretically possible to determine the distribution in a reaction of ordinary isotopes of different masses. In usual practice, however, only the isotopes of hydrogen have a sufficient percentage of mass difference to permit reasonably accurate measurements. The availability of radioactive isotopes and the development of efficient techniques for measuring radioactivity have been largely responsible for the growth of tracer chemistry. Like isotopic mass difference, radioactivity almost never alters the chemical nature of a system into which it is introduced as a constituent. A radioactive element is usually added to a reaction in the form of a common compound. If every molecule or complex which contains this element is in rapid equilibrium with its constituents, the radioactive substance quickly assumes a statistical distribution which is in proportion to the distribution of the ordinary isotope. Deviations from rapid equilibrium are measurable in terms of deviations from this statistical distribution of radioactivity. The method requires chemical separation of the species present, accurate measurement of the radioactivity, and appropriate calculations. The objective is a knowledge of the relative lability, or its opposite, the "inertness," of the chemical bonds in the species studied.

Preparation of Radioisotopes[179, 180, 181]

Very few naturally occurring radioactive elements are useful in tracer

178. Pokras, Kilpatrick, and Bernays, *J. Am. Chem. Soc.*, **75**, 1254 (1953).
179. Friedlander and Kennedy, "Introduction to Radiochemistry," New York, John Wiley & Sons, Inc., 1949.

chemistry. Complexes of such metals as uranium and thorium may be studied by application of natural tracers, but very careful separations and detailed calculations of the effects of various isotopes are necessary. Radioactive isotopes also occur naturally in potassium, rubidium, samarium, lutetium, and rhenium. All these isotopes have half-lives of the order of 10^8–10^{12} years; hence their activities are at low levels.

Most of the useful tracer elements are produced artificially. The nuclear reactions producing the active isotopes may be induced by bombardment with alpha particles, deuterons, protons, neutrons, electrons, γ-rays, or x-rays. Neutron-bombardment reactions produce many of the radioisotopes obtainable from the Oak Ridge National Laboratory. Production of the radioactive carbon of mass number 14 is illustrated by the reaction $N^{14}(n, p)C^{14}$. The production of radioactive bromine may also be effected by neutron bombardment; in this case the reaction takes place with emission of γ radiation: $Br^{79}(n, \gamma)Br^{80}$. Both the radioactive elements produced by these neutron reactions emit β^- particles at measurable rates. It should be pointed out that these nuclear reactions are independent of the chemical form of the target element, so far as their actual occurrence is concerned. The state of aggregation and chemical form do affect the efficiency of bombardment, since they determine the number and position of atoms within the target area.

Since the actual amounts of radioactive material produced for tracer use are quite small, ordinary handling procedures are not applicable. If, however, sufficient quantities of inactive material of the same chemical form are added, the active and inactive portions may be chemically treated as a unit. The fraction of radioactive material present may be found by measurement of the activity and weighing of the entire mass. The tracer in such a case is contained in a chemical substance—the "carrier"—which holds it during manipulations and separations. Carriers with their radioactive fractions may be chemically separated from other carriers whose chemical nature is not objectionable, but whose active fractions are a radioactive impurity.

If target bombardment results in transmutation, so that the desired active product is not isotopic with the remainder of the target, chemical and physical means are useful in separation. Such common techniques as ion exchange, volatilization, electrolysis, solvent extraction, adsorption on precipitates, and leaching have been profitably used. For example, bombardment of magnesium oxide with neutrons or deuterons produces radio-

180. Wahl and Bonner, "Radioactivity Applied to Chemistry," New York, John Wiley & Sons, Inc., 1951.
181. Moeller, "Inorganic Chemistry," pp. 52–77, New York, John Wiley & Sons, Inc., 1952.

active sodium by the reactions $Mg^{24}(n, p)Na^{24}$ and $Mg^{24}(d, \alpha)Na^{22}$. The sodium is recovered by leaching the target with hot water.

When the desired product is isotopic with the target, separations are theoretically possible by means of such methods as gaseous diffusion, thermal diffusion, mass spectrography, and fractional distillation[182]. Practically, however, tracers are difficult to separate from targets by these techniques. Szilard and Chalmers[183] have described a neutron bombardment of ethyl iodide, $I^{127}(n, \gamma)I^{128}$, followed by water extraction of most of the iodine activity. Evidently the energy of the neutrons is partially diverted to break the carbon-iodine bonds. This type of process has been found to be applicable to a number of radioactive preparations. The necessary characteristics of the process are rupture of only those bonds involving activated atoms, slow exchange between the freed radioactive material and the original substance, and reasonable ease of separation of the activated substance in its new chemical form. The Szilard-Chalmers process has been used for production of radioactivity in metals by neutron bombardment of metal complexes. If the metal in a complex does not undergo appreciable exchange with uncomplexed metal ions of the same species, the radioactive metal ions produced by neutron collisions remain free of complexing during the separation process. Successful Szilard-Chalmers preparations of radioactive metals have been made by neutron irradiation of salts of bis(ethylenediamine)platinum(II), tris(ethylenediamine)cobalt(III), tris(ethylenediamine)iridium(III), and tris(ethylenediamine)rhodium(III), as reported by Steigman[184]. Mann[185] has used bis(ethylacetoacetato)copper(II) in the Szilard-Chalmers process, and Duffield and Calvin[186] have used disalicylaldehyde o-phenylenediimine copper(II).

Detection and Measurement of Radioactivity

A typical tracer study involves introduction of a tracer of known activity and chemical form into a system, carrying out a known reaction in the system, separating the chemical entities, determining the activity of each, and calculating the deviations from purely statistical distribution. As an example, the work of Grinberg and Filinov[187] may be cited. These authors prepared radioactive bromine as potassium bromide, KBr*, where the asterisk denotes the active element. In one part of the study a known weight of tracer potassium bromide was added to a solution of a known weight of

182. Moeller, *ibid.*, pp. 38–52.
183. Szilard and Chalmers, *Nature*, **134,** 462 (1934).
184. Steigman, *Phys. Rev.*, **59,** 498 (1941).
185. Mann, *Nature*, **142,** 710 (1938).
186. Duffield and Calvin, *J. Am. Chem. Soc.*, **68,** 557, 1129 (1946).
187. Grinberg and Filinov, *Compt. rend. acad. sci. U.R.S.S.*, **23,** 912 (1939); **31,** 453 (1941).

potassium tetrabromoplatinate(II). After a short time the two compounds were separated (e.g., by precipitation of silver bromide or $[Pt(NH_3)_4]$-$[PtBr_4]$). The activity of each was determined and found to be exactly that dictated by statistical considerations for the equilibria

$$K_2[PtBr_4] + KBr^* \rightleftharpoons K_2[PtBr_3Br^*] + KBr;$$
$$K_2[PtBr_3Br^*] + KBr^* \rightleftharpoons K_2[PtBr_2Br_2^*] + KBr;$$
$$K_2[PtBr_2Br_2^*] + KBr^* \rightleftharpoons K_2[PtBrBr_3^*] + KBr;$$
$$K_2[PtBrBr_3^*] + KBr^* \rightleftharpoons K_2[PtBr_4^*] + KBr.$$

That is, assuming equimolar amounts of complex and potassium bromide, four-fifths of the activity is transferred to the complex. This demonstrates rapid exchange between bromide ions and the bromo groups of the complex and indicates a lability of the complex.

The example just given points out the fundamental importance of accurate measurement of radioactivity in tracer studies. Nearly all common tracers emit β^- particles, and some emit γ radiation. Heavy, naturally radioactive elements frequently emit α particles. All these types of radiation may be detected by the classical method of permitting them to strike a photographic film, which on development shows blackening caused by ionization of the emulsion material. Photographic techniques are useful for microscopic study of particle tracks, but they are not suitable for continuous measurement of radiation rates.

Applications

Radioactive tracers have become increasingly important in recent years in the study of complexes. Their principal use has been in exchange studies, the data from which have led to many significant conclusions regarding bond type. The example given above from the work of Grinberg and Filinov[187] showed rapid exchange between free bromide ions and the bromo groups of $[PtBr_4]^=$. A large degree of ionic character appears to be present in the platinum-bromine bond. The same series of studies demonstrated rapid bromide exchange for the complexes $[PtBr_6]^=$ and $[Pt(NH_3)_2Br_2]$. When radioactive platinum was used, however, in the form of $[Pt^*Cl_6]^=$, no metal exchange was observed with $[Pt(NH_3)_2Cl_4]$, nor with $[Ir(py)_2Cl_4]$ and $[Ir^*Cl_6]^=$ or $[Ir^*Cl_6]^\equiv$. These results suggest either that the metal-chlorine bonds exhibit much more covalent character than the metal-bromine bonds, or, as is more likely, that the metal-nitrogen bonds in these platinum group complexes are primarily covalent. In the latter case, regardless of the rapidity of the halogen exchange, no radioactive metal atom could be attached to a nitrogen-donor group, since only the inactive metal atoms were originally so attached. Thus no activity can appear in the nitrogen-containing fraction of the complex mixture.

Polesitskii[188] used radioactive iodine in his study of the tetraiodomer-curate(II) complex, formed according to the equation

$$HgI_2 + 2I^- \rightleftharpoons HgI_4^{=}.$$

Mercury(II) iodide was shaken with radioactive potassium iodide in one solution, and radioactive mercury(II) iodide with inactive potassium iodide in another. Silver ion was added to precipitate silver iodide and silver tetraiodomercurate(II). Completely statistical distribution of activity in the precipitates showed complete exchange and led the author to conclude that all four coordination positions in the mercury(II) complex are equivalent.

Tracers have played a significant part in several investigations of tris-(oxalato) complexes of aluminum, iron(III), chromium(III), and cobalt(III). Thomas[189] suggested that the resolved form of the chromium salt racemizes by a mechanism whose rate-determining step is

$$d\text{- or } l\text{-}[Cr(C_2O_4)_3]^{=} \rightleftharpoons [Cr(C_2O_4)_2]^- + C_2O_4^{=}$$

Thomas, Wahl[190], and Burrows and Lauder[191], furthermore, reported that the iron and aluminum complexes are resolvable, as the cobalt and chromium complexes are known to be. Long[192] and Johnson[193], however, were unable to confirm these resolutions. In addition, Long prepared radioactive oxalate by deuteron bombardment of carbon and successive conversion to carbon monoxide, carbon dioxide, and oxalate. In solution this active oxalate was mixed with the tris(oxalato) complex of each of the four metals. Exchange proved to be rapid for iron and aluminum, while no exchange was measurable with cobalt and chromium. These results indicate predominantly ionic bonds in the iron and aluminum complexes and predominantly covalent bonds in the cobalt and chromium complexes. Resolution of the first two complexes therefore seems unlikely, as does the ionic mechanism for racemization of the chromium complex.

An extensive review of the use of tracers in studying substitution reactions in complexes has been given by Taube[194]. The most important concept advanced by Taube is that the covalent or ionic character of metal-ligand bonds is not the fundamental factor influencing rates of exchange involving these bonds. It is rather the electron structure of the central metal ion which exerts a direct effect. Among the inner orbital complexes, those having one or more vacant inner d orbitals show much faster rates of substitu-

188. Polesitskii, *Compt. rend. acad. sci. U.R.S.S.*, **24**, 540 (1939).
189. Thomas, *J. Chem. Soc.*, **119**, 1140 (1921).
190. Wahl, *Ber.*, **60**, 399 (1927).
191. Burrows and Lauder, *J. Am. Chem. Soc.*, **53**, 3600 (1931).
192. Long, *J. Am. Chem. Soc.*, **61**, 570 (1939).
193. Johnson, *Trans. Faraday Soc.*, **28**, 845 (1932).
194. Taube, *Chem. Rev.*, **50**, 69 (1952).

tion than those in which at least one electron occupies each inner d orbital. Taube proposes that substitution reactions in these cases take place through formation of an intermediate which uses the vacant orbital, thus increasing the normal coordination number by one. This type of intermediate can result from complexes with filled d orbitals only through pairing or promotion of electrons, both of which require considerable energy. An example of the application of this concept may be found in the substitution reactions of vanadium(III) complexes, which have a vacant d orbital, and chromium(III) complexes, which do not. The reactions may be described in terms of electron structure in the following manner.

V(III) $d^1d^1d^0D^2SP^3 \to [d^1d^1D^3SP^3] \to d^1d^1d^0D^2SP^3$ lower-energy intermediate; rapid reaction

Cr(III) $d^1d^1d^1D^2SP^3 \to [d^2d^1D^3SP^3] \to d^1d^1d^1D^2SP^3$ higher-energy intermediate; slow reaction

Experimental observations confirm the marked difference in rates of exchange among complexes of these two trivalent metals.

Complexes of the outer-orbital type, which are not subject to the direct effect of d-orbital structure, show a regular variation in substitution rates with charge on the central metal ion. Increasing charge corresponds to decreasing rate of exchange, and the secondary effect of covalent character is more important here. Covalent character likewise accounts for rate differences in cases of similar electron structure among inner-orbital complexes, the more covalent complexes undergoing slower substitutions. In general, Taube has suggested that degree of covalence is an index of substitution rates when there is no significant variation in electron structure in the complexes under consideration, or when covalent character has a direct influence on the electron structure. But covalent character alone is not a reliable guide in prediction of substitution rates, since in many cases its effects are opposite to the determining effects of electron structure.

Establishment of the formulas of complexes has been possible through tracer studies. Adamson[195] has studied the cyano complex of cobalt(II) and established its formula as $[Co(CN)_5]^=$ rather than $[Co(CN)_6]^{4-}$, as previously supposed. The cyano groups in the complex show rapid exchange (2 minutes) with radioactive potassium cyanide, but exchange with $[Co(CN)_6]^=$ is negligible after several days. Adamson suggests that the cobalt(II) complex is an example of a true five-coordinate species in solution.

Long[196] has reported a tracer study of the tetracyanonickelate(II) ion, using radioactive cyanide and radioactive nickel. The rate of exchange be-

195. Adamson, *J. Am. Chem. Soc.*, **73**, 5710 (1951).
196. Long, *J. Am. Chem. Soc.*, **73**, 537 (1951).

tween the radioactive cyanide and $[Ni(CN)_4]^=$ is immeasurably fast. This fact suggests that radioactive nickel ion of $[Ni^*(H_2O)_x]^{++}$, should exchange rapidly with that in tetracyanonickelate. Such is not the case, however; addition of hydrated nickel ion to a solution containing tetracyanonickelate ion results in the precipitation of nickel cyanide as a suspension. Then addition of dimethylglyoxime precipitates the amount of nickel added as $[Ni^*(H_2O)_x]^{++}$, with no loss of radioactivity. Evidently the precipitated nickel cyanide actually contains two unlike kinds of nickel. Long postulates the formula $Ni[Ni(CN)_4]$ for solid nickel cyanide.

Johnson and Hall[197] have found that four-coordinate complexes of nickel which are shown by magnetic or x-ray studies to have covalent bonds do not exchange appreciably with radioactive nickel ion. Similarly, the six-coordinate complexes which can be resolved into optical isomers do not exchange, with the exception of tris(dipyridyl) nickel(II) ion. This complex shows a measurable rate of exchange, and it also racemizes measurably rapidly, as may be expected. Although bis(salicylaldoxime) nickel and bis-(salicylaldimine) nickel are diamagnetic in the solid state and therefore covalent, both complexes exchange with radioactive nickel in methyl cellosolve solution. Johnson and Hall interpret this evidence to signify a change of bond type upon solution.

Using a tracer method, Cook and Long[198] have successfully measured the dissociation constant of the stable complex ion tris(*o*-phenanthroline)iron (II), which is used analytically as ferroin indicator. Radioactive iron was used in preparing the complex. Then known amounts of the complex were dissolved in known volumes of water and treated with measured quantities of sulfuric acid. Upon acidification the following reaction takes place.

$$[Fe(o\text{-phen})_3]^{++} + 3H^+ \rightleftharpoons Fe^{++} + 3 \; H\text{-}o\text{-phen.}^+$$

The *o*-phenanthrolinium ion has a known dissociation constant, and the original concentrations of complex and added acid were known. Next a hundred-fold excess of ordinary iron(II) ion was added to the solution, and the complex was precipitated with $[CdI_4]^=$ ion. It was assumed that precipitation was complete before any shift in equilibrium took place and before any exchange could occur between added iron(II) ion and complexed radioactive iron(II) ion. Both these assumptions are reasonable, since the ferroin complex is quite stable and slow to exchange. After precipitation, the total amount of radioactivity in the filtrate was measured and attributed to the iron(II) ion originally dissociated from the complex. The added excess of iron(II) ion acted as a carrier, assuring nearly complete recovery of the activity in solution. The ratio of filtrate activity to original complex activity

197. Johnson and Hall, *J. Am. Chem. Soc.*, **70**, 2344 (1948).
198. Cook and Long, *J. Am. Chem. Soc.*, **73**, 4119 (1951).

was taken as the degree of dissociation of the complex in acid solution. All other necessary values for calculation of the dissociation constant were known, and the constant could then be found.

$$[Fe(o\text{-phen})_3]^{++} \rightleftharpoons Fe^{++} + 3\ o\text{-phen}$$

$$K_d = \frac{[Fe^{++}][o\text{-phen}]^3}{[Fe(o\text{-phen})_3^{++}]} = 8 \times 10^{-22}$$

By considering individual ion activity coefficients, Cook and Long arrived at a lower value of 7×10^{-22}, which is in rather good agreement with the value 5×10^{-22} found by Lee, Kolthoff, and Leussing[199], who used cell measurements.

DIALYSIS AND ELECTROLYTIC TRANSFERENCE

The diffusion of ions through membranes and their migration toward electrodes have been of occasional value in the study of the nature of complexes. Physical methods involving these phenomena are particularly suited to the determination of effective ionic weights.

An ordinary electrolyte, when subjected in solution to the effect of an electric current, shows the familiar migration of the positively charged ion to the cathode and the negative ion to the anode. If an electrolytic cell containing such a system is divided with porous walls, or even imaginary boundaries, into compartments, and a sample of solution from each compartment is analyzed after electrolysis, the differences in concentrations in the compartments may be used to calculate the fractions of the current carried by each of the two kinds of ions present. These fractions, known as transport numbers, are characteristic of individual ionic species, being large for rapidly moving ions and small for slow ions.

If a metal ion has been complexed by a sufficient number of negative coordinating groups to render the overall charge of the complex negative, the electrolytic migration will be opposite to that of the uncomplexed metal ion. Under these circumstances the formal calculation of transport numbers yields a negative value for the metal. For example, the addition of silver ion to an excess of a cyanide salt, followed by electrolysis, shows that the silver migrates toward the anode compartment. Furthermore, analysis of the solution in the anode compartment shows that each silver ion entering the anode compartment has been accompanied by two cyanide ions. These observations correspond to the formation of the dicyanoargentate ion.

$$Ag^+ + 2CN^- \rightarrow [Ag(CN)_2]^-$$

Hittorf[200] has made transference studies of several complex species in

199. Lee, Kolthoff and Leussing, *J. Am. Chem. Soc.*, **70**, 2348 (1948).
200. Hittorf: "Über die Wanderungen der Ionen wahrend der Elektrolyse," Leipzig, W. Engelmann, 1912.

solution. His data for the tetraiodo complex of cadmium, $[CdI_4]^=$, show negative cadmium transport numbers for concentrated solutions. As more water is added to the solution, the cadmium transport number increases in value, evidently because of the dissociation of the complex and formation of cationic species. Hittorf has shown that a similar dissociation occurs with the trichloroaurate(I) ion, $[AuCl_3]^=$.

Electrolytic diffusion measurements are conveniently made by dialysis or diffusion of ions through membranes. Most of the dialysis studies of complexes carried out since 1930 are the work of Brintzinger[201]. The general technique used is fairly simple. The electrolyte to be studied is dissolved in a solution containing an excess of another electrolyte such as sodium or potassium chloride. The resulting solution is placed in a cup having a membranous bottom. The cup is suspended so that the bottom is in contact with a known volume of solution containing the foreign electrolyte in the same concentration as in the solution which also contains the unknown. Both the solutions are stirred for a known length of time, and the solution in the cup is then analyzed. This procedure is repeated for the unknown solution, using several different time intervals. Then a like procedure is followed for a reference electrolyte whose rate of diffusion is known. The initial and final concentrations of electrolyte in the cup are used to calculate the dialytic constant λ from the relation

$$C_t = C_0 e^{-\lambda t}$$

where C_0 is the original concentration exclusive of foreign electrolyte, and C_t is the concentration at time t. With a proper choice of membrane material, the values of λ for different ionic weights obey the relation

$$\lambda \sqrt{I} = \text{constant},$$

where I is the ionic weight. Thus

$$\frac{I_x}{I_r} = \left(\frac{\lambda_r}{\lambda_x}\right)^2 ,$$

where the subscripts x refer to the electrolyte to be determined, and the subscripts r indicate the reference electrolyte. This method is therefore applicable to the determination of ionic weights by comparison with a standard.

Brintzinger has reported very extensive dialysis studies of complex ions in the presence of various other ions. His most general conclusion is that the species generally regarded as complex, such as $[Co(NH_3)_6]^{+++}$ and $[Co(NH_3)_5Cl]^{++}$, are in the presence of other ions complexed even further,

201. Brintzinger, *Z. anorg. allgem. Chem.*, **220**, 172 (1934); **225**, 221 (1935); **227**, 341, 351 (1936); **232**, 415 (1937); **256**, 98 (1948), and many other publications.

to form such "two-shelled" complexes as $\{[Co(NH_3)_6][SO_4]_4\}^{5-}$ and $\{[Co(NH_3)_5Cl][SO_4]_4\}^{6-}$. The experimentally found ionic weights for such species are in remarkably good agreement with those calculated from the proposed formulas. There are, however, certain serious criticisms of the method of dialysis. The most important of these is the fact that a reference ion must be used in each experiment, and the degree of complexing or hydration in the reference ion is often uncertain. In addition, the pore size of the membrane used is considered by many workers to be a much more critical variable than is supposed by Brintzinger. Jander[202] and Kiss[203] have shown to their satisfaction that slight variations in pore size or insufficient quantities of foreign electrolyte result in wide variation in the "dialytic constant." These criticisms are apparently justified. It is not reasonable, however, to discredit the possibility of existence of such two-shelled complexes as are proposed by Brintzinger. Laitinen, Bailar, Holtzclaw, and Quagliano[204] have shown that the half-wave potential of the hexammine cobalt(III) ion is shifted to more negative values in the presence of indifferent electrolyte anions which are good coordinating agents, such as sulfate, tartrate, and citrate. Diffusion rates in the presence of these coordinating ions are slower than with chloride or nitrate. These findings suggest formation of a two-shelled "super-complex" which is both more stable and slower to diffuse than the hexammine cobalt(III) ion. Other methods should be applied to this problem.

Thermal Measurements

The measurement of temperature has been useful in studying partial or complete decomposition of coordination compounds, as well as their phase changes, vapor pressures, and other thermodynamic properties such as heats of formation, reaction, and solution.

Ephraim[205] has reported an extensive series of studies of the decomposition temperatures of polyhalides and of ammine complexes of the transition elements. His interpretations of the data arising from these studies lead to several generalizations concerning thermal stability of complexes.

1. If the metal ion of an ammine complex may exist in more than one oxidation state, the higher state corresponds to the more stable complex. This statement is illustrated by the much greater thermal stability of $[Co(NH_3)_6]Cl_3$ as compared with $[Co(NH_3)_6]Cl_2$.

2. Divalent metals of small ionic volume show greater tendencies toward complex formation than those of larger ionic volume, and their complexes

202. Jander and Spandu, Z. physik. Chem., **A188**, 65 (1941).
203. Kiss and Acs, Z. anorg. allgem. Chem., **247**, 190 (1941).
204. Laitinen, Bailar, Holtzclaw, and Quagliano, J. Am. Chem. Soc., **70**, 2999 (1948).
205. Ephraim, Ber., **36**, 1177, 1815, 1912 (1903); Z. phys. Chem., **81**, 513, 539 (1912); **83**, 196 (1913); **84**, 98 (1913); Ber., **45**, 1322 (1912); **50**, 1069 (1917); Ephraim and Wagner, Ber., **50**, 1088 (1917); Ephraim and Muller, Ber., **54B**, 973 (1921).

are more stable. The hexammines of divalent manganese, cobalt, nickel and iron follow the relationship $(VT)^{1/3}$ = constant, where V is the ionic volume and T is the absolute decomposition temperature. Other hexammine complexes obey the relationship only approximately.

3. Hexammine complex salts containing large anions are more stable than their analogs containing smaller anions. For example, in the series [Ni(NH$_3$)$_6$]X$_2$, the chloride decomposes at 164°C, the bromide at 195°C, and the iodide at 221°C.

4. Ammine complex salts containing large anions tend to show an increased coordination number in the cation, so that the disparity in size of the cation and anion is a minimum. For example, [Ni(NH$_3$)$_6$] [Co(NH$_3$)$_2$(NO$_2$)$_4$] is difficultly crystallized from solution, but addition of ammonia results in crystallization of [Ni(NH$_3$)$_8$][Co(NH$_3$)$_2$(NO$_2$)$_4$]. It is questionable whether the additional ammonia molecules are truly coordinated to the nickel ion; they are more likely to be held merely by the requirements of the crystal lattice.

The work of Biltz[206] is important among thermal studies of complexes. This work will not be discussed in detail here, but it should be mentioned that Biltz has collected significant phase transition data from studies of stepwise dissociations of hexammine complexes, performed at either constant pressure or constant temperature. Divalent hexammines in general decompose directly to diammines, without intermediate stepwise loss of coordinated groups. The diammines usually have a greater relative thermal stability than do the hexammines.

Phase-change measurements may also be made with solutions of complex compounds. Hagenmuller[207] has used cryoscopic measurements of aqueous solutions of nitrite complexes as the basis of continuous variations analyses. Deviations of freezing points from additivity indicate the existence of [Hg(NO$_2$)$_4$]$^=$, [Cd(NO$_2$)$_4$]$^=$, [Cd(NO$_2$)$_3$]$^-$, [Cu(NO$_2$)$_3$]$^-$, [Pb(NO$_2$)$_4$]$^=$, and [Pb(NO$_2$)$_3$]$^-$. Hagenmuller assumes that the trinitrite complexes are singly hydrated to complete the coordination sphere.

OTHER METHODS

Many other physical methods have received infrequent attention in the study of coordination compounds. Most of these methods are not suited to wide application in this field; they are instead particularly adaptable to certain unusual types of problems. Several examples of the use of such methods are given below.

Gustavson[208] has carried out identification and separation of basic salts

206. Biltz, *Z. physik. Chem.*, **67**, 561 (1909); *Z. anorg. Chem.*, **109**, 132 (1920).
207. Hagenmuller, *Ann. chim.*, **6**, 5 (1951).
208. Gustavson, *Svensk Kem. Tid.*, **56**, 14 (1944); *J. Intern. Soc. Leather Trades Chem.*, **30**, 264 (1946).

of chromium(III), using selective adsorption on ion exchange columns. Since the basic salts consist of mixtures of complexes of both negative and positive charges, depending upon the number of hydroxo groups within the coordination sphere, both cationic and anionic exchange treatments are necessary for separation. Elution of the adsorbed complexes, followed by analysis of the eluate, determines the composition of both the cationic and anionic complexes present. Gustavson has used this method to study basic chromium chlorides, sulfates, oxalates, and thiocyanates.

Mellor[209] has proposed that ion exchange resins be prepared with complex-forming ligands polymerized into their structure so that some donor groups are left free. Trace quantities of metal ions could then be removed from a solution passed through such a resin.

Continuous variations studies with solution surface tension as a variable have been carried out by Arcay and Marcot[210] and by Kazi and Desai[211]. Arcay and Marcot report the formation of compounds having the compositions $2HgCl_2 \cdot KCl$, $HgCl_2 \cdot KCl$, and $HgCl_2 \cdot 2KCl$, while Kazi and Desai conclude that $CdI_2 \cdot KI$ and $CdI_2 \cdot 2KI$ form in solution.

Resolution of optically active complexes in solution has been accomplished in some instances by shaking the solution with finely ground crystals of one optical isomer of quartz. Columns packed with the ground quartz have also been used. In either case a selective adsorption effect is responsible. Sometimes the effect seems to be of a true equilibrium nature, since the time of contact with the quartz is immaterial so long as it is sufficient to bring about appreciable adsorption. In other cases, however, the selectivity appears to take place kinetically, with one isomer adsorbed more rapidly, but both adsorbed equally after a long period of time. In numerous other instances no separation has been achieved by the use of this method. Karagunes and Coumoulos[212] have resolved tris(ethylenediamine)chromium(III) chloride with quartz. Tsuchida[213] has used the method to resolve chlorobis(dimethylglyoximino)-ammine-cobalt(III). Frequent applications of quartz resolution have been made by Bailar and his co-workers[214]. Only partial resolutions have been achieved by this method.

Biltz and Stollenwerk[215] have employed a pressure method to study the

209. Mellor, *Australian J. Sci.*, **12,** 183 (1950).
210. Arcay and Marcot, *Compt. rend.*, **209,** 881 (1939).
211. Kazi and Desai, *Current Sci., India*, **22,** 15 (1953).
212. Karagunes and Coumoulos, *Nature*, **142,** 162 (1938); *Atti X° Congr. Intern. Chim.*, **2,** 278 (1938).
213. Tsuchida, Kobayashi, and Nakamura, *J. Chem. Soc. Japan*, **56,** 1339 (1935); Tsuchida, Kobayashi, and Nakamura, *Bull. Chem. Soc. Japan*, **11** (1), 38 (1936).
214. See, for example, Busch and Bailar, *J. Am. Chem. Soc.*, **75,** 4574 (1953); Kuebler and Bailar, *ibid.*, **74,** 3535 (1952); Bailar and Peppard, *ibid.*, **62,** 105 (1940).
215. Biltz and Stollenwerk, *Z. anorg. allgem. Chem.*, **114,** 174 (1920).

formation of silver ammine complexes. These investigators passed ammonia gas into an evacuated vessel containing silver chloride. The gaseous pressure was observed to rise steadily until a reaction took place between the gas and solid. During the reaction the pressure remained nearly constant, and then it rose again. Since the quantity of ammonia admitted at any time was known, the quantity combined with the solid could be calculated from the pressure data. The results give evidence for the formation of $AgCl \cdot NH_3$, $2AgCl \cdot 3NH_3$, and $AgCl \cdot 3NH_3$. The ordinary ammine complex, corresponding to $AgCl \cdot 2NH_3$, does not appear to form under these conditions.

When solutions of two metal salts are mixed to form an ideal solution, the volume of the final solution is equal to the sum of the volumes of the component solutions. If there is complex formation between the two salts, however, a non-ideal solution results, whose volume is not the sum of the original volumes. Davis and Logan[216] have identified reactions of metal-pyridine complexes with cyanate and thiocyanate ions by noting contractions in volume. Among the metals tested, the copper(II) complexes are characterized by the least contraction upon addition of cyanate or thiocyanate solutions. Cobalt(II) complexes are intermediate, and nickel(II) complexes show the greatest contractions. The addition of cyanate causes a greater contraction than the addition of thiocyanate. Davis and Logan advance the hypothesis that the amount of contraction may be related to the degree of metal-ligand affinity in these instances.

Slightly soluble salts are normally somewhat more soluble in concentrated solutions of other salts, because of the increased ionic strength of the solution and the correspondingly decreased activity coefficients of the ions of the slightly soluble salt. Sometimes, however, abnormal increases in solubility indicate complex formation. Hayek[217] has concluded from solubility studies that the increased solubility of mercury(II) iodide and mercury(II) oxide in mercury salt solutions is a result of complexing. A competition appears to exist between the water molecules of the hydrated mercury(II) ions and the neutral mercury(II) oxide or mercury(II) iodide molecules. Coordination of these molecules to form such species as $[Hg(HgI_2)_x(H_2O)_y]^{++}$ and $[Hg(HgO)_x(H_2O)_y]^{++}$ accounts for the increased solubility. Hayek suggests that the complexes $[Hg(HgI_2)](ClO_4)_2$ and $[Hg(HgO)_2](ClO_4)_2$ form in mercury(II) perchlorate solution in the presence of the respective slightly soluble mercury compounds. This explanation agrees substantially with the proposal of Sidgwick and Lewis[218] concerning solubility of beryllium oxide in beryllium salt solutions through formation of complexes of the type $[Be(BeO)_x]^{++}$.

216. Davis and Logan, *J. Am. Chem. Soc.*, **58,** 2153 (1936).
217. Hayek, *Z. anorg. allgem. Chem.*, **223,** 382 (1953).
218. Sidgwick and Lewis, *J. Chem. Soc.*, 1287 (1926).

Immiscible solvent distribution studies have been reported by Sinha and Ray[219], who investigated pyridine complexes of copper(II). Pyridine and benzene were added to solutions of copper(II) perchlorate, and the distribution of pyridine between the aqueous and benzene phases was measured as a function of the total quantity of pyridine. The amount of coordinated pyridine was calculated from the known distribution coefficients for the two solvents. When the total amount of pyridine had any value between ten and thirty times the amount of copper salt, only the dipyridine and tetrapyridine complexes were observed to form. Related studies by Macdonald, Mitchell, and Mitchell[220], with iron(III) thiocyanate complexes in an ether-water system, indicate that from one to six thiocyanate groups may coordinate with the iron(III) ion, forming all the complexes in the series $[Fe(SCN)]^{++}$ to $[Fe(SCN)_6]^{=}$.

Complex formation in solutions containing lead nitrate and either potassium or ammonium nitrate is indicated by the compressibility studies of Venkatasubramanian[221]. This investigator measured ultrasonic velocities in the solutions and estimated the compressibilities of the solutions as a function of composition. Minima in the compressibility-composition curves corresponded to formation of $Pb(NO_3)_2 \cdot KNO_3$, $Pb(NO_3)_2 \cdot 2KNO_3$, $Pb(NO_3)_2 \cdot 4KNO_3$, $Pb(NO_3)_2 \cdot NH_4NO_3$, and $Pb(NO_3)_2 \cdot 2NH_4NO_3$.

219. Sinha and Ray, *J. Indian Chem. Soc.*, **25**, 247 (1948).
220. Macdonald, Mitchell, and Mitchell, *J. Chem. Soc.*, 1574 (1951).
221. Venkatasubramanian, *Current Sci., India*, **20**, 13 (1951).

19. Coordination Compounds in Electrodeposition

Robert W. Parry

University of Michigan, Ann Arbor, Michigan

and

Ernest H. Lyons, Jr.

The Principia, Elsah, Illinois

Coordination compounds are widely used in electrodeposition. Deposits obtained from the simple salt solutions are sometimes loose, nonadherent, coarsely crystalline, and generally undesirable, while metal deposits from appropriate complex salt solutions are often smooth, adherent, and of high protective and decorative value.

The methods used in developing suitable plating baths are largely empirical; the art of electrodeposition is far ahead of its science. Thompson[1] suggested that further progress in the development of the science of electrodeposition might be achieved by a systematic application of Werner's coordination theory.

The Theory of Electrodeposition from Complex Compounds

The mechanism of electrode reactions, even for the so-called simple ions, is a subject of great complexity. As yet no theory can adequately explain all phases of the cathodic evolution of hydrogen from dilute acid[2]. It is not surprising that the much more complex phenomenon of metal deposition is not well understood[3]. The most widely used coordination compounds in commercial electrodeposition are the anionic metal cyanides, such as $[Ag(CN)_2]^-$ and $[Cu(CN)_3]^=$. Many investigators have found it difficult

1. Thompson, *Trans. Electrochem. Soc.*, **79**, 417 (1941).
2. Bockris, *J. Electrochem. Soc.*, **98**, No. 11, 153c (1951); Bockris and Potter, *J. Electrochem. Soc.*, **99**, 169 (1952); Eyring, Glasstone, and Laidler, *Trans. Electrochem. Soc.*, **76**, 145 (1939); Hickling and Salt, *Trans. Faraday Soc.*, **38**, 474 (1942).
3. Blum, Beckman, and Meyer, *Trans. Electrochem. Soc.*, **80**, 287 (1941).

to picture the reduction of a negatively charged complex on a negatively charged cathode surface.

The Alkali Metal Reduction Hypothesis. One of the earliest mechanisms[4], usually attributed to Hittorf, suggested that positively charged potassium ions are initially reduced to give potassium metal, and that the discharged potassium metal reduces silver from the cyanide complex. No direct experimental evidence was ever produced. It is highly improbable that alkali metal could plate out first[5] unless the free energy of the solid alkali is greatly lowered by instantaneous alloy formation on the electrode surface. Such alloy formation[6] may occur with electrodes such as mercury and possibly lead, but is highly improbable for other metals. The hypothesis is now obsolete.

A rather similar hypothesis[7] assumes that nascent hydrogen is liberated from the alkaline solution and reduces the silver cyanide complex in a secondary chemical process. No unequivocal evidence to support or refute such a mechanism is available. Butler[8] suggests that such a mechanism is apparently operative in some electrolytic organic reductions. An extension to complex compounds is speculative.

The Dissociation of the Complex to give "Simple" Metal Ions. This concept might be called the classical picture of complex ion reduction. It is assumed that complex ions dissociate to give low concentrations of simple metal cations which can be reduced at the cathode[9, 10, 11].

$$[Ag(CN)_2]^- \rightarrow Ag^+ + 2CN^-$$

$$Ag^+ + e^- \rightarrow Ag$$

The concept apparently developed from application of thermodynamic instability constants to the calculation of electrode potentials in the presence of complex ions. In most cases experimental differentiation between this mechanism and direct reduction of the complex has not been achieved; however, some evidence to support the dissociation hypothesis has been cited. From very dilute solutions of silver nitrate or copper sulfate, ranging

4. Classen and Hall, "Quantitative Analysis by Electrolysis," 5th ed. p. 48, New York, John Wiley & Sons, Inc., 1913; Dean and Chang, *Chem. Met. Eng.*, **19**, 83 (1918); Hedges, *J. Chem. Soc.*, **1927**, 1077; Levasseur, *Technique Moderne*, **19**, 29 (1926).
5. Glasstone, *J. Chem. Soc.*, **1929**, 690, 702; Sanigar, *Rec. trav. chim.*, **44**, 556 (1925).
6. Piontelli, *Gazz. chim. ital.*, **69**, 231 (1939).
7. Jolibois, *Helv. chim. Acta*, **23**, 412 (1940); Jolibois, *Compt. rend.*, **225**, 1227 (1947).
8. Butler, "Electrocapillarity," p. 199, London, Methuen and Co. Ltd., 1940.
9. Spitzer, *Z. Elektrochem.*, **11**, 345; 391 (1905).
10. Petrocelli, *Trans. Electrochem. Soc.*, **77**, 133 (1940); Stout and Faust, *Trans. Electrochem. Soc.*, **61**, 341 (1932).
11. Levin, *J. Gen. Chem.*, *U.S.S.R.*, **14**, 31 (1944); *J. Phys. Chem.*, *U.S.S.R.*, **18**, 53 (1944); cf., *Chem. Abs.*, **39**, 1597 (1945).

in concentration from 10^{-6} to $10^{-10}N$, finely crystalline, adherent deposits of silver or copper can be deposited by allowing the solution to flow rapidly between charged electrodes[12, 13]. The size of crystallites in silver deposits obtained from silver nitrate solutions decreased[4b] as the concentration of silver nitrate was reduced from 10^{-2} to $10^{-4}N$. Bancroft[13] stated that deposits become more finely crystalline as the potential difference between the metal electrode and the solution is increased,* but extension to the mechanism of silver cyanide reduction is certainly open to question. Theoretical arguments have been used against the hypothesis.

From the equilibrium constant for the reaction $[Ag(CN)_3]^= \rightleftharpoons Ag^+ + 3CN^-$ [15], Haber[16] calculated the ratio between time of formation and time of dissociation of the complex ion. This ratio is:

$$\frac{\text{Time of formation of complex}}{\text{Time of dissociation of complex}} = K_{\text{equilib.}} = 1.3 \times 10^{-22}$$

It was shown that if the time of formation for a given amount of complex is 10^{-3} or 10^{-4} seconds, more than a thousand years are required for dissociation of the same amount of complex. Such a situation precludes electrodeposition of silver by dissociation of the cyanide ion.

Alternatively, the time of dissociation of a complex ion may be set at 10^{-2} seconds or any other reasonable value to permit dissociation before deposition, and the time of formation of the ion may be calculated. Such a calculation shows that the complex ion must form in *less* than 10^{-22} seconds. If the coordinating anions move at least an atomic diameter (about 10^{-8} cm) to form the complex, they must have velocities several million times greater than that of light. The situation is not altered by substituting the dicyanide for the tricyanide of silver. Haber concluded that reduction of silver must take place by direct reduction of the anion and not by an intermediate dissociation process.

Similar conclusions were drawn from studies[17] of current-voltage curves for the reduction of $[Cu(CN)_3]^=$.

* Glasstone and Sanigar[14] have shown that the correlation between electrode potential and the physical properties of the deposit is not rigorous. The physical properties of silver deposited from argentocyanide solutions containing Na^+, K^+ or anions such as $PO_4^\equiv$, $CO_3^=$, $SO_4^=$, could not be correlated with the small changes in electrode potential which accompanied the introduction of these ions to the solution.

12. Vahramian and Alemyan, *J. Phys. Chem., U.S.S.R.*, **9**, 517 (1937); *Acta Physiochimica, U.S.S.R.*, **7**, 95 (1937); cf., *Chem. Abs.*, **31**, 6975 (1937); **32**, 2844 (1938).
13. Bancroft, *J. Phys. Chem.*, **9**, 290 (1905).
14. Glasstone and Sanigar, *Trans. Faraday Soc.*, **25**, 590 (1929).
15. Bodlander and Eberlin, *Z. anorg. Chem.*, **39**, 197 (1904).
16. Haber, *Z. Elektrochem.*, **10**, 433 (1904).
17. Masing, *Z. Elektrochem.*, **48**, 85 (1942).

Since such calculations are based on questionable assumptions, an experimental answer to the question has been sought.

The Direct Reduction of the Complex Ion. The direct process[15, 18, 19] for representative complex ions is shown in the following equations:

$$[Ag(CN)_2]^- + e^- \rightarrow Ag + 2CN^-$$

$$[Cu(NH_3)_2]^+ + e^- \rightarrow Cu + 2NH_3$$

This assumes reduction of a negatively charged anion at a negatively charged electrode[5a], which is reasonable since a negatively charged cyanide ion may be attracted and bound to a complex ion which already bears negative charge:

$$[Cu(CN)_2]^- + CN^- \rightarrow [Cu(CN)_3]^-$$

In such cases localized charge distribution may be of more importance than the over-all ionic charge.

Furthermore, certain complex anions undergo direct cathodic reduction.† In the reduction of potassium ferricyanide at a platinum microelectrode, the rate of reduction is controlled by the rate at which ferricyanide ions diffuse to the electrode surface[20]. Radioactive iron(III) ion does not exchange with ferricyanide ion at an appreciable rate[21]; thus no dynamic equilibrium exists between iron ions in the complex and iron ions in solution. Similar observations were made for iron(II) ions and ferrocyanide. Since the equilibrium

$$[Fe(CN)_6]^= \rightleftharpoons Fe^{+++} + 6CN^-$$

is established *very* slowly, it cannot be regarded as essential to the cathode reaction. Moreover, ferrocyanide, as well as the corresponding cyanides of nickel and cobalt, can be reduced electrolytically to give almost quantitative yields of complex cyanides containing univalent iron, cobalt, or nickel[22]. The fact that ferrocyanide is not in labile equilibrium with iron(II) ions in solution makes a mechanism involving previous dissociation untenable. An iron alloy may be deposited from a solution containing iron only as $K_3[Fe(CN)_6]$[10b]. Thus, though ferricyanide ions do not dissociate readily to produce hydrated iron(III) ions or other complexes, the entire

---

† In using the term "direct cathodic reduction" no definite mechanism for the electron transfer is implied.

18. Bodlander, *Z. Elektrochem.*, **10**, 604 (1904); Foerster, *"Electrochemie Wasseriger Losungen,"* 3rd ed., p. 229, footnote 1, Leipzig, J. A. Barth, 1922.
19. Newton and Furman, *Trans. Electrochem. Soc.*, **80**, 26 (1941).
20. Laitinen and Kolthoff, *J. Am. Chem. Soc.*, **61**, 3344 (1939).
21. Thompson, *J. Am. Chem. Soc.*, **70**, 1045 (1948).
22. Treadwell and Huber, *Helv. chim. Acta*, **26**, 10 (1943).

anion can be reduced to give iron in the divalent, monovalent, or zero valent state.

The cathodic reduction of negative ions is likewise observed with the cyano complexes of manganese[23], molybdenum[24], chromium[25], tungsten[26], and platinum[27]. Rates of substitution reactions with these ions[28] indicate that they are not in mobile equilibrium with the coordinating groups, a conclusion confirmed in some instances by radioactive tracer experiments[29]. Other examples are the electroreduction of citrate complexes of copper[30], of plumbate[31], of stannate, and of chromate. A large number of organic anions are also reduced at the cathode.

A good metallic deposit of cobalt can be obtained with high current efficiency from solutions of $[Co(pn)_2Cl_2]^+$ and $[Co(en)_3]^{+++}$ [32], yet Flagg[33] found no exchange between simple radioactive cobalt(II) ion and the pro-pylenediamine complex. Since, at room temperature, racemization of the optically-active $[Co\ en_3]^{+++}$ complex in water solution requires several weeks, equilibrium between the ethylenediamine complex and cobalt ions in solution or in other complexes must be established very slowly. A thin chromium plate can be obtained from ammonium trisoxalatochromi-um(III)[34], yet exchange between the complex ion and radioactive oxalate ions in the solution is very slow[35], showing that there is no labile equilibrium between the complex and simple chromium(III) ions. Metal deposition apparently occurs through reduction of the *anion* complex.

Deposition from these compounds probably proceeds through a lower valence state. Thus, in the reduction of $[Co(NH_3)_6]^{+++}$, $[Co(NH_3)_5NO_2]^{++}$, $[Co(NH_3)_4(NO_2)_2]^+$, $[Co(NH_3)_3(NO_2)_3]$, $[Co(NH_3)_2(NO_2)_4]^-$, and related aquo and chloro ammines, the polarographic waves[36] consist of two parts.

23. Grube and Brause, *Ber.*, **60**, 2273 (1927).
24. Collenberg, *Z. physik. Chem.*, **146**, 81, 177 (1930); Kolthoff and Tomiscek, *J. Phys. Chem.*, **40**, 247 (1936).
25. Hume and Kolthoff, *J. Am. Chem. Soc.*, **65**, 1897 (1943).
26. Collenberg, *Z. physik. Chem.*, **109**, 353 (1924).
27. Terrey, *J. Chem. Soc.*, **1928**, 202.
28. Taube, *Chem. Rev.*, **50**, 69 (1952).
29. Menken and Garner, *J. Am. Chem. Soc.*, **71**, 371 (1949).
30. Kalousek, *Collection Czechoslav. Chem. Communs.*, **11**, 592 (1939).
31. Glasstone and Hickling, "Electrolytic Oxidation and Reduction," London, Chapman and Hall, Ltd., 1935; Latimer, "Oxidation States of the Elements," New York, Prentice-Hall, Inc., 1928.
32. Kramer, Swann, and Bailar, *Trans. Electrochem. Soc.*, **90**, 55 (1946).
33. Flagg, *J. Am. Chem. Soc.*, **63**, 557 (1941).
34. Mazzucchelli and Bacci, *Gazz. chim. ital.*, **62**, 756 (1932).
35. Long, *J. Am. Chem. Soc.*, **61**, 570 (1939).
36. Kolthoff and Lingane, "Polarography," p. 285, New York, Interscience Publishers, Inc., 1941; Laitinen, Bailar, Holtzclaw, and Quagliano, *J. Am. Chem. Soc.*, **70**, 2999 (1948); Willis, Friend, and Mellor, *J. Am. Chem. Soc.*, **67**, 1680 (1945).

The first, corresponding to a gain of one electron, apparently represents reduction to the cobalt(II) state, and the second, corresponding to two electrons, represents reduction to the metal. The half-wave potential of the latter is always very nearly that of the aquated cobalt(II) ion, which is presumably formed because cobalt(II) ammines are unstable:

$$[Co(NH_3)_6]^{+++} + e^- \rightarrow [Co(NH_3)_6]^{++}$$

stable   unstable

$$[Co(NH_3)_6]^{++} + 6H_2O \rightarrow [Co(H_2O)_6]^{++} + 6NH_3 \text{ (very rapid)}$$

$$[Co(H_2O)_6]^{++} + 2e^- \rightarrow Co + 6H_2O.$$

As explained later, a two-step process is likely for other cobalt(III) and chromium(III) compounds, and possibly for chromate.

From thiosulfate solutions, good deposits of copper and zinc may be obtained[37], but cadmium from thiosulfate contains up to 5 per cent sulfur, and nickel from 22 to 70 per cent sulfur. X-ray analysis of the nickel-sulfur deposit indicates the presence of nickel sulfides such as Ni_2S_3. The deposition of semi-crystalline nickel sulfide suggests that dissociation of the thiosulfate complex does not precede reduction of the nickel ions.

Similarly, nitrogen has been detected in a copper-lead alloy plate from a solution containing ethylenediamine complexes[38]. Up to 17 per cent of halogen has been found[39] in deposits of antimony, cadmium, bismuth, copper, and tin obtained from halide solutions of the metal ions. Thus, with stable complexes, reduction appears to occur directly from the complex ion. For complexes such as $[Ag(CN)_2]^-$, which is in labile equilibrium with the Ag^+ and CN^- ions, experimental demonstration of the mechanism is not conclusive; however, theoretical considerations favor direct reduction.

Deposits are usually not obtained[40] from aqueous solutions of complex ions with electronic configurations involving hybridized orbitals from the inner electron shells, that is, the "inner orbital" ions of Taube[28]. From ions of "outer orbital" configuration, deposits are generally obtained. This rule holds for aquo complexes as well as for others, and suggests that the complex ion is directly involved.

Reduction of an Intermediate Complex Cation. To avoid difficulty due to charge repulsion at the cathode, Glasstone[5b, 41] suggested that a complex cation is formed from the complex anion; this cation then under-

37. Gernes, Lorenz, and Montillon, *Trans. Electrochem. Soc.*, **77**, 177 (1940).
38. Roszkowski, Hanley, Schrenk and Clayton, *Trans. Electrochem. Soc.*, **80**, 235 (1941).
39. Stone, thesis, Indiana University.
40. Lyons, *J. Electrochem. Soc.*, **101**, 363, 376, (1954); Lyons, Bailar, and Laitinen, *ibid*, **101**, 410 (1954).
41. Glasstone, *J. Chem. Soc.*, **1930**, 1237.

goes cathodic reduction:

$$2[Ag(CN)_2]^- \rightarrow [Ag_2CN]^+ + 3CN^-$$

$$[Ag_2CN]^+ + e^- \rightarrow Ag + AgCN$$

The existence of cationic complexes in iodide or cyanide solutions containing an excess of silver ion is fairly well established[41, 42], but the presence of appreciable amounts of the complex cation in plating solutions containing a ten-fold excess of complexing cyanide anion is open to question[43]. Job[44] found appreciable amounts of a cationic cobalt complex $(CoCl)^+$ in a solution containing an excess of hydrochloric acid, but an extrapolation to silver solutions is speculative.

The hypothesis has been extended to the plating of copper, zinc, cadmium, and mercury[41], and to silver deposition from complex iodides[45]. Glazunow[46] assumes that complex cations must be present in all complex salt solutions and reduction of these cations gives rise to three possibilities: (1) new complexes arise which cannot exist in the free state and decompose quickly with deposition of metal; (2) new complexes arise which give rise to insoluble oxides, chlorides, etc., on the electrode surface; or (3) new stable complexes arise which contain the metal in a lower valence state. The first possibility is illustrated by the deposition of zinc from complex cyanides.

$$[Zn(CN)_4]^- \rightarrow [Zn(CN)]^+ + 3CN^-$$

$$[Zn(CN)]^+ + e^- \rightarrow ZnCN$$

$$2ZnCN \rightarrow Zn + Zn(CN)_2$$

$$Zn(CN)_2 + 2CN^- \rightarrow [Zn(CN)_4]^-$$

The second possibility was used[46c, 46d] to explain the preparation of explosive antimony by electrolytic reduction of solutions containing antimony chloride complexes of the type $[SbCl_2]^+$ and $[SbCl]^{++}$:

$$[SbCl_2]^+ + e^- \rightarrow SbCl_2$$

$$SbCl_2 + 2e^- \rightarrow Sb + 2Cl^- \text{ or } SbCl_2 \rightarrow Sb + Cl_2$$

If the unstable $SbCl_2$ molecule is formed more rapidly than it decomposes, the unstable neutralized complex $SbCl_2$ is included in the metal deposit, and

42. Hellwig, *Z. anorg. Chem.*, **25,** 157 (1900).
43. Erdey-Gruz, *Z. physik. Chem.*, **172,** 157 (1935).
44. Job, *Ann. chim.*, [11] **6,** 97 (1936).
45. Schlotter, Korpiun, and Burmeister, *Z. Metallkunde*, **25,** 107 (1933).
46. Glazunov, *Chem. Listy*, **32,** 246 (1938); Glazunov, Starosta, and Vondrasek, *Z. physik. Chem.*, **A185,** 393 (1939); Glazunov, *Rev. met.*, **43,** 214 (1946); Glazunov and Lazarev, *Chem. Listy.*, **34,** 89 (1940); Glazunov and Schlotter, *First Intern. Electrod. Conf.*, (1937); cf. *Chem. Abs.*, **31,** 7766 (1939).

gives rise to explosive antimony. At lower current density, $SbCl_2$ molecules decompose as fast as they are formed; this gives stable antimony.

The third possibility is illustrated by reduction of ferricyanide to ferrocyanide.

Copper has been deposited[46b] on thin glass fibers stretched across the surface of a polished copper cathode in copper cyanide solution. The presence of copper on the nonconducting glass fiber was interpreted as evidence for secondary deposition; however, copper on these fibers might result from the metal lattice growing out over the glass fiber in a primary reduction process.

The Kinetics and Mechanism of Electrodeposition From Complex Ions

If dissociation takes place before reduction, any one of at least three steps may be rate determining: (1) diffusion of ions to the electrode surface, (2) dissociation of the complex to give so-called simple ions, (3) reduction of the simple ion and incorporation of metal atoms into the lattice. A number of investigators[47] have suggested slow dissociation as the rate determining step. In most cases it is impossible to distinguish experimentally between slow dissociation and slow reduction.

Alternatively, if deposition occurs by direct reduction of the complex ion, the process can be broken down into two major steps: (1) transfer of ions to the electrode surface and (2) reduction of the ion on the electrode surface. Experimentally these processes are studied by polarization curves. If transfer of ions to the electrode surface is the rate controlling factor, the potential of the cathode will rise above the reversible electrode potential for the solution as a whole, and the increase is termed *concentration* polarization. If the reduction process is slow while the transfer process is rapid, the potential of the cathode will again rise above the equilibrium electrode potential before metal is deposited. The latter increase in potential is termed *chemical* polarization. Much experimental work on the kinetics of the electrode processes involving complex ions has attempted to differentiate between concentration and chemical polarization.

The Transfer of Ions to the Electrode as the Rate Determining Process. Ions to be reduced reach the electrode surface by (1) diffusion, (2) mechanical stirring or (3) electrolytic migration. It is supposed that mechanical stirring cannot move ions directly to the electrode since a thin unstirred liquid layer is generally considered to adhere tenaciously to the metal surface. Ions must diffuse through this adhering film. The effects of

47. Dole, *Trans. Electrochem. Soc.*, **82**, 241 (1942); Esin, *Acta Physicochimica.*, *U.R.S.S.*, **16**, 102 (1942); cf., *Chem. Abs.*, **37**, 2273 (1943); LeBlanc and Schick, *Z. Elektrochem.*, **9**, 636 (1903); *Z. physik. Chem.*, **46**, 213 (1903).

electrolytic migration in the negative field of the cathode are generally not of great importance, and can be made negligible by the presence of an excess of an inert electrolyte. An excellent discussion of ion movement in solution is given by Kolthoff and Lingane[48]. Frequently, diffusion controls the rate of ion migration to the electrode.

If transport of ions to the electrode by diffusion is the limiting process, the current flowing can be calculated from Fick's law of diffusion. By determining the effect of a change in conditions of diffusion on the current flowing at a given potential, concentration polarization may be identified.

The Reduction of Ions on the Electrode as the Slow Process. The reduction process has been considered in three somewhat different ways. First, it has been assumed that the metal ions are discharged, then the metal atoms find places in the metal lattice. Either step may be rate determining. LeBlanc[49] thought that the slow step was dehydration or decoordination of the metal ion. Other workers[50] assume that free metal atoms accumulate around the electrode until metal crystallization occurs. An effort has been made to correlate the physical properties of the metal plate with the expected concentration of metal atoms in the cathode film. Here crystallization would be rate determining.

A second point of view suggests that an ion must first find a suitable place on the lattice before reduction occurs[51, 52]. Two possible energy barriers may be pictured, corresponding to desolvation and adsorption of the ion on the electrode surface, and to transfer of an electron from the electrode to the adsorbed ion. Either process may be rate determining. By applying the theory of absolute reaction rates, the Nernst equation for the potential of a reversible electrode is obtained. In addition, an equation was developed[53] to give the current flowing to the electrode at any voltage V as a function of the variables controlling both ion diffusion and ion reduction on the electrode surface.

The third hypothesis pictures the adsorption and reduction process as occurring in a single step[54]. No attempt is made to differentiate separate

48. Kolthoff and Lingane, "Polarography," Chapt. II, New York, Interscience Publishers, Inc., 1941.
49. LeBlanc, *Trans. Faraday Soc.*, **9**, 251 (1914).
50. Aten and Boerlage, *Rec. trav. chim.*, **39**, 720 (1920); Brandes, *Z. physik. Chem.*, **142**, 97 (1929); Fink, *J. Phys. Chem.*, **46**, 76 (1942); Hughes, *Dept. of Scientific and Ind. Research Bull.*, No. 6, (1922); Hunt, *Trans. Electrochem. Soc.*, **65**, 413 (1934); Hunt, *J. Phys. Chem.*, **36**, 1006, 2259 (1932).
51. Erdey-Gruz and Volmer, *Z. physik Chem.*, **A157**, 165 (1931).
52. Glasstone, Laidler, and Eyring, "Theory of Rate Processes," pp. 575–81, New York, McGraw-Hill Book Co., 1941.
53. Glasstone, Laidler, and Eyring, "Theory of Rate Processes," p. 579, Eq. 75, New York, McGraw-Hill Book Co., 1941.
54. Blum and Rawdon, *Trans. Amer. Electrochem. Soc.*, **44**, 397 (1923).

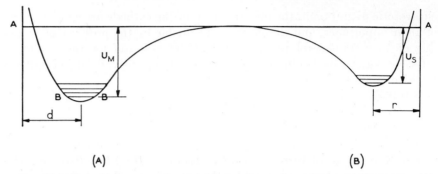

(A)   (B)

Fig. 19.1. Potential energy of a metal ion at the surface of the metallic lattice (A), and in the complexed state (B). Distance of separation great.

steps in the process. Because of inherent simplifications in this mechanism it may readily be applied to the reduction of complex ions[55-59].

A metal may be pictured as metal ions surrounded by mobile, loosely held electrons[58, 59]. The variation of the energy of a metal ion near the surface of the metal is represented by the potential energy diagram in Fig. 19.1A. The energy of an isolated ion in vacuo is represented by the horizontal line A; the ion loses energy U_m when it is bound to the metal surface and comes to rest at an equilibrium distance "d" from the bulk of the metal. The first horizontal line, BB, represents the ground energy level of the ion and the other lines represent higher energy levels. As the temperature of the metal increases there is greater probability that higher energy levels will be occupied.

Similarly, Fig. 19.1B is a potential energy diagram for a metal ion in the vicinity of a water molecule, group of water molecules, or other coordinating groups. U_s is the energy of hydration or energy of coordination and solvation for the ion. If a solvated ion from the solution approaches the metal surface, the two curves may overlap and combine to give a curve of the type shown in Fig. 19.2 (A or B). Now we have two equilibrium positions for the ion, separated by an energy barrier C. The height of this barrier is determined by how close the ion may approach to the metal surface. In some cases the potential hill may completely vanish at the moment of impact and reappear immediately as the ion rebounds. At the present time we have little information concerning such energy barriers.

55. Butler, *Trans. Faraday Soc.*, **19,** 729 (1924).
56. Gurney, *Proc. Roy. Soc. London*, **A136,** 378 (1932).
57. Fowler, *Proc. Roy. Soc. London*, **A136,** 391 (1932).
58. Butler, "Electrocapillarity," pp. 30–34, London, Methuen and Co. Ltd., 1940.
59. Gurney, "Ions in Solution," Chapt. IV, London, Cambridge University Press, 1936.

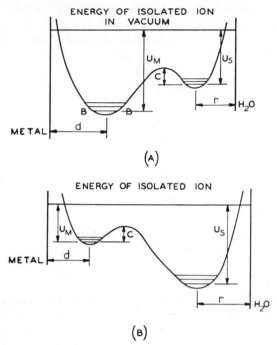

Fig. 19.2. New potential energy relationship associated with approach of solvated ion to electrode.

If the potential valleys are of equal depth, there will be no tendency for transfer of ions from one side to the other, but if energy levels in the metal are available below the levels of the ion in solution (Fig. 19.2A), spontaneous transfer of ions will take place from the solution to the metal surface, providing the ions can get over the energy barrier in the middle. For many cases this hump may be negligible, as for readily reversible electrodes, but in other cases the rate of the transfer may be limited by this barrier. The height of the barrier determines an activation energy for the process. If the number of positive ions being deposited initially exceeds the number of ions leaving the metal surface, the metal will acquire a positive charge, which retards and finally stops further deposition of positive ions on the metal surface. In electrodeposition an extraneous negative potential is imposed on the electrode to prevent this accumulation. The imposed E.M.F. maintains the energy levels for positive ions in the metal below those in the solution.

The reverse situation, illustrated in Fig. 19.2B, comes about when ions on the metal surface have higher potential energy than solvated or coordinated ions. Positive ions are then transferred spontaneously from the metal to the solution, a negative charge builds up on the electrode and a positive charge in the solution until the energy levels of ions on the electrode and in the solution are equal. If metal is to be deposited from solution, a larger external negative potential must be imposed on the cathode until energy levels in the metal are below those of the ions in the solution. The first situation, Fig. 19.2A, might be represented by a noble metal such as silver while the second situation, Fig. 19.2B, would represent a less noble metal such as zinc. In general, the effect of complex formation is to lower the potential energy of ions in solution relative to the potential energy of "simple" hydrated ions. As a result, the dips on the right in Fig. 19.2A and 19.2B will usually be deeper for the complex ions than for the simple hydrated ions. This means, for instance, that the potential for the reaction:

$$[Ag(CN)_2]^- + e^- \rightarrow Ag + 2CN^-$$

will be more negative (reaction has less tendency to go) than the potential for the corresponding reaction involving the simple hydrated ion of silver.

$$[Ag(H_2O)_2]^+ + e^- \rightarrow Ag + 2H_2O$$

This treatment does not require dissociation of the complex into simple ions, but rather assumes that the complex is in direct equilibrium with the electrode surface. The possibility that the reduction process is sometimes slow is suggested by the energy barrier in Fig. 19.2.

Rate Determining Steps in the Reduction of a Number of Complex Ions. Electrode polarization has been used as a criterion for identifying the slow process in electrode reactions. Conclusions are generally based on the shape of experimentally determined current voltage curves or upon the variation of such curves with changes in experimental conditions. The study of such curves is subject to a number of experimental errors[2a, 50a, 60]. Further, detailed interpretation of the data varies, depending upon the assumptions used. It is possible, however, in some cases to distinguish between diffusion and retarded reduction as the rate controlling process.

In the deposition of silver from solutions of the complex ions $[Ag(NH_3)_2]^+$ and $[Ag(CN)_2]^{-}$ [5a, 61], the maximum current density which gives 100 per cent cathode efficiency for metal deposition is determined by the rate at which complex ions can diffuse to the surface of the cathode. With ammonia, thiocyanate, and iodide complexes of silver, the rate of diffusion of

60. Butler, "Electrocapillarity," p. 167, London, Methuen and Co. Ltd., 1940; Glasstone, *J. Chem. Soc.*, **127**, 1824 (1925); Kohlschutter and Torricelli, *Z. Elektrochem.*, **38**, 213 (1932); Smartsev, *Compt. Rend. Acad. Sci.*, *U.S.S.R.*, **2**, 478 (1935); *Khim. Referat Zhur.*, **4**, no. 5, 119 (1941); *Acta Physicochim. U.R. S.S.*, **16**, 206 (1942); Mathers and Johnson, *Trans. Electrochem. Soc.*, **81**, 267 (1942).
61. Glasstone, *J. Chem. Soc.*, **1932**, 2849.

ions to the cathode determines cathode potential while the diffusion of ions from the anode determines anode potential (concentration polarization)[62].

Erdey-Gruz and Volmer[43, 51] concluded from current-voltage curves that under conditions such that concentration polarization is minimized, metal discharge is the rate-controlling step in deposition from ammoniacal solutions of silver bromide or chloride. For an ammoniacal solution of silver oxide, as well as for solutions of $[AgI_2]^-$ $[AgBr_2]^-$, $[Ag(CN)_2]^-$, and $[AgCl_2]^-$, the rate appears to be determined by the orientation of the ions in the lattice before reduction. Equations were derived for the curves under different circumstances of lattice formation.

These methods (see also Ref. 63) have been applied to other systems[64], but are subject to errors in measuring the active electrode surface and excessive concentration polarization around small active areas of crystal growth[65].

In the deposition of copper from solutions containing pyrophosphate, oxalic acid, or thiocyanate, concentration polarization was observed[64, 66]. With ammonia, ammonium oxalate, and thiosulfate as complexing agents the slow process was attributed to ion discharge. LeBlanc and Schick[47c] believe that the rate of copper deposition from potassium cyanide solution is limited by a slow dissociation of the $[Cu(CN)_3]^=$ complex. This idea has been used[67] to explain deposition of copper-gold alloys from cyanide solution. The rate of deposition of gold, but not that of copper, was that calculated from diffusion theory. It was concluded that the rate of discharge of gold cyanide is probably determined by the rate of diffusion of the complex ions to the electrode, but the rate of discharge of copper cyanide ions is probably determined both by diffusion and by rate of dissociation (or rate of reduction) of the complex at the electrode surface. However, Glasstone[5a] found that the potential of a copper electrode in a copper cyanide solution is dependent upon the concentration of cyanide. Relatively small increases in cyanide content bring about considerable increase in potential required for copper deposition. If the cyanide concentration is large or becomes large due to accumulation of cyanide around the cathode, hydrogen may be evolved along with copper. He concluded that polarization of the cathode is due to depletion of complex copper cyanide ions and accumulation of simple cyanide ions. This suggests diffusion as the rate controlling process, as is indicated by current-voltage data[67, 68].

62. Levin, *J. Phys. Chem., U.S.S.R.*, **17**, 247 (1943); **19**, 365 (1945); cf. *Chem. Abs.*, **38**, 1960 (1944); 40, 1738 (1946).
63. Butler, "Electrocapillarity," p. 169, London, Methuen and Co. Ltd., 1940.
64. Levin, *J. Phys. Chem., U.S.S.R.*, **15**, 948 (1941); cf. *Chem. Abs.*, **36**, 6087 (1942).
65. Vahramian, *Acta Physicochimica*, **19**, 148, 159 (1944).
66. Levin and Stonikova, *J. Gen. Chem., U.S.S.R.*, **13**, 667 (1943).
67. Esin and Alfimova, *J. Phys. Chem., U.S.S.R.*, **8**, 137 (1936); cf. *Chem. Abs.*, **31**, 1706 (1947).

The rate of deposition of zinc and cadmium from solutions of metal ammines or metal cyanides is controlled by the diffusion of ions to the electrode[41, 61, 67, 69, 70]. Both diffusion and retarded discharge play a part in the reduction of zinc from zincate solutions[70].

Only concentration polarization has been found[61, 71] in the deposition of mercury from $[Hg(CN)_4]^=$, though both diffusion and slow reduction are important in the deposition of mercury from $Hg(CN)_2$ (or perhaps $[Hg(CN)_2(H_2O)_2]$).

In the deposition of bismuth from hydrochloric or nitric acid solutions, concentration polarization predominates[72], while chemical polarization due to slow discharge is important in the deposition of bismuth from sulfuric acid solutions. Similarly, deposition of antimony[73] from hydrochloric acid solution is limited by ion diffusion, while ion discharge is important in the deposition from sulfuric acid solution.

In these experiments, concentration of the solution, current density, and temperature and other factors, play such large roles in determining the identity of the rate determining step that a distinct and unambiguous answer is obtainable only for certain ions under specific conditions.

Extensive investigations on electrode kinetics are summarized by Delahay[73a]. The most notable result is the determination of reaction rate constants for metal deposition. In some instances, it appears that the complex involved in the deposition mechanism has a lower coordination number than that of the predominant species in the solution[73B].

Electronic Configuration and Deposition Mechanism

The electronic configurations of the ions to be deposited exercise a controlling influence[40]. For example, the electronic structure of the aquated iron(II) ion is represented:

$$\left[Fe(H_2O)_6\right]^{++} \qquad 1s^2 2s^2 2p^6 3s^2 3p^6$$

68. Esin and Mantansev, *J. chim. phys.*, **33**, 631 (1936).
69. Levin, *J. Gen. Chem.*, *U.S.S.R.*, **14**, 795 (1944); cf., *Chem. Abs.*, **39**, 3736 (1945).
70. Esin and Beklemysheva, *J. Phys. Chem.*, *U.S.S.R.*, **10**, 145 (1937); cf., *Chem. Abs.*, **32**, 430 (1938); *J. Gen. Chem.*, *U.S.S.R.*, **6**, 1602 (1936).
71. Esin and Alfimova, *J. Gen. Chem.*, *U.S.S.R.*, **7**, 2030 (1937); Esin and Malarzev, *Z. physik. Chem.*, **A174**, 384 (1935).
72. Esin, Lashkarev, Levitina, and Rusanova, *J. Applied Chem.*, *U.S.S.R.*, **13**, 56 (1940); **17**, 114 (1944).
73. Esin, *J. Applied Chem.*, *U.S.S.R.*, **17**, 114 (1944); cf., *Chem. Abs.*, **39**, 1359 (1945).
73a. Delahay, New Instrumental Methods in Electrochemistry, New York, Interscience Publishers, Inc., 1954.
73b. Gerischer, *Z. Electrochem.*, **57**, 604 (1953).

in which the crosses represent electrons donated by water molecules to the sp^3d^2 hybridized orbitals. The presence of four unpaired electrons is indicated by magnetic data. In the hexacyano ion, however, the single electrons become paired, and the hybridization is d^2sp^3, involving $3d$ levels as well as $4s$ and $4p$:

$$\left[\text{Fe(CN)}_6\right]^{4-} \quad 1s^2 2s^2 2p^6 3s^2 3p^6$$

in which the crosses represent electrons from the cyano groups. The ion is diamagnetic, indicating that no unpaired electrons are present.

Iron is readily deposited from the aquated ion, but not from the cyano ion, (except as an alloy under special conditions)[10b]. In aqueous solutions, deposition generally does not occur where hybridization involves an inner orbital. Such a configuration may represent unusual stability, and apparently less energy is required to reduce hydrogen ion than to break up hybridization. Consequently, hydrogen rather than metal is discharged.

Inner orbital complexes react slowly or not at all in substitution reactions[28] except when half filled orbitals are present; a similar situation seems to hold for electron transfer reactions[40]. These observations suggest that dissociation of a coordinated group from an inner orbital complex, $AX_n \rightarrow AX_{n-1} + X$, occurs only with difficulty. Since the configuration is also unfavorable for electrodeposition, it is inferred that difficulty of dissociation is reflected in the deposition reaction, and that an intermediate of the type AX_{n-1} is important[73b].

Reduction of ferricyanide ion to ferrocyanide is reversible. Evidently little activation energy is needed to transfer an electron to the complex. Reduction to iron, however, does not generally occur. Since there appears to be no difficulty in transferring a single electron to the iron(III) complex, it has been suggested[40] that the obstacle lies in the stripping of the coordinated groups. Dissociation would be the first step in this process. The difficulty of dissociating an inner orbital complex would be shown by very large potential energy humps in Figs. 19.1 and 19.2.

With the aquated iron(II) ion, on the other hand, substitution and electron transfer studies indicate that dissociation occurs. Likewise the metal may be deposited. The necessary electrons are relatively easy to add, and loss of water groups takes place readily.

"Flash" deposits are sometimes obtained from inner orbital complexes. In some instances, the deposits appear to be the result of codeposition of impurities, and in others, the nature of the basis metal may permit deposition until it is completely coated. In either case, deposition soon ceases.

To account for the attachment of the metal ion to the cathode surface, it has been suggested[40] that the dissociated ion, AX_{n-1}, replaces the lost coordinated group with a molecule on the aquated cathode surface. Subsequently this water bridge is eliminated, perhaps because of the electrostatic attraction of the cathode for the positive metal ion, and a metallic bond is established. As other metal atoms are deposited in neighboring positions, the remaining coordinate bonds are replaced by metallic bonds. Transfer of electrons to depositing ions is needed only to maintain the average electrical potential of the cathode. Details, in terms of Pauling's theory of the metallic state, are given in reference 40, and provide an explanation for the nature of inclusions in deposits. There is evidence that non metal inclusions consist largely of residual coordinated groups.

Reversibility in the deposition of metal ions is found only when no rearrangement of the electronic configuration of the ion is necessary to attain the configuration of the metallic atoms. Among transition elements, rearrangement of electrons is associated with deposition; this requires expenditure of energy and is responsible for the observed irreversibility. In Figs. 19.1 and 19.2, this would correspond to potential humps higher than those for such metals as zinc and lead, but not quite as high as that for hydrogen, which is commonly codeposited with these metals.

Another cause of irreversibility is the tendency of such metals as tin, bismuth, and gallium to form multinuclear aquo or hydroxo complexes which are slow to dissociate. The effect of chloride ions in reducing the irreversibility is presumably to be attributed to formation of mononuclear chloro complexes.

COORDINATION COMPOUNDS AS IMPORTANT FACTORS IN ELECTRODEPOSITION

It is well known that metal deposits obtained from solutions of complex ions frequently have better physical properties than those from simple salt solutions. Further, small quantities of addition agents produce truly remarkable changes in the physical properties of the deposited metal. The causes of these phenomena are not understood, though both are of substantial technological importance.

Crystal Structures of Electrodeposits

Metal deposits obtained from solutions of complex salts are made up of submicroscopic crystals[3, 46a], but it is not true that the crystals must be smaller than the wave length of light to produce bright deposits. Bright and dull deposits of chromium contain crystals of comparable size[74], but in bright deposits, crystals show regular orientation. Blum[4, 75] emphasized the importance of crystal orientation and suggested that copper deposited from

74. Wood, *Trans. Faraday Soc.*, **31**, 1248 (1935).
75. Blum, Beckman, and Meyer, *Trans. Electrochem. Soc.*, **80**, 249, 288, 254 (1941).

cyanide complexes is dull, not because of crystal size, but because of random orientation. Recent investigations[76], however, indicate that neither crystal size nor orientation is directly related to brightness. It can only be asserted that the surface must be smooth enough for specular reflection, regardless of the structure beneath.

It has been suggested[11, 13] that the increased deposition potential on the cathode as a result of complex formation is responsible for small-grained, and sometimes oriented, deposits; however, this does not explain the actual function of the complex ion, but rather emphasizes a nonrigorous correlation[14] between electrode potential and character of deposited metal.

Kohlschütter[77] suggested that insoluble cyanides deposited on the electrode surface prevent the growth of large crystals, and attention has been directed[43, 65] toward the possible adsorption of complexing ions on the electrode. Microscopic studies[43, 50a, 60c, 60d, 65, 78] show that from perchlorate or nitrate solutions silver is not deposited uniformly over the face of a silver crystal but only on a number of active centers on the crystal face. The number of such active centers on the crystal surface is increased by a *decrease* in the concentration of the silver salt in the solution[12]. If the current is interrupted for a short time, the old crystal surfaces will not develop again, but when electrolysis is resumed, new localized sites become active and crystallites grow from the new sites[12, 60d]. In silver nitrate solution from which all organic matter had been removed, localized passivation and activation of the silver crystal face did not develop[65]. Addition of 0.2 per cent dextrin solution brought about a strong passivation, suggesting that passivation is due to adsorption of surface-active organic impurities.

In contrast to the behavior for simple salts, an entire face of the crystal may develop in solutions of complexes such as cyanide. In general, the materials present in the solution determine which crystal face develops* [43]. The absence of passivation in the electrodeposition of silver from cyanide solutions is accounted for by the high adsorption of the cyanide-silver complex, which prevents adsorption of surface-active impurities[65].

A study[32] of the deposition of cobalt and nickel from a wide variety of complexes suggested that the nature of the coordinating group as well as

---

* It is interesting in this connection that the crystalline form of an electrodeposited metal is dependent upon the bath from which it is obtained. For instance, body-centered cubic chromium is formed in the essential absence of trivalent chromium, whereas deposition of the hexagonal form depends upon the presence of trivalent chromium[75b].

76. Clark and Simonsen, *J. Electrochem. Soc.*, **98**, 110 (1951); Denise and Leidheiser, *ibid.*, **100**, 490 (1953).
77. Kohlschütter, *Z. Elektrochem.*, **19**, 181 (1913).
78. Vahramian, *Compt. Rend. Acad. Sci.*, *U.R.S.S.*, **22**, 238 (1939); *Acta Phys. Chim. U.R.S.S.*, **7**, 683 (1937).

the thermodynamic stability of the complex ions is important in determining whether good plates will be formed. In general, large coordinating groups or those containing aromatic ring systems gave poor plates. It was also observed that complexes which are reduced either with great difficulty or too easily gave poor plates. Complexes in an intermediate range of stability (i. e., [Co(en)$_3$]$^{+++}$) gave good plates.

The Effect of Brighteners. Mathers[79]† suggested that brighteners and addition agents may owe their action to ability to form complexes with the metal ions in solution. Mathers used the terms "complex ion" and "complex compound" very broadly and implied that all ions present in the ionic atmosphere are part of the complex.

However, it does not seem justifiable to postulate that all addition agents form Werner type coordination compounds with metal ions in solution. A survey of over one hundred organic addition agents used in the plating of nickel failed to reveal any relation between structure of the compounds and efficacy as brighteners or polarizers[81]. In the deposition of silver and copper, on the other hand, various substances such as glycine, tartaric acid, citric acid, and metaphosphoric acid can improve the quality of the deposit even when the addition agent is present in very small concentrations (.01M in 1M AgNO$_3$)[82]. The addition agents were found in the deposits in small amounts, and it was established by transference studies that each of the agents was able to form complex cations with silver or copper ions. From this, a close correlation between the efficacy of an addition agent and its ability to form complex compounds was suggested. However, no single simple explanation will correlate all of the observed facts with the structures of the wide variety of addition agents now in use.

An addition agent is usually a substance added in relatively small amounts to modify physical properties of the deposit. Addition agents are often used to produce bright deposits, to reduce or "level" surface irregularities on the cathode, or to alter stresses in the deposits.

Addition agents may be grouped in three classes: (a) *Grain refining* agents, such as gelatin in copper sulfate and many other baths, reduce the

---

† Mutscheller[80] suggested earlier that gelatin forms complexes with the *anions* in solutions of CuSO$_4$ and AgNO$_3$, but his definition of complex was much broader than that used for the metal complexes now under consideration.

79. Mathers, *Proc. Am. Electroplaters Soc.*, June, 134 (1939); Mathers and Kuebler, *Trans. Am. Electrochem. Soc.*, **29**, 417 (1916); **36**, 234 (1919); **38**, 133 (1920).
80. Mutscheller, *Met. and Chem. Eng.*, **13**, 353 (1915).
81. Raub and Wittum, *Metal Ind.*, (*N. Y.*), **38**, 206, 315, 429 (1940).
82. Fuseya and Maurata, *Trans. Am. Electrochem. Soc.*, **50**, 235 (1926); Fuseya and Nagano, *Trans. Am. Electrochem. Soc.*, **52**, 249 (1927); Fuseya, Murata, and Yumato, *Tech. Reports Tohoku Imp. Univ.*, **9**, no. 1, 33 (1929); cf., *Chem. Abs.*, **24**, 3445 (1930).

grain size of the deposit, and often diminish the tendency of the deposit to form "trees" and nodules; (b) *active* agents, including brighteners such as zinc, cadmium, sulfonated aryl aldehydes, safranines, etc., in nickel baths[83], which modify the surface of the deposit, and usually the structure as well, and often produce the desired effects only over a narrow range of current density, temperature, pH, and other conditions; and (c) *carrier* agents, such as naphthalene disulfonic acids or *p*-toluenesulfonamide in nickel baths[83], which greatly extend the effective operating range of the active brightener, impart greater tolerance towards impurities, and in some instances enhance brightness.

Bright deposits ordinarily have a banded structure, the cause of which is unknown. They are almost invariably more brittle than typical deposits made in the absence of the brightener. This is usually attributed to the inclusion of the brightener, or its decomposition product, in the deposit, resulting in a strained or distorted metal lattice.

Brightening is only one result of the action of addition agents. Far more frequently, addition agents cause the formation of spongy deposits; this, of course, is not desirable for electroplating. Other results are "wrinkled" deposits, discolorations, and roughness resembling that of sand paper. Studies have usually been directed toward brightness; a thorough study of addition agents seems not to have been made.

Grain refining agents are generally colloidal. Most active agents are electron donors and a tendency toward coordination is to be expected. Apparently at least two donor pairs are required[84]. Where the coordination is very strong, as between glycine and many metals, spongy deposits are produced. This is attributed to failure to convert coordinate linkages to metallic bonds on the cathode, so that the agent is included in the deposit, making it impossible to build up a normal metallic lattice. It is suggested that an effective brightener must have sufficiently strong coordinating tendency to modify the cathode surface by preventing formation of protruding crystal edges, and yet not so strong that it cannot readily be decoordinated to form metallic bonds. Probably a few residual coordinated groups remain in the deposit—enough to produce the characteristic banded structure as well as the desired smooth, bright surface.

A possible explanation of smoothing action lies in the tendency of decoordinated groups to remain at the cathode surface and form new linkages with metal ions as they diffuse toward the cathode. By this action, atoms may be "fed" into the proper level, and the build-up of crystals may be prevented. This is closely related to adsorption processes suggested by others[85]. The function of the carrier type of addition agent is not under-

83. Pinner, Soderberg, and Baker, *Trans. Electrochem. Soc.*, **80,** 539 (1941).
84. Roth and Leidheiser, *J. Electrochem. Soc.*, **100,** 490 (1953).
85. Henricks, *Trans. Electrochem. Soc.*, **82,** 237 (1942).

stood; in some instances the carrier may coordinate with trace impurities and prevent them from influencing the deposit.

It is usually relatively difficult to find brighteners for metals which are deposited reversibly or very nearly so, such as tin and lead. On the other hand, many brighteners are known for metals which are deposited irreversibly, such as nickel. In fact, irreversibility is generally accompanied by a tendency to smooth, fine-grained, semi-bright deposits even in the absence of specific addition agents. It is suggested that in these instances, the coordinating tendency is so strong that even water functions to some extent as an addition agent.

Complexes and Throwing Power

In the practice of electroplating, an important consideration is ability to deposit coatings of relatively uniform thickness on articles of irregular shape, even though the current distribution is far from uniform, as on protruding edges or in recesses. This ability, known as "throwing power," represents the net result of several characteristics of the bath and also of the geometry of the plating cell. Polarization, conductivity, and variation of current efficiency with current density are important. "Throwing power is not a single measurable property of a solution"[75]; a definitive discussion has not been given and is perhaps impossible.

In a general way, throwing power seems to parallel the stability of the complex ions in the baths. Thus, in industrial practice, silver and copper cyanide baths have the highest throwing powers, the cadmium bath is somewhat inferior, and the cyanide zinc bath is still poorer. This is exactly parallel to the stability constants of the cyano complexes. All of these baths, as well as the the stannate bath, have much better throwing power than the corresponding sulfate baths or the silver nitrate bath.

Furthermore, the throwing power of cyanide baths may be improved by increasing the concentration of cyanide, although at the expense of cathode efficiency. The improvement of throwing power by complexing has been considered to be the result of diminution of "free" metal ions in the bath. However, since deposition appears to occur directly from complex ions, this explanation is unsatisfactory. Neither can the influence on cathode efficiency explain the results, since efficiencies in the silver bath are close to 100 per cent.

It seems likely that concentration effects at the cathode surface are important. Glasstone[5a] observed that small changes in cyanide concentration have large effects on electrode potential. However, ordinary polarization measurements do not parallel throwing power very closely.

All commercial baths with good throwing power are alkaline. It is not known whether this rule applies to other baths. Metals remain in alkaline solution only by forming complexes, and hence good throwing power is to be expected; it is unlikely that alkalinity exerts any direct influence. There seem to be no data on the throwing power of highly stable complexes in acid solution. That of the chromium bath is very poor but this bath is exceptional in many ways.

THE PLATING OF SPECIFIC METALS FROM AQUEOUS SOLUTIONS OF COMPLEX IONS

Metals which can be deposited from aqueous solution in nearly pure form (i.e., not as amalgams or alloys) are located in one area of the periodic table. Furthermore, if the metals are classified according to the inner or outer orbital configuration of their complexes, they fall into four fairly well defined regions (see Fig. 19.3). The plating of pure zirconium, columbium, molybdenum, tungsten, and tantalum is still classed as doubtful[86] though several alloys of the latter group of metals can be plated from aqueous solution.

If one considers the hydrated ion a complex, complex ions are involved in all cases of electrodeposition from aqueous solution; however, in agreement with general practice, solutions containing the hydrated ions will be classed as solutions of the simple salts unless hydrate isomerism is observed, as in the case of chromium. In only a few cases have the complex ions present in specific plating solutions been identified. Even isolation of a specific solid complex such as one of the cyanides of copper gives no assurance that the particular complex is present as such in solution.

Metals forming cyanide anions with low coordination numbers tend to deposit readily. Dicyanide is very favorable, tetracyanide intermediate, and hexacyanide and octocyanide are very unfavorable for deposition[1]. Since metals of Group IB form the dicyanide while members of Group VIII form the hexacyanide and molybdenum and tungsten form the octocyanide, this generalization also emphasizes periodic relationships. In solutions of copper cyanide, increase in cyanide concentration reduces cathode efficiency, since copper complexes of higher coordination number, $[Cu(CN)_3]^=$ and $[Cu(CN)_4]^\equiv$, are formed. Likewise in the cadmium bath, which contains largely $[Cd(CN)_3]^-$, an increase in cyanide ion concentration lowers the current efficiency. Pure zinc cyanide baths contain chiefly $[Zn(CN)_4]^=$ [98] and show such low current efficiencies that cyanide and zincate solutions are mixed to produce commercial baths. Mercury deposits readily from cyanide solution and the deposition is not affected by excess cyanide. The solution appears to contain $[Hg(CN)_4]^=$ with traces of $[Hg(CN)_3]^-$. Deposition comes largely from the tetracyano ion, which is scarcely affected by excess cyanide[41]. These observations are in accord with the hypothesis that one of the cyanide groups is lost by dissociation as the first step in the deposition process.

86. Blum, *Monthly Rev. Am. Electroplater's Soc.*, **27**, 923 (1940).

H																	He
Li	Be											B	C	N	O	F	Ne
Na	Mg											Al	Si	P	S	Cl	A
K	Ca	Sc	Ti§	V§	Cr‡	Mn‡	Fe‡	Co‡	Ni‡	Cu*	Zn*	Ga†	Ge†	As†	Se†	Br	Kr
Rb	Sr	Y	Zr§	Cb§	Mo§	Tc‡	Ru§§	Rh§§	Pd§§	Ag*	Cd*	In*	Sn†	Sb†	Te†	I	Xe
Cs	Ba	La	Hf§	Ta§	W§	Re‡	Os§§	Ir§§	Pt§§	Au*	Hg*	Tl*	Pb*	Bi†	Po†	At	Rn
Fr	Ra	Ac	Th§	Pa§	U§												

FIG. 19.3. The periodic table of the elements and electrode reversibility

* Forms outer orbital complexes; can be deposited reversibly.
† Forms outer orbital complexes; deposition is usually irreversible.
‡ Forms inner and outer orbital complexes; can be deposited irreversibly from the latter.
§§ Forms inner orbital complexes only; can be deposited irreversibly.
§ Forms inner orbital complexes only; deposition in pure form has not been established.

H																	He
Li	Be											B	C	N	O	F	Ne
Na	Mg											Al	Si	P	S	Cl	A
K	Ca	Sc	Ti	V	Cr§	Mn§§	Fe§§	Co§§	Ni§§	Cu*	Zn*	Ga†	Ge§	As§	Se§	Br	Kr
Rb	Sr	Y	Zr	Cb	Mo	Tc	Ru‡	Rh‡	Pd‡	Ag*	Cd*	In*	Sn**	Sb	Te§	I	Xe
Cs	Ba	La	Hf	Ta	W	Re§	Os‡	Ir‡	Pt‡	Au*	Hg*	Tl†	Pb**	Bi**	Po	At	Rn
Fr	Ra	Ac	Th	Pa	U												

FIG. 19.4. The periodic table of the elements and their plating characteristics

* Plates from cyanide solution.

† Deposits from cyanide solution with more difficulty than * group.

‡ Will not plate from cyanide solution. Cyanide complexes are very stable. Less stable ammine, nitro, and nitroso complexes are used.

** Deposits well from solutions containing anions of low complexing ability. (NO_3^-, ClO_4^-)

§ Deposits from solutions containing the metal as the oxyanion.

§§ Will not plate from cyanide solution.

The deposition of metals other than those of Groups IB and IIB from cyanide solutions may occasionally be promoted by the presence of a second complex-forming ion such as tartrate and by the deposition of certain alloys rather than that of the pure metal. The effect of the complex forming ion is not understood, but the function of the alloy seems to be related to the reduction of the free energy of the metal in the deposit.

Group VIII metals are deposited from ammines or nitroso complexes and not from cyanides. Both cobalt and nickel may be plated from ethylene-diamine complexes; ammonia complexes are useful in deposition of platinum and palladium, while ruthenium may be plated from nitroso ammine complexes. Ammine complexes are not suitable for the technical plating of silver and gold in Group IB because of low anode corrosion.

The elements near each end of the plating groups are more difficult to deposit. Oxyanions such as $CrO_4^=$, ReO_4^-, GeO_4^{4-}, SnO_4^{4-}, $AsO_3^\equiv$, $SeO_3^=$, and $TeO_3^=$ may be used. Except for chromium, the baths range from moderately to strongly alkaline.

Lead, tin, and bismuth appear to be deposited from the simple hydrated ions better than from "complex" ions. Solutions containing complex ions of low coordinating ability, such as BF_4^-, NO_3^-, and ClO_4^-, are suitable. In the absence of addition agents, deposits of these metals are frequently coarsely crystalline.

Other elements can be deposited about equally well from simple or complex solutions. This group includes cobalt, copper, iron, gallium, manganese, nickel, rhenium, thallium, bismuth, and zinc (see Fig. 19.4).

Deposition of Pure Metals from Aqueous Solution

Arsenic, Antimony, and Bismuth. Arsenic is deposited from solutions of arsenite or thioarsenite ions, preferably with small amounts of cyanide[87] or chloride[88]. At the dropping mercury electrode, it is deposited from acid solutions, if chlorides are present[89].

Chlorides are also necessary for the polarographic reduction of antimony-(V)[90]. Reduction of antimony(III) to the metal apparently does not require halides. The so-called "explosive" antimony is deposited from chloride solution at current densities so high that appreciable amounts of chloride are included in the deposit (see p. 631). Other coordinating substances investi-

87. Hammett and Lorch, *J. Am. Chem. Soc.*, **55**, 71 (1933).
88. Rodionov, Russian Patent 27,546 (1927); Torrance, *Analyst*, **63**, 104 (1938).
89. Khlopin, *Zhur. Obschei Khim.*, **18**, 264 (1948); Kolthoff and Lingane, "Polarography," p. 261, New York, Interscience Publishers, Inc., 1941.
90. Lingane and Nichida, *J. Am. Chem. Soc.*, **69**, 530 (1947).

gated include fluoride[91], sulfate[92], tartrate[91d, 92], oxalate[91d], and sulfide[93]. The fluoride bath is preferred. Deposits are also obtained from antimony polysulfide[93].

Bismuth is deposited from solutions of the fluosilicate, fluoborate, perchlorate[94] and nitrate[95]. Since these anions have little tendency to form complexes, it is probably the aquated ion which is reduced. Chloride complexes, as $NaBiCl_4$, have also been used[94b, 96].

Cadmium. Cadmium forms only outer orbital complexes, and accordingly it appears to be deposited from all of its water-soluble compounds. Commercial cadmium plating is conducted from cyanide baths containing addition agents[97]. Cadmium sulfate baths used in electrowinning give rough, crystalline, "treed" deposits unless an addition agent such as gelatin is used[97c]. The cyanide bath requires addition agents to give smooth, bright deposits. Organic agents such as sulfonic acids, resins, aldehydes, and licorice extract, and inorganic agents such as nickel or cobalt salts, are used, often simultaneously.

Both $Na_2[Cd(CN)_4]$ and $Na[Cd(CN)_3]$ exist in solution[41, 98] and also in crystalline form[1]. Excess cyanide lowers the current efficiency[99], probably by increasing the proportion of the tetracyano complex. On the other hand, conductivity, anode corrosion, and throwing power are improved.

Poor deposits are obtained from the ammine, $[Cd(NH_3)_4]^{++}$[100], as well

91. Betts, *Trans. Am. Electrochem. Soc.*, **8**, 186 (1905); Bloom, British Patents 567794 (1945) and 559164 (1944); U. S. Patent 2389131 (1945); British Patent 294143 (1927); Mathers, *Mental Cleaning and Finishing*, **7**, 339 (1935); Mathers and Means, *Trans. Am. Electrochem. Soc.*, **31**, 289 (1917); Mathers, Means, and Richards, *Trans. Am. Electrochem. Soc.*, **31**, 293 (1917).

92. Piontelli and Tremolada, *Met. ital.*, **32**, 417 (1940); cf., *Chem. Abs.*, **37**, 1336 (1943).

93. Salmoni, *Atti X congr. intern chim.*, **3**, 614 (1939); cf. *Chem. Abs.*, **33**, 8504 (1939).

94. Harbaugh and Mathers, *Trans. Electrochem. Soc.*, **64**, 293 (1933); Kern and Jones, *Trans. Am. Electrochem. Soc.*, **57**, 255 (1930); Piontelli, *Atti X congr. intern. chim.*, **3**, 609 (1939); cf , *Chem. Abs.*, **33**, 9148 (1939).

95. Vozduizhenskii, Kamaletdinov, and Khusianov, *Trans. Butlerov Inst. Chem. Tech.*, *Kazan*, No. 1, 102 (1934); cf. *Chem. Abs.*, **29**, 3918 (1935).

96. Levin, *J. Applied Chem., U.S.S.R.*, **17**, 613 (1944); cf. *Chem. Abs.*, **40**, 2075 (1946).

97. Hall and Hogaboom, "Plating and Finishing Guidebook," 14th ed., p. 15, New York, The Metal Industry Publishing Co., 1945; Russell and Woolrich, British Patent 12526 (1849); Soderberg and Westbrook, *Trans. Electrochem. Soc.*, **80**, 492 (1941).

98. Britton and Dodd, *J. Chem. Soc.*, **1932**, 1940.

99. Irenas, *Monthly Rev. Am. Electroplater's Soc.*, **30**, 603 (1943).

100. Brand, *Z. anal. Chem.*, **28**, 581 (1889); Clark, *Ber.*, **11**, 1409 (1879); Davison, *J. Am. Chem. Soc.*, **27**, 1275 (1905); Yver, *Bull. soc. chim.*, *Paris*, **34**, 18 (1880).

as from the acetate, formate, lactate, succinate, and oxalate[101]. Deposits from the thiosulfate bath may contain 5 per cent sulfur[37], and those from complex halide solutions contain halides[79a]. The sulfamate[102], fluoborate[103], and ethylenediamine[104] baths have also been studied.

Chromium. In chromium(III) baths, the formation of chromium(II) at the cathode is vital[105], since chromium(III) complexes are inner orbital. The deposits are poor, although acceptable for electrowinning[106], and cathode efficiencies are low. Additions of acetate, tartrate[107], benzoate, and salicylate[108] are not beneficial, but oxalates are helpful. It is reported[34, 109] that better results are obtained with the blue ammonium trisoxalatochromate(III) than with the red ammonium diaquobisoxalatochromate(III); the presence of ammonium ion is essential. Deposits are also obtained from citrate complexes[110]. Contrary to some reports, there is no significant difference between plating from the violet hexaquochromium(III) sulfate or chloride, and from the green chloraquo or sulfatoaquo isomers[105]. Deposits are not obtained from $[Cr(NH_3)_6]Cl_3$, $[Cr(NH_3)_5Cl]Cl_2$, $[Cr(en)_3]Cl_3$, $[Cr(en)_3](CNS)_3$, $[Cr(urea)_6]Cl_3$, or $K_3[Cr(ox)_3] \cdot 3H_2O$[105].

Commercially, chromium is plated from chromic acid solutions containing sulfate ion in the proportion of 1 part to 100 parts CrO_3[111]. Fluosilicic acid, fluorides, and fluoborates may replace a portion or all of the sulfate. The cathode efficiency is low-rarely greater than 15 per cent.

The mechanism of reduction is not understood. Although chromium(III) ion is produced in the operation, radioactive trivalent chromium, when added to the bath, does not enter the deposit[112]. A divalent complex is probably involved. At the dropping mercury electrode, both trivalent and divalent states are recognized in the reduction[113].

Cobalt. Cobalt is generally deposited from sulfate baths; ammonium salts, boric acid, and sodium fluoride or chloride may be added[114]. The

101. Mathers and Marble, *Trans. Am. Electrochem. Soc.*, **25,** 297 (1914).
102. Piontelli and Giulotto, *Chimica e industria, Italy*, **21,** 278 (1939); Piontelli, *Korrasion u. Metallschutz.*, **19,** 110 (1943); cf., *Chem. Abs.*, **38,** 2571 (1944).
103. Anantharaman and Balachandra, *J. Electrochem. Soc.*, **100,** 232 (1953); Narcus, *Metal Finishing*, **43,** 188 (1945).
104. Harford, U. S. Patent 2377228 (1945), 2377229 (1945).
105. Parry, Swann, and Bailar, *Trans. Electrochem. Soc.*, **92,** 507 (1947).
106. Lloyd, Rawles, and Feeney, *Trans. Electrochem. Soc.*, **89,** 443 (1946).
107. Britton and Wescott, *Trans. Faraday Soc.*, **28,** 627 (1932).
108. LeBlanc, *Trans. Am. Electrochem. Soc.*, **9,** 315 (1906).
109. Mazzucchelli, *Atti acad. Lincei.*, **12,** 587 (1930).
110. Kasper, *J. Research., Nat. Bur. Standards*, **11,** 515 (1933); Yntema, *J. Am. Chem. Soc.*, **54,** 3775 (1932).
111. Dubpernell, *Trans. Electrochem. Soc.*, **80,** 589 (1941).
112. Ogburn and Brenner, *Trans. Electrochem. Soc.*, **96,** 347 (1949).
113. Lingane and Kolthoff, *J. Am. Chem. Soc.*, **62,** 852 (1940).
114. Soderberg, Pinner, and Baker, *Trans. Electrochem. Soc.*, **80,** 579 (1941); Watts, *Trans. Am. Electrochem. Soc.*, **23,** 99 (1913).

aquated ion is readily, though irreversibly, reduced. Poor results are obtained from thiocyanate solution[115], but bright plates are reported from a triethanolamine bath[116].

Cobalt(III) complexes show varying results[32]. These inner orbital complex ions are reduced to outer orbital cobalt(II) complexes prior to deposition, as is clearly shown at the dropping mercury electrode[36], in accordance with the discussion on p. 629. No deposit is obtained from inner orbital cobalt(II) complexes.

Copper. Commercial copper deposition[117] is carried out from sulfate baths[118], used chiefly for electrorefining and electrotyping, and from cyanide baths[1, 119], used largely for electroplating.

In sulfate baths, copper is present mainly as the tetraquocopper(II) ion. It has been supposed that its planar configuration indicates inner orbital configuration, but recently the existence of two series of copper(II) complexes has been demonstrated[40, 120], one of which does not permit electrodeposition and is presumably inner orbital, whereas the other gives electrodeposits and is outer orbital[120]. The aquated ion belongs to the latter series.

Added tartrates form a complex with iron which accumulates in the bath and prevents contamination of the deposit from this source[121]. Urea and thiourea produce bright plates[122], but it has not been shown that they form complexes in the bath.

Since copper is univalent and diamagnetic in cyanide baths, it has only outer orbital configuration. The tricyano complex is the principal constituent, and it is in dynamic equilibrium with di- and tetracyano ions[1]. It is assumed that deposition occurs from the dicyano ion, the supply of which is replenished by rapid dissociation of other complexes. Thus, factors promoting a shift in equilibrium toward higher coordination numbers, such as increase in cyanide-copper ratio, or reduction in temperature, decrease the cathode efficiency. If the cyanide-copper ratio is sufficiently low, and a large amount of sodium or potassium hydroxide is added, a "high speed" copper bath is obtained[119a], which at high temperatures has anode and cathode efficiencies approaching 100 per cent, even at high current densities. High temperatures favor the dicyano ion. The bath is vigorously stirred so as to reduce concentration polarization.

115. Mathers and Johnson, *Trans. Electrochem. Soc.*, **74**, 229 (1938).
116. Brockman and Nowlen, *Trans. Electrochem. Soc.*, **69**, 553 (1936).
117. Bandes, *Trans. Electrochem. Soc.*, **88**, 263 (1945).
118. Winkler, *Trans. Electrochem. Soc.*, **80**, 521 (1941).
119. Benner and Wernlund, *Trans. Electrochem. Soc.*, **80**, 355 (1941); Graham and Read, *Trans. Electrochem. Soc.*, **80**, 341 (1941).
120. Ray and Sen, *J. Indian Chem. Soc.* **25**, 473 (1948); Sen, Mizushima, Curran, and Quagliano, *J. Am. Chem. Soc.*, **77**, 211 (1955).
121. Rasumovinkov and Maslenikov, *J. Inst. Metals, Russian*, **42**, 590 (1928); cf., *Chem. Abs.*, **24**, 3443 (1930).
122. Keller, U. S. Patent 2462870.

In the conventional cyanide plating bath, both anode and cathode efficiencies are low. Under some conditions the anode efficiency may fall to zero unless Rochelle salt (potassium sodium tartrate) is added[123]. Graham and Read[119b] suggest that the tartrate forms temporary complexes with electrolysis products in the anode film. Citrate has also been used[124]. Sodium sulfite and thiosulfate are recommended as addition agents[119b].

Strangely enough, both anode and cathode efficiencies are improved by increasing the *total* concentration of the tricyano ion. This unexpected effect on anode corrosion is attributed[10a] to depolarization as follows:

$$2[Cu(CN)_3]^= + Cu \rightarrow 3[Cu(CN)_2]^- + e^-.$$

Since cyanide baths are extremely toxic and have other defects[125], many other complexes have been investigated, but no bath equivalent in all respects to the cyanide solution has been developed. Pyrophosphate baths have had some application[126]. Copper(II) complexes which give acceptable results include the ammine[19, 127], oxalate[125, 127c], formate[128], ethylenediamine[129], diethylenetriamine[129b, 130], thiosulfate[37, 131], thiourea[115, 132*], thiocyanate[133], and the sulfamate[102]. Monoethanolamine[45, 52], diethanolamine[46], and triethanolamine[134] give poor deposits unless oxalate is added, possibly forming mixed oxalato-amine complexes. Good deposits are obtained from baths containing copper(I) chloride complexes and gelatin[135].

123. McCullough and Gilchrist, U. S. Patent 1863869.
124. Smith and Munton, *Metal Finishing.*, **39**, 415 (1941).
125. Fink and Wong, *Trans. Electrochem. Soc.*, **63**, 65 (1933).
126. Coyle, *Proc. Am. Electroplater's Soc.*, p. 113 (1941); Gamov and Fomenko, Russian Patent 54546 (Feb. 28, 1939); cf., *Chem. Abs.*, **35**, 2800 (1941); Gershevich and Gamburg, *Korroziya i Borba s Nei.*, **6**, no. 2, 46 (1940); cf., *Chem. Abs.*, **36**, 4031 (1942); Stareck, U. S. Patent 2250556; British Patent 509650; Canadian Patent 379802; German Patent 680304.
127. Hansel, German Patent 688696 (1940); Kudra and Kleibs, *Zapiski Inst. Khim.*, *Akad. Nauk.*, *U.S.S.R.*, **6**, No. 3–4, 203 (1940); cf. *Chem. Abs.*, **35**, 2796 (1941); Levin, *J. Applied Chem.*, *U.S.S.R.*, **13**, 686 (1940); **14**, 68 (1941); cf. *Chem. Abs.*, **35**, 3536 (1941); **36**, 972 (1942).
128. Stareck and Passal, U. S. Patent 2383895 (1945).
129. Brockman and Mote, *Trans. Electrochem. Soc.*, **73**, 371 (1938); Greenspan, U. S. Patent 2195454; *Trans. Electrochem. Soc.*, **78**, 303 (1940); Wilson, U. S. Patent 2411674 (Nov. 26, 1946).
130. Brockman, *Trans. Electrochem. Soc.*, **71**, 255 (1937).
131. Govaerts and Wenmaekers, German Patent 406350 (1924); 384250 (1923); Thompson, *Chem. & Met. Eng.*, **10**, 458 (1912).
132. Gockel, *Z. Elektrochem.*, **40**, 302 (1934).
    * Thiourea shows a strong tendency to stabilize univalent copper. It is likely that the solution contains appreciable amounts of the copper(I) complex.
133. Schlotter, *Oberflachentech.*, **12**, 45 (1935).
134. Brockman and Brewer, *Trans. Electrochem. Soc.*, **69**, 535 (1936); Brockman and Tebeau, *Trans. Electrochem. Soc.*, **73**, 365 (1938); Schweig, British Patent 503095 (March 31, 1939).
135. Diev and Lashkarev, *J. Applied Chem.*, *U.S.S.R.*, **12**, 585 (1939); cf., *Chem. Abs.*,

Two-step reduction processes are observed with copper(II) complexes of ammonia[19, 89b, 127], bromide and chloride[136], thiocyanate[136a, 136b], thiourea, and pyridine[136a, 136b]. These agents stabilize the copper(I) state sufficiently for it to be observed in the deposition process. Satisfactory deposits are obtained from copper(I) thiosulfate[37] and thiocyanate[101] baths.

Gallium and Germanium. Gallium is deposited from sulfate or alkaline gallate solutions[137]. The process is irreversible, presumably because the metal ion is bound in a colloidal sol by hydrolysis[138].

Deposits of germanium are obtained from both sulfate and germanate solutions[139]. Oxalate, tartrate, carbonate, and phosphate additions have been suggested[140]; it is not known whether complexes are formed.

Inner orbital complexes are not formed by these metals.

Gold. Although deposition from many gold complexes has been investigated, only the cyanide and chloride baths have found extensive application[141]. The former contains the outer orbital dicyanoaurate(I) ion. In early days it was prepared from the ferrocyanide, which was available in higher purity than the cyanide. The suggestion that the gold(III) complex is formed[142] is doubtless in error. The ferrocyanide is still employed in the "salt water" process[141b].

The tetrachloroaurate(III) complex is used mainly in electrorefining. It has square planar configuration, and therefore is presumably of inner orbital dsp^2 type. At the cathode, it is reduced to the unstable dichloroaurate(I)[143], which has outer orbital configuration. The bromide bath behaves similarly. Iodide baths[144] contain gold as the monovalent complex, $[AuI_2]^-$. Thiourea[145], thiocyanate, thiosulfate, polysulfide, phosphate, and

33, 8504 (1939); Kameyama and Makishima, *J. Soc. Chem. Ind., Japan*, **34,** 462 (1932); **36,** 365 (1933); **38,** 18 (1935).

136. Kolthoff and Lingane, "Polarography," p. 176, 279, New York, Interscience Publishers, Inc., 1941; Verdieck, Ksychki, and Yntema, *Trans. Electrochem. Soc.*, **80,** 41 (1941).

137. Fogg, *Trans. Electrochem. Soc.*, **66,** 107 (1934); Sebba and Pugh, *J. Chem. Soc.*, **1937,** 1371.

138. Moeller and King, *J. Am. Chem. Soc.*, **74,** 1355 (1952).

139. Alimarin and Ivanov-Emin, *J. Applied Chem., U.S.S.R.*, **17,** 204 (1944); Fink and Dokras, *Trans. Electrochem. Soc.*, **93,** 80 (1949); Hall and Koenig, *Trans. Electrochem. Soc.*, **65,** 215 (1934).

140. Schwartz, Heinrich, and Hollstein, *Z. anorg. allgem. Chem.*, **229,** 154 (1936).

141. Frary, *Trans. Am. Electrochem. Soc.*, **23,** 25, 49 (1913); Weisberg and Graham, *Trans. Electrochem. Soc.*, **80,** 509 (1941).

142. Beutel, *Z. angew. Chem.*, **25,** 995 (1912).

143. Bjerrum, *Bull. soc. chim. Belges*, **57,** 432 (1948).

144. Schlotter, U. S. Patent 1857664 (May 10, 1932); German Patent 608268 (Jan. 19, 1935).

145. Schonmann, German Patent 731043 (Dec. 24, 1942).

sulfite baths[141a, 144b] have been described. Kushner summarized noncyanide baths[146], and general commercial practice[147].

Indium. Indium, plated from simple sulfate or from cyanide solutions[148], has recently found rather extensive use as a wear and corrosion resistant coating for bearing surfaces. It is the only trivalent metal known to be deposited readily from a cyanide bath[149]. The complex cyanides are not well understood; Thompson[1] states that only the tetracyanide, $[In(CN)_4]^-$, is well known, although the experimental basis for this statement is not given. The coordination number of six, attributed to indium[150], is observed in certain compounds[151]. Regardless of its formula, the cyano complex is unstable and slowly precipitates the hydroxide from water. Stability is improved by the presence of a large excess of alkali cyanide together with other substances, such as glucose, tartrates, and glycine[149].

Deposits from sulfate baths containing formate[152], citrate[153], fluoride[154], hydroxylamine, or pyridine[152] are good, but oxalate or acetate gives poor results.

Indium forms only outer orbital complexes. The low current efficiencies in both the sulfate and cyanide baths[155] and the corresponding polarographic irreversibility[156] are probably the results of hydrolysis[157]. In the presence of chloride ions, the reduction becomes reversible[158], presumably because the chloro complex is less readily hydrolyzed.

Iron. Iron is electroplated from sulfate or chloride baths[159]. The presence of iron(III) ions is undesirable. Chloro or sulfato complexes probably exist in solution along with aquated iron(II) ions. The chloride bath gives better deposits at high temperatures; the sulfate, at low temperatures.

146. Kushner, *Products Finishing*, **6,** no. 3, 22 (1941).
147. Kushner, *Products Finishing*, **4,** No. 12, 30 (1940), **5,** Nos. 1–12 (1940–41).
148. Hall and Hogaboom, "Plating and Finishing Guidebook," 14th ed., p. 61, New York, The Metal Industry Publishing Co., 1945.
149. Gray, *Trans. Electrochem. Soc.*, **65,** 377 (1934).
150. Moeller, *J. Am. Chem. Soc.*, **62,** 2444 (1940); **64,** 2234 (1942).
151. Ensslin and Dreyer, *Z. anorg. allgem. Chem.*, **249,** 119 (1942); Klemm and Kilian, *Z. anorg. allgem. Chem.*, **241,** 93 (1939).
152. Dennis and Geer, *J. Am. Chem. Soc.*, **26,** 437 (1904).
153. Westbrook, *Trans. Am. Electrochem. Soc.*, **57,** 289 (1930).
154. Hartz, British Patent 564053 (Sept. 11, 1944).
155. Linford, *Trans. Electrochem. Soc.*, **79,** 443 (1941), Whitehead, *Metal Finishing*, **42,** 405 (1944).
156. Kolthoff and Lingane, "Polarography," p. 274, New York. Interscience Publishers, Inc., 1941.
157. Hattox and DeVries, *J. Am. Chem. Soc.*, **58,** 2126 (1936); Takagi, *J. Chem. Soc.*, **1928,** 301.
158. Kolthoff and Lingane, "Polarography," p. 263, New York, Interscience Publishers, Inc., 1941.
159. Thomas, *Trans. Electrochem. Soc.*, **80,** 499 (1941).

Sulfamate[102] and fluoroborate[103b, 159] baths have been suggested. Iron is present probably as the aquated ion. Deposition from an alkaline' bath containing ethylenediaminetetracetic acid and triethanolamine has recently been reported[160]. In this bath iron is undoubtedly present as a complex ion, but its nature has not been established.

Iron forms both inner and outer orbital complex ions. Deposition is possible from the outer orbital aquo, chloro, and sulfato complexes, but not from the inner orbital cyano, o-phenanthroline, and α,α'-dipyridyl complexes, although certain alloys may be deposited from the cyanide complex ions, as discussed on page 667.

Lead. The best lead deposits are obtained from solutions containing anions of low complexing power. Lead nitrate, perchlorate, and salts of fluoro acids, especially fluoroantimonate, fluorostannate, fluoroborate, and fluorosilicate have been tried[161]. The last two have found commercial application[162]. The sulfamate bath also gives good deposits[102, 163]. Lead is present probably as the aquated lead(II) ion. The deposition is reversible both at lead and at mercury cathodes[164], as would be expected from the outer orbital configuration of the ion.

In alkaline solutions, the acetate[165] gives poor deposits[161]. A bath containing potassium bisoxalatoplumbate(II) with excess potassium oxalate gives good deposits, but the corresponding ammonium bath gives spongy metal[166]. Lead tartrate in the presence of sodium acetate gives compact deposits[161, 167].

Manganese. Manganese is usually deposited from a sulfate solution containing excess ammonium sulfate[168], although the corresponding chlorides may be used. Because of the strong tendency of manganese to form coordination compounds[169], it is probable that deposition occurs from outer orbital sulfato or chloro complexes. Deposits are not obtained from the inner orbital hexacyanomanganate(II), except at a mercury cathode, at which the high hydrogen overvoltage and the free energy of amalgam formation allow

160. Foley, Linford, and Meyer, *Plating*, **40**, 887 (1953).
161. Mathers, *Trans. Am. Electrochem. Soc.*, **23**, 153 (1913).
162. Gray and Blum, *Trans. Electrochem. Soc.*, **80**, 645 (1941).
163. Mathers and Forney, *Trans. Electrochem. Soc.*, **76**, 371 (1939).
164. Kolthoff and Lingane, "Polarography," p. 267, New York, Interscience Publishers, Inc., 1941.
165. Friend, "A Textbook of Inorganic Chemistry," vol. 5, p. 433, London, C. Griffin Co., 1921.
166. Classen, *Ber.*, **15**, 1096 (1882).
167. Glazunov and Jenicek, *Korrosion u. Metallschutz*, **17**, 384 (1941); cf. *Chem., Abs.*, **36**, 5095 (1942).
168. Bradt and Taylor, *Trans. Electrochem. Soc.*, **73**, 327 (1938).
169. Morgan and Burstall, "Inorganic Chemistry—A survey of Modern Developments," p. 195, Cambridge, England, W. Heffer & Sons, 1936.

deposition to proceed[170]. The addition of excess ammonium thiocyanate has been recommended[168] for the sulfate bath. Manganese(II) fluoroborate, benzoate, acetate, and citrate solutions all give deposits, as do sodium citrate solutions of manganese(II) dithionate, tartrate, formate, acetate, and fluorosilicate[168, 171]. Complexes with amines, such as mono-, di-, or triethanolamines, also give deposits[172].

Mercury. Mercury is readily deposited from the complex cyanide bath; the tetracyanomercury(II) ion predominates[41, 98], although there may be small amounts of the tricyano ion[1]. Little activation is needed, even with the divalent ion. Reduction probably proceeds through the univalent state, which forms only outer orbital complexes. Acetate solutions have also been studied[173].

Nickel. Commercial nickel plating baths contain nickel sulfate and chloride[83], usually with boric acid. An all-chloride bath is also used[174]. Chloride is necessary to dissolve the nickel anode under operating conditions[175], probably through forming a chloroaquo complex. Deposition occurs from both aquo and chloro complexes. According to magnetic data[28], these ions have two unpaired electrons, indicating outer orbital sp^3d^2 hybridization. The cyano complex has no unpaired electrons, so that the hybridization is inner orbital dsp^2. Deposits from cyanide baths[176] appear to be only flash deposits and plating soon ceases[84]. The deposition of nickel alloys from cyanide baths is discussed on page 667.

Ammoniacal solutions of a number of nickel salts[114b] contain the tetrammine complex[177], and give good deposits. Dark deposits of so-called *black nickel* which contain sulfur are obtained from baths prepared by dissolving nickel carbonate in concentrated solutions of potassium thiocyanate[114b], probably giving [Ni(SCN)$_4$]$^=$.

Plating solutions containing such complex-forming substances as oxalate[95], citrate[178], pyrophosphate[95], tartrate[179], lactate[178a, 178b], thiocya-

170. Kolthoff and Lingane, "Polarography," p. 254, New York, Interscience Publishers, Inc., 1941.
171. Bradt and Oaks, *Trans. Electrochem. Soc.*, **71**, 279 (1937); **69**, 567 (1936); U. S. Patent 2398614 (Apr. 16, 1946).
172. Dean, U. S. Patent 2317153 (Apr. 20, 1943); cf., *Chem. Abs.*, **37**, 5663 (1943).
173. Malkin, *Ber. Inst. physik. Chem., Akad. Wiss. Ukr.S.S.R.*, **11**, 109 (1938); cf., *Chem. Abs.*, **34**, 2261 (1940).
174. Wesley and Carey, *Trans. Electrochem. Soc.*, **75**, 209 (1939).
175. Dorrance and Gardiner, *Trans. Am. Electrochem. Soc.*, **54**, 303 (1928).
176. Bennett, Rose, and Tinkler, *Trans. Am. Electrochem. Soc.*, **28**, 339 (1915); Watts, *Trans. Am. Electrochem. Soc.*, **27**, 141 (1915).
177. Kato, *J. Chem. Soc., Japan*, **58**, 1146 (1937).
178. Ballay, *Compt. rend.*, **198**, 1494 (1934); Franssen, *Oberflachenteck.*, **14**, 174 (1937); cf., *Chem. Abs.*, **31**, 8387 (1947); Nichols, *Trans. Electrochem. Soc.*, **64**, 265 (1933).
179. Mathers, Webb, and Schaff, *Metal Cleaning and Finishing*, **6**, 412, 148 (1934).

nate[115, 180], fluoride[181], triethanolamine[116], and sulfamic acid[102] have been studied. In general the deposits are fairly good, but the baths offer no advantages over the chloride or sulfate bath.* Fluoroborate and sulfamate baths are occasionally used.

In the presence of excess thiosulfate, the deposits are smooth, adherent, and metallic, but contain from 22 to 70 per cent sulfur[37]. Ni_2S_3 was identified by means of x-ray diffraction. The presence of sulfide may be taken to indicate that coordinate bonds are not always easily converted to metallic bonds.

A study[32] of electrodeposits from nickel complexes showed that the smaller the coordinating group, the better the form of the deposit. Thus the tris(ethylenediamine) complex gives better plates than the corresponding propylenediamine compound, which in turn is better than the butylenediamine ion. It is possible that the larger groups prevent close approach of the nickel ion to the cathode so that conversion of coordinate bonds to metallic bonds is more difficult than with the smaller groups.

Metals which are irreversibly reduced, such as nickel, tend to be deposited more smoothly than those which are deposited reversibly, perhaps because the hindrance to deposition precludes the formation of large crystals. Accordingly, nickel deposits are particularly susceptible to the influence of addition agents. Nevertheless, the formulation of a nickel bath to yield bright deposits under the conditions encountered in industry is difficult. Two classes of addition agents are recognized, the active agents and the carriers[83] (see discussion, page 643). Although the mechanism by which these function is unknown, there is probably a better empirical knowledge of nickel brighteners than of those for other metals.

The Platinum Group Metals: Ruthenium, Rhodium, Palladium, Osmium, Iridium, Platinum. The water-soluble compounds of the platinum metals all seem to be inner orbital complexes. Nevertheless, deposits have been reported. Lyons suggests that this may result from the extreme stability of the metallic state,† so that the energy required to break the inner orbital hybridization does not greatly exceed that needed to discharge

---

* Triethanolamine and ammoniacal citrate baths permit direct plating on zinc. Ordinary baths plate nickel on zinc by displacement and such deposits are spongy and do not afford a satisfactory base for subsequent electrodeposits. The deposition potential of nickel in these special baths is apparently raised to that of zinc (see alloy plating, page 666). A nickel sulfate bath containing substantial amounts of sodium sulfate has also been used; a sulfato complex was probably formed.

† The heat of sublimation of platinum is 4.86 electron-volts[182].

180. Schone, *Metal Finishing*, **41, 77** (1943).
181. Loose, Can. Patent 401154; Spiro and Wohlgemuth, British Patent 584977 (Jan. 28, 1947).
182. Kelley, "Heats of Fusion of Inorganic Compounds," *U. S. Bureau of Mines Bull.*, 393 (1936).

the hydrogen ion[40]. The current efficiencies are quite low, and the deposition reactions are irreversible. The deposition of heavy coatings seems generally to be difficult, and most investigators have been satisfied with "flash" deposits. Information on the plating of osmium, iridium, and ruthenium is scanty, and it may be that only "flash" deposits are obtained. With rhodium, platinum, and palladium, heavier deposits are obtained, although with difficulty. Cyanide complexes give no deposits of the platinum metals[183].

Electrodeposition of these metals is not well developed, owing largely to these difficulties and to the expense of the metals. Rhodium plating has received attention because of the high reflectivity, corrosion resistance, and hardness of the deposit. It appears to be the easiest of the group to electrodeposit.

Rhodium is generally plated from acid electrolytes[184]. The most common baths are: (1) a solution of rhodium sulfate in sulfuric acid; (2) a solution of rhodium phosphate in phosphoric acid; or (3) a mixture of the two. Additional alkali sulfates or phosphates may be added[185]. The solutions are undoubtedly complex, and may contain ions of the type $[Rh(SO_4)_3]^=$ or $[Rh(PO_4)_2]^{=\,186}$. No simple solid phosphates of rhodium have been isolated; only complex phosphates of variable composition have been produced.

Addition agents suggested for the sulfate bath include the complex forming substances, di- and trimethyl- and ethylamines and tartaric and lactic acids[187].

Complexes recommended for rhodium plating include chlorides, as $Na_3[RhCl_6]$, $K_3[RhCl_6]$, $(NH_4)_3[RhCl_6]$, and $H_3[RhCl_6]$[188]; and nitrites, as $(NH_4)_3[Rh(NO_2)_6]$[189] and $[Rh(NH_3)_4(NO_2)_2]NO_2$[190]. Good deposits of rhodium have been reported from solutions prepared by dissolving rhodium hydroxide in sulfamic acid[102a], nitric acid[191], fluoroboric acid, and perchloric acid[192].

Platinum black is a typical powdery deposit, obtained from the hexa-

183. Grube and Reinhardt, Z. Elektrochem., **37,** 316 (1931).
184. Schumpelt, Trans. Electrochem. Soc., **80,** 489 (1941).
185. Fink and Lambros, Trans. Electrochem. Soc., **63,** 181 (1933).
186. Yamamato, Rept. Chem. Research, Prefectural Inst. Advancement Ind., Tokyo., no. 2, 2–12 (1940); cf., Chem. Abs., **35,** 7840 (1941).
187. Spies, German Patent 692122 (May 16, 1940).
188. Weisberg, Metal Finishing, **38,** 587 (1940).
189. Keitel, U. S. Patent 2067534 (Jan. 12, 1937); Can. Patent 365965 (May 11, 1937); Zimmermann, U. S. Patent 2067747 (June 12, 1937).
190. Keitel, U. S. Patent 1779436 (Oct. 28, 1930); Zschiegner, U. S. Patent 1779457 (Oct. 28, 1930).
191. British Patent 480145 (Feb. 17, 1938).
192. Fink and Deren, Trans. Electrochem. Soc., **66,** 471 (1934); Grube and Kesting, Z. Elektrochem., **39,** 951 (1933).

chloroplatinate(IV) ion; the reduction proceeds through the tetrachloroplatinate(II) ion to the free metal[183]. Although inner orbital in configuration, the latter ion is thermodynamically unstable[137b] and disproportionates to metal and the tetravalent ion. Sometimes this results in colloidal metal in the plating bath[193]. The instability of this inner orbital complex probably reflects the high stability of the metal.

Bright platinum[184] is generally plated from a bath prepared by boiling potassium hexachloroplatinate(IV) with a solution of disodium and diammonium phosphates. A color change during boiling and the dissolving of the precipitate of $(NH_4)_2[PtCl_6]$ suggest formation of an ammine-phosphato complex, but it has not been isolated. Thick deposits cannot be obtained, the current efficiency is low, and the bath deteriorates in use, since metal must be replenished by adding more complex, and thus phosphates and chlorides accumulate. Deterioration is less marked if accumulation of chloride is avoided by replenishing with dinitrodiammineplatinum(II).

A somewhat superior bath is prepared from ammonium nitrate, ammonium hydroxide, sodium nitrite, and $[Pt(NH_3)_2(NO_2)_2]$. The complex expected under these conditions is tetrammineplatinum(II) nitrite, $[Pt(NH_3)_4](NO_2)_2$[184]. The bath is replenished with the dinitrodiammineplatinum(II), and excessive accumulation of salts is avoided by decomposition of ammonium nitrite.

Although rhodium is deposited at the dropping mercury electrode[194], platinum is not deposited but catalyzes hydrogen evolution[87, 194, 195]. Grube[196], however, reported the reduction of platinum from the tetracyano ion on a mercury cathode.

Palladium is similar to platinum. A solution containing palladium(II) chloride, disodium and diammonium phosphates, and benzoic acid has been used[184]. Solutions containing dinitrodiamminepalladium(II),

$$[Pd(NH_3)_2(NO_2)_2],$$

have also been recommended[197]. Baths prepared with ammonium tetrachloropalladate(II) give good deposits, but corresponding potassium or sodium salts give no deposit[196]. Since the tetrachloropalladate(II) ion is said[198] to be rapidly reduced by hydrogen in the cold, easy electrodeposition

193. McCaughey, *Trans. Electrochem. Soc.*, **15**, 523 (1909); McCaughey and Patton, *Trans. Electrochem. Soc.*, **63**, 181 (1910).
194. Willis, *J. Am. Chem. Soc.*, **66**, 1067 (1944).
195. Latinen and Onstott, *J. Am. Chem. Soc.*, **72**, 4565 (1950).
196. Grube and Beischer, *Z. Elektrochem.*, **39**, 38, 131 (1933).
197. Klochko and Medvedeva, *J. Applied Chem.*, *U.S.S.R.*, **15**, 25 (1942).
198. Ipatiev, and Tronev, *J. Gen. Chem.*, *U.S.S.R.*, **5**, 643 (1935).

would be expected. Unlike platinum, palladium is deposited at the dropping mercury electrode from the tetrachloro complex[194].

Ruthenium may be deposited from a solution prepared by dissolving the nitrosochloride, $[Ru(NO)Cl_3] \cdot H_2O$, in dilute sulfuric, phosphoric, hydrochloric, or oxalic acid. Since the normal coordination number of ruthenium is six, water or sulfate may be coordinated in the remaining positions. Nitrosoammine complexes of unspecified composition have also been recommended[199].

Little is known of the deposition of osmium and iridium, though baths containing chloro complexes have been described[200]. Ions of the type $[IrCl_6]^=$ would be expected[201] in these baths. Ruthenium, osmium, and iridium are not deposited at the dropping mercury cathode[194].

Polonium. Polonium, or radium F, has not been available in sufficient quantities to permit study of its complex compounds on a macro scale; however, certain of them are known to be isomorphous with complexes of lead, tellurium, and tin. By assuming that they have similar formulas, compounds such as $(NH_4)_2[PoCl_6]$ and $(NH_4)_3[PoCl_6]$ have been suggested[202]. Haissinsky[203] states that polonium forms complexes with a large number of ions such as sulfate, acetate, oxalate, and even ions of low complexing tendency such as nitrate. Polonium is readily deposited from solutions of such complexes, which are, of course, outer orbital in type. A summary of the electrochemistry of polonium is given by Haissinsky[203].

Rhenium. Electroplated rhenium is bright and hard, resistant to hydrochloric acid[139b], but readily attacked by nitric acid or moist air[204]. Baths are prepared by dissolving potassium perrhenate, $KReO_4$, in dilute solutions of sulfuric[139b, 204], phosphoric[139b], oxalic[139b], and hydrofluoric acids[205]. Dilute nitric and hydrochloric acids are unsatisfactory[204]. Perrhenate baths somewhat resemble chromate baths. A solution of the chloride complex, $K_2[ReCl_6]$, gives only traces of metal on a platinum cathode, even at high current density[206]. With a mercury cathode an amalgam of rhenium is formed.

Selenium. Selenium is semimetallic in nature and forms few coordina-

199. Zimmerman and Zschiegner, U. S. Patent 2057638; French Patent 799251; British Patent 466126; German Patent 647334 (1936).
200. Rossman, *Metal Ind.*, (*N. Y.*), **29**, 245 (1931).
201. Morgan and Burstall, "Inorganic Chemistry—A survey of Modern Developments," p. 233, Cambridge, England, W. Heffer & Sons, 1936.
202. Emeleus and Anderson, "Modern Aspects of Inorganic Chemistry," p. 371, New York, D. Van Nostrand Co., Inc., 1938.
203. Haissinsky, *Trans. Electrochem. Soc.*, **70**, 343 (1936).
204. Lundell and Knowles, *J. Research Natl. Bur. Standards*, **18**, 629 (1937).
205. Holemann, *Z. anorg. allgem. Chem.*, **235**, 1 (1937).
206. Holemann, *Z. anorg. allgem. Chem.*, **211**, 195 (1933).

tion compounds. It is deposited in alloys with such metals as copper, bismuth, or nickel from an acid solution containing $SeO_3^=$ and various addition agents such as oxalic acid[207]. These alloys probably resemble the nickel-sulfur deposits mentioned above. Pure selenium may be plated on the anode by electrolysis of solutions of selenides, such as Na_2Se[208].

Silver. Univalent silver forms only outer orbital ions, from which it deposits so readily that it tends to form coarse crystals. No addition agent has been found which will give compact, smooth deposits from the aquated silver ion in nitrate, perchlorate, or fluoroborate baths.

The sole bath of commercial importance is the cyanide[209], which has been used with only minor modification since its introduction in 1838. The principal complex ion is the dicyano, $[Ag(CN)_2]^-$; the existence of tri- or tetracyano ions is negligible under most conditions[1]. Correspondingly, the cathode efficiency is not much affected by changes in cyanide ion concentration or in temperature; it is substantially 100 per cent under most conditions. Evidently the dicyano ion is well suited to the deposition mechanism. The ferrocyanide used in early baths[141a] was undoubtedly converted to the dicyano ion.

A number of complexing agents have been proposed to replace the toxic cyanide. Chloride, $[AgCl_2]^-$, and iodide, $[AgI_2]^-$, were suggested early[141a]. Plates comparable to those from cyanide solution have been obtained from iodide baths[127c, 144]; the addition of citric acid[210] has also been recommended. Thiosulfate complexes, probably $[Ag(S_2O_3)_2]^=$ [169, 201, 211], give good plates[141a, 212], but such deposits are adherent only when very thin[210]. Although the thiourea complex gives good results[115, 132], the bath does not compare favorably with the cyanide solution[213].

A variety of ammines has been tested. Baths containing $[Ag(NH_3)_2]^+$ [214] or the ethylenediamine ion, $[Ag(en)]^+$, give good plates, but anode efficiency is poor. Good deposits are obtained from baths containing AgCN dissolved in various amines[215]; guanidine hydrocyanide and ethylenediamine hydrocyanide give plates equal to those from the cyanide bath. Possibly deposition occurs from the cyano complex. Plates from the tri-

207. Jilek and Lukas, *Chem. Listy*, **21**, 576 (1927), Mougey and Wirshing, U. S. Patent 2338529 (Jan. 1944).
208. Bloom, U. S. Patent 2414438 (Jan. 1947); cf., *Chem. Abs.*, **41**, 3383 (1947).
209. Promisel and Wood, *Trans. Electrochem. Soc.*, **80**, 459 (1941).
210. Fleetwood and Yntema, *Ind. Eng. Chem.*, **27**, 340 (1935).
211. Morgan and Burstall, "Inorganic Chemistry—A survey of Modern Developments," p. 64, 66, Cambridge, England, W. Heffer & Sons, 1936.
212. Yuzhnyi, *Khim. Referat. Zhur.*, **1**, no. 11–12, 104 (1938), cf., *Chem. Abs.*, **33**, 8506 (1939).
213. Walter, Adler, and Riemer, *Monatsch.*, **65**, 59 (1935).
214. Hughes, and Withrow, *J. Am. Chem. Soc.*, **32**, 1571 (1910).
215. Gilbertson and Mathers, *Trans. Electrochem. Soc.*, **79**, 439 (1941).

ethanolamine bath are good, but those from guanidine and cyclohexyl-amine solutions are unsatisfactory.

Silver salt solutions containing complex-forming organic acids, such as tartaric, acetic, oxalic, and citric, are inferior to the cyanide bath[141a]. Fairly good deposits of silver are obtained from a solution of silver sulfamate containing a small amount of tartaric acid[102b].

Tellurium. Tellurium resembles selenium. It may be deposited on steel as an adherent metal plate from a strongly alkaline solution of an alkali metal tellurite[216], or from a solution of tellurium dioxide in a mixture of sulfuric and hydrofluoric acids[217]. Nitric and hydrochloric acids give inferior deposits. Tellurium may be separated from selenium by electrolysis in a mixture of hydrofluoric and sulfuric acids, in which the existence of fluoride complexes, $[TeF_5(H_2O)]^-$ and $[TeF_6]^=$, is probably important.

Tin. Inasmuch as its d orbitals are full, tin does not form inner orbital complexes. Correspondingly, electrodeposits appear to be obtained from all water-soluble compounds. Reversible deposition would therefore be expected, with the formation of coarse crystals, as observed. However, the tendency of tin to hydrolyze is apparently responsible for a small degree of irreversibility in the absence of halides. Thus, at the dropping mercury electrode, the reduction is irreversible unless chloride is present[158]. The fact that the sulfate bath responds more readily to addition agents than the chloride bath is doubtless due to this irreversibility, and the scarcity of effective addition agents even for the sulfate bath indicates that the deposition is not far from being reversible. It may be assumed that in the latter bath, the tin is present as partly hydrolyzed, aquated ions, while in the chloride bath, the hexachloro ion or a mixed chloroaquo complex, which is not readily hydrolyzed, is present. Effective addition agents for a mixed fluoride-chloride bath have been found[218].

The commercial sulfate bath[219] contains tin(II) sulfate, sulfuric acid, and various addition agents. Sometimes sulfate is replaced wholly or partially by phenolsulfonate or other organic sulfonates, or by fluoroborate, but this does not appear to influence the cathode reaction. During operation, the tin(II) ion appears to hydrolyze slowly, probably with oxidation, and to precipitate. In conformity with the near reversibility of the reduction, the current efficiency approximates 100 per cent.

Various complexing agents such as fluoride, oxalate, tartrate, citrate, pyrophosphate, cyanide, thiosulfate, and hydroxylamine have been investigated[220]. Good deposits are obtained over a narrow current density range

216. Woll and Gore, U. S. Patent 2258963 (Oct. 14, 1941).
217. Mathers and Turner, *Trans. Am. Electrochem. Soc.*, **54**, 293 (1928).
218. British Patent 592442 (Sept. 1947).
219. Pine, *Trans. Electrochem. Soc.*, **80**, 631 (1941).
220. Kern, *Trans. Am. Electrochem. Soc.*, **23**, 193 (1913).

from tin(II) oxalate in oxalic acid[60e, 221]. Oxidation of the complex causes deterioration of the bath. Similarly, polarographic irreversibility is observed with tartrate solutions[222], which is probably due to hydrolysis. Irreversibility in oxidation to the tin(IV) complex results from the required change in configuration.

Electrodeposition from an alkaline stannite bath shows high efficiency as expected, but the deposits are spongy or powdery because the ion disproportionates spontaneously into the metal and stannate ion[223]. Better deposits are obtained from the hexahydroxystannate(IV) ion. This stannate bath[224] has come into extensive use since it was found that if the tin anodes are coated by preliminary electrolysis at high current density, the products of subsequent anodic dissolution are in the quadrivalent state exclusively. Without this pretreatment, stannite soon appears in the bath, and the deposits become spongy. If stannite is present, it may be oxidized by hydrogen peroxide. The bath consists of sodium or potassium stannate with an excess of the corresponding hydroxide. Sodium acetate is sometimes added. Addition agents are generally omitted, since none of them are very effective.

Deposition from stannate ion doubtless passes through the divalent state, but since stannite ions are reduced and deposited as fast as they are formed, they do not accumulate in the bath with consequent risk of spongy deposits. Reduction from tin(IV) to tin(II) is irreversible, possibly because it requires a change in configuration; this may account for the rather low cathode efficiencies. The two-step reduction is observed polarographically[224A]; the first step is irreversible, and the second nearly reversible. The ineffectiveness of addition agents is to be associated with the reversible nature of the second step.

Good deposits are obtained from the tin(II) polysulfide complex, but the bath is difficult to maintain.

Thallium. As its electronic structure permits only outer orbital ions, thallium is electrodeposited with very little activation[225]. Solutions of thallium(I) sulfate, carbonate, or perchlorate have been used[225a, 226]. The

221. Hothersall and Bradshaw, *J. Electrodepositors Tech. Soc.*, **15**, 49 (1939); Mathers and Cockrum, *Trans. Am. Electrochem. Soc.*, **29**, 411 (1916).
222. Lingane, *J. Am. Chem. Soc.*, **65**, 866 (1943).
223. Sidgwick, "The Chemical Elements and Their Compounds," p. 621, Oxford, 1950.
224. Oplinger and Bauch, *Trans. Electrochem. Soc.*, **80**, 617 (1941); Sternfels and Lowenheim, *Trans. Electrochem. Soc.*, **82**, 77 (1942); **84**, 195 (1943).
224a. Lingane, *J. Am. Chem. Soc.*, **67**, 919 (1945).
225. Brown and McGlynn, *Trans. Am. Electrochem. Soc.*, **53**, 351 (1928); Kolthoff and Lingane, "Polarography," p. 260, New York, Interscience Publishers, Inc., 1941.
226. Hopkins, "Chapters in the Chemistry of the Less Familiar Elements," Champaign, Ill., Stipes Publishing Co., 1939.

univalent ion has weak coordinating tendencies, but a few complexes, such as $KTl(CN)_2$, have been established[225a, 227]. Deposition of a silver-thallium alloy from a cyanide bath has been reported[228]. The trivalent ion readily complexes, but reduction undoubtedly proceeds through the univalent state.

Zinc. As with other metals which form only outer orbital complexes, zinc appears to be deposited from all of its soluble compounds, although the deposits are not always compact. Deposition from the aquated ion, as in sulfate[229], chloride-acetate[230], or fluoroborate baths[231], is very nearly reversible. Accordingly cathode efficiencies are substantially 100 per cent, and effective addition agents are relatively scarce.

A solution of zinc cyanide in sodium cyanide contains the tetracyano ion, $[Zn(CN)_4]^=$ and, perhaps, traces of the tricyano ion $[Zn(CN)_3]^-$. White matte deposits of zinc are obtained at current efficiencies usually less than 15 per cent. On the other hand, from a solution of sodium zincate, in which zinc probably exists as $[Zn(OH)_4]^=$, efficiencies are as high as 90 per cent, but the deposits are spongy and poor[232]. A suitable mixture of the two baths gives excellent deposits at current efficiencies of 80 to 90 per cent. Cyanohydroxo complexes may be present.

Deposition from the cyanozincate bath is irreversible. The reasons for this are not clear, although it is possible that the zincate, at least, may form polynuclear complexes which are slow in decoordinating. The highest cathode efficiencies obtained with cyanide baths are observed with gold and silver, in which the ions are dicovalent; the removal of four cyanide groups, as with zinc, may require a longer time and produce a hindrance.

Addition agents are generally employed in alkaline baths. However, bright deposits are produced without addition agents by "bright dipping" the plated surface in dilute nitric or chromic acid, provided no traces of heavy metals, especially lead and copper, are present in the bath. Many so-called brighteners act only to remove these metals as sulfides; soluble sulfides, polysulfides, thiosulfates, and thiocyanates, have been used. Operation in the presence of a suspended precipitate of zinc sulfide is common. The function of the bright dip is not understood; zinc is dissolved, but without the usual characteristics of bright dipping[233]. Often it appears that

227. Bassett and Corbet, *J. Chem. Soc.*, **125,** 1660 (1924).
228. Hensel, *Am. Inst. Mining Met. Engrs., Inst. Metals Div., Tech. Pub.* No. **1930** (1945); cf., *Chem. Abs.*, 40, 307 (1946).
229. Lyons, *Trans. Electrochem. Soc.*, **80,** 387 (1941).
230. Hogaboom, U. S. Patent 2421265 (May, 1947).
231. Anantharaman and Balachandra, *J. Electrochem. Soc.*, **100,** 237 (1953).
232. Hull and Wernlund, *Trans. Electrochem. Soc.*, **80,** 407 (1941).
233. Soderberg, *Trans. Electrochem. Soc.*, **88,** 115 (1945).

a powder or film is removed from the surface. Bright dips are also effective on deposits from sulfate baths. It is claimed that bright dipping has a passivating effect on the surface.

True brighteners produce bright deposits without a bright dip. Compounds which have been used are various organic resins[234], ketones[235], molybdic oxide[236], piperonal or vanillin[237], or thiourea with various metals[236, 238]. Most of these may form complexes with the zinc, but the existence of the complexes in the baths has not been demonstrated. For proper operation, the cyanide-metal ratio must be carefully controlled, suggesting that certain cyano complexes are necessary for brightening.

Deposits from ammoniacal solution, in which the tetrammine ion, $[Zn(NH_3)_4]^{++}$, predominates, are similar to those from the sulfate bath. Zinc sulfate in a bath containing ammonium thiocyanate and ammonium chloride gives deposits covered with gray powder, which can be buffed to a bright coat[37]. Triethylamine and polyamines such as ethylenediamine have been recommended as brighteners[239].

Metals Whose Deposition from Aqueous Solution in Pure Form is Doubtful—Tungsten, Molybdenum, Tantalum, Zirconium, and Columbium

Although thin metallic plates of tungsten and molybdenum have been reported[46c, 110b, 239-243], it appears that the deposits are alloys and deposition ceases as soon as the codepositing metal impurity is exhausted.

Results with tantalum, zirconium, and columbium are similar[86]; deposition of these metals in the pure form has yet to be demonstrated.

Failure to obtain deposits of these metals as well as others of the vanadium and titanium groups is not surprising since all of their complexes are inner orbital. The oxygen complexes in particular are very stable, forming such ions as vanadyl and zirconyl, which strongly resist dissociation. Such complexes will form in water solution unless a still stronger coordi-

234. Henricks, U. S. Patent 2101580; 2101581.
235. Mattacotti, U. S. Patent 2109887.
236. Westbrook, U. S. Patent 2080520.
237. Westbrook, U. S. Patent 2218734; 2233500.
238. Hoff, U. S. Patent 2080479; Hull, U. S. Patent 2080423.
239. Bray and Howard, U. S. Patent 2393741 (Jan. 1946); cf., *Chem. Abs.*, **40**, 2395 (1946); Harford, U. S. Patent 2384300 (Sept. 1945); U. S. Patent 2384301 (1945).
240. Fink and Jones, *Trans. Electrochem. Soc.*, **59**, 461 (1931); Holt, *Trans. Electro-Chem. Soc.*, **71**, 301 (1937).
241. Glazunov and Jolkin, *Atti X cong. intern. chim.*, **4**, 353 (1939); cf., *Chem. Abs.*, **34**, 3184 (1940).
242. Price and Brown, *Trans. Electrochem. Soc.*, **70**, 423 (1936).
243. Hokhshtein, *J. Gen. Chem.*, *U.S.S.R.*, **7**, 2486 (1937); cf., *Chem. Abs.*, **32**, 2434 (1938).

nating agent is present. In either case, the discharge of hydrogen ion will probably require less energy than that required to discharge the metal from the complex.

The Electrolytic Separation of Metals and the Deposition of Metal Alloys from Solutions of Complex Compounds

The deposition potential of a metal can be markedly altered by complexing the metal ions in solution (Chapter 11). As is seen in Table 19.1, the magnitude of the shift brought about by a given complexing agent is different for different metals; thus it is frequently possible to separate by complex formation the deposition potentials of two metals whose deposition potentials in simple aqueous solution are very close together. This permits selective deposition of the metals, as in the purification of metals and in quantitative electrometric analysis[244]. Copper or bismuth cannot be selectively deposited from a solution containing the simple salts, but pure copper may be selectively deposited leaving bismuth in solution if tartrate is added. Similarly, antimony may be separated from many metals such as copper, bismuth, or lead, since antimony deposits with great difficulty from aqueous alkaline solutions containing tartrate or fluoride. Zinc may be separated from iron by using a cyanide bath in which the iron forms very stable inner orbital complexes.

The plating of metal alloys may be considered from an analogous viewpoint. The deposition potentials for each component of the alloy should have nearly the same value. Table 19.1 shows that the deposition potentials for copper and zinc may be brought together through complex formation with cyanide in the brass plating bath.

Thermodynamically, alloy deposition is more complicated than that of pure metals. The Nernst equation for the potential of a metal in an alloy must include a term for its activity in the alloy as well as for the activity of the metal ions in solution.*

$$E = E_0 - \frac{RT}{nF} \ln \frac{(\text{activity metal ions in solution})}{(\text{activity metal in alloy})}$$

The activity of a metal, "A," in the alloy is dependent upon the type of alloy formed. If, in a binary alloy, the solid is a two phase mixture of crystals of two metals, the activity of the metal "A" in the alloy is the same as that of the pure metal alone. If, however, the alloy is a single phase solid solution of metal "A" in a second metal "B," the activity of metal "A" in the alloy may be reduced appreciably. Under these conditions metal may

---

* The Nernst equation is used only for thermodynamic calculations and does not imply any definite mechanism for the reduction process. The actual plating potential will include another term which represents the excess potential necessary to keep the deposition process going at an appreciable rate.

244. Sand, "Electrochemistry and Electrochemical Analysis," Chapt. IV, Vol. II, London, Blackie and Son, Limited, 1940.

TABLE 19.1. THE VARIATION OF THE ELECTRODE POTENTIALS FOR ZINC
AND COPPER AS POTASSIUM CYANIDE IS ADDED TO THE SOLUTION

| Metal | 0.1 Mole Metal Sulfate per Liter | Electrolyte 0.1 Mole Metal Cyanide Plus | | |
		0.2M KCN	0.4M KCN	1.0M KCN
Zinc	−0.816	−1.033	−1.182	−1.231
Copper	0.292	−0.611	−0.964	−1.169

be deposited as an alloy from a complex ion which does not permit deposition of the pure metal. Stout and Faust[10b] were able to deposit ternary alloys of copper, iron, and nickel from a solution containing iron as the complex ferricyanide, $[Fe(CN)_6]^{\equiv}$, although iron will not deposit as the pure metal from ferricyanide solution. Similarly, a tungsten-iron alloy has been reported from a solution containing iron as ferrocyanide[245]. This explanation applies also to the deposition of other tungsten alloys, since pure tungsten cannot be deposited from aqueous solution[240b].

If the two metals "A" and "B" form an intermetallic compound of the type AB_2, the deposit may consist of the pure compound, or of solid solutions of A or B in AB_2, or of two or three phase mixtures[246]. To shift electrode potentials, a single agent which forms complexes with all metal ions to be deposited may be used, as in the silver-cadmium cyanide bath[247]; or two complexing agents may be selected so that the metals are present in different complex ions, as in a bath which contains silver as the cyanide and lead as the complex tartrate[248]. The latter type of bath permits more or less independent control of the activities of the two metal ion components. For example, in the silver-lead bath, excess cyanide reduces silver ion activity with relatively small effect on the activity of lead ions. Similarly, in a copper-tin alloy-plating bath, copper is present as the complex cyanide, and tin as the stannate ion. This permits control of copper activity by adjustment of cyanide concentration, and of tin activity by adjustment of alkali concentration.*

Alloy plating baths are usually of a type known to be suitable for deposition of at least one of the alloy components.† Cyanide is the most common

---

* Addition of alkali has a secondary effect on the activity of copper, but the effect is small in comparison to that on the activity of tin.

† However, an alloy of nickel and iron may be deposited at a current efficiency of nearly 60 per cent from a bath containing iron as potassium ferrocyanide, $K_4[Fe(CN)_6]$, and nickel as potassium nickelocyanide, $K_4[Ni(CN)_6]^{249}$ though neither pure iron nor pure nickel can be plated readily from cyanide solution.

245. Berghaus, German Patent 674430 (Apr. 14, 1939), cf., *Chem. Abs.*, **33**, 4886 (1939).
246. Allmand and Ellingham, "The Principles of Applied Electrochemistry," p. 128, New York, Longmans, Green and Co., 1924.
247. Faust, Henry, and France, *Trans. Electrochem. Soc.*, **72**, 479 (1937).
248. Faust and Thomas, *Trans. Electrochem. Soc.*, **75**, 185 (1939).
249. Stout and Carol, *Trans. Am. Electrochem. Soc.*, **58**, 357 (1930).

complexing agent; however, tartrate, oxalate, thiocyanate, amines, etc. have been used. The literature on alloy plating is summarized by Faust[250].

Cyanide Solutions for Alloy Plating. Many binary and ternary alloys have been deposited from cyanide solutions. Binary alloys include: alloys of copper with zinc[251], nickel, iron, cadmium, tin, gold, and other metals; alloys of silver with metals such as cadmium, indium, palladium, nickel, lead, and thallium; and alloys of gold with nickel, tin, etc.[250b]. Ternary alloys include combinations such as: cadmium-zinc-mercury[252], copper-cobalt-tin[253], copper-nickel-zinc[254], cadmium-zinc-antimony[255], copper-cadmium-zinc[256] and copper-tin-zinc[229]. Certain of these metals do not form cyanide complexes and are present in other forms.

Attempts to identify ions present in alloy plating solutions have not given convincing results (for example see[257]). However, it is probable that ions such as $[Cu(CN)_3]^=$ and $[Zn(CN)_4]^=$, which exist in the copper and zinc baths, are present also in the brass baths. In some cyanide solutions, other complex forming ions are essential. For instance, potassium tartrate is necessary for the satisfactory deposition of iron from the iron-nickel-copper alloy bath[11b], and additions of sodium acetate are recommended for zinc-cadmium alloy plating[258]. Ammonia is considered by some to be valuable in improving brass deposits.

Solutions for Alloy Plating Which Contain Complexing Agents Other than Cyanide. A number of alloys have been deposited from solutions containing complex forming salts of the organic acids. A copper-tin alloy may be deposited from a bath containing the oxalates[259]. A copper-zinc alloy is plated from a basic solution of the sulfates and sodium tartrate[260]. Silver-nickel, and silver-lead alloy deposits have been obtained from solutions of tartrates, citrates, or oxalates[115]. An alloy of tungsten and nickel is deposited[261] from a bath of sodium tungstate, citric acid, nickel sulfate, and ammonium hydroxide containing ions such as the complex

250. Faust, *Trans. Electrochem. Soc.*, **80**, 301 (1941); **78**, 383 (1940).
251. Coates, *Trans. Electrochem. Soc.*, **80**, 445 (1941).
252. Roberts, U. S. Patent 2250842 (1941).
253. Sklarew and Cinamon, U. S. Patent 2216605 (Oct. 1940).
254. Faust and Montillon, *Trans. Electrochem. Soc.*, **65**, 361 (1934); **67**, 281 (1935).
255. Stout and Goldstein, *Trans. Electrochem. Soc.*, **63**, 99 (1933).
256. Ernst and Mann, *Trans. Electrochem. Soc.*, **61**, 363 (1932).
257. Pan, *Trans. Electrochem. Soc.*, **62**, 63 (1932).
258. Belyaev and Agababov, *Korroziya i Borba s. Nei*, **5**, 137 (1939); cf., *Chem. Abs.*, **36**, 347 (1942).
259. Bechard, *J. Electrodepositers' Tech. Soc.*, **11**, 15 (1936).
260. Sukhodski, Kheifetz, and Chapurskii, *Repts. Central Inst. Metals, Leningrad*, no. 17, 209 (1934); cf., *Chem. Abs.*, **29**, 5357 (1945).
261. Vaaler and Holt, *Trans. Electrochem. Soc.*, **90**, 43 (1946).

nickel citrate, nickel tetrammine and complex nickel tungstate. Alloys of tungsten with iron, manganese, and silver have been obtained from similar baths. Molybdenum-cobalt and molybdenum-iron alloys are deposited[262] from solutions containing tartrates, glycols, glycerol, and sugars, which supposedly form complexes with iron and cobalt. A solution containing both citrate ions and fluoride ions has been specified for plating alloys of tungsten with nickel, iron, cobalt, and antimony[245, 263]. A nickel-iron alloy may be deposited from a formate-sulfate bath[264].

Alloys of copper-zinc, nickel-cobalt, nickel-iron, cadmium-zinc, karat gold, cadmium-silver, copper-tin, and silver-lead are deposited on the commercial scale. Certain alloy deposits may be obtained from solutions containing the aquated ions. Thus, zinc-cadmium alloys are deposited[265] from solutions of the sulfates, and lead-tin alloys from mixtures of the fluoroborates[266].

Deposits from nickel and tin chloride-fluoride solutions contain 50 atom-per cent of each metal over a considerable range of nickel-tin ratios in the bath[267]. This has been interpreted to indicate that deposition occurs from a double fluoride complex containing an atom of each metal; the existence of such a complex has been demonstrated by application of the method of continuous variations (p. 569)[267A]. Similar deposits are said to have resulted from an acetate bath. The concept is interesting, but constant composition deposits have not as yet been reported for other baths.

ELECTRODEPOSITION FROM NONAQUEOUS SOLUTIONS

The use of nonaqueous solvents in metal deposition was reviewed by Audrieth and Nelson[268] in 1931. Anhydrous liquid ammonia, the nitrogen prototype of water, has been studied as a solvent by a number of workers[268, 269]. Copper, silver, gold, beryllium, zinc, cadmium, mercury, thallium, tin, lead, arsenic, chromium, manganese, iron, nickel, cobalt, palladium and platinum, can be plated from liquid ammonia solution, but attempts to deposit aluminum, thorium, bismuth, antimony, molybdenum, and

262. Yntema, U. S. Patent 2428404 (Oct. 7, 1947).
263. Berghaus, German Patent 674430 (Apr. 14, 1939); cf., *Chem. Abs.*, **33**, 4886 (1939).
264. Kersten and Young, *Ind. Eng. Chem.*, **28**, 1176 (1936).
265. Fink and Young, *Trans. Electrochem. Soc.*, **67**, 131 (1935).
266. Blum and Haring, *Trans. Electrochem. Soc.*, **40**, 147 (1921); Carlson and Kane, *Monthly Rev. Am. Electroplaters' Soc.*, **33**, 255 (1946).
267. Cuthbertson, Parkinson, and Rooksby, *J. Electrochem. Soc.*, **100**, 107 (1953); Rooksby, *J. Electrodepositors' Tech. Soc.*, **27**, 129 (1951).
267A. Rau, thesis, University of Illinois, 1955.
268. Audrieth and Nelson, *Chem. Revs.*, **8**, 335 (1931).
269. Audrieth and Yntema, *J. Phys. Chem.*, **34**, 929 (1930); Booth and Merlub-Sobel, *J. Phys. Chem.*, **35**, 3303 (1931); Taft and Barham, *J. Phys. Chem.*, **34**, 929 (1930).

tungsten were unsuccessful. Beryllium is of particular interest since it cannot be plated from aqueous solution.

From a solution of their salts in formamide or acetamide, lead, copper, zinc, tin, thallium, cadmium, nickel, and cobalt have been deposited[270, 271]. Iron and metals above zinc in the electromotive series could not be deposited. An alloy of aluminum and iron has been plated from formamide[272]. Cathode current-voltage curves for metal deposition in formamide and pyridine have been reported[66]. Pyridine as a solvent permits the deposition of silver, magnesium, calcium, zinc, copper, iron, potassium, sodium, and lithium. No plate was obtained with beryllium[268].

Miscellaneous organic solvents from which metals have been deposited include glacial acetic acid[273], acetone[268], ether[127b, 274], ethyl bromide and benzene mixture[272b], substituted benzenes[275], and phosphorous oxychloride[276]. Of particular interest is an ethyl bromide-benzene bath containing dissolved metallic aluminum and a small amount of aluminum bromide. Aluminum was deposited from this bath at a current efficiency of 60 per cent[272b].

In general, the salts which are most soluble in a variety of solvents are the nitrates, bromides, iodides, thiocyanates, and cyanides[268]. Nonaqueous baths resemble aqueous baths in that small amounts of addition agents, temperature, and current density are of major importance in determining the type of plate obtained.

Solvents such as liquid ammonia, liquid hydrogen cyanide, glacial acetic acid, anhydrous amines, ether, and acetone are of particular importance in studying the electrochemistry of coordination compounds. Since ions in solution are always solvated,* the so-called simple ions in water are complexes of the type $[M(H_2O)_x]^{y+}$; in liquid ammonia the "simple" ions are metal ammines of the form $[M(NH_3)_x]^{y+}$; and in liquid hydrogen cyanide they are probably complexes of the type $[M(CN)_x]^{z-}$. An aquated ion in liquid ammonia is a complex ion just as metal ammines are complexes in water. Thus, the distinction between simple and complex ions is entirely

---

* Energy considerations do not permit the existence of the unsolvated simple ion M^+ in the body of the solution, though it may be adsorbed on the electrode surface.

270. Rohler, *Z. Elektrochem.*, **16**, 419 (1910).
271. Yntema and Audrieth, *J. Am. Chem. Soc.*, **52**, 2693 (1930).
272. Blue and Mathers, *Trans. Electrochem. Soc.*, **63**, 231 (1933); **65**, 339 (1934).
273. Stillwell and Audrieth, *J. Am. Chem. Soc.*, **54**, 472 (1932).
274. Kudra and Kleibs, *J. Phys. Chem.*, *U.S.S.R.*, **15**, 228 (1941); cf., *Chem. Abs.*, **36**, 6417 (1942).
275. Gorenbein, *J. Gen Chem. U.S.S.R.*, **8**, 233 (1938); cf., *Chem. Abs.* **32**, 5310 (1938); Plotnikov and Gorenbein, *Mem. Inst. Chem., Acad. Sci. Ukrain.S.S.R.* **4**, No. 3, 249 (1937); cf., *Chem. Abs.*, **32**, 5310 (1938).
276. Cady and Taft, *J. Phys. Chem.*, **29**, 1057, 1068 (1925).

arbitrary[277]. Metals have been deposited from a variety of nonaqueous solvents such as ammonia, formamide, sulfur dioxide and acetone, and little distinction need be made between reduction of solvated and other complexes. The potential energy treatment of Gurney and Fowler (see page 634) can be applied equally well to all situations.

Since the more reactive metals cannot be deposited from water solution, it is necessary to use other solvents to obtain metallic deposits. The deposition potential of the metal must not exceed the reduction potential of the solvent. A number of the more reactive metals can be deposited from nonaqueous solvents which are very weak Bronsted-Lowry acids. For example, beryllium is deposited from solutions of its salts in anhydrous liquid ammonia[269b], and aluminum alloys can be plated from solutions containing aluminum chloride and another appropriate metal salt such as iron(III) chloride in anhydrous formamide[272]. There is no general correlation between metal activity and the deposition of the metal from basic solvents. Beryllium can be deposited from liquid ammonia, and the active alkali metals can be reduced to give their characteristic blue solution in liquid ammonia, but much more noble metals such as aluminum, magnesium, antimony and bismuth cannot be deposited or reduced in liquid ammonia solution.

277. Densham, *Trans. Faraday Soc.*, **33**, 1513 (1937).

20. The Use of Coordination Compounds in Analytical Chemistry

James V. Quagliano
Notre Dame University, Notre Dame, Indiana

and

Donald H. Wilkins
University of Illinois, Urbana, Illinois

When a metal ion becomes part of a complex, it achieves new properties which may be strikingly different from those of the original ion. Such changes include those in color, stability toward oxidation or reduction, magnitude of ionic charge (frequently even a change in sign), and solubilities and crystalline form of the salts. These new properties used in the identification or determination of either the metallic ion or the coordinating agent illustrate applications of complexing to analytical chemistry. Such applications to qualitative analysis are found in the dissolution of silver chloride in ammonium hydroxide and in the generation of a red color when iron(III) ion is treated with thiocyanate. In quantitative analysis, coordination compounds are widely used in gravimetric, volumetric and colorimetric determinations, as well as in polarimetry and microscopy. In the broadest sense, any analysis carried out in solution might be considered to involve coordination, for "the chemistry of solutions is the chemistry of complexes."

APPLICATIONS TO PRECIPITATION METHODS

Insoluble Inner Complexes

Inner complexes often have properties useful in analysis and remarkably different from the ions from which they are generated. These complexes were formerly called "inner complex salts," but the term is a misnomer, for they are not salts; their usefulness in analytical chemistry depends largely upon their nonsalt-like character. An inner complex is a completely chelated, nonionic structure, formed, usually, by the union of a metal ion with a bidentate group which has a charge of minus one. Obviously, for such a

672

group to form an inner complex, the coordination number of the metal ion must be twice its ionic charge; this is frequently, but not always, the case. Inner complexes containing beryllium, aluminum, cobalt(III), iron(III), and chromium(III) are common; those containing cobalt(II) or iron(II) are rare because the usual coordination number of these ions is six; they could form inner complexes by union with a tridentate ligand of uninegative charge.

The value of inner complexes in analytical chemistry rests largely upon three properties:

(1) Many of them are insoluble in aqueous media, but may be extracted into organic solvents immiscible with water, thereby permitting a separation of certain ions from a large volume of aqueous solution into a small volume of organic solvent. The extractability is often a function of the pH of the aqueous phase, so that selective extraction and subsequent return to a new aqueous phase are possible(p. 44).

Solubility characteristics of inner complexes may be quite different if the organic coordinating agent contains a functional group of such a nature, or in such a position, that it cannot take part in coordination. For example, the zinc derivative of 8-hydroxyquinoline is quantitatively insoluble in water, whereas the zinc compound of 5-sulfo-8-hydroxyquinoline is readily soluble.

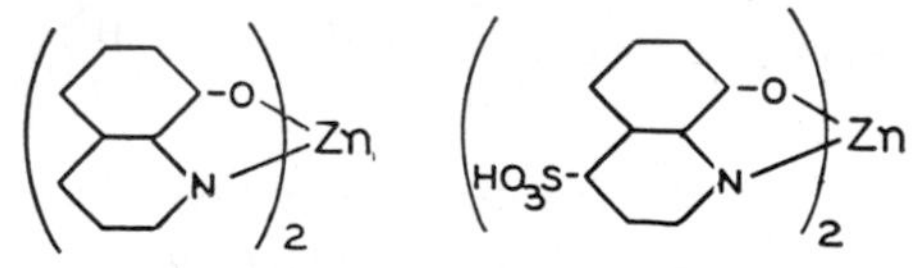

Strictly speaking, such substances are not true inner complexes, for they give ions in aqueous solution; however, they are often referred to as inner complexes because the coordinate bonds about the metal ion are the same as in the derivatives of the ligands which do not contain solubilizing groups.

(2) The formation of inner complexes is sometimes accompanied by pronounced color changes which permit colorimetric measurements. This development of color is striking, but it is by no means as general as many chemists suppose.

(3) The metal ion to be determined is often a part of a complex of high molecular weight; this gives a favorable conversion factor.

Correlation of structures of organic coordinating agents with structures of specific metal ions with which they react is largely empirical. The relationships are doubtless very complex, involving not only the varying nature of the bond between the metal and the ligand, but also steric factors and solubilities.

Dioximes. The use of inner complexes in analytical chemistry began with

Tschugaeff[1], who discovered that biacetyldioxime (dimethylglyoxime) reacts with nickel ion to give an insoluble red compound. This reaction has been extensively studied, for it furnishes a very sensitive and specific method for the determination of nickel by direct weighing.

In general, compounds designated by the formula

$$R—C\hspace{-2pt}=\hspace{-2pt}NOH$$
$$R—C\hspace{-2pt}=\hspace{-2pt}NOH$$

(in which R represents an aliphatic, aromatic, or heterocyclic group) precipitate comparable red compounds, so the functional group

$$—C\hspace{-2pt}=\hspace{-2pt}NOH$$
$$—C\hspace{-2pt}=\hspace{-2pt}NOH$$

is apparently responsible for the reaction. The dimethyl compound is the best known and most widely used glyoxime, but several other members of the series possess distinct advantages over it.

Furildioxime[2], 1,2-cyclohexanedionedioxime[3], and 1,2-cycloheptane-dionedioxime[4]

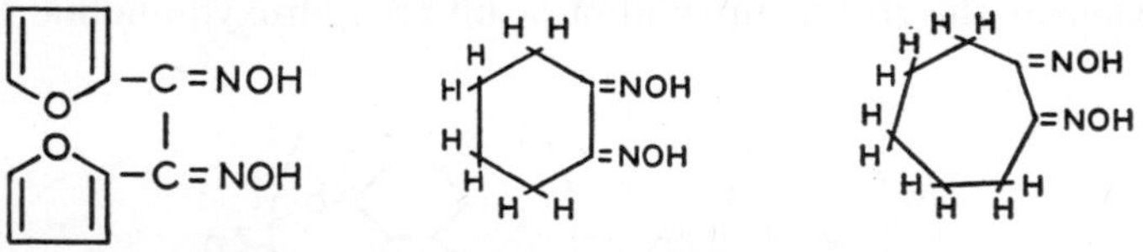

are all more soluble in water than dimethylglyoxime and give more favorable conversion factors. The nickel derivative of the cycloheptane compound, moreover, may be precipitated from slightly acid solution.

Diaminoglyoxime[5], $H_2N—C\hspace{-2pt}=\hspace{-2pt}NOH$, can be used in place of the dimethyl

$$H_2N—C\hspace{-2pt}=\hspace{-2pt}NOH$$

analog, but replacement of the NH_2 group by $NH_2CONH—$ so increases the acidity of the molecule that it acts as a dibasic acid[6], and in ammoniacal solution produces a precipitate of the formula

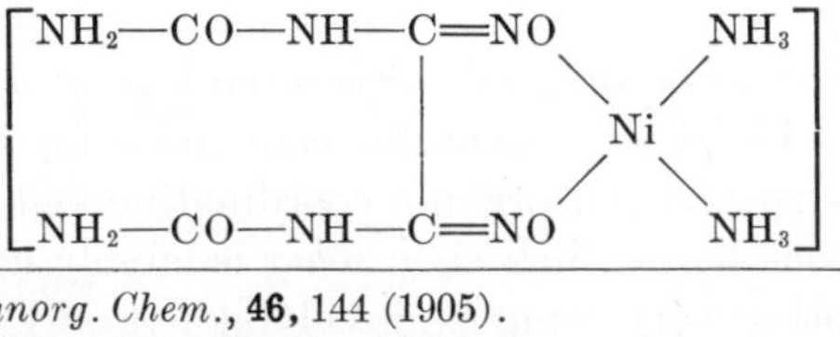

$$\left[\begin{array}{cc} NH_2—CO—NH—C\hspace{-2pt}=\hspace{-2pt}NO & NH_3 \\ & \diagdown \diagup \\ & Ni \\ & \diagup \diagdown \\ NH_2—CO—NH—C\hspace{-2pt}=\hspace{-2pt}NO & NH_3 \end{array}\right]$$

1. Tschugaeff, Z. anorg. Chem., **46**, 144 (1905).
2. Soule, J. Am. Chem. Soc., **47**, 981 (1925).
3. Wallack, Ann., **437**, 148, 175 (1924).
4. Voter and Banks, Anal. Chem., **21**, 1320 (1949).
5. Chatterjee, J. Indian Chem. Soc., **15**, 608 (1938).
6. Feigl and Christiani-Kronwald, Z. anal. Chem., **65**, 341 (1924).

The dioximes also yield (yellow) precipitates with palladium salts, but not with the ions of any other metals. The palladium(II) derivative of dimethylglyoxime is insoluble in dilute mineral acid solutions, whereas the nickel compound must be precipitated in a buffered acetate or ammoniacal medium; the ortho-dioxime group may thus be considered specific for both palladium(II) and nickel(II) ions. Palladium(II) dimethylglyoxime, unlike the nickel(II) derivative, is soluble without decomposition in solutions of alkali hydroxide[7] to form the ion

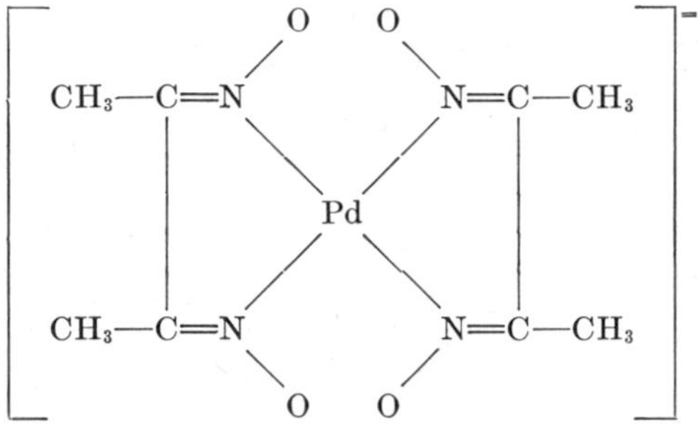

$$
\begin{bmatrix}
& O \quad O & \\
CH_3-C{=}N & \quad N{=}C-CH_3 \\
& Pd & \\
CH_3-C{=}N & \quad N{=}C-CH_3 \\
& O \quad O &
\end{bmatrix}^{-}
$$

The specificity of the ortho-dioxime group toward nickel and palladium vanishes when the oxime groups are attached to an unsaturated ring. Thus, α,β-naphthquinonedioxime and orthoquinonedioxime act as dibasic acids and precipitate many metal ions from neutral solutions[8].

The symmetrical dioximes exist in three isomeric forms:

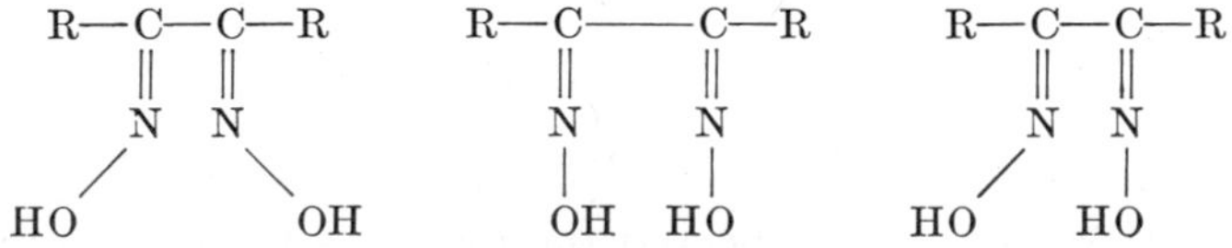

$$
\begin{array}{ccc}
\underset{\substack{\| \; \| \\ N \; N \\ HO \qquad OH \\ \text{Anti}}}{R-C-C-R} &
\underset{\substack{\| \quad \| \\ N \quad N \\ OH \; HO \\ \text{Syn-}}}{R-C\text{-----}C-R} &
\underset{\substack{\| \; \| \\ N \; N \\ HO \quad HO \\ \text{Amphi-}}}{R-C-C-R}
\end{array}
$$

Of the three isomers of biacetyldioxime, only the anti-isomer forms the characteristic red, insoluble nickel(II) compound; the syn-isomer is incapable of reacting with metallic salts, and the amphi-isomer gives a yellow or green-yellow compound in which one molecule of dioxime is combined with one nickel ion, the hydrogens of both oxime groups being replaced by the metal[6, 9].

Following the demonstration of the existence of two tautomeric forms of

7. Feigl and Suter, *J. Chem. Soc.*, **1948**, 378.
8. Feigl, *Ind. Eng. Chem., Anal. Ed.*, **8**, 401 (1936).
9. Tschugaeff, *Ber.*, **39**, 3382 (1906); **41**, 1678, 2219 (1908); *J. Chem. Soc.*, **105**, 2187 (1914); Atack, *J. Chem. Soc.*, **103**, 1317 (1913); Pfeiffer, *Ber.*, **63**, 1811 (1930); Hieber and Leutert, *Ber.*, **60**, 2296, 2310 (1927); Tschugaeff and Lebedinski, *Z. anorg. Chem.*, **83**, 1 (1913).

the oxime group[10]

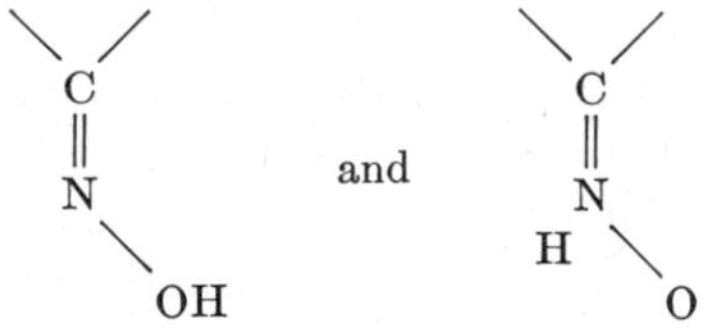

Pfeiffer[9e, 11] proposed that the nitrone form is involved in the formation of the nickel derivative, which then contains nickel-nitrogen bonds in five-membered rings.

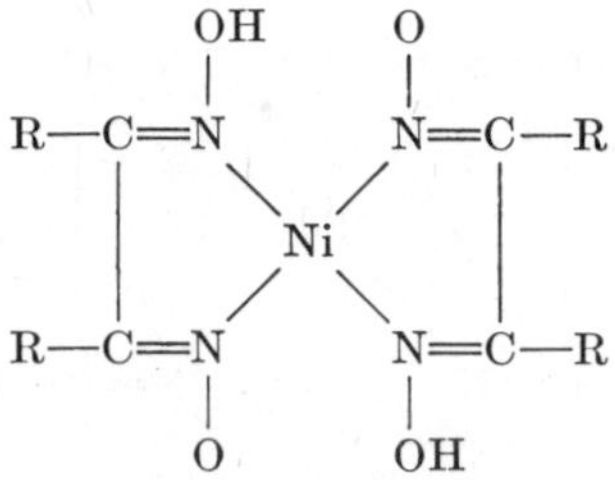

From the facts that the anti-isomer of α-benzilmonoxime (I), the mono-ethers of α-benzildioxime (II), and α-benzilmonoximeimine (III) form red precipitates with nickel(II), Pfeiffer inferred that the nickel ion is bonded to the nitrogen atom of the dioxime group rather than to the oxygen atom.

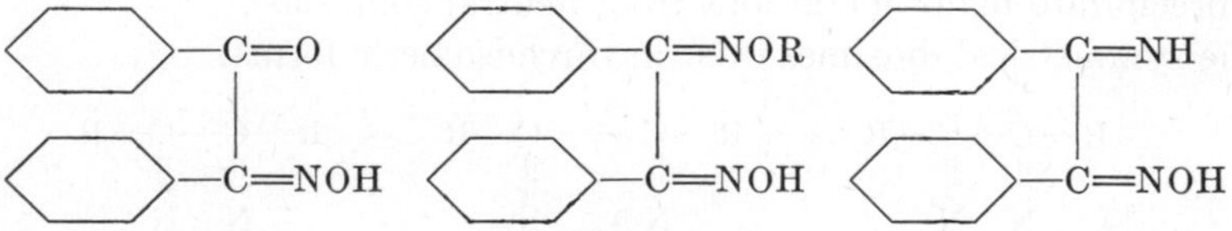

Brady and Meurs[12] have proposed the following formula for the nickel derivative of biacetyldioxime:

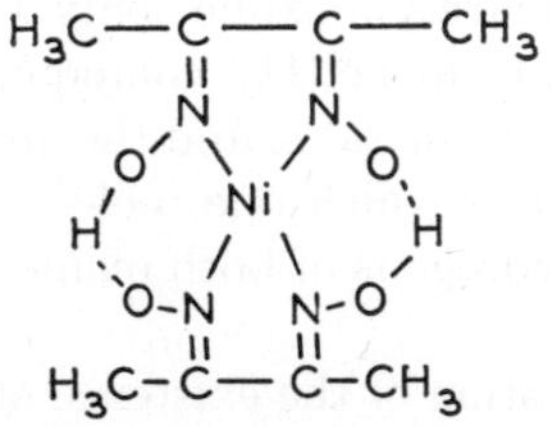

The postulated hydrogen bonding eliminates the possibility of cis-trans

10. Brady and Mehta, *J. Chem. Soc.*, **125**, 2297 (1924).
11. Pfeiffer and Richarz, *Ber.*, **61**, 103 (1928).
12. Brady and Meurs, *J. Chem. Soc.*, **1930**, 1599.

isomerism and also explains the lack of reactivity of the hydroxyl group. The nitrogen-nickel bonds are covalent and planar and two isomeric nickel derivatives of unsymmetrically substituted dioximes correspond to cis and trans configurations[13].

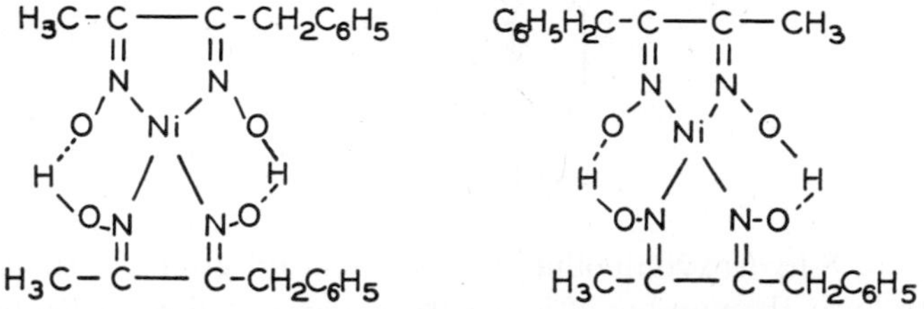

Similar isomerism exists in the case of the palladium derivative[11]. Isomerism of several sorts may be found in complexes, and since the isomers may differ in color and in solubility, their existence is of great analytical interest.

In the determination of nickel with dimethylglyoxime, the precipitate may be dried and weighed, or redissolved and titrated. In acid solution, it hydrolyzes to hydroxylamine, which can be titrated with a bromate-bromide mixture, or oxidized by iron(III) ion, the resulting iron(II) ion being titrated[14].

An interesting application of the reaction between biacetyldioxime and nickel ion is found in the determination of biacetyl, $(CH_3CO)_2$, in butter and other natural products. The biacetyl is converted to the oxime and precipitated[15].

8-Hydroxyquinoline and Derivatives. In 8-hydroxyquinoline and its derivatives, the hydroxyl and heterocyclic nitrogen combine with metal ions to form chelate rings.

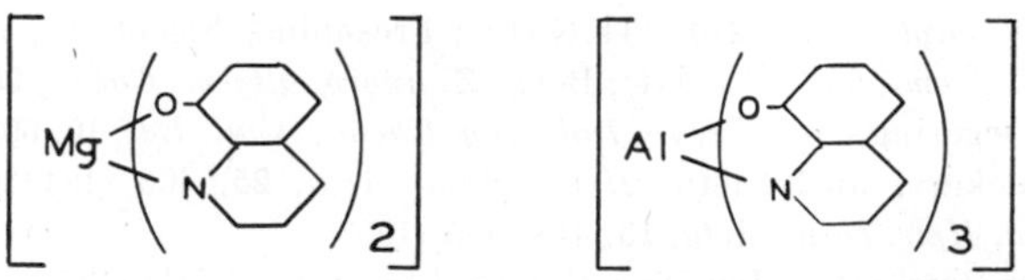

8-Hydroxyquinoline has been used in the determination and detection of over thirty elements[16]. Attempts have been made to increase the selectivity

13. Sugden, *J. Chem. Soc.*, **1932**, 246; Cavell and Sugden, *J. Chem. Soc.*, **1935**, 621.
14. Tougarinoff, *Ann. soc. sci. Bruxelles*, **54B**, 314 (1934).
15. Barnicoat, *Analyst*, **60**, 653 (1935).
16. Berg, "Die Chemische Analyse," 2nd ed., Vol. 34, Enke, Stuttgart, 1938; "Organic Reagents for Metals," 4th ed., London, Hopkin and Williams, 1943; Yoe and Sarver: "Organic Analytical Reagents," New York, John Wiley & Sons, Inc., 1945.

and sensitivity of these reactions by the use of derivatives[17], and by variations in the pH of the solutions[18].

8-Hydroxyquinaldine[19] (2-methyl-8-hydroxyquinoline) is a useful

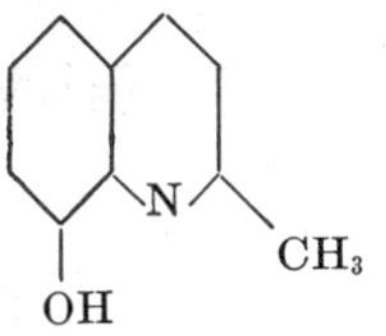

derivative of 8-hydroxyquinoline, but the methyl group in the 2-position appears to limit the number of ions with which it will react. In particular, 8-hydroxyquinaldine does not precipitate aluminum from acetic acid solutions buffered with acetate, whereas 8-hydroxyquinoline gives quantitative precipitation[20].

Many techniques have been devised for the termination of analyses involving 8-hydroxyquinoline and its derivatives. The usual methods involve weighing the precipitate directly or igniting it to the oxide, but sometimes it is more convenient to redissolve the precipitate and titrate. 8-Hydroxyquinoline precipitates are conveniently titrated either by oxidation or by bromination. For example, the 8-hydroxyquinoline may be oxidized by an excess of hexanitratocerate(IV), the excess being back titrated with oxalate[21]. The reaction is not strictly stoichiometric, but a reproducible empirical factor may be determined. The bromination technique, using standard bromate, is extremely sensitive.

Hydroxyoximes. The hydroxyoxime grouping is found in salicylaldoxime, 2-hydroxy-4-methoxyacetophenoneoxime, 2-hydroxy-5-methoxyacetophenoneoxime, and o-vanillinoxime. With copper, it forms salts in

17. Molland, *Compt. rend.*, **210**, 144 (1940); Fresenius, Fischbach, and Frommes, *Z. anal. Chem.*, **96**, 433 (1934); Berg, *Z. anorg. allgem. Chem.*, **204**, 208 (1932), Boyd, Degering, and Shreve, *Ind. Eng. Chem., Anal. Ed.*, **10**, 606 (1938); Wenger, Duckart, and Rieth, *Helv. chim. Acta*, **25**, 406 (1942); Gutzeit and Monnier, *Helv. chim. Acta*, **16**, 478, 485 (1933).
18. Moyer and Remington, *Ind. Eng. Chem., Anal. Ed.*, **10**, 212 (1938); Soto, *J. Chem. Soc., Japan*, **54**, 725 (1933); **56**, 314 (1935); Fleck and Ward, *Analyst* **58**, 388 (1933); **62**, 378 (1937); Marsson and Hasse, *Chem. Ztg.*, **52**, 993 (1928); Halberstadt, *Compt. rend.*, **205**, 987 (1937).
19. Doebner and Miller, *Ber.*, **17**, 1698 (1884); Merritt and Walker, *Ind. Eng. Chem., Anal. Ed.*, **16**, 387 (1944).
20. Merritt, *Record Chem. Progr.*, **10**, No. 2, 59 (1949).
21. Nielson, *Ind. Eng. Chem., Anal. Ed.*, **11**, 649 (1939); Gerber, Claassen, and Boruff, *Ind. Eng. Chem., Anal. Ed.*, **14**, 658 (1942).

which the phenolic hydrogen is assumed to be replaced with the formation of an inner complex.

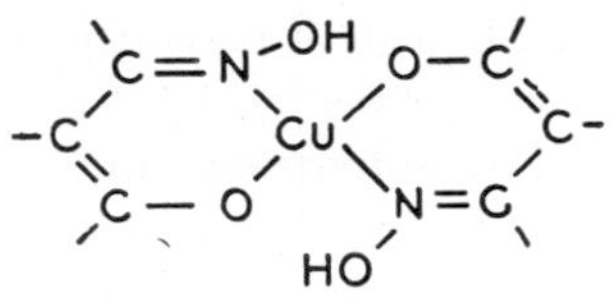

The reactions of the isomeric methyl ethers of salicylaldoxime support this.

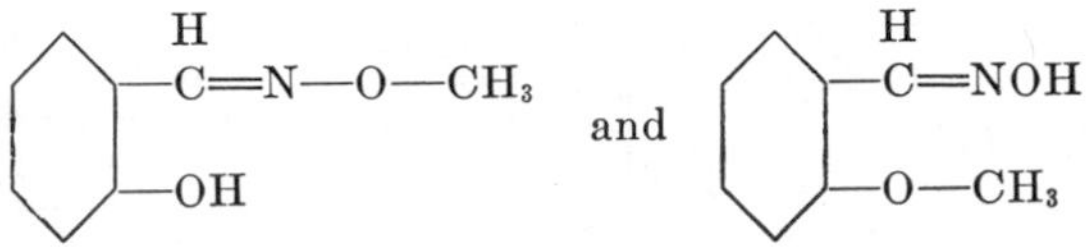

The compound containing the free phenolic hydroxyl group reacts with copper(II) ion, whereas the isomeric phenolic ether does not.

The functional group must be a part of an aromatic system to react with metal ions. Thus, acetonylcarbinol and chloralacetophenone contain the characteristic group of atoms but do not form complexes with copper(II). Apparently, an acidic hydrogen, such as is present in phenols, is necessary. Other reagents containing this functional group do not offer any special advantages over the more readily available salicylaldoxime. However, in some cases, the metal derivatives are more intensely colored[22].

The acyloin oxime group is found in a number of compounds which possess valuable analytical properties. It acts as a dibasic acid, with the oxime group tautomerizing to the nitrone form under the influence of alkali:

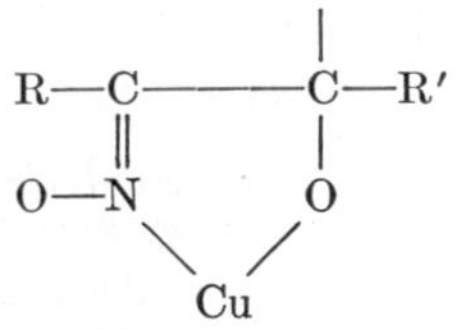

The nature of the R and R′ groups has little effect on the water-insolubility or the color of the copper(II) salt, but has a marked effect on the solubility in excess ammonia. Feigl believes that, if the R and R′ radicals are capable of coordinating with the copper ion, the inner complex formed is incapable of adding ammonia and is insoluble in aqueous ammonia[23].

α-Benzoinoxime exhibits a selective action in precipitating only copper ion from ammoniacal solutions. In acidic solutions, the reagent is useful for

22. Flagg and Furman, *Ind. Eng. Chem., Anal. Ed.*, **12**, 529 (1940).
23. Feigl and Bondi, *Ber.*, **64**, 2819 (1931).

the determination of molybdenum[24] and tungsten[25], even though the precipitate is of indefinite composition and must be converted to some other form for weighing.

Nitroso Hydroxylamines. The use of the nitroso hydroxylamine group in analytical procedures is best represented by the extensive use of cupferron and neocupferron (phenylnitrosohydroxylamine and naphthylnitrosohydroxylamine). Both reagents react with the ions of a large number of heavy-metals, forming inner complexes insoluble in acid solutions:

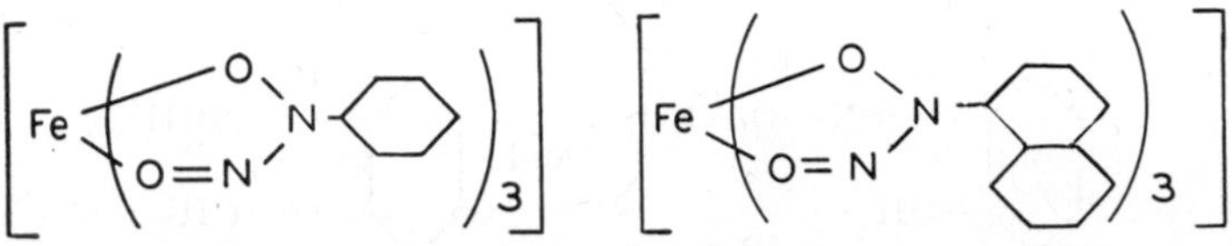

Those obtained from the naphthyl compound are less soluble than the derivatives of the phenyl compound; this illustrates the general rule that an increase in molecular weight lowers the water solubility of inner complexes.

Nitrosophenols. Several nitrosophenols find use in analytical chemistry. It is interesting that 2-nitroso-1-naphthol is eight times as sensitive as the isomeric 1-nitroso-2-naphthol in the precipitation of cobalt[26]. Since the nitrosophenol precipitates often carry reagent with them, and are not sufficiently stable to be dried, they must be ignited and weighed as the oxide. Nitrosonaphthols are used primarily for the determination of cobalt[27], but have also been used to determine iron[28], palladium[29], and copper[30]. Potassium has been determined indirectly by precipitation of potassium hexanitrocobaltate(III), and by the subsequent determination of the cobalt in the precipitate with 1-nitroso-2-naphthol.

Amino Acids. The amino acids are useful reagents, especially for divalent elements of the transition series. The solubilities of the metal com-

24. Sterling and Spuhr, *Ind. Eng. Chem., Anal. Ed.*, **12**, 33 (1940); Arrington and Rice, *U. S. Bur. Mines, Rept. Inv.*, **1939**, 3441; Knowles, *J. Research Natl. Bur. Standards*, **9**, 1 (1932); Taylor-Austin, *Analyst*, **62**, 107 (1937); Thompson and Stott, *Foundry Trade J.*, 123 (Aug. 23, 1934).

25. Steele, *Iron Steel Ind.*, **11**, 267 (1938); Baker, *Chemist-Analyst*, **30**, No. 2, 31 (1941); Isibasi, *J. Chem. Soc., Japan*, **61**, 125 (1940); Yagoda and Fales, *J. Am. Chem. Soc.*, **60**, 640 (1938).

26. Giua and Cherchi, *Gazz. chim. ita.*, **49**, 284 (1919).

27. Mayr and Feigl, *Z. anal. Chem.*, **90**, 15 (1932); Clennell, *Mining Mag.*, **36**, 270 (1927); Philippot, *Bull. soc. chim., Belg.*, **44**, 140 (1935); Eder, *Chem. Ztg.*, **46**, 430 (1922); Craig and Cudroff, *Chemist-Analyst*, **24**, No. 4, 10 (1927); Hoffman, *J. Research Natl. Bur. Standards*, **8**, 659 (1932).

28. Ilinski and Knorre, *Ber.*, **18**, 2728 (1885); Knorre, *Z. angew. Chem.*, **1904**, 641, 676; Jolles, *Z. anal. Chem.*, **36**, 149 (1897); Mathers, *J. Am. Chem. Soc.*, **30**, 209 (1908).

29. Schmidt, *Z. anorg. Chem.*, **80**, 335 (1913).

30. Burgass, *Z. angew. Chem.*, **1896**, 596; Knorre, *Ber.*, **20**, 283 (1887).

plexes are pH dependent, and useful separations may be accomplished by an adjustment of the pH of the precipitating medium. Aromatic ligands are ordinarily much weaker coordinating agents than their aliphatic analogs; however, the favorable disposition of coordinating groups in anthranilic acid makes it a reasonably good complexing agent, and it forms complexes suitable for analytical procedures with cadmium[31], cobalt[32], copper[32, 33], and zinc[31c, 34].

There are numerous sulfur compounds applicable to the formation of inner complexes not listed under the functional groups mentioned. Among these are 2-benzothiazolethiol[35], 2,5-dimercapto-1,3,4-thiodiazole[36], rubeanic acid[37], and thiocarbanilide[37e, 38].

Complex Ions as Precipitants

Many complex ions are stable enough to be used as precipitants of ions to be detected or quantitatively determined. The precipitates may often be dried and weighed; in other cases, they are ignited to oxide, or redissolved and then determined colorimetrically or by titration. The ammines of cobalt and chromium have received the most study as precipitants, but even with these, the field has hardly been touched.

Complex Cations as Precipitants. When hexamminecobalt(III) ion is added to neutral, basic, or acidic solutions of metavanadate ion, the insoluble compounds, $[Co(NH_3)_6] (VO_3)_3$, $[Co(NH_3)_6]_4 (V_2O_7)_3$, and $[Co(NH_3)_6]_4$-$(V_6O_{17})_3$ are formed, respectively[39]. The yellow precipitate formed in acid solution separates vanadium quantitatively from phosphate, arsenate, iron(III), copper(II), and calcium ions. Hexamminecobalt(III) ion may

31. Funk, *Z. anal. Chem.*, **123**, 241 (1942); Wenger and Masset, *Helv. chim. Acta*, **23**, 34 (1940); Funk and Ditt, *Z. anal. Chem.*, **91**, 332 (1933).
32. Funk and Ditt, *Z. anal. Chem.*, **93**, 241 (1933); Wenger, Cimerman, and Corbaz, *Mikrochemie*, **27**, 85 (1939).
33. Wenger and Besso, *Mikrochemie*, **29**, 240 (1941).
34. Anderson, *Ind. Eng. Chem., Anal. Ed.*, **13**, 367 (1941); Caldwell and Moyer, *J. Am. Chem. Soc.*, **57**, 2372 (1935); Cimerman and Wenger, *Mikrochemie*, **18**, 53 (1935); Wenger, *Helv. chim. Acta*, **25**, 1499 (1942); Mayr, *Z. anal. Chem.*, **92**, 166 (1933).
35. Spacu and Kuras, *J. prakt. Chem.*, **144**, 106 (1935); Dubsky, Mikrochemie, **28**, 145 (1940); Spacu and Kuras, *Z. anal. Chem.*, **102**, 24 (1935).
36. Dubsky, Okac, and Trtilek, *Mikrochemie*, **17**, 332 (1935); Ray and Gupta, *J. Indian Chem. Soc.*, **12**, 308 (1935).
37. Ray, *Z. anal. Chem.*, **79**, 94 (1929); Wolbling and Steiger, *Mikrochemie*, **15**, 295 (1934); Feigl and Kapulitzas, *Microchemie*, **8**, 239 (1930); Center and MacIntosh, *Ind. Eng. Chem., Anal. Ed.*, **17**, 239 (1930); Wolbling, *Ber.*, **67**, 773 (1934).
38. Wohler and Metz, *Z. anorg. allgem. Chem.*, **138**, 368 (1924); Singleton, *Ind. Chemist*, **3**, 121 (1927).
39. Parks and Prebluda, *J. Am. Chem. Soc.*, **57**, 1676 (1935).

also be used as a precipitant for the quantitative determination of ferrocyanide ion[40] in the absence of chromate, dichromate, and vanadate ions.

The nitratopentamminecobalt(III) ion, $[Co(NH_3)_5NO_3]^{++}$, has been employed in the determination of semi-micro quantities of phosphates[41]. The insoluble, high molecular weight complex compound, $[Co(NH_3)_5NO_3]$-$[H_3PMo_{12}O_{41}]$, has the advantage of a favorable conversion factor and avoids the post-precipitation and occlusion phenomena which are so troublesome with ammonium molybdate. It is interesting to note that the complex cations, $[Co(NH_3)_6]^{+++}$ and $[Co(NH_3)_5Cl]^{++}$ failed to give satisfactory precipitates in this procedure. Inconsistent results were obtained in attempts to use the complex ammines in the determination of germanates and arsenates.

Frequently, metal cations can be converted to anions and precipitated by the addition of complex cations. Thus, after the addition of excess iodide, bismuth may be precipitated as the orange-yellow complex, trans-$[Co\ en_2\ (SCN)_2][BiI_4]$[42]. Bismuth can be determined also by precipitation of $[Cr(NH_3)_6][BiCl_6]$, which is then analysed by ammonia distillation[43]. Similarly, antimony[44] can be precipitated and weighed as the stable and very insoluble chromium compound $[Cr\ en_3][SbS_4]$. For the determination of semi-micro quantities of antimony, the method is more rapid and convenient than the usual method of weighing as antimony(III) sulfide. Feigl and Miranda[45] used the tris(α,α'-dipyridyl)iron(II) ion for the detection of complex anions which have large atomic volumes, such as $[CdI_4]^=$, $[HgI_4]^=$, $[Co(CN)_6]^\equiv$, and $[Ni(CN)_4]^=$. The similar tris(orthophenanthroline)iron(II) ion is also useful for the precipitation of these anions.

Complex Anions as Precipitants. Complex anions can, of course, be used as precipitants, too, as is illustrated by the well-known determination of ammonium and potassium ions[46] by the precipitation of their chloroplatinates. Potassium is also determined by precipitation of $K_2Na[Co(NO_2)_6]$[47] or the still less soluble salt $K_2Ag[Co(NO_2)_6]$[48].

Cadmium can be separated from zinc and determined quantitatively by precipitation as the insoluble thiourea complex $[Cd(thiourea)_2]$

40. Hynes, Malko, and Yanowski, *Ind. Eng. Chem., Anal. Ed.*, **8**, 356 (1936).
41. Furman and State, *Ind. Eng. Chem., Anal. Ed.*, **8**, 420 (1936).
42. Spacu and Spacu, *Z. anal. Chem.*, **93**, 260 (1933).
43. Mahr, *Z. anal. Chem.*, **93**, 433 (1933).
44. Spacu and Pop, *Z. anal. Chem.*, **111**, 254 (1938); Spacu and Pop, *Mikrochemie ver. Mikrochim. Acta*, **3**, 27 (1938).
45. Feigl and Miranda, *Ind. Eng. Chem., Anal. Ed.*, **16**, 141 (1944).
46. Tenery and Anderson, *J. Biol. Chem.*, **135**, 659 (1940); Salit, *J. Biol. Chem.*, **136**, 191 (1940).
47. Snell and Snell, "Colorimetric Methods of Analysis," New York, D. Van Nostrand, 1936.
48. Burgess and Kamm, *J. Am. Chem. Soc.*, **34**, 652 (1912).

$[Cr(SCN)_4]_2$[49]. The great variety of coordinating agents that can be used to alter the properties of the ion to be determined and the tremendous array of complex ions that can be used as precipitants makes the number of combinations almost without limit.

Applications to Volumetric Analysis

The phenomena of coordination find wide application in volumetric analysis, both in the use of complexing ligands and in the use of preformed complex ions. Coordinating agents are used to "sequester" or "mask" interfering ions or to discharge their colors, to change oxidation-reduction potentials, and to alter or intensify the colors of ions to be determined. Thus, citrates, tartrates, malates, and other organic hydroxy anions, which can form five- of six-membered chelate rings, are used to prevent the precipitation of metallic hydroxides in alkaline solution[50]. Fluoride ion forms such stable complexes with many metallic ions that the usual characteristic reactions of the simple ions no longer appear; e.g., the reaction of the fluoride ion with iron(III) ion forms the colorless, soluble hexafluoroferrate(III) ion, which is so stable that copper can be determined iodometrically in its presence[51]. The addition of excess fluoride ion to a solution of an iron salt lowers the oxidation potential of the iron(II)–iron(III) system sufficiently to make possible the use of diphenylamine as an indicator in the titration of iron(II) with dichromate[52]. Phosphate ion also reacts with iron(III) ion to form a colorless, soluble complex and is used frequently instead of fluoride[53], as in the well-known iron-permanganate titration.

Titration of Liberated Hydrogen Ion

In general, the formation of an inner complex from a salt and an organic substance liberates an equivalent quantity of hydrogen ion; the metal can be determined by titration of the liberated hydrogen ion. This is illustrated in the volumetric determination of nickel[54]. Obviously, such a method can be used only with organic substances which do not themselves liberate protons, except when coordinated with metal ions.

Titration of Metal Ions with a Complexing Agent

When the complex ion, formed between a metal ion and a donor molecule, is sufficiently stable, i.e., K_d is a small number, it may be possible, by use of a suitable indicator system, to titrate the metal ion with the complex-

49. Mahr and Ohle, *Z. anal. Chem.*, **109**, 1 (1937).
50. Willard and Young, *J. Am. Chem. Soc.*, **50**, 1322, 1334, 1368 (1928).
51. Park, *Ind. Eng. Chem., Anal. Ed.*, **3**, 77 (1931).
52. Szebelledy, *Z. anal. Chem.*, **81**, 97 (1930).
53. Schollenberger, *J. Am. Chem. Soc.*, **53**, 88 (1931).
54. Holluta, *Monatsch.*, **40**, 281 (1919).

ing agent. Chelating agents, especially those containing enough donor atoms within one molecule to saturate the coordination sphere of the metal ion, are more generally useful in this technique, since monodentate donor species commonly undergo stepwise reaction with the metal ion, with the result that a plot of concentration of uncombined metal ion against moles of complexing agent gives no sharp break[55]. However, a number of well-known determinations are based on titration of metal ions with monodentate donors. The cyanometric titrations of nickel and cobalt ions serve to illustrate this point.

Indicator Systems. Although a number of indicator systems can be devised for determinations of this type, only two have found extensive use. The first is the pH indicator. Since complexing agents are basic substances (amines, anions of weak acids, and the like) the first addition of excess complexing agent is accompanied by a rapid rise in pH. This principle has been applied to the determination of a wide variety of metal ions by titration with the anions of ammonia triacetic acid[56], uramil diacetic acid[57], and ethylenediaminetetraacetic acid[58].

The second technique involves tying up the metal ion in a colored complex of lesser stability than that formed between the metal ion and the complexing agent which serves as the titrant. The success of this method depends on a sharp color change accompanying the destruction of the indicator complex. Since donor molecules or ions which undergo color change upon reaction with a metal ion are also color sensitive toward hydrogen ion, titrations of this type are carried out in buffered solutions. Schwarzenbach and coworkers[59] have employed purpureate ion (murexide) in the formation of indicator complexes with calcium, magnesium, cadmium, zinc, and copper.

MUREXIDE

These investigators[60] have also used o,o'-dihydroxyazo dyes in indicator

55. Schwarzenbach, *Chimia*, **3,** 1 (1949); *Anal. chim. Acta*, **7,** 141 (1952).
56. Schwarzenbach and Biedermann, *Helv. chim. Acta*, **31,** 331 (1948).
57. Schwarzenbach and Biedermann, *Helv. chim. Acta*, **31,** 456 (1948).
58. Schwarzenbach and Biedermann, *Helv. chim. Acta*, **31,** 459 (1948).
59. Schwarzenbach, Biedermann, and Bangerter, *Helv. chim. Acta*, **29,** 811 (1946); Schwarzenbach and Gysling, *Helv. chim. Acta.*, **32,** 1108, 1314 (1949).
60. Schwarzenbach and Biedermann, *Helv. chim. Acta*, **31,** 678 (1948); Schwarzenbach and Biedermann, *Chimia*, **2,** 56 (1948).

complexes in the titration of magnesium, calcium, zinc, and cadmium with disodium ethylenediaminetetraacetic acid. This indicator technique has been used most extensively in the determination of water hardness[59a].

Polydentate complexing agents have also been utilized in procedures based on amperometric titrations[55b, 61], polarimetric titrations[62], potentiometric titrations[63], and spectrophotometric titrations[64].

Applications of the Technique. The most widely employed complexing agent, ethylenediaminetetraacetic acid, is quite nonspecific in its action, and may be applied to the analysis of the alkaline earth ions, almost all of the dipositive and tripositive transition element ions, and the metallic ions of periodic groups IB, IIB, and IIIB, as well as to the analysis of lead and bismuth. Specificity of the reagent for the alkaline earth ions or for lead or bismuth ions may be attained by masking the transition metal ions with cyanide[65]. This masking technique has been applied to the determination of the calcium ion content of mineral waters containing large amounts of copper, cobalt, zinc, nickel, and iron salts[66].

It is also possible to determine a particular ion selectively by the proper choice of an indicator complex and by adjusting the pH of the medium. Thus, it is possible to determine the total hardness of water (magnesium and calcium ion) by titrating an aliquot with ethylenediaminetetraacetic acid, using Eriochrome Black T as the indicator, at a pH of about 10[59a, 60b],

ERIOCHROME BLACK T

and then to determine the calcium ion independently by titrating a second aliquot of the sample with the same reagent in strongly alkaline solution, using murexide as the indicator[59a, 67].

This technique has also been applied to the determination of magnesium

61. Pribil and Matyska, *Collection Czechoslov. Chem. Communs.*, **16**, 139 (1951).
62. Pribil and Matyska, *Chem. Listy*, **44**, 305 (1950).
63. Hahn, *Anal. chim. Acta*, **4**, 583 (1950); Pribil, Koudela, and Matyska, *Collection Czechoslov. Chem. Communs.*, **16**, 80 (1951); Pribil and Malicky, *Collection Czechoslov. Chem. Communs.*, **14**, 413 (1949); Pribil and Horacek, *Collection Czechoslov. Chem. Communs.*, **14**, 626 (1949).
64. Sweetster and Bricker, *Anal. Chem.*, **25**, 253 (1953).
65. Flaschka and Huditz, *Z. anal. Chem.*, **137**, 172 (1952).
66. Botha and Webb, *J. Inst. Water Engrs.*, **6**, 459 (1942).
67. Cheng, Kurtz, and Bray, *Anal. Chem.*, **24**, 1640 (1952).

in plant materials[68], the estimation of the effectiveness of polyphosphates in sequestering calcium ions[69], and to a number of microdeterminations[70].

Complex Ions as Oxidation-Reduction Indicators

If a complexing agent gives stable, highly colored complexes with a metal in two different oxidation states, and if the oxidation-reduction potential of the resulting couple is suitable, the couple can be used as an oxidation-reduction indicator. Such cases are rare, but the 1,10-phenanthroline-iron and ruthenium complexes furnish interesting and important examples. Tris-(orthophenanthroline)iron(II) ion (ferroin)

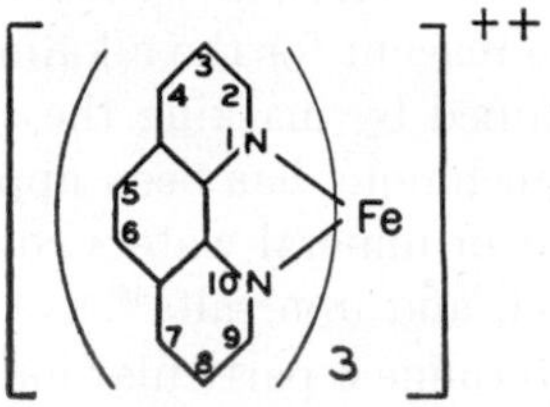

is an intense red color and the corresponding iron(III) ion is a faint blue. The reaction* is reversible; both complexes are stable in acid media, and the system has a high oxidation-reduction potential (1.10 volts in $0.1F$

$$[Fe(C_{12}H_8N_2)_3]^{+++} + e^- \rightleftarrows [Fe(C_{12}H_8N_2)_3]^{++}$$

acid)[71]. The potential may be varied to suit the requirements of the analysis by placing substituents in various positions in the organic rings. The change in potential brought about by the substitution of methyl groups for hydrogen atoms has been found to be an additive function, so if the oxidation potentials for the complexes with methyl groups in the 3, 4, or 5 positions are known, the potential for any combination of methyl substitutions can be calculated[71]. As Table 20.1 shows, methyl groups in the 3 or 8 positions lower the value by 0.03 volt; in the 5 or 6 positions, lower it by 0.04 volt; and in the 4 or 7 positions, lower it by 0.11 volt. Substitution of a nitro group in position 5 of 1,10-phenanthroline changes the oxidation-reduction potential of the couple to 1.25 volts, which makes this couple an excellent indicator for cerate oxidimetry[72].

* See footnote, page 399, Chapter 11 for discussion of sign conventions used; the convention adopted by polarographers is used in this chapter.

68. Forster, *Analyst*, **78**, 179 (1953).
69. Kurias, *Textil-Rundschau*, **5**, 224 (1950); cf. *Chem. Abs.*, **44**, 8824e (1950).
70. Flaschka, *Mikrochemie ver. Mikrochim.*, *Acta*, **39**, 38 (1952); Debney, *Nature*, **169**, 1104 (1952); Flaschka, *Mikrochemie ver Mikrochim. Acta*, **39**, 315 (1952).
71. Brandt and Smith, *Anal. Chem.*, **21**, 1313 (1949).
72. Salomon, Gabrio, and Smith, *Arch. Biochem.*, **11**, 433 (1946); Smith and Fritz *Anal. Chem.*, **20**, 874 (1946).

TABLE 20.1. EFFECT OF THE INTRODUCTION OF METHYL GROUPS ON THE REDOX
POTENTIALS OF THE 1,10-PHENANTHROLINE-IRON COUPLE

Methyl Substituted Derivative	Redox Potential, Found	Volts in 0.1F acid, Calc.
unsubstituted	1.10	—
3	1.07	—
4	—	0.99
5	1.06	—
3, 4	0.97	0.96
3, 8	1.03	1.04
4, 5	0.95	0.95
4, 6	0.95	0.95
4, 7	0.88	0.88
5, 6	1.00	1.02
3, 4, 6	0.92	0.92
3, 4, 7	0.88	0.85
3, 5, 7	0.93	0.92
3, 5, 8	0.99	0.99
3, 4, 6, 7	0.84	0.81
3, 4, 6, 8	0.89	0.89
3, 4, 7, 8	0.85	0.82
3, 4, 6, 8	0.93	0.96

Several modifications of the 1,10-phenanthroline-ruthenium structure
have been studied, but none has come into use as an indicator. Dwyer[73] investigated the ruthenium(II)–ruthenium(III) couple and found it to have
an oxidation-reduction potential of −1.29 volts in 1N nitric acid. Cagle and
Smith studied the use of tris(α,α'-dipyridyl)iron(II) ion and its methyl
derivatives and found them to be suitable as indicators in the determination of iron[74].

Stiegman and his co-workers found the oxidation potential of the ruthe-
nium(II)–ruthenium(III) dipyridyl system to be 1.33 volts in 1N nitric
acid[75]. Brant and Smith, however, report that this value is 1.25 volts[71].
The change in the redox potential of metallic couples by coordination is
well known, and is discussed in Chapter 11. Many applications of the
phenomenon have been made in analytical chemistry.

73. Dwyer, Humpoletz, and Nyholm, *J. Proc. Roy. Soc. N. S. Wales*, **80**, 212 (1946).
74. Cagle and Smith, *J. Am. Chem. Soc.*, **69**, 1860 (1947); *Ind. Eng. Chem., Anal. Ed.*,
     19, 384 (1947).
75. Steigman, Biernbaum, and Edmonds, *Ind. Eng. Chem., Anal. Ed.*, **14**, 30 (1942).

The Application of Coordination Compounds to Colorimetric Methods of Analysis

The display of colors shown by coordination compounds of the transition metals is utilized in the manufacture of pigments (Chapter 22) and in analysis by colorimetric methods. The familiar qualitative tests for iron[76] and cobalt[77] with thiocyanate depend upon this property; the thiocyanate group probably coordinates through the nitrogen atom.

At low concentrations of thiocyanate, iron forms the deep red complex $[Fe(NCS)]^{++}$. At higher concentrations, other red complexes of the type $[Fe(NCS)_n]^{3-n}$ are formed, where n may be any interger from one to six[78]. Partition studies with the solvents ether and water[79], thermometric titrations[80], and spectrophotometric studies[78] indicate that these species are in stepwise equilibrium. The complexes are stable in strongly acidic solutions, and so have a definite advantage over other, more sensitive reagents.

Cobalt(II) ion reacts with thiocyanate in aqueous solutions containing alcohol or acetone, producing complex species which may be extracted into ether-alcohol solutions[77c]. Spectrophotometric studies indicate that the cobalt ion reacts stepwise, forming a series of complexes of the formula $[Co(NCS)_n]^{2-n}$, where n is an interger between one and four, inclusive[81]. The intense blue coloration developed in ether-alcohol solutions has been variously attributed to dehydration effects of the solvent[82] and to a change in the coordination number of the cobalt ion[81b].

The use of complexing agents in quantitative colorimetric analyses is well illustrated by the application of 1,10-phenthroline, α,α'-dipyridyl, and α,α',α''-tripyridyl.

α,α',α''-tripypidyl

1,10-Phenanthroline has been applied to the colorimetric determination of

76. Frank and Oswalt, *J. Am. Chem. Soc.*, **69,** 1321 (1947); Woods and Mellon, *Ind. Eng. Chem., Anal. Ed.*, **13,** 551 (1941); Peters and French, *Ind. Eng. Chem., Anal. Ed.*, **13,** 604 (1941).
77. Tomula, *Z. anal. Chem.*, **83,** 6 (1931); Uri, *Analyst*, **72,** 478 (1947); Young and Hall, *Ind. Eng. Chem., Anal. Ed.*, **18,** 264 (1946).
78. Babko, *J. Gen. Chem., U.S.S.R.*, **16,** 1549 (1946); cf. *Chem. Abs.*, **41,** 4732e (1947).
79. Macdonald, Mitchell, and Mitchell, *J. Chem. Soc.*, **1951,** 1574.
80. Chatterjee, *Science and Culture*, **15,** 209 (1949).
81. Katzin and Gebert, *J. Am. Chem. Soc.*, **72,** 5659 (1950); Lehne, *Bull. soc. chim., France*, **1951,** 76; Babko and Drako, *J. Gen. Chem. U.S.S.R.*, **19,** 1809 (1949); cf. *Chem. Abs.*, **44,** 1355 (1950); Babko and Drako, *Zavodskaya Lab.*, **16,** 1162 (1950); cf. *Chem. Abs.*, **47,** 3175 (1951).
82. West and De Vries, *Anal. Chem.*, **23,** 334 (1951).

iron in fruit and wine[83], in leather[84], and in biological materials[85]. A large number of modified 1,10-phenanthroline derivatives have been studied in recent years. The substitution of methyl groups for hydrogen atoms is an additive function with regard to the wave length of maximum absorption and molecular extinction coefficient. This relationship was discovered for iron(II) complexes by Brandt and Smith[71] and for copper by McCurdy[86]. A most sensitive colorimetric reagent for iron is 4,7-diphenyl-1,10-phenanthroline; the iron(II) complex has a molecular extinction coefficient of 22,400. In addition to iron(II), cobalt(II), molybdenum(?), ruthenium(II), and copper(I) give colored solutions with this reagent. However, the copper(I) complex does not form at a pH less than 7[86]. The iron(II) complex may be extracted into solvents such as isoamyl alcohol over a pH range of 2 to 9, whereas the cobalt(II) complex is not extractable.

α,α'-Dipyridyl has found use in colorimetric methods of analysis, the complexes being very similar to those of 1,10-phenanthroline, but not so stable[87]. Several substituted dipyridyls do not give colored complexes with iron(II) ion[88]. Perhaps this can be explained on steric grounds in the following cases:

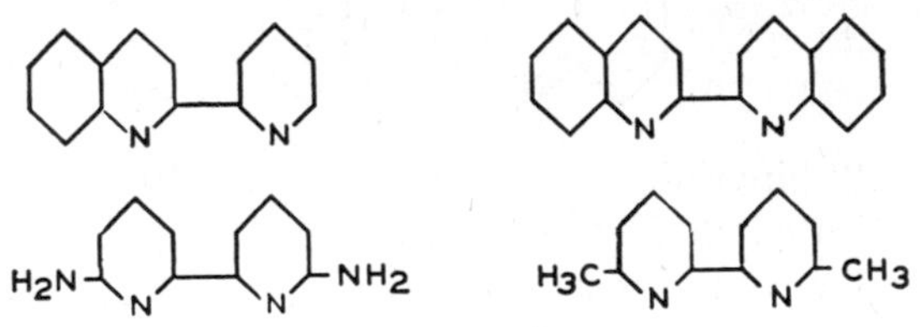

but in the case of

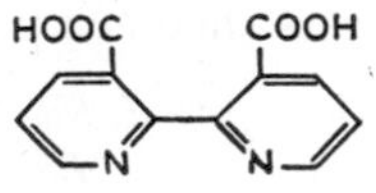

it must be attributed to a lessening of the basicity of the nitrogen atoms. α,α',α''-Tripyridyl has been applied to the spectrophotometric deter-

83. Byrne, Saywell and Cruess, *Ind. Eng. Chem., Anal. Ed.*, **9**, 83 (1937).
84. Smith and Fritz, *J. Am. Leather Chemists Ass'n.* **42**, 195 (1947).
85. Willard and Hummel, *Ind. Eng. Chem., Anal. Ed.*, **10**, 13 (1938).
86. McCurdy, thesis, University of Illinois, 1951; Smith and McCurdy, *Anal. Chem.*, **24**, 371 (1952).
87. Blau, *Monatsch.*, **19**, 647 (1898); Parker and Griffin, *Can. J. Research*, **17B**, 66 (1939).
88. Willink and Wibaut, *Rec. trav. chim.*, **54**, 275 (1935).

mination of iron[89] and cobalt(II)[90]. The reagent is not particularly sensitive for cobalt[91] but it may be used over a wide range of concentrations (0.5 to 50 ppm) and the cobalt complex is stable over the pH range 2 to 10. Surprisingly, copper(I) ion does not form a colored complex with tripyridyl, although it does so with α,α'-dipyridyl[92] and with 1,10-phenanthroline[93]. The stereochemistry of tripyridyl is evidently such that it is not as strong a coordinating agent as its bidentate analogs. Morgan and Burstall[94] have isolated and characterized a number of complexes of α,α'-dipyridyl, α,α',α''-tripyridyl, and $\alpha,\alpha',\alpha'',\alpha'''$-tetrapyridyl; tripyridyl occupies three coordination positions in compounds of the type, [Pt tripy Cl$_3$]Cl[94e, 90b]. It is probably significant in the chemistries of these higher polypyridyls that they tend to form bridged structures and in so doing enter into the coordination spheres of two metal atoms simultaneously.

Hoste[95] pointed out the specificity of 6,6'-substituted dipyridyls for copper(I), stating that 2,2'-biquinoline forms the most stable complexes of this series. Indeed, copper(I) is almost unique among the metal ions in forming colored complexes with compounds such as 2,2'-biquinoline[96],

6,6'-dimethyl-2,2'-bipyridine, and 2,9-dimethyl-1,10-phenanthroline[71]. Of the many substituted derivatives available, 2,9-dimethyl-4,7-diphenyl-1,10-phenanthroline is the most sensitive reagent for copper now available[97]. Copper(I) ion reacts with biquinoline, whereas iron(II) ion does not.

8-Hydroxyquinoline is also used for the colorimetric determination of many metallic ions. Alten, Weiland, and Loofman[98] coupled the hydroxyquinolate of aluminum, in the precipitate, with a diazo compound to obtain a strongly colored dye, which was then compared with a standard.

89. Moss and Mellon, *Ind. Eng. Chem., Anal. Ed.*, **14**, 862 (1942).
90. Moss and Mellon, *Ind. Eng. Chem., Anal. Ed.*, **14**, 931 (1942); Morgan and Burstall, *J. Chem. Soc.*, **140**, 1649 (1937); **135**, 20 (1932).
91. Moss and Mellon, *Ind. Eng. Chem., Anal. Ed.*, **15**, 74 (1943).
92. Ignatieff, *J. Soc. Chem. Ind.*, **56**, 407t (1937); Gerber, Claassen, and Boruff, *Ind Eng. Chem., Anal. Ed.*, **14**, 364 (1942).
93. Tartarini, *Gazz. chim. ital.*, **63**, 597 (1933); Wenger and Duckert, *Helv. chim. Acta*, **27, 757** (1944).
94. Morgan and Burstall, *J. Chem. Soc.*, **1937**, 1649; **1938**, 1672, 1675, 1662; **1934**, 965, 1498.
95. Hoste, *Anal. chim. Acta*, **4**, 23 (1950).
96. Breckenridge, Lewis, and Quick, *Can. J. Research*, **B17**, 258 (1939).
97. Smith and Wilkins, *Anal. Chem.*, **25**, 510 (1953).
98. Alten, Weiland, and Loofmann, *Angew. Chem.*, **46**, 668 (1933).

Magnesium and some other quinolates give a green color when dissolved in dilute acid and treated with iron(III) chloride[99], or they can be converted to iron(III) quinolate, which is dissolved in alcohol to give a green-black color[100]. Alternatively, the quinolate precipitates may be dissolved in dilute hydrochloric acid and the absorption of the solution measured; 8-hydroxyquinoline absorbs strongly at 252 mμ. Aluminum, gallium, and indium hydroxyquinolates fluoresce strongly in chloroform. Lacroix has given a comprehensive theoretical treatment of the equilibria involved in the extraction of some hydroxyquinolates[101].

Dithizone (diphenylthiocarbazone)

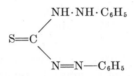

is used primarily in qualitative analysis, particularly in trace analysis[102]. It forms highly colored inner complexes with a great number of metallic ions, doubtless through chelation. Most of these inner complexes are extractable into carbon tetrachloride, but under proper conditions, separations of individual elements can be made. The ions which give colored complexes may be divided into five groups[102, 103]:

(1) Copper, silver, gold, mercury, and palladium ions—extractable from dilute mineral acid solutions.

(2) Zinc, cobalt, nickel, palladium, and rather large quantities of cadmium and tin ions—extractable from acetic acid solutions.

(3) Silver, mercury, copper, gold, palladium, cobalt, nickel, cadmium, and large amounts of zinc ions—extractable from sodium hydroxide solutions.

(4) Tin(II), thallium(I), bismuth, and lead ions—extractable from slightly alkaline solutions containing cyanide.

(5) Cobalt, nickel, and cadmium ions—extractable from strongly alkaline solutions containing tartrate.

Two types of complexes may be formed when a metal ion combines with dithizone, a complex containing the bidentate keto form of dithizone, in which one hydrogen has been displaced from the imido group (I), and a

99. Gerber, Claassen, and Boruff, *Ind. Eng. Chem., Anal. Ed.*, **14**, 658 (1942); Weeks and Todd, *Ind. Eng. Chem., Anal. Ed.*, **15**, 297 (1943); Wolff, *Compt. rend. soc. biol.*, **127**, 1445 (1938).
100. Lavollay, *Bull. soc. chim. Biol.*, **17**, 432 (1935).
101. Lacroix, *Anal. chim. Acta*, **1**, 260 (1947).
102. Fischer, *Wiss. Veröffentlich, Siemens-Konzer*, **4**, 158 (1925).
103. Fischer, *Z. angew. Chem.*, **47**, 685 (1934); Fischer and Leopoldi, *Z. anal. Chem.*, **107**, 241 (1936).

complex containing a tridentate enol form of the ligand, which structure envisions replacement of both hydrogen ions from the hydrazide function (II).

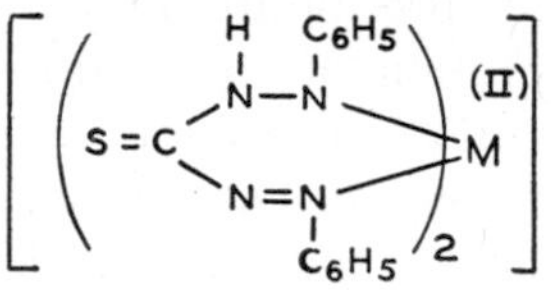

It is significant that those metal ions which are good sulfur coordinators (groups 1 and 3 above) show the greatest tendency to form the "enol" type of complex (II). Formation of the "enol" species takes place only in basic solution.

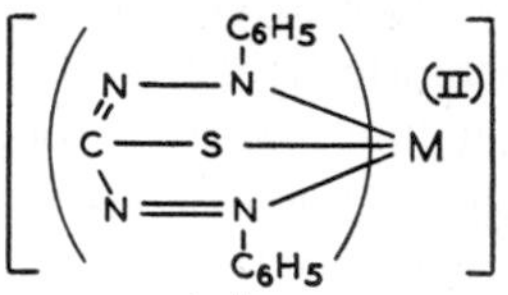

The selectivity of the dithizone is generally increased by:

(1) Addition of complexing reagents to remove interfering metal ions; this is exemplified in group 4 above.

(2) Control of pH of the solution to be extracted; compare groups 1, 2, 3, and 5.

(3) Oxidation or reduction of interfering metals; platinum(II) follows the same pattern as does palladium; however platinum (IV) does not react with dithizone[104].

Diphenylcarbazide and diphenylcarbazone react with the ions of

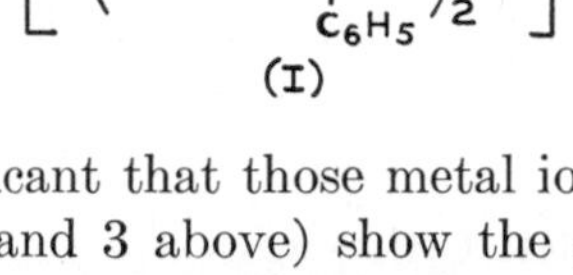

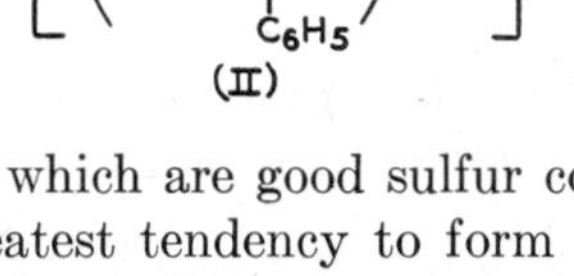

heavy metals to form inner complexes[105], which are extractable into organic solvents such as benzene and chloroform. Unipositive copper and silver give complexes in which the ratio of metal ion to ligand is one to one and in which the ratio is two to one. Since these reagents do not contain a co-ordinating sulfur atom, they react with an entirely different group of metallic ions than does diphenylthiocarbazone. They are useful for the determination of chromium, which forms a soluble red-violet compound in dilute mineral acid solution, and, by an indirect procedure, for the determination of lead, through the precipitation of the chromate[106].

Colored lakes, even though they be insoluble in water, can often be used in colorimetric work by extracting them into organic solvents. Chloroform

104. Sandell, "Colorimetric Determination of Traces of Metals," New York, Interscience Publishers, Inc., 1944.
105. Feigl and Lederer, *Monatsch.*, **45**, 63, 115 (1924).
106. Letonoff and Reinhold, *Ind. Eng. Chem., Anal. Ed.*, **12**, 280 (1940).

is more generally useful for inner complexes than other organic solvents[107]. By the introduction of solubilizing groups into organic molecules which normally give insoluble inner complexes, it is often possible to obtain materials which are water soluble and suitable for colorimetric determinations. Thus, alizarin sulfonic acid gives a soluble aluminum complex, whereas alizarin itself gives an insoluble one[108]. The structural formula for the sulfonic dye is probably

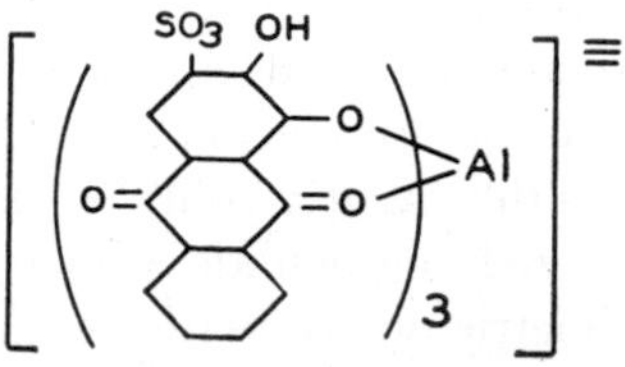

Similarly, the cobalt(III) compound of 1-nitroso-2-naphthol is insoluble, but the disulfonic derivative is soluble[109].

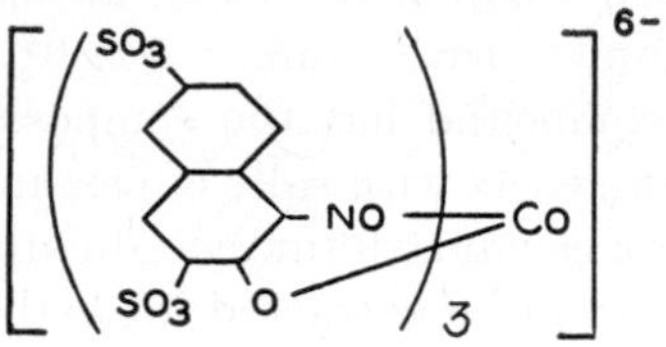

In these cases, as in many others, the introduction of solubilizing groups does not greatly change the coordinating ability.

Quinalizarin (1,2,5,8-tetrahydroxyanthroquinone) has been used for the

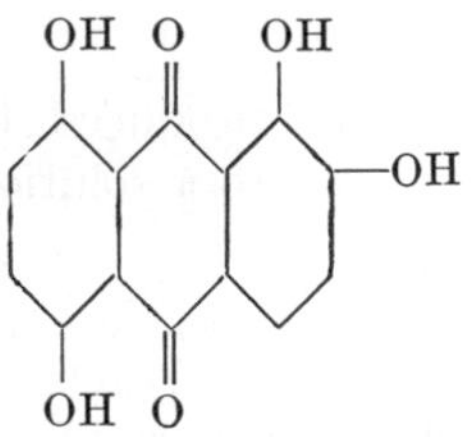

colorimetric detection of germanium and the rare earths and for the determination of beryllium, gallium, magnesium, aluminum, and boron[110]. Willard and Fogg[111] have developed a quantitative procedure for the deter-

107. Feigl, *Anal. Chem.*, **21**, 1298 (1949).
108. Atack, *J. Soc. Chem. Ind.*, **34**, 936 (1915).
109. van Klooster, *J. Am. Chem. Soc* , **43**, 746 (1921).
110. Komarowsky and Poluektov, *Mikrochemie*, **18**, 66 (1935).
111. Willard and Fogg, *J. Am. Chem. Soc.*, **59**, 40 (1937).

mination of gallium based on the pink to amethyst color of the gallium quinalizarin compound.

Boron, a powerful oxygen coordinator, forms an inner complex with hydroxyanthraquinone in concentrated sulfuric acid solution[112], and magnesium, scandium, the rare earths, nickel, cobalt, and beryllium ions give sensitive reactions with this reagent in sodium hydroxide solution[113].

Thiourea and its derivatives have been used for the detection and determination of a number of ions which are good sulfur coordinators[114]. Bismuth ion[115] forms a yellow compound upon the addition of thiourea. Mahr[116] has proposed a method for the determination of cadmium, chromium, and mercury by precipitation as the slightly soluble compounds [M(thiourea)$_2$] [Cr(NH$_3$)$_2$(SCN)$_4$]$_2$. These red compounds are soluble in organic ketones and are suitable for colorimetric determinations.

Storfer has used thiourea for the detection of ferricyanide through the formation of the red-violet compound [Cu(thiourea)$_3$]$_3$[Fe(CN)$_6$]·2H$_2$O[117]. The reagent will detect 0.48 mg of ferricyanide at a dilution of 1:100,000.

Thiourea forms colored compounds which are suitable for colorimetric determination of osmium[118], ruthenium[114, 115a, 119] and other platinum metals[120]. The osmium compound has the composition [Os(NH$_2$CSNH$_2$)$_6$] Cl$_3$·H$_2$O. Thiocarbanilide reacts with salts of osmium and ruthenium, both of which are good nitrogen and sulfur coordinators[119, 121]. The resulting highly colored complexes can be extracted into ether, which increases the sensitivity of the test and suggests that the compounds are probably inner complexes.

Utilization of Fluorescence in the Application of Complexes to Analytical Chemistry

The intense green fluorescence produced by the addition of morin (3,5,7,2′,4′-pentahydroxyflavone) to a solution of an aluminum salt[122]

112. Smith, *Analyst*, **60**, 735 (1935).
113. Fischer and Wernet, *Angew. Chem.*, **A60**, 729 (1948).
114. Yoe and Overholser, *Ind. Eng. Chem., Anal. Ed.*, **14**, 435 (1942).
115. Mahr, *Z. anal. Chem.*, **94**, 161 (1933); **97**, 96 (1934).
116. Mahr, *Angew. Chem.*, **53**, 257 (1940).
117. Storfer, *Mikrochemie*, **17**, 170 (1935).
118. Tschugaev, *Compt. rend.*, **167**, 235 (1918); Gilcrist, *J. Research, Natl. Bur. Standards*, **6**, 421 (1931).
119. Singleton, *Ind. Chemist*, **3**, 121 (1927); Wohler and Metz, *Z. anorg. allgem. Chem.*, **138**, 368 (1924).
120. Whitmore and Schneider, *Mikrochemie*, **17**, 279 (1935).
121. Wolbling, *Ber.*, **67**, 773 (1934).
122. Goppelsroder, *J. prakt. Chem.*, **101**, 408 (1867).

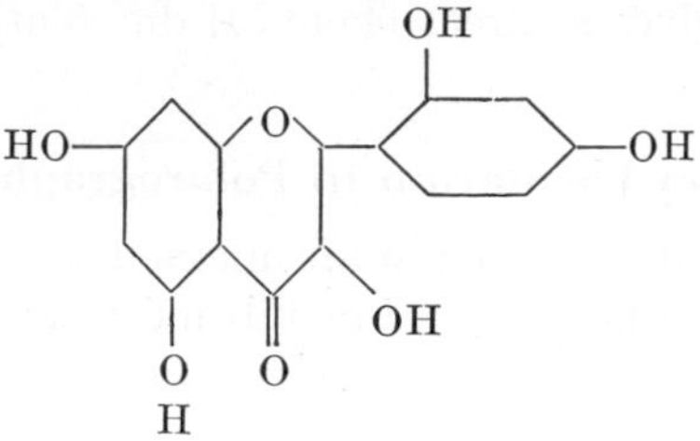

can be used for the determination of small quantities of aluminum[123]. Good oxygen coordinators, such as beryllium, gallium, indium, and scandium, also form complexes which show a strong green fluorescence[47]. However, these ions are easily separated from aluminum ion.

1-Amino-4-hydroxyanthroquinone gives an intense red fluorescence with

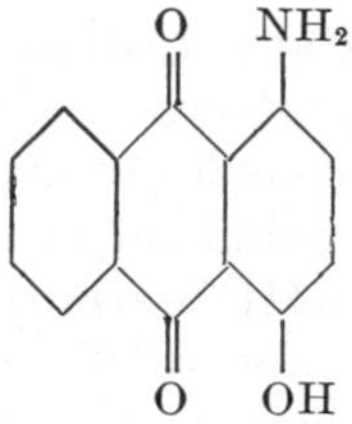

beryllium ion in alkaline solution and with thorium in acid solution. The reagent is less sensitive, but more specific, than morin[124].

Benzoin

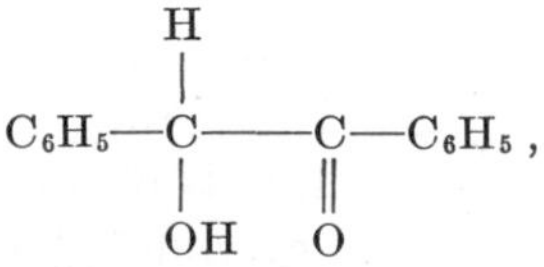

has been suggested as a qualitative reagent for the fluorometric determination of zinc[123]. In the presence of magnesium hydroxide as an adsorbing agent, the reagent is highly specific, only beryllium, boron, and antimony interfering. The stability of the fluorescent material suggests that the zinc replaces the hydroxyl hydrogen and forms a five-membered ring with the oxygen atoms.

White and Lowe[125] used the fluorescence of the sodium salt of 4-sulfo-2-hydroxy-α-naphthalene-azo-β-naphthol (Pontachrome Blue Black R) for the quantitative determination of aluminum. Although not as sensitive as

123. White and Neustadt, *Ind. Eng. Chem., Anal. Ed.,* **15,** 599 (1943).
124. Fletcher, White, and Sheftel, *Ind. Eng. Chem., Anal. Ed.,* **18,** 179 (1946).
125. White and Lowe, *Ind. Eng. Chem., Anal. Ed.,* **9,** 430 (1937).

morin, this reagent gives a direct chemical differentiation between aluminum and beryllium.

The Role of Complex Formation in Polarographic Analysis

Where applicable, the polarographic method is convenient and rapid. This is especially true where several metals must be determined simultaneously or where simple precipitation or titration procedures are not available[126].

Complex formation may be utilized to provide a system especially suited for the determination of a particular substance and to mask the effect of interfering ions. A third function of complex formation is dependent upon the stabilization of valence states of metal ions through coordination (Chapter 11). This latter effect often makes possible the simultaneous polarographic determination of two metal ions whose uncomplexed forms (aquated ions) normally reduce at potentials which are too nearly the same to give distinct polarographic curves.

The first of the functions of complex formation mentioned above may be illustrated by the relationships found among the complex ions of rhodium[127]. The chloro complex of rhodium(III) is reduced to free metal upon contact with elemental mercury while the rhodium(III) complexes with nitrite, oxalate, tartrate and ethylenediamine do not give polarographic reduction waves, apparently because of their great stability. However, rhodium may be determined when present in the tripositive state in a complex ion of intermediate stability, such as $[Rh(NH_3)_5Cl]^{++}$ or $[Rh(CNS)_6]^{\equiv}$.

The polarographic determination of manganese in the presence of copper, chromium, zinc, cobalt, nickel, and iron provides an excellent example of the masking effect exerted by particular complexing agents on the ease of reduction of metal ions. If the sample is contaminated with iron, copper, chromium, or zinc, the addition of cyanide[128] facilitates the determination of manganese (so long as the iron is in the dipositive state) since the cyano complexes of these other metals are not reduced at the dropping mercury electrode. Similarly, the addition of tartrate eliminates the reduction waves of cobalt(II), nickel(II), and iron(III)[129].

The separation of very similar half-wave potentials of metals is, of course, a less extreme case of the phenomenon of masking. Perhaps the most interesting examples are found among the complexes of cobalt and nickel. Although the polarographic reduction curves for hexaquocobalt(II) and hexaquonickel(II) ions overlap, the two metals may be estimated from a

126. Kolthoff and Lingane, "Polarography," 2nd Ed., Vol. II, p. 582, New York, Interscience Publishers, Inc., 1952.
127. Reference 126, p. 490.
128. Verdier, *Collection Czechoslov. Chem. Communs.*, **11**, 238 (1939).
129. Verdier, *Collection Czechoslov. Chem. Communs.*, **11**, 233 (1939).

single polarogram by the use of a pyridine-pyridinium chloride supporting electrolyte[130]. A determination of cobalt in the presence of nickel also involves the oxidation of the cobalt(II) to the tripositive state with perborate in an ammonia-ammonium chloride solution[131]. The resulting hexamminecobalt(III) ion is reduced at $-.53$ volts vs. S.C.E., while the nickel(II)-ammonia complex is reduced at a much more negative potential. A similar technique is used for the oxidation of cobalt(II) to cobalt(III) in the presence of ethylenediaminetetraacetic acid[132].

Estimation of the several metals in an alloy is among the most practical applications of the polarographic method[126]. Here, the ease and rapidity of routine analyses are of considerable value. The following scheme for the determination of copper, zinc, and nickel will serve to illustrate. After dissolution and preliminary treatment, the polarogram obtained from an ammonia-ammonium carbonate solution of the mixed salts gives one wave attributable to the copper and a second which arises from both the nickel and the zinc. The nickel may then be determined from a second polarogram run on a cyanide medium. Neutralization and addition of cyanide ion to an aliquot of the test solution leads to the formation of very stable zinc and copper complexes which are not reduced polarographically. However, the nickel cyanide complex gives a well-defined wave.

A very clever application of complex formation in the polarographic determination of metal ions was reported by Willard and Dean[133]. The *o,o'*-dihydroxyazo dye, 5-sulfo-2-hydroxy-α-benzene-azo-β-naphthol

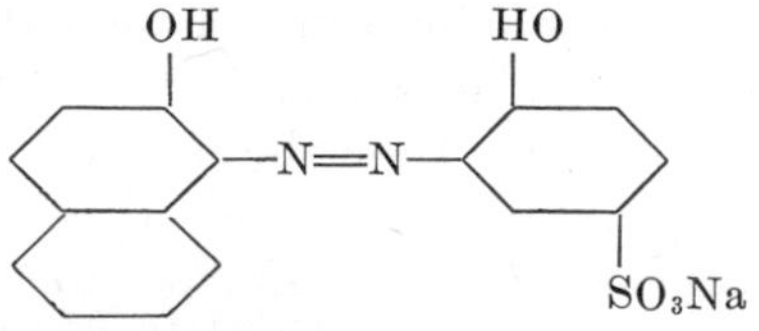

is more difficultly reduced in the presence of aluminum ion than in its normal state. Apparently, stabilization of the dye in a complex of the type [Al(dye)$_2$] results in two waves in the reduction curve of the dye, and the second wave is proportional, in height, to the concentration of aluminum ion.

The application of the polarographic method to the study of complex ions is further discussed in Chapter 18.

130. Lingane and Kerlinger, *Ind. Eng. Chem., Anal. Ed.*, **13**, 77 (1941).
131. Watters and Kolthoff, *Anal. Chem.*, **21**, 1466 (1949).
132. Souchay and Faucherre, *Anal. chim. Acta*, **3**, 252 (1949).
133. Willard and Dean, *Anal. Chem.*, **22**, 1264 (1950).

21. Coordination Compounds in Natural Products

Gunther L. Eichhorn

Louisiana State University, Baton Rouge, Louisiana
and the National Institutes of Health, Bethesda, Maryland

As a consequence of the ability of coordinated metal ions to influence many of the complex reactions upon which the vital processes of living organisms depend, coordination compounds of many varieties are found widely distributed in nature. A comprehensive coverage of so vast a subject in a short chapter is impossible; instead, it is our purpose to demonstrate how the versatility of coordination reactions has been incorporated into nature's pattern, to record some of the progress that has been made in the elucidation of this pattern, and to illustrate how a knowledge of coordination chemistry can yield clues to the mechanisms of biochemical processes and thus serve as a valuable tool in biochemical research.

Excellent treatises are available on some of the naturally occurring coordination compounds[1]; particular emphasis has therefore been placed upon topics not covered elsewhere from the point of view of coordination chemistry, and an attempt has been made to set the whole subject matter into a context that provides the maximum possible opportunity for an understanding of the dynamic relationships that exist between the natural coordination compounds.

The Detection of Coordination Compounds in Natural Products

Clues to the existence of complex compounds in nature range from those that offer conclusive proof to those that provide circumstantial evidence; they have been classified into four categories, in the order of decreasing amount of available knowledge concerning the nature of the compound:

(1) The isolation and determination of structure of the coordination compound, with metal ion and donor molecule intact.

1. Lemberg and Legge, "Hematin Compounds and Bile Pigments," New York, Interscience Publishers, Inc., 1949; Martell, and Calvin, "Chemistry of the Metal Chelate Compounds," Chapt. 8, New York, Prentice-Hall, Inc., 1952.

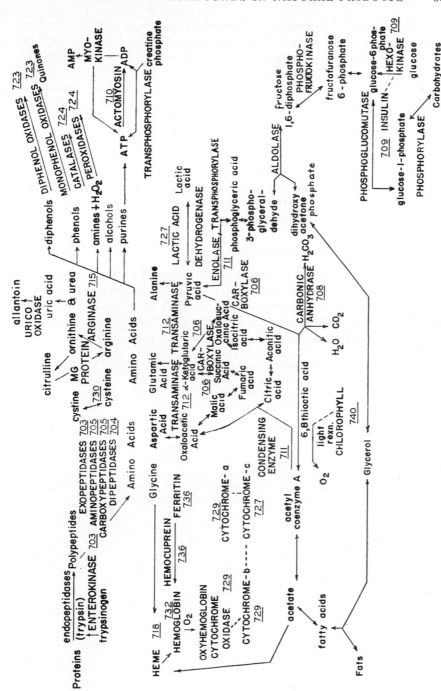

Fig. 21.1. Some dynamic relationships between the natural coordination compounds. Numbers refer to page numbers.

(2) The activation of a specific biochemical process by a metal ion. Frequently such a metal is part of an enzyme system, and it is possible to deduce some of the donor-acceptor relationships from a knowledge of the structure of the coenzyme, the reactants, and the products.

(3) Observations on the mineral nutritional requirements of organisms. When these include, even in trace amounts, metals with high coordinating ability, the existence of complexes may be suspected and tested by radioactive tracer techniques or through feeding of competing coordinating agents to the organism.

(4) Detection of organic metabolic intermediates that are good coordinating agents (e.g., compounds containing two donor groups separated by two or three carbon atoms). Relationships between such molecules may suggest the participation of metal ions in the form of complexes.

Functions of Complex Compounds

Some of the reactions that are known or believed to occur in plant or animal metabolism have been outlined in Fig. 21.1; the names of coordination compounds have been capitalized, so that their omnipresence becomes evident from an inspection of the chart. Dotted lines have been used to represent functional relationships between two compounds.

For the benefit of the inorganic chemist unversed in the biochemical literature a brief explanation of this chart will be presented.

It may be observed that many of the capitalized compounds are catalytic agents. Biochemical catalysts are called enzymes; they are generally involved in the chemical transformation of a specific compound or group of compounds. The latter are known as the substrates of the enzyme. An enzyme is frequently named by addition of the suffix "ase" to the name of its substrate. Enzymes generally consist of a protein portion that accounts for the bulk of the weight of the molecule, and of a non-protein part, the "prosthetic group" of the enzyme. Coenzymes are relatively simple organic molecules in whose absence the enzyme cannot function. The distinction between coenzymes and prosthetic groups is not clear-cut; the most important difference probably lies in the greater ease with which the former may be detached from the protein component of the enzyme. Many enzymes are coordination compounds; frequently the donor groups are contributed by the prosthetic group or by the coenzyme.

The reactions outlined in the chart include processes that occur in plant or animal metabolism; a large number of them are found in both types of organism. Whereas plants are capable of producing the matter required for their structure and maintenance from simple compounds through photosynthesis, animals ingest rather complicated "food" materials: the proteins, fats, and carbohydrates, which are condensation products of amino acids, fatty acids, and monosaccharides, respectively.

Proteins, fats, and carbohydrates are related to each other in both plant and animal metabolism, because they can be broken down into simple substances, which may, in turn, be condensed into the appropriate large molecules as required by the organism.

To illustrate this relationship let us consider the molecule of pyruvic acid, which is centrally located on the chart. This molecule may be produced by "transamination" (page 712) from alanine, one of the amino acids formed by the degradation of proteins. The chain of events by which proteins (upper left) are decomposed is initiated by the so-called endopeptidases (page 703), which split the protein into relatively large fragments, the polypeptides. The degradation process is then taken over by the exopeptidases which have been so named because they remove the terminal amino acids, the acids on the "outside" of the polypeptide chain. Some of these amino acids are molecules of alanine, which may then be converted into pyruvic acid.

Pyruvic acid may result from the metabolism of fats (lower left) in the following manner: Fat degradation ultimately yields acetic acid, or acetate ion, which may be converted into an extremely reactive form, acetyl coenzyme A. When the acetyl group is so combined, it may react with carbon dioxide to produce pyruvic acid, or it may pass through the tricarboxylic acid cycle (see below) to oxaloacetic acid, which is converted to pyruvic acid through decarboxylation.

The formation of pyruvic acid from carbohydrates may be followed in the lower right section of the chart.

A group of substances that play a central role in biochemistry are the compounds of the tricarboxylic acid cycle. The cycle consists of the removal of citric acid in a series of reactions, in which two of its carbon atoms are lost by decarboxylation (in the presence of carboxylase enzymes), and the replenishment of citric acid through the condensation of the enol form of oxaloacetic acid with acetyl coenzyme A in the presence of "condensing enzyme" (page 711). The cycle may be followed in the center of the chart.

In the upper right section are outlined some of the enzymatic reactions which result in the oxidation of the decomposition products of the amino acids into quinoid compounds. Here also are summarized some of the reactions which provide the energy for muscular activity through the splitting of phosphate bonds; e.g., the conversion of adenosine triphosphate (ATP) (page 710) into adenosine diphosphate (ADP).

The left central section of the chart includes relationships between the compounds involved in the metabolism of iron, e.g., the oxygen carrying molecule hemoglobin, and some of the oxidizing enzymes of the "cytochrome system". The latter is engaged in numerous oxidation-reduction reactions; the dotted lines that could be drawn between the cytochromes and many of the compounds on the chart have been omitted for the sake of simplicity.

It must be remembered that the comprehension of the coordination aspects of biochemical processes is limited in the same manner as is the pure organic chemistry involved. The structures of relatively small molecules that arise as intermediates or through degradative action may be completely known, but the structures of larger aggregates, such as the proteins and the nucleic acids, cannot be completely described in terms of the relative positions of all the atoms with respect to each other.

The participation of complex compounds in nearly every phase of biological activity may be classified under the following general headings:

(1) Bond formation and cleavage.

(2) Exchange of functional groups.

(3) Blocking of functional groups.

(4) Influence upon stereochemical configuration.

(5) Oxidation-reduction reactions.

(6) Storage and transfer.

(7) Transmission of energy.

The first four of these functions prescribe that a complex must be produced as an intermediate in a reaction, the completion of which depends upon the decomposition of the complex. These intermediates are labile coordination compounds, and generally involve metal ions, such as magnesium, that are not exceedingly strong electron acceptors. To perform the last three functions the complexes must remain more or less intact; as a result, the coordination compounds are more inert than those in the first four groups, and they include metals like copper and iron, or else very strong coordinating agents.

BOND FORMATION AND BOND CLEAVAGE

Metal ions play an important role in many of the bond-making and bond-breaking reactions of natural processes. In the catalysis of bond formation the metal ion can serve as a point of attachment for the two donor atoms between which reaction is to take place. The acceleration of bond cleavage as a result of coordination may be attributed to the polarization of electrons toward the metal[2], and therefore away from the organic molecule; the activation energy necessary for the severence of the weakest link in such a molecule may thus be considerably lowered. Many bond-forming and bond-breaking reactions are reversible, and catalyzed by similar metal-enzyme compounds.

Cleavage of Peptide Bonds

The metabolic decomposition of proteins into amino acids occurs through a complicated series of reactions, in which the large molecules are first fragmented into polypeptides by the endopeptidases, and the resulting polypeptides are further degraded by aminopeptidases and carboxypeptidases, which act, respectively, upon the amino and carboxyl terminals of the peptide, thus splitting off amino acids one by one from each end. When only

2. Smith, *Proc. Natl. Acad. Sci. U. S.*, **35**, 80 (1949); Kroll, *J. Am. Chem. Soc.*, **74**, 2063 (1952); Eichhorn and Bailar, *J. Am. Chem. Soc.*, **75**, 2905 (1953).

two amino acids remain, the dipeptide is susceptible to the action of a dipeptidase.

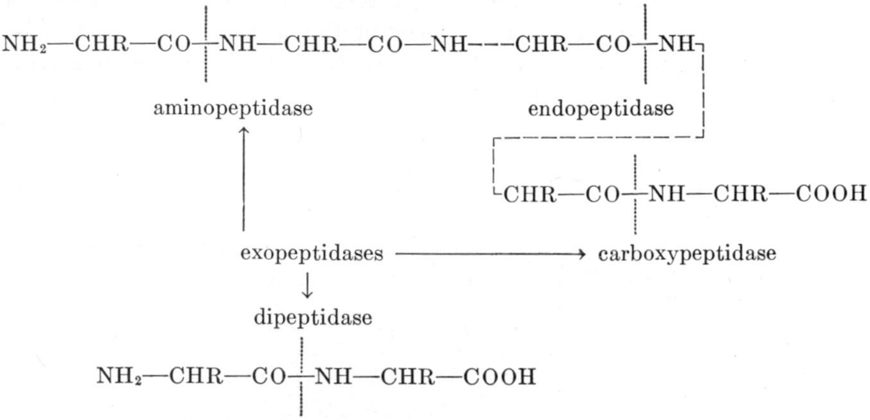

NH₂—CHR—CO⊢NH—CHR—CO—NH———CHR—CO⊢NH┐

        aminopeptidase   endopeptidase

            ↑   └CHR—CO⊢NH—CHR—COOH

       exopeptidases ————————→ carboxypeptidase
                    ↓
             dipeptidase

NH₂—CHR—CO⊢NH—CHR—COOH

Endopeptidases. Not much information is available about the participation of metal ions in the action of the endopeptidases. It is known, however, that the enzyme enterokinase, which is involved in the removal of a protective polypeptide from trypsinogen, producing the active enzyme trypsin, is a calcium protein[3]. Recently, it has been demonstrated that the activity of trypsin may be enhanced by the addition of a variety of metal ions and chymotrypsin by calcium[4]. It is possible that the metal ions in these reactions are coordinated in a fashion similar to the linkage in the exopeptidase complexes.

Exopeptidases. That many exopeptidases are metal complexes has been amply demonstrated in a variety of activation and inhibition experiments[5]. Many of the enzymes lose their activity if the metal is removed, and regain it upon readdition of the ion; inhibition by powerful complexing agents, such as cysteine, cyanide, and sulfide, also constitutes evidence that metal ions are involved. It has been demonstrated in the case of leucine aminopeptidase that the initial rate of the enzyme catalyzed reactions is much higher if the enzyme is treated with metal ion prior to the addition of substrate, rather than if the metal and substrate are added at the same time. This leads to the conclusion that the formation of bonds between the metal ion and the protein portion of the enzyme is a time consuming process, indicating that these bonds are of essentially covalent character[6].

3. McDonald and Kunitz, *J. Gen. Physiol.*, **25**, 53 (1941).
4. Green, Gladner, and Cunningham, *J. Am. Chem. Soc.*, **74**, 2122 (1952).
5. Smith, "Enzymes and Enzyme Systems," Edsall, pp. 49–76, Cambridge, Harvard University Press, 1951.
6. Smith and Bergmann, *J. Biol. Chem.*, **138**, 789, (1941); **153**, 627 (1944).

Dipeptidases. *Glycylglycine Dipeptidase.* The structure of the dipepti-
dase-substrate intermediates has been formulated with the metal coordinated to the amino group, the peptide nitrogen, and the carboxyl group of
the substrate, the remaining covalences of the metal being satisfied by
positions on the enzyme protein. Thus the cobalt(II) enzyme glycylglycine
dipeptidase[7] may be depicted[1b]:

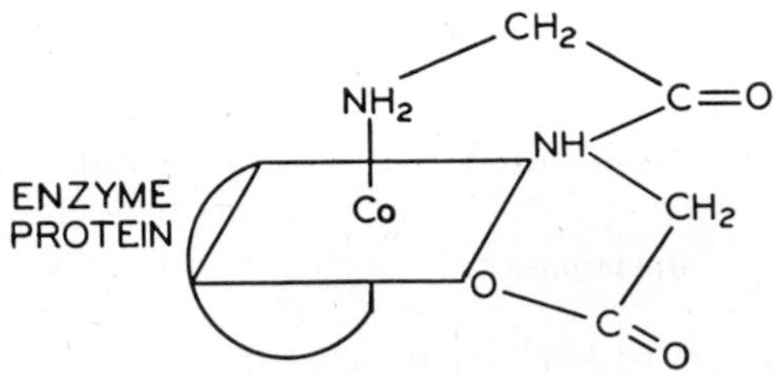

Coordination to the amino and peptide nitrogens is suggested by the failure of the enzyme to act upon the dipeptide having two methyl groups substituted on the amino nitrogen or one methyl group on the peptide nitrogen[8]. Glycylglycine dipeptidase has no effect upon glycylglycylglycine.
Smith has shown that the susceptibility of a molecule to cleavage by
glycylglycine dipeptidase may be correlated with the intensity of absorption of its cobalt(II) complex[7]: the absorption of the glycylglycine complex
is much higher than that of either the glycine or glycylglycylglycine complexes. Similar data have been obtained by Klotz[9], who has shown that the
spectra of the copper(II) complexes of peptides containing even numbers of
glycine molecules are more intense than those of the odd-numbered glycine
peptide complexes. The generalization that intensity of absorption can be
used as a qualitative indication of the stability of a complex, and so provide
evidence for the correlation of stability with enzyme susceptibility[10] appears to have been misleading in this instance, since the stabilities of glycylglycine complexes have since been determined quantitatively and found to
be lower than those of glycine[11]. The spectra may be explained by the
assumption that coordination of a polypeptide always requires the participation of either an amino group or a carboxyl group; this postulate leads
to a structure for the triglycine complex (A) that resembles the glycine
complex, and to structures for di- and tetraglycine complexes (B) that

7. Smith, *ibid.*, **173,** 571 (1948).
8. Smith, *ibid.*, **176,** 21 (1948).
9. Klotz, Feller, and Urqhart, *J. Phys. Coll. Chem.*, **54,** 18 (1950).
10. Smith, "The Enzymes," Sumner and Myrbaeck, Vol. I, p. 817, New York,
    Academic Press, Inc., 1951.
11. Monk, *Trans. Faraday Soc.*, **47,** 297 (1951).

contain fused ring systems:

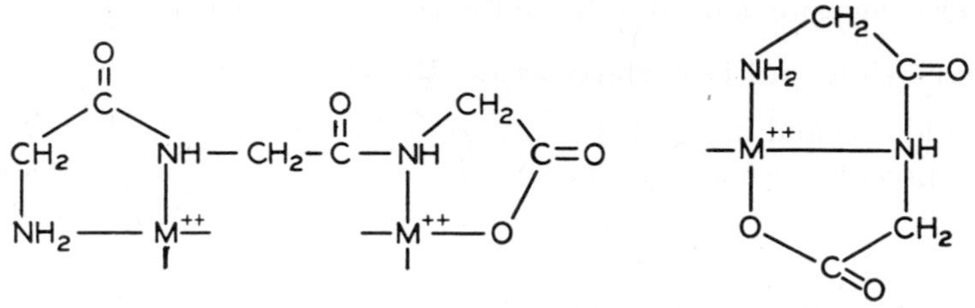

A   B

The spectra of complexes of higher polypeptides of glycine show no sharp differences depending upon the presence of odd or even numbers of glycine molecules, since all of the complexes probably contain the condensed ring structure (B). The inability of glycylglycine dipeptidase to act upon triglycine can be interpreted on the basis of this structure if it is assumed that structure B is essential for enzyme activity.

Other Dipeptidases. Dipeptidases in general are specific in their action only upon one dipeptide, and in their requirement of a particular metal ion. However, the same substrate may be acted upon by different enzymes in different tissues, and these enzymes sometimes require different metals (e.g., zinc or magnesium for various glycyl-L-leucine dipeptidases)[12]. Apparently the metal specificity in these cases depends not so much upon the donors in the substrate as it does upon the donors in the enzyme protein.

Aminopeptidases and Carboxypeptidases. The complex intermediates in the action of these enzymes[5, 13] may be formulated like those for the dipeptidases; possibly coordination with the substrate involves only two rather than three donors, the amino and peptide groups in the aminopeptidases, and the carboxyl and peptide groups in the carboxypeptidases. Klotz[13a] has suggested that the metal may be coordinated to the substrate at only one position; he postulates that the metal stabilizes a complex between the peptide bond and hydroxyl ion:

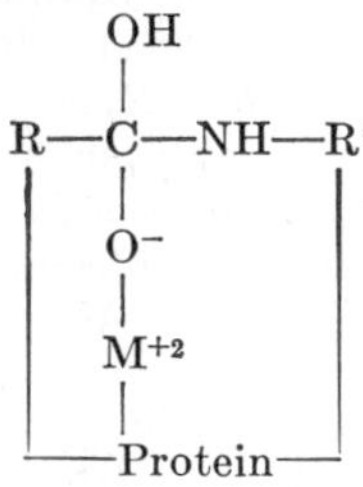

---

12. Smith, *J. Biol. Chem.*, **176,** 9 (1948).
13. Smith and Hanson, *ibid.*, **176,** 997 (1948); **179,** 802 (1949); Smith, in "The Enzymes," pp. 838–40.
13a. Klotz, "The Mechanism of Enzyme Action," McElroy and Glass, pp. 257–285, Baltimore, Johns Hopkins Press, 1954.

The metal has a twofold purpose in this scheme: to attract hydroxyl ions to the cleavage site, and to stabilize the transition state.

Carboxylation and Decarboxylation Reactions

The addition and removal of carbon dioxide are also widely occurring reversible processes which are catalyzed by metal ions[14] through the formation of complex intermediates. Some of these reactions, such as the decarboxylation of pyruvic acid, may be accompanied by oxidation or reduction[15], whereas others, such as the decarboxylation of α-ketoglutaric acid, are not[16]. The metal ion is generally magnesium, and sometimes manganese, although these may be replaced by other metal ions[17]; in addition, some carboxylase reactions require the presence of diphosphothiamine, Vitamin B_1 pyrophosphate, as coenzyme.

Metal-containing carboxylase enzymes catalyze the conversion of oxalosuccinic acid to α-ketoglutaric acid[20], and of α-ketoglutaric to succinic acid[18].

$$
\begin{array}{ccc}
\mathrm{CH_2{-}{-}{-}CH{-}CO{-}COOH} & & \mathrm{CH_2{-}CH_2{-}CO{-}COOH} \\
\mathrm{\ \ \ |\qquad\ \ |} & \rightarrow & \mathrm{\ \ \ |} \qquad\qquad\qquad + CO_2 \\
\mathrm{COOH\ \ COOH} & & \mathrm{COOH}
\end{array}
$$

oxalosuccinic acid α-ketoglutaric acid

$$\downarrow \tfrac{1}{2}O_2$$

$$
\begin{array}{c}
\mathrm{CH_2{-}{-}{-}CH_2} \\
\mathrm{\ \ |\qquad\ \ |} \qquad + CO_2 \\
\mathrm{COOH\ \ COOH}
\end{array}
$$

The first of these reactions, as well as the decarboxylation of oxaloacetic acid[16b, 17] proceeds through the influence of metal ions even in the absence of enzyme protein[20]. Since many of these acids are polyfunctional, a number of different structures have been assigned to the complex intermediates, among them the formulation of the complex as a six-membered chelate

14. Green, Herbert, and Subrahmanyan, *J. Biol. Chem.*, **138**, 327 (1941); Kossel, *Z. Physiol. Chem.*, **276**, 251 (1942); Veenesland, Ref. 10, Vol. II, pp. 183–215; Ochoa, *ibid.*, Vol. II, 929–1023; *Physiol. Rev.* **31**, 56 (1951).

15. Lipmann, *Enzymologia*, **4**, 65, (1937); Lipmann, *J. Biol. Chem.*, **155**, 55 (1944); Kolnitsky and Werkman, *Arch. Biochem.*, **2**, 113 (1943); Utter and Werkman, *ibid.*, **2**, 491 (1943); Koepsell and Johnson, *J. Biol. Chem.*, **145**, 379 (1942); Koepsell and Johnson and Meek, *ibid.*, **154**, 535, (1944); Stumpf, *ibid.*, **159**, 529 (1945).

16. Krampitz and Werkman, *Biochem. J.*, **35**, 595 (1941); Speck, *J. Biol. Chem.*, **178**, 315 (1949); Veenesland, *J. Biol. Chem.*, **178**, 591 (1949).

17. Krebs, *Biochem. J.*, **36**, 303 (1942).

18. Green, Westerfeld, Veenesland, and Knox, *J. Biol. Chem.*, **145**, 69 (1942).

20. Kornberg, Ochoa, and Mehler, *ibid.*, **174**, 159 (1948).

involving the carbonyl and the carboxyl groups in β-positions to each other[20]:

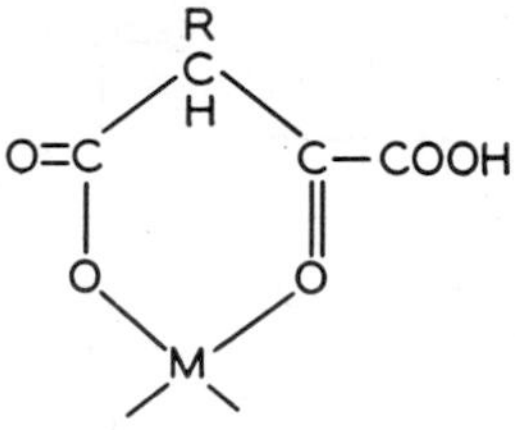

$$
\begin{array}{c}
\text{R} \\
\text{C} \\
\text{H} \\
\text{O=C} \qquad \text{C—COOH} \\
\text{O} \qquad \text{O} \\
\text{M} \\
\end{array}
$$

(A)

Martell and Calvin[1b] have pointed out that acetoacetic acid,

$$CH_3—CO—CH_2—COOH,$$

should be capable of this type of chelation, but its decarboxylation is not affected by metal ions. Moreover, esterification of the α-carboxyl group of oxaloacetic acid prevents the metal ion catalysis of the decarboxylation[21], thus implicating this group in the process, a circumstance not explainable on the basis of the above formulation; consequently a chelate between the keto and the α-carboxyl groups has been proposed, and the mechanism of the decarboxylation has been formulated as follows[1b]:

$$
\text{O=C}\!\!-\!\!-\!\!\text{C}\!-\!\overset{R}{\text{C}}\text{H}\!-\!\text{CO}\!-\!\text{O}^- \qquad \longrightarrow \qquad \text{O=C}\!\!-\!\!-\!\!\text{C}\!=\!\text{CHR} \;+\; CO_2
$$

(B)

Such a mechanism suggests that there may be no fundamental difference between these so-called decarboxylations of β-ketoacids and the decarboxylations of α-ketoacids, such as pyruvic and α-ketoglutaric, which may form complexes of type B, but not of type A.

Recently Westheimer and Graham[22] have studied the iron(III) complexes of dimethyl oxaloacetic acid. The initially formed yellow complex is con-

21. Steinberger and Westheimer, *J. Am. Chem. Soc.*, **73**, 429 (1951).
22. Westheimer and Graham, Paper at conference on Coordination Chemistry, Indiana University (1953).

verted to a blue substance as a result of the decarboxylation:

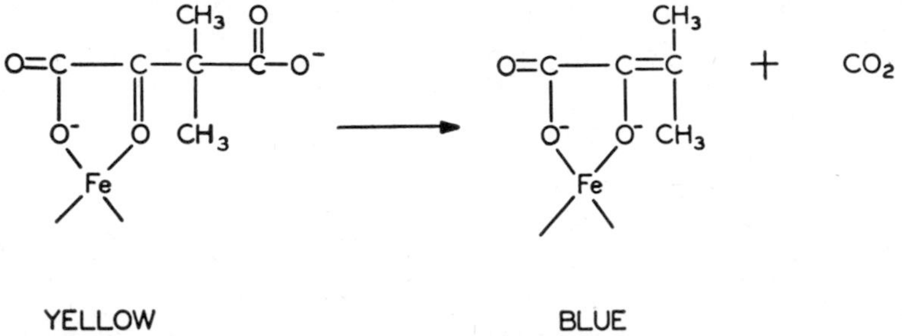

YELLOW   BLUE

When the β-carboxyl group is esterified, the production of the iron complex is not hindered, but esterification of the α-carboxyl group prevents the formation of any yellow color, providing further evidence that the alpha, and not the beta, carboxyl group is involved in the chelation.

Since decarboxylation reactions are catalyzed by metal ions in the absence of protein, the purpose of the latter becomes problematic; it is reasonable to suppose that, in addition to its rather marked influence upon the rate of the reaction, the protein is responsible for rendering an enzyme specific for one, and only one substrate, a specificity of which the simple metal ion is quite incapable. The function of diphosphothiamine may be to increase the stability of the complex between substrate, metal, and protein. Perhaps the amino group of thiamine combines with the carbonyl group of the keto acid to produce a Schiff's base, which then constitutes the active substrate for decarboxylation.

Carbonic Anhydrase. This enzyme[23] catalyzes the reaction between water and carbon dioxide to produce carbonic acid, and for that reason is very important in the regulation of pH. The enzyme, which contains zinc, obviously cannot function through the mechanism that has been postulated for the keto acids; it may possibly involve an intermediate zinc-carbonato complex.

Phosphorylation

Many biological bond-forming and bond-breaking processes, especially those connected with carbohydrate and nucleoprotein metabolism, are accompanied by the synthesis or destruction of phosphate bonds; indeed, the energy required for many biochemical reactions is derived from the cleavage of phosphate bonds, especially the conversion of adenosine triphosphate (ATP) to adenosine diphosphate (ADP). Many of the enzymes associated with these reactions, the phosphorylases that catalyze the phosphorolytic degradation of organic molecules, and the phosphatases that are

23. Vallee and Altschule, *Physiol. Rev.* **29**, 370 (1949).

engaged in the cleavage of phosphate bonds, have metal ion constituents[24], usually magnesium, and are inhibited by competing complexing agents.

Since magnesium forms relatively strong bonds with phosphates, the presence of this ion in phosphorylating enzymes points to the formation of complex intermediates in which the donor and the recipient of the phosphate are brought together through complex formation with the metal ion. Thus a possible intermediate in the phosphorylation of glucose by ATP under the influence of magnesium-containing hexokinase may be formulated as follows:

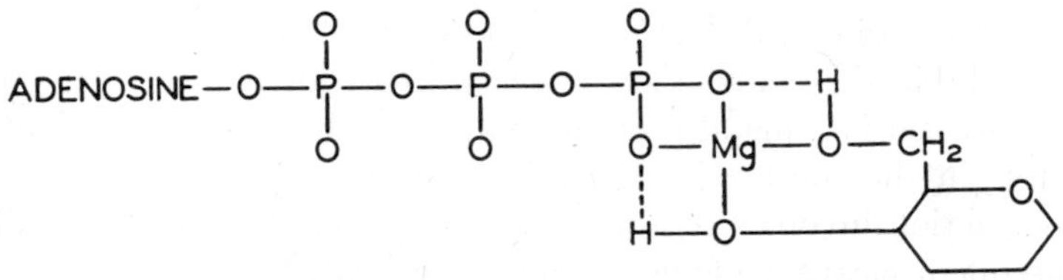

The existence of such an intermediate would indicate that the magnesium can perform a dual function by bringing about contact between the reacting molecules, and by labilizing the phosphorus-oxygen bond. More work on the magnesium complexes of carbohydrates and of ATP should prove of great value in the further elucidation of these reactions.

Insulin. A very important biochemical coordination compound possibly related to carbohydrate phosphorylation reactions is the zinc protein, insulin[26]. Removal of zinc greatly decreases the stability of this molecule, suggesting that coordination stabilization may be one of the functions of the metal. Insulin reacts readily with other divalent metals, such as cadmium, cobalt, and nickel[26, 27].

Little is known concerning the exact mechanism of the metabolic function of insulin, but it has been proposed that insulin stimulates carbohydrate metabolism through its antagonism toward a "diabetogenic hormone" (pituitary factor)[28], which, in turn, inhibits the phosphorylation of glucose. These relationships might be interpreted by postulating that the hormone

24. Roche, Ref. 10, Vol. I, 473–510; Frisell and Hellermann, *Ann. Rev. Biochem.*, **20**, 24 (1951); Humphrey and Humphrey, *Biochem. J.*, **47**, 238 (1950); Meyerhof and Lohmann, *Biochem. Z.* **271**, 102 (1934); Warburg and Christian, *ibid.*, **311**, 209 (1942); **314**, 149, (1943); Jenner and Kay, *J. Biol. Chem.*, **93**, 733 (1931); Roche, Nguyen-von-Thoai, and Danzas, *Bull. Soc. Chim. Biol.*, **26**, 411 (1944); Massart and Vandendriessche, *Naturwis.*, **28**, 143 (1940); Nguyen-von-Thoai, Roche, and Roger, *Biochim. and Biophys. Acta*, **1**, 61 (1947).
26. Scott and Fischer, *Biochem. J.*, **29**, 1048 (1935).
27. Spiga and deBarbieri, *Boll. Soc. Ital. Biol. Sper.*, **21**, 64 (1946).
28. Bjering, *Acta Med. Scand.*, **94**, 483 (1936); Baldwin, "Dynamic Aspects of Biochemistry," p. 413, Cambridge University Press, 1952.

can coordinate either with the magnesium of the phosphorylase, or with the zinc of insulin; whenever the former occurs, phosphorylation is barred, but when the hormone is tied to insulin, magnesium is again free to catalyze the phosphorylation reaction.

Insulin-Zn-diabetogenic hormone $\rightarrow$ diabetogenic hormone-Mg-phosphorylase

(phosphorylation occurs)   (no phosphorylation)

Actomyosin. The mechanical energy of muscle contraction, like the chemical energy of carbohydrate metabolism, is derived from the decomposition of ATP into ADP, and is brought about through the contractile protein actomyosin. Although it has been claimed that magnesium ions actually inhibit the contraction reaction[29], predominating opinion holds that actomyosin is a metal-protein complex and that the metal plays an active role in the contraction[24c, 30]. A possible explanation of this role is that contraction involves coordination of magnesium with the ATP, and the consequent cleavage of the phosphate radical:

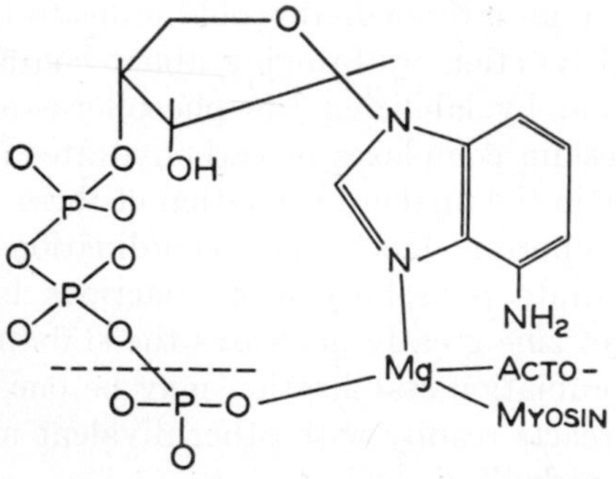

The existence of a metal-actomyosin-ATP complex has been discussed by Walaas[31]. The proposed structure of a complex intermediate bears much resemblance to a structure recently proposed for the Vitamin B_{12} molecule.

Other Condensation and Cleavage Reactions

Several other bond-forming and bond-breaking enzymes are metalloproteins that do not fit into any of the categories that have already been discussed.

29. Braverman and Morgulis, *J. Gen. Physiol.*, **31**, 411 (1948); Mommaerts, *Science*, **104**, 605 (1946); Watanabe, Yago, Sugekawa, and Tonomura, *J. Chem. Soc. Japan*, **73**, 761 (1952).
30. Spicer and Bowen, *J. Biol. Chem.*, **188**, 741 (1951); Perry, *Biochem. J.*, **47**, xxxviii (1950); Swanson, *J. Biol. Chem.*, **191**, 577 (1951); Szent-Gyoergyi, "Chemistry of Muscular Contraction," 2nd Ed., New York, Academic Press, 1951; Portzehl, *Z. Naturforsch.*, **76**, 1 (1952).
31. Walaas, *Nord. Med.*, **43**, 1047 (1950).

Condensing Enzyme. This enzyme is the catalyst for the condensation of acetate in the form of acetyl coenzyme-A (produced by decarboxylation of pyruvic acid or the degradation of fatty acids) with oxaloacetic acid enol to form citric acid. The latter then passes through the tricarboxylic acid cycle, losing in the process two carbon atoms and forming again oxaloacetate which may undergo another condensation. This condensation is therefore of fundamental importance; the so-called condensing enzyme requires magnesium, calcium, or manganese for its activity[32]*; these metals probably function by exercising their ability to bring the condensing molecules into contact:

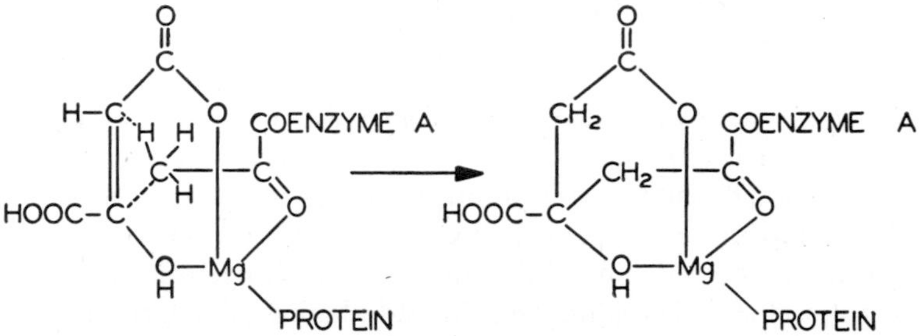

Enolase. Another very important enzyme is the magnesium-containing enolase, which catalyzes the dehydration of D-2-phosphoglyceric acid to phosphoenolpyruvate[33]. The natural enzyme apparently contains magnesium, although manganese or zinc may be substituted. The following type of intermediate may be postulated for such a reaction:

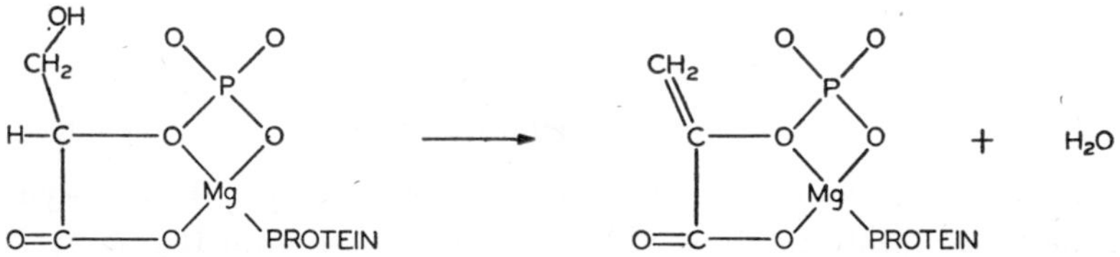

According to this mechanism, the protein magnesium complexes with the phosphate and carboxyl groups, producing a five-membered chelate ring. Coordination of the oxygen on the central carbon atom labilizes the bond

* Note added in proof: It now appears that the metal requirement is for the production of acetyl coenzyme A. The metal may be omitted when preformed acetyl CoA is used. There is no evidence at present that metal ions are involved in the condensation. See Ochoa in "Methods in Enzymology," Colowich and Kaplan, Vol. I, p. 685. Academic Press, Inc., 1955.

32. Stern and Ochoa, *J. Biol. Chem.*, **191**, 161 (1951).
33. Kun, *Proc. Soc. Exptl. Biol. Med.*, **75**, 68 (1950); Warburg and Christian, *Biochem. Z.* **310**, 384 (1941).

between the carbon atom and the proton. The latter is consequently released, thus placing a negative charge on the carbon. The molecule then regains neutrality by the loss of a hydroxyl ion and the formation of a double bond; the net result of the loss of a proton and a hydroxide ion is the dehydration of the molecule.

EXCHANGE OF FUNCTIONAL GROUPS—TRANSAMINATION

Closely related to the bond-breaking and bond-forming reactions are the group transfer reactions, in which metal ions may participate because (a) they are able to bring reacting molecules together to form an activated complex, (b) they can serve in the cleavage of bonds that occurs prior to the transfer, and (c) the relative stabilities of the complexes of the reaction products may exceed the stabilities of the complexes of the reacting substances.

Probably the most important exchange reaction of this sort is transamination[34], which provides a link between carbohydrate and protein metabolism through the transfer of amino groups from amino acids to keto acids. An example of a transamination whose natural occurrence has been demonstrated is the reaction of glutamic acid with pyruvic or oxaloacetic acid[34, 35] to produce α-ketoglutaric acid and alanine or aspartic acid

$$HOOC—CH_2—CH_2—\underset{\underset{NH_2}{|}}{CH}—COOH + CH_3—\overset{\overset{O}{\|}}{C}—COOH \rightarrow$$

glutamic acid   pyruvic acid

$$HOOC—CH_2CH_2—\underset{\underset{O}{\|}}{C}—COOH + CH_3—\underset{\underset{NH_2}{|}}{CH}—COOH$$

α-ketoglutaric acid   alanine

These reactions are catalyzed by transaminase enzymes, the coenzyme of which has been firmly established as pyridoxal[36] (vitamin B$_6$) or pyridoxamine[36a] phosphate.

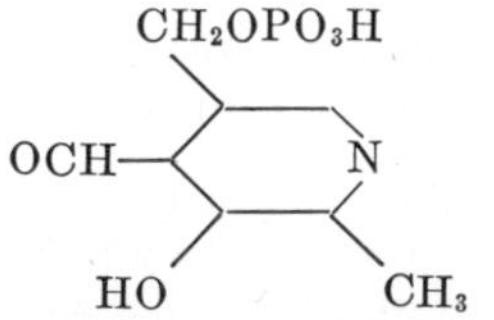

$$CH_2OPO_3H$$

OCH   N

HO   CH$_3$

34. Cohen, *J. Biol. Chem.*, **136**, 565 (1940); Cohen, Ref. 10, Vol. I, p. 1040.
35. Nisonoff and Barnes, *J. Biol. Chem.*, **199**, 699 (1952); Green, Leloir, and Nocito, *ibid.*, **161**, 559 (1945).
36. Lichstein, Gunsalus, and Umbreit, *J. Biol. Chem.*, **161**, 311 (1945).
36a. Meister, Sober, and Peterson, *J. Am. Chem. Soc.*, **74**, 2385 (1952).

The requirement of the vitamin has led to the speculation[37] that the amino acid initially forms a Schiff's base with the pyridoxal (see equation below), that subsequently the double bond shifts to the amino acid carbon atom, while a hydrogen is transferred from the latter to the pyridoxal, and that finally the newly created double bond is cleaved, yielding a keto acid and pyridoxamine. The latter is then supposed to transfer the amino group that it has just picked up to a keto acid, the overall effect being the transfer of the amino group from the amino acid to the keto acid, with pyridoxal acting as catalyst.

The nonenzymatic transfer of amino groups from a large number of amino acids to pyridoxal, and from pyridoxamine to α-ketoglutaric acid at 100° has been thoroughly investigated[38]. It has been discovered that the reaction is inhibited by ethylenediaminetetraacetic acid and catalyzed by copper(II), aluminum(III), iron(II), and iron(III) (in order of decreasing activity). It has been postulated that the intermediates in these transamination reactions are metal complexes of the Schiff's bases described above; the mechanism may be depicted as follows:

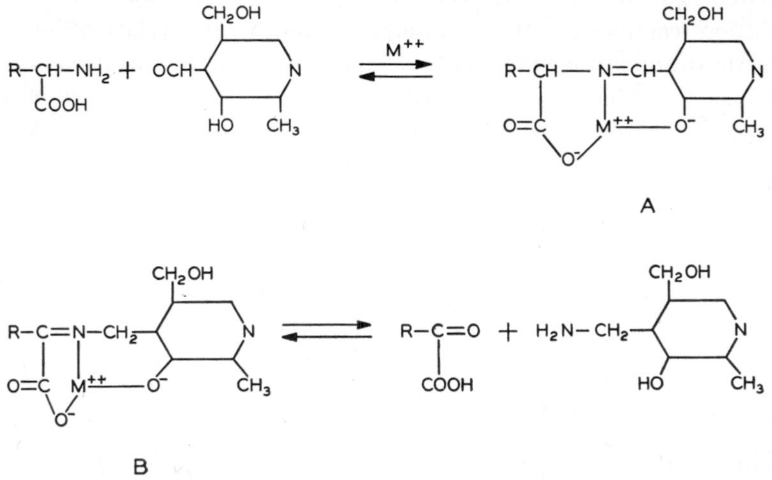

A

B

Coordination with the metal ion stabilizes these Schiff's bases because the presence of the carboxyl group makes possible the formation of a second ring. (When the production of such a fused ring system is prevented by the absence of an additional donor group, metal ion coordination decreases the stability of the Schiff's base.) Confirmatory evidence for the existence of the postulated Schiff's base complexes at room temperature has been ob-

37. Schlenk and Fischer, *Arch. Biochem.*, **12**, 69 (1947).
38. Snell, *J. Am. Chem. Soc.*, **74**, 979 (1952); Snell, *ibid.*, **67**, 194 (1945).

tained recently through spectrophotometric investigations of systems containing copper(II) and nickel(II) ions in solution together with pyridoxal and alanine, or with pyridoxamine and pyruvic acid[39]. Solutions of the metals in the presence of two such reactants exhibit completely different absorption phenomena from those of the complexes of pyruvic acid or alanine alone, or of the vitamin alone, thus indicating Schiff's base complex formation. Moreover, the spectra of the pyruvic acid-pyridoxamine complex solutions gradually change upon standing until they have become identical with those of the pyridoxal-alanine complexes, indicating that under the experimental conditions employed, the equilibrium favors Schiff's base A, which is produced by a double bond shift from the initially formed B.

Although the formation of metal-Schiff's base complexes as intermediates in nonenzymatic transaminations appears thus to have been well established, the enzymatic reaction does not necessarily follow the same course. Indeed, the presence of metal ions in transaminase itself has not been established; only a trace of metal would be required, however, in the catalytic process that has been described.

Other Vitamin B$_6$ Catalyzed Reactions. Closely related to the transamination reactions are the deamination[41] and decarboxylation[42] of amino acids, the deamidation of amino acid amides, and the racemization of amino acids[43], all of which are catalyzed by vitamin B$_6$ in the presence of metal ions, and probably involve the same type of Schiff's base complex intermediates. Thus it has been observed that L-alanine undergoes extensive racemization in the presence of both aluminum ion and pyridoxal, although it is quite stable in the presence of aluminum ion alone. The racemization can be explained in terms of an equilibrium between structures A and B; reformation of A from B and subsequent hydrolysis results in the production of the racemate.

BLOCKING OF FUNCTIONAL GROUPS

Many biochemical processes involve reactions of polyfunctional molecules at one specific point with reagents that could presumably attack elsewhere. A possible function of coordination with a metal, therefore, is to block those groups whose participation in the reaction is to be avoided.

39. Eichhorn and Dawes, *J. Am. Chem. Soc.*, **76**, 5663 (1954).
41. Metzler and Snell, *J. Biol. Chem.*, **198**, 363 (1952).
42. Schales, Ref. 10, Vol. II p. 246; Gunsalus, Bellamy, and Umbreit, *J. Biol. Chem.*, **155**, 685 (1944).
43. Olivard, Metzler, and Snell, *ibid.*, **199**, 669 (1952).

Arginase

The degradation of arginine to ornithine is an illustration of a reaction in which coordination blocking may be involved.

$$HOOC—CH—(CH_2)_3—NH—C—NH_2 \quad \rightarrow$$

with NH_2 below the first CH and $\|\ NH$ below the C.

arginine

$$HOOC—CH—(CH_2)_3—NH_2 + NH_2—CO—NH_2$$

with NH_2 below the CH.

ornithine   urea

The catalyst for the reaction is the enzyme arginase[44], which in its natural form apparently contains manganese, but it may also become activated by divalent cobalt, nickel, and iron[45]. The products of the reaction are urea and ornithine; the latter, but not the former, inhibits the decomposition reaction. Moreover, other amino acids besides ornithine are inhibitors[46], although the inhibiting capacity appears to depend upon the structural similarity of the amino acid to ornithine (lysine is next in line after ornithine). It is probable therefore, that the enzyme metal is coordinated with the ornithine portion, rather than the guanidine part, of the arginine; the mechanism of the reaction is then illustrated by the following equation:

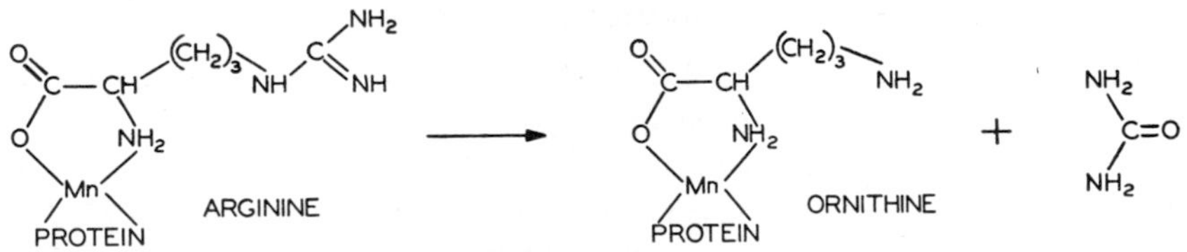

The inhibition by amino acids is probably due to their ability to compete with arginine for the metal ion. The inclusion of manganese in a second, seven-membered or larger, chelate ring involving one of the guanidine nitrogens is not out of the question, and, if it occurs, may explain the exercise by the metal of its bond-breaking capacity; it is probable that one of these nitrogens is attached to the enzyme, if not through the metal, then at some other point; otherwise the superior inhibiting power of lysine remains unexplained.

It has been shown that the reverse of the arginase catalyzed reaction,

44. Greenberg, Ref. 10, Vol. I, Chapt. 25.
45. Hellerman and Perkins, *J. Biol. Chem.*, **112**, 175 (1935).
46. Hunter and Downs, *J. Biol. Chem.*, **157**, 427 (1945).

the conversion of ornithine to arginine[46a] or citrulline[46b], may be achieved in the laboratory by blocking the α-amino group through coordination with copper, thus leaving only the ω-amino group vulnerable to attack by urea. Since this reaction *is* reversible, it appears reasonable to suppose that one of the functions of the metal in arginase is to prevent the urea that has been removed from the end of the arginine molecule from attaching itself to the α-amino group, a process that would result in the formation of a biochemically unknown substance.

Glutathione

Another possible illustration of coordination blocking may be that concerned with the biosynthesis of the widely distributed tripeptide, glutathione,

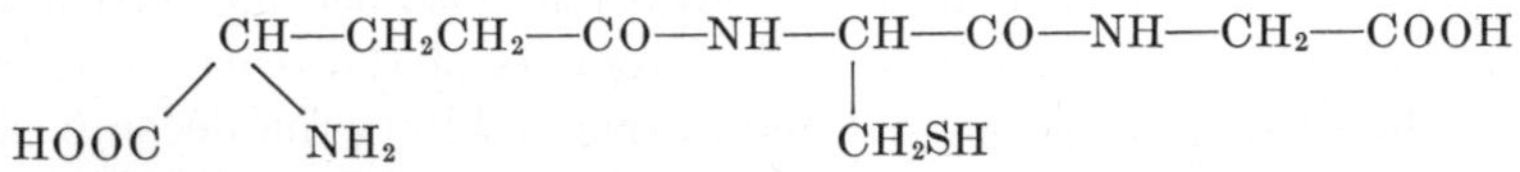

$$CH\!-\!CH_2CH_2\!-\!CO\!-\!NH\!-\!CH\!-\!CO\!-\!NH\!-\!CH_2\!-\!COOH$$

$$HOOC \quad NH_2 \qquad\qquad CH_2SH$$

Whereas peptide bonds are generally formed between α-amino and α-carboxyl groups, the glutamic acid is in this instance bound through the γ-carboxyl. It is easy to visualize how such a linkage could be achieved if it is supposed that the α-carboxyl group is tied up along with the α-amino group by chelation with a metal ion.

STEREOCHEMICAL SPECIFICITY

Many of the enzymes that have been discussed up to this point are specific for their substrates to the extent that they will act upon one optical isomer and have no effect at all upon its antipode[47]. Thus glycyl-L-leucine dipeptidase does not attack glycyl-D-leucine, and arginase splits L-arginine only[48]. This specificity becomes plausible when it is remembered that prior to coordination to the substrate the metal is already coordinated to an enzyme protein that is optically active by virtue of its being composed of optically active amino acids. Further coordination with optically isomeric substrates would therefore result in the formation of diastereoisomers. It becomes evident from a consideration of enzyme specificity that only one of these diastereoisomers is capable of existence; possibly steric hindrance between the organic groups is responsible for the instability of the unattainable diastereoisomer[10]. The influence exerted by coordinated op-

46a. Turba and Schuster, *Z. physiol. Chem.*, **283**, 27 (1948).
46b. Kurtz, *J. Biol. Chem.*, **122**, 477 (1938).
47. Bergmann, Zervas, Fruton, Schneider, and Schleich, *J. Biol. Chem.*, **109**, 325 (1935).
48. Reisser, *Z. Physiol. Chem.*, **49**, 210 (1906); Edlbacher and Bonem, *ibid.*, **145**, 69 (1925).

tically-active molecules upon entering optically-active donors has been discussed by Bailar *et al.* See (Chapter 8.)

THE PORPHYRINS

It has been noted in the introduction to this chapter that the biochemical functions of metal ions discussed in the preceding sections are such that the complexes produced must be relatively labile. On the other hand, those functions which remain to be considered require that the metal ion be rather firmly held by the donor molecules. A group of such molecules that appear to have been especially constructed for this purpose are the porphyrins.

These compounds are derivatives of the parent substance porphine[49], which consists of four pyrrole nuclei joined at their α-carbon atoms by methene groups. All of the porphyrin complexes to which reference will be made here are derivatives of protoporphyrin, which has the following structure[50]:

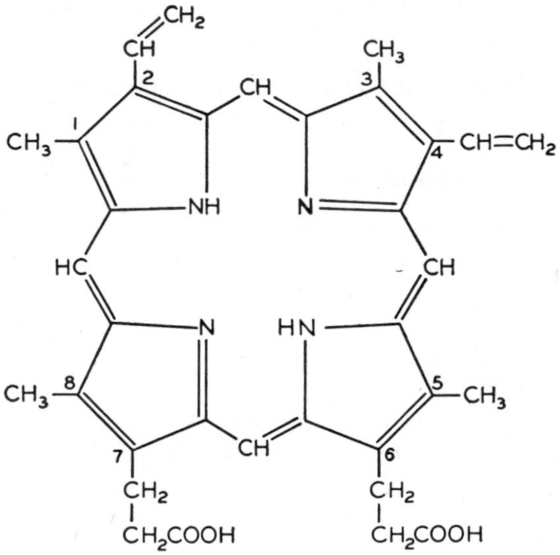

Stability of Porphyrin Complexes

Porphyrin molecules form complexes with metal ions by coordination through the four pyrrole nitrogen atoms; since two hydrogen atoms are lost in the process, the porphyrin can neutralize a dipositive charge on the metal ion in addition to occupying four positions in its coordination sphere.

49. Fischer and Gleim, *Ann.*, **521**, 157 (1935).
50. Fischer and Orth, "Die Chemie des Pyrrols." Leipzig, Akademische Verlagsgesellschaft M. B. H., 1937. Vol. II, p. 396.

The porphyrin complexes contain four six-membered chelate rings (generally the ring size of greatest stability when double bonds are involved) which have been fused together in a manner such that each nitrogen atom is part of two of the rings. All of the atoms in the porphine nucleus of the porphyrin molecule lie in the same plane[51]*; consequently the resonance stabilization of the organic molecule is very high, and, since the coordinated metal ion must occupy a position that is coplanar with the rest of the molecule, it can serve as a nucleus for enhanced resonance stabilization by producing four additional fused rings. Another unique feature of the porphyrin complexes, shared only with the closely related phthalocyanine dyes (see page 73), is the completely enveloping cyclization of the organic molecule, a factor that may also contribute to the great stability of these substances.

Because of this stability, the structure of porphyrin-containing complexes is much more completely known than are the structures of other naturally occurring coordination compounds, since the protein may be removed without destruction of that part of the molecule in the immediate environment of the metal ion[52]. Another consequence of porphyrin stability is the survival of the structure intact in a variety of inanimate materials that have their origins in the prehistoric decay of living matter[53].

Heme, Hemin, and Hematin

Because many of the naturally occurring porphyrin complexes contain iron as the metallic constituent, the iron complexes of the porphyrins have been exhaustively studied. The most common of these, iron(II) protoporphyrin, or heme, presumably has two coordination positions above and below the plane of the porphyrin molecule occupied by water molecules. The magnetic moment of heme indicates the presence of four unpaired electrons, suggesting ionic (outer orbital) bonding[54a]; this relatively loose bonding in heme is in sharp contrast to that of the nickel(II) porphyrin complexes[55], for which strictly covalent bonding is indicated by magnetic measurements. It

---

* This conclusion is based on the similarity of the structures of porphyrins and phthalocyanines.

51. Robertson and Woodward, *J. Chem. Soc.*, **1937**, 219; Robertson and Woodward, *ibid.*, **1940**, 36.
52. Nencki and Zaleski, *Z. Physiol. Chem.*, **30**, 384 (1900).
53. Treibs, *Angew. Chem.*, **49**, 682 (1936).
54. Pauling, and Coryell, *Proc. Natl. Acad. Sci. U. S.*, **22**, 159 (1936); Pauling and Coryell, *ibid.*, **22**, 210 (1936); Haurowitz and Kittel, *Ber.*, **66B**, 1046 (1933); Pauling, Whitney, and Felsing, *J. Am. Chem. Soc.*, **59**, 633 (1937).
55. Haurowitz and Klemm, *Ber.*, **68B**, 2312 (1935); Klemm and Klemm, *J. prakt. Chem.*, **143**, 82 (1935); Klemm; *Angew. Chem.*, **48**, 617 (1935).

is of considerable interest that the iron complexes of the porphyrins are among the least stable of the heavy metal porphyrins, and have evidently been selected by nature because their stability can be enhanced through further coordination; such an increase in stability cannot occur in other porphyrin complexes, since they have already attained the maximum stability of which they are capable.

Heme is very sensitive to reaction with oxygen[56], which results, through the formation of a labile oxygen complex intermediate, in the conversion to the iron (III) protoporphyrin, hemin[52]; the charge on this ion is neutralized by its association with an anion[56]:

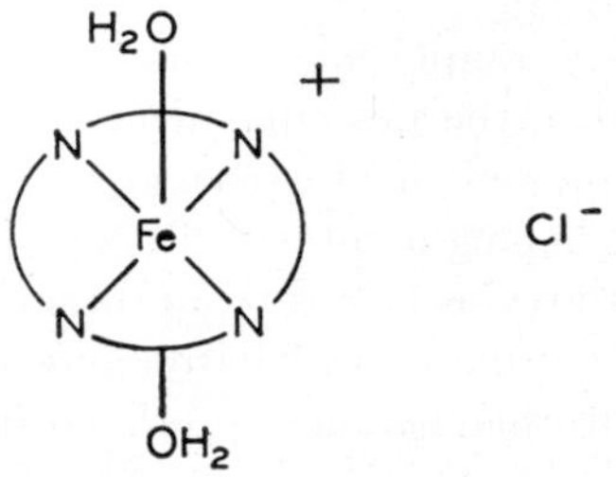

Treatment of hemin with base at room temperature results in the neutralization of the propionic acid carboxyl groups, and the removal of a hydrogen ion from a coordinated water molecule[56, 57]:

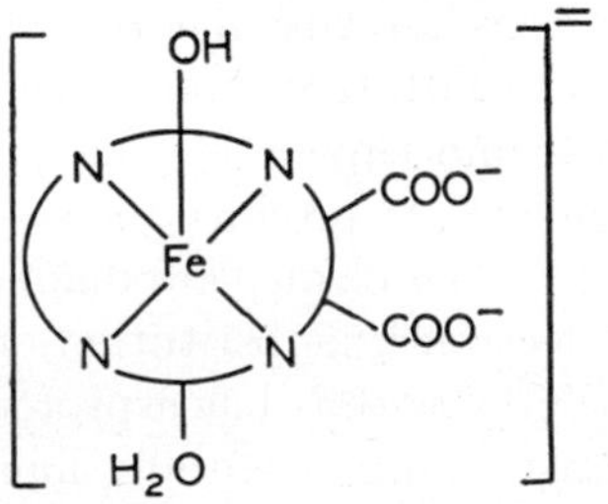

Titration of this anionic complex with acid results in the utilization of only two equivalents of hydrogen ion, a phenomenon which has been interpreted as indicating that one carboxyl group has regained its proton, and that the second hydrogen ion has neutralized the hydroxyl group, which has been replaced from the coordination sphere by the unprotonated carboxylate group of a neighboring ion, thus producing the binuclear complex α-hema-

56. Lemberg and Legge, Reference 1a, p. 166.
57. Hamsick, Z. Physiol. Chem., **182**, 117 (1929); Hamsick, ibid., **190**, 199 (1930); Morrison and Williams, J. Biol. Chem., **123**, lxxxvii (1938).

tin[56]:

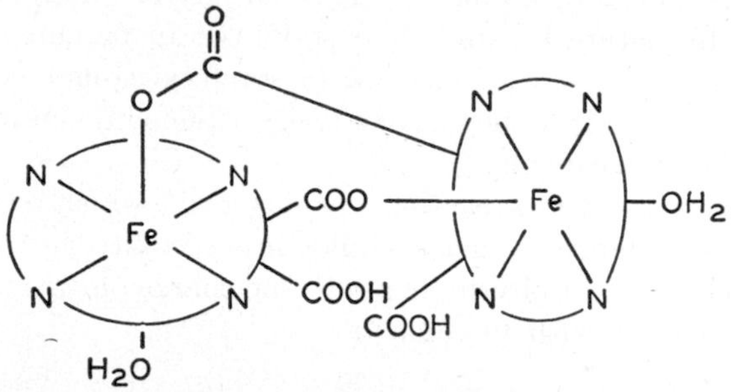

This molecule serves as a simple model that demonstrates two types of linkage commonly found in the proteinated natural porphyrin complexes. The utilization of the propionic acid carboxyl group for chemical bonding is probably a feature of hemoglobin as well as of peroxidase, although in these compounds the carboxyl is linked to a protein, rather than to another iron atom. Carboxylate coordination with iron may also occur in peroxidase, but the carboxyl group in this instance is derived from the protein.

Hemochromes and Hemichromes

Since the iron in all of its naturally occurring porphyrin complexes is coordinated to a protein, complexes in which its extra valences are occupied by simple monodentate basic groups can serve as models for the larger molecules. For reasons already mentioned, nickel porphyrins are incapable of further reaction with bases, but both heme and hemin can fill the coordination positions unoccupied by the porphyrin nitrogens with ammonia, amines, cyanide, etc., to produce the so-called hemochromes and hemichromes, respectively[58]. The former are diamagnetic[54a], and the latter have only one unpaired electron[54a]; substitution of the water molecules of heme and hemin by basic groups thus has a profound effect upon the iron to porphyrin linkage, transforming essentially ionic bonds into essentially covalent bonds. Reference has already been made to the importance of this transition in the natural porphyrin compounds.

Although dipyridyl and ortho-phenanthroline are among the strongest electron donors to ferrous ion, these molecules are incapable of hemochrome formation, probably because the donor atom is sterically hindered in its approach to the porphyrin iron atom[59]. Ethylenediamine does react, not as a chelating agent, since the replaceable groups are not in *cis* positions but as a monodentate, as evidenced by the fact that two molecules of the amine coordinate with every iron atom.

58. Lemberg and Legge, Ref. 1a, p. 174.
59. *Ibid.*, p. 176.

The coordination of iron porphyrin with imidazole is of particular interest, since the linkage of iron to the proteins of hemoglobin and the cytochromes has been postulated to occur through an imidazole nitrogen of histidine. Three molecules of imidazole have been found to combine with hemin[60]; since the formation of imidazolium salts with the propionic acid side chains can account for a maximum of two moles, it has been demonstrated that at least one, and possibly two, imidazole molecules may be coordinated with the iron.

Oxidation-reduction Potentials

Because hemochrome-hemichrome systems are models of the biochemically active oxidation-reduction catalysts, their oxidation potentials are of considerable interest. When the water molecules of heme and hemin are replaced by basic groups, the potential decreases[61], revealing that coordination with the nitrogen bases stabilizes the iron(II). The oxidation potentials of the heme-hemin and hemochrome-hemichrome systems are pH dependent, and the slopes of potential vs. pH curves are independent of the nature of the coordinated bases, approximating a value of 0.059 in all complexes except those with cyanide and imidazole[1b]. This constancy has been interpreted by Martell and Calvin as resulting from the displacement of one of the coordinated hemochrome bases by hydroxide ion during the oxidation. The constancy of the oxidation potential of the cyanide complexes has been attributed to the great stability of these complexes, and their consequent inertness toward hydroxide ion. The increased slope observed for the imidazole system may be due to the dissociation of a hydrogen ion from the uncoordinated nitrogen in the imidazole molecule.

Reaction with Oxygen, Cyanide, Carbon Monoxide, and Hydrogen Peroxide

Carbon monoxide[62], cyanide[62b, 63] and hydrogen peroxide[64] react readily with the simple iron porphyrin complexes in reactions analogous to those that occur in the proteinated biologically active materials. Carbon monoxide reacts with heme, but not with hemin, whereas cyanide ion coordinates with hemin, and not with heme. This behavior toward carbon monoxide and

60. Hamsick, Z. Physiol. Chem., 241, 156 (1936).
61. Ref. 1a, p. 195.
62. Anson and Mirsky, J. Physiol. London, 60, 50 (1925); Hill, Proc. Roy. Soc. London 100B, 419 (1926); Hill, ibid., 105B, 112 (1930); Milroy, J. Physiol., 38, 392 (1909); Pregl, Z. Physiol. Chem., 44, 173 (1905); Lemberg and Legge, Ref. 1a, p. 185.
63. Hogness, Tscheile, Sidwell, and Barron, J. Biol. Chem., 118, 1 (1937).
64. Von Euler and Josephson, Ann., 456, 111 (1927); Haurowitz, Enzymologia, 4, 139 (1937); Haurowitz, Brdicka, and Kraus, ibid., 2, 9 (1937).

cyanide is applicable to the protein-containing porphyrin complexes, and has been utilized to differentiate between natural porphyrin complexes of iron in the di- and tripositive states. Coordination of oxygen with heme, however, results in rapid oxidation of the iron to the tripositive state; one of the functions of the protein in hemoglobin must therefore be the stabilization of the iron(II)-oxygen complex (see page 732), and the protein in cytochrome-c is apparently designed to prevent any kind of reaction with molecular oxygen. The functions of catalase and peroxidase require weak coordination of these compounds with hydrogen peroxide; their protein components are evidently responsible for weakening the rather strong bonds between hydrogen peroxide and hemin. One of the prime effects, therefore, of the presence of proteins in biologically active molecules is to regulate the strength of the bonds between the porphyrin iron atom and various potential coordinating donors to which the iron becomes attached during the course of a catalytic process.

OXIDATION-REDUCTION

Oxidation-reduction reactions are of fundamental importance in biochemical processes; they are of such wide occurrence that one of the chief requirements of an oxidant is its specificity toward a particular substrate. The role of coordination compounds becomes immediately apparent, since coordination of the same metal ion with different donor molecules may result in the formation of complexes exhibiting a wide variation in oxidation potentials (see Chapter 11). Another attribute of complexes which is useful in promoting specificity is their ability to attach themselves to the substrate through functional groups of the donor molecule.

The oxidizing enzymes may be classified into two categories: (1) those that are directly responsible for the oxidation of a substrate, and (2) those that participate in the chain of transmission of the oxidizing power of molecular oxygen to the final substrate. Among the first group are certain enzymes, the reduced form of which can be oxidized by molecular oxygen; these will be discussed in the following section.

Oxidases

Phenol Oxidases. Among the enzymes susceptible to oxidation by molecular oxygen are some that do not contain a porphyrin prosthetic group, but appear to have the metal directly attached to the protein. The most thoroughly investigated of these substances are the phenol oxidases; these are capable of converting phenols or amines to quinones, which, according to Warburg[65], may in turn be instrumental in the oxidation of other

65. Warburg, "Heavy Metal Prosthetic Groups and Enzyme Action," Oxford, Clarendon Press, 1949.

compounds. The metallic component of these enzymes is copper[66], and their oxidizing ability depends upon the reduction of copper(II) to copper(I)[66b, 66c].

Phenol oxidases have been placed in two groups, the monophenol and the polyphenol oxidases[67]. The latter are capable of the rapid oxidation of ortho-diphenolic compounds, and the slower oxidation of monophenolic substances, to quinones. The oxidation of the monophenols is, presumably, a two-step process, consisting of the initial insertion of a hydroxyl group in a position ortho to the already existing one[68], and a subsequent manifestation of polyphenolic oxidase activity. Monophenol oxidases, whose existence is a matter of controversy, are incapable of reacting with diphenol substances.

The behavior of the monophenol and diphenol oxidases may be explained by the hypothesis that a monophenol oxidase contains one readily replaceable coordinated group, being firmly linked to the protein in three positions, whereas diphenol oxidase contains two labile donors, being securely attached to the protein at only one point. The failure of a monophenol oxidase to coordinate with diphenols may then be attributed to steric hindrance, and the ability of a diphenol oxidase to act upon monophenols or diphenols can be explained on the basis of the replacement of either one or both of the labile groups in the formation of the enzyme-substrate complex. Such a scheme could have validity even if the distinction between monophenol and polyphenol oxidases is an artifact; it could then explain the behavior toward phenolic substrates of the oxidases with various modifications of their protein component.

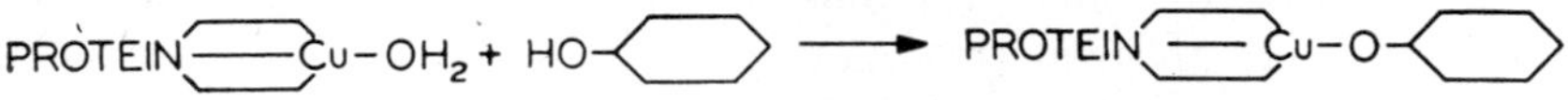

MONOPHENOL OXIDASE

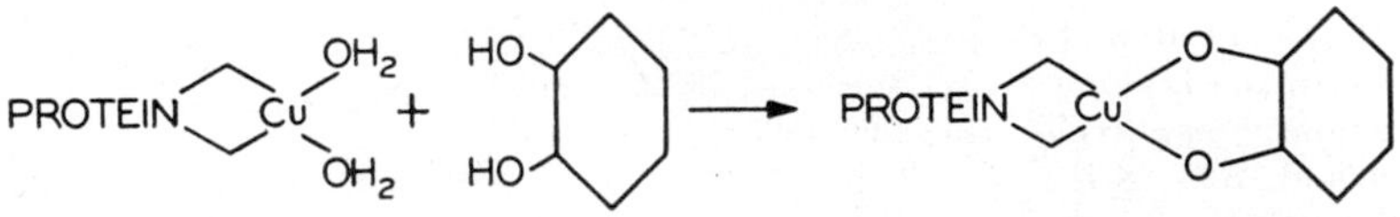

DIPHENOL OXIDASE

66. Kubowitz, *Biochem. Z.*, **292**, 221 (1937); Kubowitz, *ibid.*, **299**, 32 (1939); Keilin and Mann, *Proc. Roy. Soc. London*, **B125**, 187 (1938).
67. Baldwin, Ref. 28b, p. 156.
68. Dawson and Tarpley, Ref. 10, Vol. II, pp. 454–98; Raper, *Ergeb. Enzymforsch.*, **1**, 270 (1932).

Once coordination has been achieved, oxidation presumably occurs through electron transfer from the phenolic group to the copper[69].

Some evidence has been accumulated to suggest that the difference between monophenol and diphenol oxidases may be artificial, and that diphenolases may lose their monophenolase activity as a result of structural modifications during the purification procedure[68a, 70]. According to Dawson and Tarpley[68a], there are only three well-characterized phenol oxidases: tyrosinase, the enzyme responsible for the eventual conversion of tyrosine to a melanine-like substance that accounts for plant and animal pigmentation, laccase[71, 72], a diphenolase without monophenol oxidase activity, and ascorbic acid oxidase, a specific phenol oxidase for the conversion of its substrate to dehydroascorbic acid[73].

Peroxidases and Catalases. In contrast to the phenol oxidases, two groups of autoxidizable redox enzymes, the peroxidases and catalases, have porphyrin prosthetic groups, and as a result much more is known of the way in which iron, their metallic constituent, is bound to the substrate and to the organic portion of the molecule.

Both types of enzymes are associated with the degradation of hydrogen peroxide, which arises as a by-product of the oxidation reactions catalyzed by other enzymes and must be rapidly transformed because of its high toxicity. Catalases are capable of bringing about the decomposition of hydrogen peroxide into water and oxygen[74] and of oxidizing primary and secondary alcohols at the expense of hydrogen peroxide[75]. Whether the first of these two processes is designed to eliminate hydrogen peroxide in an emergency, after too rapid accumulation, has been a controversial issue[76]. Peroxidases cause the oxidation via hydrogen peroxide of a large number of substances, e.g., aminophenols, diamines, diphenols, and some leuco dyes[75b].

69. Martell and Calvin, Ref. 1b, p. 388.
70. Mallette and Dawson, *Arch. Biochem.*, **23**, 29 (1949).
71. Bertrand, *Compt. rend.*, **121**, 166 (1895).
72. Bertrand, *Bull. Soc. Chim. Biol.*, **27**, 396 (1945); Bertrand, *Compt. rend.*, **221**, 35 (1945).
73. Zilva, *Biochem. J.*, **28**, 663 (1934); Tauber, Kleiner, and Mishkind, *J. Biol. Chem.*, **110**, 211 (1935); Tauber and Kleiner, *Proc. Soc. Exptl. Biol. Med.*, **32**, 577 (1935); Srinivasan, *Current Sci.*, **4**, 407 (1935); Ghosh and Guba, *J. Ind. Chem. Soc.*, **14**, 721 (1937); Johnson and Silva, *Biochem. J.*, **31**, 438 (1937); Stotz, *J. Biol. Chem.*, **133**, c (1940); Lovett-Janison and Nelson, *J. Am. Chem. Soc.*, **62**, 1409 (1940).
74. Lemberg and Legge, Ref. 1a, p. 401; Zeile and Hellstroem, *Z. Physiol. Chem.*, **192**, 171 (1930).
75. Keilin and Hartree, *Biochem. J.*, **39**, 293 (1945); Chance, Ref. 10, Vol. II, p. 448.
76. Theorell, *ibid.*, p. 397.

Catalases and peroxidases are iron(III) protoporphyrin complexes[74b, 77] that differ in the nature of the protein component, the principal function of which appears to be the regulation of the lability of hydrogen peroxide in the hydrogen peroxide complex; (a secondary effect of the protein in the case of catalase is a high degree of stabilization of iron(III); unlike the iron in peroxidase, that in catalase cannot be reduced by the action of dithionite[78]). Hemin itself exhibits some catalase activity, but the reaction is very slow because of the relative inertness of the iron-H_2O_2 bond[64a]. This bond has been considerably weakened in peroxidase to permit more rapid reaction, but is most labile in catalase, which, according to some, must function when too much hydrogen peroxide has accumulated. Another apparent difference between the two enzyme types is the existence of only one iron porphyrin prosthetic group in a molecule of peroxidase[79] and of four such groups in a molecule of catalase[80].

It has been concluded from a study of titration data that the iron atom in horseradish peroxidase is coordinated to a carboxyl group of the protein; at the same time one of the propionic acid side chains of the porphyrin may be tied to the protein at another point[81], possibly to a tyrosine hydroxyl group to form an ester type linkage. It has not been definitely established whether the sixth position of the peroxidase, the one to which hydrogen peroxide becomes attached in the catalysis, is occupied by water[82] or a hydroxyl group[81b, 82, 83]. These features have been incorporated in the following diagram:

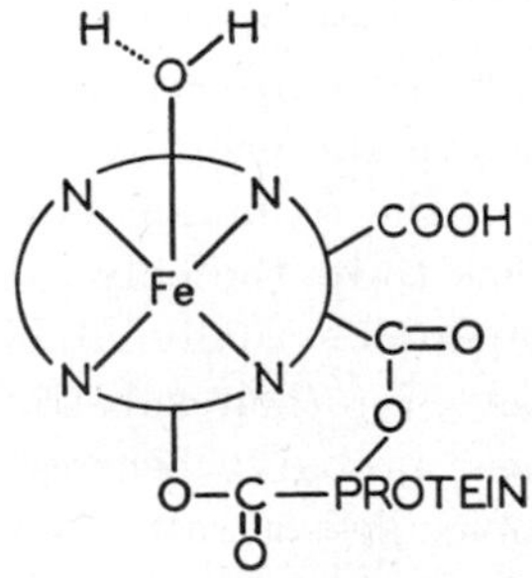

77. Theorell, *Arkiv. Kemi. Mineral. Geol.*, **14B**, No. 20 (1940); Theorell, Bergstrioni, and Alleson, *Arkiv. Kemi. Mineral. Geol.*, **16A**, No. 13 (1942); Stern, *J. Biol. Chem.*, **112**, 661 (1936).
78. Keilin and Hartree, *Biochem. J.*, **39**, 148 (1945).
79. Theorell, *Arkiv. Kemi. Mineral. Geol.*, **15B**, No. 24 (1940).
80. Agner, *ibid;* *16A*, No. 6 (1943); Theorell, *Adv. Enzym.*, **7**, 265 (1947); Lemberg and Legge, Ref. 1a, p. 414.
81. Theorell, *Arkiv. Kemi. Mineral. Geol.*, **16A**, No. 14 (1942); Theorell and Paul, *ibid.*, **18A**, No. 12 (1944).
82. Chance, *Arch. Biochem. Biophys.*, **40**, 153 (1952).
83. Agner and Theorell, *Arch. Biochem.*, **10**, 321 (1946), for catalase.

Unreacted peroxidase contains five unpaired electrons[84], indicating ionic bond character. Substitution of the labile group with fluoride leaves the magnetic moment unchanged, but coordination with cyanide or hydrogen sulfide results in a transition to the covalent type, as manifested by a reduction of the magnetic moment to that corresponding to one unpaired electron[84]. The nitric oxide complex is diamagnetic as a result of the pairing of the unpaired electrons of the metal and donor molecules and reduction of the iron(III) to iron(II) by the nitric oxide. Carbon monoxide produces a diamagnetic, covalent complex with the reduced form of the peroxidase, but it does not inhibit the activity of the enzyme, since that depends upon the availability of the oxidized form of the molecule.

Because of the lability of the complexes of catalases and peroxidases with hydrogen peroxide their investigation has proved to be a more difficult task than is the study of the complexes with the inhibitors; Chance has been able to overcome this difficulty with a good deal of success by application of a technique for the study of extremely rapid reactions[85]; he has proposed the existence of four types of complexes between enzyme and peroxides[86]. The most significant of these are the "primary enzyme-substrate compounds," and the "secondary enzyme-substrate compounds" that are formed initially by a change in the structure of the primary complexes[87]. The spectra of the primary compounds suggest that the hydrogen peroxide molecule, in addition to its coordination with iron, is also somehow tied to a methene bridge of the porphine ring[86]. The spectra of the secondary compounds resemble those of the cyanide and hydrogen sulfide complexes[87c]; hence they are probably simple coordination compounds. In peroxidases the formation of the primary and secondary compounds is essential if the reaction with the reductant is to occur[88], but in catalases the primary compound seems to be the only catalytically active component, and the secondary compound actually inhibits catalase activity[89].

The specificity of catalases for their substrate is considerably greater than that of the peroxidases, probably because the catalase protein permits reaction only with molecules of restricted size and shape (activity toward alkyl peroxidases decreases with chain length) and the peroxidase prosthetic group apparently lies exposed, thus minimizing steric hindrance in the coordination with a substrate[86].

84. Theorell, *Arkiv. Kemi. Mineral. Geol.*, **16A**, No. 3 (1942).
85. Chance, *Rev. Sci. Instruments*, **18,** 601 (1947).
86. Chance, Ref. 10, Vol. II, p. 440.
87. Chance, *J. Biol. Chem.*, **179,** 1331, 1341 (1949); Chance, *J. Am. Chem. Soc.*, **72,** 1577 (1950); Chance, *Arch. Biochem.*, **21,** 416 (1949).
88. Chance, *Arch. Biochem.*, **22,** 224 (1949).
89. Chance, *J. Biol. Chem.*, **179,** 1341 (1949).

Dehydrogenases

Many redox enzymes cannot react directly with molecular oxygen, and are therefore reoxidized through the cytochrome system. Some of these enzymes such as yeast lactic acid dehydrogenase, which catalyzes the interconversion of pyruvic acid and lactic acid[90], may be metalloproteins. The hydrogenase enzymes can catalyze the reaction of molecular hydrogen with oxygen to form water, with carbon dioxide to produce formic acid, etc.[91]. Evidence for the presence of a hematin prosthetic group in this enzyme consists of the inhibition by cyanide ion in the oxidized, but not in the reduced form, inhibition by carbon monoxide[93], but only in the dark, and the fact that deficiency of iron in organisms induces decreased hydrogenase activity[91, 94].

It should be pointed out that, of the known dehydrogenases, those that have been shown to be metal complexes are very much in the minority.

The Cytochrome System

The enzymes that act as the middlemen in the delivery of the oxidizing power of molecular oxygen to the eventual substrate belong to the cytochrome system; these are a group of iron-porphyrin-protein complexes that differ from each other in the nature of the protein[95], and possibly in the attachment of the latter to the prosthetic group. The need for the cytochrome system apparently arises from the fact that autoxidation of most substrates would entail such high oxidation potentials that the cells would be damaged or destroyed[96]. The existence of the system thus substitutes a series of redox reactions of low potential for one such reaction whose potential is too high. The order in which the various cytochromes take part in the scheme is not at all definite at this time. It appears certain that cytochrome oxidase is oxidized directly by the oxygen that it receives from oxyhemoglobin. Cytochrome oxidase, in turn, may act upon cytochrome-*a*, which oxidizes cytochrome-*c*, which in turn acts upon cytochrome-*b*[96].

Cytochrome-*c*. Of the various components of the cytochrome system, present structural knowledge is most adequate for cytochrome-*c*, because that compound is the only soluble, and therefore easily separable, member of the group.

90. Bach, Dixon, and Zerfas, *Biochem. J.*, **40**, 229 (1946).
91. Umbreit, Ref. 10, Vol. II, Chapt. 54; Green and Strickland, *Biochem. J.*, **28**, 898 (1934); Stephenson and Strickland, *ibid.*, **26**, 712 (1932); **27**, 1517, 1528 (1933).
93. Hoberman and Rittenberg, *J. Biol. Chem.*, **147**, 211 (1943).
94. Waring and Werkman, *Arch. Biochem.*, **1**, 425 (1942–3); **4**, 75 (1944).
95. Warburg, Ref. 65, p. 66.
96. Lemberg and Legge, Ref. 1a, p. 376.

The magnetic moment of ferrocytochrome-*c* is zero[97]. That of ferricyto-chrome-*c* is pH dependent, and five different spectrophotometrically distinguishable species of the oxidized form of the enzyme have been dis-covered[99]. Two of these forms are found in highly acid solutions (pH = 0.7 and 1.4) and have five unpaired electrons, but the three species that pre-dominate at higher pH levels (starting at pH 4.75) have only one such electron[99]. It thus appears that the iron of cytochrome-*c*, except in the oxidized state in highly acid solution, is essentially covalently bound, in contrast to the iron in peroxidase and catalase. In line with this indicated stability, cytochrome-*c* does not react readily with oxygen, carbon monox-ide, hydrogen sulfide, azide, and similar coordinating agents[97]; indeed, it had been believed for some time that no such reaction occurs. The reac-tion of ferrocytochrome-*c* with carbon monoxide[97] and of ferricytochrome-*c* with cyanide[100] and azide[101] has now been demonstrated, but the rate of formation of the former, and the stability of the latter, are so low as to render any physiological importance of these compounds quite unlikely[99]. The cytochromes are the only known naturally occurring iron-porphyrin complexes whose biochemical function may not involve a change in the coordination sphere of the metal ion.

Each molecule of cytochrome-*c* contains one hematin group[102], which is apparently bound to the protein at four places. The two coordination positions of the iron that are unoccupied by the porphyrin nitrogens are apparently attached to a basic donor in the protein since cytochrome-*c* has a hemochrome type spectrum[103]; titration data indicate that the donor may be histidine imidazole[97]. The other two links between protein and the prosthetic group involve the side chains of the porphyrin[103]. The par-ticular porphyrin that can be isolated from cytochrome-*c* resembles proto-porphyrin in all aspects but one; namely, the addition of two cysteine molecules across the double bonds of the vinyl groups[104]. These cysteine molecules are the terminal groups of the protein; the firmness of the attach-ment of protein to prosthetic group in this compound is evidenced by the fact that the iron may be removed without disturbing this attachment. The structure of cytochrome-*c* may then be represented as follows:

97. Theorell and Akesson, *J. Am. Chem. Soc.*, **63**, 1804, 1812, 1818, 1820 (1941).
99. Paul, Ref. 10, Vol. II, p. 376.
100. Horecker and Kornberg, *J. Biol. Chem.*, **165**, 11 (1946); Potter, *ibid.*, **137**, 13 (1941).
101. Horecker and Stannard, *J. Biol. Chem.*, **172**, 589 (1948).
102. Theorell, *Biochem. Z.*, **279**, 463 (1935); **285**, 207 (1936); Zeile and Reuter, *Z. Phys. Chem.*, **221**, 101 (1933); Ref. 97.
103. Lemberg and Legge, Ref. 1a, p. 351.
104. Hill and Keilin, *Proc. Roy. Soc. London*, **107B**, 286 (1930); Theorell, *Biochem. Z.*, **301**, 201 (1939); **298**, 242 (1938).

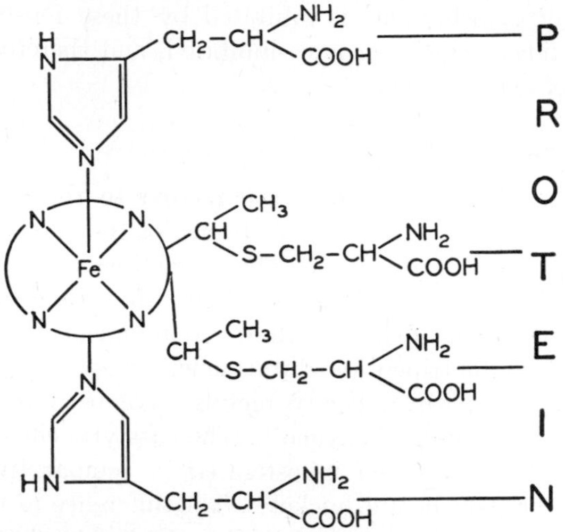

Although cytochrome-c itself does not react with molecular oxygen it may be converted by the action of pepsin into an autoxidizable fragment of one-sixth of the total molecular weight of the enzyme[105].

Cytochromes a and b. Not much is known about the structure of these components of the cytochrome system. Both are apparently mixtures of substances, but one of the presumed components of cytochrome-a is now believed to be identical with cytochrome oxidase[106].

Cytochrome Oxidase. The porphyrin of cytochrome oxidase differs from protoporphyrin in the substitution of a CHO group for the methyl group in the 3-position[107]. The properties of the compound have been investigated mainly through spectrophotometric measurements and inhibition techniques[108]. Since the oxidase is inhibited by carbon monoxide, which prevents oxidation of the reduced form[108, 109], and by cyanide,[109] sulfide, and azide, which prevent reduction of the oxidized form[110], the presence of a labile coordinate link is indicated, suggesting that oxidation of cytochrome oxidase may take place through the formation of an unstable oxygen complex intermediate.

That cytochrome oxidase is essential to the oxidation of the cytochromes[111] has been demonstrated by the observation that, even though complexes of cytochrome-c with cyanide and azide are extremely unstable,

105. Tsou, *Nature*, **164**, 1134 (1949).
106. Keilin and Hartree, *Proc. Roy. Soc. London*, **127B**, 167 (1939).
107. Paul, Ref. 10, Vol. II, p. 363.
108. Warburg, *Biochem. Z.*, **177**, 471 (1926); Warburg, *Naturwiss.*, **15**, 546 (1927).
109. Krebs, *Biochem. Z.*, **193**, 347 (1928); **204**, 322 (1929).
110. Keilin, *Proc. Roy. Soc. London*, **104B**, 206 (1929); **121B**, 165 (1936).
111. Warburg, *Naturwiss.*, **22**, 441 (1934).

the oxidation of cytochrome-c is inhibited by these ions[110]. Actually it must be the oxidase which becomes inhibited, and therefore incapable of the oxidation of cytochrome-c.

The Cysteine-Cystine System

Many biological redox reactions are related to the oxidation of the sulfhydryl group of cysteine, and the reverse of that reaction, the reduction of the disulfide link of cystine. These reactions may not involve free cysteine or cystine molecules; it is more likely that these substances function as part of a protein, their immediate environment in many substances being suggested by the tripeptide glutathione.

Pure cysteine, from which heavy metals have been removed, is very slowly oxidized by molecular oxygen[113]. The catalytic effect of metal ions upon this oxidation has been investigated in comparative experiments with divalent iron, cobalt, and nickel[114]. The difference in the behavior of the three ions in their reaction with cysteine is highly instructive in view of the specificity of metal ions in biochemical reactions. All three metal ions react with cysteine in the absence or in the presence of oxygen; only in the case of nickel are the complexes produced under the two conditions identical, indicating that the nickel complex is the only one that is not susceptible to oxidation.

The cobalt(II) complex does absorb oxygen; quantitative determinations of oxygen uptake have revealed that the amount of oxygen consumed depends upon the cobalt concentration, if cysteine is in excess, and upon the cysteine concentration, if cobalt is in excess. In either case, one-half mole, and no more, of oxygen is consumed per mole of cobalt or three moles of cysteine, and no free cystine is produced. The oxidized molecule is apparently the 1:3 cobalt(III) cysteine complex:

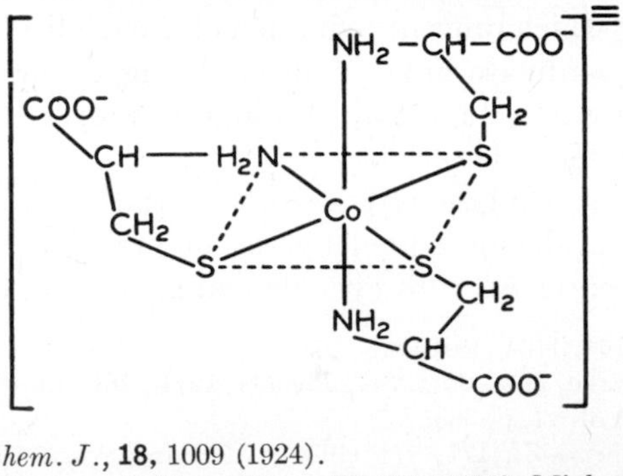

113. Harrison, *Biochem. J.*, **18**, 1009 (1924).
114. Michaelis and Barron, *J. Biol. Chem.*, **83**, 191 (1929); Michaelis and Yamaguchi, *ibid.*, **83**, 367 (1929); Michaelis, *ibid.*, **84**, 777 (1929); Schubert, *J. Am. Chem. Soc.*, **53**, 3851 (1931).

The reaction with iron is quite different from that with cobalt. The oxygen uptake depends upon the cysteine concentration, even when the latter is present in great excess. The introduction of oxygen (air) into such a solution results in the formation of a violet color that fades upon standing, only to be revived by repeated shaking with air, until all of the cysteine has been completely consumed. The violet complex is probably tris(cysteine)-iron(III), analogous to the cobalt complex pictured above. It is apparently readily transformed into the 1:1:1 iron(II) cysteine-cystine complex:

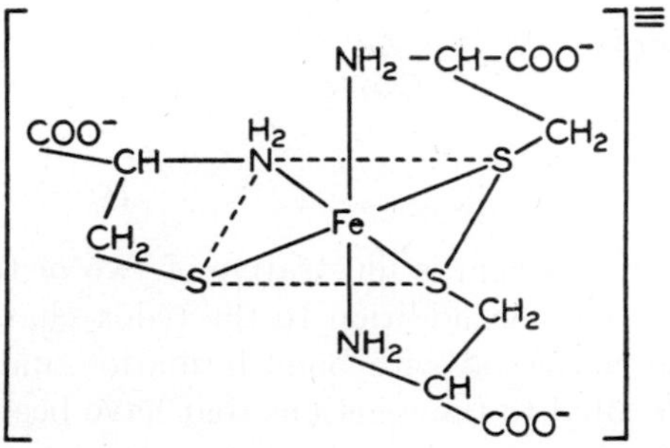

Because of the instability of the three-membered chelate ring, the cystine molecule is subsequently lost, replaced by two more cysteines, and the cyclic process is renewed. Thus iron can serve as a catalyst for the oxidation of cysteine to cystine. Nickel cannot take its place because it is too difficult to oxidize, and cobalt cannot function because of the high stability of the cobalt(III) complex.

Michaelis and Schubert postulate that the metal may be bound to the carboxyl and sulfur groups of cysteine as it is in the complexes of thioglycolic acid, which they also investigated[115], and which bear some resemblance to the complexes of cysteine. Martell and Calvin[1b] have pointed out that in the light of present knowledge and experimental data it is more appropriate to assume that the amino groups, rather than the carboxyl groups, are coordinated. Further support for the latter theory may be gained from the observation that the glutathione sulfhydryl group may be oxidized by iron in a fashion that resembles the oxidation of cysteine; a similar violet color is produced during the progress of the oxidation[113]. In glutathione, coordination of the carboxyl group of cystine is prevented through the engagement of the latter in a peptide bond. It is possible that the glycine carboxyl group participates in the chelation; in any case, the

115. Michaelis and Schubert, *J. Am. Chem. Soc.*, **52**, 4418 (1930); Schubert, *J. Am. Chem. Soc.*, **54**, 4077 (1932).

possible structures (A) and (B) both involve nitrogen coordination:

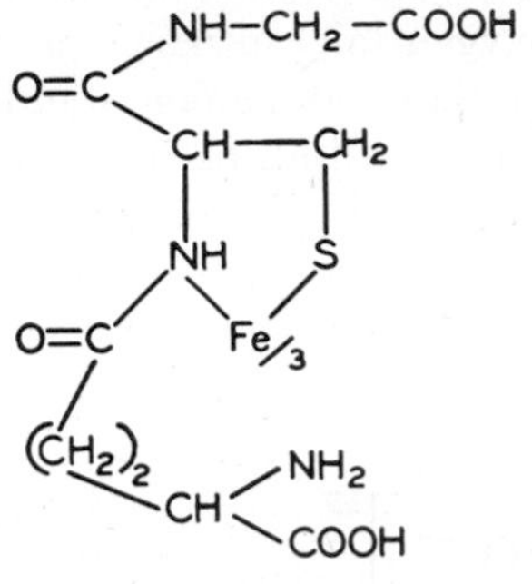

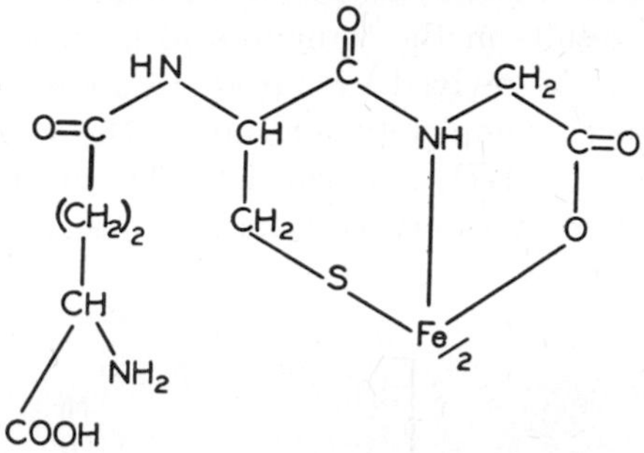

A   B

The cysteine-cystine system is illustrative of two of the catalytic functions of metal ions, since, in addition to the redox character of the reactions, they are also concerned with bond formation and cleavage, and in this sense may be related to the reactions that have been considered in an earlier section.

STORAGE AND TRANSFER

A common feature of the coordination compounds described up to this point is their role as catalysts in chemical reactions. The nature of coordination compounds would suggest another role—the storage and transfer of either metal ions or donor molecules. Complexes which perform such functions, as well as some whose biochemical function is not yet understood, will be considered in this section.

The Transportation of Oxygen

Hemoglobin. Of all iron porphyrin complexes, the hemoglobin molecule is uniquely constructed for the purpose of oxygen transport. Unproteinated ferroheme compounds form extremely unstable complexes with oxygen; they are easily transformed to the iron(III) complexes. On the other hand, when the protein is linked as in reduced cytochrome-c, the heme iron is not affected by oxygen at all. Hemoglobin represents an intermediate stage; it is a molecule capable of complexing with oxygen without a resultant oxidation of the iron. The stability of the iron to oxygen linkage must be great enough to prevent decomposition of the oxyhemoglobin during its circulation through the body, yet weak enough to permit dissociation when contact with an oxidase has been established. Just how the globin-heme linkage satisfies all of these requirements cannot be understood until the nature of the globin has been further elucidated.

The prosthetic group of hemoglobin is iron(II) protoporphyrin (heme). It is believed that the propionic acid carboxyl groups of the porphyrin are tied to the protein as in horseradish peroxidase[116] (page 725). It has been established further that the protein is also linked to the heme by coordination with iron, but whether this occurs at one or two points, and through what basic group of the protein, are issues which have not yet been settled.

The theory that iron is coordinated to globin through two histidine imidazole groups is based upon studies of the pH dependent factor in the heat of oxygenation of hemoglobin, which corresponds to the heat of dissociation of histidine[117], and upon a difference in the titration curves of hemoglobin and oxyhemoglobin, that has been interpreted as reflecting the presence in hemoglobin of an imidazole grouping whose acidity increases upon oxygenation as a result of removal from the iron coordination sphere[118]. According to this view one histidine is more tightly bound than the other by virtue of a more favorable spatial relationship; upon oxygenation the "proximal" histidine remains coordinated, while the "distal" histidine dissociates.

There is, however, some objection to the "imidazole hypothesis", based on the ability of the oxylabile group to react with carbon dioxide to produce carbamino compounds, a reaction not shown by imidazole itself[119]. Moreover, Haurowitz has accumulated evidence[120] in favor of the theory that globin is bound to iron at only one point, and that the group displaced by oxygen is actually a water molecule. He has shown that at low water vapor pressures the spectrum of hemoglobin is converted to a hemochromogen-like spectrum, a phenomenon that can be reversed by raising the humidity, whereas the spectrum of oxyhemoglobin is independent of the water vapor pressure. These facts lead to the conclusion that hemoglobin contains coordinated water which may be removed through dehumidification of the environment, or through displacement by oxygen.

From the composition and molecular weight[121] of hemoglobin it has been concluded that each molecule contains four heme groups, and it has

116. Granick, *Chem. Eng. News*, **51**, 668 (1953).
117. Wyman, *J. Biol. Chem.*, **127**, 1, 581 (1939).
118. Wyman and Ingalls, *ibid.*, **139**, 877 (1941); Coryell and Pauling, *J. Biol. Chem.*, **132**, 769 (1940).
119. Roughton, *Harvey Lectures*, **39**, 96 (1944); Lemberg and Legge, Ref. 1a, p. 238.
120. Haurowitz, "Hemoglobin," Roughton and Kendrew, p. 53, Barcroft Symposium, New York, Interscience Publishers, Inc., 1949; Haurowitz, *J. Biol. Chem.*, **193**, 443 (1951).
121. Adair, *Proc. Roy. Soc. London*, **108A**, 627 (1924); Svedberg and Nichols, *J. Am. Chem. Soc.*, **49**, 2920 (1927); Svedberg and Fahraeus, *ibid.*, **48**, 430 (1926).

been shown that these lie on the surface of the globin molecule[122]. All of the known and postulated structural characteristics of the coordination chemistry of hemoglobin have been incorporated in the following two diagrams:

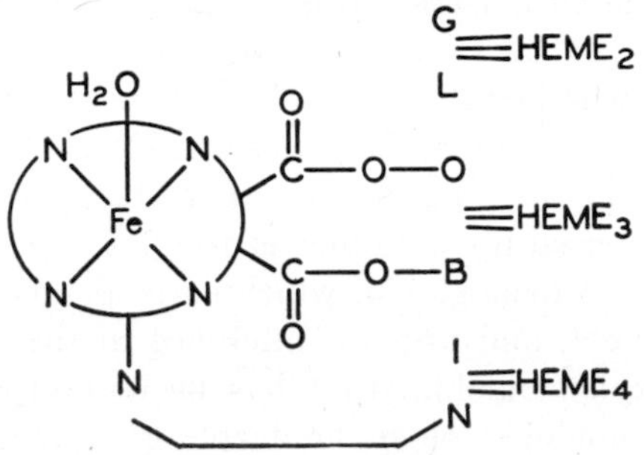

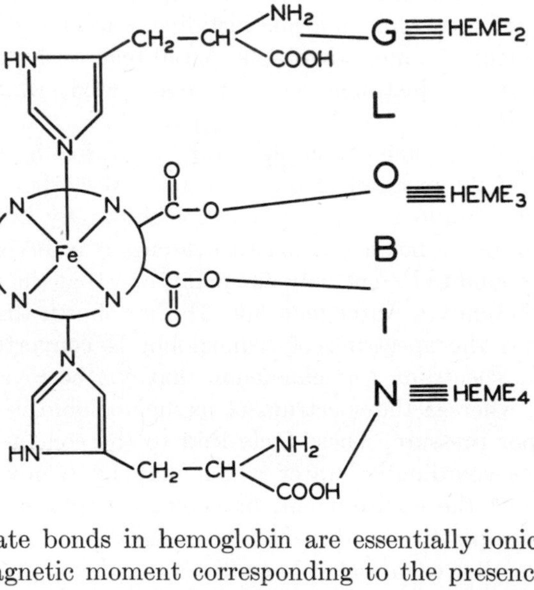

The coordinate bonds in hemoglobin are essentially ionic[54b], as manifested by a magnetic moment corresponding to the presence of four unpaired electrons; consequently the molecule is susceptible to reaction not only with oxygen, but with the usual monodentate complexing agents[123]. Oxyhemoglobin and carbonmonoxyhemoglobin are diamagnetic, indicating that the replacement of the water molecule (or "distal" imidazole group) causes the iron to form octahedral covalent bonds with the donor atoms. Hemiglobin (methemoglobin), which may be produced by oxidation of hemoglobin with a number of oxidants, e.g., potassium ferricyanide or

122. Granick, *J. Gen. Physiol.*, **25**, 571 (1942).
123. Stitt and Coryell, *J. Am. Chem. Soc.*, **61**, 1263 (1939); Holden, *Australian J. Exptl. Biol. Med. Sci.*, **21**, 159 (1943); Hill, *Biochem. J.*, **19**, 341 (1925).

copper(II) ion, contains five unpaired electrons[124]; oxidation of the iron atom thus has no effect upon the ionic character of the bonds emanating from it. The magnetic moment of hemiglobin, like that of hemoglobin, is diminished as a result of complexation with cyanide, nitric oxide, etc.; however, only in the case of the nitric oxide complex does the magnetic moment correspond to that calculated from the spin contribution. Pauling[125] has recalculated magnetic moments on the assumption that the orbital contribution may not be neglected, and has shown that a large variation is possible, since the unpaired electron may be in the $3d$ or the $4p$ shell, or a hybrid of these two energy states.

Hemoglobin coordinates more strongly with carbon monoxide[126] than with oxygen; the latter is readily displaced by carbon monoxide groups, the toxicity of which may therefore be attributed to its ability to render the hemoglobin molecule incapable of performing its oxygen-carrying function.

Hemocyanin. In addition to hemoglobin, one other natural product is concerned with the oxygen transport function; this is the copper(I) protein, hemocyanin, which is found in invertebrate animals[127]. Like hemoglobin, this substance is capable of reversible reaction with oxygen, cyanide, and carbon monoxide[128]; the stability of carbonmonoxyhemocyanin is very low. Evidence for and against the presence of a porphyrin in hemocyanin is inconclusive; and almost nothing is known of the structure of this compound. It is of considerable interest, however, that nature has perfected the synthesis of oxygen-carrying compounds utilizing two metals that are as different in their properties as copper and iron.

Synthetic Oxygen-carrying Chelates. A complete understanding of the oxygen-carrying ability of hemoglobin and hemocyanin is limited by the lack of knowledge of protein structure. For this reason the study of two types of oxygen-carrying complexes unencumbered by protein molecules has been undertaken in the hope that these simple models may prove useful in throwing light upon the more complicated natural products. These are the cobalt(II) complexes of bis(salicylaldehyde)ethylenediamine[129] and their derivatives, and the cobalt(II) complexes of histidine[130].

124. Ref. 54d.
125. Pauling, Ref. 120a, p. 162.
126. Lemberg and Legge, Ref. 1a, p. 215.
127. Dawson and Mallette, *Adv. Prot. Chem.*, **II,** 179 (1945).
128. Wolvekamp, Ref. 120a, p. 301.
129. Pfeiffer, Breit, Luebbe, and Tsumaki, *Ann.*, **503,** 84 (1933); Tsumaki, *Bull. Chem. Soc. Japan,* **13,** 252 (1938); Calvin and co-workers (Bailes, Wilmarth, Barkelew, Aranoff, Hughes, and Harle), *J. Am. Chem. Soc.*, **68,** 2254, 2257, 2263, 2273, 2612 (1946).
130. Burke, Hearon, Caroline, and Schade, *J. Biol. Chem.*, **165,** 723 (1946); Michaelis, *Arch. Biochem.*, **14,** 17 (1942); Hearon, Burke, and Schade, *J. Natl. Cancer Inst.*, **9,** 337 (1949).

For a discussion of the structural features of these interesting materials the reader is referred to the treatise by Martell and Calvin[1b] (see also Chapter 1). It has been concluded from a study of the polarographic half-wave potentials for the reduction of oxygen in the presence of various chelating agents related to the oxygen carriers that the oxygen-carrying ability of a molecule is related to its ability to catalyze the reduction of oxygen. This property is determined by the ability of the metal to furnish electrons to oxygen, which may, in turn, be correlated with the stability of the complex.

It is noteworthy that only cobalt, of all the metals in the first transition series, can serve in these simple oxygen-carrying chelates; iron(II) is irreversibly oxidized, and the copper(II) and nickel(II) complexes have little tendency to react with oxygen at all. The hemoglobin molecule has been so constructed that the coordination of iron(II) with oxygen is stabilized; there is therefore an analogy between cobalt in the model compounds and iron in hemoglobin. Because of this stabilizing ability of the organic portion of the hemoglobin molecule, cobalt hemoglobin does not readily react with oxygen, and this substance is therefore analogous to the copper and nickel complexes of the models.

Storage of Metal Ions

Ferritin. The synthesis of so important and elaborate a molecule as hemoglobin is undoubtedly a complicated process, the nature of which is being slowly unravelled. An important advance in this direction has been the discovery of ferritin, an iron(III) protein complex, whose sole function appears to be the storage of iron until it is needed for hemoglobin synthesis[131].

The molecule has evidently been exceedingly well constructed for the efficient storage of iron, since from 17 to 23 per cent of its total weight consists of this metal. The iron may be removed by treatment of ferritin with sodium thiosulfate and by dialaysis of the iron(II) as the dipyridyl complex. It is not possible to reconvert the apoferritin thus produced to ferritin by the readdition of iron either in the form of its divalent or trivalent salts or as a colloidal suspension of iron(III) hydroxide.

The magnetic moment of ferritin, like that of hematin and some of the methemoglobin derivatives (page 734), corresponds to the presence of three unpaired electrons per iron atom. The structure of ferritin is believed to involve long chains or layers of protein through peptide bonds. Thus there may be some analogy between the structures of ferritin and the chromium complex produced in the tanning of leather.

Hemocuprein, and the Requirements of Copper in Hemoglobin

131. Michaelis, *Adv. Prot. Chem.*, III, 53 (1947).

Synthesis. Mann and Keilin[132] have isolated from blood cells a metallo-protein containing 0.34 per cent copper that is so loosely held that it is removed by treatment with trichloroacetic acid. The function of "hemocuprein" is not known; it is possible, however, that the compound is concerned with the role of copper in the synthesis of hemoglobin. A large number of experiments have proved that copper in trace amounts is essential for this synthesis[133]; for example, the administration of iron does not aid an anemic animal in hemoglobin production unless the iron is accompanied by copper[134, 135]. The latter, moreover, is quite specific in its action; substitution of any of a large variety of other metal ions has proved ineffective[134b].

The suggestion that copper is active in porphyrin formation[136] and is subsequently replaced from the porphyrin complex by iron appears to be inconsistent with the observation that the addition of iron as the porphyrin complex has no effect on hemoglobin synthesis in the absence of copper[137]. Moreover, since copper forms more stable complexes with the porphyrins than does iron, it is difficult to envisage such a replacement reaction. On the other hand, it is more plausible to assume that the function of copper is the liberation of iron from ferritin; perhaps the hemocuprein molecule approaches a molecule of ferritin, and, as a result of the attraction of copper for the ferritin protein, the latter becomes detached from iron, which is then free to enter into the hemoglobin production sequence. It is possible also that copper is responsible for the coordination of iron to globin at the proper places by blocking other positions on the globin, which might otherwise become attached. Our understanding of the function of hemocuprein and the role of copper in hemoglobin synthesis leaves much to be desired.

Cyanocobalamin. Another coordination compound that may play a part in hemoglobin synthesis is the anti-anemic cobalt-containing vitamin B_{12}, cyanocobalamin[138-143]. Knowledge of the structure of the compound

132. Mann and Keilin, *Nature*, **142**, 148 (1938).
133. Josephs, *J. Biol. Chem.*, **96**, 559 (1932).
134. Elvehjem and Hart, *ibid.*, **95**, 363 (1932); Keil and Nelson, *ibid.*, **93**, 49 (1931); Hart, Steenback, Waddell, and Elvehjem, *ibid.*, **77**, 777 (1928); Elvehjem, *Physiol. Rev.*, **15**, 471 (1935).
135. Polonovsky and Briskas, *Compt. Rend. Soc. Biol.*, **129**, 379 (1938).
136. Cunningham, *Biochem. J.*, **25**, 1267 (1931).
137. Kohler, Elvehjem, and Hart, *J. Biol. Chem.*, **128**, 501 (1939).
138. Diehl, *Rec. Chem. Progress*, **13**, 9 (1952).
139. Buchanan, Johnson, Mills, and Todd, *J. Chem. Soc.*, **1950**, 2845.
140. Schmid, Abnoether, and Karrer, *Helv. chim. Acta*, **36**, 65 (1953).
141. Diehl, Van der Haar, and Sealock, *J. Am. Chem. Soc.*, **72**, 5312 (1950).
142. Brink, Kuehl, and Folkers, *Science*, **112**, 354 (1950).
143. Brockmann, Roth, Broquist, Hultquist, Smith, Fahrenbach, Cosulich, Parker, Stohstad, and Jukes, *J. Am. Chem. Soc.*, **72**, 4325 (1950).

is constantly increasing, since this recently discovered vitamin is receiving a great deal of attention.*

Acid hydrolysis of the vitamin yields a nucleotide and two moles of ethanolamine in addition to a large molecule to which the cobalt is still attached[139]. Whether either the nucleotide or the ethanolamine is coordinated to cobalt has not been ascertained, although it has been the subject of considerable speculation. When the cobalt-containing hydrolysis product is subjected to oxidation by 5 per cent aqueous permanganate, eight organic acids are produced, among them oxalic, succinic, and methyl- and dimethyl- succinic acids, in addition to four others whose structures are undetermined[140].

The oxidation state of cobalt in the vitamin is plus three, as has been deduced from the fact that the substance is diamagnetic[141]. An unusual feature of the vitamin, in view of its biological importance, is that one of the coordination positions of the cobalt is occupied by a cyanide ion[142]. The cyanide may be replaced by hydroxide through acid hydrolysis[144, 145], and treating with base yielding hydroxocobalamin, another compound that is frequently associated with the vitamin; it may be reconverted into the vitamin, cyanocobalamin, by treatment with cyanide ion.

When hydroxocobalamin is dissolved, it is supposed that the hydroxide group leaves the coordination sphere, and is replaced by water, thus forming aquocobalamin hydroxide[145]. This substance gives two different responses when it is treated with various anions. Reaction with cyanide (yielding the vitamin), nitrite, or thiocyanate results in the displacement of the water molecule from the coordination sphere. Chloride and sulfate, on the other hand, are not capable of this kind of substitution, and consequently they simply replace the hydroxide anion, forming the respective aquocobalamin salts[146]. The reaction of aquocobalamin hydroxide with basic groups, e.g., ammonia, amino acids, peptides, etc., also leads to the replacement of coordinated water; these substances have been termed "cobalichromes," in analogy with the hemichromes[145, 147]. It has been suggested that the biological action of cyanocobalamin involves an equilibrium with cobalichromes, and that the cyanide ion functions in the inhibition of various enzymes[145a].

* Note added in proof: The elucidation of the structure of vitamin B_{12} is an outstanding example of the rapid progress made in the coordination chemistry of natural products since this chapter was written. See *Nature* **176**, 325, 328 (1955).

144. Veer, Edelhauser, Wijmenga, and Lens, *Biochem. Biophys. Acta*, **6**, 225 (1950); Wijmenga, Veer, and Lens, *ibid.*, **6**, 229 (1950).
145. Cooley, Ellis, Petrow, Beaven, Holiday, and Johnson, *J. Pharm. Pharmacol.*, **3**, 271 (1951); Buhs, Newstead, and Trenner, *Science*, **113**, 625 (1951).
146. Ellis and Petrow, *J. Pharm. Pharmacol.*, **4**, 152 (1952); Welch and Nichol, *Ann. Rev. Biochem.*, **21**, 646 (1952).
147. Petrow, unpublished work; *ibid.*, **21**, 647.

When cyanocobalamin is treated with an excess of cyanide ion, one other coordinated group is replaced, yielding the dicyano complex[145a]; this reaction reveals that the vitamin contains only one weak coordinate covalent bond. X-ray studies have indicated that the four strongly co-ordinated groups, irreplaceable by cyanide, are coplanar; as a result it has been proposed that cobalamin may be a porphyrin complex. A recent study has shown that hydrogenation of vitamin B_{12} in the presence of PtO_2 results in the liberation of five to six moles of ammonia[140]; the sub-sequent discovery that a large number of cobalt ammines lose their ammonia when subjected to the same treatment led to the suggestion that ammonia may also be coordinated to cobalt in the vitamin. It appears, however, that such coordination is unlikely, in view of the inertness of the coordinated groups in question toward reaction with cyanide ion.

Polarographic reduction of the vitamin has been interpreted as indicating a two-electron reduction to a cobalt(I) complex[138]. Reduction via platinum catalyzed hydrogenation[138] leads to a complex of cobalt(II) that can be reoxidized to cobalt(III) with ferricyanide, or by treatment with excess cyanide ion, which results in the formation of the dicyano complex. The polarographic wave of the cobalt(II) complex indicates two one-electron reductions, and the ultimate conversion to metallic cobalt.

Calcium Proteinates. It has been estimated that half of the calcium present in blood plasma is in the form of ionic calcium, and that the other half is coordinated to a protein. It has been proposed that the function of the calcium-protein complex is the regulation of the ionic calcium content[148].

TRANSMISSION OF ENERGY—CHLOROPHYLL

Many of the coordination compounds that have been discussed through-out this chapter are important both in plant and animal metabolism. The best known and most unique complex of plant materials is the chlorophyll molecule, whose function is the capture of photons of light and their trans-mission to a system which may convert them into the energy required for a chemical reaction.

Calvin[149] has pointed out that a possible specific point to which the light energy may be transferred by chlorophyll is the disulfide link in 6,8-thioctic acid,

$$
\begin{array}{c}
CH_2 \\
\diagup \quad \diagdown \\
CH_2 \qquad CH—(CH_2)_4—COOH \\
\diagdown \quad \diagup \\
S—S
\end{array}
$$

a compound capable of promoting the oxidative decarboxylation of pyruvic

148. Greenberg, *Adv. Prot. Chem.*, **I**, 147 (1944).
149. Calvin, *Ind. Eng. News*, **31**, 1735 (1953).

acid into acetyl, which may then be fed into the tricarboxylic acid cycle of the "dark reaction" of photosynthesis. Through the agency of chlorophyll, however, the energy for the dissociation of the disulfide bond may be delivered to this molecule in the presence of light. Since the "dark reaction" depends upon the existence of the disulfide, the "dark reaction" stops; at the same time the free radical sulfur atoms, produced as a result of the cleavage, become active in the reducing portion of the photosynthetic cycle, the so-called "light reaction," whose ultimate goal is the fixation of carbon dioxide, and which is accompanied by the elimination of molecular oxygen.

The structure of the chlorophyll molecule as it occurs in the natural state is not known, since the protein component is dissociated from the prosthetic group during the extraction of chlorophyll. The prosthetic group itself exists in various modifications, all of which are complexes of magnesium with porphyrins. The predominant chlorophyll type in green plants is chlorophyll-a, which has the structure[150];

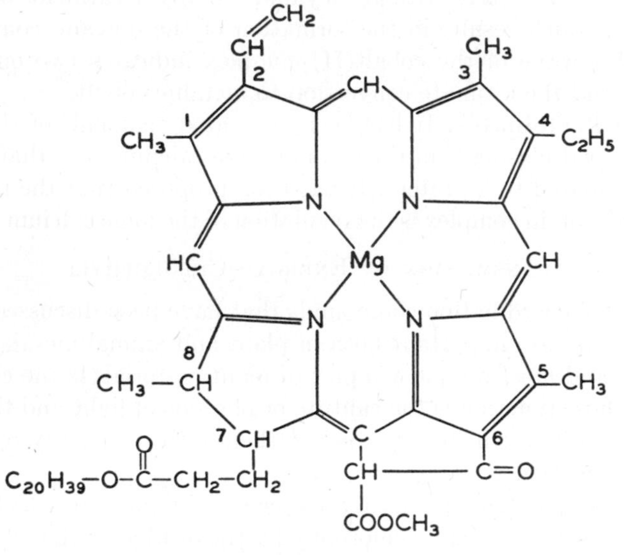

The other chlorophylls have prosthetic groups that differ in only a few respects; chlorophyll-b, for example, has a formyl group substituted for the 3-methyl, and bacteriochlorophyll has an acetyl in place of the vinyl group at position 2, while the 3 and 4 pyrrole carbon atoms have been reduced[151].

150. Fischer, *Naturwiss.*, **28**, 401 (1940).
151. Rabinowitsch, "Photosynthesis," I, Chapt. 16, New York, Interscience Publishers, Inc., 1945; Loomis, Ref. 10, Vol. II, p. 1059.

The ability of the chlorophyll molecule to act as an agent for the transmission of light energy is due to its capacity to absorb light and to be raised to an excited energy state. The factors that influence this excitation are also the factors that determine the absorption spectrum[152]; analyses of the spectra of chlorophyll and related compounds have shown that the reduction of one of the pyrrole rings[153] and the introduction of magnesium[154] are the two most important structural modifications of protoporphyrin that affect the absorption spectrum and give the characteristic green color[155].

The chlorophyll molecule in the excited state may regain its ground state condition by a variety of paths[156]; among these are luminescence, and the transfer of energy to a chemical reaction system. Models have been devised, in which chlorophyll has been permitted to initiate reactions other than photosynthesis[157]; of more importance from the point of view of coordination chemistry, it has been demonstrated that the magnesium complex of phthalocyanine, in hot hydrocarbon solvents, exhibits both the phenomenon of luminescence[158] and the ability to stimulate chemical reactions, such as the conversion of tetralin hydroperoxide to α-tetralone[159]. The substitution of zinc for magnesium yields a compound that luminesces, but not nearly to the extent of the magnesium complex; the iron, copper, and nickel complexes do not luminesce at all[159, 160]. The reason for the metal specificity in the production of luminescent porphyrin and phthalocyanine complexes cannot be clearly understood until the phenomenon of luminescence itself has been more thoroughly elucidated. Hill[160] has observed that the magnesium and zinc complexes, which exhibit this property, possess an inert gas configuration, whereas the iron, copper, and nickel complexes do not.

It is possible to make some further observations of differences in the structures of luminescing and nonluminescing complexes, which may or may not prove helpful in the correlation of this property with structure. Most of the complexes of iron, copper, and nickel, whose structures have been determined, are octahedral or square planar; in either case four of the bonds connecting the metal to the coordination donors are coplanar. In general, the influence of the metal ion is all-important in the determina-

152. Rabinowitsch, "Photosynthesis," Vol. II, p. 619.
153. Stern and Wenderlein, *Z. Physik. Chem.*, **174A**, 81 (1935).
154. Stern and Wenderlein, *ibid.*, **176A**, 81 (1936).
155. Rabinowitch, Ref. 151, Vol. II, p. 619.
156. Rabinowitch, *ibid.*, Vol. II, p. 796.
157. Warburg and Luettgens, *Biokhimija*, **11**, 303 (1946).
158. Helberger, *Naturwiss.*, **26**, 316 (1938).
159. Helberger and Hever, *Ber.*, **72**, 11 (1939).
160. Hill, *Adv., Enzym.*, **12**, 1, (1951).

tion of the geometrical configuration of the complex. The porphyrin and phthalocyanine molecules, however, have the unusual property of forcing the planar configuration upon the metal ion, if coordination is to take place, since the donor atoms are held in the same plane by the rigid structure of these molecules. Magnesium and zinc generally form only tetrahedral complexes; magnesium, in particular has no d-orbitals available for strong planar bond formation. Therefore the planar bonds in these complexes must be strained, and the electrons that make up these bonds may be partly responsible for the ability to absorb and to reemit energy. It is significant that the magnesium phthalocyanine complex in the solid state is combined with two molecules of water that are not thermolabile[161], thus defying the usual coordination number of four for magnesium. Chlorophyll itself is very hygroscopic, and the presence of half a mole of water per mole of chlorophyll has been noted[162]. Evidently enough electron bensity resides outside the plane of the molecule to make such bonding possible; perhaps the excited and unexcited states of chlorophyll are differentiated by the presence or absence of coordinated molecules of water.

161. Linstead and Lowe, *J. Chem. Soc.*, **1934**, 1022.
162. Rabinowitch, Ref. 151, Vol. I, p. 450.

22. Dyes and Pigments

Roy D. Johnson

American Embassy, Melbourne, Australia

and

Niels C. Nielsen

University of Missouri, Columbia, Missouri

The importance of coordination in dyeing has been systematically investigated only during the past few decades. Although Werner[1] called attention to it in 1908, Morgan and his co-workers must be credited with the first complete studies in the field.

Purely inorganic coordination compounds comprise only a small fraction of the pigments and dyes being used. Most dyestuffs are synthetic organic compounds; and, of these, the large class of metal-dye compounds called "dye lakes" are of greatest interest to the coordination chemist.* The lakes are of two types: coordination compounds and metal salts of dyes. Many commercial dyes contain both types of lakes.

Although the term "mordant dyeing" has been applied to any process which involves the application of some compound in addition to the organic dyestuff, there is now a tendency to consider mordant dyes as those which contain groups capable of acting as electron-pair donors in the formation of coordinate covalent bonds. Work which is now in progress on the role of metal ions in dye-fiber interactions makes it appear certain that coordination phenomena are involved in that aspect of dyeing, also.

MINERAL COLORS AND INORGANIC COMPLEXES AS MORDANTS

Many coordination compounds are highly colored, but few of them have found use as coloring agents. One inorganic pigment which is used extensively, except in the United States, is mineral khaki, which is formed

---

1. Werner, *Ber.*, **41**, 1062 (1908).

* A review of the literature on color lakes containing an extensive bibliography has been presented by W. B. Blumenthal in *Am. Dyestuff Reptr.*, **35**, 520 (1946). Other reviews may be found in Refs. 18, 45, 48b.

by the precipitation of mixed iron and chromium hydroxides on cotton fabrics. The cloth is impregnated with the metal salts, treated with an alkaline solution, and aged. Polynuclear complexes, related to those used in chrome tanning, are formed by oxolation and olation (Chapter 13). Cane sugar, glucose, glycerol, and other nonelectrolytes containing OH groups are added to prevent precipitation of the pigment by forming complexes with the metal ions[2, 3]. The colloidal behavior of these solutions also indicates complex formation.

Complex iron cyanides such as Prussian Blue have been used in the dyeing of textiles. Although early investigations of the chemical nature of these complexes produced conflicting evidence, x-ray analysis[4] shows that Prussian Blue has a cubic lattice with Fe(II) and Fe(III) ions placed alternately at the corners of the cube (p. 90). The cyanide groups are situated along the edges of the cube and serve to join neighboring metal ions. Alkali metal ions appear at the centers of alternate cubes. Numerous studies of these compounds are indicative of the variations in composition[5]. Salts of the $[Fe(CN)_6]^{4-}$ and $[Fe(CN)_6]^{3-}$ complex ions may be formed with many metals to produce colored materials whose insolubility suggests their usefulness as pigments. The familiar Iron Blues are well known examples of these compounds[6]. A newer pigment, Inorganic Maroon, has the approximate composition $K_2Cu[Fe(CN)_6]$[7]. The high tinctorial power of this compound suggests further investigation of the heavy metal salts of the complex iron cyanides which may be applicable in the dyeing of the newer synthetic fibers (see page 766). Heavy metal cyanides also have been employed for the production of colored gold plating[8].

The heavy metal ferro- and ferricyanides can be characterized as polynuclear coordination compounds. This can be explained by the tendency of the cyanide group to complex with most of the heavy metal ions and to its unparalleled ability to behave as a bridging group. Hydroxide groups behave in the same manner, but the number of metal ions which form stable OH bridges is very much smaller[9]. Often the OH group losses pro-

2. Daruwalla, and Nabar, *J. Soc. Dyers Colourists*, **68**, 168 (1952); Bhende and Ramachandran, *J. Sci. Ind. Research (India)*, **7B**, 176 (1948); **8B**(1), 10 (1949).

3. Daruwalla and Nabar, *Kolloid. Z.*, **127**, 33 (1952).

4. Keggin, *Nature*, **137**, 577 (1936).

5. Schaeppi and Treadwell, *Helv. Chim. Acta*, **31**, 577 (1948); Saxena and Bhattacharya, *J. Indian Chem. Soc.*, **28**, 703 (1951); Bhattacharya and Sexton, *J. Indian Chem. Soc.*, **29**, 263 (1952); Bhattacharya and Saxena, *J. Indian Chem. Soc.*, **29**, 284, 529, 535, 632 (1952); Bhattacharya and Saxena, *J. Indian Chem. Soc.*, **28**, 141, 221, (1951).

6. American Cyanamid Co., *Nitrogen Chemicals Digest*, Volume VII, "The Chemistry of the Ferrocyanides," New York, American Cyanamid Company, 1953.

7. Gessler and Goepfert, U. S. Patent 2564756 (1951); cf. *Chem. Abs.*, **45**, 10613 (1951).

8. Thews, *Metal Finishing*, **49** (9), 80 (1951).

9. Scott and Audrieth, *J. Chem. Ed.*, **31**, 168 (1954).

tons, leaving oxide ion linkages between the metal ions. Certain well known inorganic pigments may be coordination compounds, for simple ratios of hydrated oxides to normal metal salts prevail in practically all basic salts such as white lead and malachite[10]. This hypothesis has been verified in some cases[11], but other explanations have also been given to account for the formation of complex basic salts[12, 13]. These inorganic polymers illustrate a modification rather than a contradiction of Werner's hypothesis.

Among the inorganic complexes used as mordants are the familiar phosphotungstic and phosphomolybdic acids (see Chapter 14). The complexity of these materials has made it difficult to evaluate their exact behavior in mordanting operations. Several formulas for the mordanted products have been suggested[14]. The addition of the acid to the dye produces both physical and chemical changes, the latter probably involving coordination of several dye molecules (R) to the complex acid to give structures of the type:

$$
\begin{array}{ccc}
R & & R \\
\diagdown & & \diagup \\
R\!\!-\!\!\text{Complex Acid}\!\!-\!\!R \\
\diagup & & \diagdown \\
R & & R
\end{array}
$$

Some basic dyes are susceptible to mordanting with potassium ferrocyanide and sodium sulfite, if copper sulfate is first added to the dye solution. The use of the tannin-tartar emetic mordant system is well known. After initial interaction between tannic acid and the basic dye molecule, the antimony salt combines with the tannic acid portion of the molecule or, more specifically, with the *ortho*-hydroxy groups present in the digallic acid constituent of the tannic acid[15].

A recent patent proposes the use of metal carbonyls of the iron group for mordanting acetate rayons. The process is suitable for a large number of lake-forming dyes which contain nitro groups[16].

METAL COMPLEXES OF ORGANIC DYESTUFFS

Any organic compound containing intramolecular hydrogen bonds will, in general, react with metal ions to form coordinate covalent bonds. Co-

10. Werner, *Ber.*, **40**, 4441 (1907).
11. Weinland, Stroh, and Paul, *Ber.*, **55**, 2706 (1922).
12. Feitknecht, *Helv. Chim. Acta.*, **13**, 22 (1930); **16**, 427, 1302 (1933); **18**, 28, 40 (1935); **19**, 448, 467, 831 (1936).
13. Thomas, "Colloid Chemistry," New York, McGraw-Hill Book Co., 1934.
14. Pratt, "The Chemistry and Physics of Organic Pigments," New York, John Wiley & Sons, Inc., 1947.
15. Ref. 14, p. 178.
16. Grimmel, British Patent 631,765.

ordination can occur with any class of dyes which has derivatives containing the necessary donor groups in the proper positions. The most characteristic groupings found in commercial dyes are —OH, —COOH, =O, =NOH, and —NH₂ in *ortho* or *peri* positions with respect to each other or, in the case of the azo or azomethine dyes, in the *ortho* positions with respect to the —N=N— or —N=C— linkages.

—NO, —OH Substituted Dyes

Naphthol Green B (structure I) was the first commercially available

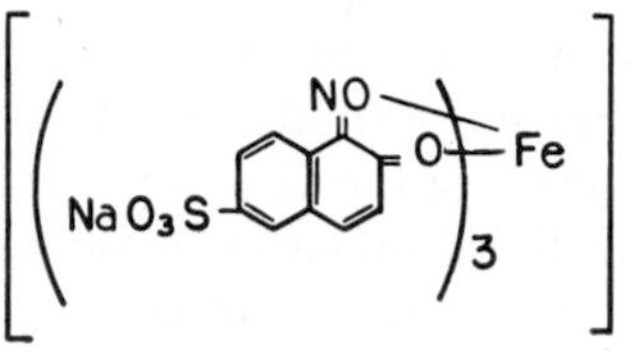

I

soluble acid dye containing a coordinated metal ion[17]. The —NO, —OH groups characteristic of this dyestuff occur in many metallized dyes.

The *o*-nitrosophenols are polygenetic dyes with colors ranging from green (with Fe) to brown (with Cr) and yellow (with Zn)[18]. The similarity between the zinc and barium compounds suggests that salt formation, rather than coordination, may occur. Pigment Green B, the bisulfite compound of 1-nitroso-2-naphthol complexed with iron, is suitable for filling rubber[19]. Various substituents have led to numerous other dyes in the Pigment Green series.

The coordination phenomena occurring with the nitrosophenols have been investigated[20]. When Gambine Y (1,2-naphthoquinone-1-oxime) was allowed to react with [Co(NH₃)₆]Cl₃ at room temperature, a simple salt was formed. Upon warming the salt, six molecules of ammonia were evolved and the chelate compound (structure II) was formed.

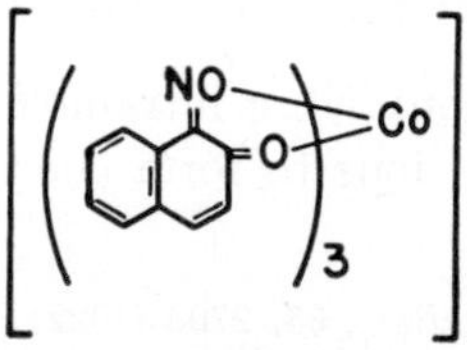

II

17. Hofmann, *Ber.*, **24**, 3741 (1891).
18. Venkataraman, "The Chemistry of Synthetic Dyes," New York, Academic Press, 1952.
19. E. I. duPont de Nemours and Co., U. S. Patent 2092750 (1937).
20. Morgan and Main Smith, *J. Chem. Soc.*, **119**, 704 (1921).

Morgan and Main Smith reported that air oxidation of a mixture of 7-hydroxy-1,2-naphthoquinone-1-oxime and a cobalt salt gave the compound shown in structure(III), while oxidation by hydrogen peroxide in the presence of ammonia gave a more complex salt (structure IV). According to them, the $[Co(NH_3)_5]^{3+}$ ion neutralized the three charges on the complex with the sixth coordination position of the pentammine being filled by one of the phenolic oxygens. This is not clearly shown by their

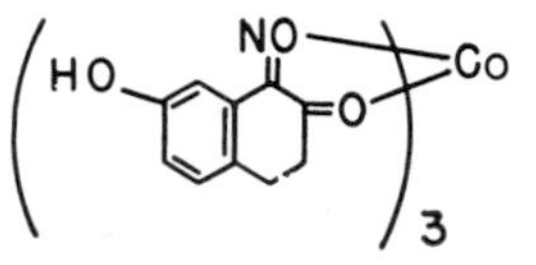

III 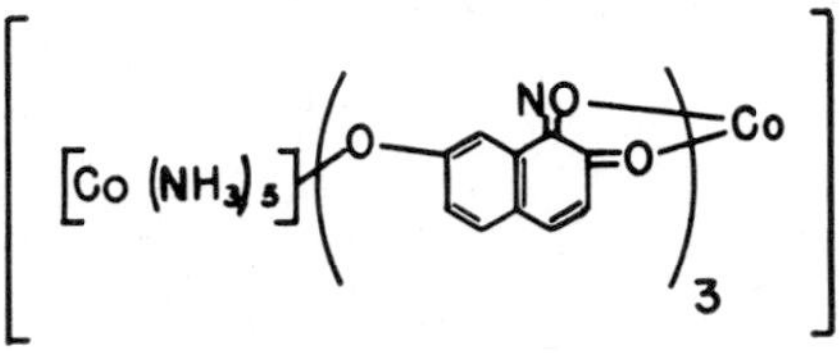   **IV**

formulation (IV). The formation of the three chelate rings widely separates the three hydroxyl groups in position 7 so that not more than one of them could possibly satisfy a secondary valence of a given cobalt. Analysis showed that the compound contained a mole of water, and Lamb and Larson[21] have shown that the $[Co(NH_3)_5H_2O]^{3+}$ ion is more stable than the $[Co(NH_3)_6]^{3+}$ ion. This suggests that the lake is probably a simple salt of the former. Under more stringent conditions, the dye might replace the water molecule as in the analogous reaction:

$$[Co(NH_3)_5H_2O]Cl_3 \rightarrow [Co(NH_3)_5Cl]Cl_2 + H_2O$$

In a study of the cobaltammine and iron lakes of dinitrosoresorcinol the cobaltammine lakes were shown to be monochelate. Evidently, the chelate ring is formed with the two intermediate functional groups, leaving the salt forming function to the terminal functional groups. Similar results were obtained with the green iron(III) lakes[22].

o-Nitrosophenol combines quantitatively with copper(II), mercury(I), nickel(II), palladium(II) and cobalt(III)[23], while 2-nitroso-1-naphthol and the related Nitroso-R salt have been suggested as analytical reagents for cobalt[24] and for the colorimetric and photometric determination of iron[25].

21. Lamb and Larson, *J. Am. Chem. Soc.*, **42,** 2024 (1920).
22. Morgan and Moss, *J. Chem. Soc.*, **121,** 2857 (1922).
23. Cronheim. *J. Org. Chem.*, **12,** 1 (1947).
24. Jung, Cardini, and Fuksman, *Anales Assoc. quim. Argentia*, **31,** 122 (1943); Haywood and Wood, *J. Soc. Chem. Ind.*, **62,** 37 (1943); Willard and Kaufmann, *Anal. Chem.*, **19,** 505 (1947).
25. Sideris, Young, and Chun, *Ind. Eng. Chem., Anal. Ed.*, **16,** 276 (1944).

The α-oximinoketones form metal complexes of the type

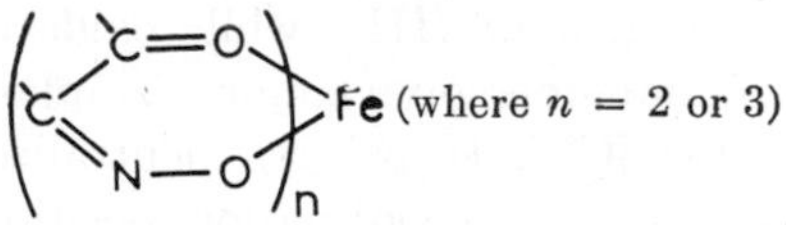

These have been patented for use on photo images[26]. Nilssen[27] has reported that iron forms complexes with the compound

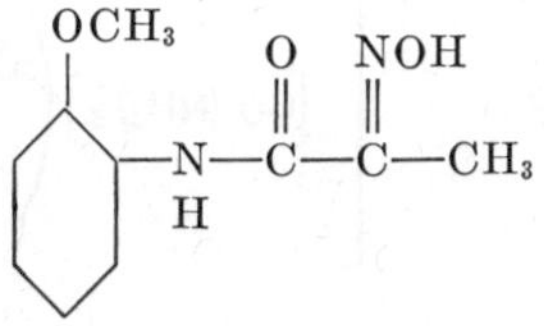

The stoichiometry and structure of the resulting complex have not been investigated, but it seems possible that the oxime group is not involved in the coordination[28].

In the case of the 1-nitroso derivatives of 2-hydroxy-3-naphthoic acid arylamides, two ferric compounds, formulated as structures (V) and (VI), have been prepared[29].

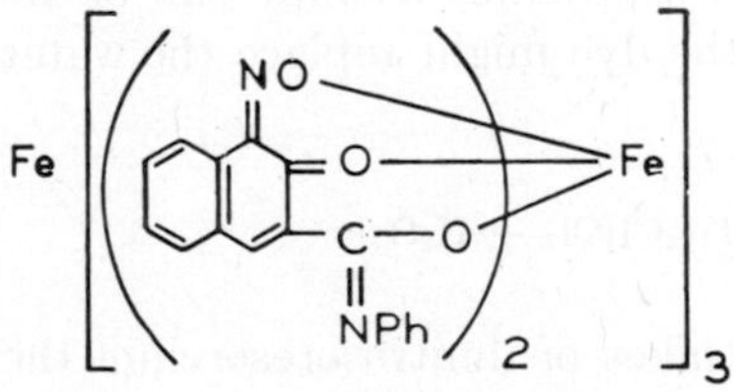

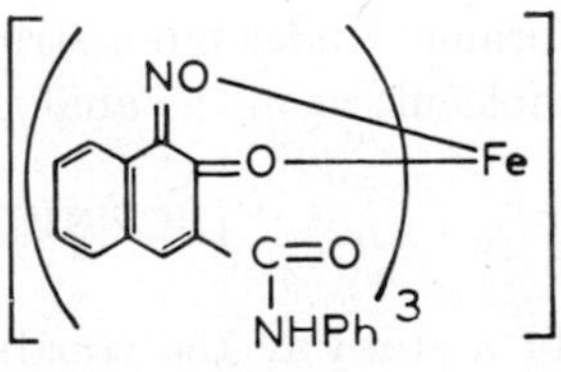

The formation of compound (V) requires "enolization" in the arylamide group. Evidence for this comes from the preparation of the iron lake of the N-benzyl derivative in which "enolization" cannot occur, and only compound (VI) is formed[30].

The commercial use of the iron complexes of the o-nitrosophenols, to the

26. Sargent, U. S. Patents 2533181 and 2533182.
27. Nilssen, *Soc. Dyers and Colourists, Symposium on Fibrous Proteins*, **1946**, 142.
28. Ref. 18, p. 404.
29. Unpublished. See Ref. 18, p. 404.
30. Forster, Kudva, and Venkataraman, *J. Indian Chem. Soc., Ind. and News Ed.*, **6**, 119 (1943).

exclusion of other well known metal complexes, is indicative of the stability of these materials.

Ortho-Dihydroxy Substituted Dyes

Numerous dyes of all classes contain the *ortho*-dihydroxy group or the related quinoid structure (=O, —OH); the most important of these are the alizarin dyes. An understanding of the coordination phenomena involved has resulted from investigations of simpler ring systems and of derivatives of anthracene. Colorless 2,4,5-trihydroxytoluene will complex with copper(II), iron(II) and cobalt(II) to give wool dyes ranging from medium brown to black in color[31]. The compounds are formulated as

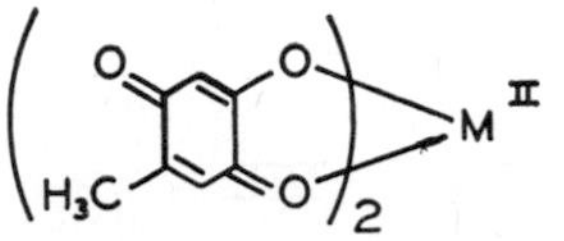

The oxidation of the organic molecule is analogous to that observed in the complexes of Diamond Black PV(VII)[32].

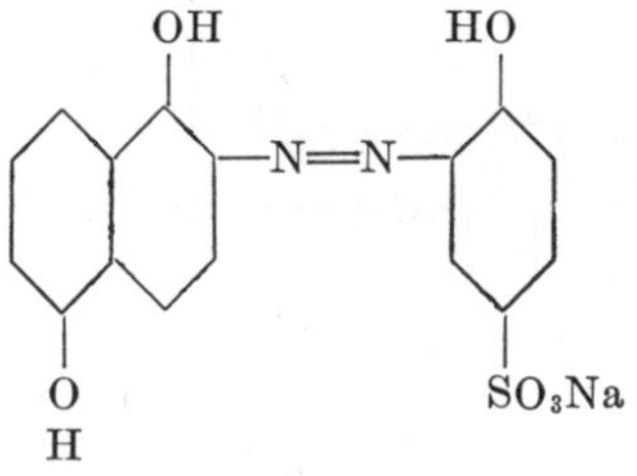

VII

When treated with chromic acid, this type of dye oxidizes to a quinoid form with which the chromium, in its reduced state, can coordinate. The evidence for this mechanism is neither extensive nor accurate enough to warrant assignment of specific structures to the resulting compounds, most of which are impure.

Alizarin is a polygenetic dye with colors ranging from rose-red with aluminum salts to violet-black with iron compounds. Turkey-Red lake is the most important commercial dye of this series. The lakes of alizarin are

31. Burton and Stoves, *J. Soc. Dyers Colourists*, **66**, 474 (1950).
32. Morgan and Main Smith, *J. Chem. Soc.*, **125**, 1731 (1924).

often regarded as adsorption complexes[33], but a pure compound has been isolated and assigned structure (VIII)[34].

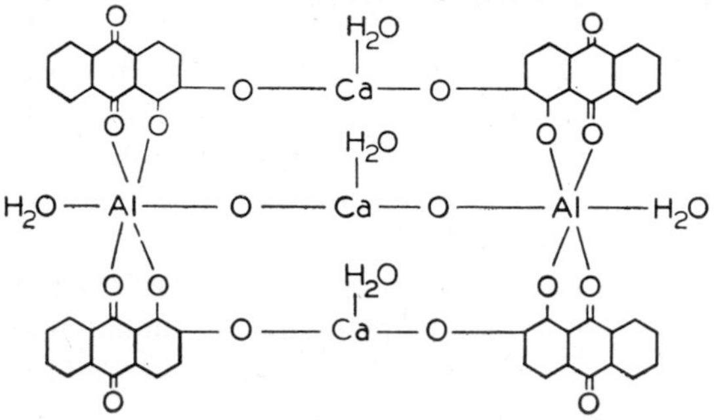

VIII

Alizarin forms a cobalt(III) complex containing two cobalt atoms for each five ammonia molecules[35]. This was first reported to have structure (IX), but is probably the salt shown in structure (X).

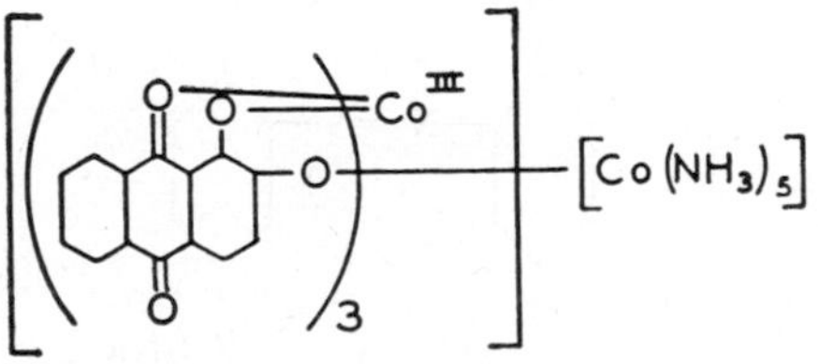

IX

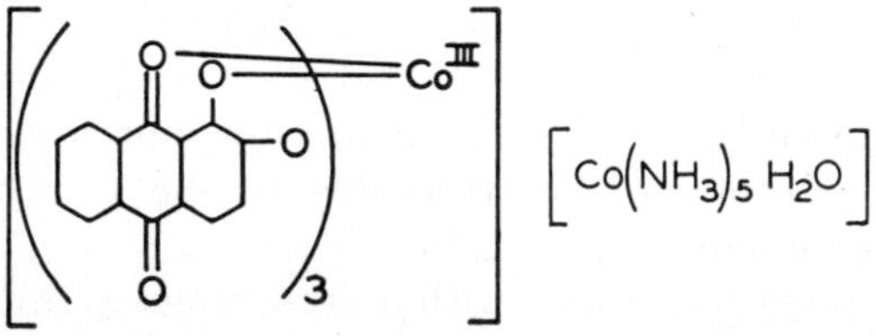

X

An interesting complex analogous to Turkey Red contains both di- and

33. Bancroft, *J. Phys. Chem.*, **36**, 3137 (1932); Reference 14, p. 110.
34. Fierz-David and Rutishauser, *Helv. Chim. Acta*, **23**, 1298 (1940).
35. Morgan and Main Smith, *J. Chem. Soc.*, **121**, 160 (1922).

trivalent cobalt (XI)

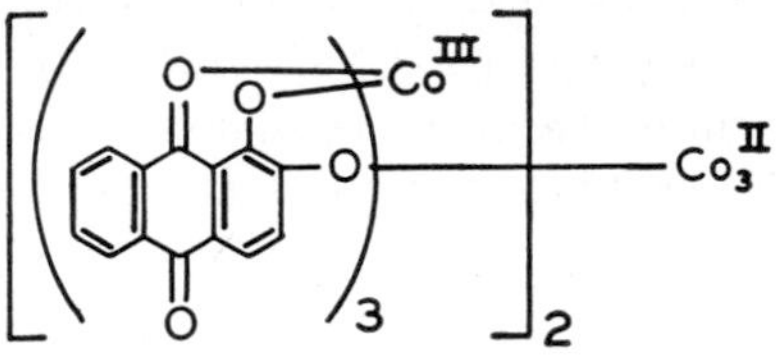

XI

Purpurin gives a mixture of two cobalt lakes in approximately equal proportions, while, with alizarin cyanine, cobalt is reported to form a lake containing two chelate rings (XII).

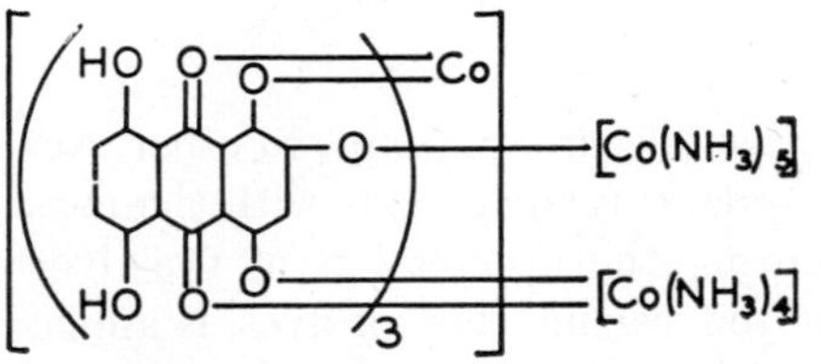

XII

A similar structure results when an amine group is substituted in the 3-position; however, 2-nitroalizarin reacts with cobalt to form only a single chelate ring. Many complexes of alizarin are salts rather than coordination compounds[36, 37].

Complexes of 1-hydroxyanthraquinone with several transition metal ions have been investigated[38] and formulated as

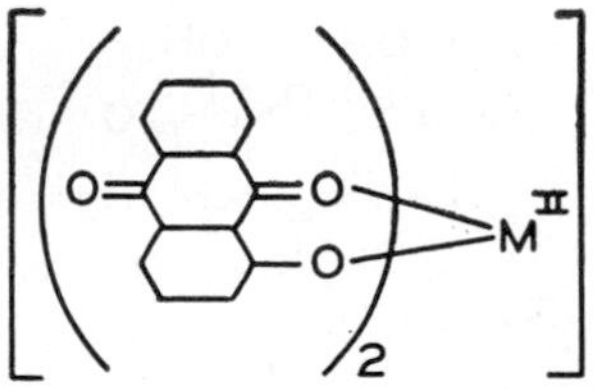

on the basis of analytical and spectral data. Beryllium forms similar compounds with naphthazarin and alkannin. It also forms a polymer with a metal-ligand ratio of 1:1[39].

36. Dorta-Schaeppi, Hürzeler, and Treadwell, *Helv. Chim. Acta*, **34**, 797 (1951).
37. Liebhafsky and Winslow, *J. Am. Chem. Soc.*, **60**, 1776 (1938); **69**, 1130 (1947); Flagg, Liebhafsky, and Winslow, *J. Am. Chem. Soc.*, **71**, 3630 (1949).
38. Geyer and Smith, *J. Am. Chem. Soc.*, **64**, 1649 (1942).
39. Underwood, Toribara and Neuman, *J. Am. Chem. Soc.*, **72**, 5597 (1950).

Many compounds related to alizarin are of commercial importance as dyes, and most of them are applied in conjunction with metal salts. Typical examples are anthragallol, Alizarin Cyanine NS, Anthracene Blue WR, Bordeaux B, and Alizarin Red S. More complex derivatives such as Alizarin Irisol R (XIII) are also useful for the preparation of barium and aluminum lake pigments.

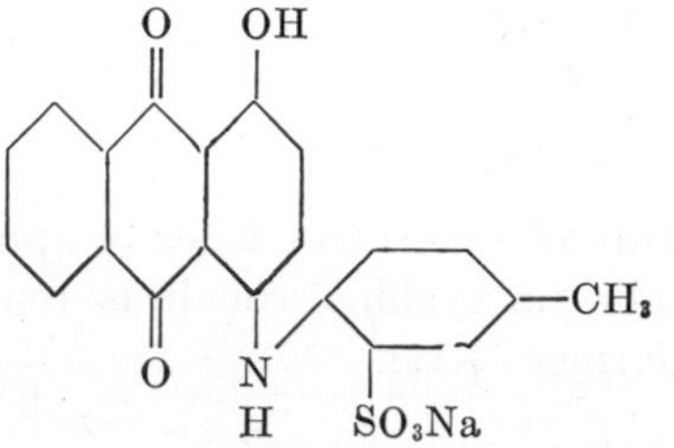

XIII

The presence of *ortho*-dihydroxy groups in other classes of dyes plays an important role in mordanting operations with the indication that complex formation occurs during the application of the dyestuffs. Gallocyanine (XIV), a member of the oxazine class of dyes, is applied on a chrome mordant. Among the xanthenes, Gallein (XV) and Coerulein (XVI) are applied on chromed wool.

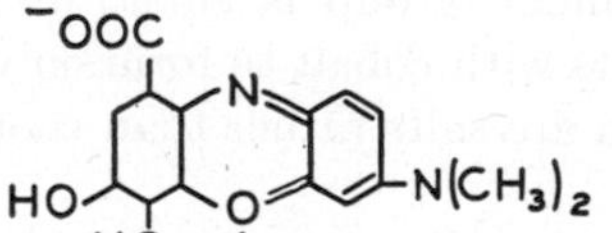

XIV

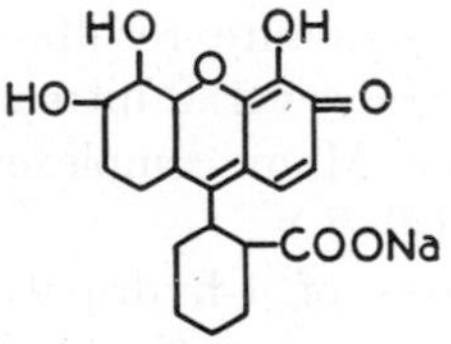

XV

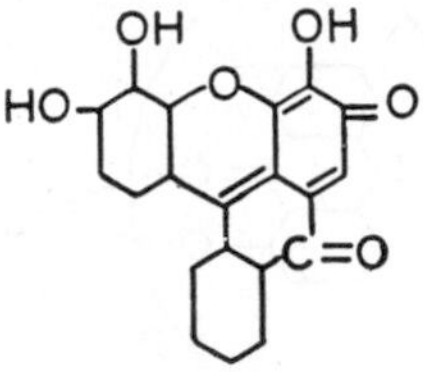

XVI

The thiazine class of dyes is represented by Brilliant Alizarin Blue 3R (XVII), which yields blue chromium lakes.

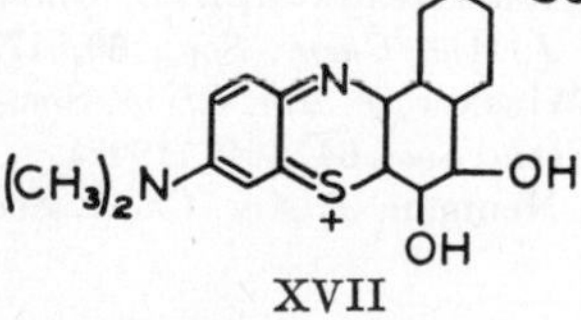

XVII

In dyeing, the variations in color or shade resulting from changes in the metal ions present in the bath or on the fiber suggest the formation of coordination compounds rather than salts. The presence of the *ortho*-dihydroxy group characterizes all members of each class which are useful in mordanting operations. It is reasonable to assume that stable coordination compounds could be prepared and characterized in order to clarify the role of complex formation in the dyeing process.

—COOH, —OH Substituted Dyes

Azosalicylic acids constitute the largest class of com ercial dyes which are characterized by the presence of —COOH and – OH groups on adjacent carbons and are suitable for the dyeing of fabrics by the chrome process. The simpler dyes include the Alizarin Yellows, Ergansoga Brown 3R, Diamond Flavine G, and Eriochrome Flavine A. All are formed by coupling diazonium salts with salicylic acid.

The constitution of some of these complexes has been determined[40]. Alizarin Yellow 2G reacts with chromium compounds to form the complex ion

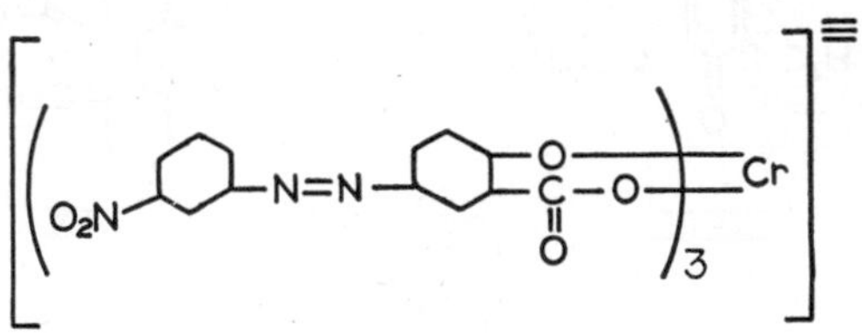

which has been isolated as the chromium(III) salt. Other compounds having different Cr:dye ratios have also been prepared[41]. One of these has been assigned the structure

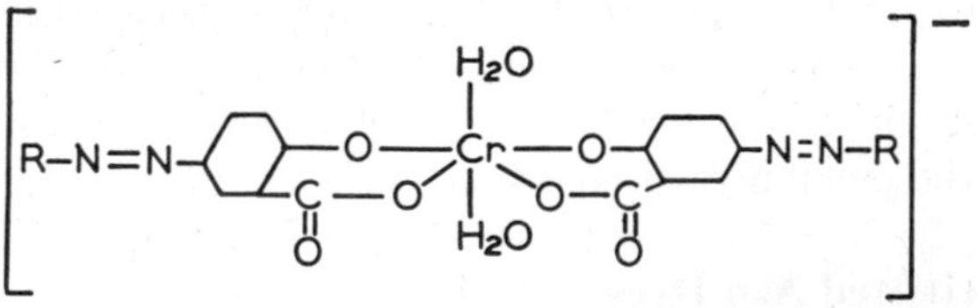

The two coordinated water molecules may be replaced by ammonia.

Drew and Fairbairn[42] prepared chromium complexes of azosalicylic acids containing both two and three salicylic acid groups per chromium ion. More recently, coordination compounds were prepared from tetrammine copper(II) sulfate and aquopentamminecobalt(III) chloride and the

40. Morgan and Main Smith, *J. Chem. Soc.*, **121**, 2866 (1922); *J. Soc. Dyers Colourists*, **41**, 223 (1925).
41. Brass and Wirtnitzer, *Atti X congr. intern. chim.*, **3**, 46 (1939).
42. Drew and Fairbairn, *J. Chem. Soc.*, **1939**, 823.

azosalicylic acid dye, Mordant Yellow O[43]. Two ammonias in the copper complex were replaced by one dye molecule, while all of the ligands in the simple cobalt complexes were replaced to yield a complex ion $[Co(dye)_3]^{6-}$.

Many triphenylmethane derivatives contain salicylic acid residues, and lake formation has been indicated by several workers[44]. No evidence is available regarding the structure of these compounds[45]. A group of dyes known as the Chromoxanes is especially useful for application with chrome mordants. By heating the chromium ammonium salt of salicylic acid with the dye Eriochrome Azurol B (XVIII), a compound is formed which will dye blue on both protein and animal fibers[46].

In the xanthene class, compounds such as Chromogen Red B (XIX) are useful for chrome printing on cotton.

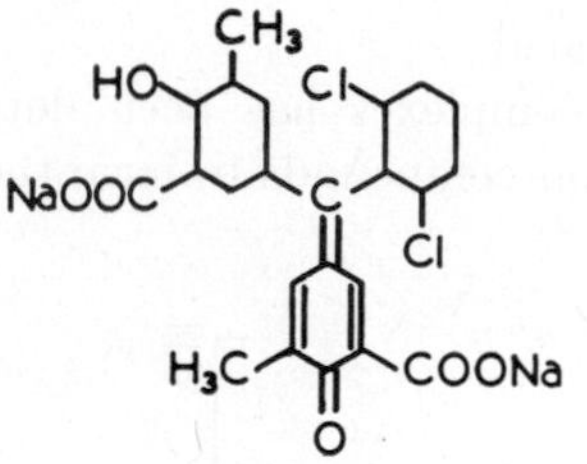

<u>XVIII</u> 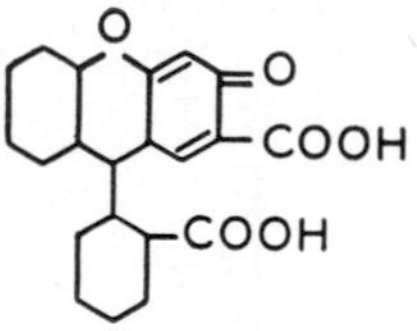   <u>XIX</u>

Azine dyes can also be adapted for chrome printing on cotton by substitution of a salicylic acid group on a ring nitrogen.

Because of the complexity of the metal derivatives of the ortho-hydroxy-carboxy triphenylmethanes and azosalicylates, it is difficult to isolate them in pure enough form to allow study of their structures. Further work is needed. Some of these compounds may well be simple salts, but others, having either the —OH or —COOH group adjacent to the azo bond, afford the possibility of coordination with the azo group.

Ortho-Substituted Azo Dyes

Most commercially important azo dyes are characterized by the follow-

43. Ref. 18, p. 567.
44. Middleton, *J. Am. Chem. Soc.*, **48**, 2125 (1926), Hammett and Sottery, *J. Am. Chem. Soc.*, **47**, 142 (1925); Corey and Rogers, *J. Am. Chem. Soc.*, **49**, 216, (1927).
45. Wittenberger, *Melliand Textilber.*, **32**, 454 (1951). See ref. 85 and 88.
46. Ref. 18, p. 731.

ing substituents[47, 48]:

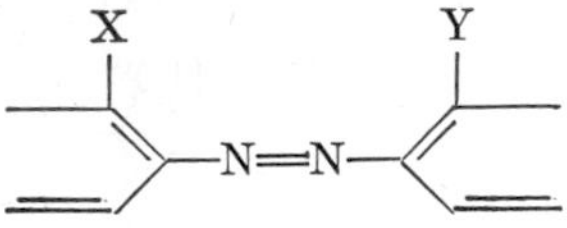

	X	Y
	—OH	—OH
	—OH	—COOH
	—OH	—NH$_2$
	—OH	—H
	—NH$_2$	—H

The aromatic nuclei containing the *ortho*-substituents may be either benzene, naphthalene, or pyrazalone rings. The latter two are encountered most frequently in the patent literature. The mordanting metals commonly used are chromium for wool dyes and copper for cotton dyes, but compounds of manganese, iron, cobalt, nickel, vanadium, tungsten, molybdenum, tellurium, zirconium, and titanium have also been patented. Boyle[49] has reviewed the patent literature on soluble chromium dyes up to 1939. A more recent compilation of commercially available metal-complexes of azo dyes includes the Benzo Fast Copper, the Chlorantine Fast, the Palatine Fast, and the Coprantine dyes[50].

The Palatine Fast and Neolan colors have one metal atom per dye molecule. Palatine Fast Blue CGN (XX) may be formulated as[51]

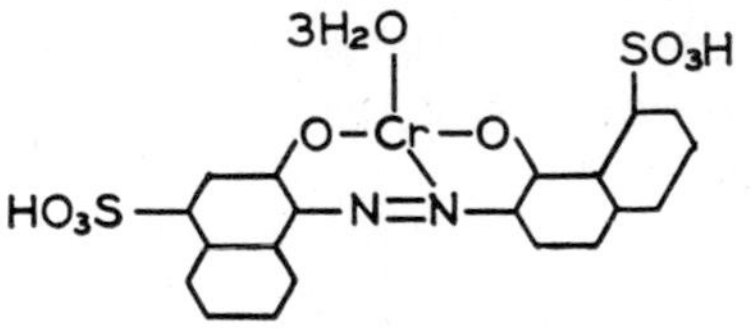

XX

These two classes of dyes include fifty individual compounds ranging in shades from yellow to black[52]. Most of the colors are chromium complexes, although copper was once employed in preparing several members of the group.

Neolan Red B is the chromium complex of Eriochrome Red B (XXI) while the complex formed by chromium and Eriochrome Blue Black R

47. Knight, *J. Soc. Dyers Colourists*, **66**, 34 (1950).
48. Mackenzie, Millson, and West, *Ind. Eng. Chem.*, **44**, 1017 (1952); Pfitzner, *Angew. Chem.*, **62**, 242 (1950).
49. Boyle, *Am. Dyestuff Reptr.*, **28**, 741 (1939).
50. Specklin, *Teintex*, **15**, 451 (1950).
51. Valko, *Oesterr. Chem. Ztg.*, **40**, 465 (1937).
52. Ref. 18, pp. 534–9.

(XXII) is sold as Neolan Blue B. Some Palatine Fast colors are also being marketed for leather dyeing under the name Erganil dyes.

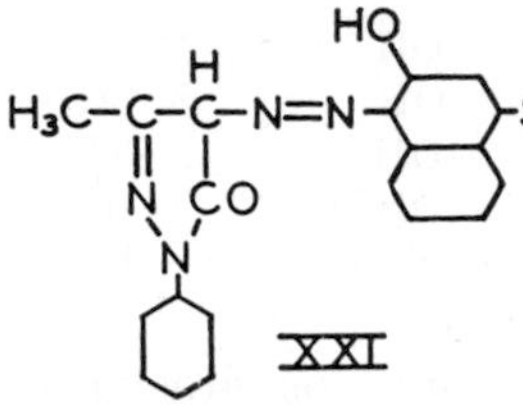

Knowledge of the constitution and structures of the metal complexes of azo dyes is more extensive than for any other class of coloring agents. As early as 1900, an alcohol-soluble copper compound of o-hydroxyazobenzene which contained two azo dye molecules for each copper atom was reported[53]. Werner[54] included this compound in his newly developed theory; however, the exact formulation of the azo dye lakes was not attempted until a much later date when Morgan and his students initiated a systematic investigation[55]. Eriochrome Red B (XXI) and Palatine Chrome Black 6B each contain two hydroxyl groups in positions *ortho* to the azo bond. With Eriochrome Red B, three different compounds were isolated; these had dye:metal ratios of 3:1, 3:2, and 1:1. Palatine Chrome Black 6B, $HO \cdot C_{10}H_6 \cdot N_2 \cdot C_{10}H_5(OH) \cdot SO_3H$, formed two lakes having dye:metal ratios of 3:1 and 1:1. Because of the presence of the sulfonic acid groups, the ratios are not representative of the number of metal ions coordinated with a single azo group. In the above dyes, there are three azo groups for each coordinated metal ion. The same ratio was obtained for the cobalt complex of an o-amino, o'-hydroxyazo dye, Metachrome Brown B. These results led Morgan to conclude that only one hydroxy group was included in the coordination sphere of the metal ion. The error in his interpretation resulted from the presence of the sulfonic acid groups which also interacted with the metal ammine complexes used in the preparations.

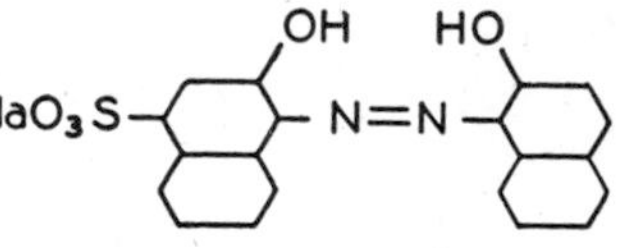

Drew and his co-workers may be credited with clarifying the structures of the azo dye complexes. Copper lakes of 2-hydroxy-5-methylazobenzene, o-hydroxyazobenzene, 2-hydroxy-5,5'-dimethylazobenzene, benezeneazo-β-naphthol, and m-tolylazo-β-naphthol, showed, on analysis, a dye:copper ratio of 2:1[56]. All of the compounds were anhydrous and did not add organic amines, so the two molecules of dye in each compound must have formed four bonds with the copper ion, thus satisfying its normal coordina-

53. Bamberger, *Ber.*, **33**, 1951 (1900).
54. Werner, *Ber.*, **41**, 2383 (1908).
55. Morgan and Main Smith, *J. Chem. Soc.*, **125**, 1731 (1924).
56. Drew and Landquist, *J. Chem. Soc.*, **1938**, 292.

tion number. The general structure of these lakes may be represented as

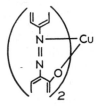

Analogous results were obtained with dyes having a single *ortho*-carboxy group, except for a marked decrease in the stability of the complexes. The dye:metal ratio was the expected 2:1, but dihydrates also formed, and the water could be replaced by pyridine or aniline. Since *ortho*-carboxy and *ortho*-hydroxy complexes should be identical with respect to coordinative saturation, it is difficult to understand the ability of the former to add additional donor molecules.

The copper lake of 2,2'-dicarboxyazobenzene (dye:metal = 1:1) formed a stable monohydrate, thus satisfying the coordination number of four for the copper ion. The copper derivatives of *o*-carboxybenzeneazo-*p*-cresol and *o*-carboxybenzeneazo-β-naphthol also gave a ratio of 1:1 and added one molecule of either pyridine or aniline. The *o,o'*-dihydroxyazo and azomethine dyes formed copper complexes containing one metal ion per dye molecule and capable of giving monopyridine and monoquinoline derivatives. Pfeiffer's[57] work supports that of Drew.

Investigations of the chromium, iron, nickel, and zinc compounds of mono- and di-*ortho*-substituted azo dyes were also made[42]. By treating *o*-hydroxybenzeneazo-β-naphthol with chromium(III) chloride, a salt-like material, Cr(dye)Cl, containing water, was formed. It could be converted to a compound containing non-ionic chlorine by heating. A dipyridine derivative was also prepared in which chromium has its preferred coordination number of six.

The chromium lakes of 2-hydroxy-5-nitrobenzeneazo-β-naphthol and 2-hydroxy-5-sulfobenzeneazo-β-naphthol gave the same dye:metal ratios as those which had only *ortho* substituents. The only differences noted were in the solubility of the complexes and the high water content of the solid material. A single hydroxy group in the *ortho* position was not capable of holding a chromium(III) ion in stable union with the dye. All of the dihydroxy dyes gave the expected 1:1 complexes with nickel(II), zinc(II), and iron(III). In addition, the iron(III) lakes gave other dye:metal ratios similar to those given by the chromium(III) compounds. The nickel(II) and zinc(II) complexes, like those of copper(II), formed monopyridine deriva-

57. Pfeiffer, Hesse, Pfitzner, Scholl and Thielert, *J. prakt. Chem.*, **149**, 217 (1937).

tives, thus demonstrating a coordination number of four, the azo group taking part in the formation of one coordinate covalent bond.

With o-carboxy, o'-hydroxy dyes, nickel(II), chromium(III), and iron (III) compounds containing one mole of dye per metal ion were isolated. Copper and zinc ions combined with this structure to give salts, one of which Drew formulated as $Cu[Cu(dye)_2NH_3]\cdot 6H_2O$. Analogous aluminum lakes were also prepared[58] but in the case of chromium, definite compounds of monohydroxy dyes were not obtained. The lake from o-hydroxybenzene-azo-β-naphthol, formulated as $[Al(dye)]Cl\cdot 5H_2O$, was not stable to treatment with ammonium hydroxide or potassium chromate. With 2'-hydroxy-4'-sulfobenzene-4-azo-1-phenyl-3-methyl-1-pyrazol-5-one, a compound having the composition $Al(dye)\cdot 6H_2O$ was isolated.

o-Hydroxybenzeneazo-β-naphthol gives hydrated $V(dye)_2$ which is readily converted to $VO(dye)$. The latter adds one mole of pyridine, and, like the other vanadyl complexes which were prepared, it is similar to the complexes of chromium(III)[59].

Beech and Drew[60] investigated the effect of sulfonic acid groups on the coordinating tendencies of the o,o'-dihydroxyazo dyes. By permitting copper(II) chloride to react with 2'-hydroxy-5'-sulfobenzeneazo-β-naphthol, an unusual compound was formed:

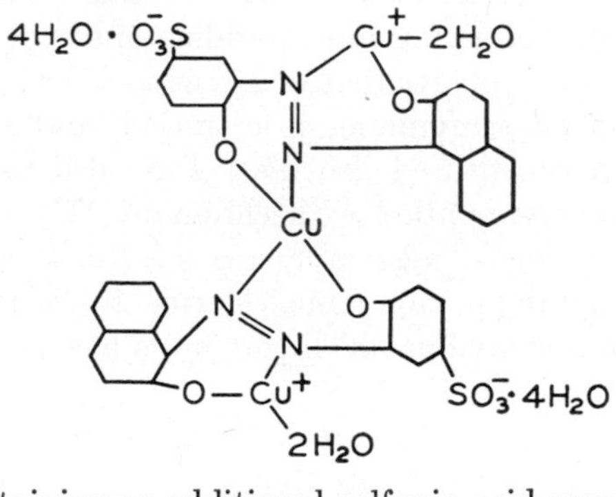

A similar dye, containing an additional sulfonic acid group on the naphthalene ring, may be metallized with copper(II) chloride to give a compound which has been assigned a structure having two copper(II) ions coordinated to a single azo group.

These results suggested that the sulfonic acid groups present on the dye nucleus serve to neutralize part of the charge on the metal ion. The latter, therefore, does not require both hydroxyl groups for neutralization, and it is possible for two metal ions to be attracted to the vicinity of a single azo

58. Beech and Drew, *J. Chem. Soc.*, **1940,** 603.
59. Drew and Dutton, *J. Chem. Soc.*, **1940,** 1064.
60. Beech and Drew, *J. Chem. Soc.*, **1940,** 608.

TABLE 22.1. METAL COMPLEXES OF AZO AND AZOMETHINE DYES

Dye	Composition of Lake	Configuration
Benzeneazo-β-naphthol	Co(dye)$_3$	planar
	Ni(dye)$_2$	
5-Chloro-2-hydroxybenzeneazo-β-naphthylamine	Co(dye)$_2$	tetrahedral
	Ni(dye)OH	
	Ni(dye)OH·H$_2$O	
2'-Hydroxybenzal-2-hydroxy-5-chloro-aniline	Co(dye)·2H$_2$O	tetrahedral
	Ni(dye)·H$_2$O	
2'-Carboxybenzene-4-azo-1-phenyl-3-methylpyrazole-5-one	Co(dye)·H$_2$O	tetrahedral
	Ni(dye)·H$_2$O	

group, each forming a coordinate covalent bond with one of the nitrogen atoms. Subsequent evidence fails to support this conclusion.

The chromium complex of 2'-hydroxy-3'-sulfo-5'-methylbenzene-4-azo-1-phenyl-3-methyl-1-pyrazol-5-one and related dyes, when prepared with disalicylato chromic acid or its ammonium salt, contain a salicylaldehyde residue which completes the coordination sphere of the chromium ion[61]. Similarly, nickel and copper complexes of formazyl compounds of the type shown below (XXIII) add a mole of ammonia, ethanolamine, or pyridine[62].

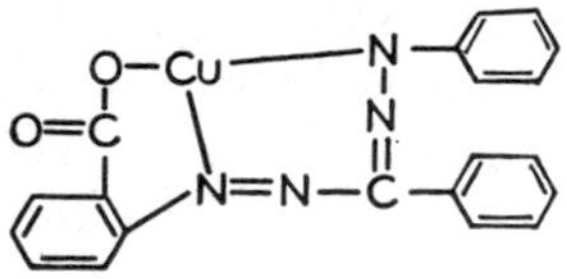

XXIII

In recent years, several workers have made use of magnetic measurements and complete analyses to establish the composition and structure of a series of dyes representing a variety of substituents. Some of the results are summarized in Table 22.1[63]. In addition, the replacement of coordinated groups from cobalt complexes by dye molecules was examined[64]. Table 22.2 lists some of the compounds obtained in this investigation. The studies also included dyes in which the "ortho" substituent is a nitrogen atom in a heterocyclic ring[65]. Simple salts were used in most cases, so the coordination positions remaining unfilled after the formation of the metal-dye complex contain water molecules as indicated in Table 22.3.

Except for the work with dyes containing sulfonic acid groups, and the behavior of organometallic compounds with respect to the azo bond, all

61. Shetty, *Helv. Chim. Acta*, **35**, 716 (1952).
62. Wizinger and Biro, *Helv. Chim. Acta*, **32**, 901 (1949).
63. Callis, Nielsen, and Bailar, *J. Am. Chem. Soc.*, **74**, 3461 (1952).
64. Bailar and Callis, *J. Am. Chem. Soc.*, **74**, 6018 (1952).
65. Liu, thesis, University of Illinois, 1951.

TABLE 22.2. METAL COMPLEXES OF AZO AND AZOMETHINE DYES

Dye	Metal Salt	Composition of Lake
Benzeneazo-β-naphthol	$[Co(NH_3)_6]Cl_3$	$Co(dye)_3$
2'-hydroxybenzal-2-hydroxy-5-chloroaniline	$Co(OAc)_2 \cdot 4H_2O$	$Co(dye)$ and $Co(dye)_3$
	$[Co(NH_3)_6]Cl_3$	$Co_2(dye)_3(NH_3)_3$
	$[Co(dien)_2]Cl_3$	$[Co\ dien\ dye]\ Cl$
	$[Co(NH_3)_5SCN]Cl_2$	$Co_2(dye)_3(NH_3)_3$
	$Na_3Co(NO_2)_6$	$Co_2(dye)_3(NH_3)_3$
	$[Cr(NH_3)_6](NO_3)_3$	$Cr_2(dye)_3(NH_3)_2H_2O$
	$Zn(OAc)_2 \cdot 2H_2O$	$Zn(dye)$
	$ZnCl_2$	$Zn(dye)$

evidence indicates that the azo group occupies only one of the coordination positions available in the sphere of a metal ion. Consideration of this fact is important in the choice of other coordinating agents which might be added to dye baths, or in evaluating interactions between metallized dyes and fibers.

Miscellaneous Dyes

Phthalocyanines. The phthalocyanines constitute an important series of fast blue to green pigments[66]. Although earlier workers had apparently prepared a copper phthalocyanine, it was the excellent work of Linstead and his students[67] which resulted in a complete picture of the structure and properties of this new chromophore. The work has since been confirmed by the x-ray studies of Robertson and others[68].

The structure of the phthalocyanines was found to be similar to that of porphin, the fundamental nucleus of chlorophyll (page 74) and hemin (page 74). The phthalocyanine nucleus may be derived by replacing the methine groups by nitrogen atoms. The products are known as azaporphins. All attempts to prepare the simple azaporphins appear to have failed.

The phthalocyanines have a coplanar structure and are capable of occupying four coordination positions and neutralizing two charges of a metal ion. The stability of complexes of the chromophore has been demonstrated by preparing derivatives of more than twenty elements. These include representatives of each group of the periodic table. Divalent metals dis-

66. For reviews, see: Dahlen, *Ind. Eng. Chem.*, **31**, 839 (1939); Haddock, *J. Soc. Dyers Colourists*, **61**, 68 (1945); Haddock and Linstead, "Thorpe's Dictionary of Applied Chemistry," p. 617, 4th ed., Vol. IX, London, Longman's.

67. Linstead *et al.*, *J. Chem. Soc.*, **1934**, 1016, 1017, 1022, 1027, 1031, 1033; **1936**, 1719, 1725, 1737, 1739, 1744; **1937**, 911, 922, 929, 933; **1938**, 1157; **1939**, 1809, 1820; **1940**, 1070, 1076, 1079; Brit. Pat. 389,842 (1933); 390,148 (1933); 410,814 (1934); 441,332 (1936); Dent, *J. Chem. Soc.*, **1938**, 1.

68. Robertson, *J. Chem. Soc.*, **1935**, 615; **1936**, 1195, 1736; **1937**, 219; **1940**, 36; Endermann, *Z. physik. Chem.*, **190**, 129 (1942).

TABLE 22.3. METAL COMPLEXES OF AZO DYES

Dye	Composition of Lakes
α-Pyridylazo-β-naphthol	[Cu dye H$_2$O]NO$_3$
	[Cu dye]NO$_3$
	[Ni dye H$_2$O]NO$_3$
	[Ni dye]NO$_3$
	[Co(dye)$_2$]Cl*
	[Cr(dye)$_2$]NO$_3$
α-Pyridylazoresorcinol	[Cu dye H$_2$O]
	[Cu dye]
	H$_2$[Ni(dye)$_2$]·H$_2$O
	Co[Co(dye)$_2$]$_3$·3H$_2$O
	[Cr(dye)$_2$]
	[Cr dye (H$_2$O)$_3$]·3H$_2$O
α-(o-Carboxyazobenzene)-o'-chloroace-	[Cu dye H$_2$O]
toacetanilide	[Cu dye]
	H$_2$[Ni(dye)$_2$]
	H[Cr(dye)$_2$]
2-Carboxybenzene-4-azo-1-phenyl-3-	[Cu dye]
methylpyrazol-5-one	[Ni dye (H$_2$O)$_2$]
	[Co dye H$_2$O]
	[Co dye (H$_2$O)$_3$]*
	[Co(dye)$_2$]·2H$_2$O*

* Prepared from [Co(NH$_3$)$_6$]Cl$_3$.

place the two hydrogen atoms to form a nonionic complex. Trivalent ions form compounds of the type (Phthalocyanine MX), while tetravalent ions give (Phthalocyanine MX$_2$) compounds. The metal phthalocyanine may be used directly or, in some cases, the metal may be removed by treatment with acid.

Although a great many phthalocyanines have been synthesized, the copper derivative is the most important and is sold commercially in the Monastral Fast Blue, Heliogen Blue, and Vulcan Blue series. These are valuable because of their brilliant shades, high tinctorial strength, insolubility in water, and stability. In the usual organic solvents, they vary from total insolubility to very slight solubility. They are soluble in most strong acids but reprecipitate upon dilution. The pigments are relatively stable to heat, light, and chemical reagents. The pigment properties have been successfully modified by halogenation and sulfonation. The soluble sulfonated phthalocyanines thus produced are somewhat less stable than the insoluble pigments. Helberger[69] has shown that some metal phthalocyanines exhibit brilliant chemiluminescence when oxidized under certain conditions. The phthalocyanines have numerous applications wherever coloring materials are used.

69. Helberger, *Naturwissenschaften*, **26**, 316 (1938).

Other Nitrogen-donor Dyes. Patents have been issued on dyes from 2,4-diarylpyrroles such as 2,2′,4,4′-tetraphenylazadipyrromethine

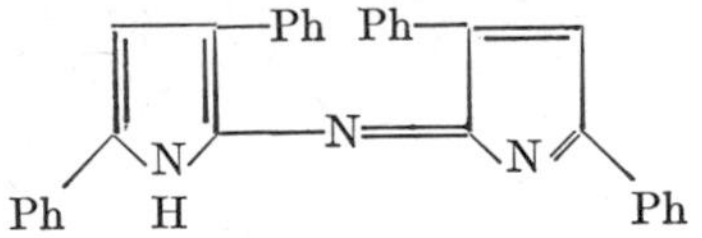

This compound forms metal complexes similar to those of the phthalocyanines[70].

Kunz prepared the copper and iron compounds of indigo[71]. The structure of the copper compound has been given as[72]

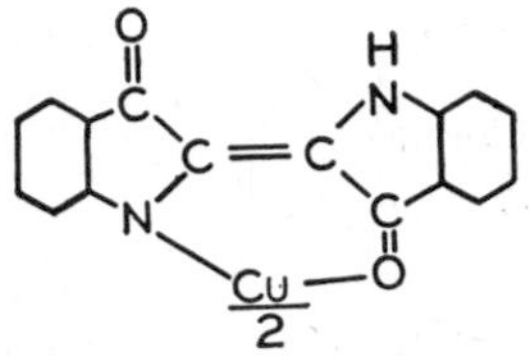

Drew and Kelly[73] obtained highly colored metallic compounds of dithio-β-isoindigo.

The primary application of these results has been in the solubilization of indigo and other vat dyes through complex formation. In the reaction, the active groups are the carbonyl functions[74].

Sulfur Containing Dyes. These dyes are probably the least understood from the point of view of the structure of the organic compounds present in the commercial products; however, the extensive use of metal salts in the preparation of these materials suggests that coordination phenomena are involved[75]. Thionyl Purple 2B forms bordeaux red lakes when copper, cobalt, or nickel salts are added[76]. Structures have been proposed for several sulfur dyes including Pyrogene Green[77]

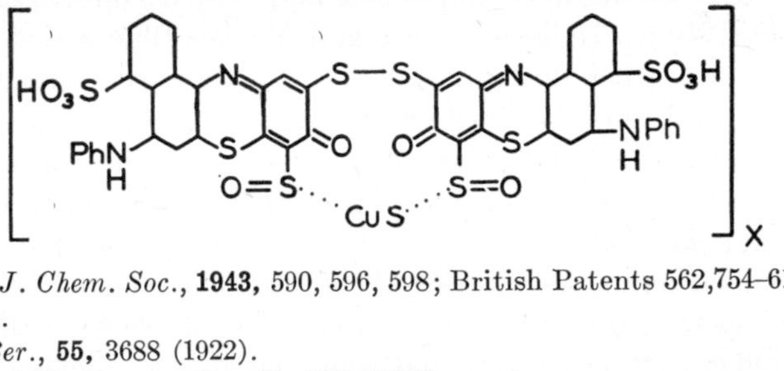

70. Rogers, *J. Chem. Soc.*, **1943**, 590, 596, 598; British Patents 562,754–61 (1950) and others.
71. Kunz, *Ber.*, **55**, 3688 (1922).
72. Kuhn and Machemer, *Ber.*, **61**, 118 (1928).
73. Drew and Kelly, *J. Chem. Soc.*, **1941**, 625, 630, 637.
74. Ref. 18, pp. 1047–48.
75. Ref. 18, pp. 1063–4, 1071 ff.
76. Vlies, *J. Soc. Dyers Colourists*, **29**, 316 (1913).
77. Fierz-David et al., *Helv. Chim. Acta*, **15**, 287 (1932); **16**, 585 (1933); *J. Soc. Dyers Colourists*, **51**, 50 (1935); *Naturwissenschaften*, **20**, 945 (1932).

Copper, nickel, and cobalt lakes of two *o*-mercaptoazo compounds containing the grouping

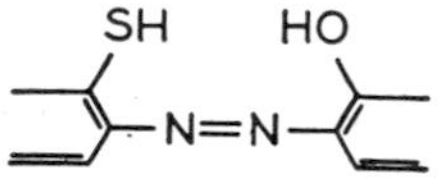

show a dye:metal ratio of 2:1[78]. The sulfur-containing dyes offer a fertile field of research for the coordination chemist.

The Dye-Metal-Fiber Interactions*

In practice, the application of a dye involves both physical and chemical changes. The physical phenomena involved appear to be independent of the type of fiber, while chemical changes are related to the structure of the material being dyed. Textile fibers may be divided into four classes on the basis of their chemical structure: cellulose and rayons; proteins, which include wool and silk; synthetic polyamides which are chemically related to the proteins; and miscellaneous polymers.

Cotton, which is nearly pure cellulose, may be dyed by colors having the chromophore in the anion. The principal attraction involves hydrogen bonding with the possibility of some electrostatic forces if the hydroxyl groups of the cellulose have some acidic character. The direct cotton dyes are often *o*-hydroxy- or *o*-aminoazo dyes in which chelation assists in the formation of hydrogen bonds between the dye molecules and the cellulose chain:

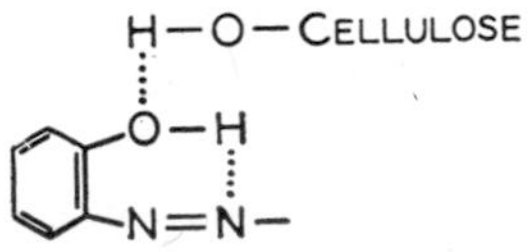

This bonding implies that chelation of the proton with the azo group increases the accessibility of the electron pair involved in the formation of the hydrogen bond with the cellulose. The chelation of a metal ion would probably result in the formation of a more stable chelate ring but would also introduce the probability of delocalizing the electron pair as well as converting the dye to a cation. Evidence suggests that the presence of a metal ion results in the formation of a chemical bond between it and the cellulose groups. Systems containing $[Cu(NH_3)_4]^{++}$ show a decrease in pH upon addition of polyhydroxy compounds such as cellulose or sucrose[79]. The

78. Burawoy and Turner, *J. Chem. Soc.*, **1952**, 1286.

* See Ref. 18, Chap. VI, XLI, p. 567; Race, Rowe, and Speakman, *J. Soc. Dyers Colourists*, **62**, 372 (1946); Giles, *J. Soc. Dyers Colourists*, **60**, 303 (1944); Justin-Mueller, *Teintex*, **15**, 57 (1950).

79. Arkhipov and Kharitonova, *J. Appl. Chem. U.S.S.R.* **24**, 733 (1951); *J. Soc. Dyers Colourists*, **67**, 471 (1951).

following reaction has been suggested:

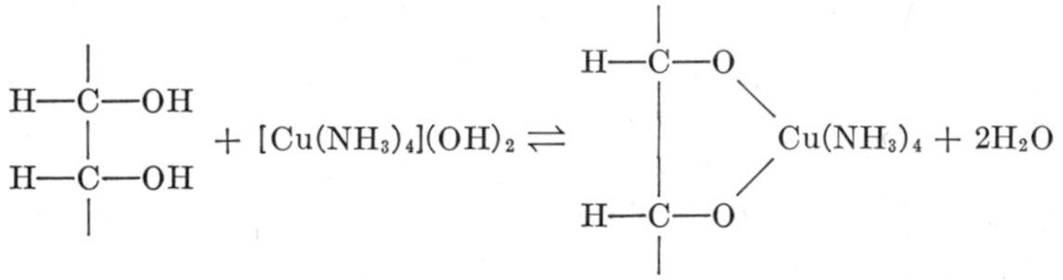

$$
\begin{array}{c}
\text{H—C—OH} \\
| \\
\text{H—C—OH} \\
|
\end{array}
+ [\text{Cu(NH}_3)_4](\text{OH})_2 \rightleftharpoons
\begin{array}{c}
\text{H—C—O} \\
\diagdown \\
\diagup \\
\text{H—C—O} \\
|
\end{array}
\text{Cu(NH}_3)_4 + 2\text{H}_2\text{O}
$$

Rayons, which are derivatives of cellulose, may be classified into two groups: nitro rayon, cuprammonium, viscose; and cellulose acetate. The first group may be dyed in the same manner as cotton. Cellulose acetate, however, is dyed by materials which dissolve in the fiber. Most cellulose acetate dyes are sparingly soluble in water and are handled as dispersions.

Wool and silk have similar dyeing properties since both consist of protein chains. Wool contains sulfur in the form of cystine and as disulfide linkages between the keratin residues. The latter may also be joined by salt groups. Wool is, therefore, capable of reacting with both anionic and cationic dyes.

In the dyeing of wool, as in the case of cotton, hydrogen bonding seems to be involved. Much evidence has also been found for direct chemical combination between metal ions and protein fibers. Dichromate ions are absorbed and are reduced to chromium(III) ions on heating. The combination of chromed wool with a dye may involve chemical bonding, but many chrome dyes have no salt or chelating groups, and the interaction probably involves adsorption. Where lake formation with a dye is possible, it is necessary to have the chromium present as the chromium(III) ion[80]. A systematic investigation of the interaction of chromium complexes with collagen, collagen with the amino groups blocked, silk fibroin, and polycaprolactam led to the conclusion that cationic chromium reacts with carboxy groups while chromium anions react with amino groups in protein fibers[81]. Others have questioned these results[82], but Shuttleworth[83] appears to have resolved the conflicting data by examining the adsorption of eighteen chromium complexes on amino, sulfonic acid, and carboxylic resins. The chief mechanism is coordination of the complexes with carboxy groups; it can be related to the dissociation constants of the ligands.

Wool absorbs nickel ions from solutions of $[\text{Ni(NH}_3)_4](\text{OH})_2$ with no increase in the nitrogen content of the wool[84]. The coordinated ammonia

80. Gaunt, *J. Soc. Dyers Colourists*, **65**, 429 (1949).
81. Strakhov, *J. Appl. Chem. U.S.S.R.*, **24**, 142 (1951); *J. Soc. Dyers Colourists*, **67**, 292 (1951).
82. Gustavson, *J. Soc. Leather Trades Chem.*, **36**, 182 (1952).
83. Shuttleworth, *J. Amer. Leather Chemist's Assoc.*, **47**, 387 (1952).
84. Bell and Whewell, *J. Soc. Dyers Colourists*, **68**, 299 (1952).

molecules may be replaced by the amine groups of the wool; however, modification of the amine groups does not decrease the amount of nickel ion absorbed although it does decrease the rate of the process. Similar modifications of the disulfide and carboxy groups have little effect on the adsorption of nickel ion, and it appears that main chain $>CO$ and $>NH$ groups are involved.

Another investigation of the interaction between metal ions and wool indicates that bonding is dependent on the nature of the metal ion involved[85]. Wool was treated with salts of lead, cadmium, zinc, copper, iron, bismuth, and mercury. Upon treatment with ions of the first four metals, the cystine content of the wool decreased and the nitrogen content of the bath increased. X-ray studies suggested that the metal ions, except perhaps copper, were present in the wool as metal sulfides. In all cases, the metal content of the wool was in excess of the noncystine sulfur present, and some of the metal must have been bound by functional groups of the keratin.

The dyeing of synthetic fibers has presented many problems which vary with the chemical nature of the materials[86]. A survey has been made of the dyeing methods suitable for three typical products: "Nylon," "Orlon" acrylic fiber, and "Dacron" polyester fiber[87]. Of the three, "Nylon" compares favorably with wool in ease of dyeing.

A series of metal complexes of azo dyes, known as the Perlon Fast colors, has been developed for the dyeing of Perlon, a nylon-type fiber[88]. Examples are Perlon Fast Yellow G (XXIV) and Perlon Fast Red 3BS (XXV).

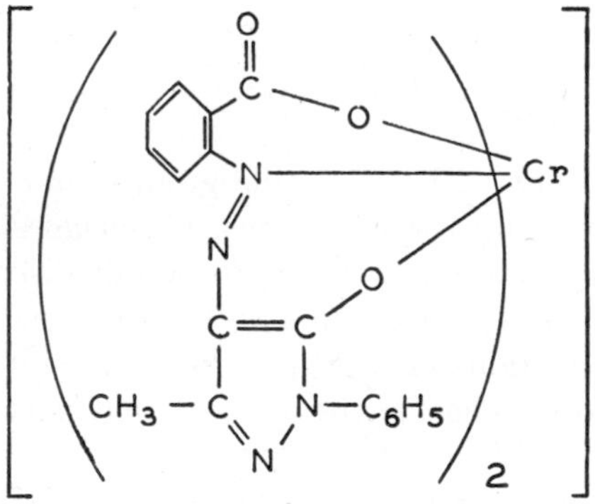

XXIV

85. Schoberl, *Melliand Textilber.*, **33,** 4 (1952); *J. Soc. Dyers Colourists*, **68,** 226 (1952).
86. Baumann, *Am. Dyestuff Reptr.*, **41,** P. 453 (1952).
87. Turnbull, *Am. Dyestuff Reptr.*, **41,** P. 75, P. 82 (1952).
88. Anacker, *Melliand Textilber.*, **30.** 256 (1949); Knight, *J. Soc. Dyers Colourists*, **66,** 169 (1950).

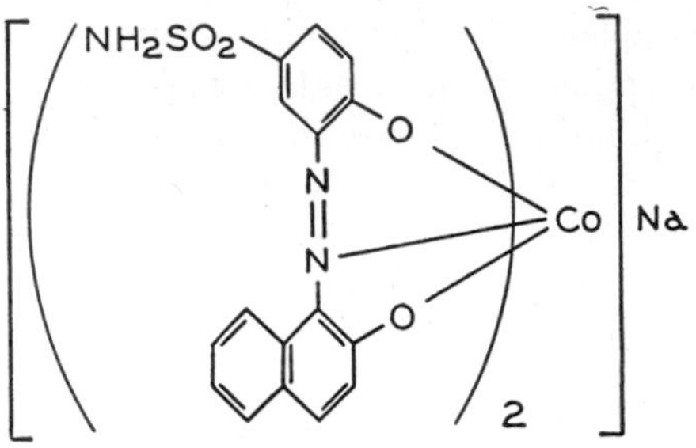

XXV

Nylon may be chromed prior to the addition of the dye; whereas wool reduces the dichromate to chromium(III) on heating, this reduction does not occur on nylon fibers without the addition of a reducing agent. The reduction is catalyzed by the presence of a dye which forms a complex with the reduced chromium ion. Once the chromium ion has been fixed on the nylon, chelation with a lake-forming dye follows. If nylon is treated directly with CrF_3 or $Cr_2(SO_4)_3$, there is a strong tendency for the metal ions to migrate into the dye solution and form insoluble complexes.

Undoubtedly, the fixation of chromium on a fiber is more than a simple interaction between chromium(III) ions and donor groups. The necessity for starting with an oxyanion suggests the occurrence of an olation-type reaction with chains of —Cr—O—Cr—O— groups being bonded to evenly spaced groups on the material being dyed. This would result in the proper distribution and bonding of chromium atoms prior to their reduction to a lower oxidation state.

The principle of impregnating a synthetic fiber with copper ion prior to application of a dye has proved very useful in the dyeing of acrylonitrile fibers such as "Orlon," "Dynel," and "Acrilan." The copper(I) ions form coordinate covalent bonds with the nitrile groups, and, upon addition of the dye, probably form copper-dye linkages. This suggests that the copper ions must be spaced at intervals in order to permit discrete bonding with the larger dye molecules. In connection with this point, it may be noted that "Dynel," which contains only 40 per cent acrylonitrile, is dyed more effectively by this process than is the 100 per cent acrylonitrile polymer, "Orlon"[89].

Although copper(I) salts may be added directly, it is preferable to use a copper(II) salt and reduce it with hydroxylamine hydrogen sulfate. The use of the hydrochloride tends to retard the process. This may be due to the formation of chloride compounds with the copper(I) ion. The copper may also be applied in the form of a salt of an acid or a direct dye having

89. Douglas, *J. Soc. Dyers Colourists*, **67**, 133 (1951); Hatfield and Sharing, *J. Soc. Dyers Colourists*, **64**, 381 (1948).

one, but not more than one, sulfonic or carboxy group in the molecule[90].

From this brief discussion of the dye-metal-fiber interactions, it appears certain that much work remains to be done to insure a more complete understanding of the chemical reactions which are taking place. The information concerning dye-metal interactions, while far from complete, is sufficiently advanced to enable reasonable predictions of the behavior of metal ions with numerous classes of dyes. A more concentrated effort in the direction of metal-fiber bonding seems indicated.

90. Blaker and Laucius, *Am. Dyestuff Reptr.*, **41,** P. 39 (1952); Fronmuller, *Am. Dyestuff Reptr.*, **41,** P. 578 (1952); Szlosberg, *Am. Dyestuff Reptr.*, **41,** P. 510 (1952); Field and Fremon, *Text. Research J.*, **21,** 531 (1951); Field, *Am. Dyestuff Reptr.*, **41,** P. 475 (1952).

23. Water Softening Through Complex Formation

Roy D. Johnson

American Embassy, Melbourne, Australia

and

Clayton F. Callis

Monsanto Chemical Co., Dayton, Ohio

Water softening may be defined as the process of effectively removing ions, such as calcium and magnesium, which cause the precipitation of soaps. It is evident that water softening, thus defined, is somewhat simpler than water conditioning in boiler systems[1] where heating and evaporation complicate the precipitation problem. The general methods used for water softening are distillation, precipitation, ion exchange, and the effective removal of ions from solution by the formation of soluble complexes. This discussion will be confined to softening of water through complex formation.

This phenomenon of "tying-up" alkaline earth ions in soluble complex ions, and thus preventing the formation of precipitates, is generally termed "sequestration"[2]. The tests commonly used for determining the sequestering ability of a "sequestering agent" depend upon the prevention or diminution of precipitation as measured by nephelometry or by the formation of soap foams[3,4]. The weight of sequestering agent per unit quantity of multivalent positive ion needed to prevent the precipitation of alkaline earth salts under operating conditions is known as the sequestration value. Ma-

1. Schwartz and Munter, *Ind. Eng. Chem.*, **34**, 32 (1942).
2. Hall, U. S. Patent 1,956,515 (1934); Reissue 19, 719 (1935).
3. Van Wazer, "Encyclopedia of Chemical Technology," Vol. XI, pp. 403–41. New York, Interscience Publishers, Inc., 1953.
4. For example, Andress and Wüst, *Z. anorg. allgem. Chem.*, **237**, 113 (1938); **241**, 196 (1939); Rudy, Schloesser and Watzel, *Angew. Chem.*, **53**, 525–31 (1940); Hafford, Leonard, and Cummins, *Ind. Eng. Chem.*, *Anal. Ed.*, **18**, 411–15 (1946); Miles and Ross, *J. Amer. Oil Chem. Soc.*, **24**, 23 (1947); Davies and Monk, *J. Chem. Soc.*, **1949**, 413–22. Also, private communication from R. K. Skaar, Food Machinery and Chemical Corporation.

terials useful as sequestering agents include the chain or polyphosphates and certain polyamino acids. The phytates have also been suggested.

THE CHAIN OR POLYPHOSPHATES [5-10]

The phosphates most commonly used as sequestering agents for water softening are the sodium salts of the chain phosphates, i.e., sodium acid pyrophosphate, tetrasodium pyrophosphate, sodium tripolyphosphate, and the sodium salts of the low and high molecular weight glassy phosphates[11].

Polyphosphates, One of Three Groups of Condensed Phosphates

On the basis of the present evidence (reviewed in refs. 3, 8, and 10) including x-ray studies of crystalline phosphates and physical-chemical studies of solutions of the phosphates, it is believed that the so-called "condensed phosphates" are built-up by sharing oxygen atoms between structural units, each unit consisting of a tetrahedral grouping of four oxygen atoms around a central phosphorus atom. It has been shown[3] that the condensed phosphates can be conveniently divided into three groups: the chain, the ring, and the branched phosphates, depending on the number of shared oxygens per tetrahedron.

The chain phosphates are generally called polyphosphates and consist of unbranched P-O-P chains. The ring phosphates consist of simple rings of interconnected phosphorus and oxygen atoms, and are included in the class of metaphosphates. At present only the six- and eight-membered rings are known (trimeta- and tetrametaphosphate). The branched phosphates, often referred to as ultraphosphates, include structures in which one or more PO_4 groups share oxygen atoms with three neighboring groups. These branched phosphates, on dissolution in water, are rapidly converted into groups in which no, one, or two oxygens are shared[12]. This means that only

5. Graham, *Proc. Royal. Soc.*, **123**, 253 (1833).
6. Partridge, Hicks and Smith, *J. Am. Chem. Soc.*, **63**, 454 (1941); Morey and Ingerson, *Am. J. Sci.*, **242**, 1 (1944).
7. Quimby, *Chem. Revs.*, **40**, 141 (1947); "Thorpe's Dictionary of Applied Chemistry," 4th ed., Vol. 9, p. 508, New York, Longmans, Green and Co., 1949; Topley, *Quart. Revs.*, **3**, 345 (1949).
8. Van Wazer, *et al.*, *J. Am. Chem. Soc.*, **72**, 639, 644, 647, 906 (1950); **75**, 1563 (1953).
9. Quimby, *J. Phys. Chem.*, **58**, 603 (1954).
10. Callis, Van Wazer and Arvan, *Chem. Revs.*, **54**, 777 (1954).
11. "Sodium Phosphates for Industry," Catalog of the Monsanto Chemical Company, Inorganic Chemicals Division; "Victor Chemicals," Catalog of Victor Chemical Works; "Blockson Chemicals," Catalog of the Blockson Chemical Company; "Westvaco Chemicals," Catalog of Westvaco Chemical Division, Food Machinery and Chemical Corporation.
12. Pfanstiel and Iler, *J. Am. Chem. Soc.*, **74**, 6059–64 (1952); Strauss, Smith and Wineman, *J. Am. Chem. Soc.*, **75**, 3935–40 (1953).

orthophosphates, simple rings, or unbranched chains are present a short while after dissolution, and of these only the unbranched chains or poly-phosphates are effective in alkaline earth ion sequestration.

The chain phosphates constitute a homologous series of polymeric compounds represented by the formula $M_{(n+2)}P_nO_{(3n+1)}$ ($1 < M_2O/P_2O_5 < 3$), in which M represents an equivalent of metal, and n is the number of phosphorus atoms in the chain. Thus, the monomer is the orthophosphate (not one of the phosphates which softens by sequestration), the dimer is the pyrophosphate, and the trimer is the triphosphate or tripolyphosphate. In the sodium system, higher crystalline polymers are not known, and Partridge, Hicks, and Smith[6] have shown from an equilibrium phase diagram that triphosphate is the only crystalline compound between the pyro- and metaphosphate compositions. However, thermal evidence for the formation of a crystalline lead tetraphosphate has recently been published[13], and all possible chain lengths up to several hundred are present in solutions of the glassy phosphates[8c].

The sodium phosphate glasses, introduced as water softeners by Hall[2] in 1932, were the first phosphates used in this application. They are prepared by quenching sodium oxide-phosphoric oxide melts in the composition range, $1 < Na_2O/P_2O_5 < 1.34$. An infinite number of products may be produced within this range. It has been shown from solubility fractionation and end-group titration studies[8c] that in aqueous solution these glasses exhibit a size distribution of linear molecule-ions, the average of which is a first-order function of the Na_2O/P_2O_5 mole ratio, i.e., theoretically,

$$\frac{Na_2O + H_2O}{P_2O_5} = \frac{\bar{n} + 2}{\bar{n}} \tag{1}$$

where $Na_2O \gg H_2O$ and $\bar{n}$ is the number-average number of phosphorus atoms in the chain. As $\bar{n}$ approaches infinity, the general formula of the chain phosphates approaches that of the metaphosphate composition, $M_nP_nO_{3n}$. This metaphosphate composition is the limiting composition for both the chain and branched regions, as well as being the empirical composition for the ring compounds. Actually, high-molecular weight chain compounds with empirical compositions analytically indistinguishable from that of the ring compounds are known, and the thermal interrelationships of a number of crystalline varieties of this metaphosphate composition have been studied[7]. These crystalline and glassy chain phosphates, with compositions near that of the metaphosphate, are not used in commercial water softening primarily because of undesirable physical properties, such as slow rate of dissolution. The Na_2O/P_2O_5 mole ratios generally chosen for the commercial glasses are 1.11 and about 1.33 for the high- and low-molecular

13. Osterheld and Langguth, *J. Phys. Chem.*, **59**, 76 (1955).

Table 23.1. Relative Sequestering Ability of Several Polyphosphates at Room Temperature

Polyphosphate	Grams of Ca[a] per 100 Grams of Phosphate	Grams of Mg[b] per 100 Grams of Phosphate	Grams of Iron[c] Per 100 Grams of Phosphate
Sodium triphosphate	13.4	6.4	0.184
Sodium phosphate glass with $Na_2O/P_2O_5 = $ ca. 1.3	18.5	3.8	0.092
Sodium phosphate glass with $Na_2O/P_2O_5 = 1.1$	19.5	2.9	0.031
Tetrasodium pyrophosphate	4.7	8.3	0.273

[a] At optimum pH of 10 to 11. See reference 4d for details.

[b] pH adjusted to 10, soap present[4g].

[c] Ferric sulfate solution mixed with phosphate in sodium sesquicarbonate solution followed by addition of hydrogen peroxide[4g].

weight glasses, respectively[11]. The average number of phosphorus atoms in the chains can be estimated from equation (1). Glasses with a 1.11 ratio have an average chain length of about 14, and those with the higher ratio have an average chain length of approximately 6. Some products of intermediate composition are also marketed.

The Sequestering Action of the Polyphosphates

The addition of a polyphosphate to water containing calcium or magnesium ions leads to precipitation of calcium or magnesium phosphate. This precipitation continues until an excess of the phosphate has been added. Then the precipitate is peptized, dispersed, and redissolved in a sequestering action. The sequestering ability of the phosphates is dependent upon many factors, the principal ones of which are discussed below.

Factors Affecting the Sequestering Ability of Polyphosphates

Nature of the Polyphosphate (or Precipitating Anion) and the Metal Ion

Measurements of the sequestering ability of the polyphosphates give widely different results depending upon the anion used (sometimes a precipitating anion other than phosphate is added), the metallic ion and the pH. One common test consists of measuring the amount of a soluble salt of the metal in question which can be added to a solution of the phosphate before precipitation occurs. Table 23.1 lists values for several polyphosphates[11a, 14]. By this test, the glassy phosphates are better sequestrants for soluble calcium salts than are tri- or pyrophosphates. However, with magnesium ion and soap present (Table 23.1), the tetrasodium pyrophosphate and sodium triphosphate show up as better sequestering agents.

14. "Technical Bulletin number 808, Sodium Tripolyphosphate," New York, Westvaco Chemical Division, Food Machinery and Chemical Corporation.

TABLE 23.2. NATURAL pH AND FREE ALKALINITY OF THE POLYPHOSPHATES[11a]

Polyphosphate	Natural pH of 1% Soln.	% Free Alkalinity as Na_2O
Tetrasodium pyrophosphate	10.25	23.3
Sodium acid pyrophosphate	4.2	Equal to tetrasodium pyrophosphate in buffering ability
Sodium triphosphate	9.9	16.7
Sodium phosphate glass with $Na_2O/$ P_2O_5 = ca. 1.33	7.9	8.5
Sodium phosphate glass with $Na_2O/$ P_2O_5 = ca. 1.11	6.9	2.7

In the presence of anions such as fluoride and oxalate, which form highly insoluble precipitates with calcium, the sequestering powers of the polyphosphates are more nearly equal, and, in fact, the differences in sequestering abilities are negligible[11a]. It is obvious that an indiscriminate comparison of these sequestering values will lead to confusing conclusions.

pH of Solutions. The phosphates differ greatly in their natural alkalinity and in their ability to control the pH of a solution by buffering action. The natural pH of one per cent solutions and the free alkalinity of the sequestering polyphosphates are given in Table 23.2. The sodium phosphate glasses are not good buffering agents, as shown by their low free alkalinity; however, if the pH buffering requirements are neglected, the glasses sequester as well as the crystalline phosphates under most conditions, and better under some conditions, as shown by the data of Table 23.1.

The pH of the solution has an important effect on the stability of the phosphates. The condensed phosphates react with water to form less condensed phosphates and ultimately orthophosphates through rupture of P-O-P linkages. The hydrolytic degradation of pyro- and triphosphate has been carefully studied by Van Wazer, Griffith, and McCullough[15]. The hydrolyses follow the first-order rate law and are catalyzed by acid and not by base. The degradation of the polyphosphates is extremely slow at neutral or alkaline pH and room temperature, but is accelerated by a number of factors, the more important of which are increasing temperature and decreasing pH. The presence of cations (other than tetramethyl ammonium), colloidally precipitated metal oxides, and the enzymes known as phosphatases also accelerate the breakdown..

Comparisons of the rates of reversion of the polyphosphates to orthophosphates in dilute solutions[11c] without pH control or adjustment have shown tetrasodium pyrophosphate to be the most stable, followed in order by sodium triphosphate, the sodium phosphate glasses, and sodium acid pyrophosphate. The reversion in one hour at 100°C, as measured by the

15. Van Wazer, Griffith and McCullough, *J. Am. Chem. Soc.*, **77**, 287 (1955).

build-up of orthophosphate, varies from less than 1 per cent for tetrasodium pyrophosphate and 8 per cent for sodium triphosphate, to about 55 per cent for sodium acid pyrophosphate. The products of the degradation may or may not possess complexing ability. Sodium triphosphate gives one mole of pyro- and one mole of orthophosphate, the former having sequestering ability. Both Bell[16] and Thilo[17] report trimetaphosphate as one of the products of the hydrolysis of the long chain phosphates.

The Nature of the Sequestering Reaction and the Stability of the Complex Ions Formed

In the sequestering tests described above, the amount of an ion needed to form a barely discernible precipitate depends upon the solubility of the precipitate and the formation of a soluble complex ion. By neglecting the dispersing action and colloid stabilization of phosphates, we can represent this action as follows:

$$Ca^{++} + \text{polyphosphate molecule-ion} \rightleftharpoons \text{Ca-polyphosphate complex} \qquad (2)$$

$$Ca^{++} + \text{precipitating anion} \rightleftharpoons \text{Ca precipitate}, \qquad (3)$$

in which the precipitating anion can be the phosphate or some other anion. Precipitation of calcium will occur if the equilibrium concentration of calcium is great enough to exceed the solubility product of the precipitate. Thus, the differences noted with different anions can be correlated with the respective solubility products. A number of studies of the complex ions of polyphosphates have been reported[18], but most of them fail to describe accurately the complex ions by chemical formulas and true equilibrium constants primarily because (a) the theoretical treatment for chain molecule-ions has not been thoroughly developed, (b) electrochemical measurements are often complicated by irreversibility of the reactions, (c) the available range of concentrations is restricted because of precipitate formation, and (d) it is difficult to obtain single species of the chain phosphates with a degree of polymerization greater than three. In addition to the precipitation tests discussed earlier, a number of other techniques, including pH titration, membrane potentials, conductivity, transference number measurements, polarography, ion-exchange equilibrium and colorimetric studies have been applied to these systems.

16. Bell, *Ind. Eng. Chem.*, **39**, 137 (1947).
17. Thilo, *Chem. Technik.*, **4**, 345–51 (1952).
18. Van Wazer and Campanella, *J. Am. Chem. Soc.*, **72**, 655 (1950); Rogers and Reynolds, *J. Am. Chem. Soc.*, **71**, 2081 (1949); Rosenheim, Frommer, Glaser and Handler, *Z. anorg. Chem.*, **153**, 126 (1926); Bassett, Bedwell and Hutchinson, *J. Chem. Soc.*, **1936**, 1412; Kolthoff and Watters, *Ind. Eng. Chem., Anal. Ed.*, **15**, 8 (1943); Laitinen and Onstott, *J. Am. Chem. Soc.*, **72**, 4729 (1950); Bobtelsky and Kertes, *J. Appl. Chem.* **4**, 419 (1954).

Gray and Lemmerman (as reported by Quimby[9]) carried out a conductometric study, using Job's method of continuous variation, on the calcium triphosphate system at concentrations low enough to prevent precipitation at any ratio of calcium to triphosphate. Their results are consistent with the existence of a soluble 1:1 calcium:triphosphate complex. The boundary between homogeneous and heterogeneous regions at 60°C was determined turbidimetrically, after attainment of steady state. (Figure 23.1). The homogeneous region comes close to the calcium axis and is usually not detected upon adding sodium triphosphate to calcium solutions. On branch DE of the curve, more than one mole of triphosphate per mole of calcium is required to prevent precipitation. The shift of the curve to the right as sodium salts are added suggests that the precipitates contain sodium, but the equilibrium solid phases have not been completely characterized. From measurements of the clarification of calcium oxalate suspensions, Gray and Lemmerman[9] have estimated the dissociation constant to be 3.1×10^{-7} at 30°C, assuming that the 1:1 calcium:triphosphate complex is the only one involved.

Rogers and Reynolds[18b] report that pyrophosphate forms complexes of the type $M^{II}(P_2O_7)^=$ with divalent ions such as magnesium, and com-

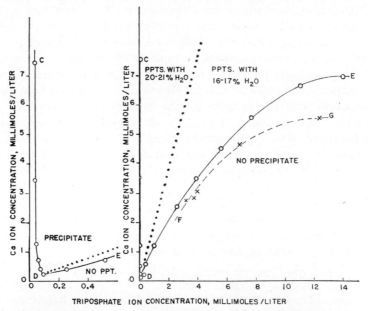

FIG. 23.1. Homogeneous and heterogeneous regions at 60°C for the CaCl₂-Na₅P₃O₁₀-H₂O system. Solid curve obtained turbidimetrically. Dashed curve FG gives saturated solutions obtained from compositions between dotted line and curve DE. (Reproduced from *J. Phys. Chem.*, **58**, 613 (1954))

TABLE 23.3. DISSOCIATION CONSTANTS FOR SEVERAL CONDENSED PHOSPHATES FROM CONDUCTIVITY DATA[19]

Polyphosphate	Acid	Dissociation Constant for the Na Salt	Ca Salt
Trimetaphosphate	8.3×10^{-3}	68×10^{-3}	0.33×10^{-3}
Tetrametaphosphate	1.8×10^{-3}	9×10^{-3}	$K_1\ 2.2 \times 10^{-3}$
			$K_2\ 1.3 \times 10^{-5}$
Pyrophosphate	$K_3\ 2.7 \times 10^{-7}$		
	$K_4\ 2.4 \times 10^{-10}$	4.5×10^{-3}	
Triphosphate		3.0×10^{-3}	

TABLE 23.4. APPARENT DISSOCIATION CONSTANTS OF CALCIUM COMPLEXES[20]
(Ionic strength 0.15, pH 7.4, temp. 37°C)

Phosphate	$pK_c(= -\log K_c)$
Triphosphate	4.14
Pyrophosphate	3.47
Tetrametaphosphate	3.06
Trimetaphosphate	2.32

plexes of the types $M^{III}(P_2O_7)^-$ and $M^{III}(P_2O_7)_2^{-5}$ with such metals as iron and aluminum. Considerable data on the relative stability of polyphosphate complexes were obtained by Monk[19] from solubility and conductivity measurements in solutions of low ionic strength. Some of the data are reproduced in Table 23.3. Gosselin and Coghlan[20] measured the apparent dissociation constants of a number of calcium phosphate complex ions, utilizing the equilibrium technique of ion exchange[21]. Linear variation of the distribution coefficients with the molar concentration of the phosphate was cited as evidence that the complex ions formed were of the 1:1 type. The values reported (Table 23.4) are not true dissociation constants because the identity and concentration of the phosphate, which enters into the calculations, cannot be inferred from the available information, so the values in the table are smaller than the true pK_c's, and smaller than the values reported by Monk from conductivity data.

As would be expected from modern electrochemical theory[22], both the ring and the chain phosphates undergo association with cations at relatively low concentration. In spite of the relatively high negative charge on the ring compounds, the ring phosphates form less stable complexes than do the chain phosphates. This difference is in accord with the known fact that ring phosphates are not effective in the prevention of precipitation in water softening. Van Wazer and Campanella[18a] suggested that the chain

19. Monk, *et al.*, *J. Chem. Soc.*, **1949**, 423–27, 427–29, 2693–95; **1950**, 3475–78; **1952**, 1314–17, 1317–20.
20. Gosselin and Coghlan, *Archiv. Biochem. and Biophys.*, **45**, 301 (1953).
21. Schubert, Russell, and Myers, *J. Biol. Chem.*, **185**, 387 (1950).
22. Fuoss, *Chem. Rev.*, **17**, 27 (1935).

phosphate complexes are more stable because the chain compounds can form chelate rings with the metal atom, as in (I) or (II), whereas the ring compounds cannot do so because of mechanical constraint. Polarographic and pH studies[18a] indicate that to a first order approximation the complexing ability of a chain phosphate is proportional to the total number of phosphorus atoms in the polyphosphate, regardless of chain length. It is also

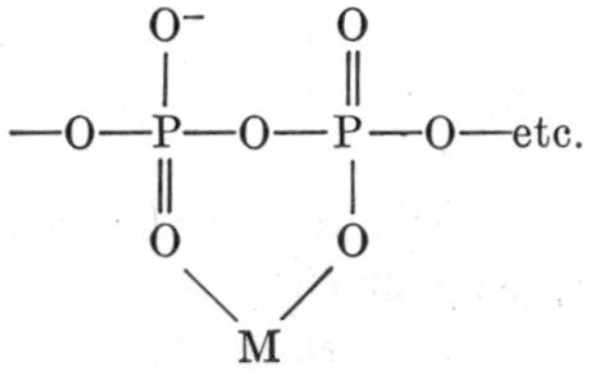

(I) 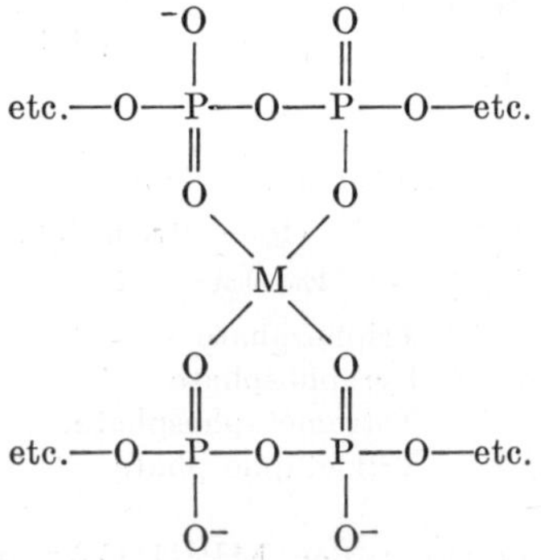   (II)

postulated that the formation of polydentate structures is inhibited by the presence of negative charges on the individual PO_4 groups which tend to prevent coiling, and cross-linking of chains through the metal atom is supported by changes in polarographic diffusion currents. Estimates of molecular weights range from 10^3 to 10^5 for complex ions formed from barium and a glass with an average chain length of five and of 10^3 to 10^7 for complexes from a long-chain glass with approximately the metaphosphate composition. From this work, it is also shown that the barium ion is associated with four phosphorus atoms and the sodium with two phosphorus atoms.

The pH titration studies of Van Wazer and Campanella[18a] also indicate that cations can be divided into three groups based on their ability to form complexes with the polyphosphates: (1) quaternary ammonium ions, which form no complexes; (2) alkali and similar cations, which form weak complexes; and (3) the other metal ions which form strong complexes. Estimates of the dissociation constants were made, but the assignment of definite structures and the establishment of the relative covalent and ionic contributions to the stability of the complexes is uncertain on the basis of the available evidence.

Threshold Treatment

A complementary phenomenon to sequestration is used in "threshold" water conditioning. Here, very low concentrations of condensed sodium phosphates act as deterrents to the crystallization of calcium carbonate.

The triphosphate, $Na_5P_3O_{10}$, and the phosphate glasses may be used successfully in concentrations of 1 to 5 parts per million[23]. The "threshold" is the point at which sufficient sodium phosphate has been added to prevent crystallization. The concentrations required are considerably below the amounts required to completely complex the calcium. Presumably, the phenomena are due to the adsorption of the complex phosphate on the submicroscopic nuclei[23a, 23c, 23f] in such a manner as to prevent crystal growth and precipitation. Microscopic studies indicate that the sodium phosphates cause distortion of the calcite crystals, the amount of distortion increasing as the amount of phosphate is increased. In addition to preventing precipitation, solutions of threshold concentrations slowly remove old calcium carbonate scale if they are circulated through a given system for a period of several months. Crystalline sodium trimetaphosphate has little or no inhibiting effect except in the presence of alkalies, which presumably convert it to the triphosphate.

Polyamino Acids[24]

The use of synthetic polyamino acids as sequestering agents is relatively recent. The most important of these substances are triglycine (III), and ethylenediaminetetraacetic acid (IV). Ender named these compounds Trilon A and Trilon B, respectively[25].

$$
\begin{array}{ccc}
CH_2CO_2H & HO_2CCH_2 & CH_2CO_2H \\
\diagup & \diagdown & \diagup \\
N{-}CH_2CO_2H & NCH_2CH_2N & \\
\diagdown & \diagup & \diagdown \\
CH_2CO_2H & HO_2CCH_2 & CH_2CO_2H \\
(III) & & (IV)
\end{array}
$$

Trilon B is one of the most powerful coordinating agents known, and its disodium salt is widely used under the trade names "Versene," "Sequestrene," and "Nullapon." It is significant that it forms stable complexes with calcium and magnesium—elements which do not react strongly with most

23. Buchrer and Reitemeier, *J. Phys. Chem.*, **44**, 552 (1940); Fink and Richardson, U. S. Patent 2358222 (1940); Hatch and Rice, *Ind. Eng. Chem.*, **31**, 51 (1939); Reitemeier and Buchrer, *J. Phys. Chem.*, **44**, 535 (1940); Rice and Partridge, *Ind. Eng. Chem.*, **31**, 58 (1939); Raistrick, *Disc. Faraday Soc.*, **1949**, 234.
24. Martell and Bersworth, *Proc. Sci. Sect. Toilet Goods Assoc.*, No. 10, Dec. 1948; Martell, Plumb, and Bersworth, *Technical Bulletin Bersworth Chemical Co.*, Framingham, Mass.; "Sequestrene," *Technical Bulletin*, Alrose Chemical Company, Providence, Rhode Island; "The Versenes," *Technical Bulletin № 2*, 4th Ed., Bersworth Chemical Company, Framingham, Mass., 1952.
25. Ender, *Fette und Seifen*, **45**, 144 (1938); Ley, *Ber.*, **42**, 354 (1909).

complexing agents. A considerable literature has grown up about its use in water softening, both in the technical journals, and in patents[25a].

Ethylenediaminetetraacetic Acid

Schwarzenbach and Ackermann[26g-26i] have measured the dissociation constants of ethylenediaminetetraacetic acid, and have shown that two hydrogens are held in the form of zwitter ions:

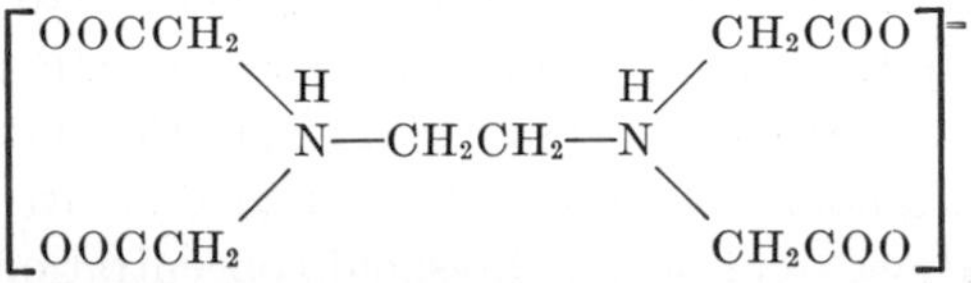

$$
\begin{bmatrix}
OOCCH_2 & & & CH_2COO \\
& \diagdown H & & H \diagup \\
& N - CH_2CH_2 - N & \\
& \diagup & & \diagdown \\
OOCCH_2 & & & CH_2COO
\end{bmatrix}^{-}
$$

(V)

Three structures have been postulated for calcium salts of Trilon B, (VI), (VII), and (VIII). Structure (VI) is of the type usually associated with divalent ions. Structure (VII) was proposed by Pfeiffer[26a-26c].

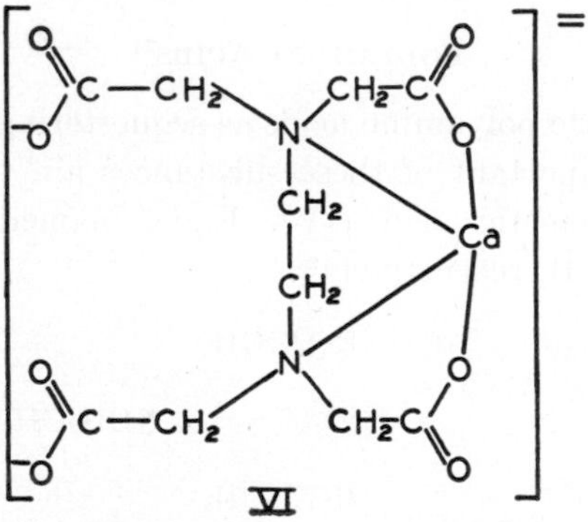

VI

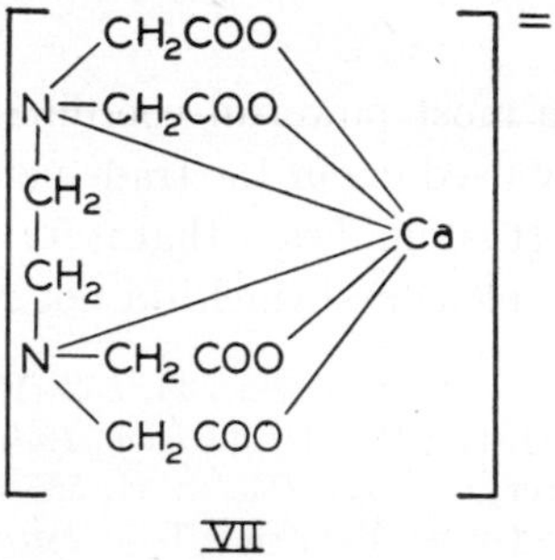

VII

25a. For example, I. G. Farbenindustrie A. G., French 811938 (1937); German 718981 (1942); Munz, U. S. Patent 2240957 (1941); Bersworth, U. S. Patent 2396938 (1946).
26. Pfeiffer and co-workers, *Ber.*, **75B**, 1 (1942); **76B**, 847 (1943); *Z. anorg. allgem. Chem.*, **258**, 247 (1949); Brintzinger and co-workers, *Z. anorg. allgem. Chem.*, **249**, 113 (1942); **251**, 285 (1943); **256**, 65 (1948); Schwarzenbach and Ackermann, *Helv. Chim. Acta*, **30**, 1798 (1947); **31**, 459, 1029 (1948); **32**, 839 (1949).

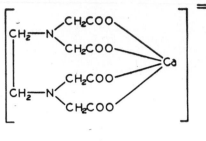

VIII

Formula (VIII) was suggested because calcium shows little tendency to form complexes with amines in aqueous solution. Martell and his associates[24a,b] have shown, however, that the addition of calcium chloride to a solution of the disodium salt (V), results in a marked drop in the pH of the solution. If the nitrogens were not involved in complex formation, there should be no change in the pH of the solution. Further, (VII) is favored over (VI) on the basis of titration of one mole of the amino acid in the presence of

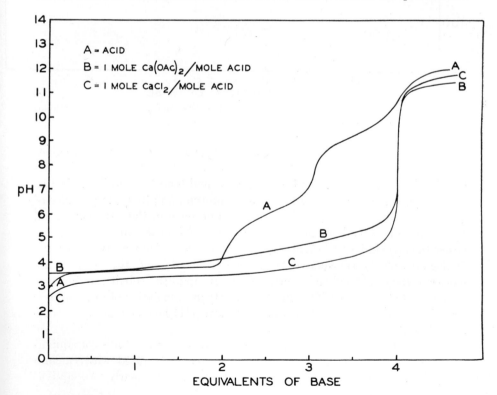

FIG. 23.2. The effect of calcium salts on the neutralization curve of ethylenediaminetetraacetic acid.

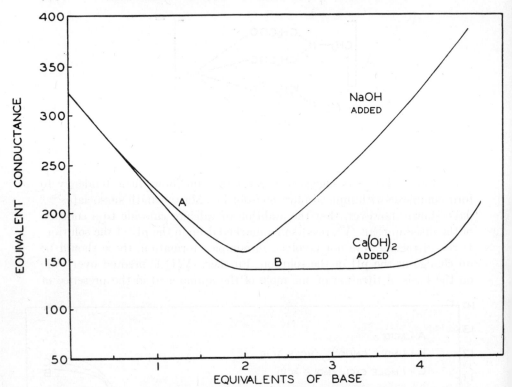

FIG. 23.3. Conductometric titration of ethylenediaminetetraacetic acid with sodium hydroxide and calcium hydroxide.

one mole of calcium salt[24b] (Fig. 23.2). The considerable change in pH values in the presence of acetate ion supports the hypothesis that all of the carboxyl groups in ethylenediaminetetraacetic acid tend to coordinate. If two of the carboxyl groups were free to act as proton acceptors, the presence of the acetate ion should make little or no difference in the titration curve. Structure (VI) should be optically active, but Pfeiffer was unable to resolve either the strychnine or brucine salts of the calcium complex. However, the analogous cobalt(III) complex has been resolved[27] and the hexadentate nature of the ethylenediaminetetraacetato group in the cobalt complex was demonstrated by means of the infrared spectrum[27]. Isolation of anhydrous[26e] sodium ethylenediaminetetraacetatocobaltate(III) lends support to structure (VII).

Additional data on the calcium complex are shown by studies of equivalent conductance[24a] (Fig. 23.3). When the acid is titrated with calcium hydroxide, the equivalent conductance decreases until nearly two equiva-

27. Busch and Bailar, *J. Am. Chem. Soc.*, **75**, 4574 (1953).

TABLE 23.5. FORMATION CONSTANTS FOR ALKALINE EARTH ELEMENT COMPLEXES WITH ETHYLENEDIAMINETETRAACETIC ACID

Divalent ion	log Kk_1	log Kk_2
Mg	2.28	8.69
Ca	3.51	10.59
Sr	2.30	8.63
Ba	2.07	7.76

lents of base have been added, and remains constant until four equivalents have been added. Presumably, the decrease represents the removal of the two strongly acidic hydrogens, and the flat portion of the curve denotes the removal of calcium ions and the neutralization of the third and fourth hydrogens of the acid. Addition of excess calcium hydroxide increases the equivalent conductance.

Schwarzenbach and Ackermann[26g-26i] studied the relative complexing tendencies of ethylenediaminetetraacetic acid and homologous compounds with three, four, and five carbon atoms between the nitrogen atoms. The trimethylenediamine (C_3) compound showed strong complex formation, but not as strong as the ethylenediamine compound. The higher homologs were much less effective. Consequently, they concluded that the fused ring system was not obtained with the molecules containing four or five carbon chains, and that in the formation of complexes of them, the aminodicarboxylic groups act independently. Qualitatively, the sequestering action of the tetrasodium salt of ethylenediaminetetraacetic acid is strong enough to dissolve precipitates such as $Ca_3(PO_4)_2$, CaC_2O_4, $MgCO_3$, $BaSO_4$, and alkaline earth salts of soaps[24d]. Schwarzenbach and Ackermann[26g-26i] have obtained equilibrium constants for the formation of a number of complexes (Table 23.5). Kk_1 is the equilibrium constant for the reaction

$$M^{++} + HY^{\equiv} \rightleftharpoons MHY^{-} \tag{4}$$

and Kk_2 is the constant for the reaction

$$M^{++} + Y^{4-} \rightleftharpoons MY^{=} \tag{5}$$

The values were obtained by titrating ethylenediaminetetraacetic acid with potassium hydroxide in the presence of the various metal ions. Similar titrations with sodium and lithium hydroxides indicated slight complex formation with these metals. The investigators assumed no complex formation with potassium, apparently without investigating the behavior of rubidium and cesium. It is difficult to use the data in a quantitative sense since the equilibria are very sensitive to the addition of ions to the solution. It is evident that the complexes are more stable in alkaline solution. Further, when acid salts are used, complex formation is accompanied by a drop in the pH of the solution.

The great stability of the calcium and magnesium compounds of ethylenediaminetetraacetic acid is the basis for an excellent method of determining hardness in water[26g, 28]. The water is titrated with a standard solution of disodium ethylenediaminetetraacetate, using, as the indicator, the wine-red magnesium complex of the dye Eriochrome Black T. The calcium ion is first tied up by the complexing agent, and then the "free" magnesium ion. The next drop of the ethylenediaminetetraacetate solution destroys the magnesium-dye complex, and the color of the solution becomes a clear blue. Alternatively, the end point can be determined by pH indicators or by potentiometric methods[29].

Triglycine

The complexing action of triglycine is similar to that of ethylenediamine-tetraacetic acid, two moles of triglycine being required per mole of calcium ion. By analogy, we would expect the complex structure (IX).

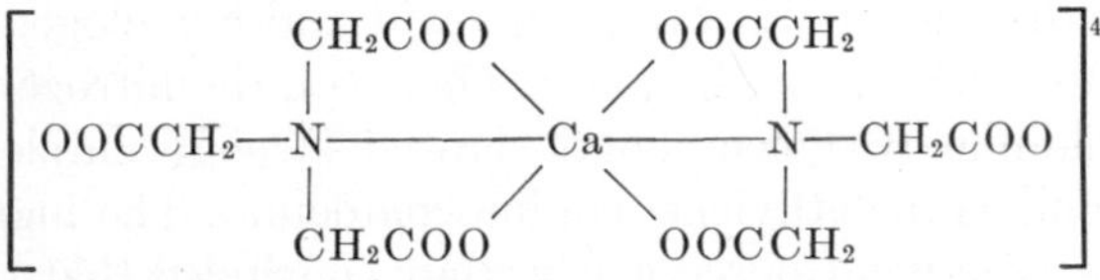

$$\left[\begin{array}{c} CH_2COO \qquad\qquad OOCCH_2 \\ \\ OOCCH_2-N-\!\!\!-\!\!\!-Ca-\!\!\!-\!\!\!-N-CH_2COO \\ \\ CH_2COO \qquad\qquad OOCCH_2 \end{array} \right]^{4-}$$

(IX)

Extent of the Sequestering Ability of the Polyamino Acids

The ability of the polyamino acids to form complexes with metals varies widely. Complexes similar to those of calcium have been obtained with magnesium, strontium, barium, copper(II), mercury(II), cadmium, zinc, and nickel. Of the tripositive ions, bismuth, cobalt, and chromium give stable complexes, while iron forms relatively weak ones. Lead, lanthanum, neodymium, thorium and uranium(IV) have little tendency for complex formation with these compounds.

The polyamino acids are strong sequestering agents above a pH of 5, and the higher the pH the stronger their sequestering power. The poly-amino acids may be used independently as water softeners and, in addition, may be incorporated in liquid or solid soaps to give them a detergent-like action in hard water.

PHYTATES

Phytic acid is the hexaphosphate ester of the inactive form of inositol[30].

28. Bredermann and Schwarzenbach, *Chimia*, (Switz.), **2**, 56 (1948); Diehl, Goetz and Hach, *J. Am. Waterworks Assoc.*, **42**, 40 (1950); Goetz, Loomis and Diehl, *Anal. Chem.*, **22**, 798 (1950).
29. Hahn, *Anal. Chim. Acta*, **4**, 583 (1950).
30. Suzuki, Yoshemura, and Takaishi, *Bull. Tokyo Imper. Univ., College of Agric.*, **7**,

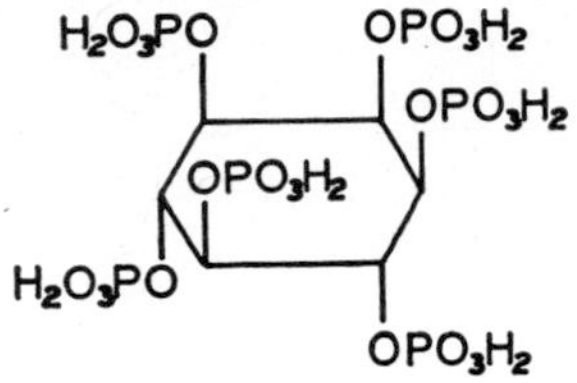

$$H_2O_3PO \quad\quad OPO_3H_2$$

The phytate ion is known to form metal complexes, but few of its derivatives have been studied, and apparently, it has not been used commercially. Arvan[31] studied the behavior of calcium ion in the presence of phytate ion. He found that immediate precipitation resulted if the calcium:sodium phytate ratio exceeded 1:1. Even at lower ratios, a substance of the composition $Ca_2Na_8C_6H_6O_{24}P_6 \cdot 3H_2O$ slowly precipitated after 36 hours. Addition of sodium carbonate or sodium oxalate to the solutions did not give immediate precipitation, although it did so at the same pH in the absence of phytate.

The possibility of complex formation indicated by this chemical evidence was not supported by Arvan's spectrophotometric studies in the ultraviolet region, and it is possible that the solubility of calcium in concentrations less than or equal to phytate concentration is due, wholly or in part, to crystal distortion of the type described under threshold treatment for water conditioning.

495 (1907); Newberg, *Biochem. Z.*, **9**, 557 (1908); Anderson, thesis, Cornell University, 1919; Starkenstein, *Biochem. Z.*, **30**, 56 (1910); Vorbrodt, *Bull. intern. acad. sci. Cracovie*, **ser. A**, 414 (1910).

31. Arvan, thesis, University of Illinois, (1949).

Index

etn, see Ethylamine

etu, su Ethylenethiocarbamide and ethylenethiourea

Exchange between oxalate

and trisoxalato aluminum(III) ions, 326

and trisoxalato chromium(III) ions, 326, 629

and trisoxalato iron(III) ions, 326

Exchange of functional groups, metal catalyzed, 712

Exchange rate

and structural features of complex ion, 213

relation to bond type, 615

Exchange reactions

as criterion for bond type, 211

of complexes, 611–618

of ferrocyanides, 628

of platinum(II) complexes, relationship to stability, 12

of trisoxalato complexes, 326, 629

results compared with magnetic susceptibility data, 211

results compared with stability of isomers, 211

Exchange resins, use of, 622

Exopeptidases, metal activation of, 703

Expansion of crystal lattice as size of ligand increases, 139

Explosive character of some ammines, 61

Fajans' Quanticule Theory, 132, 203

Ferricyanide, see Hexacyanoferrate(III)

Ferritin, 736

Ferrocene, 494

Ferro- and ferricyanide pigments, 744

structures of, 90

Ferrocyanide, see Hexacyanoferrate(II)

Ferroin, 686

Ferromagnetism, 600

Fiber-metal-dye interactions, 763

First absorption band of complexes, 565

First order, compounds of, 158

Fischer's Salt, 97

Five-coordinate configurations, 387

Five-membered rings, stability of, 227

Flash electrodeposits, 639, 739

Flavo salts, 98

Jörgensen's structure of, 107

Flocculation of metal oxide sols, 468

Fluoresence of complexes, analytical uses of, 694

Fuoride ion

as masking agent for molybdate and tungstate, 16

donor properties of, 4–20

reaction with peroxidase, 726

stabilization of high oxidation states by, 9

Fluoro complexes

coordination numbers in, 144

of aluminum, occurrence and properties of, 6

of antimony, configuration of, 8

of tellurium, electrodeposition from, 662

rate of hydrolysis of, 218

stabilization of high oxidation states in, 9

use in separation of niobium and tantalum, 16

use in separation of zinconium and hafnium, 16

Force constants of coordinate bonds from Raman spectra, 213

Forced configurations, 412

for tetracovalent complexes, 354, 363

Formamide, electrodeposition from solutions in, 670

Formate as bridging group, 33

Formation constants, *see also* Dissociation constants, Instability constants, and Stability constants

determination by electrode potentials, 593

determination by polarography, 405

of metal chelates, 177

Formato complexes of chromium, 460

Formatopentammine cobalt(III) ion, 33

Formazyl compounds, metal complexes of, 759

F-strain in complexes, 236

Four-coordinate, see Tetracoordinate

Four membered rings

evidence for, 226

in bridged molecules, 226

Fourteen-member ring, 260

Fourth absorption band, 567

Functional groups, blocking by metal ions, 714

β-Furfuraldoxime, complexes of, 78